Teacher's Edition

Houghton Mifflin
Math
North Carolina

Grade 1

Volume 2

HOUGHTON MIFFLIN   BOSTON

ISBN: 0-618-40312-4

2 3 4 5 6 7 8 9 WC 09 08 07 06 05 04

An Introduction to
Houghton Mifflin
Math
North Carolina

Your Teacher's Edition is a key component for effective and easy teaching of mathematics. This section will give you an overview of *Houghton Mifflin Math.* You will learn about how the exciting features of the program can help you meet the needs of all your students, prepare students for high-stakes testing, and make lessons fun and engaging for your students and you.

Program Authors & Consultants

Authors

Dr. Carole Greenes
Professor of Mathematics Education
Boston University
Boston, Massachusetts

Dr. Matt Larson
Curriculum Specialist for Mathematics
Lincoln Public Schools
Lincoln, Nebraska

Dr. Miriam A. Leiva
Distinguished Professor of Mathematics Emerita
University of North Carolina
Charlotte, North Carolina

Dr. Jean M. Shaw
Professor Emerita of Curriculum and Instruction
University of Mississippi
Oxford, Mississippi

Dr. Lee Stiff
Professor of Mathematics Education
North Carolina State University
Raleigh, North Carolina

Dr. Bruce R. Vogeli
Clifford Brewster Upton Professor of Mathematics
Teachers College, Columbia University
New York, New York

Dr. Karol Yeatts
Associate Professor
Barry University
Miami, Florida

Consultants

Strategic Consultant
Dr. Liping Ma
Senior Scholar
Carnegie Foundation for the Advancement of Technology
Palo Alto, California

Language and Vocabulary Consultant
Dr. David Chard
Professor of Reading
University of Oregon
Eugene, Oregon

North Carolina Teacher Advisory Panel Members

Stephanie McDaniel
Grade 1
B. Everett Jordan Elementary School
Graham, NC

Yvette Smith
Grade 1
Northeast Elementary School
Pikeville, NC

Caroline Annas
Grade 2
Shepherd Elementary School
Moorsville, NC

Del Daniels
Grade 2
Meadow Lane Elementary School
Goldsboro, NC

Tracy McKeel
Grade 3
Rosewood Elementary School
Goldsboro, NC

Fran Coleman
Grade 3
Rosenwald Elementary School
Fairmont, NC

Janet Lee Blue
Grade 4
Rosenwald Elementary School
Fairmont, NC

Lynnetta Burton
Grade 4
Pleasant Grove Elementary School
Burlington, NC

Amy Janning
Grade 5
Spring Creek Elementary School
Goldsboro, NC

Brenda Sharts
Elementary Director
Cleveland County Schools
Shelby, NC

Teacher Reviewers

KINDERGARTEN

Karen Sue Hinton
Washington Elementary School
Ponca City, OK

Hilda Kendrick
W. E. Wilson Elementary School
Jefferson, IN

Debby Nagel
Assumption Elementary School
Cincinnati, OH

GRADE 1

Stephanie McDaniel
B. Everett Jordan Elementary School
Graham, NC

Juan Melgar
Lowrie Elementary School
Elgin, IL

Sharon O'Brien
Echo Mountain School
Phoenix, AZ

GRADE 2

Sally Bales
Akron Elementary School
Akron, IN

Rose Marie Bruno
Mawbey Street Elementary School
Woodbridge, NJ

Megan Burton
Valley Elementary School
Pelham, AL

GRADE 3

Jenny Chang
North Elementary School
Waukegan, IL

Patricia Heintz
PS 92
Harry T. Stewart Elementary School
Corona, NY

Allison White
Kingsley Elementary School
Naperville, IL

GRADE 4

Kathy Curtis
Hoxsie School
Warwick, RI

Lynn Fox
Kendall-Whittier Elementary School
Tulsa, OK

Barbara O'Hanlon
Maurice & Everett Haines
Elementary School
Medford, NJ

Connie Rapp
Oakland Elementary School
Bloomington, IL

Pam Rettig
Solheim Elementary School
Bismarck, ND

Tracy Smith
Carstens Elementary School
Detroit, MI

GRADE 5

Jim Archer
Maplewood Elementary School
Indianapolis, IN

Linda Carlson
Van Buren Elementary School
Oklahoma City, OK

Maggie Dunning
Horizon Elementary School
Hanover Park, IL

Mike Intoccia
McNichols Plaza
Scranton, PA

Jennifer LaBelle
Washington Elementary School
Waukegan, IL

Peg McCann
Warwick Neck School
Warwick, RI

GRADE 6

Robin Akers
Sonoran Sky Elementary School
Scottsdale, AZ

Ellen Greenman
Daniel Webster Middle School
Waukegan, IL

Angela McCray
Abbott Middle School
West Bloomfield, MI

Houghton Mifflin Math

Reaching All Learners, All Of The Time.

HOUGHTON MIFFLIN

Houghton Mifflin Math A+

Time-Tested Approaches Ensure Proven Results

Houghton Mifflin Math really works! Here's why:

★ It's proven with scientifically based research.

★ It's based on more than 30 years of studies on how students learn best.

★ It incorporates models and strategies from high-performing classrooms.

★ It meets the needs of all learners.

A Complete System of Intervention and Challenge Means Success for All Learners

With a variety of specialized, focused teaching support, you can effectively manage instruction to meet the diverse needs of all students in your classroom.

Reaching All Learners

Practical point-of-use support is built into each lesson so that your English learners, gifted and talented students, early finishers, and struggling students can all reach their goals.

 MathTracks MP3 Audio CD

Our unique audio tutor on audio CD reteaches lessons just as you would to students who have missed instruction or who need a little extra support in mastering content and building confidence.

Ways to Success Intervention CD-ROM

Built into every lesson, this special safety net of support ensures that students stay on track with diagnostic reteaching and plenty of practice.

Chapter Challenges

Encourage advanced students to put their skills to the test and expand their thinking with challenging activities and projects linked to each chapter.

Lesson Planner

Customize daily instruction with this powerful CD-ROM to meet your state standards and school calendar, then personalize the lessons to match your teaching style, the needs of your students, and the materials you have on hand.

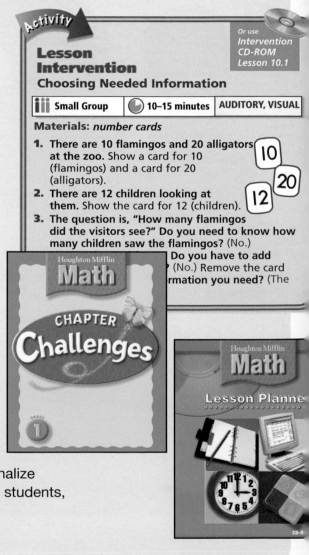

Activity

Or use Intervention CD-ROM Lesson 10.1

Lesson Intervention
Choosing Needed Information

| Small Group | 10–15 minutes | AUDITORY, VISUAL |

Materials: *number cards*

1. **There are 10 flamingos and 20 alligators at the zoo.** Show a card for 10 (flamingos) and a card for 20 (alligators).
2. **There are 12 children looking at them.** Show the card for 12 (children).
3. **The question is, "How many flamingos did the visitors see?"** Do you need to know how many children saw the flamingos? (No.) Do you have to add ? (No.) Remove the card rmation you need? (The

Houghton Mifflin
Math

CHAPTER Challenges

GRADE **1**

Houghton Mifflin
Math

Lesson Planne

PLUS, a wide selection of leveled resources for Practice, Reteach, Enrichment, Problem Solving, Homework, and English learners links to each lesson for your convenience!

Compelling Literature and Real-World Connections Give Immediate Meaning to Math

With engaging literature plus strong connections, our program reinforces math concepts and demonstrates the value of mathematics in everyday life, for every student.

- Authentic literature selections enable young learners to connect mathematics to their own world.

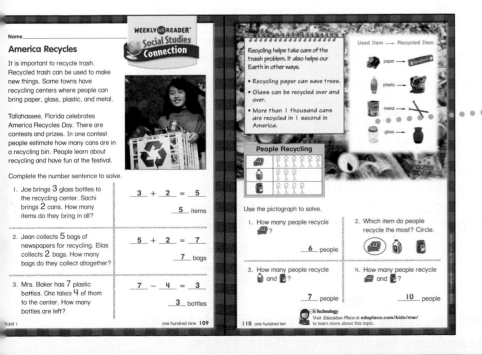

- A special partnership with *Weekly Reader®* makes our real-world and curriculum connections dynamic, relevant, and just right for your students.

A Plan for Test-Taking Success Builds Skills and Confidence

With a four-tiered plan that systematically builds critical skills, your students are sure to perform well on standardized tests, every time.

1 Using a series of guided questions, students effectively build the reasoning and thinking skills necessary for test-taking achievement.

2 With daily exposure to typical test content and questions, plus instruction on critical test-taking strategies, students feel more comfortable and focused on test days.

3 Powerful practice in listening, reading, and problem-solving strategies prepares students for the challenges of test taking.

4 With authentic practice that replicates the typical content, question format, materials, and administrative conditions of test day, you can build students' confidence and test-taking skills, all while ensuring success.

And, our comprehensive, daily vocabulary plan reinforces the mathematical language included on state tests.

Technology Solutions Help You Manage the Big Jobs of Your Classroom

A wealth of technology on CD-ROM and the Web provides everything you need to make your job easier and builds motivation and skill in your students.

Just for Students

eMathBook
With content identical to the student books, an eGlossary, and printable homework masters, our eMathBook—available on CD-ROM and via the Web—makes math readily accessible to students on the go.

Especially for Teachers

Ways to Success Intervention CD-ROM
Developed to engage students and offer self-help and extra support, our easy-to-use CD-ROM features diagnostic and prescriptive reteaching, focused practice, plus background-building opportunities for customized intervention that links to each lesson.

Ways to Assess CD-ROM (Test and Spiral Review Generator)
Create, print, and administer customized assessments in print or online form for all lessons in *Houghton Mifflin Math*. With ready-made Chapter and Unit tests, plus multiple-choice, fill-in-the-blank, and free-response question formats, you can easily choose which tests best fit your classroom. And you can instantly generate spiral reviews based on specific lesson objectives, student needs, and your own teaching sequence.

For Students, Teachers, Parents, and Caregivers

Education Place®
Packed with an array of FREE materials and support for the lessons in *Houghton Mifflin Math*, including a Math Vocabulary Glossary, Games, Brain Teasers, Extra Practice, Homework Help, Teaching Models, Manipulatives, Family Letters, and so much more, our award-winning Web site has it all!
Visit **www.eduplace.com/math/mw/** today.

Technology that gets you and your students ready for success!

Components

	K	1	2	3	4	5	6
Student Book	●	●	●	●	●	●	●
Student Book, Multi-Volume Set	●	●	●				
Big Book	●						
Teacher's Edition	●	●	●	●	●	●	●
Read-Aloud Anthologies, Volumes 1–4	●	●	●				
Trade Book Literature Library	●	●	●	●	●	●	●
Unit Resource Folders	●	●	●	●	●	●	●
Reteach/Practice/ Enrichment	●	●	●	●	●	●	●
Problem Solving/Homework/English Learners	●	●	●	●	●	●	●
Assessments/Learning Tools	●	●	●	●	●	●	●
Practice Workbook	●	●	●	●	●	●	●
Homework Workbook		●	●	●	●	●	●
English Learners Handbook	●	●	●	●	●	●	●
Building Vocabulary Kit	●	●	●	●	●	●	●
Test Prep Blackline Masters		●	●	●	●	●	●
Chapter Challenges	●	●	●	●	●	●	●
Combination Classroom Guide	●	●	●	●	●	●	●
Kindergarten Kit	●						
Busy Bear Puppet	●						
Math Songs for Young Learners	●						
Student Manipulatives Kit	●	●	●	●	●	●	●
Custom Manipulatives Kits	●	●	●	●	●	●	●
Overhead Manipulatives Kit	●	●	●	●	●	●	●
Math Center	●	●	●	●	●	●	●
Lesson Transparencies	●	●	●	●	●	●	●
Daily Routines Flip Chart	●	●	●	●	●	●	●
Teaching Transparencies	●	●	●	●	●	●	●
Test Prep Transparencies		●	●	●	●	●	●
Lesson Planner CD-ROM	●	●	●	●	●	●	●
Ways to Success Intervention CD-ROM		●	●	●	●	●	●
Chapter Intervention Blackline Masters		●	●	●	●	●	●
eMathBook (Student Book on CD-ROM)	●	●	●	●	●	●	●
Ways to Assess CD-ROM (test and spiral review generator)		●	●	●	●	●	●
MathTracks MP3 Audio CD		●	●	●	●	●	●
Learner Profile		●	●	●	●	●	●
Education Place Web site	●	●	●	●	●	●	●

Manipulatives

Program Manipulatives	Suggested Alternatives	K	1	2	3	4	5	6
Algebra Tiles	Bars and squares made from grid paper or construction paper						●	●
Attribute Blocks	Seashells, pasta, buttons	●	●	●				
Balance Scales	Ruler, paper cups, and string	●	●	●	●	●	●	●
Bill Set	Bills made from construction paper and markers	●	●	●	●	●	●	●
Blank Number Cubes with Labels	Number cards, spinners	●	●	●	●	●	●	●
Coin Set	Real coins, buttons	●	●	●	●	●	●	●
Connecting Cubes	Paper clips, string and beads or pasta	●	●	●	●	●	●	●
Counting Chips	Buttons, coins, beans	●						
Demonstration Clock	Clockface with two lengths of string fastened to the center for the hands	●	●	●	●	●	●	●
Fraction Tiles	Bars and squares made from grid paper or construction paper				●	●	●	●
Geometric Solids	Cans, boxes, balls, cones, modeling clay shapes	●	●	●	●	●	●	●
Geotool Compass							●	●
Pattern Blocks	Shapes cut out of different-colored construction paper or cardboard	●	●	●	●	●	●	●
Place-Value Blocks/ Base-Ten Blocks	Grid paper cutouts	●	●	●	●	●	●	●
Protractor							●	●
Ruler, inch and centimeter	One-inch or one-centimeter grid paper strips					●	●	●
Transparent Spinner	Construction paper, paper clip, and pencil	●	●	●	●	●	●	●
Two-Color Counters	Coins, washers, or beans with one side painted	●	●	●	●	●	●	●

Scope and Sequence

In the Program...

Number and Operations

Addition

	K	1	2	3	4	5	6
Adding decimals				●	●	▲	▲
Adding fractions				●	●	▲	▲
Adding integers and rational numbers					●	●	▲
Adding measurements						●	▲
Adding mixed numbers						●	▲
Adding money	●	●	●	●	▲	▲	▲
Adding multi-digit numbers	●	●	●	▲	▲	▲	▲
Adding whole numbers	●	●	▲	▲	▲	▲	▲
Basic facts	●	●	▲				
Equations						●	▲
Estimating sums		●	●	▲	▲	▲	▲
Expressions					●	●	▲
Inverse operations					●	▲	▲
Mental math		●	●	●	●	▲	▲
Missing addends	●	●	●	▲	▲		
Number sentences	●	●	●	▲	▲		
Problem-solving applications	●	●	●	▲	▲	▲	▲
Properties of addition		●	●	▲	▲	▲	▲
Regrouping to add			●	●	▲	▲	▲
Strategies for adding	●	●	●	●	▲		
Three or more addends		●	▲				

Comparing and Ordering Numbers

	K	1	2	3	4	5	6
Decimals				●	●	▲	▲
Decimals and fractions				●	●	●	▲
Decimals, fractions, and percents						●	▲
Fractions				●	●	●	▲
Integers					●	▲	▲
Money amounts	●	●	●	●	▲		
Percents						●	▲
Rational numbers						●	●
Using <, >, and = symbols			●	●	▲	▲	▲
Whole numbers	●	●	●	▲	▲	▲	▲

Counting, Reading, Writing Numbers

	K	1	2	3	4	5	6
Decimals				●	●	●	▲
Fractions		●	●	●	▲	▲	▲
Integers						●	●
Mixed numbers				●	●	▲	▲
Money	●	●	▲	▲			
Ordinal Numbers	●	●	●	▲			
Percent						●	●
Powers and exponents						●	●
Rational numbers						●	●
Roman and other numerals				●	●	▲	▲
Scientific notation						●	●
Square numbers				●	●	●	▲
Square roots							●
Whole numbers	●	●	●	●	●	▲	▲

KEY Teach and Apply ●   Practice and Apply ▲   Teacher's Edition Lesson ★

In Level 1...

Number and Operations

Addition

adding money 609, 622
adding whole numbers
  basic facts 35–54, 125–137, 429–446, 557–570
  fact families 155–156, 429–446, 465–470, 591–594
  one-digit numbers without regrouping
    models 605–606
    place value chart 605–606
  related facts 153–154, 465–470, 591–592
  three addends 443–444, 569–570
  two-digit numbers without regrouping
    models 607–608
    number form 607–614
    place-value chart 608, 610–612
estimating sums 615–616
horizontal addition 35–48
hundred chart 324, 326, 328
meaning of sum 39–40
mental math 45–46, 603–604
missing addends 48, 130, 156, 432, 445–446
number sentences 39–40, 42, 51–53, 135–137, 154, 470, 571–572, 592
problem-solving applications 51–53, 135–137, 571–573, 615–617
properties of addition
  Associative Property 443–444
  Commutative Property 45–46, 435–436, 569–570
  Zero Property 41–42
relating addition and subtraction 153–154, 465–470, 591–592, 637–638
strategies for adding
  counting on 125–128, 133–134, 429–430, 439–440
  drawing a picture 133–134
  making ten 431–434, 439–440, 559–562
  using double facts 129–131, 133–134, 439–440, 557–558
  using models 35–50, 125–126, 133–134, 429–435, 557–568
  using number lines 127–128, 133–134, 429–430
  using properties 41–42, 45–46, 435–436, 569–570
using symbols 39–40
vertical form 49–50

Comparing and Ordering Numbers

money amounts 402, 407
whole numbers
  before, after, between 17–18, 303–304
  greater than, less than 23–24
  is equal to 21–22, 313–314
  is greater than, is less than 21–24, 311, 313–314
  more, fewer, same 7–8
  more than, less than 327–328
  two-digit numbers 303–304, 311–314
  using models 311–314
  using a number line 23–24, 303–304
  using place value 311–314
  writing <, >, or = 313–314, 566
Ordering
whole numbers
  before, after, between 17–18, 303–304
  two-digit numbers 303–304

Number and Operations

Number and Operations

	K	1	2	3	4	5	6

Decimals

	K	1	2	3	4	5	6
Adding decimals				●	●	▲	▲
Comparing decimals				●	●	▲	▲
Decimal notation			●	●	▲	▲	▲
Decimals and fractions				●	●	▲	▲
Decimals and mixed numbers				●	●	▲	▲
Decimals and percents						●	▲
Dividing decimals						●	▲
Estimating decimals					●	●	▲
Modeling decimals				●	▲		
Multiplying decimals						●	▲
Ordering decimals				●	●	▲	▲
Place value of decimals				●	●	▲	▲
Reading decimals			●	●	●	▲	▲
Repeating and terminating						●	●
Rounding decimals					●	▲	▲
Subtracting decimals				●	●	▲	▲
Writing decimals			●	●	▲	▲	▲

Division

	K	1	2	3	4	5	6
Basic facts			●	●	▲		
Checking division with multiplication				●	▲	▲	▲
Dividing decimals						●	▲
Dividing fractions						●	▲
Dividing integers and rational numbers							●
Dividing mixed numbers						●	▲
Dividing money				●	●	▲	▲
Dividing whole numbers			●	●	●	▲	▲
Division as equal groups			●	▲	▲		
Equations						●	▲
Estimating the quotient				●	●	▲	▲
Expressions					●	▲	▲
Fact families				●	▲		
Missing factors				●	▲	▲	▲
Number sentences				●	▲		
Problem-solving applications			●	●	▲	▲	▲
Relating multiplication and division				●	▲	▲	▲
Relating subtraction and division				●	▲		
Remainders				●	●	▲	
Strategies for dividing			●	●	▲		

Counting, Reading, Writing Numbers

fractions 239–246
money
  amounts
    dime 389–390, 393–404
    half-dollar 402
    nickel 389–392, 395–404
    penny 389–404
    quarter 399–404
on a counting board 634
ordinal numbers 305–306
skip-counting
  by 2's 322–324
  by 5's 325–326, 389–390
  by 10's 277–278, 389–390
whole numbers
  0 through 9 9–12
  10 through 20 13–16
  forward and backward 19, 304
  one hundred 291–292
  through 100 277–295
  word form 9–16, 277–278, 280–284, 291–292

KEY   Teach and Apply ●   Practice and Apply ▲   Teacher's Edition Lesson ★

Scope and Sequence

In the Program...
Number and Operations

	K	1	2	3	4	5	6
Estimating							
Benchmarks		●	●	●	▲	▲	▲
Estimated or Exact Answer?				●	●	●	●
Estimating decimals				●	●	●	▲
Estimating differences			●	●	▲	▲	▲
Estimating fractions					●	▲	▲
Estimating measures	●	●	●	▲	▲	▲	▲
Estimating money			●	●	●	▲	▲
Estimating products				●	●	▲	▲
Estimating quotients				●	●	▲	▲
Estimating sums		●	●	▲	▲	▲	▲
For reasonableness of answer			●	●	▲	▲	▲
Quantities	●	▲					
Using a referent	●	●	▲	▲			
Using strategies		●	●	●	●	▲	▲
Fractions							
Adding fractions				●	●	▲	▲
Comparing fractions			●	●	●	▲	▲
Decimals and fractions				●	●	▲	▲
Decimals and percents						●	▲
Dividing fractions						●	▲
Equivalent fractions				●	●	▲	▲
Improper fractions			●	●	●	▲	▲
Meaning of fractions	●	●	●	●	●	▲	▲
Measurement and fractions				●	▲	▲	▲
Mixed numbers				●	▲	▲	▲
Modeling fractions	●	●	●	▲	▲	▲	▲
Multiplying fractions						●	▲
Ordering fractions				●	▲	▲	▲
Ratios and fractions						●	▲
Reciprocals						●	●
Simplifying fractions					●	●	▲
Subtracting fractions				●	●	▲	▲
Integers and Rational Numbers							
Absolute value						●	▲
Adding and subtracting integers					●	●	▲
Comparing and ordering						●	▲
Graphing on the number line					●	●	▲
Meaning					●	●	▲
Multiplicative inverse							●
Multiplying and dividing integers							●
Negative numbers on a thermometer				●	●	▲	▲
Operations with rational numbers							●
Opposites					●	●	●
Scientific notation						●	●

KEY Teach and Apply ● Practice and Apply ▲ Teacher's Edition Lesson ★

In Level 1...
Number and Operations

Estimating
benchmarks (measures) 511, 513
measures 503–506, 511–514
quantities 307–308
sums 615–616
using a referent 115, 307–308, 315–316
using strategies
 rounding to the nearest ten 653
whole numbers 307–308

Fractions
equal parts 237–238
fractional parts
 of a set 245–246
 of a whole 237–243
meaning of fractions 237–238
modeling fractions
 less than one whole 237–246
reading fractions 237–246
unit fractions
 one half 239–240
 one third, one fourth 241–243

Number and Operations

	K	1	2	3	4	5	6
Mental Math							
Addition		●	●	●	●	▲	▲
Division				●	▲	▲	▲
Multiples and powers of 10		●	●	●	▲	▲	▲
Multiplication				●	▲	▲	▲
Patterns	●	●	▲	▲	▲	▲	▲
Problem-solving applications			●	▲	▲	▲	▲
Subtraction		●	●	▲	▲	▲	▲
Use properties		●	●	●	●	▲	▲
Mixed Numbers							
Adding mixed numbers					●	▲	▲
Decimals and mixed numbers				●	●	▲	▲
Dividing mixed numbers						●	▲
Meaning of mixed numbers				●	▲	▲	▲
Multiplying mixed numbers						●	▲
Subtracting mixed numbers					●	▲	▲
Using a number line with mixed numbers				●	▲	▲	▲
Writing mixed numbers				●	▲	▲	▲
Multiplication							
Arrays			●	▲			
Basic facts		●	●	●	▲		
Concrete/pictorial representations	●	●	●	▲			
Drawing a picture to multiply		●	●	▲			
Equations						●	▲
Estimating products				●	●	▲	▲
Expressions					●	▲	▲
Horizontal and vertical forms				●	▲		
Mental math				●	▲	▲	▲
Missing factors					●	▲	▲
Multiplication as equal groups	●	●	●	▲			
Multiplying decimals						●	▲
Multiplying fractions						●	▲
Multiplying integers and rational numbers							●
Multiplying mixed numbers						●	▲
Multiplying money				●	●	▲	▲
Multiplying three factors				●	▲	▲	▲
Multiplying whole numbers		●	●	▲	▲	▲	▲
Number sentences			●	▲	▲		
Problem-solving applications		●	●	▲	▲	▲	▲
Properties of multiplication			●	●	▲	▲	▲
Related facts				●	▲		
Related to other operations			●	●	▲	▲	▲
Skip-counting to multiply	●	●	●	▲			
Square numbers				●	▲	▲	▲
Strategies			●	●	▲		

KEY Teach and Apply ●   Practice and Apply ▲   Teacher's Edition Lesson ★

In Level 1...

Number and Operations

Mental Math
addition 603–604, 615–616
counting on, counting back 627
multiples of 10 293–296, 569–570, 603–604, 611, 625–636. 631–632
patterns 333–334
subtraction 625–626
use properties
　make a ten, use a double 569–570, 613
　to add in any order 443–444, 569–570

Multiplication Readiness
concrete/pictorial representations 322–326
drawing a picture to multiply 324
equal groups 323–324
multiplying with 2
　skip-counting 322–324
　using a hundred chart 324
multiplying with 5
　skip-counting 325–326
　using a hundred chart 326
multiplying with 10
　skip-counting 277–278
problem-solving applications 324, 326
skip-counting 322–326
strategies
　using patterns 333–334

Scope and Sequence

In the Program...

Number and Operations

	K	1	2	3	4	5	6
Number Theory							
Even and odd numbers	●	●	●	▲	▲	▲	▲
Factor trees					●	▲	▲
Factors			●	●	▲	▲	▲
Figurate numbers					●	▲	▲
Greatest common factor						●	▲
Least common denominator						●	▲
Least common multiple						●	▲
Multiples				●	●	●	▲
Prime factorization						●	▲
Prime and composite numbers					●	●	▲
Reciprocals							▲
Rules for divisibility						●	▲
Place Value							
Decimals				●	●	▲	▲
Expanded form			●	▲	▲	▲	▲
Millions and billions					●	●	▲
Money				●	●	▲	▲
Standard form	●	●	●	▲	▲	▲	▲
Using a place-value chart		●	●	●	▲	▲	▲
Whole numbers	●	●	●	▲	▲	▲	▲
Ratio, Proportion, and Percent							
Estimation with percents						●	●
Finding a percent of a number						●	●
Meaning of percents				●	●	●	●
Percents related to circle graphs						●	●
Percents related to fractions and/or decimals				●	●	●	●
Rates				●	●	▲	▲
Reading and writing ratios						●	●
Writing and solving proportions						●	●
Subtraction							
Basic facts	●	●	●	▲			
Checking subtraction		●	●	●	▲	▲	▲
Equations						●	▲
Estimating differences			●	●	▲	▲	▲
Expressions						●	▲
Mental math		●	●	▲	▲	▲	▲
Number sentences	●	●	●	▲	▲	▲	▲
Problem-solving applications	●	●	▲	▲	▲	▲	▲
Properties of subtraction				●	▲	▲	▲
Regrouping to subtract			●	▲	▲	▲	▲
Strategies for subtracting	●	●	●	▲	▲	▲	▲
Subtracting decimals				●	●	▲	▲
Subtracting fractions				●	●	●	▲
Subtracting integers						●	●
Subtracting mixed numbers					●	●	▲
Subtracting measurements						●	▲
Subtracting money	●	●	●	●	▲	▲	▲
Subtracting whole numbers	●	●	▲	▲	▲	▲	▲
Subtracting with zeros				●	●	▲	▲

KEY Teach and Apply ● Practice and Apply ▲ Teacher's Edition Lesson ★

In Level 1...

Number and Operations

Number Theory

Even numbers 331–332
Odd numbers 331–332

Place Value

addition 607–614
expanded form 289–290
standard form 9–24, 277–295
subtraction 629–638
whole numbers
  through 20 9–24
  through 100 277–297, 311–314
  using models 9–18, 21–27, 277–294
word form 9–16, 277–278, 280–284, 291–292
Place-value chart
  in addition 605–612
  in subtraction 629–638
  through 99 279–284, 287–288, 311–314

Subtraction

basic facts
  to 10 63–75
  to 12 457–478, 459–475
  to 20 581–594
checking subtraction with addition 637–638
comparing 149–150
difference 67–68
fact families
  through 10 155–156, 465–470
  through 12 465–470
  through 20 591–594
horizontal form 65–68
inverse relationship to addition 153–154, 465–470, 591–592, 637–638
mental math 625–626
missing numbers 48, 304, 432, 445–446, 590
number sentences 73–74, 154, 434, 470
problem-solving applications 146, 148, 150, 159–161, 473–475, 584, 592, 595–596
related facts 153–154, 465–470, 591–592
strategies
  counting back 145–146, 157–158
  drawing a picture 157–158
  using a number line 147–148, 157–158, 457–458
  using addition 157–158
  using double facts 581–582
  using models 61–75, 625–630
  using part-part-whole 459–462, 467–470, 583–586, 589–590
subtracting money 633
subtracting whole numbers
  modeling with base-ten blocks 629–630
  one-digit numbers without regrouping
    models 627–628
    number form 627–628
    place-value chart 627–628
  two-digit numbers without regrouping
    models 629–630
    number form 629–638
    place-value chart 629–632
using a number line 147–148, 157–158, 457–458
  using symbols 65–66
  vertical form 75–76
  zero in subtraction 71–72

In the Program...

Algebra

	K	1	2	3	4	5	6
Readiness and Applications							
Addition and subtraction number sentences	●	●	●	▲	▲		
Analyze change	●	●	●	▲	▲	▲	▲
Fact families			●	●	●	▲	
Inverse operations			●	●	▲	▲	▲
Meaning of equality				●	●	▲	▲
Missing addends	●		●	▲	▲		
Missing digits			▲	●	●	▲	▲
Missing factors			●	●	●	▲	▲
Missing measurements and units			●	●	●	●	▲
Missing operations	●	●	●	●	▲		
Multiplication and division number sentences			●	●	▲		
Proportional reasoning	●	●	●	●	▲	▲	▲
Symbols showing relations	●	●	●	▲	▲	▲	▲
Variables			●	●	▲	▲	▲
Venn diagrams		●	●	●	●	▲	▲
Writing and solving number sentences or equations	●	●	●	●	●	●	●
Coordinate Graphs							
Graphing ordered pairs			●	●	▲	▲	▲
Ordered pairs			●	●	▲	▲	▲
Equations and Inequalities							
Equations with more than one variable						●	●
Graphing an equation						●	▲
Linear equations						●	▲
Modeling equations		●	●	●	▲	▲	▲
Formulas					●	●	▲
Solving addition and subtraction equations						●	▲
Solving equations by using inverse operations						●	▲
Solving multiplication and division equations						●	▲
Writing an equation or number sentence				●	●	▲	▲
Writing and solving proportions						●	▲
Writing and solving percent equations						●	▲

KEY Teach and Apply ● Practice and Apply ▲ Teacher's Edition Lesson ★

In Level 1...

Algebra

Readiness and Applications

addition and subtraction number sentences 39–40, 42, 51–53, 73–74, 135–137, 154, 434, 470, 571–572, 592

analyze change 215–218

classifying and sorting 183–185, 187–188, 189, 191–192, 193–194

fact families—addition and subtraction
 through 10 155–156, 465–470
 through 12 465–470
 through 20 591–594

inverse operations 153–154, 465–466

meaning of equality 39–40, 65–66

missing addends 48, 130, 156, 432, 445–446

missing operation symbols 135–137

proportional reasoning
 equivalences in measures and money 365, 375, 377, 389–390, 393–394, 403–404, 525–526
 fraction of a set 245–246
 trading coins 390, 397

symbols showing relations 313–314

writing and solving number sentences
 addition 39–40, 42, 51–53, 135–137, 154, 434, 470, 571–572, 592
 subtraction 73–74, 154, 470

Venn diagrams 194

Equations and Inequalities

using <, >, and = symbols 23–24, 313–314, 566

Scope and Sequence

In the Program...

Algebra

	K	1	2	3	4	5	6
Expressions							
Evaluate by substitution					●	●	▲
Evaluate by using order of operations					●	●	▲
Exploring expressions		●	●	●	▲		
Expressions with exponents						●	▲
Inverse relationship of addition and subtraction		●	●	▲	▲	▲	▲
Inverse relationship of multiplication and division					●	▲	▲
Order of operations					●	▲	▲
Pi as a ratio						●	▲
Writing expressions					●	●	▲
Patterns and Functions							
Continuing patterns	●	●	●	●	▲	▲	▲
Describing patterns	●	●	●	●	▲	▲	▲
Function tables						●	●
Input/output tables	●	●	●	▲	▲	▲	▲
Measurement patterns			●	●	▲	▲	▲
Numerical patterns	●	●	●	▲	▲	▲	▲
Patterns in the coordinate plane						●	▲
Special patterns and sequences	●	●	●	▲	▲	▲	▲
Tessellations			●	●			▲
Using patterns to solve problems	●	●	●	▲	▲	▲	▲
Visual patterns	●	●	●	▲	▲	▲	▲
Properties							
Associative Property		●	●	●	▲	▲	▲
Commutative Property		●	●	▲	▲	▲	▲
Distributive Property					●	●	▲
Equality Property							●
Identity Property				●	▲	▲	▲
Inverse Property							●
Zero Property		●	●	●	▲	▲	▲

KEY Teach and Apply ● Practice and Apply ▲ Teacher's Edition Lesson ★

In Level 1...

Algebra

Expressions

exploring Expressions 567–568
fact families
through 10 155–156, 465–470
through 12 465–470
through 20 591–594

Patterns and Functions

functions 132, 462
completing and/or continuing patterns
numerical patterns 50, 322–336, 389–390, 472, 603–604
visual patterns 219–222, 227–228
describing patterns 50, 219–222, 227–228, 323–335, 472
in a hundred chart 324, 326–328, 330
skip-counting
by 2's 322–324
by 5's 325–326
by 10's 277–278, 389–390
special patterns and sequences
even and odd numbers 331–332
one more one less, ten more ten less 327–328
time patterns 367, 378
using patterns
in addition 50, 322–326, 603–604
in multiplication 322–326, 389–390
in subtraction 71–72, 625–626
to solve problems 219–220, 333–335

Properties

Associative Property
of addition 443–444
Commutative Property
of addition 45–46, 435–436, 569–570
Zero Property
of addition 41–42

Geometry

In the Program...

	K	1	2	3	4	5	6
Basic Figures							
Attributes of plane figures		●	●	●	▲	▲	▲
Basic figures: square, rectangle, triangle, and circle	●	●	●	▲	▲	▲	▲
Classifying and sorting figures and shapes	●	●	●	●	▲	▲	▲
Geometric patterns	●	●	●	▲	▲	▲	▲
Pattern blocks: triangle, square, rhombus, trapezoid, hexagon	●	●	●	●	▲		
Real-life objects	●	●	▲	▲			
Sides, corners, square corners		●	●	▲			
Plane Figures and Spatial Sense							
Angles			●	●	▲	▲	▲
Circles	●	●	●	●	▲	▲	▲
Circumference						●	▲
Comparing angles				●	●		▲
Complex figures		●	●	▲	▲	▲	▲
Constructing angles						●	▲
Constructing circles, using a compass						●	▲
Classifying polygons				●	●		▲
Congruent figures		●		●	▲	▲	▲
Intersecting lines				●	▲	▲	▲
Line of symmetry	●	●	●	▲	▲	▲	▲
Line segments				●	▲	▲	▲
Lines				●	▲	▲	▲
Making and drawing polygons		●	●	▲	▲	▲	▲
Making and drawing quadrilaterals		●	●	▲	▲	▲	▲
Measuring angles, using a protractor					●	▲	▲
Orientations						●	▲
Parallel lines				●	▲	▲	▲
Perpendicular lines				●	▲	▲	▲
Polygons				●	▲	▲	▲
Points				●	▲	▲	▲
Pythagorean Theorem							●
Quadrilaterals				●	▲	▲	▲
Radius, diameter, chord					●	●	▲
Rays				●	▲	▲	▲
Relating solid and plane figures	●	●	▲	▲	▲	▲	▲
Right angles				●	▲	▲	▲
Sides, angles, and diagonals of polygons				●	●	●	▲
Similar figures				●	▲	▲	▲
Symmetry	●	●	●	▲	▲	▲	▲
Subdividing and combining		●	●	▲	▲	▲	▲
Tesselations and tangrams			●	▲	▲	▲	▲
Vertex			●	▲	▲	▲	▲
Visual Thinking	●	●	●	▲	▲	▲	▲

KEY Teach and Apply ● Practice and Apply ▲ Teacher's Edition Lesson ★

In Level 1...

Geometry

Basic Figures

combining shapes 186
corners 185–186, 191–192
geometric patterns 219–221
plane figures
 circle 185–189
 identifying, classifying, and describing 185–189
 rectangle 185–186
 square 185–186
 triangle 185–186
pattern blocks 197–198, 215–218
sides 185–186

Plane Figures and Spatial Sense

drawing geometric figures 184–186
circle 185–189
congruent figures 226
identifying, classifying, and describing 185–189
rectangle 185–186
square 185–186
triangle 185–186
relating solids and plane figures 195–196
symmetry 223–224
Using visual thinking, spatial reasoning, and geometric modeling to solve
 problems 225–226

Scope and Sequence

In the Program...

Geometry

Solid Figures (3-dimensional objects)

	K	1	2	3	4	5	6
Complex figures				●		●	▲
Cone	●	●	●	▲	▲	▲	▲
Cube	●	●	●	▲	▲	▲	▲
Cylinder	●	●	●	▲	▲	▲	▲
Face, edge, vertex			●	▲	▲	▲	▲
Identifying, classifying, and describing solid figures		●	●	▲	▲	▲	▲
Nets			●	●	●	▲	▲
Prisms	●	●	●	▲	▲	▲	▲
Pyramids		●	●	▲	▲	▲	▲
Sphere	●	●	●	▲			

Transformations

	K	1	2	3	4	5	6
Constructions, using a compass to draw arcs						●	▲
Degrees turned						●	▲
Flips (Reflections)	●	●	●	●	●	▲	▲
Slides (Translations)	●	●	●	●	●	▲	▲
Transformations in the coordinate plane						●	●
Turns (Rotations)	●	●	●	●	●	▲	▲

Measurement

Area and Perimeter

	K	1	2	3	4	5	6
Complex figures					●	●	▲
Estimating area, using square units			●	▲			
Finding area, using a formula					●	●	▲
Finding area, using square units			●	▲			
Finding circumference						●	●
Finding perimeter			●	●	▲	▲	▲
Finding perimeter, using a formula						●	●
Meaning of area			●	▲	▲	▲	▲
Meaning of perimeter			●	▲	▲	▲	▲
Problem-solving applications			●	●	▲	▲	▲
Pythagorean theorem						●	●
Relating area and perimeter				●	●	▲	▲
Surface area						●	▲
Surface area, using a formula					●	●	▲

Capacity

	K	1	2	3	4	5	6
Conversion table		●	●	●	▲	▲	▲
Customary system		●	●	●	▲	▲	▲
Equivalent units		●	●	▲	▲	▲	▲
Estimating capacity	●	●	●	▲	▲	▲	▲
Measuring capacity	●	●	●	▲	▲	▲	▲
Metric system		●	●	●	▲	▲	▲
Problem-solving applications	●	●	●	▲	▲	▲	▲

In Level 1...

Geometry

Solid Figures (3-dimensional objects)

cone 191–192
cube 191–192
cylinder 191–192
face 191–192
identifying, classifying, and describing 191–192, 193–194, 195–196
pyramid 191–192
real-life objects 191–192
rectangular prism 191–192
sphere 191–192

Transformations

readiness
  flip 215–218
  slide 215–218
  turn 215–218

Measurement

Capacity

comparing 523–524
estimating 523–524, 527–528
customary system
  comparing 525–526
  conversion table 525
  cup, pint, quart 525–526
  measuring 525
metric system
  comparing 527–529
  estimating 527–529
  liter 527–529
problem solving 498–514, 523–534

KEY Teach and Apply ●   Practice and Apply ▲   Teacher's Edition Lesson ★

Measurement

Length

	K	1	2	3	4	5	6
Centimeter		●	●	▲	▲	▲	▲
Choosing appropriate unit		●	●	●	▲	▲	▲
Conversion table			●	●	▲	▲	▲
Customary measurement		●	●	▲	▲	▲	▲
Distance formula							●
Equivalent units			●	●	▲	▲	▲
Estimating length	●	●	●	▲	▲	▲	▲
Fractions and measurement			●	▲	▲	▲	▲
Foot, yard			●	▲	▲	▲	▲
Inch	●	●	▲	▲	▲	▲	▲
Indirect measurement					●	●	●
Kilometer				●	▲	▲	▲
Measuring instruments		●	●	▲	▲	▲	▲
Measuring length	●	●	●	▲	▲	▲	▲
Meter		●	●	●	▲	▲	▲
Metric measurement		●	●	●	▲	▲	▲
Mile				●	▲	▲	▲
Problem-solving applications	●	●	●	●	▲	▲	▲

Money

	K	1	2	3	4	5	6
Adding and subtracting money		●	●	●	▲	▲	▲
Comparing amounts			●	●	▲	▲	▲
Consumer applications	●	●	●	▲	▲	▲	▲
Counting coins and bills	●	●	▲	▲	▲		
Counting on with money	●	●	▲	▲	▲		
Decimals, fractions, and money				●	▲		
Equivalent amounts	●	●	●	▲	▲		
Estimating money			●	●	▲		
Identifying coins and bills	●	●	▲	▲			
Making change			●	▲	▲	▲	▲
Multiplying and dividing money				●	●	▲	▲
Place value					●	▲	▲
Problem-solving applications	●	●	●	●	▲	▲	▲
Rounding money				●	▲		
Symbolic notation	●	●	●	▲	▲	▲	▲

Temperature

	K	1	2	3	4	5	6
Celsius scale			●	▲	▲	▲	▲
Estimating temperature				●	▲		
Fahrenheit scale		●	●	▲	▲	▲	▲
Interpreting a thermometer		●	●	▲	▲		
Negative numbers					●	▲	▲
Relating Celsius scale to Fahrenheit scale						●	●
Writing temperature			●	●	▲	▲	▲

Measurement

Length

centimeter
  measuring 505–506
choosing appropriate unit 533–534
comparing length 499–500
estimating length 503–506
inch
  measuring 503–504
non-standard units 501–502
problem solving 498–514, 523–534

Money

adding money 609, 622
coins
  dime 389–390, 393–404
  half-dollar 402
  nickel 389–392, 395–404
  penny 389–404
  quarter 399–404
comparing amounts 402, 407
consumer applications
  making purchases 405–407
counting coins 389–404
counting on 389–404
equivalent amounts 399–401, 403–404
modeling and writing amounts 389–404
problem-solving applications 390, 392, 394, 396, 404–407
subtracting money 633
symbolic notation
  cent symbol (¢) 389–404, 633
value of money 389–404

Temperature

Fahrenheit 531–532
interpreting a thermometer 531–532

KEY Teach and Apply ▓ Practice and Apply ● Teacher's Edition Lesson ▲

Scope and Sequence

Measurement

Time

	K	1	2	3	4	5	6
A.M. and P.M.			●	●	▲		
Analog clock	●	●	●	▲			
Calendar concepts	●	●	▲	▲			
Digital clock	●	●	●	▲			
Elapsed time		●	●	▲	▲	▲	▲
Equivalent units			●	●			
Estimating time	●	●	▲	▲			
Ordinal numbers	●	●	▲	▲			
Problem-solving applications	●	●	▲	▲	▲		▲
Schedules		●	●	▲	▲		
Sequencing events	●	●	▲	▲			
Telling time	●	●	●	▲	▲		
Time line				●	●	▲	▲
Time zones				●		●	▲

Volume

	K	1	2	3	4	5	6
Estimating volume				●	▲	▲	▲
Finding volume, counting cubic units				●	▲	▲	▲
Finding volume, using a formula					●	●	▲
Meaning of volume				●	●	▲	▲
Problem-solving applications				●	●	●	▲

Weight and Mass

	K	1	2	3	4	5	6
Conversion table				●	●	▲	▲
Equivalent units				●	●	▲	▲
Estimating weight and mass	●	●	●	●	▲	▲	▲
Finding weight and mass			●	●	▲	▲	▲
Gram and kilogram		●	●	●	▲	▲	▲
Ounce				●	●	▲	▲
Pound		●	●	▲	▲	▲	▲
Problem-solving applications	●	●	●	●	▲	▲	▲
Ton				●		●	▲

KEY Teach and Apply ● Practice and Apply ▲ Teacher's Edition Lesson ★

Measurement

Data Analysis and Probability

Data Analysis

	K	1	2	3	4	5	6
Analyzing and interpreting data	●	●	●	●	▲	▲	▲
Average				●	▲	▲	▲
Bar graphs	●	●	●	▲	▲	▲	▲
Box-and-whisker plots							●
Choosing an appropriate display				●	●	▲	▲
Circle graph			●	●	●	●	▲
Cluster						●	▲
Collecting, organizing, and displaying data	●	●	●	●	▲	▲	▲
Double bar graphs					●	▲	▲
Double line graphs						●	▲
Frequency tables/tally charts	●	●	●	●	●	▲	▲
Gap						●	▲
Histogram					●	●	▲
Line graphs		●			●	▲	▲
Line plots		●	●	●	▲	▲	▲
Making tables and charts	●	●	▲	▲	▲	▲	▲
Mean				●	▲	▲	▲
Measures of central tendency			●	●	●	▲	▲
Median			●	●	▲	▲	▲
Misleading data or graphs						●	▲
Mode			●	●	▲	▲	▲
Organized lists			●	●	●	●	●
Outliers					●	●	▲
Pictographs	●	●	●	▲	▲	▲	▲
Problem-solving applications	●	●	●	▲	▲	▲	▲
Quartiles							●
Range			●	●	▲	▲	▲
Reading tables and charts	●	●	●	▲	▲	▲	▲
Sampling techniques						●	●
Scatter plot							●
Stem-and-leaf plots					●	●	▲
Surveys	●	●	●	●	▲	▲	▲

Probability

	K	1	2	3	4	5	6
Calculating probability of simple event				●	●	▲	▲
Compound events					●	▲	▲
Developing and analyzing predictions and inferences	●	●	●	●	▲	▲	▲
Fair or unfair			●	▲			
Fundamental Counting Principle							●
Likelihood of an event	●	●	●	▲	▲	▲	▲
Permutations and combinations							●
Possible outcomes				●	●	▲	▲
Probability experiments	●	●	●	●	▲	▲	▲
Problem-solving applications	●	●	●	▲	▲	▲	▲
Recording outcomes	●	●	●	▲	▲	▲	▲
Representing likelihood as a number from 0 to 1					●	●	●
Theoretical probability						●	▲
Using a tree diagram or grid					●	▲	▲
Using coins, cubes, or spinners	●	●	●	▲	▲	▲	▲

KEY Teach and Apply ●   Practice and Apply ▲   Teacher's Edition Lesson ★

Data Analysis and Probability

Data Analysis

collecting and organizing 87–88
reading and interpreting data
  bar graphs 95–96, 101–103
  pictographs 89–92
  pictures 405–407
tables or charts 379–380
formulate questions 458, 638
graphs
  bar graph
    making 97–99
    reading and interpreting 95–96, 101–103
  line plots 478
  pictograph
    making 91–92
    reading and interpreting 89–90
making a table 334–335, 447–448
sorting 87–88, 91–93, 97–98
survey 93
tally charts 87–88, 96, 99, 248, 253, 285, 478

Probability

develop and analyze predictions and inferences 99, 247–248, 251–252
likelihood of an event 247–249
making predictions 247–249
probability experiments 247–248
recording outcomes 247–248
tally 247–248
using cubes 249, 251
using spinners 247–248

Scope and Sequence

In the Program...

Problem Solving

	K	1	2	3	4	5	6
Applications / Decisions							
Addition applications	●	●	●	▲	▲	▲	▲
Building new knowledge	●	●	●	●	●	●	●
Choosing a computation method		●	●	●	●	●	▲
Choosing an operation		●	●	●	▲	▲	▲
Curriculum connections		●	●	●	●	●	●
Data applications	●	●	●	▲	▲	▲	▲
Decimal applications				●	●	●	▲
Division applications			●	●	▲	▲	▲
Estimated or exact answers			●	●	●	●	▲
Fraction applications		●	●	●	●	▲	▲
Geometry applications		●	●	●	●	▲	▲
Integer applications						●	▲
Interpreting remainders				●	●	●	▲
Measurement applications	●	●	●	●	▲	▲	▲
Money applications	●	●	●	●	▲	▲	▲
Multiplication applications		●	●	▲	▲	▲	▲
Number and operations	●	●	●	●	▲	▲	▲
Percent applications						●	▲
Place-value applications		●	●	●	▲	▲	▲
Probability applications		●	●	●	▲	▲	▲
Ratio applications						●	▲
Solving multi-step problems		●	●	●	●	▲	▲
Subtraction applications	●	●	▲	▲	▲	▲	▲
Time applications		●	●	▲	▲	▲	▲
Too much information or too little information		●	●	▲	▲	▲	▲
Using a bar graph		●	●	●	▲	▲	▲
Using a diagram					●	▲	▲
Using a formula					●	●	▲
Using a number sentence	●	●	●	▲	▲		▲
Using a pattern	●	●	●	▲	▲	▲	▲
Using a pictograph	●	●	●	▲	▲	▲	▲
Using a picture, graph, or map	●	●	●	▲	▲	▲	▲
Using a table or chart	●	●	●	▲	▲	▲	▲
Using an equation						●	▲
Using estimation			●	●	●	▲	▲
Using functions and graphs					●	●	●
Strategies							
Act it out with models	●	●	●	●	▲	▲	▲
Choose a method		●	●	●	▲	▲	▲
Draw a picture or diagram	●	●	●	●	●	▲	▲
Find a pattern	●	●	●	▲	▲	▲	▲
Guess and check	●	●	●	●	▲	▲	▲
Make a model	●	●	●	●	●	●	▲
Make a table or chart	●	●	●	●	▲	▲	▲
Make an organized list			●	●	●	▲	▲
Monitor and reflect on the process	●	●	●	▲	▲	▲	▲
Solve a simpler problem				●	●	▲	▲
Use logical reasoning	●	●	●	●	▲	▲	▲
Work backward				●	●	▲	▲
Write a number sentence or equation	●	●	●	●	●	▲	▲

KEY Teach and Apply ● Practice and Apply ▲ Teacher's Edition Lesson ★

In Level 1...

Problem Solving

Applications

addition applications 51–53, 135–137, 571–573, 615–617
building new knowledge 39–40, 65–66, 75–76, 243, 313–314, 367, 401, 443–444, 605–614, 627–638
choosing a strategy 27, 53, 79, 103, 133–134, 137, 161, 199, 229, 253, 335, 381, 449, 475, 573, 617, 641
choosing an operation 159–161, 473–475, 639–640
curriculum connections 30, 82, 106, 140, 164, 202, 232, 256, 298, 310, 318, 338, 384, 452, 464, 518, 536, 598, 610, 620, 634, 644
data applications 89–92, 95–96, 101–103, 379–380, 458
fraction applications 238, 240, 242, 246
geometry applications 188, 194, 196–199, 208–210, 227–230
measurement applications 498–514, 523–534
money applications 390, 392, 394, 396, 404–407
number and operations applications 8, 25–27
place-value applications 282, 292–295, 315–316
probability applications 249–250, 252–253
solving multi-step problems 632, found in every Problem Solving lesson
subtraction applications 146, 148, 150, 159–161, 473–475, 584, 592, 595–596
time applications 360, 364, 367, 371, 374, 376, 378–381
too much information 595–596
using a bar graph 95–96, 101–103
using a number sentence 39–40, 42, 51–53, 73–74, 135–137, 154, 470, 571–572, 592
using a pattern 50, 219–222, 227–228, 333–335
using a pictograph 89–92
using a picture 251–253, 405–407
using a table or chart 379–380

Strategies

act it out 77–79
choose an operation 159–161
draw a picture or diagram 25–27, 199
find a pattern 50, 219–222, 227–228, 333–335
guess and check 615–617
make a table 334–335, 400, 447–448
monitor and reflect on the process 315–316, 533–534
use logical reasoning 92, 99, 134, 515–516
write a number sentence 39–40, 42, 51–53, 73–74, 135–137, 154, 434, 470, 571–572, 592

Reasoning and Proof

Analyzing

	K	1	2	3	4	5	6
Algebraic Thinking				▲	▲	▲	▲
Analyzing	●	●	●	●	▲	▲	▲
Checking reasonableness of answers	●	●	●	●	▲	▲	▲
Classifying	●	●	●	●	●	▲	▲
Creating and solving problems	●	●	●	●	●	●	●
Developing arguments and proof	●	●	●	●	▲	▲	▲
Drawing conclusions	●	●	●	●	●	▲	▲
Explaining reasoning	●	●	●	●	●	▲	▲
Generalizing	●	●	●	●	●	●	▲
Identifying relationships				●		●	▲
Identifying relevant information		●	●	▲	▲	▲	▲
Logical thinking	●	●	●	●	▲	▲	▲
Making and investigating conjectures	●	●	●	●	▲	▲	▲
Making decisions	●	●	●	●	▲	▲	▲
Making predictions	●	●	●	●	▲	▲	▲
Number relationships	●	●	●	●	●	●	▲
Reading mathematics	●	●	●	●	▲	▲	▲
Reasonableness of method and solution		●	●	●	▲	▲	▲
Using logic	●	●	●	●	▲	▲	▲
Using strategies to find solutions	●	●	●	●	▲	▲	▲
Visual thinking	●	●	●	▲	▲	▲	▲

Communication

Analyzing and Evaluating Strategies

	K	1	2	3	4	5	6
Act it out with models	●	●	●	●	▲	▲	▲
Choose a method		●	●	●	▲	▲	▲
Choose an operation	●	●	●	▲	▲	▲	▲
Draw a picture or diagram	●	●	●	●	●	●	▲
Find a pattern	●	●	●	▲	▲	▲	▲
Guess and check	●	●	●	●	▲	▲	▲
Make a table or chart	●	●	●	●	▲	▲	▲
Make an organized list			●	●	●	●	▲
Monitor and reflect on the process	●	●	●	●	▲	▲	▲
Solve a simpler problem				●	●	●	▲
Use logical reasoning	●	●	●	●	▲	▲	▲
Work backward				●	●	▲	▲
Write a number sentence or equation	●	●	●	●	●	▲	▲

KEY Teach and Apply ● Practice and Apply ▲ Teacher's Edition Lesson ★

Reasoning and Proof

Analyzing

analyzing 215–218, 309, 531–532
checking reasonableness of answers 315–316, 533–534
classifying and sorting 183–184, 187–189, 193–194
creating and solving problems 43, 69, 93, 151, 437, 587
developing arguments and proof 183–184, 187–189, 193–194
drawing conclusions 183–184, 187–189, 193–194
explaining reasoning 315–316, 533–534
generalizing 183–184, 187–189, 193–194
identifying relevant information 595–596
justifying thinking 315–316, 533–534
logical thinking 92, 134, 515–516
making and investigating conjectures 615–617
making decisions
  choosing a method 27, 53, 79, 103, 133–134, 137, 161, 199, 229, 253, 335, 381, 449, 475, 573, 617, 641
  choosing a strategy 27, 53, 79, 103, 133–134, 137, 161, 199, 229, 253, 335, 381, 449, 475, 573, 617, 641
  choosing an operation 159–161, 473–475, 639–640
  determining reasonableness of an answer 315–316, 533–534
  too much information 595–596
making predictions 247–249
number relationships 65–66
reading mathematics 42, 96, 186, 210, 280, 312, 460, 568, 630
reasonableness of method and solution 315–316, 533–534
using logic 92, 99, 134, 515–516
using strategies to find solutions 27, 53, 79, 103, 133–134, 137, 161, 199, 229, 253, 335, 381, 449, 475, 573, 617, 641
visual thinking 225–226

Communication

Analyzing and Evaluating Strategies

act it out with models 77–79
choose a method 27, 53, 79, 103, 133–134, 137, 161, 199, 229, 253, 335, 381, 449, 475, 573, 617, 641
choose an operation 159–161
draw a picture or diagram 25–27, 199
find a pattern 50, 219–222, 227–228, 333–335
guess and check 615–617
make a table or chart 334–335, 400, 447–448
monitor and reflect on the process 315–316, 533–534
use logical reasoning 92, 99, 134, 515–516
write a number sentence 39–40, 42, 51–53, 73–74, 135–137, 154, 434, 470, 571–572, 592

Scope and Sequence

In the Program...

Communication

	K	1	2	3	4	5	6
Analyzing and Evaluating Thinking							
Determining reasonableness of an answer		●	●	●	▲	▲	▲
Estimating or exact answer			●	●	●	▲	▲
Explaining reasoning	●	●	●	●	▲	▲	▲
Identifying relevant information		●	●	▲	▲	▲	▲
Justifying thinking	●	●	●	●	▲	▲	▲
Making predictions	●	●	●	●	▲	▲	▲
Too much or too little information		●	●	▲	▲		▲
Communicating Mathematical Thinking							
Clarifying understanding	●	●	●	●	▲	▲	▲
Drawing a picture or diagram	●	●	●	●	▲	▲	▲
Using manipulatives	●	●	●	●	●	▲	▲
Talk About It/Write About It		▲	▲	▲	▲	▲	▲
Organizing and Consolidating Thinking							
Classifying	●	●	●	●	●	▲	▲
Drawing conclusions		●	●	●	▲	▲	▲
Generalizing	●	●	●	●	●	▲	▲
Using Mathematical Language							
Creating and solving problems	●	●	●	●	●	●	●
Describing problems and solutions	●	●	●	●	▲	▲	▲
Vocabulary		▲	▲	▲	▲	▲	▲
Connections							
Building Upon Prior Knowledge							
Adding	●	●	●	▲	▲	▲	▲
Dividing			●	●	▲	▲	▲
Multiplying		●	●	●	▲	▲	▲
Subtracting	●	●	●	▲	▲	▲	▲
Using money	●	●	●	●	▲	▲	▲
Recognizing and Applying Mathematics in Context							
Curriculum connections	●	●	●	●	●	●	●
Real-life applications	●	●	●	●	●	●	●
Recognizing and Using Connections							
Decimals, fractions, and mixed numbers				●	●	▲	▲
Drawing conclusions		●	●	●	●	▲	▲
Generalizing	●	●	●	●	●	▲	▲
Measurement and time	●	●	●	●	▲	▲	▲
Money	●	●	●	▲	▲	▲	▲
Patterns	●	●	●	▲	▲	▲	▲
Related facts	●	●	●	●	▲		

In Level 1...

Communication

Analyzing and Evaluating Thinking

determining reasonableness of an answer 315–316, 533–534
estimating or exact answer 315–316
explaining reasoning 315–316, 533–534
identifying relevant information 595–596
justifying thinking 315–316, 533–534
making predictions 247–249
too much information 595–596

Communicating Mathematical Thinking

clarifying understanding (See Explain Your Thinking in lessons.)
drawing a picture 25–27, 199
Talk About It 14, 19, 35, 61, 64, 74, 87, 88, 92, 99, 189, 191, 192, 240, 242, 247, 288, 290, 309, 332, 378, 396, 404, 407, 462, 499, 504, 509, 511, 513, 523, 524, 525, 526, 527, 570, 582, 608, 628
using manipulatives 9–18, 21–27, 35–50, 61–75, 125–126, 133–134, 277–294, 311–314, 429–435, 557–568, 625–630

Organizing and Consolidating Thinking

classifying 183–184, 187–189, 193–194
drawing conclusions 183–184, 187–189, 193–194
generalizing 183–184, 187–189, 193–194

Using Mathematical Language

creating and solving problems 43, 69, 93, 151, 437, 587
describing problems and solutions 7–8, 23–24, 185–189, 193–196, 207–210, 215–216, 247–249, 305–306, 311–312, 329–330, 503–504, 505–506, 511–512, 513–514, 525–526, 527–528, 531–532
Math At Home—Vocabulary 3, 121, 179, 273, 355, 425, 495, 553
Reading Math—Vocabulary 42, 72, 210, 280, 306, 312, 460, 506, 586, 630

Connections

Building Upon Prior Knowledge

adding 39–40, 443–444, 569–570, 605–614
fractions 243
numbers 313–314
subtracting 65–66, 75–76, 633, 627–638
time 365–367
using money 401, 633

Recognizing and Applying Mathematics in Context

curriculum connections 30, 82, 106, 140, 164, 202, 232, 256, 298, 310, 318, 338, 384, 452, 464, 518, 536, 598, 610, 620, 634, 644
real-life applications 87–88, 91–92, 97–98, 207–212, 363–378, 384, 389–404, 503–506, 511–514, 525–528, 531–532

Recognizing and Using Connections

drawing conclusions 183–184, 187–189, 193–194
generalizing 183–184, 187–189, 193–194
measurement 525–526, 531–532
money 399–401, 403–404
patterns 50, 219–222, 227–228, 333–335
related facts 153–154, 465–470, 591–592
time 363–376

In the Program...

Representation

Organizing, Recording, and Communicating Ideas

	K	1	2	3	4	5	6
Making a list			●	●	●	▲	▲
Using a bar graph	●	●	●	▲	▲	▲	▲
Using a circle graph			●	●	●	▲	▲
Using a double bar graph				●	●	▲	▲
Using a double line graph						●	▲
Using a line graph					●	▲	▲
Using a line plot		●	●	●	▲	▲	▲
Using a pictograph	●	●	●	▲	▲	▲	▲
Using a picture or diagram			●	●			
Using a stem-and-leaf plot					●	●	▲
Using a table or chart	●	●	●	▲	▲	▲	▲
Using measurement	●	●	●	●	▲	▲	▲
Using probability	●	●	●	▲	▲	▲	▲
Using symbols	●	●	●	▲	▲	▲	▲

Selecting, Applying, and Translating Among Representations

	K	1	2	3	4	5	6
In decimals, fractions, and money				●	▲		
In geometry	●	●	●	●	▲	▲	▲
In measurement	●	●	●	●	▲	▲	▲
In percent						●	▲
In time		●	●	▲	▲	▲	

Using Representations to Model and Interpret Mathematics

	K	1	2	3	4	5	6
Algebraic equations	●	●	●	●	●	▲	▲
Arrays			●	●	●	▲	▲
Counters, connecting cubes	●	●	●	●	▲	▲	▲
Data	●	●	●	●	▲	▲	▲
Decimal models				●	●	▲	▲
Fraction models		●	●	●	▲	▲	▲
Geoboard/dot or grid paper		●	●	●	●	▲	▲
Geometric tools (compass, protractor, straightedge)					●	●	●
Hundreds chart	●	●	●	▲	▲	▲	▲
Integer models				●	●	●	▲
Make a model (act it out)	●	●	●	●	●	▲	●
Manipulatives or models	●	●	●	●	▲	▲	▲
Modeling solids	●	●	●	●	●	●	●
Money and coins	●	●	▲	▲	▲	▲	▲
Multiplication table				●	▲		
Number lines	●	●	●	●	●	▲	▲
Part/part whole models			●	●	●	▲	▲
Pattern blocks		●	●	▲	▲	▲	▲
Percent models					●	●	●
Pictures/diagrams			●	●	●	●	▲
Place-value models		●	●	●	▲	▲	▲
Symbols	●	●	●	●	▲	▲	▲
Technology	▲	▲	▲	▲	▲	▲	▲

KEY Teach and Apply ●   Practice and Apply ▲   Teacher's Edition Lesson ★

In Level 1...

Representation

Organizing, Recording, and Communicating Ideas

using a bar graph 95–96, 101–103
using a line plot 478
using a pictograph 89–92
using a picture 251–253, 405–407
using a table or chart 379–380
using mathematical language 7–8, 23–24, 185–189, 193–196, 207–210, 215–216, 247–249, 305–306, 311–312, 329–330, 503–504, 505–506, 511–512, 513–514, 525–526, 527–528, 531–532
using measurement 499–514, 523–532
using probability 247–250, 252–253
using symbols 39–40, 65–66, 313–314, 389–404, 633

Selecting, Applying, and Translating Among Representations

in geometry 188–189, 193–194, 215–225
in measurement 501–502, 525–526
in time 363–374

Using Representations to Model and Interpret Mathematics

algebraic expressions, equations, and number sentences 39–40, 42, 51–53, 73–74, 135–137, 154, 434, 470, 571–572, 592
connecting/snap cubes 45–48, 73–74, 129, 153–155, 249–250, 251, 277–278, 331–332, 445–446
counters 9, 11, 13, 15, 35–38, 63–65, 131, 431–434, 557–562, 565, 567, 580
data 89–92, 95–96, 101–103, 379–380, 458
fraction models 236, 239–243, 245–246
geoboard/dot or grid paper 226
hundreds chart 324, 326, 327, 329
make a model (act it out) 77–80, 293–296
modeling solid shapes 191–192, 195–196
money and coins 388, 389–396, 397, 399–404, 419, 609, 633
number cards 100
number cubes 131
number lines
  adding and subtracting 127–128, 147–148, 429–430, 457–458
  counting and ordering 18
  line plots 478
  to compare and order 23–24, 303–304
  to estimate to the nearest ten 653
part/part whole workmats 37–38, 63–65, 135, 153–156, 459–462, 565, 567–568, 580, 583–584, 585, 589
pattern blocks 197–198, 215–218
pictures/diagrams 25–27, 199, 251–253, 267, 405–407
place -value (base ten) blocks 274, 281–282, 285, 287–292, 293–294, 311, 313, 315, 603–608, 625–630
place -value tables 274, 281–282, 311, 313, 605–608, 627–630
real objects 49–50, 182
spinners 247–248, 329, 636
symbols 39–40, 65–66, 313–314, 389–404, 633
technology 116, 174, 268, 350, 420, 490, 548, 654
ten frames 13–16, 431–434, 559–562, 565
thermometers 531–532, 534
Venn diagrams 158, 594

Houghton Mifflin
Math

Welcome To Grade 1 Math

Your book will help you learn about numbers, shapes, graphs, and patterns.

You will start with things you already know—counting, sorting, and ordering. You will learn about adding, subtracting, and solving problems.

You will work with your teacher and classmates to understand math.

xxii Student Handbook

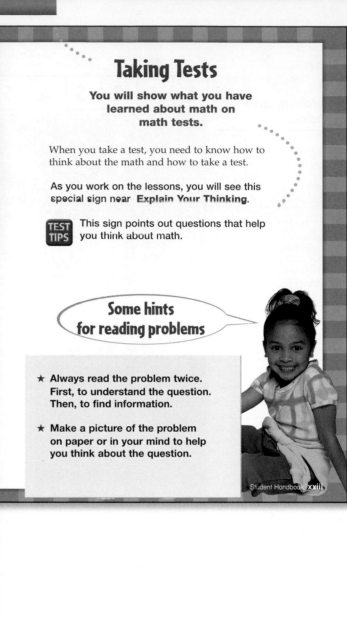

Taking Tests

You will show what you have learned about math on math tests.

When you take a test, you need to know how to think about the math and how to take a test.

As you work on the lessons, you will see this special sign near **Explain Your Thinking**.

TEST TIPS This sign points out questions that help you think about math.

Some hints for reading problems

★ Always read the problem twice. First, to understand the question. Then, to find information.

★ Make a picture of the problem on paper or in your mind to help you think about the question.

Student Handbook xxiii

Some pages in your book have special signs that help you practice taking tests.

You will find **TEST PREP** where you will practice listening to test questions.

You can use a **Practice Test** to see what taking a test is like.

These pages will help you get ready for real tests.

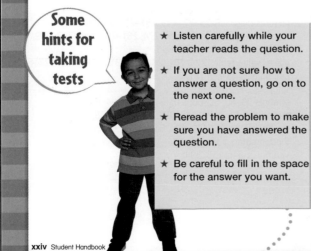

Some hints for taking tests

★ Listen carefully while your teacher reads the question.

★ If you are not sure how to answer a question, go on to the next one.

★ Reread the problem to make sure you have answered the question.

★ Be careful to fill in the space for the answer you want.

xxiv Student Handbook

Notes:

Pacing Guide

Grade One

Houghton Mifflin Math encourages you to customize instruction to meet the needs of your students. As a guide, we have identified lessons as review, core, or extend for typical first grade level content. As these categories may vary based on your local curriculum, consider this chart as a guide to help you plan your teaching year.

Unit	Chapter	Review Lessons	Number of Days	Core Lessons	Number of Days	Extend Lessons	Number of Days	Days to Assess
1	1	1–3	3	5–7	3	4	1	1
	2			1–8	8			1
	3	2	1	1, 3–8	7			1
	4	2	1	1, 3–6	5			2
2	5	3	1	1, 2, 4, 5	4			1
	6			1–7	7			2
3	7	1, 2, 4	3	5–7	3	3	1	1
	8	1, 5	2	2–4, 6–7	5	8	1	1
	9	1	1	2, 4, 6	3	3, 5	2	2
4	10			1–8	8			1
	11			1–6	6			1
	12			1–5	5			2
5	13	1	1	2, 3, 5–9	7	4	1	1
	14	1	1	2–4, 6–7	5	5	1	2
6	15			1–8	8			1
	16			1–8	8			2
7	17	1, 5	2	2–4, 6–8	6			1
	18	1	1	2–5	4			2
8	19			1–7	7			1
	20			1–7	7			1
	21			1, 2, 4–6	5	3	1	1
	22			1–3, 5–7	6	4	1	2
Totals		Review	17	Core	127	Extend	9	30

Table of Contents

As you read through the Table of Contents (it begins on the next page), you will see that *Houghton Mifflin Math* is organized into 8 units. Each unit consists of 2–4 chapters related to the big mathematical idea of the unit. Chapters have from 5 through 9 lessons, two Quick Checks, and a Chapter Review/Test. At the end of each unit is a Unit Test.

This unit/chapter organization promotes the kind of effective teaching and assessment that will help you reach all the learners in your class. Daily Lesson Quizzes make you aware of which students may be in need of help and which have mastered the material. Quick Checks and Chapter and Unit Tests are all linked to immediate and focused remediation and intervention tools—*Reteach* resources and the *Ways to Success* Intervention CD-ROM. *Enrichment* resources and *Chapter Challenge*s are available for those students who are ready for some extra challenge. If algebra is an important element in your mathematics curriculum, you will find special support for this teaching in those lessons with an Algebra label.

Be sure to look for the *Weekly Reader Connection* icons—these indicate activities for which students can find additional information by visiting the Weekly Reader link at Houghton Mifflin's Education Place Web site (**www.eduplace.com/kids/mw/**).

Number Concepts, Operations, and Graphing
STARTING THE UNIT

1 Number Concepts Through 20

2 Addition Concepts

Algebra Indicates lessons that include algebra instruction.

Technology

Ways to Assess Customized
    Spiral Review and Test Generator CD
Lesson Planner CD-ROM
Ways to Success Intervention CD-ROM
MathTracks CD-ROM
Education Place:
www.eduplace.com/math/mw
Houghton Mifflin Math eBook CD-ROM
eManipulatives
eGames

WR Indicates  WEEKLY WR READER® Connection

Addition and Subtraction Facts Through 10

STARTING THE UNIT

5   Addition Strategies Through 10

Algebra Indicates lessons that include algebra instruction.

6 Subtraction Strategies Through 10

FINISHING THE UNIT

Technology

Ways to Assess Customized
   Spiral Review and Test Generator CD

Lesson Planner CD-ROM

Ways to Success Intervention CD-ROM

MathTracks CD-ROM

Education Place:
www.eduplace.com/math/mw

Houghton Mifflin Math eBook CD-ROM

eManipulatives

eGames

 WR Indicates **WEEKLY WR READER® Connection**

Geometry and Fractions
STARTING THE UNIT

7 Plane and Solid Shapes

8 Spatial Sense and Patterns

Algebra Indicates lessons that include algebra instruction.

9 Fractions and Probability

FINISHING THE UNIT

Technology

Ways to Assess Customized
  Spiral Review and Test Generator CD
Lesson Planner CD-ROM
Ways to Success Intervention CD-ROM
MathTracks CD-ROM
Education Place:
www.eduplace.com•math/mw
Houghton Mifflin Math eBook CD-ROM
eManipulatives
eGames

 Indicates **WEEKLY WR READER® Connection**

Numbers Through 100
STARTING THE UNIT

10 Place Value to 100

11 Order and Compare Numbers

Algebra Indicates lessons that include algebra instruction.

 **Number Patterns**

FINISHING THE UNIT

Technology

Ways to Assess Customized
   Spiral Review and Test Generator CD

Lesson Planner CD-ROM

Ways to Success Intervention CD-ROM

MathTracks CD-ROM

Education Place:
www.eduplace.com/math/mw

Houghton Mifflin Math eBook CD-ROM

eManipulatives

eGames

 Indicates **WEEKLY WR READER® Connection**

Time and Money
STARTING THE UNIT

13 Time and Calendar

Algebra Indicates lessons that include algebra instruction.

14 Using Money

FINISHING THE UNIT

Technology

Ways to Assess Customized
  Spiral Review and Test Generator CD

Lesson Planner CD-ROM

Ways to Success Intervention CD-ROM

MathTracks CD-ROM

Education Place:
www.eduplace.com/math/mw

Houghton Mifflin Math eBook CD-ROM

eManipulatives

eGames

 Indicates **WEEKLY WR READER® Connection**

Addition and Subtraction Facts Through 12

STARTING THE UNIT

15 Addition Facts Through 12

Algebra Indicates lessons that include algebra instruction.

Subtraction Facts Through 12

FINISHING THE UNIT

Technology

Ways to Assess Customized
   Spiral Review and Test Generator CD
Lesson Planner CD-ROM
Ways to Success Intervention CD-ROM
MathTracks CD-ROM
Education Place:
www.eduplace.com/math/mw
Houghton Mifflin Math eBook CD-ROM
eManipulatives
eGames

 Indicates **WEEKLY WR READER Connection**

Measurement
STARTING THE UNIT

17 Length and Weight

18 Capacity and Temperature

Algebra Indicates lessons that include algebra instruction.

Technology

Ways to Assess Customized
   Spiral Review and Test Generator CD

Lesson Planner CD-ROM

Ways to Success Intervention CD-ROM

MathTracks CD-ROM

Education Place:
www.eduplace.com/math/mw

Houghton Mifflin Math eBook CD-ROM

eManipulatives

eGames

FINISHING THE UNIT

Two-Digit Addition and Subtraction
STARTING THE UNIT

19 Addition Facts Through 20

 Indicates **WEEKLY WR READER® Connection**

Algebra Indicates lessons that include algebra instruction.

22 Subtracting Two-Digit Numbers

FINISHING THE UNIT

END OF BOOK RESOURCES

Technology

Ways to Assess Customized
   Spiral Review and Test Generator CD
Lesson Planner CD-ROM
Ways to Success Intervention CD-ROM
MathTracks CD-ROM
Education Place:
www.eduplace.com/math/mw
Houghton Mifflin Math eBook CD-ROM
eManipulatives
eGames

 WR Indicates WEEKLY WR READER® Connection

Time and Money

Unit at a Glance

Assessment System

Assessing Prior Knowledge

Check whether children understand the prerequisite concepts and skills.

- **CHAPTER PRETEST** (Unit Resource Folder or *Ways to Success* Intervention CD-ROM)
- **WARM-UP ACTIVITY:** Every TE Lesson
- **UNIT LITERATURE ACTIVITY:** PE p. 354

Ongoing Assessment

Monitor whether children are acquiring new concepts and skills.

- **PROBLEM OF THE DAY:** First page of every TE lesson
- **QUICK REVIEW:** First page of every TE lesson
- **LESSON QUIZ:** First page of every TE lesson
- **COMMON ERROR:** Every TE Lesson
- **QUICK CHECK:** PE pp. 372, 383, 398, 409
- **KEY TOPIC REVIEW:** PE pp. 384, 410

Test Prep and Practice

Help children prepare for state and standardized tests.

- **DAILY TEST PREP:** Every TE Lesson
- **CUMULATIVE TEST PREP:** PE pp. 421–422
- **PROBLEM SOLVING FOR TESTS:** PE pp. 382, 408
- **TEST PREP ON THE NET:** eduplace.com/kids/mw
- **TEST-TAKING STRATEGIES:** eduplace.com/math/mw

Summary Assessment

Assess children's mastery of new concepts and skills.

- **CHAPTER TEST:**
    - ✔ PE pp. 385–386, 411–412
    - ✔ Unit Resource Folder
- **UNIT TEST:**
    - ✔ PE pp. 415–416
    - ✔ Test A, Unit Resource Folder
    - ✔ Test B, Unit Resource Folder

TEST TIPS Student Self-Assessment

Allow children to evaluate their own understanding.

- **EXPLAIN YOUR THINKING:** PE pp. 359, 363, 365, 369, 373, 375, 377, 389, 391, 393, 395, 399, 403

Performance Assessment

Evaluate children's ability to use mathematics in real-world situations.

PERFORMANCE ASSESSMENT: PE pp. 417–418
WRITE ABOUT IT OR TALK ABOUT IT: in Hands-On lessons

Technology Options

Use computer-based assessment to make testing and reporting easier.

- **WAYS TO ASSESS** (CD-ROM, LAN, or Web spiral review and test creation, administration, scoring, and report generation)
- **LEARNER PROFILE** (observations, evaluations, and reports from your handheld or desktop computer)

UNIT 5   Time and Money
Reaching All Learners

Resources	On Level Students	Extra Support Students	English Learners	Inclusion/ Special Needs	Advanced Learners	Mathematically Promising
Student Editions						
Building Vocabulary	●	●	●	●	●	●
Guided Practice ✱	●	●	●	●	●	●
MathTracks MP3 Audio CD 💿	●	●	○	○		
Teacher's Editions						
Building Vocabulary Strategies	●	●	●	○	●	○
Teacher Support	●	○	●		○	○
Intervention Activities	○	●	●	●		
Other Resources						
Chapter Challenges	○				●	●
Combination Classroom Guide	●	●	●	●	●	●
English Learners Handbook	○	○	●	○		
Ways to Success CD-ROM 💿	○	●	●	●		

KEY ● **Highly Appropriate**   ○ **Appropriate**   ✱ **Scaffolded Instruction**

Documenting Adequate Yearly Progress
National Test Correlations

UNIT 5 Objectives		ITBS	Terra Nova (CTBS)	CAT	SAT	MAT
5A	Tell time to the hour and half-hour using analog and digital clocks.	●	●	●		●
5B	Compare time, order events, and determine elapsed time.		●	●		
5C	Use a calendar.	●	●	●	●	●
5D	Find the value of a group of coins including pennies, nickels, and dimes.	●	●	●	●	●
5E	Show the same amount in different ways including ways to make $0.25.	●	●		●	
5F	Apply skills and strategies to solve problems.	●	●	●	●	●

Activities for Reaching All Learners

Differentiated Instruction

Home-School Activity

Daily Time Line

Materials: magazines, glue, index cards

Work with a partner and write a list of 6 things you do during the day. Write the time each activity takes place on an index card. Find magazine pictures that show each activity. Glue each activity in order on a sheet of paper. Glue the time each activity takes place under each picture. Display your daily time line.

Unit Vocabulary Activity

Pay It In Words

Materials: 20 picture/price cards (1¢–90¢); money word cards (10-penny, 10-nickle, 10-dime, 4-quarter, 2 half-dollar)

Shuffle and place the picture/price cards facedown. Place money cards face up in individual piles. One child chooses a picture card, tells the picture, and reads the cost (for example: marbles-23¢) The partner 'pays' for the item in word cards (2-dime and 3 penny cards). Children play 5 rounds.

Remediation

MathTracks Lessons 13.4, 13.5, 13.7, 13.9, 14.1, 14.4, 14.6

Use the MathTracks CD-ROM to help children who need a quick review or extra support for the lesson, to provide children who were absent with complete lesson presentation, or to assist children with reading difficulties.

Intervention

Ways to Success CD-ROM

Use the Ways to Success CD-ROM to help children who need extra help with lessons. This software is designed to reteach the lesson objective, provide extra guided and independent practice, and if needed, reteach a key prerequisite skill.

Unit Project

Classroom Carnival

Math Topics:

- tell time to the hour and half-hour
- determine elapsed time
- find the value of a group of dimes, nickels, pennies
- find different ways to show the same amount of money

To Begin

- Plan a classroom math carnival. Make a schedule of games and activities which lists the days and times each event will take place.
- Set up stations in the classroom for the following activities: coin toss, guess the amount, and clay shapes.

Ongoing

- For use in the Coin Toss, each player gets 5 pennies, 2 nickels, and 1 dime. Player stands behind a line on the floor and tosses the coins into a box.
- The player adds the amount that lands in the box and then records the total amount.
- For practice with elapsed time see Guess the Amount activity in Connecting to the Unit Project on page 357D. For practice in counting on coins see the Clay Shapes activity in Connecting to the Unit Project on page 387D.

To Finish

- Children share results of their coin toss.
- Guess the Amount: Count and tell children the actual number of pennies on display.
- Clay Shapes: Display the clay shapes and amounts for children to observe.
- See page 414 to Wrap Up the Unit Project.

Starting Unit 5
Accessing Prior Knowledge

UNIT 5

Time and Money

From the Read-Aloud Anthology
MY BIG NIGHT

by Harold Mitchell

illustrated by Josee Masse

Access Prior Knowledge
This story will help you review
• Addition and subtraction
  facts through 10
• Order

353a

Tonight at **7** o'clock
I'll be acting in a play.

But it's only ____ o'clock.
It's still **6** hours away.

353b from *My Big Night*

Accessing Prior Knowledge

In Unit 2, children:
• order events
• understand addition and subtraction facts through 10
• use addition strategies
• use subtraction strategies

This selection from the Unit Opener gives you the opportunity to review some of these prerequisite skills.

• You may wish to review order by telling this story: **I walked the dog. It was raining. I put on my raincoat. I dried the dog. I put on my boots.** Ask a volunteer to order the events.

• You may also wish to review addition and subtraction facts by calling out facts to 10 and having volunteers solve.

Story Summary

Today you will be reading a story about time. The title of the story is *My Big Night*. The author is Harold Mitchell.

Reading the Story

You can find the entire text of the book at the end of the Teacher's Edition on page T55.

Read the selection aloud to the children. Then read it again, having children raise their hands when they feel you have come to an important detail.

This story is available in the Read-Aloud Anthology, Volume 3

Tonight at 7 o'clock
I'll be roaring in a play.

But it's only __5__ o'clock.
It's still 2 hours away.

353c

Name_____

Use the number line.
Write the number.

0 1 2 3 4 5 6 7 8 9 10

1. The family eats dinner at 5 o'clock. Which number is just after 5? __6__

2. The play starts at 7 o'clock. Which number is just before 7? __6__

| 1 | 2 | 3 |

3. What does the girl in the story do before the play?

   She plays a ball game and eats dinner.

4. What does she do after dinner?

   She acts in a play.

5. **Talk About It** What do you do before and after dinner?

   Answers may vary.

354

Unit Bibliography

A Quarter From the Tooth Fairy
by Caren Holtzman

How Long? by Elizabeth Dale

Me Counting Time by Joan Sweeney

My Big Night by Harold Mitchell

The Purse by Kathy Caple

What Time Is It, Mr. Wolf?
by Bob Beeson

See also the **Math and Literature Bibliography** in the Teacher Support Handbook at the back of this Teacher's Edition.

Literature Activity

Purpose: This activity provides an opportunity to informally assess children's ability to order events and their understanding of the terms *just before* and *just after*.

Using This Page

- You may wish to have children work in pairs.
- Observe children as they work to complete Exercises 1–2. **What number comes after 7?** (8)
- Observe children as they work to complete Exercises 3–4. If they confuse "before" and "after," have them talk about their morning routine, and order the events.
- Have children share their responses for Exercise 5.

UNIT 5   Time and Money
Math At Home

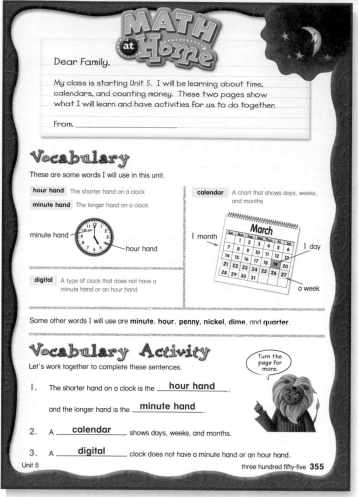

Math at Home

Dear Family,

My class is starting Unit 5. I will be learning about time, calendars, and counting money. These two pages show what I will learn and have activities for us to do together.

From. _____

Vocabulary

These are some words I will use in this unit.

hour hand   The shorter hand on a clock

minute hand   The longer hand on a clock

minute hand → (clock) ← hour hand

calendar   A chart that shows days, weeks, and months

I month | March | I day
a week

digital   A type of clock that does not have a minute hand or an hour hand

Some other words I will use are **minute**, **hour**, **penny**, **nickel**, **dime**, and **quarter**.

Vocabulary Activity

Let's work together to complete these sentences.

Turn the page for more.

1. The shorter hand on a clock is the __hour hand__, and the longer hand is the __minute hand__.

2. A __calendar__ shows days, weeks, and months.

3. A __digital__ clock does not have a minute hand or an hour hand.

Unit 5   three hundred fifty-five **355**

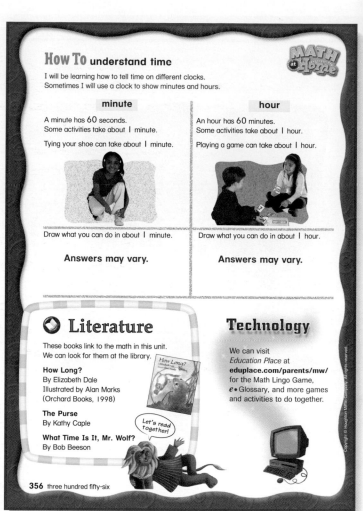

How To understand time

I will be learning how to tell time on different clocks. Sometimes I will use a clock to show minutes and hours.

minute	hour
A minute has 60 seconds. Some activities take about I minute.	An hour has 60 minutes. Some activities take about I hour.
Tying your shoe can take about I minute.	Playing a game can take about I hour.
Draw what you can do in about I minute.	Draw what you can do in about I hour.
Answers may vary.	**Answers may vary.**

Literature

These books link to the math in this unit. We can look for them at the library.

How Long?
By Elizabeth Dale
Illustrated by Alan Marks
(Orchard Books, 1998)

The Purse
By Kathy Caple

What Time Is It, Mr. Wolf?
By Bob Beeson

Let's read together!

Technology

We can visit *Education Place* at **eduplace.com/parents/mw/** for the Math Lingo Game, *e•*Glossary, and more games and activities to do together.

356 three hundred fifty-six

Discuss the letter to the family with children. You may want to use this letter as an introduction to the unit. Highlight for children what they will be learning in the unit. Tell children that as they go through the unit they will be able to answer the questions on these pages.

Math at Home is available in Spanish and other languages on Education Place.
www.eduplace.com/math/mw/

Literature

Encourage parents to find the suggested books and read them with their children.

Technology

Education Place is an award-winning website with engaging activities for students and helpful information for parents. Look for the eGlossary, the Math Lingo Game, and more.

355   UNIT 5

Building Vocabulary

Strategies for Building Vocabulary

Telling Time

Review the terms **hour hand** and **minute hand**. Have a volunteer identify each hand on a demonstration clock. Ask children to be silent for a 60-second period. Explain that the minute hand moved from one tick mark to the next tick mark during the silent period. Ask the children to think of activities they could complete while the minute hand moves once. Create a word web with their ideas.

Make another word web with activities children could complete while the hour hand moves from one hour to the next hour.

Graphic Organizer: Word Web

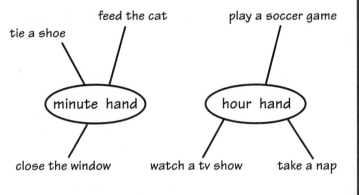

feed the cat   play a soccer game

tie a shoe

minute hand   hour hand

close the window   watch a tv show   take a nap

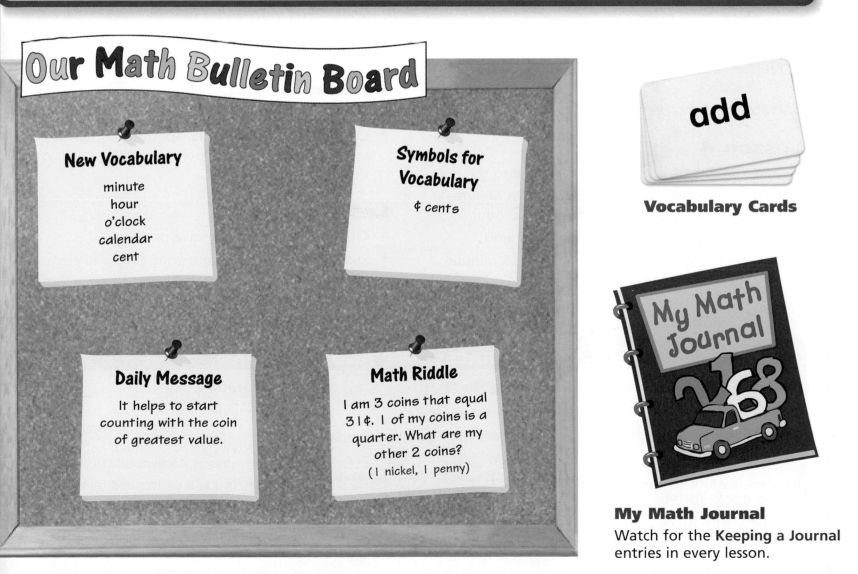

Our Math Bulletin Board

New Vocabulary

minute
hour
o'clock
calendar
cent

Symbols for Vocabulary

¢ cents

Daily Message

It helps to start counting with the coin of greatest value.

Math Riddle

I am 3 coins that equal 31¢. 1 of my coins is a quarter. What are my other 2 coins?
(1 nickel, 1 penny)

add

Vocabulary Cards

My Math Journal

Watch for the **Keeping a Journal** entries in every lesson.

Lesson by Lesson Overview
Time and Calendar

Lesson 1

- This lesson reviews ordering events.
- Real-life scenarios help children relate to the events, which they number to show order.
- Problems have children use the words *before* and *after* to describe sequence of events.

Lesson 2

- In this lesson, children compare time.
- Children estimate how long an activity will take. The activity is timed and children record the results.
- Children identify the pictured activities that take about 1 minute and they compare activities to determine which takes the longest and which takes the shortest amount of time.

Lesson 3

- This lesson teaches children to tell time to the hour on analog and digital clocks.
- Children practice writing the time two ways.
    5 o'clock   5:00
- Problem solving uses time and data in a table.

Lesson 4

- Time to the half-hour is related to time to the hour.
- Children read and write the time first as *minutes after* the hour and then as *half past* the hour.
- Problem solving features a pattern of times.
- The lesson is extended to teach time in 5-minute intervals.

Lesson 5

- Elapsed time is taught with clocks so that children can see how the hands move and count to find how long an activity lasts.
- Problems require children to order time.

Lesson 6

- Children draw hands on analog clocks and write numerals on digital clocks to show given times.
- Children compare clocks with time written out.

Lesson 7

- Calendars are familiar to children.
- This lesson extends that knowledge by having children write answers to questions about a calendar page.
- Ordinal numbers are extended to 31st.
- Children fill in the dates on a blank calendar page and color and write in response to directives about the page.

Lesson 8

- This lesson introduces the months of the year in order.
- Children answer questions about the order of months. They also compare the number of days in given months.

Lesson 9

- Children use a table to solve problems.
- Problems involve the sequencing time and elapsed time.
- Children may need to use clocks to solve problems.

SKILLS TRACE: TIME AND CALENDAR

Grade K	Grade 1	Grade 2
• identify times of day (ch. 9)	• order events	• understand and estimate lengths of time; find elapsed time (ch. 16)
• find days and months on a calendar; also yesterday, today, tomorrow (ch. 9)	• estimate 1 minute, compare times to 1 minute	• tell time to the hour; half-hour; 5 minutes; 15 minutes (ch. 16)
• identify which activities take longer and shorter (ch. 9)	• tell time to the hour and the half-hour (analog and digital)	• read and understand information on a calendar (ch. 16)
• order events (ch. 9)	• find elapsed time	• compare time in terms of hours, days, weeks, and months (ch. 16)
• read time to the hour; match analog to digital (ch. 9)	• read and use a calendar	

Chapter Planner

Lesson	Objective	Vocabulary	Materials	✔ NCTM Standards
13.1 **Order Events** p. 359A	Order events.	before after	index cards	Recognize the attributes of length, volume, weight, area, and time.
13.2 **Estimate a Minute** **(Hands-On)** p. 361A	Compare time.	minute	timer	Develop common referents for measures to make comparisons and estimates.
13.3 **Hour** p. 363A	Tell time to the hour using analog and digital clocks.	digital hour hour hand minute hand o'clock	demonstration clock	Recognize the attributes of length, volume, weight, area, and time.
13.4 **Half-Hour** p. 365A	Tell time to the half-hour.	half-hour	demonstration clock	Recognize the attributes of length, volume, weight, area, and time.
13.5 **Elapsed Time** **(Hands-On)** p. 369A	Find elapsed time.		demonstration clock, index cards labeled 1:00 - 12:00 (teacher-made), individual clocks (Learning Tool (LT) 33)	Recognize the attributes of length, volume, weight, area, and time.
13.6 **Practice Telling Time** p. 373A	Practice telling time using analog and digital clocks.		demonstration clock, index cards, paper clocks (LT 33), analog and digital clock transparencies	Recognize the attributes of length, volume, weight, area, and time.
13.7 **Days and Weeks** p. 375A	Read a calendar to find dates.	calendar	drawing paper, blank calendar (LT 35), calendar	Recognize the attributes of length, volume, weight, area, and time.
13.8 **Months** p. 377A	Use a calendar.		calendar pages, calendar for the month	Recognize the attributes of length, volume, weight, area, and time.
13.9 **Problem Solving: Use a Table** p. 379A	Use a table to solve problems about elapsed time.		schedule in table form	Solve problems that arise in mathematics and in other contexts.

Resources For Reaching All Learners

LESSON RESOURCES: Reteach, Practice, Enrichment, Problem Solving, Homework, English Learners, Daily Routines, Transparencies, Math Center.

ADDITIONAL RESOURCES FROM HOUGHTON MIFFLIN: Chapter Challenges, Combination Classroom Planning Guide, Every Day Counts, Math to Learn (Student Handbook)

Every Day Counts
The *Clock* and *Calendar* Activities in Every Day Counts support the math in this chapter.

Assessing Prior Knowledge

Before beginning the chapter, you can assess student understandings in order to assist you in differentiating instruction.

Complete Chapter Pretest in Unit Resource Folder

Use this test to assess both prerequisite skills (**Are You Ready?** — one page) and chapter content (**Check What You Know** — two pages).

Chapter 13 Prerequisite Skills Pretest

Chapter 13 New Content Pretest

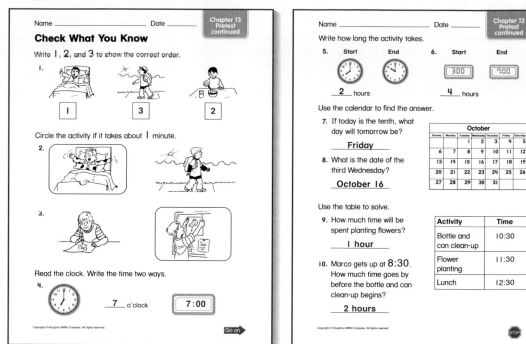

Customizing Instruction

For Students Having Difficulty

Items	Prerequisites	Ways to Success
1–4	Write and order numbers 0–20.	CD: 11.1 Skillsheet 88
5–7	Use estimation to solve reasoning problems.	CD: 11.6 Skillsheet 89

Ways to Success: Intervention for every concept and skill (CD-ROM or Chapter Intervention Skillsheets).

For Students Having Success

Items	Objectives	Resources
7	**13A** Use vocabulary relating to time and calendar.	Enrichment 13.3
1–4	**13B** Order events, compare time.	Enrichment 13.1, 13.2, 13.5
5–6	**13C** Tell and show time to the hour and half-hour.	Enrichment 13.3, 13.4
7–8	**13D** Read and use a calendar.	Enrichment 13.7, 13.8
9–10	**13E** Use a table to solve problems about elapsed time.	Enrichment 13.9

Use **Chapter Challenges** with any students who have success with all new chapter content.

Other Pretest Options

Informal Pretest

The pretest assesses vocabulary and prerequisite skills needed for success in this chapter.

Ways to Success CD-ROM

The **Ways to Success** chapter pretest has automatic assignment of appropriate review lessons.

Chapter Resources

Assessing Prior Knowledge

Just a Minute (compare times to 1 minute)

- Place a minute sand timer in the math center. Prepare a set of activity cards by writing a simple, one-step direction on each card. You might include activities such as hop on one foot or read a page.
- Invite pairs of children to come to the math center, choose an activity card, and start the timer. Partners can help each other count how many times they hop, or how many pages they read, in one minute.

Ongoing Skill Activity

"Go Fish" for a Time (analog and digital clocks)

- Prepare a set of cards that show times to the hour on analog and digital clocks.
- Invite pairs of children to play "Go Fish" with the clock cards. Children shuffle the cards and deal 4 cards to each player. They take turns asking for a clock to match one in their hand. If the other player has the card, he or she passes it over. If not, the child takes the card from the top of the pile.
- Children play until all 12 matches are made.

Connecting to the Unit Project

- To play Clay Shapes, children choose a shape card and use toothpicks and clay to create the shape.
- One child sets a money amount for each side, such as 3¢.
- Children find how much money his or her shape will cost.

Teacher Support

Professional Resources Handbook

Research, Mathematics Content, and Language Intervention

Research-Based Teaching

Telling time or reading a clock is not the same as understanding time, its sequence, its duration, and relativity (Mock, 1999). Research indicates the importance of developing the concept of duration. To associate concrete events with the passing of time, use an egg timer or an hourglass during the silence game or other activities. An appropriate starting point is to have children estimate whether an activity takes about 1 minute, more than 1 minute, or less than 1 minute. See *Professional Resources Handbook, Grade 1,* Unit 5.

For more ideas relating to Unit 5, see the Teacher Support Handbook at the back of this Teacher's Edition.

Language Intervention

Research shows that many students need to both see and hear new words. Write new words, (for example, *minute, digital, hour hand*) on the board as you introduce them.

Technology

Time-Saving Technology Support

Ways to Assess Customized Spiral Review Test Generator CD
Lesson Planner CD-ROM
Ways to Success Intervention CD-ROM
MathTracks CD-ROM
Education Place: www.eduplace.com/math/mw
Houghton Mifflin Math eBook CD-ROM
eManipulatives
eGames

Starting Chapter 13
Time and Calendar

CHAPTER OBJECTIVES

13A Develop and use math vocabulary relating to time and calendar.

13B Order events, compare time, and determine elapsed time.

13C Tell and show time to the hour and half-hour using analog and digital clocks.

13D Read and use a calendar.

13E Use information in a table to solve problems about elapsed time.

Math Background

Time and Calendar

Linking typical activities to appropriate parts of the day is important to learning to tell time. (Breakfast is in the morning; lunch is at noon.)

Units of time include seconds, minutes, hours and days. Children can appreciate the units' relative sizes by associating them with something familiar. If you play kickball for 1 hour, how many minutes have passed? Time measurement involves several concepts. *Before* and *after* are key terms in learning to order events. Reading analog and digital clocks, and learning different ways of expressing time are also key concepts. In Grade 1, children learn to tell time to the hour and half-hour and practice counting by 5s to tell time to five minutes.

Another skill is finding elapsed time, or the number of hours that pass between an event's beginning and end. Elapsed time between 2:00 P.M. and 4:00 P.M. is 2 hours. It is calculated by counting on from 2 to 3 to 4.

Children learn that a calendar shows days, weeks, and months. Children learn to name months in order, as well as days of the week.

Time and Calendar

INVESTIGATION

Find the clocks in the shop that are not working right.

Using The Investigation

- Review the terms *hour hand* and *minute hand* with children. Hold up a clock. Have volunteers identify the hour hand and the minute hand.

- Discuss *minute* and *hour* as periods of time. Explain that it takes 60 seconds for the minute hand to move from one minute to the next on the clock. Explain that it takes the hour hand one hour to move from one hour to the next.

- Have children brainstorm activities they can do in one minute and one hour.

- Read the directions to children. **Look at the clocks in the pictures. Find the clocks in the shop that are not working right.** (4 incorrect clocks: 1 with jumbled numbers, 1 with no hands, 1 with 6 hands, 1 with upside down clockface)

- Discuss other clocks that are correct.

 For more information about projects and investigations, visit Education Place. **eduplace.com/math/mw/**

Before and After School

Draw something you do in the morning before school.

Answers may vary.

These kids are busy learning at school during the day.

Draw something you do in the evening.

Answers may vary.

For Mathematically Promising Students

The *Chapter Challenges* resource book provides blackline masters for activities that explore, extend, and connect the mathematics in every chapter. To support this independent work, see the Teacher Notes for each activity.

Explore: Ordering Events, page 73, after Lesson 1
Extend: A Timely Story, page 75, after Lesson 3
Connect: Time On Saturday, page 77, after Lesson 5

Using This Page

- Give children crayons.
- Review the terms *before* and *after* with children. Share with children activities you do before and after school.
- **Think about your days during the week. In the top box, draw a picture of something you do before you come to school in the morning.** (eat breakfast, get dressed) **Then, in the bottom box, draw a picture of something you do after school in the evening.** (a sport activity, homework, eat dinner, go to bed)

NSF Children's Math Worlds

Using *Children's Math Worlds* helps develop student communication skills because of the daily work with Math Talk, a teaching practice that can be used with all lessons. The emphasis on building a helping community will also enhance student participation in all classroom discussion.

Order Events

PLANNING THE LESSON

MATHEMATICS OBJECTIVE
Order events.

Use Lesson Planner CD-ROM for Lesson 13.1.

Meeting North Carolina's Standards
2.02 Develop an understanding of the concept of time.

Daily Routines

Calendar
Write several numbers from 1 to 30 on the board in random order. Ask children to name the day and dates in order.

Sunday	Monday	Tuesday	Wednesday	Thursday	Friday	Saturday
			1	2	3	4
5	6	7	8	9	10	11
12	13	14	15	16	17	18
19	20	21	22	23	24	25
26	27	28	29	30	31	

Vocabulary
Ask children to give examples of things that can be in **order**. Suggest the letters of the alphabet, counting numbers, and days of the week. Have children identify letters **before** and **after** given letters.

Vocabulary Cards

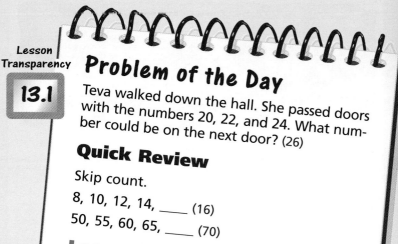

Lesson Transparency **13.1**

Problem of the Day
Teva walked down the hall. She passed doors with the numbers 20, 22, and 24. What number could be on the next door? (26)

Quick Review
Skip count.
8, 10, 12, 14, ____ (16)
50, 55, 60, 65, ____ (70)

Lesson Quiz
Meg put on her bike helmet. She rode her bike to Jin's house. Meg and Jin rode their bikes to the park.

1. What did Meg do before she rode to Jin's house? (put on her bike helmet)

2. What did she do after she rode to Jin's house? (rode to the park)

LEVELED PRACTICE

RETEACH 13.1

Name _____ Date _____ Reteach 13.1

Order Events
Many events happen in order.

1	2	3
The glass is empty before Mario begins to pour.	Mario is pouring his juice.	The glass is full after Mario pours.

Write 1, 2, and 3 to show the correct order.

1.
| 3 | 1 | 2 |

2.
| 3 | 2 | 1 |

Copyright © Houghton Mifflin Company. All rights reserved.
Use with text pages 359–360.

PRACTICE 13.1

Name _____ Date _____ Practice 13.1

Order Events
Write 1, 2, and 3 to show the correct order.

1.
| 2 | 3 | 1 |

2.
| 3 | 1 | 2 |

3.
| 1 | 3 | 2 |

Test Prep

Fill in the ○ for the correct answer. NH means Not Here.

4. Jane is sending a postcard to a friend.
   What is the *last* thing she will do?

| Write the postcard. | Put the postcard in the mailbox. | Put a stamp on the postcard. | NH |
| ○ | ● | ○ | ○ |

Copyright © Houghton Mifflin Company. All rights reserved.
Use with text pages 359–360.

ENRICHMENT 13.1

Name _____ Date _____ Enrichment 13.1

Now, Next, Then, and End
Put the events in the correct order.
Write 1, 2, 3, or 4.

1.
| 2 | 4 |
| 1 | 3 |

2.
| 1 | 3 |
| 2 | 4 |

Talk About It What do you do after the sun comes up? What do you do when it goes down?

Copyright © Houghton Mifflin Company. All rights reserved.
Use with text pages 359–360.

Reaching All Learners

Differentiated Instruction

English Learners

In order to understand concepts dealing with sequence and time, children will have to understand the term *in order*. Use Worksheet 13.1 to introduce English-language learners to this term.

Special Needs

VISUAL, TACTILE

- Write three events in random order. For example, put on your shoe, put on your sock, tie your shoe.
- Ask the child which event happens first, second, and last.
- Have the child write 1, 2, and 3 to show order.

Put on shoe.	Put on sock.	Tie shoe.
2	1	3

Early Finishers

AUDITORY

- Have children work in pairs. Have one child say a common activity that people do every day, such as putting toothpaste on a toothbrush.
- Then have the other child say the activity that happens just after that, such as brushing teeth.
- Children continue with different situations, saying the activities that happen just before and just after.

TECHNOLOGY

Spiral Review

Using the *Ways to Assess* CD-ROM, you can create **customized** spiral review worksheets covering any lessons you choose.

Lesson Planner

Use the **Lesson Planner CD-ROM** to see how lesson objectives for this chapter are correlated to standards.

Education Place

Encourage students to visit **Education Place** at eduplace.com/kids/mw/ for more student activities.

Science Connection

Tell children that all turtles lay their eggs on land. Work with children to decide on the order of events.

1. Turtle digs a hole.
2. She lays her eggs in the hole.
3. She covers the eggs with dirt.

MATH CENTER

Real-Life Activity

Help children understand the usefulness of mathematics. This activity makes math come alive by connecting the lesson skills to a real-life situation.

Homework Workbook Page 82

TEACHING LESSON 13.1

LESSON ORGANIZER

Objective Order events.

Resources Reteach, Practice, Enrichment, Problem Solving, Homework, English Learners, Transparencies, Math Center

Materials index cards

Activity

Warm-Up Activity

Modeling *Before* and *After* with a Number Line

iii Small Group	⏱ 5 minutes	Visual, Auditory

1. Draw a number line from 20 to 35 on the board.

   20 21 22 23 24 25 26 27 28 29 30 31 32 33 34 35

2. Circle the number 21. **What number comes just before 21?** (20) **What number comes just after 21?** (22)

3. Continue by having volunteers circle other numbers and asking the same questions.

Name_____

Order Events

Objective Put events in order.

Vocabulary before after

Some events happen **before** others.
Some events happen **after** others.
Many events happen in order.

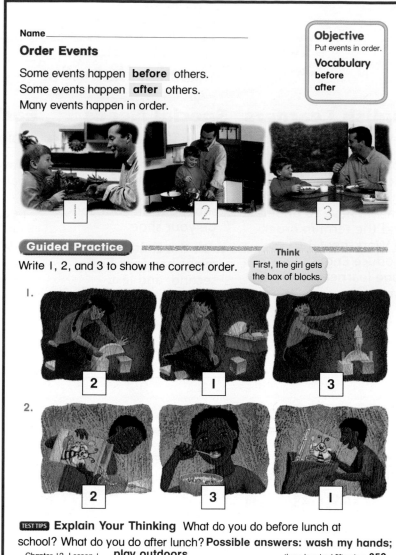

Guided Practice

Write 1, 2, and 3 to show the correct order.

Think First, the girl gets the box of blocks.

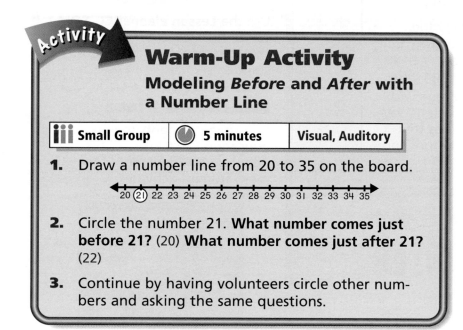

1. 2 1 3

2.  2 3 1

TEST TIPS **Explain Your Thinking** What do you do before lunch at school? What do you do after lunch? **Possible answers: wash my hands; play outdoors**

Chapter 13 Lesson 1   three hundred fifty-nine **359**

---

1 Introduce

Discuss Order

iiii Whole Group	⏱ 10–15 minutes	Visual, Auditory

1. Draw simple sketches on the board showing an egg being cracked into a pan, a fried egg in a pan, a person eating a fried egg. Label the pictures 1, 2, and 3.

2. Explain that some events happen in order, like things you do to make a fried egg. Point to the first picture. **First, you crack an egg into a pan.** Point to the middle picture. **Then you cook the egg.** Point to the last picture. **Finally, you eat the egg after you cook it.**

3. Ask volunteers for other examples of things they might do in order. Children can act out these examples or draw pictures.

2 Develop

Guided Learning

Teaching Example Introduce the objective and vocabulary to children. Guide them through the example to show how the steps of making soup need to happen in order. 1. Cut up the vegetables and get all the ingredients together. 2. Put the pot with the vegetables and water on the stove to cook. 3. Eat the soup when it is done.

Guided Practice

Have children complete **Exercises 1–2** as you observe. Give children the opportunity to answer the Explain Your Thinking question and discuss their responses with the class.

Write 1, 2, and 3 to show the correct order.

Remember to think about which event happens first.

1. [2] [1] [3]

2. [1] [3] [2]

Draw three pictures in order to show things you did today.

3.
Answers may vary.		
[1]	[2]	[3]

Problem Solving ▶ Reasoning

Mato brushes his teeth.
Next he reads a story.
Then he goes to bed.

4. What does Mato do before he reads a story?

   brushes his teeth

5. What does Mato do after he reads a story?

   goes to bed

360 three hundred sixty

At Home Discuss your child's daily routine. Have your child use the words **before** and **after** to tell about the events.

Daily Test Prep

How many fewer birds are there than kittens?

2 ● 3 ○ 4 ○ 5 ○

Pet Shop Animals						
Kittens						
Rabbits						
Fish						
Birds						

0 1 2 3 4 5 6

Activity

Lesson Intervention
Order the Steps of an Event

Or use Intervention CD-ROM Lesson 13.1

👥 Small Group	⏱ 5–10 minutes	Auditory, Visual

Materials: *index cards*

1. Give each group of 3 children the following events on index cards: *cook dinner, eat dinner, wash dishes.* Give one card to each child.

[cook dinner] [eat dinner] [wash dishes]

2. **In what order do these 3 events happen?** Have children agree on the order, then arrange themselves in order. **What happens first?** (cook dinner) **What comes next?** (eat dinner) **What happens last?** (wash dishes)

3. Have the groups of 3 come up with their own events and put them in order for the rest of the class.

---

3 Practice

Independent Practice

Be sure children understand what the pictures show. Have children complete **Exercises 1–3** independently.

Problem Solving

After children complete **Exercises 4–5**, call on volunteers to share their answers. Discuss other things children may do at night.

Common Error

Misinterpreting Pictured Events

To help children decide the order in which events would happen, have them make up a story to match the pictures. Use their stories to determine if they understand the concept.

4 Assess and Close

Andrew put on his coat and boots. Next, he went outside. Then he built a snowman.

What did Andrew do before he went outside? (put on his coat and boots)

What did he do after he went outside? (built a snowman)

Keeping a Journal

Draw three pictures to show things you did before you came to school today. Label your pictures 1, 2, and 3 to show the order.

Hands-On Activity: Estimate a Minute

PLANNING THE LESSON

MATHEMATICS OBJECTIVE
Compare time.

Use Lesson Planner CD-ROM for Lesson 13.2.

Daily Routines

Calendar
Have children name the dates of all the Saturdays in the month. Ask them what pattern they see.
(increase by 7)

Sunday	Monday	Tuesday	Wednesday	Thursday	Friday	Saturday
				1	2	3	4
5	6	7	8	9	10	11
12	13	14	15	16	17	18
19	20	21	22	23	24	25
26	27	28	29	30	31	

Vocabulary
Show a demonstration clock and introduce a **minute**. Explain that it is a unit of time.

Vocabulary Cards

Meeting North Carolina's Standards
2.02 Develop an understanding of the concept of time.

Lesson Transparency **13.2**

Problem of the Day
Raul dropped his bat. Then he ran to first base. What did he probably do before he did those two things? (hit the ball with the bat)

Quick Review
Write the number.
twenty-one (21)   thirty-three (33)
nineteen (19)   eleven (11)

Lesson Quiz
1. Does it take less than a minute or more than a minute to eat dinner? (more than a minute)
2. Does it take less than a minute or more than a minute to take a photograph? (less than a minute)

LEVELED PRACTICE

RETEACH 13.2

Name _____ Date _____   Reteach 13.2

Activity: Estimate a Minute

If you know how long a minute is, you can find out what takes more or less than 1 minute.

less than 1 minute	about 1 minute	more than 1 minute

Circle the answer. **Answers will vary.**

1. About how long does it take to watch a TV show?	about 1 minute (more than 1 minute) less than 1 minute	
2. About how long does it take to wash your face?	(about 1 minute) more than 1 minute less than 1 minute	Soap
3. About how long does it take to write your first and last name?	In 1 minute I wrote: my first name my first and last name I had time left over. **Answers will vary.**	Tito Ruiz

Copyright © Houghton Mifflin Company. All rights reserved.   Use with text pages 361–362.

PRACTICE 13.2

Name _____ Date _____   Practice 13.2

Activity: Estimate a Minute

Circle activities you know take about 1 minute.
Draw an X on the activity if it takes more than 1 minute.

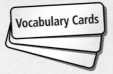

1.   2.
3.   4.

Test Prep

Fill in the ○ under the correct answer. NH means Not Here.

5. Which of these activities takes more than 1 minute?

NH

○   ○   ●   ○

Copyright © Houghton Mifflin Company. All rights reserved.   Use with text pages 361–362.

ENRICHMENT 13.2

Name _____ Date _____   Enrichment 13.2

This Will Only Take a Minute

Color the activities that take about 1 minute (Red)

Color the activities that take more than 1 minute (Green)

1. red	2. red	3. green
4. green	5. green	6. red
7. green	8. red	9. red

Write About It What are some things that take you about 1 minute to do?
Answers will vary.
_____

Copyright © Houghton Mifflin Company. All rights reserved.   Use with text pages 361–362.

Practice Workbook Page 83

Reaching All Learners
Differentiated Instruction

English Learners

In order to estimate time, children will have to understand the words *longest* and *shortest*. Use Worksheet 13.2 to introduce English-language learners to these words.

Special Needs
AUDITORY, TACTILE

Materials: *counters*

- Ask the child to estimate how many counters he or she can line up in a row in 1 minute.
- Have the child start when you say "go."
- After 1 minute, have the child count how many counters are lined up. Compare that number to the estimate.

Early Finishers
TACTILE, KINESTHETIC

Materials: *index cards, timer*

- On index cards, write several activities that will take about one minute to do. For example: writing 5 addition sentences, solving 3 subtraction problems, or measuring 3 lines.
- Using a timer, have children choose a card and try to complete the activity in less than a minute.

TECHNOLOGY

Spiral Review

To reinforce skills on lessons taught earlier, create **customized** spiral review worksheets using the *Ways to Assess* CD-ROM.

eBook

An electronic version of this lesson can be found in **eMathBook**.

Games

Students can practice their math vocabulary using the Math Lingo game, available on the *Ways to Success* CD-ROM.

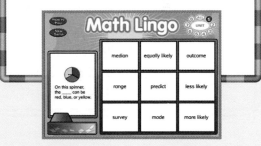

Social Studies Connection

Working in small groups, challenge children to list as many occupations as they think of in 1 minute. After you have timed them for a minute, have groups compare their lists.

MATH CENTER

Vocabulary Activity

This vocabulary-building activity helps children understand and remember new words. Encourage children to use the words in math discussion.

PROBLEM SOLVING 13.2

Name _____ Date _____ | Problem Solving 13.2

Estimate a Minute

Read each problem.
Circle your answer.
Draw a picture to help you answer.

| The school bus will come in about 1 minute. Does Kevin have time to make a sandwich? Yes (No) | Draw or write here. I think of all the steps I take in making a sandwich. They take more than 1 minute. |

1. Annette's friend rings the doorbell. Can Annette answer the door in less than 1 minute? (Yes) No | Draw or write here.

2. Dan has 20 pages to read in his book. Can he read them in less than 1 minute? Yes (No)

3. Shana sends a letter to Grandma. Can she put a stamp on the letter in less than 1 minute? (Yes) No

Use with text pages 361–362.

HOMEWORK 13.2

Name _____ Date _____ | Homework 13.2

Activity: Estimate a Minute

| You can read a page in about 1 minute. | It takes more than 1 minute to read a book. | You can read a sign in less than 1 minute. STOP |

Use a clock to time 1 minute.
Draw >, <, or = next to each activitiy.

= about 1 minute, > more than 1 minute, < less than 1 minute

1. Take a bath.	>	2. Write the alphabet.	>
3. Open a gift.	=	4. Open a door.	<
5. Eat breakfast.	>	6. Write your name.	=

7. Think of two activities that take more than 1 minute and two that take less than 1 minute. Act them out to see if you are right. | Draw here.

Use with text pages 361–362.

ENGLISH LEARNERS 13.2

Name _____ Date _____ | English Learners 13.2

Estimate a Minute

longest

shortest

Circle the picture that is the longest.

1.

Circle the picture that is the shortest.

2.

To the Teacher: Use the pictures and sentences at the top of the page to demonstrate the meaning of the words *longest* and *shortest*. Then have children circle the pictures to show which are the *longest* and *shortest*.

Use with text pages 361–362.

TEACHING LESSON 13.2

LESSON ORGANIZER

Objective Compare time.

Resources Reteach, Practice, Enrichment, Problem Solving, Homework, English Learners, Transparencies, Math Center

Materials Timer

Activity

Warm-Up Activity
Modeling Time

⭑⭑⭑⭑ Whole Group	⏱ 5 minutes	Auditory, Tactile

1. Ask children what they know about time. **What day is today? What day of the week was yesterday? Is it morning or afternoon?** Continue with more specific questions to find out what they know about time.

2. **What time do you go to bed? How long is your favorite after school activity?**

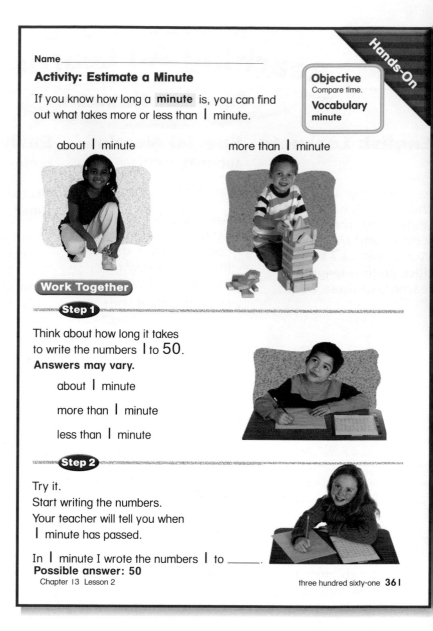

Name_____

Activity: Estimate a Minute

Objective Compare time.

Vocabulary minute

If you know how long a **minute** is, you can find out what takes more or less than 1 minute.

about 1 minute   more than 1 minute

Work Together

Step 1

Think about how long it takes to write the numbers 1 to 50.
Answers may vary.

  about 1 minute

  more than 1 minute

  less than 1 minute

Step 2

Try it.
Start writing the numbers.
Your teacher will tell you when
1 minute has passed.

In 1 minute I wrote the numbers 1 to _____.
Possible answer: 50

Chapter 13 Lesson 2   three hundred sixty-one **361**

---

① Introduce
Activity

Model Estimating a Minute

⭑⭑⭑⭑ Whole Group	⏱ 10–15 minutes	Visual, Auditory

Materials: *timer*

1. Ask children to wait while you write on the board for one minute. Set a timer for one minute. Start writing addition sentences. Stop after a minute. **How long did I keep you waiting?** Explain to children that you wrote on the board for 1 minute.

2. Assign children an exercise or routine that they enjoy. **Now you are going to draw as many flowers on the page as you can when I say go.** Have children draw and stop after a minute. **How long were you drawing?** Explain that the exercise lasted for 1 minute.

3. **How long is a minute?** (Accept reasonable answers.)

② Develop

Teaching Example Introduce the objective and vocabulary to children. Tell them that they can estimate how long it takes for 1 minute to pass. **Close your eyes. I will tell you when the minute starts. Raise one hand when you think one minute has passed.** After the minute passes, discuss how long different children waited to raise their hands.

Work Together

Step 1. Have children guess how long it takes to write the numbers 1 to 50. Encourage children to share their estimates and explain why they chose them.

Step 2. Next, time the children for one minute as they write. Have children count their numbers. Direct children to complete the sentence.

Discuss how long it took most children to write the numbers. Guide them to think in terms of 1 minute or more than 1 minute.

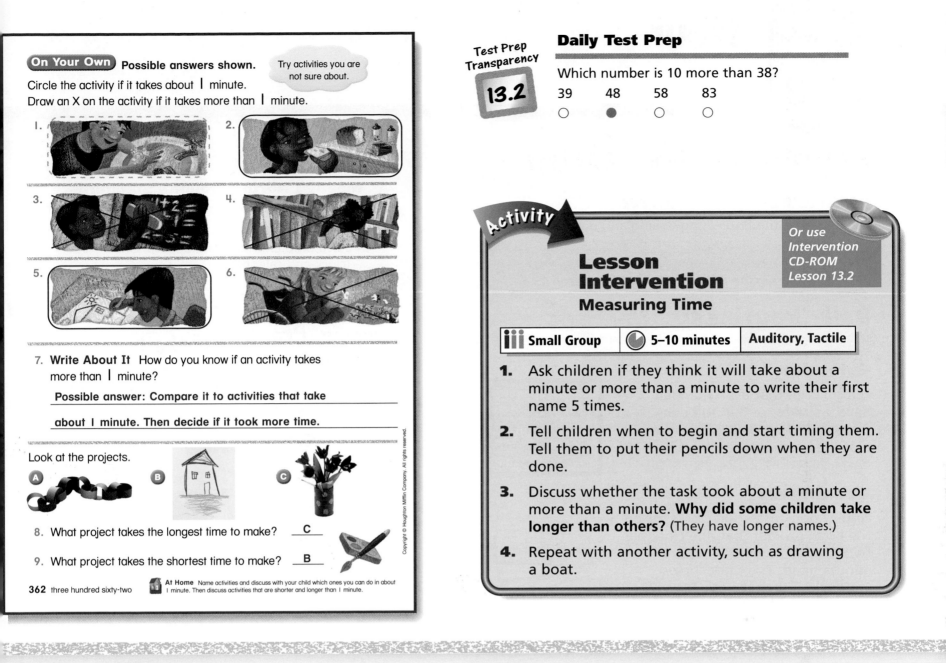

On Your Own Possible answers shown.

Circle the activity if it takes about 1 minute.
Draw an X on the activity if it takes more than 1 minute.

Try activities you are not sure about.

1.

2.

3.

4.

5.

6.

7. **Write About It** How do you know if an activity takes more than 1 minute?

Possible answer: Compare it to activities that take about 1 minute. Then decide if it took more time.

Look at the projects.

Ⓐ  Ⓑ Ⓒ

8. What project takes the longest time to make? __C__

9. What project takes the shortest time to make? __B__

362 three hundred sixty-two

At Home Name activities and discuss with your child which ones you can do in about 1 minute. Then discuss activities that are shorter and longer than 1 minute.

Daily Test Prep

Which number is 10 more than 38?

39 48 58 83
○ ● ○ ○

Activity

Lesson Intervention

Measuring Time

Or use Intervention CD-ROM Lesson 13.2

| 👥 Small Group | 🕐 5–10 minutes | Auditory, Tactile |

1. Ask children if they think it will take about a minute or more than a minute to write their first name 5 times.

2. Tell children when to begin and start timing them. Tell them to put their pencils down when they are done.

3. Discuss whether the task took about a minute or more than a minute. **Why did some children take longer than others?** (They have longer names.)

4. Repeat with another activity, such as drawing a boat.

---

❸ Practice

On Your Own

Children complete **Exercises 1–6** independently. Use the **Write About It** in **Exercise 7** to discuss children's ideas. Then have children complete **Exercises 8–9**.

Common Error

Misunderstanding the Problem

Children may be so intent on looking at the pictures that they may misunderstand the problem. Have children read aloud carefully to find out what they need to do, or read the directions and discuss.

❹ Assess and Close

What is something that takes about a minute to do?
(Responses will vary.)

What is something that takes more than a minute to do?
(Responses will vary.)

Keeping a Journal

Write a list of 5 things that take you about a minute to do.

Hour

PLANNING THE LESSON

MATHEMATICS OBJECTIVE
Tell time to the hour using analog and digital clocks.

Use Lesson Planner CD-ROM for Lesson 13.3.

Daily Routines

Calendar

Tell children that even numbers have 0, 2, 4, 6, or 8 in the ones place. Ask children to name dates that are even numbers. (2, 4, 6, 8, 10, 12, 14, 16, 18, 20, 22, 24, 26, 28, 30)

Sunday	Monday	Tuesday	Wednesday	Thursday	Friday	Saturday
				1	2	3	4
5	6	7	8	9	10	11
12	13	14	15	16	17	18
19	20	21	22	23	24	25
26	27	28	29	30	31	

Vocabulary

Display demonstration clocks set on the hour. Explain that one clock has two hands—an **hour hand** and a **minute hand**. The clock shows 1 **o'clock**. A **digital** clock shows the same time with numbers.

Vocabulary Cards

Meeting North Carolina's Standards

2.02 Develop an understanding of the concept of time.
- Tell time at the hour and half-hour.
- Solve problems involving applications of time (clock and calendar).

Lesson Transparency **13.3**

Problem of the Day
Donato saw a solid object with 8 corners. All the edges were the same length. What object did he see? (Possible answers: number cube, block, box)

Quick Review
Which number is greater?

35, 18	51, 86	75, 48	96, 69
(35)	(86)	(75)	(96)

Lesson Quiz
Write the time another way.
1. 4 o'clock (4:00)
2. 11:00 (11 o'clock)
3. 7 o'clock (7:00)

LEVELED PRACTICE

RETEACH 13.3

Name _____ Date _____   Reteach 13.3

Hour

It is 7:00.
The minute hand is at the __12__.
The hour hand is at __7__.
It is __7__ o'clock

Read the clock. Write the time two ways.

1. __5__ o'clock — 5:00
2. __3__ o'clock — 3:00
3. __11__ o'clock — 11:00
4. __8__ o'clock — 8:00
5. __4__ o'clock — 4:00

Copyright © Houghton Mifflin Company. All rights reserved.   Use with text pages 363–364.

PRACTICE 13.3

Name _____ Date _____   Practice 13.3

Hour

Read the clock. Write the time two ways.

1. 4:00 — __4__ o'clock
2. 6:00 — __6__ o'clock
3. 9:00 — __9__ o'clock
4. 1:00 — __1__ o'clock
5. 3:00 — __3__ o'clock
6. 8:00 — __8__ o'clock

Test Prep

Fill in the ○ for the correct answer. NH means Not Here.

7. What time is it on the clock?
   12:00 ○   8:00 ○   2:00 ●   NH ○

Copyright © Houghton Mifflin Company. All rights reserved.   Use with text pages 363–364.

ENRICHMENT 13.3

Name _____ Date _____   Enrichment 13.3

Tick-Tock for an Hour

Find the pattern.
Write the time that comes next.
Show the time on the clock.

1. __9__ o'clock
2. __10__ o'clock
3. __4__ o'clock
4. __5__ o'clock

Write About It How far does the minute hand move in 1 hour? How far does the hour hand move in 1 hour?
The minute hand moves around the clock once. The hour hand moves only to the next number.

Copyright © Houghton Mifflin Company. All rights reserved.   Use with text pages 363–364.

Practice Workbook Page 84

Reaching All Learners

Differentiated Instruction

English Learners

Worksheet 13.3 introduces the words *shorter* and *longer*. English-language learners will need to understand these words as they learn to tell time on an analog clock.

Inclusion
VISUAL, TACTILE

Materials: *paper plate or LT 33, demonstration clock*

- Display a demonstration clock. Have the child use it as a model to make a paper-plate clock.
- Set the demonstration clock and have the child match the time.
- Have the child write the time.

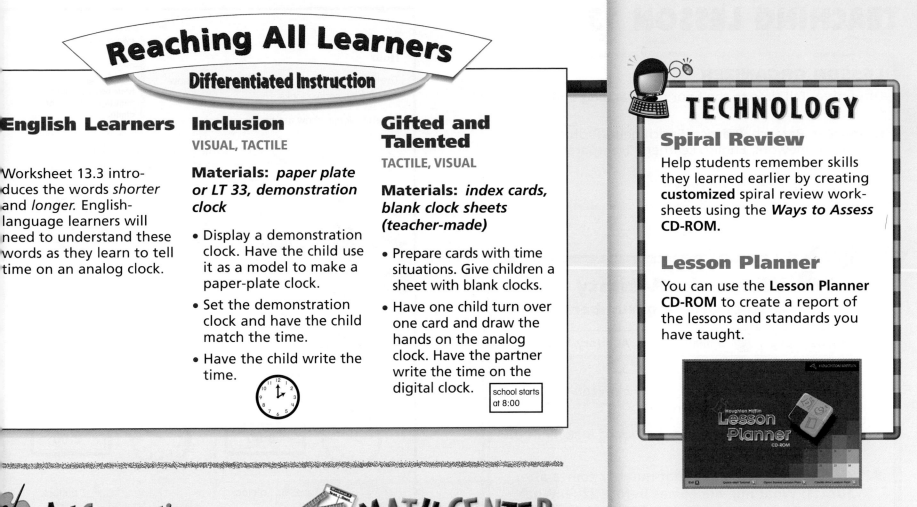

Gifted and Talented
TACTILE, VISUAL

Materials: *index cards, blank clock sheets (teacher-made)*

- Prepare cards with time situations. Give children a sheet with blank clocks.
- Have one child turn over one card and draw the hands on the analog clock. Have the partner write the time on the digital clock.

school starts at 8:00

TECHNOLOGY

Spiral Review

Help students remember skills they learned earlier by creating **customized** spiral review worksheets using the *Ways to Assess CD-ROM*.

Lesson Planner

You can use the **Lesson Planner CD-ROM** to create a report of the lessons and standards you have taught.

Art Connection

Have children draw a picture in the middle of a paper plate. Then have them write the numbers 1 to 12 around the clock face. Using fasteners, help children attach hands to their clock.

MATH CENTER

Vocabulary Activity

This vocabulary-building activity helps children understand and remember new words. Encourage children to use the words in math discussion.

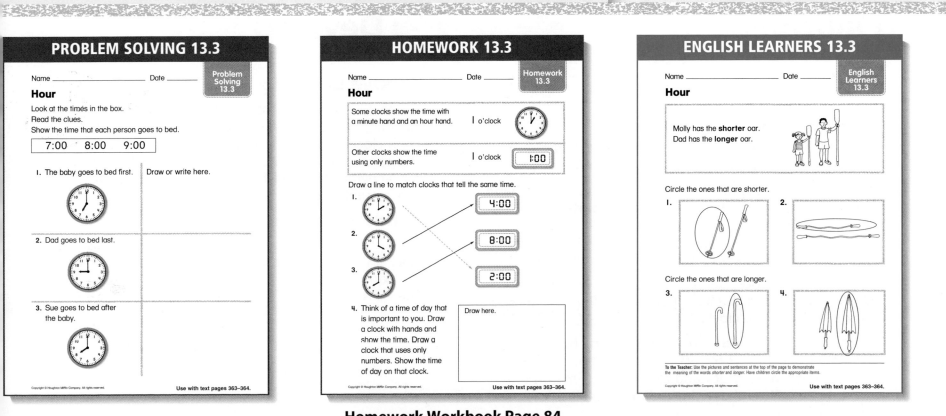

PROBLEM SOLVING 13.3

Name _____ Date _____ Problem Solving 13.3

Hour

Look at the times in the box.
Read the clues.
Show the time that each person goes to bed.

7:00   8:00   9:00

1. The baby goes to bed first. | Draw or write here.

2. Dad goes to bed last.

3. Sue goes to bed after the baby.

Use with text pages 363–364.

HOMEWORK 13.3

Name _____ Date _____ Homework 13.3

Hour

Some clocks show the time with a minute hand and an hour hand.   1 o'clock

Other clocks show the time using only numbers.   1 o'clock   1:00

Draw a line to match clocks that tell the same time.

1.   4:00
2.   8:00
3.   2:00

4. Think of a time of day that is important to you. Draw a clock with hands and show the time. Draw a clock that uses only numbers. Show the time of day on that clock.   Draw here.

Use with text pages 363–364.

ENGLISH LEARNERS 13.3

Name _____ Date _____ English Learners 13.3

Hour

Molly has the **shorter** oar.
Dad has the **longer** oar.

Circle the ones that are shorter.

1.   2.

Circle the ones that are longer.

3.   4.

To the Teacher: Use the pictures and sentences at the top of the page to demonstrate the meaning of the words *shorter* and *longer*. Have children circle the appropriate items.

Use with text pages 363–364.

Homework Workbook Page 84

TEACHING LESSON 13.3

LESSON ORGANIZER

Objective Tell time to the hour using analog and digital clocks.

Resources Reteach, Practice, Enrichment, Problem Solving, Homework, English Learners, Transparencies, Math Center

Materials Demonstration clock

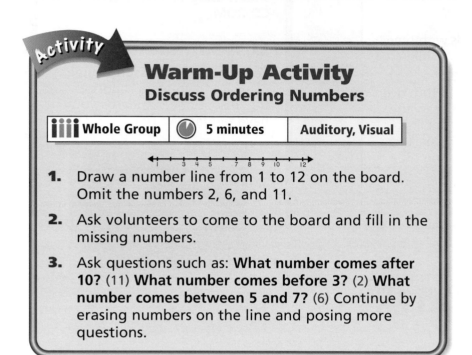

Warm-Up Activity
Discuss Ordering Numbers

| ᴵᴵᴵᴵ Whole Group | 🕐 5 minutes | Auditory, Visual |

1. Draw a number line from 1 to 12 on the board. Omit the numbers 2, 6, and 11.

2. Ask volunteers to come to the board and fill in the missing numbers.

3. Ask questions such as: **What number comes after 10?** (11) **What number comes before 3?** (2) **What number comes between 5 and 7?** (6) Continue by erasing numbers on the line and posing more questions.

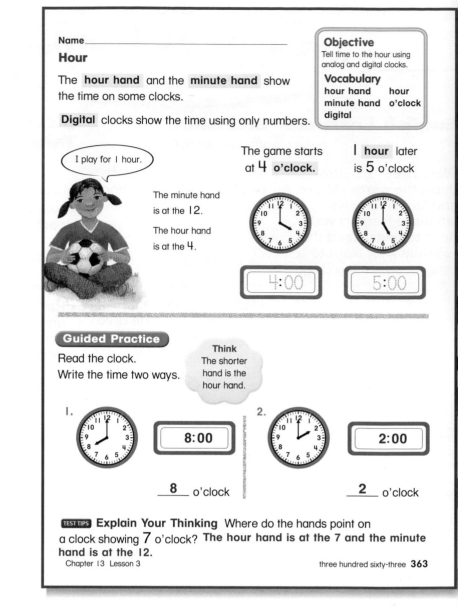

Name_____

Hour

The **hour hand** and the **minute hand** show the time on some clocks.

Digital clocks show the time using only numbers.

Objective Tell time to the hour using analog and digital clocks.

Vocabulary
hour hand   hour
minute hand   o'clock
digital

I play for 1 hour.

The minute hand is at the 12.
The hour hand is at the 4.

The game starts at 4 **o'clock.**

1 **hour** later is 5 o'clock

4:00   5:00

Guided Practice

Read the clock. Write the time two ways.

Think The shorter hand is the hour hand.

1.   8:00   _8_ o'clock

2.   2:00   _2_ o'clock

TEST TIPS Explain Your Thinking Where do the hands point on a clock showing 7 o'clock? **The hour hand is at the 7 and the minute hand is at the 12.**

Chapter 13 Lesson 3   three hundred sixty-three **363**

---

① Introduce

Model Telling Time to the Hour

| ᴵᴵᴵᴵ Whole Group | 🕐 10–15 minutes | Visual, Auditory |

Materials: *demonstration clock*

1. Display the demonstration clock and draw a digital clock on the board, both showing 2 o'clock.

2. On the demonstration clock, point out the minute hand and the hour hand. **The minute hand points to 12. The hour hand points to 2. It shows 2 o'clock.** Discuss with children that the 12 on the clock represents the hour it is, but also the 12 represents the 60 minute mark.

3. On the digital clock, point out the 2 and the 00. **This clock shows a 2 in the hour place and 00 in the minute place. It shows 2 o'clock.**

4. **What number is 1 more than 2?** (3) **In one hour, these clocks would show 3 o'clock.** Move the hour hand on the demonstration clock and rewrite the time on the digital clock. **Now these clocks show 3 o'clock.**

② Develop

Guided Learning

Teaching Example Introduce the objective and vocabulary to children. Guide them through the example to show what both clocks look like at 4 o'clock and at 5 o'clock. Discuss the concept of 60 minutes in 1 hour and remind children of the activities they did for 1 minute. Explain that 1 hour is not a number on a clock and that a clock measures time.

Guided Practice

Have children complete **Exercises 1–2** as you observe. Give children the opportunity to answer the Explain Your Thinking question. Then discuss their responses with the class.

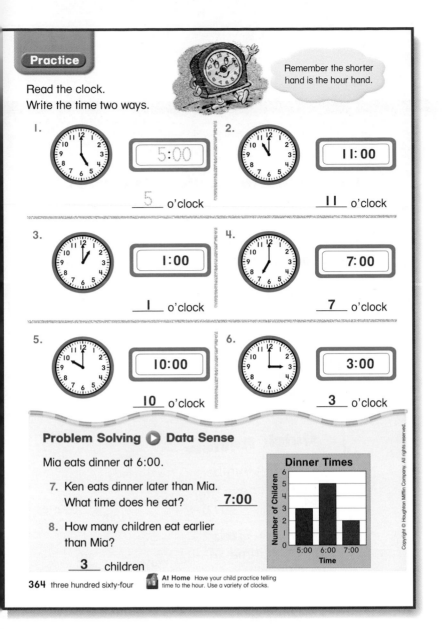

Practice

Read the clock.
Write the time two ways.

Remember the shorter hand is the hour hand.

1. 5:00
   __5__ o'clock

2. 11:00
   __11__ o'clock

3. 1:00
   __1__ o'clock

4. 7:00
   __7__ o'clock

5. 10:00
   __10__ o'clock

6. 3:00
   __3__ o'clock

Problem Solving ▶ Data Sense

Mia eats dinner at 6:00.

7. Ken eats dinner later than Mia.
   What time does he eat?   __7:00__

8. How many children eat earlier
   than Mia?

   __3__ children

Dinner Times

Number of Children (0–6) vs Time (5:00, 6:00, 7:00)

At Home Have your child practice telling time to the hour. Use a variety of clocks.

Daily Test Prep

How many equal parts?

1   2   3   4
○   ○   ●   ○

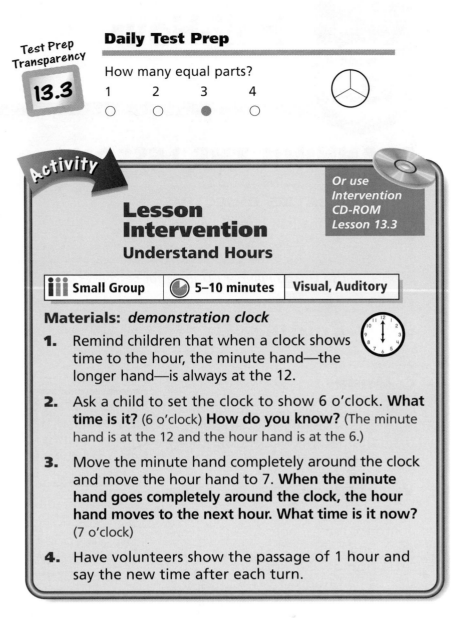

Activity

Or use Intervention CD-ROM Lesson 13.3

Lesson Intervention

Understand Hours

| 👥 Small Group | 🕐 5–10 minutes | Visual, Auditory |

Materials: *demonstration clock*

1. Remind children that when a clock shows time to the hour, the minute hand—the longer hand—is always at the 12.

2. Ask a child to set the clock to show 6 o'clock. **What time is it?** (6 o'clock) **How do you know?** (The minute hand is at the 12 and the hour hand is at the 6.)

3. Move the minute hand completely around the clock and move the hour hand to 7. **When the minute hand goes completely around the clock, the hour hand moves to the next hour. What time is it now?** (7 o'clock)

4. Have volunteers show the passage of 1 hour and say the new time after each turn.

---

3 Practice

Independent Practice

Children complete **Exercises 1–6** independently.

Problem Solving

After children complete **Exercises 7** and **8**, call on volunteers to share their answers.

Common Error

Confusing the Minute Hand and the Hour Hand
Children may confuse the hands of the clock. Remind them that the long hand is for minute and the short hand is for hour. Label the hands on a paper plate clock for children to use.

4 Assess and Close

What time is it when the minute hand is at the 12 and the hour hand is at the 6? (6 o'clock)

What time is it when both hands point to the 12? (12 o'clock)

Keeping a Journal

Draw a time on a clock. Draw and write about something you might do at that time of day.

Half-Hour

Lesson 13.4

PLANNING THE LESSON

MATHEMATICS OBJECTIVE
Tell time to the half-hour.

Use Lesson Planner CD-ROM for Lesson 13.4.

Daily Routines

Calendar
Point out today's date. Depending on the date, ask children to name the date that is 2 weeks from today, or was 2 weeks earlier.

Sunday	Monday	Tuesday	Wednesday	Thursday	Friday	Saturday
			1	2	3	4
5	6	7	8	9	10	11
12	13	14	15	16	17	18
19	20	21	22	23	24	25
26	27	28	29	30	31	

Vocabulary
Have children come to the board to draw shapes to show **one half**. Draw a circle clock face divided into halves. Discuss **half-hour** as 30 minutes since there are 60 minutes in an hour.

Vocabulary Cards

Meeting North Carolina's Standards
2.02 Develop an understanding of the concept of time.
- Tell time at the hour and half-hour.
- Solve problems involving applications of time (clock and calendar).

Lesson Transparency 13.4

Problem of the Day
Mai folds a paper clock face in half. If the number 12 is at the top part of the fold, what number is at the bottom part of the fold? (6)

Quick Review
Write the number.

6 tens 4 ones (64)   1 ten 3 ones (13)   10 tens 0 ones (100)

Lesson Quiz
Write the time another way.
1. 8:00 (8 o'clock)
2. 30 minutes after 8 (8:30, half past 8)
3. Half past one (1:30, 30 minutes after 1)

LEVELED PRACTICE

RETEACH 13.4

Name _____ Date _____

Reteach 13.4

Half-Hour

An hour has 60 minutes.
A half-hour has 30 minutes.

The hour hand is halfway between the __7__ and the __8__.

The minute hand is at the 6.

It is __30__ minutes after __7__ or half past __7__.

Say and write the time.

1. __2__ o'clock | __2:30__ | half past __2__
2. __10__ o'clock | __10:30__ | half past __10__
3. half past __7__ | __8:00__ | __8__ o'clock

Copyright © Houghton Mifflin Company. All rights reserved.
Use with text pages 365–368.

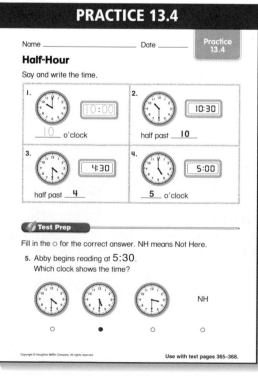

PRACTICE 13.4

Name _____ Date _____

Practice 13.4

Half-Hour

Say and write the time.

1. 10:00 __10__ o'clock
2. 10:30 half past __10__
3. 4:30 half past __4__
4. 5:00 __5__ o'clock

Test Prep

Fill in the ○ for the correct answer. NH means Not Here.

5. Abby begins reading at 5:30. Which clock shows the time?

NH

Copyright © Houghton Mifflin Company. All rights reserved.
Use with text pages 365–368.

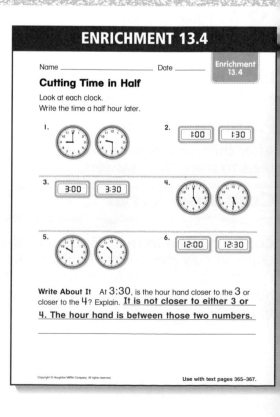

ENRICHMENT 13.4

Name _____ Date _____

Enrichment 13.4

Cutting Time in Half

Look at each clock.
Write the time a half hour later.

1.
2. 1:00 1:30
3. 3:00 3:30
4.
5.
6. 12:00 12:30

Write About It At 3:30, is the hour hand closer to the 3 or closer to the 4? Explain. It is not closer to either 3 or 4. The hour hand is between those two numbers.

Copyright © Houghton Mifflin Company. All rights reserved.
Use with text pages 365–367.

Practice Workbook Page 85

Reaching All Learners

Differentiated Instruction

English Learners

In order to tell time to the half-hour, children will have to understand the concept *half*. Use Worksheet 13.4 to develop children's understanding of this concept.

Inclusion
TACTILE, VISUAL

Materials: *demonstration clock*

Start the clock at 8 o'clock. Then move it to 9 o'clock. Elicit that 1 hour has passed. Repeat for 9:30, moving both hands. Say one half-hour has passed. The minute hand moved halfway around and the hour hand is halfway between two numbers. Write the time. Say the time as half past 9 or 30 minutes after 9.

Early Finishers
KINESTHETIC

Materials: *index cards*

- Prepare a set of cards showing times to the hour and half-hour.
- Mix the cards and place them facedown in a pile.
- Players take turns turning over a card and placing it so all cards end up in order.

Literature Connection

Refer to the unit story, *How Long?* by Elizabeth Dale. Review the activities that Caroline did to fill one, ten, fifteen, and twenty minutes. Have children draw pictures of something Caroline could do to fill thirty minutes.

MATH CENTER

Real-Life Activity

Help children understand the usefulness of mathematics. This activity makes math come alive by connecting the lesson skills to a real-life situation.

PROBLEM SOLVING 13.4

Name _____ Date _____

Problem Solving 13.4

Half-Hour

Laura works in a pet store. She feeds a different pet every half-hour. She starts at 10:00 with the fish. Show the times she feeds each animal.

Draw or write here.

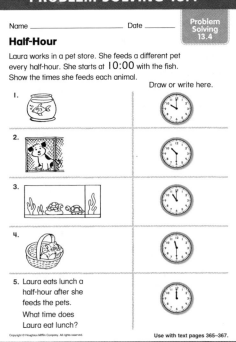

1.
2.
3.
4.
5. Laura eats lunch a half-hour after she feeds the pets. What time does Laura eat lunch?

Copyright © Houghton Mifflin Company. All rights reserved.

Use with text pages 365–367.

HOMEWORK 13.4

Name _____ Date _____

Homework 13.4

Half-Hour

An hour is 60 minutes.	A half-hour is 30 minutes.
3:00 3 o'clock	3:30 half past 3

Say and write the time.

1. half past ___
2. ___5___ o'clock
3. half past ___7___
4. ___8___ o'clock

5. Write down 3 activities you do each day. Think about the time you usually do each activity. Write the time of each activity.

Write here.

Copyright © Houghton Mifflin Company. All rights reserved.

Use with text pages 365–367.

Homework Workbook Page 85

ENGLISH LEARNERS 13.4

Name _____ Date _____

English Learners 13.4

Half-Hour

This is a sandwich.   This is **half** a sandwich.

Circle the pictures that show half.

1.
2.
3.

To the Teacher: Use the pictures and sentences at the top of the page to demonstrate the meaning of *half.* Then have children circle the pictures that show *half.*

Copyright © Houghton Mifflin Company. All rights reserved.

Use with text pages 365–367.

TEACHING LESSON 13.4

LESSON ORGANIZER

Objective Tell time to the half-hour.

Resources Reteach, Practice, Enrichment, Problem Solving, Homework, English Learners, Transparencies, Math Center

Materials Demonstration clock

Warm-Up Activity
Writing Time to the Hour

| iiii Whole Group | ⏱ 5 minutes | Auditory, Tactile |

Materials: *demonstration clock*

1. Set the demonstration clock to show 7 o'clock. Have children write the corresponding time as seen on a digital clock. (7:00)  7:00

2. Move the hands of the clock slowly to 8 o'clock. Count by 5s as you move from one number to the next around the clock. Explain that you are showing that an hour, or 60 minutes, has passed and it is an hour later. **What time does the clock show now?** (8:00) Have children write the time.

3. Call on volunteers to move the hands to show time on the hour to 12 o'clock. Have them write the time on the board.

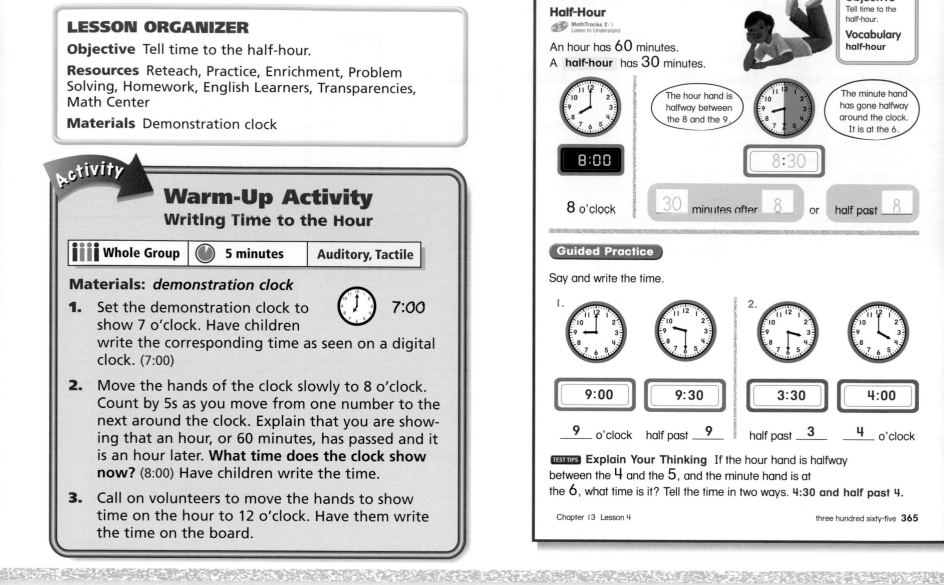

Name _____

Half-Hour

*MathTracks 2 / 1
Listen to Understand*

An hour has 60 minutes.
A **half-hour** has 30 minutes.

The hour hand is halfway between the 8 and the 9.

The minute hand has gone halfway around the clock. It is at the 6.

8:00   8:30

8 o'clock   30 minutes after 8   or   half past 8

Guided Practice

Say and write the time.

1.
9:00   9:30
9 o'clock   half past 9

2.
3:30   4:00
half past 3   4 o'clock

TEST TIPS Explain Your Thinking If the hour hand is halfway between the 4 and the 5, and the minute hand is at the 6, what time is it? Tell the time in two ways. 4:30 and half past 4.

Chapter 13 Lesson 4   three hundred sixty-five **365**

1 Introduce
Modeling Half-Hour

| iiii Whole Group | ⏱ 10–15 minutes | Visual, Auditory |

1. Draw two large clock faces on the board, showing 2 o'clock and 2:30. Point to the first clock. Ask: **What time does this clock show?** (2 o'clock) **How do you know?** (The minute hand is at 12. The hour hand is at 2.)

2. Point to the second clock. **Does this clock show 2 o'clock?** (no) Point out that the minute hand is now pointing to the 6 and the hour hand is halfway between the 2 and the 3.

3. Explain that an hour has 60 minutes and a half-hour has 30 minutes. **When the minute hand is on the 6, a half-hour, or 30 minutes, has passed. The hour hand is halfway between two numbers. Count by 5s from the 12 to the 6 to get 30 minutes.**

4. Write the words and numbers as you say: **We can write this time as 30 minutes after 2, 2:30, or half past 2.**

2 Develop

Guided Learning

Teaching Example Introduce the objective and vocabulary to children. Discuss the pictured clocks. After children trace the time in different notations, have them read each form aloud.

Guided Practice

Have children complete **Exercises 1–2** as you observe. Give children the opportunity to answer the Explain Your Thinking question. Then discuss their responses with the class.

Say and write the time.

Remember when it is 30 minutes after the hour, the minute hand is at the 6.

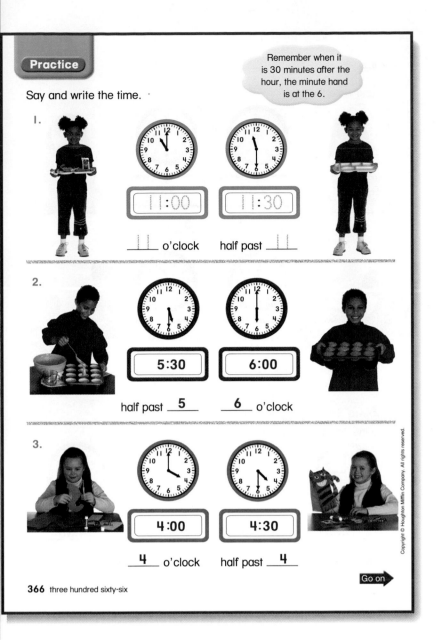

1.

11:00   11:30

___ o'clock   half past ___

2.

5:30   6:00

half past _5_   _6_ o'clock

3.

4:00   4:30

_4_ o'clock   half past _4_

366 three hundred sixty-six

Go on ▶

ACHIEVING
Mathematical Proficiency

The Importance of Vocabulary

Several mathematical concepts are associated with measuring and telling time. **Each of these concepts depends on students' knowledge and understanding of key vocabulary words.** One concept involves arranging events according to the times they take place. Children learn to use the key terms *before* and *after* in this context. Another concept involves reading an analog or digital clock to tell time.

In this chapter, children use the words *before* and *after* to order events in time. They use the words *minute hand* and *hour hand* to measure time and the words *minute, hour, o'clock,* and *half-hour* to express the time and determine elapsed time.

Defining and expanding upon key vocabulary words **helps children understand real-life math applications of telling time.**

---

③ Practice

Independent Practice

Children complete **Exercises 1–3** on page 366 independently.

Lesson continues

Technology Connection
Use Technology to Record Time

Using a word processing program, students will create a table showing their daily activities during a 3-hour period.

Show how to create a table in a word processing program.

- Have students click **Table**, then **Insert**. Create a table with 2 columns and 7 rows.
- Have students label the top cell in the first column "Time." Have them label the top cell in the second column "Activity."
- Choose a 3-hour time period. In the Time column, have students enter half-hour increments within the selected 3 hours. Then have them type in the activity or activities they are involved in during each half-hour increment.

Have students discuss which of their daily activities take about a half-hour to do and which take more or less time.

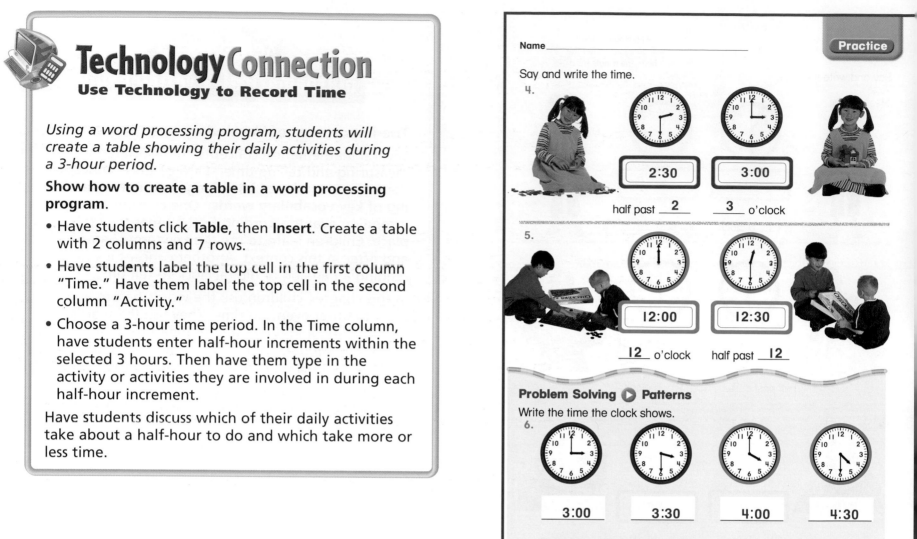

Name _____

Say and write the time.

4.

2:30   3:00

half past __2__   __3__ o'clock

5.

12:00   12:30

__12__ o'clock   half past __12__

Problem Solving ▶ Patterns

Write the time the clock shows.

6.

3:00   3:30   4:00   4:30

7. **Talk About It** Explain the pattern you see above. **Possible answer:**
It shows the time every half-hour from 3:00 to 4:30.

---

3 Practice

Independent Practice

Children complete **Exercises 4–5** on page 367 independently.

Problem Solving

After children complete **Exercise 6** on page 367, call on volunteers to share their answers. Use the **Talk About It** in **Exercise 7** to discuss the half-hour pattern.

Common Error

Misreading the Hour Hand
Some children may misread the hour hand when reading time to the half-hour. Remind them that when the hour hand is between two numbers, the lesser number tells the hour. The time is 30 minutes after the hour.

4 Assess and Close

How many minutes are there in a half-hour? (30)

What is another way to write half past six? (6:30, 30 minutes past 6)

If the hour hand is between 10 and 11 and the minute hand is at 6, what time is it? (10:30, half past 10)

Keeping a Journal

Draw a clock that shows 8:30. Explain how you know that the time is 8:30.

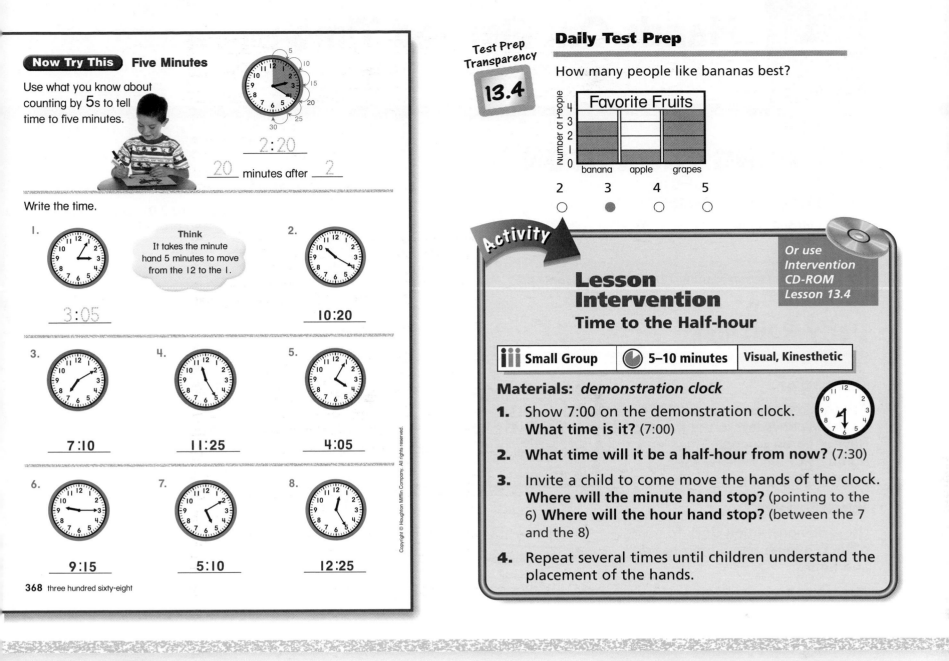

Now Try This Five Minutes

Use what you know about counting by 5s to tell time to five minutes.

2:20

_20_ minutes after _2_

Write the time.

Think It takes the minute hand 5 minutes to move from the 12 to the 1.

1. 3:05

2. 10:20

3. 7:10

4. 11:25

5. 4:05

6. 9:15

7. 5:10

8. 12:25

Daily Test Prep

How many people like bananas best?

Favorite Fruits

Number of People	banana	apple	grapes

2 3 4 5

○ ● ○ ○

Activity

Or use Intervention CD-ROM Lesson 13.4

Lesson Intervention

Time to the Half-hour

iii Small Group	5–10 minutes	Visual, Kinesthetic

Materials: demonstration clock

1. Show 7:00 on the demonstration clock. **What time is it?** (7:00)

2. **What time will it be a half-hour from now?** (7:30)

3. Invite a child to come move the hands of the clock. **Where will the minute hand stop?** (pointing to the 6) **Where will the hour hand stop?** (between the 7 and the 8)

4. Repeat several times until children understand the placement of the hands.

Now Try This

Five Minute Intervals

Materials: colored chalk

Introduce Draw a large clock face on the board. Write the numbers 1–12 around the clock with white chalk. On the outside of the circle, using colored chalk, write _5 minutes_ next to the 1, _10 minutes_ next to the 2, _15 minutes_ next to the 3, etc.

• **Count by 5s as I point to the numbers 1–12.**

• Draw the time 2:15 on the clock. Say: **We say this time is two fifteen because it is 15 minutes after 2 o'clock.** Write other times on the clock and have children say the time.

Develop Have children complete **Exercises 1 and 2** as you observe. Make sure students are able to write the minutes.

Practice Have children complete **Exercises 3–8** independently.

Hands-On: Elapsed Time

Lesson **13.5**

PLANNING THE LESSON

MATHEMATICS OBJECTIVE
Find elapsed time.

Use Lesson Planner CD-ROM for Lesson 13.5.

Daily Routines

Calendar
Ask children to name the dates of all the Wednesdays in the month. Have children compare the 4 or 5 numbers to tell which is the greatest number.

Sunday	Monday	Tuesday	Wednesday	Thursday	Friday	Saturday
			1	2	3	4
5	6	7	8	9	10	11
12	13	14	15	16	17	18
19	20	21	22	23	24	25
26	27	28	29	30	31	

Vocabulary
Use a demonstration clock to review **o'clock**, **minute hand**, **hour hand**, and **hour**.

Vocabulary Cards

Meeting North Carolina's Standards
Prepare for Grade 3 Standard 2.01 Solve problems using measurement concepts and procedures.

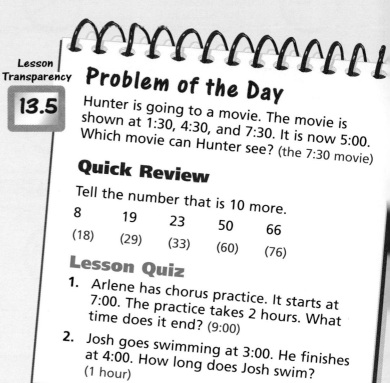

Lesson Transparency **13.5**

Problem of the Day
Hunter is going to a movie. The movie is shown at 1:30, 4:30, and 7:30. It is now 5:00. Which movie can Hunter see? (the 7:30 movie)

Quick Review
Tell the number that is 10 more.

8	19	23	50	66
(18)	(29)	(33)	(60)	(76)

Lesson Quiz
1. Arlene has chorus practice. It starts at 7:00. The practice takes 2 hours. What time does it end? (9:00)

2. Josh goes swimming at 3:00. He finishes at 4:00. How long does Josh swim? (1 hour)

LEVELED PRACTICE

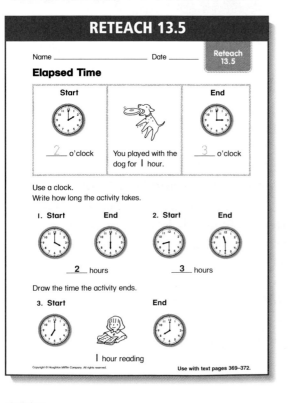

RETEACH 13.5

Name _____ Date _____   Reteach 13.5

Elapsed Time

Start		End
_2_ o'clock	You played with the dog for 1 hour.	_3_ o'clock

Use a clock.
Write how long the activity takes.

1. Start   End   2. Start   End

_2_ hours   _3_ hours

Draw the time the activity ends.

3. Start   End

1 hour reading

Use with text pages 369–372.

PRACTICE 13.5

Name _____ Date _____   Practice 13.5

Elapsed Time

Use a clock.
Show when the activity starts or ends.

	Start	How long?	End
1.		1 hour reading	4:00
2.	5:00	1 hour cooking	6:00
3.		2 hours driving	11:00

Test Prep

Fill in the ○ for the correct answer. NH means Not Here.
4. The movie starts at 5:00. It lasts 2 hours. What time is it over?

●   ○   ○   ○ NH

Use with text pages 369–372.

ENRICHMENT 13.5

Name _____ Date _____   Enrichment 13.5

The Time It Takes

Look at the time each activity starts.

Decide how many hours you think it would take you to do the activity.

Write the number of hours.

Show when the activity ends. **Answers will vary.**

1.		I play soccer for ____ hours.	
2.		We go to the zoo for ____ hours.	
3.		We play a game for ____ hours.	

Talk About It   When do you start eating lunch? When do you finish? About how long does it take you to eat your lunch?

Use with text pages 369–371.

Practice Workbook Page 86

369A   CHAPTER 13   Lesson 5

Reaching All Learners

Differentiated Instruction

English Learners

In order to understand elapsed time, children will need to know the words *start* and *end*. Use Worksheet 13.5 to introduce English-language learners to these words.

Special Needs
TACTILE, VISUAL

Materials: *demonstration clock, time cards for hours and half hours (teacher-made)*

- Place cards with the times facedown.
- Ask the child to choose a card, say the time, and set the clock. Then have the child show the time an hour later.

Gifted and Talented
TACTILE, VISUAL

Materials: *index cards*

- Give each pair of children index cards with times from 1:00 to 12:00.
- Children take turns choosing 2 cards and placing the card with the earlier time to the left of the later time.
- The partner determines how much time has passed.

TECHNOLOGY

Spiral Review

Create **customized** spiral review worksheets for individual students using the *Ways to Assess CD-ROM.*

Lesson Planner

You can customize your teaching plan or meet your curriculum requirements wtih the **Lesson Planner CD-ROM.**

Literature Connection

Refer to the unit literature selection, *My Big Night*, by Harold Mitchell. Read the first page of the story aloud. Show 7:00 on a clock. Remind children that the girl's play will happen in 6 hours. Ask a volunteer to show the current time.

MATH CENTER

Vocabulary Activity

This vocabulary-building activity helps children understand and remember new words. Encourage children to use the words in math discussion.

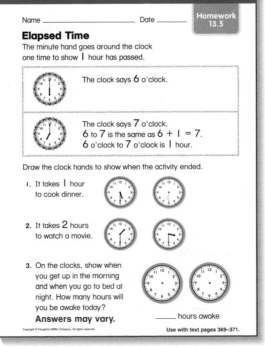

PROBLEM SOLVING 13.5

Name _____ Date _____ | Problem Solving 13.5

Elapsed Time

Read each problem.
Write the answer.
Use a clock to help you.

Basketball practice starts at 3:00.
Tyrone practices for 2 hours.
What time does he finish?
__5__ o'clock

1. Lisa goes to ballet class at 4:00.
She practices for 1 hour and 30 minutes.
What time does she finish?
__5:30__

Draw or write here.

2. Sam spends 1 hour doing math homework. He spends 1 hour reading. If he starts at 4 o'clock, what time does he finish?
__6__ o'clock

3. Kerry goes to her friend's house at 8:00 in the morning. She spends 8 hours there. What time does Kerry come home?
__4:00__

 Use with text pages 369–371.

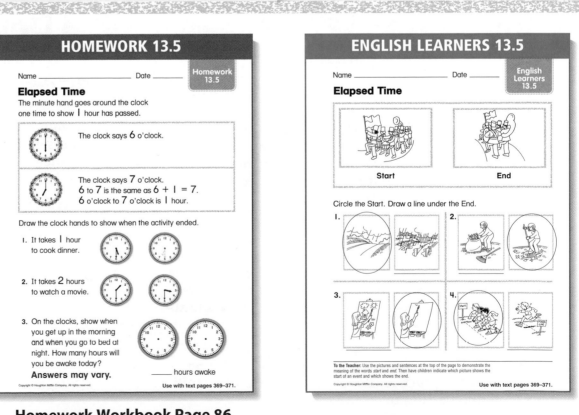

HOMEWORK 13.5

Name _____ Date _____ | Homework 13.5

Elapsed Time
The minute hand goes around the clock one time to show 1 hour has passed.

The clock says 6 o'clock.

The clock says 7 o'clock.
6 to 7 is the same as 6 + 1 = 7.
6 o'clock to 7 o'clock is 1 hour.

Draw the clock hands to show when the activity ended.

1. It takes 1 hour to cook dinner.

2. It takes 2 hours to watch a movie.

3. On the clocks, show when you get up in the morning and when you go to bed at night. How many hours will you be awake today?
Answers may vary.
_____ hours awake

Use with text pages 369–371.

ENGLISH LEARNERS 13.5

Name _____ Date _____ | English Learners 13.5

Elapsed Time

Start   End

Circle the Start. Draw a line under the End.

1.   2.

3.   4.

To the Teacher: Use the pictures and sentences at the top of the page to demonstrate the meaning of the words start and end. Then have children indicate which picture shows the start of an event and which shows the end.

Use with text pages 369–371.

Homework Workbook Page 86

TEACHING LESSON 13.5

LESSON ORGANIZER

Objective Find elapsed time.

Resources Reteach, Practice, Enrichment, Problem Solving, Homework, English Learners, Transparencies, Math Center

Materials Index cards labeled 1:00 – 12:00, demonstration clock, individual clocks (Learning Tool (LT) 33)

Activity

Warm-Up Activity
Modeling Counting Hours

| ⛄ Whole Group | 🕐 10 minutes | Auditory, Kinesthetic |

Materials: *index cards labeled 1:00 – 12:00*

1. Give one card to each child. Have children sit in order of their numbers starting at 1:00.

   "one hour later than 1:00"

2. Ask the child with 2:00 to stand up. **Who has the time showing 1 hour later than 2:00?** (3:00) Have the child stand up. **Who has the time showing one hour later than 3:00?** (4:00)

3. Continue the activity through 12:00. Explain that each time we go to the next number on the clock it represents one hour that has passed, or one hour later.

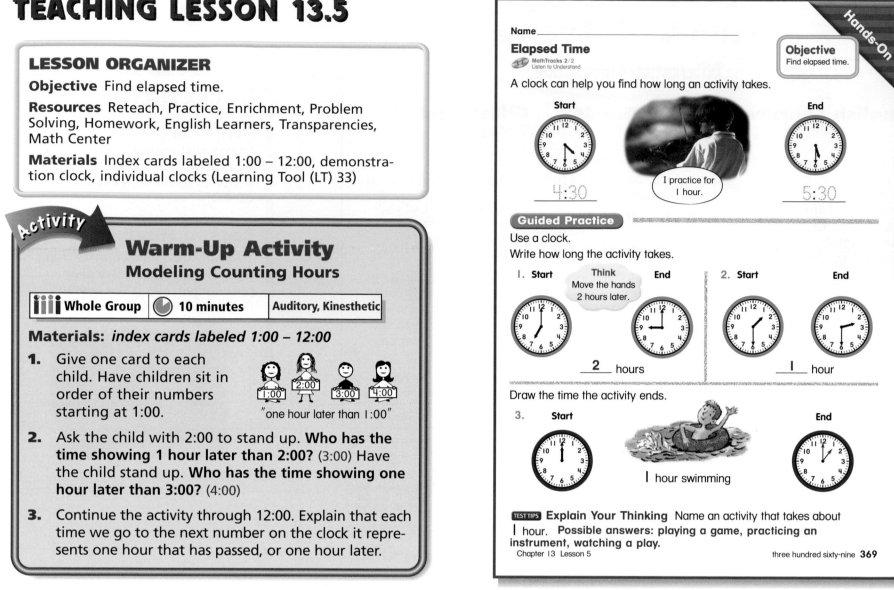

Name_____

Elapsed Time

🎧 MathTracks 2/2
Listen to Understand

Objective
Find elapsed time.

A clock can help you find how long an activity takes.

Start   End

4:30   I practice for 1 hour.   5:30

Guided Practice

Use a clock.
Write how long the activity takes.

1. Start   Think: Move the hands 2 hours later.   End

   __2__ hours

2. Start   End

   __1__ hour

Draw the time the activity ends.

3. Start   End

   I hour swimming

TEST TIPS **Explain Your Thinking** Name an activity that takes about I hour. **Possible answers: playing a game, practicing an instrument, watching a play.**

Chapter 13 Lesson 5   three hundred sixty-nine **369**

---

1 Introduce
Discuss Finding Elapsed Time

| ⛄ Whole Group | 🕐 10–15 minutes | Visual, Auditory |

Materials: *demonstration clock, individual clocks (LT 33)*

1. Set the clock to show 3:00. Have children do the same. Ask a child to tell the time. Tell a story to go along with the time. **Claire's piano lesson starts at 3:00. It ends at 4:00. How long is her lesson?** Slowly move the hands on the clock to model the passing of one hour and show 4:00. Guide children to do the same. Guide children to see that the piano lesson is 1 hour long.

2. Now set the clock at 5:30. **At 5:30 Claire began practicing on her own. She finished practicing at 6:30.** Move the hands on the clock to show 6:30. **How long did she practice on her own?** (1 hour)

3. Show 4:30 on the clock. **Jay has football practice at 4:30. Practice lasts for 2 hours. What time will it be when football practice is over?** (6:30) Move the hands to show the passing of 2 hours.

2 Develop

Guided Learning

Teaching Example Introduce the objective to the children. Explain that elapsed time means the amount of time that passes. Guide them through the example by having children set their individual clocks to show the start and end times and how long the activity lasts.

Guided Practice

Have children complete **Exercises 1–3** as you observe. Tell them to move the hands on their clocks to show the times. Give children the opportunity to answer the Explain Your Thinking question. Then discuss their responses with the class.

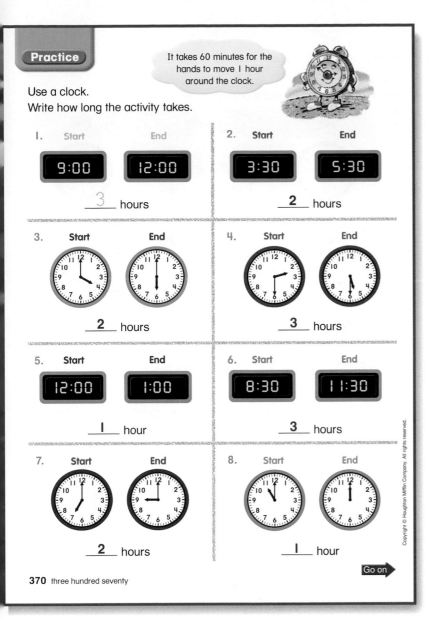

Practice

It takes 60 minutes for the hands to move 1 hour around the clock.

Use a clock.
Write how long the activity takes.

1. Start **9:00** End **12:00**
_____3_____ hours

2. Start **3:30** End **5:30**
_____2_____ hours

3. Start End
_____2_____ hours

4. Start End
_____3_____ hours

5. Start **12:00** End **1:00**
_____1_____ hour

6. Start **8:30** End **11:30**
_____3_____ hours

7. Start End
_____2_____ hours

8. Start End
_____1_____ hour

Go on ▶

Literature Connection

Refer to the unit story, *My Big Night* by Harold Mitchell. Have children answer these questions, based on the passage that appears in the student book.

- What time does the family eat dinner? (5:00)
- What time is the play? (7:00)
- How much time passes between 5:00 and 7:00? (2 hours)
- If the play lasts 1 hour, what time will it be when it ends? (8:00)

Practice

Independent Practice

Children complete **Exercises 1–8** on page 370 independently.

Lesson continues ➡

Daily Test Prep

Which shape is between the circle and triangle?

◇ □ ○ ☆ △ ▭

square   star   circle   NH
○   ●   ○   ○

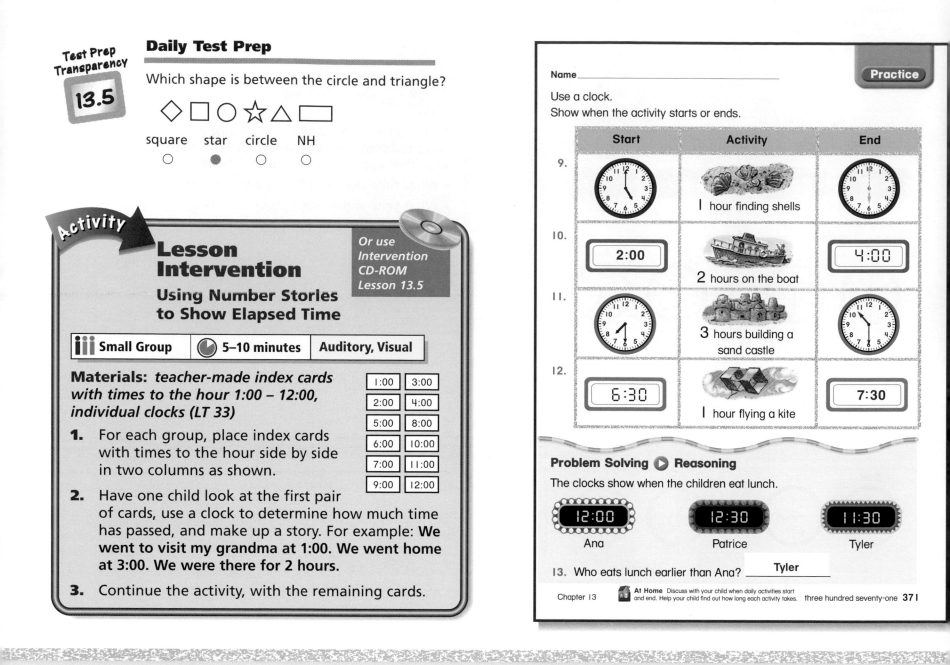

Activity

Lesson Intervention

Or use Intervention CD-ROM Lesson 13.5

Using Number Stories to Show Elapsed Time

| 👥 Small Group | 🕐 5–10 minutes | Auditory, Visual |

Materials: *teacher-made index cards with times to the hour 1:00 – 12:00, individual clocks (LT 33)*

1:00	3:00
2:00	4:00
5:00	8:00
6:00	10:00
7:00	11:00
9:00	12:00

1. For each group, place index cards with times to the hour side by side in two columns as shown.

2. Have one child look at the first pair of cards, use a clock to determine how much time has passed, and make up a story. For example: **We went to visit my grandma at 1:00. We went home at 3:00. We were there for 2 hours.**

3. Continue the activity, with the remaining cards.

Name_____   **Practice**

Use a clock.
Show when the activity starts or ends.

	Start	Activity	End
9.	(clock)	1 hour finding shells	(clock)
10.	2:00	2 hours on the boat	4:00
11.	(clock)	3 hours building a sand castle	(clock)
12.	6:30	1 hour flying a kite	7:30

Problem Solving ▶ Reasoning

The clocks show when the children eat lunch.

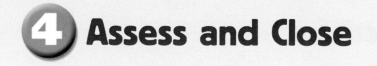

12:00   12:30   11:30
Ana   Patrice   Tyler

13. Who eats lunch earlier than Ana? ___Tyler___

3 Practice

Independent Practice

For **Exercises 9–12** on page 371, do the first exercise with children to be sure they understand the task. Then have them complete the exercises independently.

Problem Solving

After children complete **Exercise 13**, call on volunteers to share their solutions.

Common Error

Miscounting Hours

Children may count the start time as an hour. Provide practice with clock faces and have children move clock hands ahead and count on each hour.

4 Assess and Close

A band concert began at 2:00. It lasted 2 hours. What time did the concert end? (4:00)

After the concert, the band members had a party. The party started at 5:00. It ended at 7:00. How long did the party last? (2 hours)

✏️ Keeping a Journal

Write a story about an activity that you do. Tell what time you start the activity, what time it ends, and how long the activity takes.

Quick Check

Write 1, 2, and 3 to show the correct order.

1.

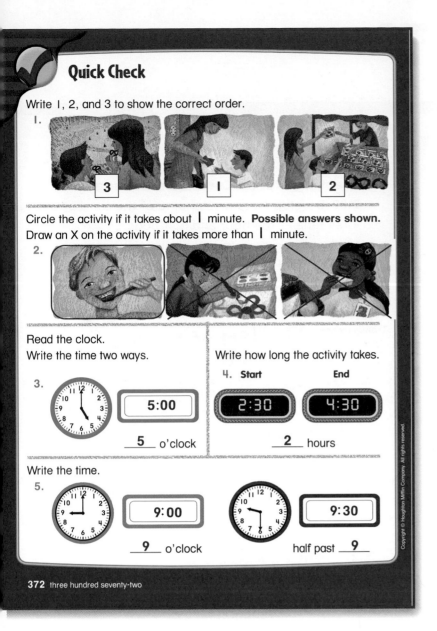

3   **1**   **2**

Circle the activity if it takes about 1 minute. **Possible answers shown.**
Draw an X on the activity if it takes more than 1 minute.

2.

Read the clock.
Write the time two ways.

3.

5:00

5 o'clock

Write how long the activity takes.

4. **Start**   **End**

2:30   **4:30**

2 hours

Write the time.

5.

9:00

9 o'clock

9:30

half past **9**

372   three hundred seventy-two

Copyright © Houghton Mifflin Company. All rights reserved.

Quick Check

Have children complete the Quick Check exercises independently to assess their understanding of concepts and skills taught in **Lessons 1–5.**

Item	Lesson	Error Analysis	Intervention
1	13.1	Child may put pictures in the wrong order.	Reteach Resource 13.1 *Ways to Success* 13.1
2	13.2	Children may misunderstand the problem.	Reteach Resource 13.2 *Ways to Success* 13.2
3	13.3	Children may confuse the minute hand and the hour hand.	Reteach Resource 13.3 *Ways to Success* 13.3
4	13.4	Children may miscount hours.	Reteach Resource 13.4 *Ways to Success* 13.4
5	13.5	Children my misread the hour hand.	Reteach Resource 13.5 *Ways to Success* 13.5

Practice Telling Time

PLANNING THE LESSON

MATHEMATICS OBJECTIVE
Practice telling time using analog and digital clocks.

Use Lesson Planner CD-ROM for Lesson 13.6.

Daily Routines

Calendar
Ask children to count how many Tuesdays are in the current month. Then have them find a month with more or fewer Tuesdays.

Sunday	Monday	Tuesday	Wednesday	Thursday	Friday	Saturday
			1	2	3	4
5	6	7	8	9	10	11
12	13	14	15	16	17	18
19	20	21	22	23	24	25
26	27	28	29	30	31	

Vocabulary
Draw analog and digital clocks showing 11:00 on the board. Ask volunteers to point to the **hour hand, minute hand,** and **digital** clock. Then ask volunteers to complete this sentence: When the (hour) hand points to 11 and the (minute) hand points to 12, the time is (11 o'clock).

Vocabulary Cards

Meeting North Carolina's Standards
2.02 Develop an understanding of the concept of time.
- Tell time at the hour and half-hour.
- Solve problems involving applications of time (clock and calendar).

Lesson Transparency 13.6

Problem of the Day
Ali went shopping at 2:30. Cindy walked her dog at half past 2. Robin swam at 30 minutes after 2. Which activity started first? (They all started at the same time, 2:30.)

Quick Review
Tell the number that is 10 less.

11	25	40	71	99
(1)	(15)	(30)	(61)	(89)

Lesson Quiz
Where are the hands on a clock pointing when it is 9 o'clock? (The hour hand points to the 9 and the minute hand points to the 12.) Write the same time as shown on a digital clock. (9:00)

LEVELED PRACTICE

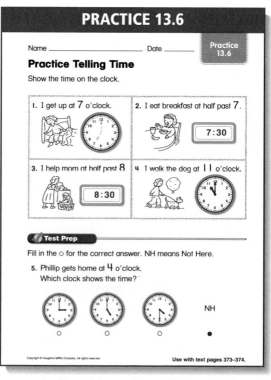

RETEACH 13.6

Name _____ Date _____   Reteach 13.6

Practice Telling Time

The same time can be shown in different ways.

clock with hands	digital clock	words
	7:30	half past 7

Show the time on both clocks.

1. 3 o'clock — 3:00
2. half past 4 — 4:30
3. 9 o'clock — 9:00
4. half past 8 — 8:30
5. half past 7 — 7:30
6. 10 o'clock — 10:00

Use with text pages 373–374.

PRACTICE 13.6

Name _____ Date _____   Practice 13.6

Practice Telling Time

Show the time on the clock.

1. I get up at 7 o'clock.
2. I eat breakfast at half past 7. — 7:30
3. I help mom at half past 8. — 8:30
4. I walk the dog at 11 o'clock.

Test Prep

Fill in the ○ for the correct answer. NH means Not Here.

5. Phillip gets home at 4 o'clock. Which clock shows the time?

○   ○   ○   NH ●

Use with text pages 373–374.

ENRICHMENT 13.6

Name _____ Date _____   Enrichment 13.6

The Time I Take

Decide what time you do each of the activities below.

Show the time on the two clocks. **Answers will vary.**

1.
2.
3.
4.

Write About It Which kind of clock do you like best? Why?
Answers will vary.

Use with text pages 373–374.

Practice Workbook Page 87

Reaching All Learners

Differentiated Instruction

English Learners

English-language learners may not have experience reading a *schedule*. Use Worksheet 13.6 to develop children's ability to read and use a schedule.

Special Needs
TACTILE, VISUAL

Materials: *demonstration clock*

- Present the child with a riddle, such as: I'm thinking of a time. The minute hand is on the 12. The hour hand is on the 4. What time is it?
- Have the child set the time on the clock and write the time.
- Repeat with times half past the hour.

Early Finishers
TACTILE, VISUAL

Materials: *index cards*

- Write times 2 different ways from 12:00 to 11:30 to the hour and half-hour on index cards.
- Have the children use the cards to play a concentration game.

TECHNOLOGY

Spiral Review

Using the *Ways to Assess* CD-ROM, you can create **customized** spiral review worksheets covering any lessons you choose.

Lesson Planner

Use the **Lesson Planner CD-ROM** to see how lesson objectives for this chapter are correlated to standards.

eBook

eMathBook allows students to review lessons and do homework without carrying their textbooks home.

Education Place

Recommend that parents visit **Education Place** at eduplace.com/parents/mw/ for parent support activities.

Social Studies Connection

Tell children that there are different time zones in the United States. For example, when it is 4:30 in Georgia, it is 1:30 in California. Show children these locations on a map of the United States. Then have children write 4:30 and 1:30 in three different ways.

MATH CENTER

Real-Life Activity

Help children understand the usefulness of mathematics. This activity makes math come alive by connecting the lesson skills to a real-life situation.

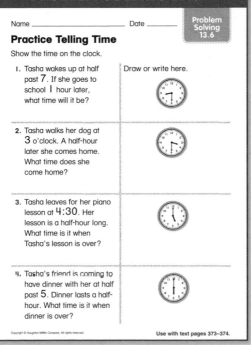

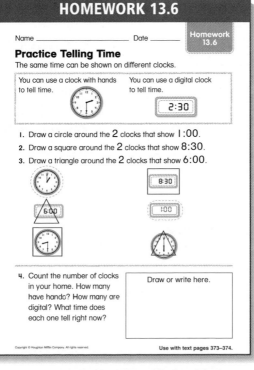

Homework Workbook Page 87

TEACHING LESSON 13.6

LESSON ORGANIZER

Objective Practice telling time using analog and digital clocks.

Resources Reteach, Practice, Enrichment, Problem Solving, Homework, English Learners, Transparencies, Math Center

Materials Paper clocks (LT 33), index cards, analog and digital clock transparencies, demonstration clock

Activity

Warm-Up Activity
Modeling Practicing Telling Time

👥 Small Group	🕐 5–10 minutes	Tactile, Visual

Materials: *paper clocks (LT 33), index cards*

1. Provide each group with a paper clock and cards with blank digital displays drawn on them.

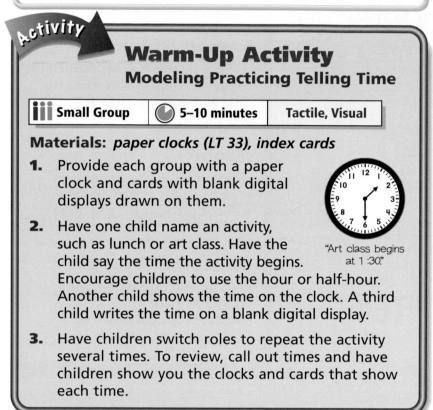

"Art class begins at 1:30."

2. Have one child name an activity, such as lunch or art class. Have the child say the time the activity begins. Encourage children to use the hour or half-hour. Another child shows the time on the clock. A third child writes the time on a blank digital display.

3. Have children switch roles to repeat the activity several times. To review, call out times and have children show you the clocks and cards that show each time.

Name_____

Practice Telling Time

Objective Show time on digital and analog clocks.

The same time can be shown in different ways.

I can use a clock with hands.

I can use a digital clock.

I can use words.

half past 9

Guided Practice

Show the time on the two clocks.

1. 8 o'clock

   8:00

2. half past 1

   1:30

3. 11 o'clock

   11:00

4. half past 5

   5:30

TEST TIPS **Explain Your Thinking** Why is it important to be able to tell time on different kinds of clocks?

Possible answer: There may be different clocks in different places you visit.

Chapter 13 Lesson 6   three hundred seventy-three **373**

①Introduce
Discuss Different Ways to Tell Time

👥 Whole Group	🕐 10–15 minutes	Visual, Auditory

Materials: *analog and digital clock transparencies*

1. On the overhead, show 9:30 on the analog clock and on the digital clock. Then write the words *half past 9.*

2. Remind children that they have learned 3 different ways to show the time. Discuss the clock face, the digital clock, and the time shown on the overhead. Ask a volunteer to read each time.

3. Show several more times to the hour or half-hour in a variety of ways. Have volunteers show the times on both clocks.

②Develop

Guided Learning

Teaching Example Introduce the objective to the children. Guide them through the example to review how to show time using different ways.

Guided Practice

Have children complete **Exercises 1–4** as you observe. Give children the opportunity to answer the Explain Your Thinking question. Then discuss their responses with the class.

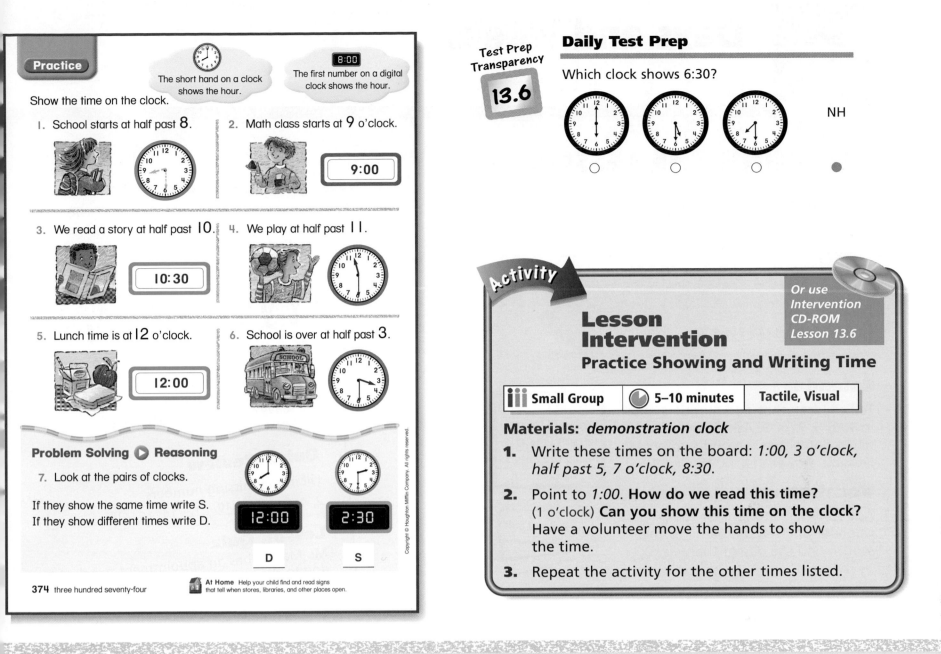

Practice

The short hand on a clock shows the hour.

The first number on a digital clock shows the hour.

Show the time on the clock.

1. School starts at half past 8.

2. Math class starts at 9 o'clock.

9:00

3. We read a story at half past 10.

10:30

4. We play at half past 11.

5. Lunch time is at 12 o'clock.

12:00

6. School is over at half past 3.

Problem Solving ▶ Reasoning

7. Look at the pairs of clocks.

If they show the same time write S.
If they show different times write D.

12:00

2:30

D   S

374 three hundred seventy-four

At Home Help your child find and read signs that tell when stores, libraries, and other places open.

Test Prep Transparency

13.6

Daily Test Prep

Which clock shows 6:30?

NH

Activity

Or use Intervention CD-ROM Lesson 13.6

Lesson Intervention

Practice Showing and Writing Time

| ⫙ Small Group | 🕐 5–10 minutes | Tactile, Visual |

Materials: *demonstration clock*

1. Write these times on the board: *1:00, 3 o'clock, half past 5, 7 o'clock, 8:30.*

2. Point to *1:00.* **How do we read this time?** (1 o'clock) **Can you show this time on the clock?** Have a volunteer move the hands to show the time.

3. Repeat the activity for the other times listed.

3 Practice

Independent Practice

Children complete **Exercises 1–6** independently.

Problem Solving

After children complete **Exercise 7,** call on volunteers to share their solutions.

Common Error

Writing Digital Time Incorrectly

Children may become confused when writing time in digital notation for the hour and the half-hour. Remind children that *o'clock* translates to *00* and that *half past* translates to *30*.

4 Assess and Close

What time is it when the hour hand is between the 5 and 6 and the minute hand points to the 6? (5:30)

Where are the hands on an analog clock pointing when it is 8 o'clock? (The hour hand points to the 8 and the minute hand points to the 12.)

Keeping a Journal

Draw a picture of your favorite school activity. Then draw two different kinds of clocks to show the time that activity takes place.

Days and Weeks

PLANNING THE LESSON

MATHEMATICS OBJECTIVE
Read a calendar to find dates.

Use Lesson Planner CD-ROM for Lesson 13.7.

Meeting North Carolina's Standards
2.02 Develop an understanding of the concept of time.
- Solve problems involving applications of time (clock and calendar).

Daily Routines

Calendar
Tell children that odd numbers end in 1, 3, 5, 7, or 9. Ask children to name dates that are odd numbers. (Possible answers: 11, 13, 15, 17, 19, 21)

Vocabulary
Ask volunteers to look at the **calendar** and tell the name of the *month* and the *day* of the *week*.

Vocabulary Cards

Lesson Transparency 13.7

Problem of the Day
Jansen went to the library at half past 3. He spent 2 hours at the library. What time did he leave? Write the time 2 ways. (5:30, half past 5)

Quick Review
Fill in the missing numbers.
2, 4, 6, __(8)__, __(10)__, 12, 14, 16, __(18)__, __(20)__, 22

Lesson Quiz
Mr. Marcus has an appointment to take his dog to the vet tomorrow. If today is Wednesday, the 16th, what is the date of the appointment? (Thursday, the 17th)

LEVELED PRACTICE

RETEACH 13.7

Days and Weeks

Name _____ Date _____ Reteach 13.7

A calendar shows the months, weeks, and days of a year.

October

Sunday	Monday	Tuesday	Wednesday	Thursday	Friday	Saturday
					1	2
3	4	5	6	7	8	9
10	11	12	13	14	15	16
17	18	19	20	21	22	23
24/31	25	26	27	28	29	30

Use the calendar to find the answer.

1. The name of the month is __October__.
2. How many days are in this month? __31__
3. How many days are in one week? __7__
4. What day comes after Thursday? __Friday__
5. What day is October 12? __Tuesday__
6. If today is October 20, what is tomorrow's date? __October 21__

Copyright © Houghton Mifflin Company. All rights reserved. Use with text pages 375–376.

PRACTICE 13.7

Days and Weeks

Name _____ Date _____ Practice 13.7

Fill in the calendar for this month. **Check students' answers.**

1. Color today (Red).
2. What is the date of the second Monday in this month? _____
3. What day is the last day in this month? _____

Test Prep

Fill in the ○ for the correct answer. NH means Not Here.

4. Andrew's birthday is on June 5. His party is two days later. What is the date of his party?

June 3   June 6   June 7   NH
○   ○   ●   ○

Copyright © Houghton Mifflin Company. All rights reserved. Use with text pages 375–376.

ENRICHMENT 13.7

Day by Day

Name _____ Date _____ Enrichment 13.7

Fill in the missing dates on the calendar. Then answer the questions.

MAY

Sun.	Mon.	Tues.	Wed.	Thurs.	Fri.	Sat.
			1	2	3	4
5	6	7	8	9	10	11
12	13	14	15	16	17	18
19	20	21	22	23	24	25
26	27	28	29	30	31	

1. On what day was the last day of April? __Tuesday__
2. Rosa's birthday is May 10. On what day is that? __Friday__
3. Each Monday, Tony has piano lessons. How many lessons will he have in May? __4__ lessons
4. On what day is June 1? __Saturday__

Talk About It What is a good way to find the date that is a week from today? __Add 7 to today's date.__

Copyright © Houghton Mifflin Company. All rights reserved. Use with text pages 375–376.

Practice Workbook Page 88

375A   CHAPTER 13   Lesson 7

Reaching All Learners
Differentiated Instruction

English Learners

English-language learners may not have the language skills to explain the process behind their thinking. Use Worksheet 13.7 to provide children with sentence frames they can use to complete the Explain Your Thinking activity.

Special Needs
TACTILE, AUDITORY

Materials: *index cards*

- Display 7 index cards labeled with the names of the days of the week in order.
- Point to and say each day with the child.
- Mix up the cards and have the child order them.

Early Finishers
TACTILE, VISUAL

Materials: *calendar*

- Have children solve problems such as: Kate goes to visit her grandparents for 1 week. She leaves on March 21. When does she return? (March 28)
- Children can write similar problems for a partner to solve.

TECHNOLOGY
Spiral Review

To reinforce skills on lessons taught earlier, create **customized** spiral review worksheets using the *Ways to Assess* CD-ROM.

Lesson Planner

You can use the **Lesson Planner CD-ROM** to create a report of the lessons and standards you have taught.

Education Place

Visit **Data Place** at eduplace.com/dataplace/ to take a survey and see graphs of the results.

Language Arts Connection

Refer to the literature selection *Me Counting Time* by Joan Sweeney. Read the selection and stop at the page of months. Have the month's calendar visible and have children refer to it as you ask questions.

MATH CENTER
Vocabulary Activity

This vocabulary-building activity helps children understand and remember new words. Encourage children to use the words in math discussion.

PROBLEM SOLVING 13.7

Name _____ Date _____ Problem Solving 13.7

Days and Weeks

February

Sun.	Mon.	Tues.	Wed.	Thurs.	Fri.	Sat.
					1	2
3	4	5	6	7	8	9
10	11	12	13	14	15	16
17	18	19	20	21	22	23
24	25	26	27	28		

Complete the calendar.
Use the calendar to find the answer.

1. The month is February.
   There are __28__ days.

2. On what day did January end? __Thursday__

3. On what day will March begin? __Friday__

4. How many Fridays are there in the month of February? __4__

Copyright © Houghton Mifflin Company. All rights reserved.   **Use with text pages 375–376.**

HOMEWORK 13.7

Name _____ Date _____ Homework 13.7

Days and Weeks
Fill in the calendar for next month. **Answers will vary.**

Sunday	Monday	Tuesday	Wednesday	Thursday	Friday	Saturday

Answer the questions. **Answers will vary.**

1. What is the name of the month? _____
2. On what day of the week does the month begin? _____
3. On what day of the week does the month end? _____
4. How many days are in this month? _____
5. Count the number of days you will go to school. Count the vacation days. Count the weekend days.

   There are _____ days of school this month
   There are _____ vacation days.
   There are _____ weekend days.
   Answers will vary.

Copyright © Houghton Mifflin Company. All rights reserved.   **Use with text pages 375–376.**

ENGLISH LEARNERS 13.7

Name _____ Date _____ English Learners 13.7

Days and Weeks

March

S	M	T	W	T	F	S
1	2	3	4	5	6	7
8	9	10	11	12	13	14
15	16	17	18	19	20	21
22	23	24	25	26	27	28
29	30	31				

The Mondays are 1, 8, 15, 22, and 29.
There are 5 Mondays in March.

How can you tell if there are more Tuesdays or Fridays in the month shown above?

The Tuesdays are __2__, __9__, __16__, __23__, and __30__.

There are __5__ Tuesdays in March.

The Fridays are __5__, __12__, __19__, and __26__.

There are __4__ Fridays in March.

5 is more than __4__.

There are more __Tuesdays__ than __Fridays__ in March.

Copyright © Houghton Mifflin Company. All rights reserved.   **Use with text pages 375–376.**

Homework Workbook Page 88

TEACHING LESSON 13.7

LESSON ORGANIZER

Objective Read a calendar to find dates.

Resources Reteach, Practice, Enrichment, Problem Solving, Homework, English Learners, Transparencies, Math Center

Materials Drawing paper, calendar, blank calendar (LT 35)

Activity

Warm-Up Activity
Modeling the Days of the Week

| iiii Whole Group | 10 minutes | Auditory, Kinesthetic |

Materials: *drawing paper, calendar (LT 35)*

1. In advance, write the names of the days of the week on 7 sheets of drawing paper. Display a calendar page for the current month.

2. Give one sheet each to 7 children. Have the child holding a card with the first day of the week stand up. **What day comes after Sunday?** (Monday) Ask that child to stand up.

3. Continue with the rest of the days. Ask the children to go to the front of the classroom and arrange themselves in order from Sunday to Saturday. Allow classmates to assist where needed.

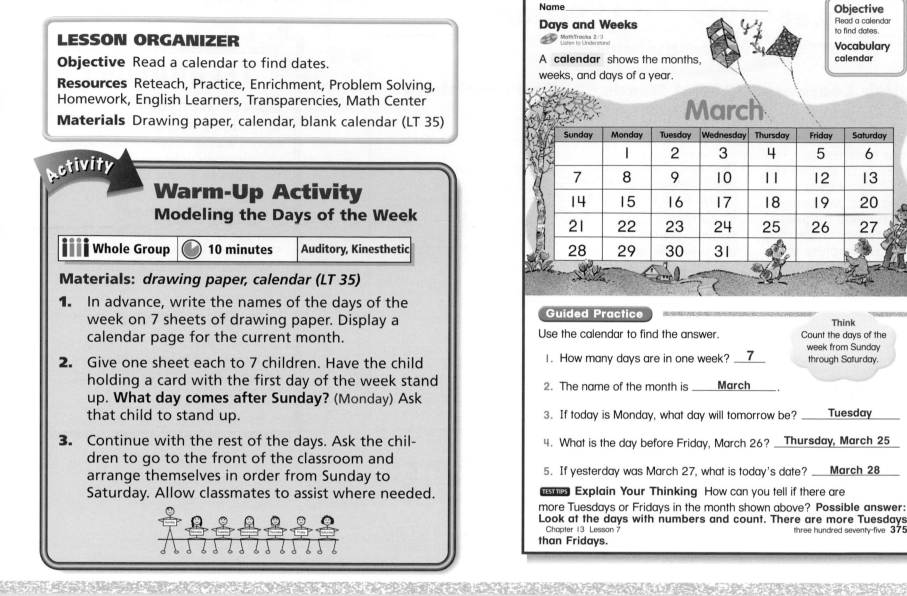

Name _____

Days and Weeks

MathTracks 2/3
Listen to Understand

A **calendar** shows the months, weeks, and days of a year.

Objective
Read a calendar to find dates.

Vocabulary
calendar

March

Sunday	Monday	Tuesday	Wednesday	Thursday	Friday	Saturday
	1	2	3	4	5	6
7	8	9	10	11	12	13
14	15	16	17	18	19	20
21	22	23	24	25	26	27
28	29	30	31			

Guided Practice

Use the calendar to find the answer.

> **Think**
> Count the days of the week from Sunday through Saturday.

1. How many days are in one week? __7__

2. The name of the month is ___March___.

3. If today is Monday, what day will tomorrow be? ___Tuesday___

4. What is the day before Friday, March 26? ___Thursday, March 25___

5. If yesterday was March 27, what is today's date? ___March 28___

TEST TIPS **Explain Your Thinking** How can you tell if there are more Tuesdays or Fridays in the month shown above? **Possible answer: Look at the days with numbers and count. There are more Tuesdays than Fridays.**

Chapter 13   Lesson 7   three hundred seventy-five **375**

---

1 Introduce
Discuss Days and Weeks

| iiii Whole Group | 10–15 minutes | Visual, Auditory |

Materials: *blank calendar (LT 35)*

1. Make a calendar for the current month. Ask children to help you as you write the days of the week on the calendar. Write a 1 on the first day in the month. **What is the first day of the month? What is the second day of the month?**

2. Ask volunteers to help you fill in the dates for the rest of the month.

3. **What day of the week is the 19th? What is the date of the second Wednesday?** Continue asking questions about the different days and dates on the calendar.

2 Develop

Guided Learning

Teaching Example Introduce the objective and vocabulary to the children. Point out the name of the month, the names of the days of the week, and the dates on the calendar.

Guided Practice

Have children complete **Exercises 1–5** as you observe. Give children the opportunity to answer the Explain Your Thinking question. Then discuss their responses with the class.

Practice

Fill in the calendar for this month.

The first date of the month can be any day of the week.

Answers may vary.

Sunday	Monday	Tuesday	Wednesday	Thursday	Friday	Saturday

Use the calendar to find the answer.   **Answers may vary.**

1. Color today ▭.
2. Color yesterday ▭.
3. Color tomorrow ▭.
4. Color the first Sunday ▭.

5. What day of the week is the ninth? _____

6. What is the date of the
   second Thursday in this month? _____

7. If today is the eleventh, what
   day of the week will tomorrow be? _____

Problem Solving ▶ Reasoning   **Answers may vary.**

8. What day of the week comes
   after the last date on your calendar? _____

9. What is the date of that day? _____

At Home Ask your child to read the dates of the Wednesdays shown on the calendar.

Daily Test Prep

Add.

$$\begin{array}{r} 6 \\ +\ 3 \\ \hline \end{array}$$

3 ○   8 ○   9 ●   10 ○

Activity

Or use Intervention CD-ROM Lesson 13.7

Lesson Intervention
Use a Calendar

⚇ Small Group	⏱ 10–15 minutes	Auditory, Visual

1. Have children use the calendar page on page 375 to solve oral problems. For example: **Liam's brother was born on Friday, March 5. Liam's birthday is 2 days later. What is the date of Liam's birthday?** (March 7)

2. Help children make up similar problems for the group to solve.

---

3 Practice

Independent Practice

Children complete **Exercises 1–7** independently.

Problem Solving

After children complete **Exercises 8** and **9**, call on volunteers to share their answers.

Common Error

Confusing Ordinal Numbers
Children may not remember ordinal numbers or may not be able to read them. Provide exercises where children match the ordinal numbers on a calendar page to ordinal number words on cards.

---

4 Assess and Close

If today is Friday, the 25th, what is the date tomorrow?
(Saturday, the 26th)

If today is Tuesday, the 3rd, what was the date yesterday?
(Monday, the 2nd)

✎ Keeping a Journal

Use the calendar for this month. Write the date of the first Monday. Then write the date of the last Friday. Write how many Saturdays there are in this month.

Months

PLANNING THE LESSON

MATHEMATICS OBJECTIVE
Use a calendar.

Use Lesson Planner CD-ROM for Lesson 13.8.

Daily Routines

Calendar
Ask children to name the current month. Then have them name last month and next month.

Vocabulary
Ask children to name the **day** and the *date,* including the *month.* Then ask them to name the day and date for yesterday and tomorrow. Help children say the months of the *year* in order.

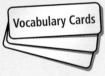
Vocabulary Cards

Meeting North Carolina's Standards
2.02 Develop an understanding of the concept of time.
• Solve problems involving applications of time (clock and calendar).

Lesson Transparency
13.8

Problem of the Day
Write the names of the days of the week in order. Underline the third day and circle the sixth day. (Sunday, Monday, Tuesday, Wednesday, Thursday, Friday, Saturday)

Quick Review
Fill in the missing numbers.
5, 7, ____ (9), ____ (11), 13, 15, 17, ____ (19), ____ (21), 23

Lesson Quiz
1. Colleen's birthday is in the fourth month of the year. In what month is Colleen's birthday? (April)

2. Laura goes to camp during the seventh month of the year. What month does Laura go to camp? (July)

LEVELED PRACTICE

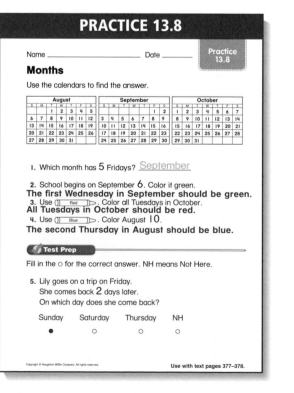

RETEACH 13.8

Name _____ Date _____
Reteach 13.8

Months

There are 12 months in one year.

January

Sunday	Monday	Tuesday	Wednesday	Thursday	Friday	Saturday
						1
2	3	4	5	6	7	8
9	10	11	12	13	14	15
16	17	18	19	20	21	22
23/30	24/31	25	26	27	28	29

January
February
March
April
May
June
July
August
September
October
November
December

Use the calendar and list of months.

Find the answer.

1. How many Mondays are in this month? __5__

2. How many days are in this month? __31__

3. What is the third month of the year? __March__

4. What month comes after June? __July__

Copyright © Houghton Mifflin Company. All rights reserved.
Use with text pages 377–378.

PRACTICE 13.8

Name _____ Date _____
Practice 13.8

Months

Use the calendars to find the answer.

1. Which month has 5 Fridays? _September_

2. School begins on September 6. Color it green.
The first Wednesday in September should be green.

3. Use [Red]. Color all Tuesdays in October.
All Tuesdays in October should be red.

4. Use [Blue]. Color August 10.
The second Thursday in August should be blue.

Test Prep

Fill in the ○ for the correct answer. NH means Not Here.

5. Lily goes on a trip on Friday.
   She comes back 2 days later.
   On which day does she come back?

Sunday   Saturday   Thursday   NH
●   ○   ○   ○

Copyright © Houghton Mifflin Company. All rights reserved.
Use with text pages 377–378.

ENRICHMENT 13.8

Name _____ Date _____
Enrichment 13.8

I Know What Day It Is

Use the calendars to answer the questions.

1. What month comes after July? __August__

2. July 4 is Independence Day. What is the day and date?
   __Thursday__ is the day, and __4__ is the date.

3. June is the sixth month of the year. What month of the year is August? __eighth__

4. Circle June 20. What day is it? __Thursday__

5. Suppose you were invited to a party on the third Friday in June. What is the date? __21__

Write About It July is the seventh month of the year now. What month of the year will it be next year? Why?
__The seventh, because the months of the year__
__come in the same order every year.__

Copyright © Houghton Mifflin Company. All rights reserved.
Use with text pages 377–378.

Reaching All Learners

Differentiated Instruction

English Learners

English-language learners may not be familiar with the endings for comparative adjectives. Use Worksheet 13.8 to teach children how adding the endings –er and –est changes the meaning of words.

Inclusion

TACTILE, VISUAL

Materials: *small calendar*

Display loose calendar pages in order. Point to and say each month. Mix up the pages and have the child put them in order. Then help the child identify the last day of a month and the first day of the next month and emphasize the sequence of days.

Gifted and Talented

TACTILE, KINESTHETIC

Materials: *blank calendar pages, poster board*

• Provide children with 12 blank calendar pages. Have children work together to make a calendar. Have them paste the pages in order on the poster board.

• Encourage children to mark special events and holidays.

TECHNOLOGY

Spiral Review

Help students remember skills they learned earlier by creating **customized** spiral review worksheets using the *Ways to Assess* CD-ROM.

eBook

An electronic version of this lesson can be found in **eMathBook.**

Education Place

Encourage students to visit **Education Place** at **eduplace.com/kids/mw/** for more student activities.

Science Connection

Name the four seasons—winter, spring, summer, fall—and explain that in most places the weather changes during the seasons. Talk about the temperature (hot or cold) in your area. Have children draw season pictures.

MATH CENTER

Vocabulary Activity

This vocabulary-building activity helps children understand and remember new words. Encourage children to use the words in math discussion.

PROBLEM SOLVING 13.8

Name _____ Date _____   Problem Solving 13.8

Months

Use the tables to answer the questions.

Month	Days		Month	Days
1. January	31		7. July	31
2. February	28		8. August	31
3. March	31		9. September	30
4. April	30		10. October	31
5. May	31		11. November	30
6. June	30		12. December	31

1. Kendra's birthday is in the 3rd month of the year. In what month is her birthday?

   March

2. What is the shortest month of the year?

   February

3. What month comes between June and August?

   July

Draw or write here.

Copyright © Houghton Mifflin Company. All rights reserved.

Use with text pages 377–378.

HOMEWORK 13.8

Name _____ Date _____   Homework 13.8

Months

There are 12 months in one year. They are:

January, February, March, April, May, June, July, August, September, October, November, December.

Use the calanders to answer the questions.

1. Which month comes before May?

   April

2. Which month has the most days?

   May

3. Which month has 5 Wednesdays?

   April

4. Finish this sentence. 30 days has September, **April**, **June**, and November.

5. In which month is your birthday? Write the month. Write the months that come before and after.

Write here.

Copyright © Houghton Mifflin Company. All rights reserved.

Use with text pages 377–378.

ENGLISH LEARNERS 13.8

Name _____ Date _____   English Learners 13.8

Months

few   fewer   fewest

You can add endings to words to tell how things are different from one another.

Label the pictures with words from the boxes.

small   smaller   smallest

1.

small   smallest   smaller

tall   taller   tallest

2.

taller   tallest   tall

To the Teacher: Use the example at the top of the page to demonstrate how to make comparative adjectives. Then have children label the pictures with the adjectives from the boxes.

Copyright © Houghton Mifflin Company. All rights reserved.

Use with text pages 377–378.

TEACHING LESSON 13.8

LESSON ORGANIZER

Objective Use a calendar.

Resources Reteach, Practice, Enrichment, Problem Solving, Homework, English Learners, Transparencies, Math Center

Materials Calendar pages, calendar for the month

Warm-Up Activity
Modeling Reading a Calendar

iiii Whole Group	5 minutes	Tactile, Visual

Materials: *calendar pages*

1. Display 3 consecutive calendar pages. Point to a page and identify it by month. Have a volunteer point to the month before and the month after. Identify each month by name.

2. Point to today's date on the calendar. Have children say the date for yesterday and the date for tomorrow.

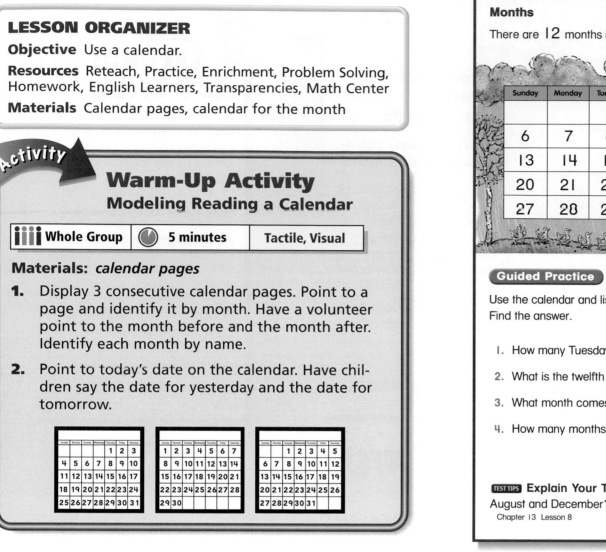

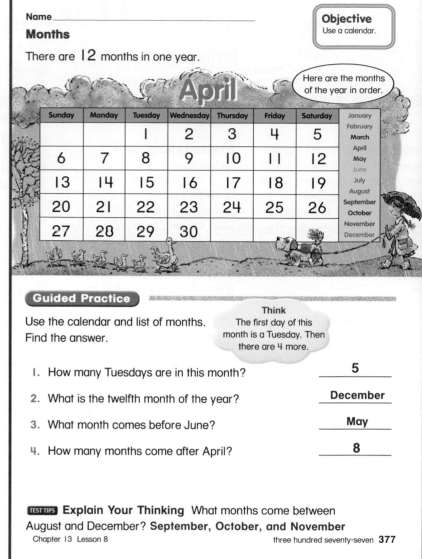

Name_____

Months

Objective
Use a calendar.

There are 12 months in one year.

Here are the months of the year in order.

April

Sunday	Monday	Tuesday	Wednesday	Thursday	Friday	Saturday
		1	2	3	4	5
6	7	8	9	10	11	12
13	14	15	16	17	18	19
20	21	22	23	24	25	26
27	28	29	30			

January
February
March
April
May
June
July
August
September
October
November
December

Guided Practice

Use the calendar and list of months. Find the answer.

Think
The first day of this month is a Tuesday. Then there are 4 more.

1. How many Tuesdays are in this month? _____ **5**

2. What is the twelfth month of the year? _____ **December**

3. What month comes before June? _____ **May**

4. How many months come after April? _____ **8**

TEST TIPS **Explain Your Thinking** What months come between August and December? **September, October, and November**

---

1 Introduce

Discuss the Calendar for the Year

iiii Whole Group	10–15 minutes	Visual, Auditory

1. Draw a 12-section grid on the board. Write the names of the months in each section. Read the names aloud as you write. When all the names are written, ask volunteers to read the names as you point to the months.

January	February	March
April	May	June
July	August	September
October	November	December

2. **What is the first month of the year?** (January) **What is the last month of the year?** (December) **What month comes after May?** (June) **What month is it now?**

3. Continue asking questions about the 12 months of the year. Ask children in what month were they born. Then have them tell which months come before and after their birthday month.

2 Develop

Guided Learning

Teaching Example Introduce the objective to children. Point out that there are 12 months in a year and that the months come in the same order every year. Have children read the names of the months in unison.

Guided Practice

Have children complete **Exercises 1–4** as you observe. Give children the opportunity to answer the Explain Your Thinking question. Then discuss their responses with the class.

Practice

Use the calendars to find the answer.

Remember some months have more days than others.

May

Sun.	Mon.	Tues.	Wed.	Thurs.	Fri.	Sat.
					1	2	3
4		6	7	8	9	10
11	12	13	14	15	16	17
18	19	20	21	22	23	24
25	26	27	28	29	30	31

June

Sun.	Mon.	Tues.	Wed.	Thurs.	Fri.	Sat.
1	2	3	4	5	6	7
8	9	10	11	12	13	14
15	16	17	18	19	20	21
22	23	24	25	26	27	28
29	30					

July

Sun.	Mon.	Tues.	Wed.	Thurs.	Fri.	Sat.
		1	2	3	4	5
6	7	8	9	10	11	12
13	14	15	16	17	18	19
20	21	22	23	24	25	26
27	28	29	30	31		

1. Which of these months has the fewest days? ___June___

2. Which month has 5 Wednesdays? ___July___

3. Cinco de Mayo is May 5. Color it 🖍.

4. Color all Fridays in July 🖍.

Algebra Readiness ▶ Patterns

Use the May calendar above. Write the dates for the Thursdays.

5. [ ] [8] [15] [22] [29]

6. **Talk About It** What pattern do you see? Possible answer: Each date is 7 more than the Thursday before it because there are 7 days in a week.

Now write the dates for the Saturdays.

7. [3] [10] [17] [24] [31]

8. **Talk About It** Is the pattern the same? Why? Yes; Possible answer: There are 7 days in a week.

At Home Help your child find your family's special days on a calendar.

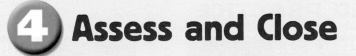

Activity

Or use Intervention CD-ROM Lesson 13.8

Lesson Intervention

Practice Reading a Calendar

👥 Small Group	⏱ 5–10 minutes	Tactile, Visual

Materials: *calendar for the month*

Sunday	Monday	Tuesday	Wednesday	Thursday	Friday	Saturday
			1	2	3	4
5	6	7	8	9	10	11
12	13	14	15	16	17	18
19	20	21	22	23	24	25
26	27	28	29	30		

1. Display the calendar for the current month. Ask a volunteer to name the month.

2. Have children refer to the calendar as you ask questions. **How many days are there in this month? What is the first day of this month? This month ends on which day of the week? What is today's date?**

3. Ask if any children know of a special day in this month. If so, have them point to the date and name the day it falls on.

3 Practice

Independent Practice

Children complete **Exercises 1–4** independently.

Algebra Readiness

After children complete **Exercises 5–7**, call on volunteers to share their answers. Use the **Talk About It** in Exercise 8 to discuss the patterns found on a calendar.

Common Error

Naming the Months Incorrectly

Children may name or sequence the months incorrectly. Provide a chart with the months in order and suggest that children refer to it if they are confused.

4 Assess and Close

How many months are in a year? (12)

What is the first month? (January) **The last month?** (December)

Which month comes after May? (June)

Keeping a Journal

Write the name of this month. Write the names of the month before and the next month.

Lesson 13.9

Problem Solving: Use a Table

PLANNING THE LESSON

MATHEMATICS OBJECTIVE
Use a table to solve problems about elapsed time.

Use Lesson Planner CD-ROM for Lesson 13.9.

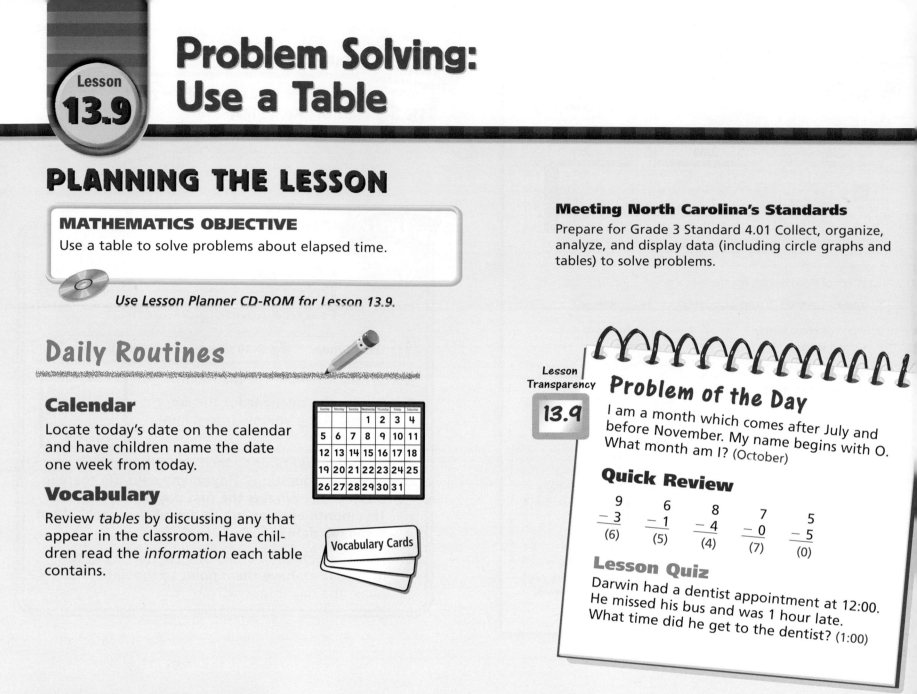

Daily Routines

Calendar
Locate today's date on the calendar and have children name the date one week from today.

Vocabulary
Review *tables* by discussing any that appear in the classroom. Have children read the *information* each table contains.

Vocabulary Cards

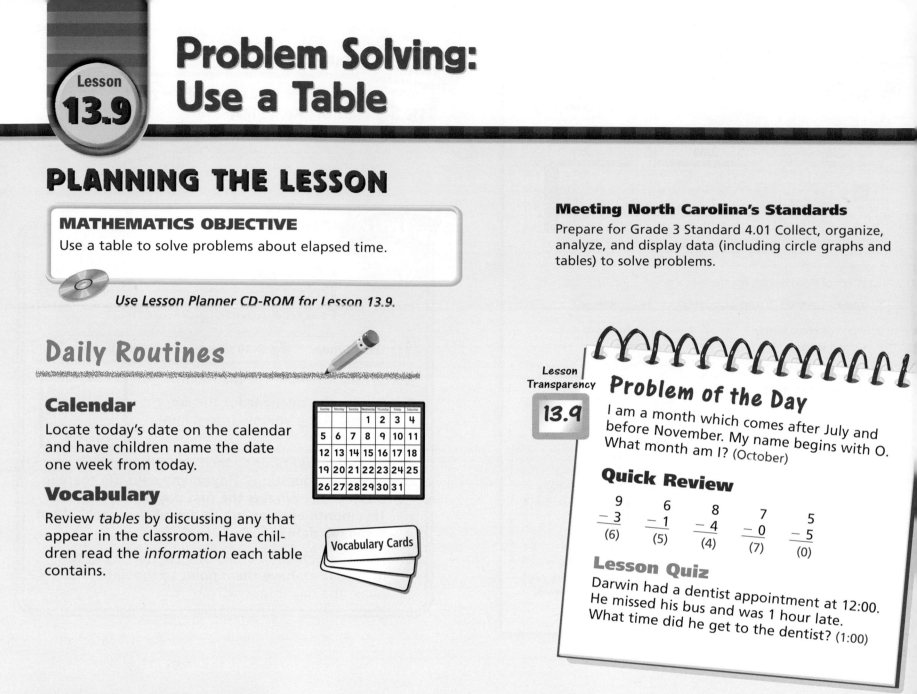

Meeting North Carolina's Standards
Prepare for Grade 3 Standard 4.01 Collect, organize, analyze, and display data (including circle graphs and tables) to solve problems.

Lesson Transparency 13.9

Problem of the Day
I am a month which comes after July and before November. My name begins with O. What month am I? (October)

Quick Review

9	6	8	7	5
− 3	− 1	− 4	− 0	− 5
(6)	(5)	(4)	(7)	(0)

Lesson Quiz
Darwin had a dentist appointment at 12:00. He missed his bus and was 1 hour late. What time did he get to the dentist? (1:00)

LEVELED PRACTICE

RETEACH 13.9

Name _____ Date _____ **Reteach 13.9**

Problem Solving Use a Table

Read It Look for information.

The children play games for 2 hours.

When do the games end?

Activity	Time
Pizza	1:00
Open Presents	3:00
Play Games	5:00

Picture It Here is a model of a problem you can follow.

When does the movie end?

Gina goes to the movies at 2:00.	The movie is 2 hours long.	Two hours from 2:00 is 4:00.
	The movie ends at 4:00.	

Solve It Use the model and the table to solve the problem.

1. The games begin at ___5:00___.

2. The children play games for 2 hours. When do the games end? The games end at ___7:00___.

Copyright © Houghton Mifflin Company. All rights reserved. **Use with text pages 379–382.**

PRACTICE 13.9

Name _____ Date _____ **Practice 13.9**

Problem Solving Use a Table

Use the table to solve the problem.

Monday Schedule

Activity	Time
Reading	9:00
Math	11:00
Lunch	12:00
Science	1:00
Art	2:00
Dismissal	3:00

Draw or write to explain.

1. Ms. Roper gets to school at 8:00. How much time does she have before Reading? ___1 hour___

2. What activity starts 2 hours before Science? ___Math___

3. What activity starts 2 hours after lunch? ___Art___

4. How many hours are there between Reading and Lunch? ___3 hours___

Copyright © Houghton Mifflin Company. All rights reserved. **Use with text pages 379–382.**

ENRICHMENT 13.9

Name _____ Date _____ **Enrichment 13.9**

Problem Solving Use a Table

1. **Read the problem**
   It is 10:00.
   How long does Kevin have to wait before swimming begins?

Activity	Time Today	Time Tomorrow
Art	9:00	
Baseball	10:00	
Lunch	11:30	
Swimming	1:00	

Picture It

Use the table.

What activity begins at 10:00? ___baseball___

When does swimming begin? ___1:00___

Solve It

Count on from baseball to swimming. How long does Kevin have to wait? ___3 hours___

2. Write different times in the table for Time Tomorrow.

Make up your own problem. ___Answers will vary.___

_____

_____

What is the answer to your problem? _____

Copyright © Houghton Mifflin Company. All rights reserved. **Use with text pages 379–382.**

Reaching All Learners
Differentiated Instruction

English Learners

English-language learners may not have the language skills to explain the process behind their thinking. Use Worksheet 13.9 to provide children with sentence frames they can use to complete the problems.

Inclusion
AUDITORY, VISUAL

Materials: index cards

- Prepare cards labeled with daily class activities.
- Have the child read each card.
- Arrange the day's schedule and ask questions. **What do we do before lunch? Do we have art today? Is math before or after lunch?**

| Science | Lunch | Math | Art |

Gifted and Talented
VISUAL, TACTILE

- Have each child write an activity that he or she does during the day and the time the activity takes place.
- Children make a table by pasting their strips onto a large sheet in time order.
- Then children write questions that can be answered using the information in the table.

TECHNOLOGY

Spiral Review

You can prepare students for standardized tests with **customized** spiral review on key skills using the *Ways to Assess* CD-ROM.

Intervention

Use the *Ways to Success* intervention software to support students who need more help in understanding the concepts and skills taught in this chapter.

Lesson Planner

You can customize your teaching plan or meet your curriculum requirements with the **Lesson Planner CD-ROM.**

Art Connection

Display the daily class schedule. Have each child draw a picture of one activity. Make a mural (or book) by placing the drawings in the correct sequence.

MATH CENTER

Number of the Week Activity

Display the Number of the Week to motivate children to use their problem-solving skills. The exercises cover topics across all math strands.

PROBLEM SOLVING 13.9

Name _____ Date _____ | Problem Solving 13.9

Use a Table

Sue leaves Detroit in the morning for New York City.

Dad gets to the New York City train station at 11:00.

How long does Dad have to wait before Sue's train arrives?

City	Time
Detroit	6:00 A.M.
Chicago	7:30 A.M
New York City	12:00 P.M.

UNDERSTAND

| What do I know? | When Dad gets to the station. |
| What do I need to find out? | How long Dad has to wait. |

PLAN

| How can I use the table to help me? | I can find the time that Sue's train arrives. |

SOLVE

| How can I figure out how long Dad has to wait? | Dad gets to the station at 11:00. Sue's train arrives at 12:00. |
| | Dad has to wait __1__ hour. |

LOOK BACK

| Is there another way I could solve the problem? | I can start at 12:00 and count back. |

Copyright © Houghton Mifflin Company. All rights reserved.
Use with text pages 379–381.

HOMEWORK 13.9

Name _____ Date _____ | Homework 13.9

Problem Solving
Use a Table

You can organize information in a table.

If Lila played outside for only a half-hour, when would she begin dinner?

Use the table to solve.

Lila plays outside

at __5__ o'clock.

A half-hour later it is __5:30__.

Lila could begin dinner at __5:30__.

Activity	Lila's Time	My Time
Play outside	5:00	
Dinner	6:00	
Homework	7:00	
Board games	7:30	
Bath	8:00	

Now fill in the table with the time you begin each activity.

1. How long do you do your homework? **Answers may vary.**

   I do homework for _____ minutes.

2. How many hours is it from the time you begin dinner until the time you take a bath?

   It is _____ hours from the time I begin dinner until the time I take a bath.

3. What activity takes the most amount of time?

   _____ is the longest activity of my evening.

Copyright © Houghton Mifflin Company. All rights reserved.
Use with text pages 379–381.

Homework Workbook Page 90

ENGLISH LEARNERS 13.9

Name _____ Date _____ | English Learners 13.9

Use a Table

Monday

Four people travel by bus. | Three people travel by car. | Six people travel by train.

On Tuesday ten people travel by bus.
Six people travel by car.
How many more people travel by bus than by car?

This is how many people travel by bus. __10__

This is how many people travel by car. __6__

__10__ − __6__ = 4

There are __4__ more people who travel by bus than by car.

To the Teacher: Use the pictures and sentences at the top of the page to help children become familiar with the vocabulary they will need to solve the word problems. Then read the sentences with children and have them complete each of them.

Use with text pages 379–381.

TEACHING LESSON 13.9

LESSON ORGANIZER

Objective Use a table to solve problems about elapsed time.

Resources Reteach, Practice, Enrichment, Problem Solving, Homework, English Learners, Transparencies, Math Center

Materials Schedule in table form

Activity

Warm-Up Activity
Modeling Planning a Schedule

iii Small Group	⏱ 5–10 minutes	Visual, Tactile

1. Invite children to be travel agents for the day. Assign each child in the group a destination city and a departure time. Have each child draw a picture of a plane and label it with its destination city and the time it leaves.

2. Have children share their drawings with the others in their group. Then arrange the planes in order of the departure times.

3. Ask the groups to share the information about their plane schedules with the class. Then ask the class questions about the plane schedules.

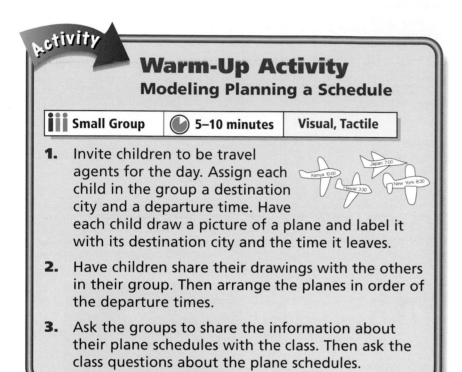

Name_____

Use a Table

MathTracks 2/4
Listen to Understand

Objective Use information in a table to solve problems about elapsed time.

Problem Solving

Use a table to get information.

The Wilsons are having a family picnic.

Dan picks up his family at the airport. Does Aunt Nora arrive before or after Grandma?

Think Find the times in the table.

Use the table to solve.

Arrival Schedule

Person	Time
Grandma	12:00
Aunt Nora	3:00
Cousin Eva	6:00
Uncle Joe	8:00

Grandma arrives at _12:00_.

Aunt Nora arrives at _3:00_.

Aunt Nora arrives _after_ Grandma.

Use a table to help you solve problems.

Molly picks up Cousin Eva at the airport. How many hours will they have to wait to pick up Uncle Joe?

Think Find the first time in the table. Count on to get to the second time.

Use the table to solve.

Cousin Eva arrives at _6:00_.

Uncle Joe arrives at _8:00_.

They wait for _2_ hours.

Chapter 13 Lesson 9   three hundred seventy-nine **379**

---

① Introduce
Discuss Reading a Table

iiii Whole Group	⏱ 10–15 minutes	Visual, Auditory

1. Draw a two-column table on the board. Write the title *Our Daily Routine* on the table. Label the columns *Activity* and *Time*. Fill in the class schedule on the table.

Our Daily Routine	
Activity	Time
Math	10:00
Lunch	11:30

2. Present problems that can be solved with the information in the table. For example: **We start math at 10:00. Is that before or after we have lunch?** (before)

3. **Jack's mother comes to help with our science project. It is 1:00. How long will she have to wait before Science begins?** (1/2 hour)

② Develop

Guided Learning

Teaching Example Introduce the objective to the children. Then explain the information in the table and how it relates to the context of the problems.

Work through the first problem to get information from the table. Then work through the second problem using the information in the table to solve.

Guided Practice

Discuss the schedule of events in the table. Have children complete **Exercises 1–2** on page 380 as you observe.

Use the table to solve the problem.

Friday Schedule

Activity	Time
Sign in	8:00
Boat trip	9:00
Lunch	12:00
Soccer game	2:00
Dinner	6:00

1. Cathy signs in at 8:00. How much time does she have until the boat trip begins?

Draw or write to explain.

Think
Count on from 8:00 to 9:00 to find how much time until the boat trip.

____1 hour____

2. What activity starts 3 hours after the boat trip?

Think
Start at 9:00 and count on 3 hours.

____lunch____

Practice

3. What activity begins 2 hours after lunch starts?

____soccer game____

4. How many hours are there between lunch and dinner?

____6____ hours

Go on

Play "How Much Time?"

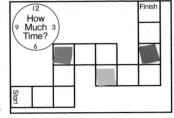

Draw a simple game board of squares on chart paper or on the board. Use a different colored self-stick note as a game piece for each team.

Separate the class into two teams and decide which team goes first. Say a story problem involving elapsed time aloud; for example:

A movie is showing at 5:30 and ends at 7:30. How long is the movie?

A player for the first team says the answer. If the answer is correct, the team gets to move one space on the board. If not, the other team gets a chance to answer.

Say another story and the second team tries to answer. Continue until one team reaches the last square.

---

3 Practice

Independent Practice

Children complete **Exercises 3** and **4** on page 380 independently.

Lesson continues

Daily Test Prep

Which of the following shows half past 7?

6:30 ○   7:00 ○   7:30 ●   NH ○

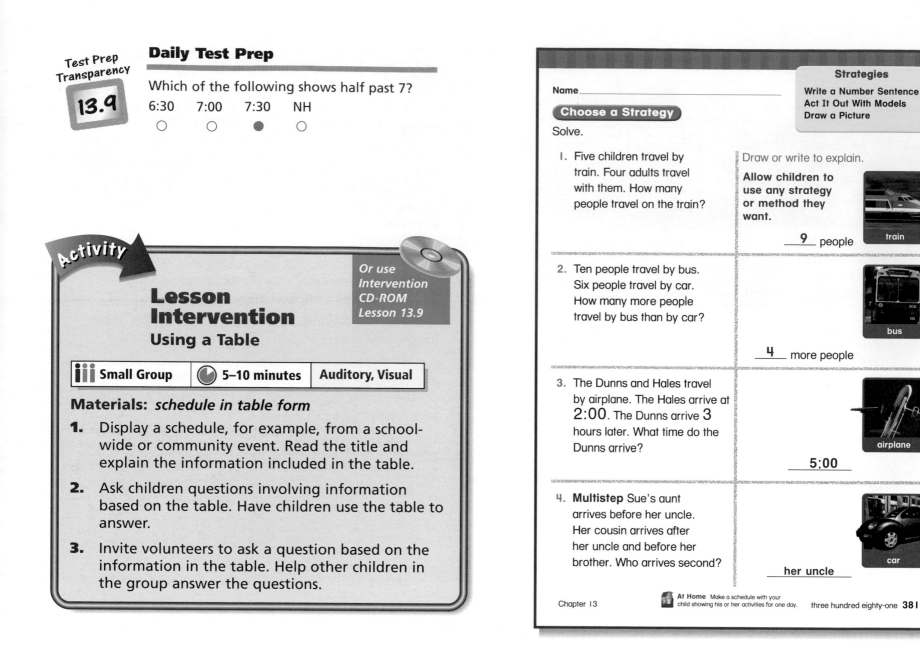

Activity

Lesson Intervention

Using a Table

Or use Intervention CD-ROM Lesson 13.9

| 👥 Small Group | ⏱ 5–10 minutes | Auditory, Visual |

Materials: *schedule in table form*

1. Display a schedule, for example, from a school-wide or community event. Read the title and explain the information included in the table.

2. Ask children questions involving information based on the table. Have children use the table to answer.

3. Invite volunteers to ask a question based on the information in the table. Help other children in the group answer the questions.

Name _____

Choose a Strategy

Strategies
Write a Number Sentence
Act It Out With Models
Draw a Picture

Solve.

1. Five children travel by train. Four adults travel with them. How many people travel on the train?

   Draw or write to explain.

   Allow children to use any strategy or method they want.

   __9__ people   *train*

2. Ten people travel by bus. Six people travel by car. How many more people travel by bus than by car?

   __4__ more people   *bus*

3. The Dunns and Hales travel by airplane. The Hales arrive at 2:00. The Dunns arrive 3 hours later. What time do the Dunns arrive?

   __5:00__   *airplane*

4. **Multistep** Sue's aunt arrives before her uncle. Her cousin arrives after her uncle and before her brother. Who arrives second?

   __her uncle__   *car*

③ Practice

Mixed Strategy Practice

Read the problem-solving strategies with children. Make sure children can read and comprehend the problems in **Exercises 1–4** on page 381. If necessary, pair more proficient readers with less proficient readers. Encourage them to discuss the problems before solving.

Common Error

Misunderstanding the Table

Children may misunderstand the information in the table. Have them use a different color for each problem and circle the information they need in the problem and in the table. Some children may need to talk through the problem.

④ Assess and Close

The soccer game was scheduled for 2:00. It was delayed 1 hour because of rain. What time did the game begin? (3:00)

The game ended at 5:00. How long was the game? (2 hours)

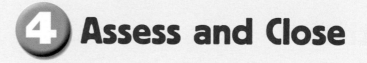 **Keeping a Journal**

Write these times in a list: 8:00, 11:00, 12:00, and 3:00. Next to each time write something you do at school or at home at that time of the day.

Carmela's Camp Schedule

Activity	Time
Swimming	8:00
Bike ride	10:00
Lunch	12:00
Soccer game	3:00
Dinner	6:00

Listen to your teacher read the problem. Solve.

Show your work using pictures, numbers, or words.

1. Carmela goes swimming at 8:00. How many hours does she have until the bike ride begins?

    __2__ hours

2. An hour after dinner starts Carmela reads a book. What time does she start reading?

    __7:00__

Listen to your teacher read the problem. Choose the correct answer.

3. 10:00   11:00   12:00   1:00
   ○   ●   ○   ○

4. 4 hours   3 hours   2 hours   1 hour
   ○   ○   ●   ○

382 three hundred eighty-two

Problem-Solving for Tests

Listening Skills

This page provides children practice with the oral problem-solving format used in some standardized test items.

You may want to read each item only once to mimic the style of oral tests.

Use with Items 1 and 2

Listening Strategy: Read the problem silently while the teacher reads it aloud.

- *This problem is on the page. Read it to yourself while I read it aloud.*
- *Listen to the whole problem. Wait until I finish to start writing. Use the table to solve the problems.*

Use with Item 3

Listening Strategy: Listen to the problem. Use the table to help you find the answer.

- *Look at the picture and listen as I read the problem.*

    Carmela goes on the bike ride at 10:00. The ride takes 1 hour. When will she return to camp?
- *You can look at the table now. Mark your answer.*

Use with Item 4

Listening Strategy: Listen for important facts and numbers.

- *Listen for the question the problem asks.*

    Carmela's soccer game starts at 3:00. It lasts for 1 hour. Dinner is at 6:00. How many hours does she have to wait after the game until dinner?
- *Use the numbers to solve the problem. Then mark your answer.*

Quick Check

Have children complete the Quick Check exercises independently to assess their understanding of concepts and skills taught in **Lessons 6–9**.

Item	Lesson	Error Analysis	Intervention
1–2	13.6	Children may confuse time on the hour or half-hour.	Reteach Resource 13.6 *Ways to Success* 13.6
3–4	13.7	Children may not remember or be able to read ordinal numbers.	Reteach Resource 13.7 *Ways to Success* 13.7
5	13.8	Children may name the months incorrectly.	Reteach Resource 13.8 *Ways to Success* 13.8
6	13.9	Children may misunderstand the information in the table.	Reteach Resource 13.9 *Ways to Success* 13.9

Name_____ **Quick Check**

Show the time on the clock.

1. Lunch starts at half past 11.

2. Art class starts at 2 o'clock.

2:00

Use the calendars to find the answer.

May

Sun.	Mon.	Tues.	Wed.	Thurs.	Fri.	Sat.
					1	2	3
4	5	6	7	8	9	10
11	12	13	14	15	16	17
18	19	20	21	22	23	24
25	26	27	28	29	30	31

3. If today is May tenth, what day of the week will tomorrow be?

    ___Sunday___

4. Color all Fridays in June ▬▬▶.

June

Sun.	Mon.	Tues.	Wed.	Thurs.	Fri.	Sat.
1	2	3	4	5	6	7
8	9	10	11	12		14
15	16	17	18	19		21
22	23	24	25	26		28
29	30					

5. Which of these months has more days?

    ___May___

Use the table to solve the problem.

6. How many hours are there between lunch and snack?

    __3__ hours

Meal Schedule	
Meal	**Time**
Breakfast	7:00
Lunch	12:00
Snack	3:00
Dinner	6:00

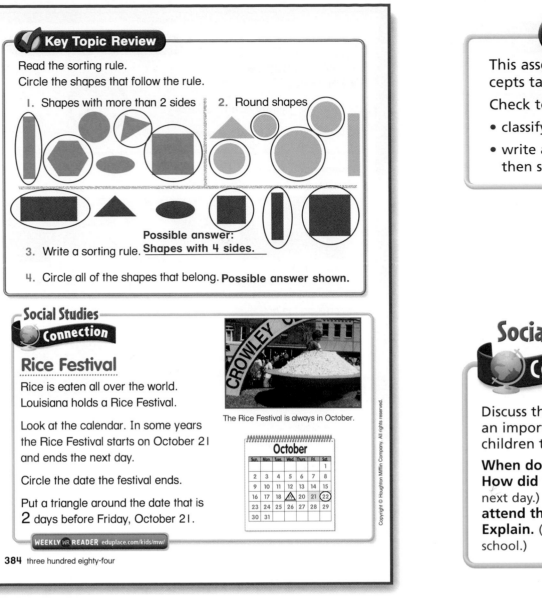

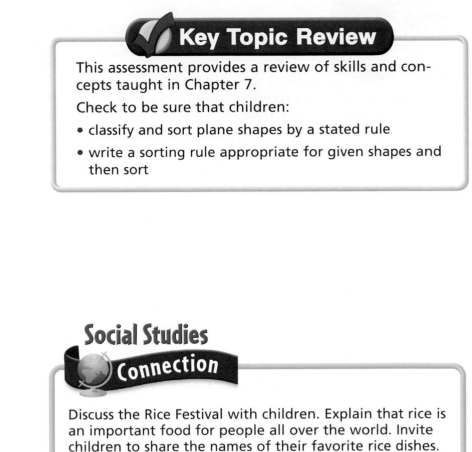

Read the sorting rule.
Circle the shapes that follow the rule.

1. Shapes with more than 2 sides   2. Round shapes

Possible answer:
3. Write a sorting rule. Shapes with 4 sides.

4. Circle all of the shapes that belong. **Possible answer shown.**

Social Studies
Connection

Rice Festival

Rice is eaten all over the world.
Louisiana holds a Rice Festival.

The Rice Festival is always in October.

Look at the calendar. In some years
the Rice Festival starts on October 21
and ends the next day.

Circle the date the festival ends.

Put a triangle around the date that is
2 days before Friday, October 21.

October

Sun.	Mon.	Tues.	Wed.	Thurs.	Fri.	Sat.
						1
2	3	4	5	6	7	8
9	10	11	12	13	14	15
16	17	18	19	20	21	22
23	24	25	26	27	28	29
30	31					

WEEKLY WR READER eduplace.com/kids/mw/

This assessment provides a review of skills and concepts taught in Chapter 7.

Check to be sure that children:

- classify and sort plane shapes by a stated rule
- write a sorting rule appropriate for given shapes and then sort

Social Studies
Connection

Discuss the Rice Festival with children. Explain that rice is an important food for people all over the world. Invite children to share the names of their favorite rice dishes.

When does the Rice Festival end? (Saturday, October 22nd) **How did you know that?** (It starts on the 21st and ends the next day.) **If you lived in Louisiana, would you be able to attend the Rice Festival without missing a day of school? Explain.** (Yes, I could go on Saturday because there is no school.)

Chapter Review/Test

Purpose: This test provides an informal assessment of the Chapter 13 objectives.

Chapter Test Items 1–15

To assign a numerical grade for this Chapter Test, use 6 points for each test item and add 10 to the score.

Check Understanding

Use children's work on word problems to informally assess progress on chapter content.

Customizing Your Instruction

For children who have not yet mastered these objectives, you can use the reteaching resources listed in the chart below.

 Assessment Options

A summary test for this chapter is also provided in the Unit Resource Folder.

Name_____ **Chapter Review/Test**

Vocabulary *e* Glossary

Show 4 o'clock.

1. Draw the minute hand ▬▬▬ .

2. Draw the hour hand ▬▬▬ .

Concepts and Skills

Write 1, 2, and 3 to show the correct order.

3.

2   1   3

Circle the activity if it takes about 1 minute. **Possible answers shown.**
Draw an X on the activity if it takes more than 1 minute.

4.   5.   6.

Read the clock.
Write the time two ways.

7.   5:00   8.   4:30

5 o'clock   half past 4

Reteaching Support

Chapter Test Items	Summary Test Items	Chapter Objectives Tested	TE Pages	Use These Reteaching Resources
1–2	7	**13A** Develop and use math vocabulary relating to time and calendar.	363A–364	Reteach Resource and *Ways to Success* CD: 13.3 Skillsheet 90
3–6, 9–10	1–4	**13B** Order events, compare time, and determine elapsed time.	359A–362, 369A–371	Reteach Resources and *Ways to Success* CD: 13.1, 13.2, 13.5 Skillsheet 91, 92, and 95
7–8, 11–12	5–6	**13C** Tell and show time to the hour and half-hour using analog and digital clocks.	363A–367, 373A–374	Reteach Resources and *Ways to Success* CD: 13.3, 13.4, 13.6 Skillsheet 93 and 94
13–14	7–8	**13D** Read and use a calendar.	375A–378	Reteach Resources and *Ways to Success* CD: 13.7, 13.8 Skillsheet 96
15	9–10	**13E** Use information in a table to solve problems about elapsed time.	379A–382	Reteach Resource and *Ways to Success* CD: 13.9 Skillsheet 97

CHAPTER SUMMARY TEST

Name _____ Date _____ Chapter 13 Test

Write 1, 2, and 3 to show the correct order.

1.

1   3   2

Circle the activity if it takes about 1 minute.

2.

3.

Read the clock.
Write the time two ways.

4.   4 o'clock   4:00

Go on

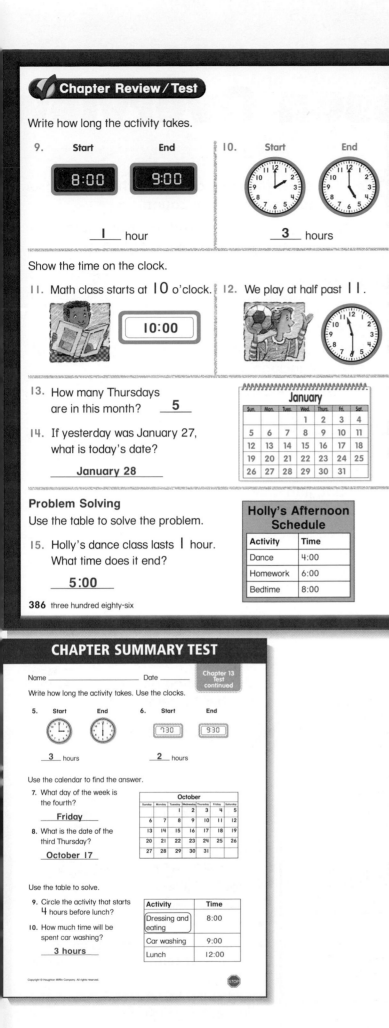

Chapter Review/Test

Write how long the activity takes.

9.
Start: 8:00
End: 9:00

___1___ hour

10.
Start
End

___3___ hours

Show the time on the clock.

11. Math class starts at 10 o'clock.

10:00

12. We play at half past 11.

13. How many Thursdays are in this month? ___5___

January

Sun.	Mon.	Tues.	Wed.	Thurs.	Fri.	Sat.
			1	2	3	4
5	6	7	8	9	10	11
12	13	14	15	16	17	18
19	20	21	22	23	24	25
26	27	28	29	30	31	

14. If yesterday was January 27, what is today's date?

___January 28___

Problem Solving

Use the table to solve the problem.

15. Holly's dance class lasts 1 hour. What time does it end?

___5:00___

Holly's Afternoon Schedule

Activity	Time
Dance	4:00
Homework	6:00
Bedtime	8:00

Use the End of Grade Test Prep Assessment Guide to help familiarize your children with the format of standardized tests.

CHAPTER SUMMARY TEST

Name _____ Date _____

Chapter 13 Test continued

Write how long the activity takes. Use the clocks.

5.
Start
End

___3___ hours

6.
Start: 7:30
End: 9:30

___2___ hours

Use the calendar to find the answer.

7. What day of the week is the fourth?

___Friday___

October

Sunday	Monday	Tuesday	Wednesday	Thursday	Friday	Saturday
		1	2	3	4	5
6	7	8	9	10	11	12
13	14	15	16	17	18	19
20	21	22	23	24	25	26
27	28	29	30	31		

8. What is the date of the third Thursday?

___October 17___

Use the table to solve.

9. Circle the activity that starts 4 hours before lunch?

10. How much time will be spent car washing?

___3 hours___

Activity	Time
Dressing and eating	8:00
Car washing	9:00
Lunch	12:00

STOP

Lesson by Lesson Overview
Using Money

Lesson 1

- This lesson reviews the value of pennies, nickels, and dimes. Children count to find the value of groups of coins as skip counting by 5s and 10s is applied to coins.
- Full size photographs of coins allow children to place coin models or real coins on the page to count.

Lesson 2

- Children count to find the value of groups of nickels and pennies. Children skip count the nickels by 5s and then count on by 1s to find the total value.
- Starting with the coin of greater value is an important strategy for counting coins.

Lesson 3

- Children learn to count to find the value of groups of dimes and pennies. The strategy is to count the dimes by 10s and count on by 1s to find the total value.
- Problem solving explores the equal amounts.

Lesson 4

- Children learn to count to find the value of groups of dimes, nickels, and pennies. The strategies of the previous lessons are combined as children count by 10s, 5s, and then 1s.

- Children show the same coins, put them order from greatest to least value and count.
- A game provides practice with counting coins and showing an amount with the fewest coins.

Lesson 5

- Children show different ways to make 25¢, including a quarter.
- Children also count to find the value of groups of coins that include a quarter.
- The lesson is extended to introduce half-dollar.

Lesson 6

- Children find different ways to show the same amount of money. Children count coins, write the amount, and draw coins to show the amount another way.
- Children draw coins to show a given amount two ways.
- Problem solving has children draw a given number of coins to show an amount.

Lesson 7

- Children use data in a picture to solve problems.
- Real-life objects with price tags are used.
- The problems involve deciding how much money is needed to buy a number of items.

SKILLS TRACE: USING MONEY

Grade K	Grade 1	Grade 2
• sort and graph coins (ch. 10)	• **identify pennies, nickels, dimes; count groups of like coins**	• identify and find the value of groups of dimes, nickels, pennies, quarters, and half-dollars (ch. 14)
• identify pennies, count pennies (ch. 10)	• **find the value of groups of nickels and pennies; dimes and pennies; dimes, nickels and pennies; quarters**	• identify coin combinations that equal a dollar (ch. 14)
• identify nickels, count nickels by 5s, trade pennies for nickels (ch. 10)	• **identify quarters, amounts that equal 25¢**	• show equal amount with different coins (ch. 14)
• identify dimes, count dimes by 10s (ch. 10)	• **find different ways to show the same amount of money**	• show an exact amount (ch. 15)
• identify quarters (ch. 10)		• compare money amounts and use the fewest coins to show an amount (ch. 15)
		• add and subtract money amounts; make change (ch. 15)

Chapter Planner

Lesson	Objective	Vocabulary	Materials	✔ NCTM Standards
14.1 **Value of Coins** **(Hands-On)** p. 389A	Identify coins—pennies, nickels, and dimes—and count groups of pennies, nickels, or dimes.	penny cent nickel dime	coin sets, overhead coins	Understand numbers, ways of representing numbers, relationships among numbers, and number systems.
14.2 **Nickels and Pennies** **(Hands-On)** p. 391A	Find the value of a group of nickels and pennies.		coin sets	Understand numbers, ways of representing numbers, relationships among numbers, and number systems.
14.3 **Dimes and Pennies** **(Hands-On)** p. 393A	Find the value of a group of dimes and pennies.		coin sets, overhead coins, blank transparency	Understand numbers, ways of representing numbers, relationships among numbers, and number systems.
14.4 **Count Coins** **(Hands-On)** p. 395A	Find the value of a group of dimes, nickels, and pennies.		coin sets, overhead coins	Understand numbers, ways of representing numbers, relationships among numbers, and number systems.
14.5 **Quarters** **(Hands-On)** p. 399A	Identify and count with quarters. Make 25 cents with pennies, nickels, and dimes.	quarter	coin sets, blank transparency, overhead coins	Understand numbers, ways of representing numbers, relationships among numbers, and number systems.
14.6 **Equal Amounts** p. 403A	Find different ways to show the same amount of money.		coin sets, overhead coins, blank transparency	Understand numbers, ways of representing numbers, relationships among numbers, and number systems.
14.7 **Problem Solving:** **Use a Picture** p. 405A	Recognize and use data from a picture to solve a problem.		coin sets, paper plates, overhead coins, blank transparency	Solve problems that arise in mathematics and in other contexts.

Resources For Reaching All Learners

LESSON RESOURCES: Reteach, Practice, Enrichment, Problem Solving, Homework, English Learners, Daily Routines, Transparencies, Math Center.

ADDITIONAL RESOURCES FROM HOUGHTON MIFFLIN: Chapter Challenges, Combination Classroom Planning Guide, Every Day Counts, Math to Learn (Student Handbook)

Every Day Counts
The *Coin Counter* activities in Every Day Counts support the math in this chapter.

Assessing Prior Knowledge

Before beginning the chapter, you can assess student understandings in order to assist you in differentiating instruction.

Complete Chapter Pretest in Unit Resource Folder

Use this test to assess both prerequisite skills (**Are You Ready?** — one page) and chapter content (**Check What You Know** — two pages).

Chapter 14 Prerequisite Skills Pretest

Chapter 14 New Content Pretest

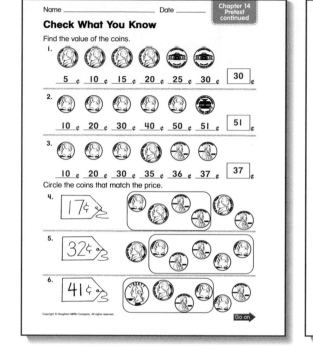

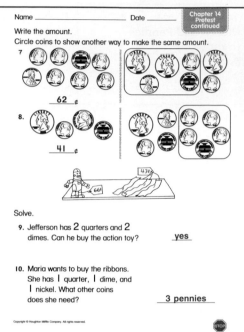

Customizing Instruction

For Students Having Difficulty

Items	Prerequisites	*Ways to Success*
1–4	Count and regroup tens and ones.	CD: 10.2 Skillsheet 98
5–8	Skip count by 5s and 10s.	CD: 12.2, 12.3 Skillsheet 99

Ways to Success Intervention for every concept and skill (CD-ROM or Chapter Intervention Skillsheets).

For Students Having Success

Items	Objectives	Resources
1–3	14A Use vocabulary relating to money.	Enrichment 14.1
4–6	14B Identify coins.	Enrichment 14.1–14.4
7–8	14C Find the value of a group of coins and find different ways to show the same amount.	Enrichment 14.2–14.6
9–10	14D Use a picture to solve a problem.	Enrichment 14.7

Use **Chapter Challenges** with any students who have success with all new chapter content.

Other Pretest Options

Informal Pretest

The pretest assesses vocabulary and prerequisite skills needed for success in this chapter.

***Ways to Success* CD-ROM**

The *Ways to Success* chapter pretest has automatic assignment of appropriate review lessons.

Chapter Resources

Activity

Assessing Prior Knowledge

Different Ways to Show an Amount (show equal amounts)

- Have available containers of 25 craft sticks.
- Tell each child to take one container and count the sticks.
- Ask children to group the craft sticks to show 25 in different ways. For example, they might show 25 individual craft sticks or five groups of 5 sticks.
- Repeat the activity for other numbers of craft sticks.

Activity

Ongoing Skill Activity

Trading Up (compare money amounts)

- Pairs of children can play a "Trading Up" game. Provide each pair with a box of pennies and nickels and a number cube labeled 1–3.
- Partners take turns rolling the number cube and taking that number of pennies from the box.
- When children have a group of five pennies, they can trade them for a nickel. Children play until they have a set amount. As an extension activity, include pennies, nickels, and dimes in the box and have the children trade nickels for dimes.

Activity

Connecting to the Unit Project

- To play Guess the Amount, display a set of pennies.
- Children observe the set of pennies for 60 seconds.
- A volunteer covers the set of pennies after 60 seconds.
- Children record their names and guesses on a chart.

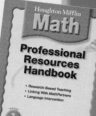

Teacher Support

Professional Resources Handbook

Research, Mathematics Content, and Language Intervention

Research-Based Teaching

One of the problems associated with teaching and learning about money is the lack of a physical size relationship among the respective coins and their value (Botula, 1999). Drum and Wesley (1999) explained that coins, although concrete models themselves, are non-proportional in relation to their values. According to Drum and Wesley, using coin models that are proportionally sized becomes the solution to the problem that teachers have had with teaching about money. These proportionate models will allow children to relate to monetary values on a concrete level. It is suggested that the teacher use normal models, such as the coins themselves, to introduce each coin by name. The proportionally-sized value models of the coins should then be substituted. See *Professional Resources Handbook, Grade 1, Unit 5.*

For more ideas relating to Unit 5, see the Teacher Support Handbook at the back of this Teacher's Edition.

Language Intervention

In East Asian countries, children learn that just as numbers can be composed and decomposed as sets and subsets, money can be composed and decomposed as well. Consistency and application of mathematical language across topics and strands builds coherence of learning and reinforces understanding. For further explanation, see "Mathematical Language and Money" in the *Professional Resources Handbook Grade 1.*

Technology

Time-Saving Technology Support

Ways to Assess Customized Spiral Review
  Test Generator CD
Lesson Planner CD-ROM
Ways to Success Intervention CD-ROM
MathTracks CD-ROM
Education Place: www.eduplace.com/math/mw
Houghton Mifflin Math eBook CD-ROM
eManipulatives
eGames

Starting Chapter 14
Using Money

CHAPTER OBJECTIVES

14A Develop and use math vocabulary relating to money.

14B Identify coins, including penny, nickel, and dime.

14C Find the value of a group of coins including pennies, nickels, dimes, and quarters, and show different ways to make the same amount.

14D Recognize and use data from a picture to solve a problem.

Math Background

Using Money

Some basic skills needed to work with coins include counting, skip counting, adding, and subtracting.

Two concepts associated with coins are important to distinguish. One is the *coin* itself. It is a single object. For example, 1 dime ≠ 2 nickels, because 1 dime simply means 1 coin, whereas 2 nickels means 2 coins. The other concept is the coin's *value*. For example, 1 dime's value = the value of 2 nickels = 10¢.

The relationships between pennies, nickels, dimes, quarters, and half-dollars are important concepts. They lead to children's understanding that different combinations of coins can represent the same value.

When finding the value of a penny collection, simple counting is used. When finding the value of a nickel collection, skip counting by 5s is used. Similarly, skip counting by 10s is used to find the value of a collection of dimes. When working with a mixed collection of coins, children should start with the coin of greatest value, then count from the coin of the next greatest value, and so on. For example,

25¢ → 35¢ → 45¢ → 50¢ → 51¢ → 52¢ → 53¢

Using The Investigation

- Review coin names with children. Hold up a *penny* and ask a volunteer to identify it and tell its value. Repeat with *nickel, dime,* and *quarter.* Talk about things children might buy with their money.

- Read the question to children. **Look at the prices in the picture. Look at the girl holding the coins. What items can she buy?** (harmonica, frog, airplane) **How many more pennies does she need to buy the horse?** (2 pennies) **How much money does she need to buy the horse and frog?** (12¢)

 For more information about projects and investigations, visit Education Place. **eduplace.com/math/mw/**

People Using Math
Selma Burke

Selma Burke was born in Mooresville, North Carolina.

Selma Burke was a sculptor, someone who shapes things out of clay. In 1940, she opened her own school to help others learn how to be sculptors.

In 1943, she won a contest to make a sculpture of President Franklin D. Roosevelt. Two years later, the sculpture was used as a model for his picture on the dime. The next time you have a dime, look at Selma Burke's art work.

Selma was **6** years old when she first made something out of clay.

1. How much money would she have, if she had 1 dime for each year of her age?

   __60__ ¢

2. How much money would you have, if you had 1 dime for each year of your age?

   Should be age x 10. ¢

CHAPTER CHALLENGES

For Mathematically Promising Students

The *Chapter Challenges* resource book provides blackline masters for activities that explore, extend, and connect the mathematics in every chapter. To support this independent work, see the Teacher Notes for each activity.

Explore: Look for Patterns, page 79, after Lesson 1
Extend: Bag of Coins, page 81, after Lesson 3
Connect: How Much Money?, page 83, after Lesson 5

Using This Page

- Read about Selma Burke to children. Then read questions to children. **You can count by tens to find the answer to Exercise 1.**

- Point out that children can also count by tens in Exercise 2.

- Tell children that Selma Burke had a special talent. She went to school and became a nurse, but she never gave up her dream of being a sculptor. **What is something you would like to do? Do you have a special talent?**

NSF Children's Math Worlds

Using lessons from the *Children's Math Worlds* is a good way to ensure that your students will develop a deep understanding of using money. The most effective approach is to use the *Children's Math Worlds* lessons along with the lessons in the chapter.

Hands-On: Value of Coins

PLANNING THE LESSON

MATHEMATICS OBJECTIVE
Identify coins—pennies, nickels, and dimes—and count groups of pennies, nickels, or dimes.

Use Lesson Planner CD-ROM for Lesson 14.1.

Meeting North Carolina's Standards
1.02 Use groupings of 2's, 5's, and 10's with models and pictures to count collections of objects.
Also 1.01

Daily Routines

Calendar
Circle the 15th on the current month's calendar. Ask children how many pennies equal this number. (15) Repeat with other dates, presenting them as numbers.

Sunday	Monday	Tuesday	Wednesday	Thursday	Friday	Saturday
			1	2	3	4
5	6	7	8	9	10	11
12	13	14	15	16	17	18
19	20	21	22	23	24	25
26	27	28	29	30	31	

Vocabulary
Display a penny. Write **penny** and 1 **cent** on the board. Introduce the **nickel** and **dime** in a similar way. Give each child a coin. Say penny, nickel, or dime and have children holding that coin stand up.

Vocabulary Cards

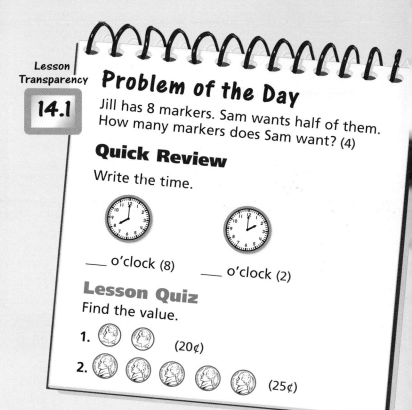

Lesson Transparency **14.1**

Problem of the Day
Jill has 8 markers. Sam wants half of them. How many markers does Sam want? (4)

Quick Review
Write the time.

_____ o'clock (8)   _____ o'clock (2)

Lesson Quiz
Find the value.
1. (20¢)
2. (25¢)

LEVELED PRACTICE

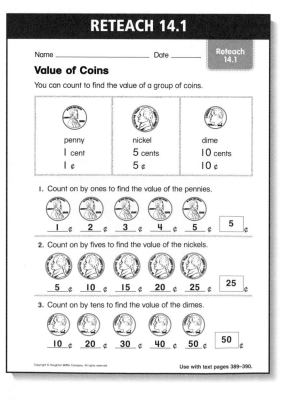

RETEACH 14.1

Name _____ Date _____   Reteach 14.1

Value of Coins
You can count to find the value of a group of coins.

penny 1 cent 1¢	nickel 5 cents 5¢	dime 10 cents 10¢

1. Count on by ones to find the value of the pennies.
1¢ 2¢ 3¢ 4¢ 5¢   [5]

2. Count on by fives to find the value of the nickels.
5¢ 10¢ 15¢ 20¢ 25¢   [25]

3. Count on by tens to find the value of the dimes.
10¢ 20¢ 30¢ 40¢ 50¢   [50]

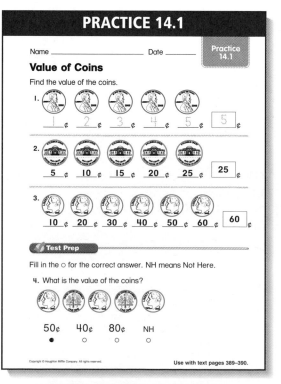

PRACTICE 14.1

Name _____ Date _____   Practice 14.1

Value of Coins
Find the value of the coins.
1. 1¢ 2¢ 3¢ 4¢ 5¢   [5]¢
2. 5¢ 10¢ 15¢ 20¢ 25¢   [25]¢
3. 10¢ 20¢ 30¢ 40¢ 50¢ 60¢   [60]¢

Test Prep
Fill in the ○ for the correct answer. NH means Not Here.
4. What is the value of the coins?
● 50¢   ○ 40¢   ○ 80¢   ○ NH

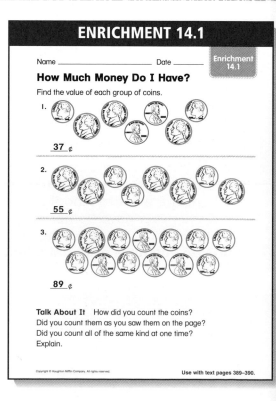

ENRICHMENT 14.1

Name _____ Date _____   Enrichment 14.1

How Much Money Do I Have?
Find the value of each group of coins.
1. __37__ ¢
2. __55__ ¢
3. __89__ ¢

Talk About It How did you count the coins? Did you count them as you saw them on the page? Did you count all of the same kind at one time? Explain.

Practice Workbook Page 91

Reaching All Learners

Differentiated Instruction

English Learners

English-language learners may not be familiar with the value of coins. They will need to learn the relative value of pennies, nickels, and dimes to solve problems that involve money.

Special Needs
AUDITORY, VISUAL

Materials: *coin sets, index cards*

- Write money amounts from the lesson on index cards. Place the cards facedown in a pile.
- Have the child turn over a card and tell him or her which coins to use. Have the child show coins as he or she counts by ones, fives, or tens.

Early Finishers
TACTILE, VISUAL

Materials: *coin sets*

- Have children work in pairs. Give each pair a set of coins.
- Have one child write an amount on a sheet of paper. Have the partner show that amount in coins.
- Children switch roles.

TECHNOLOGY

Spiral Review

Create **customized** spiral review worksheets for individual students using the *Ways to Assess* CD-ROM.

Manipulatives

Interactive **Coins and Bills** tool is available on the *Ways to Success* CD-ROM.

Lesson Planner

Use the **Lesson Planner CD-ROM** to see how lesson objectives for this chapter are correlated to standards.

Social Studies Connection

Have children look at nickels. Tell them that the building is Monticello, the home of Thomas Jefferson, the 3rd president of the United States. Elicit that it is Jefferson's face on the front of the nickel.

MATH CENTER

Vocabulary Activity

This vocabulary-building activity helps children understand and remember new words. Encourage children to use the words in math discussion.

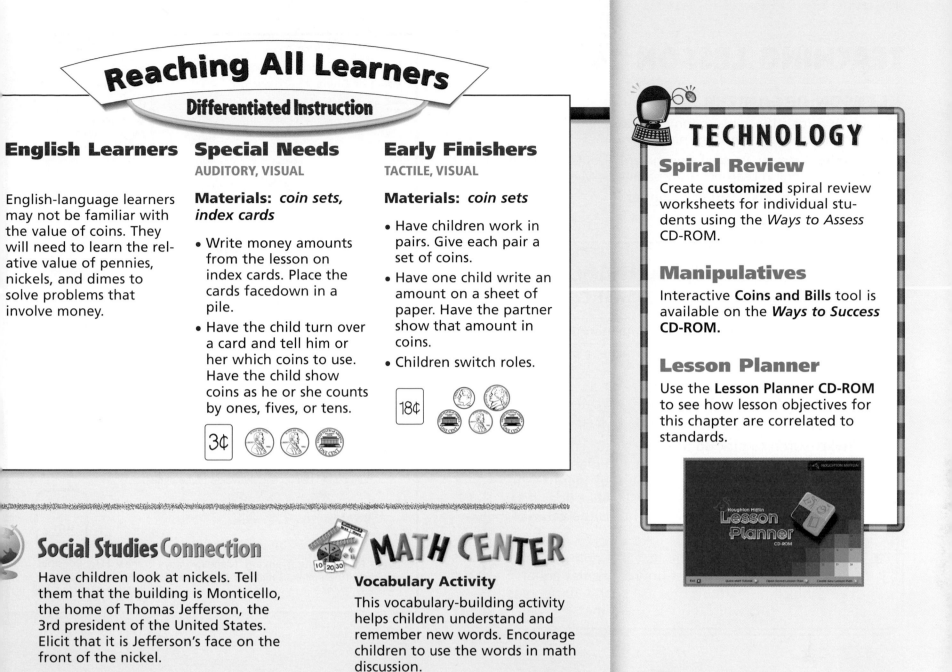

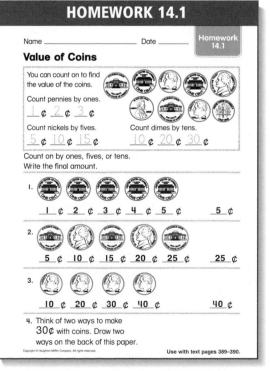

Homework Workbook Page 91

TEACHING LESSON 14.1

LESSON ORGANIZER

Objective Identify coins—pennies, nickels, and dimes—and count groups of pennies, nickels or dimes.

Resources Reteach, Practice, Enrichment, Problem Solving, Homework, English Learners, Transparencies, Math Center

Materials Coin sets, overhead coin set

Activity

Warm-Up Activity
Modeling the Value of Coins

| ㅤ Whole Group | 5 minutes | Auditory, Tactile |

Materials: *coin sets*

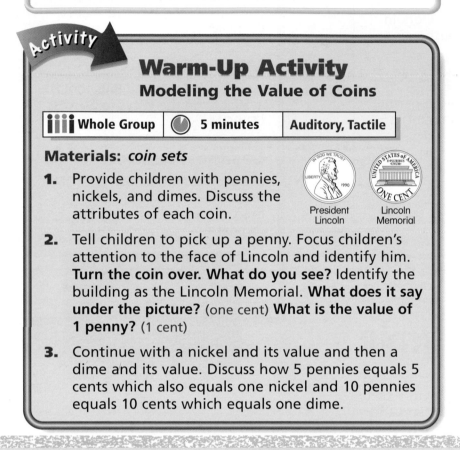

President Lincoln   Lincoln Memorial

1. Provide children with pennies, nickels, and dimes. Discuss the attributes of each coin.

2. Tell children to pick up a penny. Focus children's attention to the face of Lincoln and identify him. **Turn the coin over. What do you see?** Identify the building as the Lincoln Memorial. **What does it say under the picture?** (one cent) **What is the value of 1 penny?** (1 cent)

3. Continue with a nickel and its value and then a dime and its value. Discuss how 5 pennies equals 5 cents which also equals one nickel and 10 pennies equals 10 cents which equals one dime.

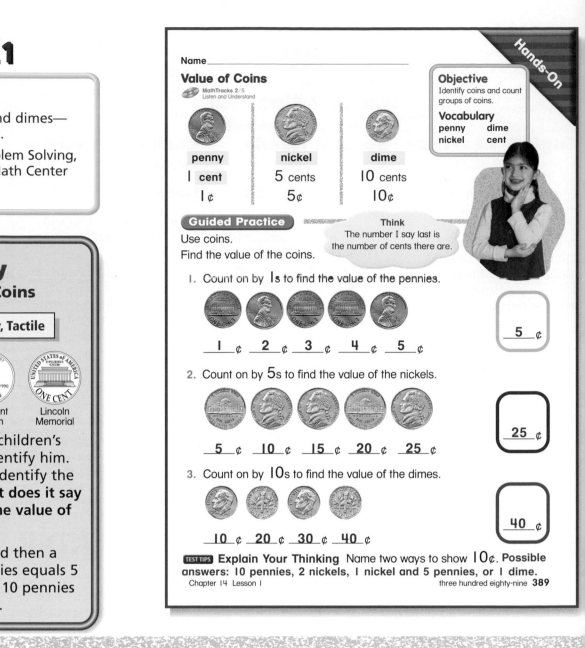

Name _____

Value of Coins

MathTracks 2/5
Listen and Understand

Objective
Identify coins and count groups of coins.

Vocabulary
penny   dime
nickel   cent

penny — 1 cent — 1¢
nickel — 5 cents — 5¢
dime — 10 cents — 10¢

Guided Practice

Use coins.
Find the value of the coins.

Think
The number I say last is the number of cents there are.

1. Count on by 1s to find the value of the pennies.

    _1_ ¢ _2_ ¢ _3_ ¢ _4_ ¢ _5_ ¢ | 5 ¢ |

2. Count on by 5s to find the value of the nickels.

    _5_ ¢ _10_ ¢ _15_ ¢ _20_ ¢ _25_ ¢ | 25 ¢ |

3. Count on by 10s to find the value of the dimes.

    _10_ ¢ _20_ ¢ _30_ ¢ _40_ ¢ | 40 ¢ |

TEST TIPS Explain Your Thinking Name two ways to show 10¢. **Possible answers: 10 pennies, 2 nickels, 1 nickel and 5 pennies, or 1 dime.**

Chapter 14 Lesson 1   three hundred eighty-nine **389**

1 Introduce
Activity
Modeling the Value of Coins

| ㅤ Whole Group | 10–15 minutes | Auditory, Tactile |

Materials: *overhead coin set, coin sets*

1. Provide children with pennies, nickels, and dimes. Display a row of 4 pennies. Show children how to count on by ones to find the value of the group of coins. Write 4 cents and 4¢ and have children read both forms.

2. Continue with modeling and show a row of 4 nickels. Show children how to count on by fives to find the value of the group of coins. Recount with the children. Write 20 cents and 20¢.

3. Repeat with a row of 4 dimes. Count by tens and write the value as 40 cents and 40¢.

2 Develop

Guided Learning

Teaching Example Introduce the objective and vocabulary to children. Guide them through the examples having them place a matching coin on top of the picture as they say the value.

Guided Practice

Have children complete **Exercises 1–3** as you observe. Give children the opportunity to answer the Explain Your Thinking question. Then discuss their responses with the class.

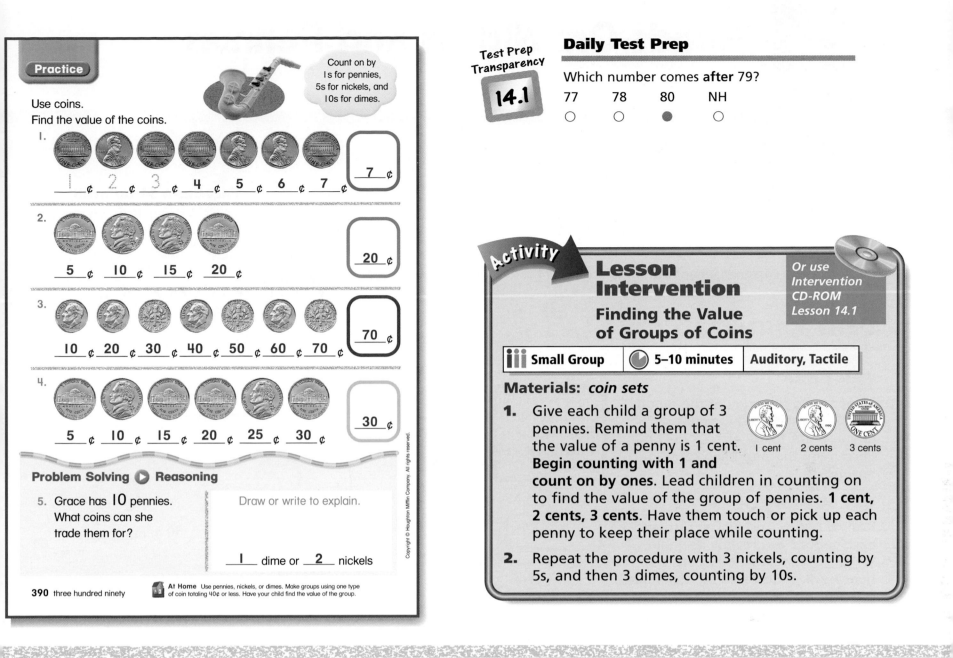

Practice

Use coins.
Find the value of the coins.

Count on by
1s for pennies,
5s for nickels, and
10s for dimes.

1. _1_ ¢ _2_ ¢ _3_ ¢ _4_ ¢ _5_ ¢ _6_ ¢ _7_ ¢   **7** ¢

2. _5_ ¢ _10_ ¢ _15_ ¢ _20_ ¢   **20** ¢

3. _10_ ¢ _20_ ¢ _30_ ¢ _40_ ¢ _50_ ¢ _60_ ¢ _70_ ¢   **70** ¢

4. _5_ ¢ _10_ ¢ _15_ ¢ _20_ ¢ _25_ ¢ _30_ ¢   **30** ¢

Problem Solving ▶ Reasoning

5. Grace has 10 pennies.
What coins can she
trade them for?

Draw or write to explain.

_1_ dime or _2_ nickels

390 three hundred ninety

 **At Home** Use pennies, nickels, or dimes. Make groups using one type of coin totaling 40¢ or less. Have your child find the value of the group.

Daily Test Prep

Which number comes **after** 79?

77   78   80   NH
○   ○   ●   ○

Activity

Lesson Intervention

Or use Intervention CD-ROM Lesson 14.1

Finding the Value of Groups of Coins

| iii Small Group | ⏱ 5–10 minutes | Auditory, Tactile |

Materials: *coin sets*

1. Give each child a group of 3 pennies. Remind them that the value of a penny is 1 cent. **Begin counting with 1 and count on by ones.** Lead children in counting on to find the value of the group of pennies. **1 cent, 2 cents, 3 cents.** Have them touch or pick up each penny to keep their place while counting.

    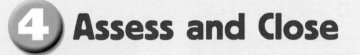
    1 cent   2 cents   3 cents

2. Repeat the procedure with 3 nickels, counting by 5s, and then 3 dimes, counting by 10s.

---

③ Practice

Independent Practice

Children complete **Exercises 1–4** independently.

Problem Solving

After children complete **Exercise 5,** call on volunteers to share their solutions.

Common Error

Misidentifying Coins

Children may have difficulty distinguishing the differences among coins. Help children identify key characteristics of each coin. For example, a penny has a copper color, a nickel is larger than a dime, a dime is silver colored and smaller than a penny.

④ Assess and Close

Explain how you would count a group of 5 nickels.
(Count on by fives: 5, 10, 15, 20, 25.)

Would you count by ones, fives, or tens to count a group of dimes? (tens)

Keeping a Journal

Draw a group of coins. Tell how to count them to find the value.

Hands-On: Nickels and Pennies

PLANNING THE LESSON

MATHEMATICS OBJECTIVE
Find the value of a group of nickels and pennies.

Use Lesson Planner CD-ROM for Lesson 14.2.

Meeting North Carolina's Standards
1.02 Use groupings of 2's, 5's, and 10's with models and pictures to count collections of objects.
Also 1.01

Daily Routines

Calendar
Point to the fifth day of the month and have children skip count by 5s as you point to 10, 15, 20, 25, 30. Encourage them to keep counting beyond 30.

Vocabulary
Review **penny** and **nickel**. Display each coin as you review its name. Write ___ cents and ___ ¢ on the board. Ask children to tell the value of each coin. Have volunteers complete the examples on the board. Ask which coin has the *greater value.* (nickel)

Vocabulary Cards

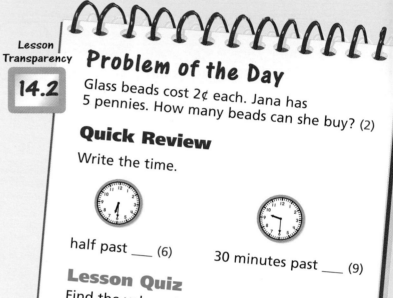

Lesson Transparency
14.2

Problem of the Day
Glass beads cost 2¢ each. Jana has 5 pennies. How many beads can she buy? (2)

Quick Review
Write the time.

half past ___ (6)

30 minutes past ___ (9)

Lesson Quiz
Find the value of the group of coins.
1. 3 nickels and 1 penny (16¢)
2. 4 nickels and 3 pennies (23¢)
3. 6 nickels and 2 pennies (32¢)

LEVELED PRACTICE

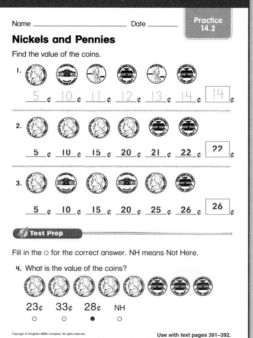

RETEACH 14.2

Name _____ Date _____
Reteach 14.2

Nickels and Pennies

Find the value of the coins.
Count the coins with the greater value first.

Count on by fives for nickels.
Count on by ones for pennies.

5 ¢ 10 ¢ 15 ¢ 20 ¢ 21 ¢ 22 ¢ | 22 | ¢

Find the value of the coins.
Count on by fives.
Then count on by ones.

1.
5 ¢ 10 ¢ 15 ¢ 16 ¢ 17 ¢ 18 ¢ | 18 | ¢

2.
5 ¢ 10 ¢ 15 ¢ 20 ¢ 25 ¢ 26 ¢ | 26 | ¢

Copyright © Houghton Mifflin Company. All rights reserved.
Use with text pages 391–392.

PRACTICE 14.2

Name _____ Date _____
Practice 14.2

Nickels and Pennies

Find the value of the coins.

1.
5 ¢ 10 ¢ 11 ¢ 12 ¢ 13 ¢ 14 ¢ | 14 | ¢

2.
5 ¢ 10 ¢ 15 ¢ 20 ¢ 21 ¢ 22 ¢ | ?? | ¢

3.
5 ¢ 10 ¢ 15 ¢ 20 ¢ 25 ¢ 26 ¢ | 26 | ¢

Test Prep

Fill in the ○ for the correct answer. NH means Not Here.

4. What is the value of the coins?

23¢   33¢   28¢   NH
○   ○   ●   ○

Copyright © Houghton Mifflin Company. All rights reserved.
Use with text pages 391–392.

ENRICHMENT 14.2

Name _____ Date _____
Enrichment 14.2

What Can I Buy?

You have nickels and pennies.
Look at the amount on the price tag.
You must use both nickels and pennies to pay for each item.
Draw the nickels and pennies you would use.
Answers will vary. Possible answers are given.

Amount	Nickels 5¢	Pennies 1¢
1. 9¢	5¢	1¢ 1¢ 1¢ 1¢
2. 12¢	5¢ 5¢	1¢ 1¢
3. 15¢	5¢ 5¢	1¢ 1¢ 1¢ 1¢ 1¢
4. 23¢	5¢ 5¢ 5¢ 5¢	1¢ 1¢ 1¢

Talk About It Would you rather use mostly pennies or mostly nickels to pay for something you want to buy?

Answers may vary.

Copyright © Houghton Mifflin Company. All rights reserved.
Use with text pages 391–392.

Practice Workbook Page 92

Reaching All Learners

Differentiated Instruction

English Learners

English-language learners may not have the language skills to explain the process behind their thinking. Use Worksheet 14.2 to provide children with sentence frames they can use to complete the Explain Your Thinking activity.

Inclusion
AUDITORY, TACTILE

Materials: *coin sets*

• Show the child a penny and a nickel and discuss the values. Have the child count out 5 pennies at a time and trade them for nickels.

• Set out a row of 2 nickels and 4 pennies. Help the child with the counting sequence of fives and ones. Repeat with other combinations.

Gifted and Talented
TACTILE, VISUAL

Materials: *coin sets, cards for 5¢–50¢ (teacher-made)*

• Have one child draw a card and use nickels and pennies to match the amount.

• Have another child draw a card and add or subtract coins from the first amount to match the new card.

TECHNOLOGY

Spiral Review

Using the *Ways to Assess* CD-ROM, you can create **customized** spiral review worksheets covering any lessons you choose.

eBook

An electronic version of this lesson can be found in **eMathBook**.

Manipulatives

Interactive **Coins and Bills** tool is available on the *Ways to Success* CD-ROM.

Science Connection

Discuss the color of a penny and explain that pennies are made of a mixture of two metals called copper and zinc. Many years ago, children collected pennies, which were melted and used to repair the Statue of Liberty.

MATH CENTER

Real-Life Activity

Help children understand the usefulness of mathematics. This activity makes math come alive by connecting the lesson skills to a real-life situation.

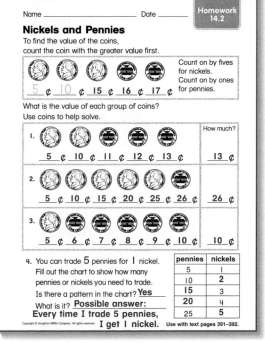

PROBLEM SOLVING 14.2

Name _____ Date _____ | Problem Solving 14.2

Nickels and Pennies

Read each problem. Write the answer.
Draw coins to find the answer.

Eric has 5 nickels in his bank. He puts in 4 pennies. How much money does he have in all?
29 ¢

1. Sandra has 4 nickels and 3 pennies. She uses 1 nickel and 1 penny to buy a pencil. How much money does she have?
Draw or write to explain.
17 ¢

2. Lee has 1 nickel and 7 pennies. May has 2 nickels and 4 pennies. Which child has more?
May

3. Tony has 6 nickels and 2 pennies in his bank. He puts in 3 more pennies. How much money does he have in all?
35 ¢

Use with text pages 391–392.

HOMEWORK 14.2

Name _____ Date _____ | Homework 14.2

Nickels and Pennies
To find the value of the coins, count the coin with the greater value first.

Count on by fives for nickels.
Count on by ones for pennies.
5 ¢ **10** ¢ **15** ¢ **16** ¢ **17** ¢

What is the value of each group of coins?
Use coins to help solve.

	How much?
1. **5** ¢ **10** ¢ **11** ¢ **12** ¢ **13** ¢	**13** ¢
2. **5** ¢ **10** ¢ **15** ¢ **20** ¢ **25** ¢ **26** ¢	**26** ¢
3. **5** ¢ **6** ¢ **7** ¢ **8** ¢ **9** ¢ **10** ¢	**10** ¢

4. You can trade 5 pennies for 1 nickel. Fill out the chart to show how many pennies or nickels you need to trade.
Is there a pattern in the chart? **Yes**
What is it? **Possible answer: Every time I trade 5 pennies, I get 1 nickel.**

pennies	nickels
5	1
10	2
15	3
20	4
25	5

Use with text pages 391–392.

ENGLISH LEARNERS 14.2

Name _____ Date _____ | English Learners 14.2

Nickels and Pennies

is the same as

Would you rather have 1 nickel or 4 pennies? Why?

1 penny is equal to **1** cent.

4 pennies are equal to **4** cents.

1 nickel is equal to **5** pennies.

1 nickel is equal to **5** cents.

1 nickel is greater than 4 pennies.

To the Teacher: Use the example at the top of the page to demonstrate the relative value of each coin. Then have children complete the sentence frames to provide the language needed to explain how to solve the word problem.

Use with text pages 391–392.

Homework Workbook Page 92

TEACHING LESSON 14.2

LESSON ORGANIZER

Objective Find the value of a group of nickels and pennies.

Resources Reteach, Practice, Enrichment, Problem Solving, Homework, English Learners, Transparencies, Math Center

Materials Coin sets

Activity

Prior Knowledge
Counting Pennies or Nickels

| 👥 Whole Group | ⏱ 5 minutes | Auditory, Tactile |

Materials: *coin sets*

1. Review how to count on by ones to count groups of pennies. Give each child a group of 5 pennies. Remind children to begin counting with 1 since the value of a penny is 1¢. Then count on by ones together to find the value of the group.

2. Continue by reviewing how to count nickels by fives.

3. **How do you know what number to begin with to count a group of coins?** (Answers may vary.) **What number do you begin with when counting pennies?** (1) **Nickels?** (5)

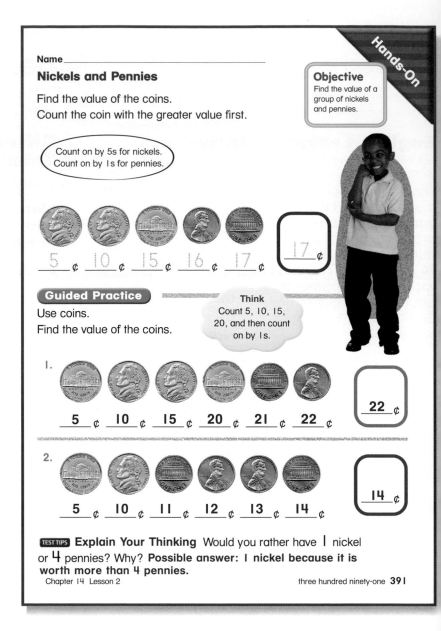

Name_____

Nickels and Pennies

Find the value of the coins.
Count the coin with the greater value first.

Objective
Find the value of a group of nickels and pennies.

Count on by 5s for nickels.
Count on by 1s for pennies.

5 ¢ 10 ¢ 15 ¢ 16 ¢ 17 ¢ |17| ¢

Guided Practice
Use coins.
Find the value of the coins.

Think
Count 5, 10, 15, 20, and then count on by 1s.

1.
5 ¢ 10 ¢ 15 ¢ 20 ¢ 21 ¢ 22 ¢ |22| ¢

2.
5 ¢ 10 ¢ 11 ¢ 12 ¢ 13 ¢ 14 ¢ |14| ¢

TEST TIPS **Explain Your Thinking** Would you rather have 1 nickel or 4 pennies? Why? **Possible answer: 1 nickel because it is worth more than 4 pennies.**

Chapter 14 Lesson 2   three hundred ninety-one **391**

1 Introduce
Model and Count Nickels and Pennies

| 👥 Whole Group | ⏱ 10–15 minutes | Tactile, Auditory |

Materials: *coin sets*

1. Demonstrate how to count a group of mixed coins. Give each child 2 nickels and 2 pennies. Ask them to make a row starting with the nickels. **When you have different coins to count, count the coin with the greater value first. Which coins will you count first?** (nickels)

2. Model how to count the nickels by fives and count on pennies by ones. Have children count along, 5, 10, 11, 12. **The value of the set of coins is 12¢.**

3. Continue to demonstrate counting with other groups of nickels and pennies. Then present other examples and have children count with coin sets.

2 Develop

Guided Learning

Teaching Example Introduce the objective to children. Guide them through the example by having them place coins over the pictures. Emphasize the importance of counting the coin with the greater value first. Stress the need to switch from counting on by fives when counting nickels in the group, to counting on by ones when counting the pennies.

Guided Practice

Have children complete **Exercises 1–2** as you observe. Give children the opportunity to answer the Explain Your Thinking question. Then discuss their responses with the class.

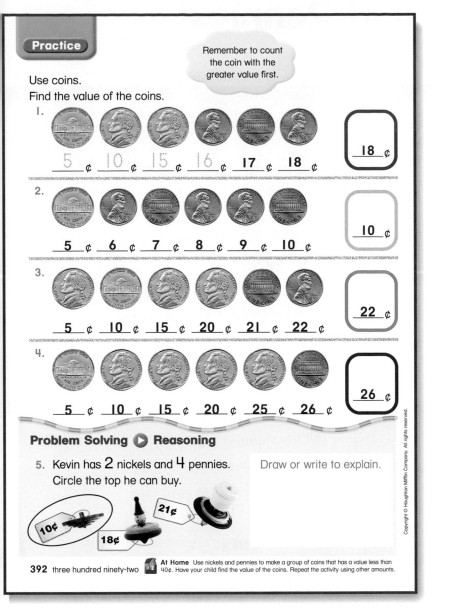

Practice

Remember to count the coin with the greater value first.

Use coins.
Find the value of the coins.

1. 5 ¢ 10 ¢ 15 ¢ 16 ¢ 17 ¢ 18 ¢   18 ¢

2. 5 ¢ 6 ¢ 7 ¢ 8 ¢ 9 ¢ 10 ¢   10 ¢

3. 5 ¢ 10 ¢ 15 ¢ 20 ¢ 21 ¢ 22 ¢   22 ¢

4. 5 ¢ 10 ¢ 15 ¢ 20 ¢ 25 ¢ 26 ¢   26 ¢

Problem Solving ▷ Reasoning

5. Kevin has 2 nickels and 4 pennies. Circle the top he can buy.

Draw or write to explain.

10¢   18¢   21¢

392 three hundred ninety-two   **At Home** Use nickels and pennies to make a group of coins that has a value less than 40¢. Have your child find the value of the coins. Repeat the activity using other amounts.

Daily Test Prep

Which number comes **just after** 29?

27 ○   30 ●   31 ○   NH ○

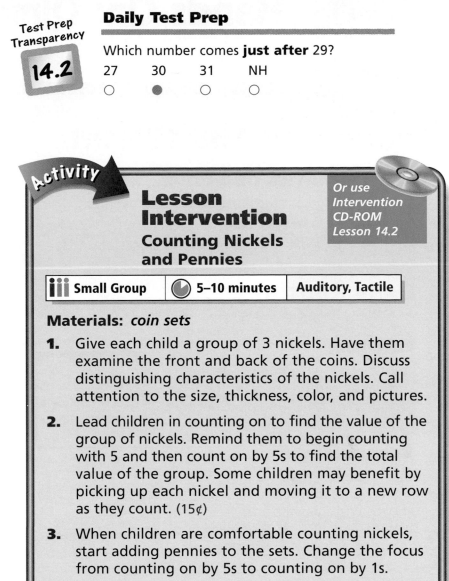

Activity

Or use Intervention CD-ROM Lesson 14.2

Lesson Intervention
Counting Nickels and Pennies

| iii Small Group | ⏱ 5–10 minutes | Auditory, Tactile |

Materials: *coin sets*

1. Give each child a group of 3 nickels. Have them examine the front and back of the coins. Discuss distinguishing characteristics of the nickels. Call attention to the size, thickness, color, and pictures.

2. Lead children in counting on to find the value of the group of nickels. Remind them to begin counting with 5 and then count on by 5s to find the total value of the group. Some children may benefit by picking up each nickel and moving it to a new row as they count. (15¢)

3. When children are comfortable counting nickels, start adding pennies to the sets. Change the focus from counting on by 5s to counting on by 1s.

③ Practice

Independent Practice

Children complete **Exercises 1–4** independently.

Problem Solving

After children complete **Exercise 5,** call on volunteers to share their solutions. Provide coins to those students who may need to use them.

Common Error

Unable to Switch from 5s to 1s

Children may struggle with counting on by 1s after counting on by 5s. Have the child count the nickels and circle the value. Then have the child count on by ones from the circled number.

④ Assess and Close

How you would count a group of 2 nickels and 3 pennies?
(Start with the nickels. Count on by 5s and then count on by 1s: 5, 10, 11, 12, 13¢.)

Do you begin counting on by 1s or 5s when you count a group of nickels and pennies? Why? (Begin counting on by 5s to count the nickels because it is easier to start with coins of greater value.)

Keeping a Journal

Draw a group of nickels and pennies. Use words and pictures to show how to find the total value.

Hands-On: Dimes and Pennies

Lesson 14.3

PLANNING THE LESSON

MATHEMATICS OBJECTIVE
Find the value of a group of dimes and pennies.

Use Lesson Planner CD-ROM for Lesson 14.3.

Meeting North Carolina's Standards

1.02 Use groupings of 2's, 5's, and 10's with models and pictures to count collections of objects.

Also 1.01

Daily Routines

Calendar

Point to the tenth day of the month and have children skip count by 10s as you point to 20 and 30. Continue counting to 100.

Sunday	Monday	Tuesday	Wednesday	Thursday	Friday	Saturday
			1	2	3	4
5	6	7	8	9	10	11
12	13	14	15	16	17	18
19	20	21	22	23	24	25
26	27	28	29	30	31	

Vocabulary

Review **dime**. Display a dime as you say its name and remind children of how to write its value. Write 10 cents and 10¢ on the board and read aloud with the class.

Vocabulary Cards

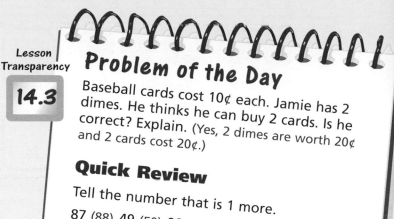

Lesson Transparency 14.3

Problem of the Day

Baseball cards cost 10¢ each. Jamie has 2 dimes. He thinks he can buy 2 cards. Is he correct? Explain. (Yes, 2 dimes are worth 20¢ and 2 cards cost 20¢.)

Quick Review

Tell the number that is 1 more.
87 (88) 49 (50) 98 (99)
Tell the number that is 10 less.
47 (37) 19 (9) 100 (90)

Lesson Quiz

How many dimes and pennies do you need?
1. 32¢ (3 dimes and 2 pennies)
2. 12¢ (1 dime and 2 pennies)
3. 45¢ (4 dimes and 5 pennies)

LEVELED PRACTICE

RETEACH 14.3

Name _____ Date _____ **Reteach 14.3**

Dimes and Pennies

Find the coins that match the price.

Count the coin with the greater value first.

10 ¢ 20 ¢ 30 ¢ 31 ¢ 32 ¢ 33 ¢ 34 ¢

Remember
Count on by 10s for dimes.
Count on by 1s for pennies.

Find the value of the coins.

1.
10 ¢ 20 ¢ 30 ¢ 31 ¢ 32 ¢ 33 ¢ | 33 |

Circle the coins that match the price.

2. 41¢

Copyright © Houghton Mifflin Company. All rights reserved. Use with text pages 393–394.

PRACTICE 14.3

Name _____ Date _____ **Practice 14.3**

Dimes and Pennies

Circle the group of coins that matches the price.

1. 32¢
2. 40¢
3. 23¢
4. 41¢

Test Prep

Fill in the ○ for the correct answer. NH means Not Here.

5. What is the value of the coins?

23¢   43¢   18¢   NH
○   ○   ○   ●

Copyright © Houghton Mifflin Company. All rights reserved. Use with text pages 393–394.

ENRICHMENT 14.3

Name _____ Date _____ **Enrichment 14.3**

Pocketful of Change

You have dimes and pennies.
Look at the amount on the price tag.
You must use both dimes and pennies to pay for each item.
Draw the dimes and pennies you would use.
Answers will vary. Possible answers are given.

	Amount	Dimes 10¢	Pennies 1¢
1.	20¢	10¢	1¢ 1¢ 1¢ 1¢ 1¢ 1¢ 1¢ 1¢ 1¢ 1¢
2.	15¢	10¢	1¢ 1¢ 1¢ 1¢ 1¢
3.	25¢	10¢ 10¢	1¢ 1¢ 1¢ 1¢ 1¢
4.	40¢	10¢ 10¢ 10¢	1¢ 1¢ 1¢ 1¢ 1¢ 1¢ 1¢ 1¢ 1¢ 1¢

Write About It If the price of an item ends in a zero, is there another way you could pay instead of using both dimes and pennies? Is it easier ? Why?

<u>Using dimes only is easier than dimes and</u>
<u>pennies because I just count on ten.</u>

Copyright © Houghton Mifflin Company. All rights reserved. Use with text pages 393–394.

Practice Workbook Page 93

Reaching All Learners
Differentiated Instruction

English Learners

English-language learners may not be familiar with the concept of prices and price tags. Use Worksheet 14.3 to build familiarity with these concepts.

Special Needs
AUDITORY, TACTILE

Materials: *coin sets*

- Trace sets of dimes and pennies, using a different color for each.
- Have the child match each set of coins to the circles and count to find the value.
- Help the child as necessary, repeating the counting pattern several times.

Gifted and Talented
TACTILE, VISUAL

Materials: *coin sets*

- Prepare problems for children, such as: You have 48¢. How many dimes and pennies do you have? (4 dimes, 8 pennies)
- You have 65¢. 4 coins are dimes. The rest are pennies. How many pennies do you have? (25 pennies)

TECHNOLOGY

Spiral Review

To reinforce skills on lessons taught earlier, create **customized** spiral review worksheets using the *Ways to Assess* CD-ROM.

Manipulatives

Interactive **Coins and Bills** tool is available on the *Ways to Success* **CD-ROM.**

Education Place

Encourage students to visit **Education Place** at **eduplace.com/kids/mw/** for more student activities.

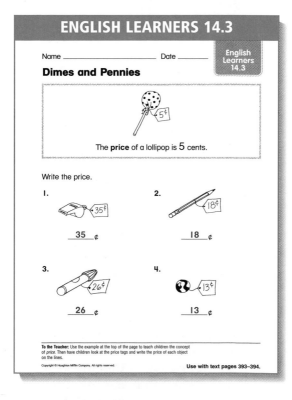

Music Connection

Have children sing a song to the tune of "The Farmer in the Dell."
"Five pennies make a nickel,
Five pennies make a nickel,
How many make a nickel?
One, two, three, four, five."

MATH CENTER

Real-Life Activity

Help children understand the usefulness of mathematics. This activity makes math come alive by connecting the lesson skills to a real-life situation.

PROBLEM SOLVING 14.3

Name _____ Date _____ Problem Solving 14.3

Dimes and Pennies

Read each question. Write the answer.
Draw coins to find the answer.

Paco has 4 pennies. He gets 1 dime each time he walks the dog. If he walks the dog 3 times, how much money will he have in all?
___34___ ¢

1. Cindy has 6 dimes. She finds 2 pennies. How much money does Cindy have in all?
___62___ ¢

Draw here.

2. Rose has 5 dimes and 4 pennies. She uses a dime to buy an apple. How much money does she have now?
___44___ ¢

3. Frank has 7 dimes in his hand. He has 4 pennies in his pocket. How much money does Frank have in all?
___74___ ¢

Copyright © Houghton Mifflin Company. All rights reserved.
Use with text pages 393–394.

HOMEWORK 14.3

Name _____ Date _____ Homework 14.3

Dimes and Pennies
To find the value of the coins,
count the coin with the greater value first.

Count on by tens for dimes.
Count on by ones for pennies.

_10_ ¢ _20_ ¢ _21_ ¢ _22_ ¢ _23_ ¢ _24_ ¢

Circle the coins that match the number of cents shown.
Use coins to help you solve.

1. 22¢	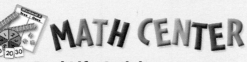
2. 30¢	
3. 15¢	

4. How many dimes and pennies would you need to make 53¢?

Draw or write to explain.

_5_ dimes _3_ pennies

Copyright © Houghton Mifflin Company. All rights reserved.
Use with text pages 393–394.

ENGLISH LEARNERS 14.3

Name _____ Date _____ English Learners 14.3

Dimes and Pennies

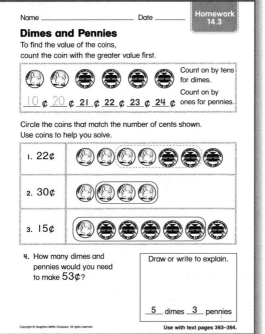

5¢

The **price** of a lollipop is 5 cents.

Write the price.

1.
35¢
___35___ ¢

2.
18¢
___18___ ¢

3.
26¢
___26___ ¢

4.
13¢
___13___ ¢

To the Teacher: Use the example at the top of the page to teach children the concept of *price*. Then have children look at the price tags and write the price of each object on the lines.

Copyright © Houghton Mifflin Company. All rights reserved.
Use with text pages 393–394.

Homework Workbook Page 93

CHAPTER 14   Lesson 3   **393B**

TEACHING LESSON 14.3

LESSON ORGANIZER

Objective Find the value of a group of dimes and pennies.

Resources Reteach, Practice, Enrichment, Problem Solving, Homework, English Learners, Transparencies, Math Center

Materials Coin sets, overhead coins, blank transparency

Activity

Warm-Up Activity
Modeling How to Count Nickels and Pennies

iiii Whole Group	⏲ 5 minutes	Auditory, Tactile

Materials: *coin sets*

1. Display 3 nickels and 4 pennies and have each child show the same coins. Remind children to arrange coins with the greater value first. **What coins are first in the row?** (nickels)

2. Review how to count groups of nickels and pennies, counting on by fives and then counting on by ones: 5¢, 10¢, 15¢, 16¢, 17¢, 18¢, 19¢.

3. **How do we know which coins to begin with when counting nickels and pennies?** (Begin with the coins of greater value—the nickels.)

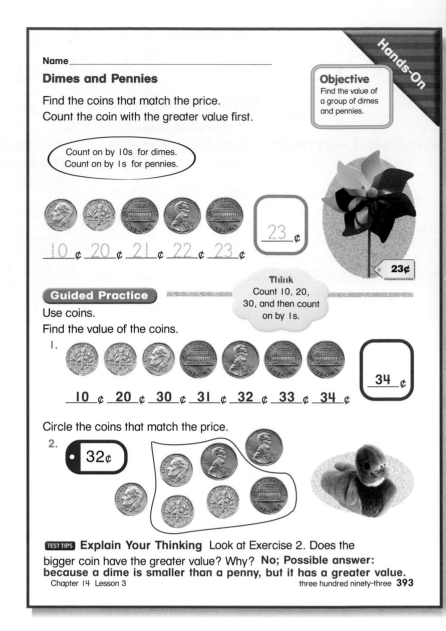

Name_____

Dimes and Pennies

Find the coins that match the price.
Count the coin with the greater value first.

Objective Find the value of a group of dimes and pennies.

> Count on by 10s for dimes.
> Count on by 1s for pennies.

_10_ ¢ _20_ ¢ _21_ ¢ _22_ ¢ _23_ ¢ | 23 | ¢

23¢

Think Count 10, 20, 30, and then count on by 1s.

Guided Practice

Use coins.
Find the value of the coins.

1.

_10_ ¢ _20_ ¢ _30_ ¢ _31_ ¢ _32_ ¢ _33_ ¢ _34_ ¢ | 34 | ¢

Circle the coins that match the price.

2.  32¢

TEST TIPS **Explain Your Thinking** Look at Exercise 2. Does the bigger coin have the greater value? Why? **No; Possible answer: because a dime is smaller than a penny, but it has a greater value.**

Chapter 14 Lesson 3   three hundred ninety-three **393**

---

1 Introduce
Model and Count Dimes and Pennies

iiii Whole Group	⏲ 10–15 minutes	Tactile, Auditory

Materials: *coin sets, overhead coins, blank transparency*

1. Demonstrate how to count a group of dimes and pennies. Give each child 2 dimes and 3 pennies. Tell them to arrange the coins in an order that is easy to count. **Which coins should we count first?** (dimes)

2. Model how to count the dimes and pennies using the overhead coins. Remind children to count the dimes by 10s and then count on by 1s for the pennies. (10¢, 20¢, 21¢, 22¢, 23¢) Repeat with other groups of dimes and pennies.

3. Draw a price tag for 34¢ on a blank transparency. Display a group of dimes and pennies. Have volunteers look at the price tag and choose the coins to match the price. **How do you know which coins to use to match the price?** Look at the price. Look at the group of coins. Think of ways to make 34¢ with those coins.

2 Develop

Guided Learning

Teaching Example Introduce the objective to children. Guide them through the example by having them place coins over the pictures to model finding the value of a group of dimes and pennies. Emphasize the importance of counting the coins of greater value first. Remind children to switch from counting on by 10s to counting on by 1s.

Guided Practice

Be sure children understand that they have two different kinds of exercises to complete. Have children complete **Exercises 1–2** as you observe. Remind students to circle groups of coins, not each individual coin in Exercise 2. Give children the opportunity to answer the Explain Your Thinking question. Then discuss their responses with the class.

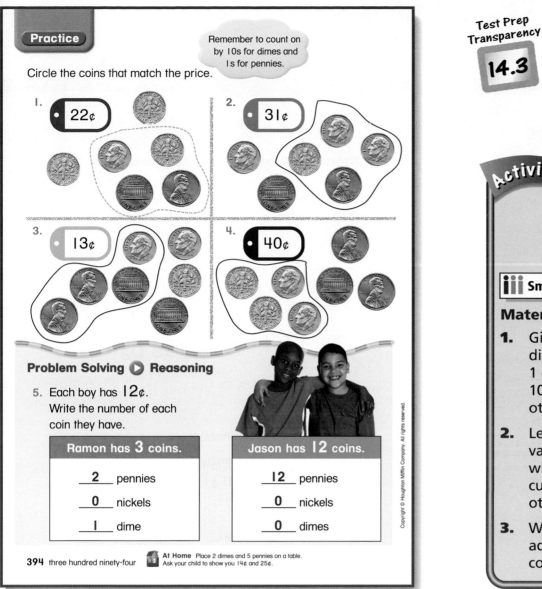

Practice

Remember to count on by 10s for dimes and 1s for pennies.

Circle the coins that match the price.

1. **22¢**

2. **31¢**

3. **13¢**

4. **40¢**

Problem Solving ▶ Reasoning

5. Each boy has 12¢.
Write the number of each coin they have.

Ramon has 3 coins.	Jason has 12 coins.
2 pennies	**12** pennies
0 nickels	**0** nickels
1 dime	**0** dimes

394 three hundred ninety-four

At Home Place 2 dimes and 5 pennies on a table. Ask your child to show you 14¢ and 25¢.

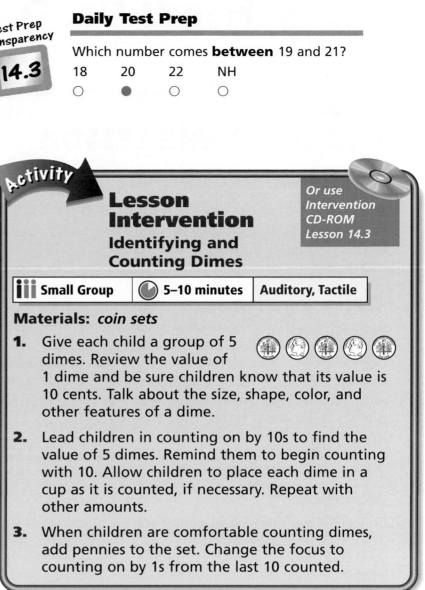

Activity

Or use Intervention CD-ROM Lesson 14.3

Lesson Intervention
Identifying and Counting Dimes

👤👤👤 Small Group	🕐 5–10 minutes	Auditory, Tactile

Materials: *coin sets*

1. Give each child a group of 5 dimes. Review the value of 1 dime and be sure children know that its value is 10 cents. Talk about the size, shape, color, and other features of a dime.

2. Lead children in counting on by 10s to find the value of 5 dimes. Remind them to begin counting with 10. Allow children to place each dime in a cup as it is counted, if necessary. Repeat with other amounts.

3. When children are comfortable counting dimes, add pennies to the set. Change the focus to counting on by 1s from the last 10 counted.

3 Practice

Independent Practice

Children complete **Exercises 1–4** independently.

Problem Solving

After children complete **Exercise 5,** call on volunteers to share their solutions. Provide coins to those who may need to use them.

Common Error

Miscounting Coins in a Mixed Set

Children may lose track of dimes and pennies when selecting pictured coins from a larger set. Have children count out the coins they need to match the price, place the coins on the matching pictures, and circle those pictures.

4 Assess and Close

Explain how to count a group of 4 dimes and 4 pennies.
(Start with the dimes. Count by 10s to 40¢ and then count on by 1s to 44¢.)

How many dimes and pennies match a price of 45¢?
(4 dimes and 5 pennies)

Keeping a Journal

Draw a price tag. Write a price on it. Write or draw the coins you could use to match the price.

Hands-On: Count Coins

PLANNING THE LESSON

MATHEMATICS OBJECTIVE
Find the value of a group of dimes, nickels, and pennies.

Use Lesson Planner CD-ROM for Lesson 14.4.

Meeting North Carolina's Standards

1.02 Use groupings of 2's, 5's, and 10's with models and pictures to count collections of objects.

Also 1.01

Daily Routines

Calendar
Display 2 dimes, 1 nickel and 2 pennies. Have a child count the value of the coins. (27 cents) Have another child find and point to the date with the same number. (27th) Repeat with different amounts.

Sunday	Monday	Tuesday	Wednesday	Thursday	Friday	Saturday
			1	2	3	4
5	6	7	8	9	10	11
12	13	14	15	16	17	18
19	20	21	22	23	24	25
26	27	28	29	30	31	

Vocabulary
Review **dime, nickel,** and **penny** and their values. Review **skip counting** and **counting on** by having children demonstrate how to skip count nickels using 5s or dimes using 10s. Then count on by 1s for pennies.

Vocabulary Cards

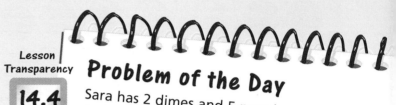

Lesson Transparency 14.4

Problem of the Day
Sara has 2 dimes and 5 pennies. A muffin costs 20¢. Can she buy the muffin? (Yes, she has 25¢.)

Quick Review
Tell which number is greater.

48, 75   21, 31   99, 100   12, 11
(75)   (31)   (100)   (12)

Lesson Quiz
Pencils are being sold for 10¢ each. Sean has 2 dimes and 3 nickels. How many pencils can he buy? (3)

LEVELED PRACTICE

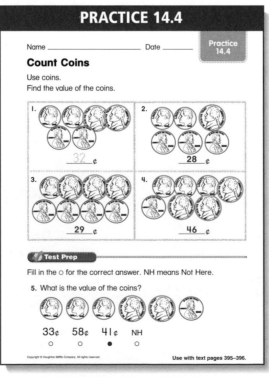

RETEACH 14.4

Name _____ Date _____ Reteach 14.4

Count Coins

Count on by tens for dimes.
Count on by fives for nickels.
Count on by ones for pennies.

10¢ 20¢ 30¢ 35¢ 36¢ 37¢ [37]¢

Use coins.
Find the value of the coins.

1. 10¢ 15¢ 20¢ 21¢ 22¢ [22]¢

2. 10¢ 20¢ 30¢ 35¢ 40¢ 41¢ [41]¢

Use with text pages 395–396.

PRACTICE 14.4

Name _____ Date _____ Practice 14.4

Count Coins

Use coins.
Find the value of the coins.

1. ___32___ ¢
2. ___28___ ¢
3. ___29___ ¢
4. ___46___ ¢

Test Prep

Fill in the ○ for the correct answer. NH means Not Here.

5. What is the value of the coins?

33¢   58¢   41¢   NH
○   ○   ●   ○

Use with text pages 395–396.

ENRICHMENT 14.4

Name _____ Date _____ Enrichment 14.4

Comparing Coins

Find the value of the coins in each box.
Circle the box in each row with the greater value.

1. ___43___ ¢   ___30___ ¢

2. ___32___ ¢   ___35___ ¢

3. ___59___ ¢   ___62___ ¢

Talk About It In Exercise 3, in which box were the coins easier to count? Why? **Answers may vary.**

Use with text pages 395–396.

Practice Workbook Page 94

Reaching All Learners

Differentiated Instruction

English Learners

In order to write and solve problems with coins, children will need to understand their singular and plural forms. Use Worksheet 14.4 to introduce these forms to English-language learners.

Special Needs
TACTILE, VISUAL

Materials: *coin sets, envelopes*

- Give the child an envelope with dimes, nickels, and pennies.
- Have the child sort the coins. Review counting by 10s, 5s, and 1s. Then have the child count the coins and write the value of the set.

Early Finishers
VISUAL, TACTILE

Materials: *coin sets, 1–6 number cube*

- Provide each child with coins and a number cube.
- The child rolls the number cube and takes that number of pennies.
- Each time the child rolls and takes pennies, he or she should also trade for nickels or dimes. Play continues until the child has exactly 3 dimes.

TECHNOLOGY

Spiral Review

Help students remember skills they learned earlier by creating **customized** spiral review worksheets using the *Ways to Assess* CD-ROM.

Manipulatives

Interactive **Coins and Bills** tool is available on the *Ways to Success* CD-ROM.

Games

Students can practice their computational skills using the **Find a Friend** game on the *Ways to Success* CD-ROM.

Social Studies Connection

Tell children that the U.S. Mint makes all the American coins. A press punches out discs called *blanks*.

After 11 copper-colored blanks are *struck*, what is the value of the coins? (11¢)

MATH CENTER

Real-Life Activity

Help children understand the usefulness of mathematics. This activity makes math come alive by connecting the lesson skills to a real-life situation.

PROBLEM SOLVING 14.4

Name _____ Date _____ **Problem Solving 14.4**

Count Coins

Read each problem. Write the answer.
Use coins to help you find the answer.

Carlos has 2 dimes, 3 nickels, and 3 pennies. Does he have enough to buy a snack for 37¢?
Yes

1. Janet has 2 dimes, 4 nickels, and 4 pennies. Can she buy crayons for 45¢? / Draw or write to explain.
No

2. Lou has 3 dimes, 5 nickels and 1 penny. Can he buy a puzzle for 50¢?
Yes

3. Rosa has 3 dimes, 5 nickels and 6 pennies. Can she buy a toy for 55¢?
Yes

Copyright © Houghton Mifflin Company. All rights reserved. — Use with text pages 395–396.

HOMEWORK 14.4

Name _____ Date _____ **Homework 14.4**

Count Coins
You can find the value of coins by counting on.

Count dimes first.
10¢ _20_ ¢

Count nickels next.
25¢ _30_ ¢ _35_ ¢

Then count pennies.
36¢ 37¢ _38_ ¢ _39_ ¢   39¢

Find the value of the coins. Use dimes, nickels, and pennies.

1. _10_ ¢ _15_ ¢ _20_ ¢ _25_ ¢ _26_ ¢   26 ¢

2. _10_ ¢ _20_ ¢ _30_ ¢ _35_ ¢ _36_ ¢   36 ¢

3. Carla has 3 dimes, 3 nickels, and 4 pennies. Can she buy an apple that costs 49¢? Circle Yes or No. / Draw or write to explain.
(Yes)   No

Copyright © Houghton Mifflin Company. All rights reserved. — Use with text pages 395–396.

ENGLISH LEARNERS 14.4

Name _____ Date _____ **English Learners 14.4**

Count Coins

1 penny   2 pennies   1 nickel   2 nickels

1 dime   2 dimes

Count the coins.

1. 3 dimes   2. 1 penny   3. 4 nickels

4. 1 nickel   5. 1 dime   6. 2 pennies

To the Teacher: Use the examples at the top of the page to demonstrate the singular and plural forms of different coins. Then have children count the coins and write how many of each there are.

Copyright © Houghton Mifflin Company. All rights reserved. — Use with text pages 395–397.

Homework Workbook Page 94

TEACHING LESSON 14.4

LESSON ORGANIZER

Objective Find the value of a group of dimes, nickels, and pennies.

Resources Reteach, Practice, Enrichment, Problem Solving, Homework, English Learners, Transparencies, Math Center

Materials Coin sets, overhead coins

Activity

Warm-Up Activity
Modeling How to Count Coins

| iiii Whole Group | ⏱ 5 minutes | Auditory, Tactile |

Materials: *coin sets*

1. Review how to count groups of coins. Have children work in pairs. Give one child nickels and one child pennies. Tell children to place two nickels and two pennies on the desk.

   5¢ 10¢ 11¢ 12¢

2. **What is the value of your coins?** (12¢) Have volunteers share how they counted to find the value of the coins.

3. Repeat with two dimes and two pennies. Make sure children understand the need to begin counting with coins of greater value.

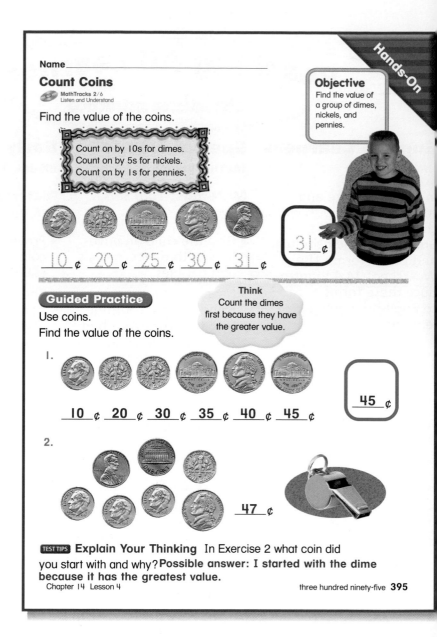

Name_____

Count Coins

MathTracks 2/6
Listen and Understand

Objective
Find the value of a group of dimes, nickels, and pennies.

Find the value of the coins.

Count on by 10s for dimes.
Count on by 5s for nickels.
Count on by 1s for pennies.

10¢ 20¢ 25¢ 30¢ 31¢   31¢

Guided Practice

Use coins.
Find the value of the coins.

Think
Count the dimes first because they have the greater value.

1.

10¢ 20¢ 30¢ 35¢ 40¢ 45¢   45¢

2.

47¢

TEST TIPS **Explain Your Thinking** In Exercise 2 what coin did you start with and why? **Possible answer: I started with the dime because it has the greatest value.**

Chapter 14 Lesson 4   three hundred ninety-five **395**

---

① Introduce
Model Counting Coins

| iiii Whole Group | ⏱ 10–15 minutes | Tactile, Auditory |

Materials: *coin sets, overhead coins*

1. Display 2 dimes, 1 nickel, and 2 pennies. Have children show the same coins. Emphasize that the coins are in order from greatest to least. **Why are the coins arranged from greatest to least in value?** (to make it easy to count them)

2. Model how to count the coins. Have children arrange and count their coins along with you. Remind children to count the dimes first, counting by 10s to 20¢. Next, count the nickel, counting on 5 from 20¢ to 25¢. Finally, count the pennies, counting on by 1s from 25¢ to 27¢.

3. **How can we count 1 dime, 2 nickels, and 3 pennies?**
   (Begin with the dime and count 10, 15, 20, 21, 22, 23¢.)

② Develop

Guided Learning

Teaching Example Introduce the objective to children. Guide them through the example by having them place coins on the pictured coins to model how to find the value of a group of dimes, nickels, and pennies. Emphasize counting the dime first since it has the greatest value.

Guided Practice

Have children complete **Exercises 1–2** as you observe. Give children the opportunity to answer the Explain Your Thinking question. Then discuss their responses with the class.

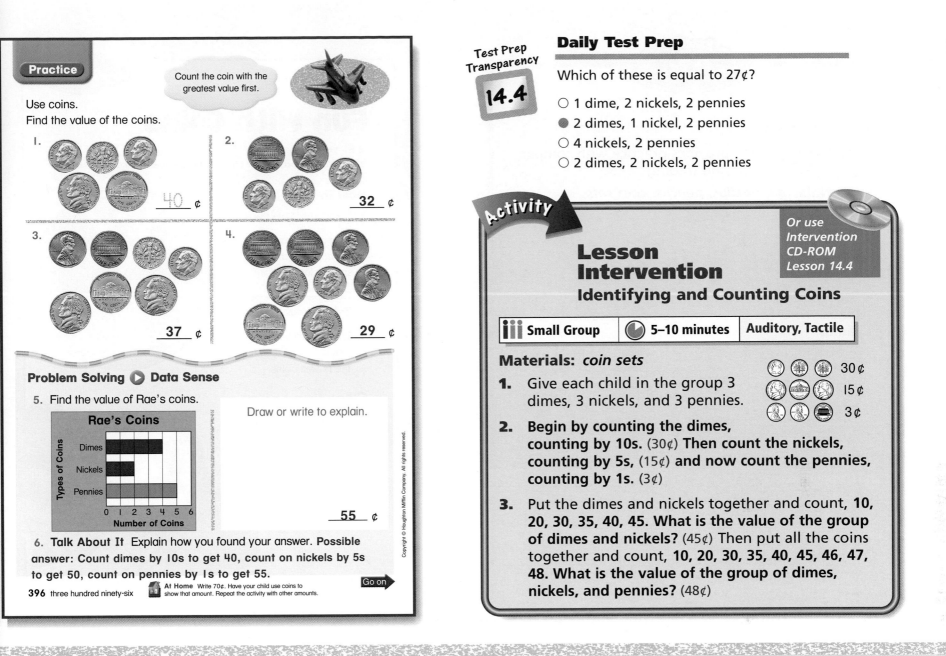

Count the coin with the greatest value first.

Use coins.
Find the value of the coins.

1. 40 ¢

2. 32 ¢

3. 37 ¢

4. 29 ¢

Problem Solving ▶ Data Sense

5. Find the value of Rae's coins.

Rae's Coins

Types of Coins: Dimes, Nickels, Pennies

Number of Coins: 0 1 2 3 4 5 6

Draw or write to explain.

55 ¢

6. **Talk About It** Explain how you found your answer. **Possible answer: Count dimes by 10s to get 40, count on nickels by 5s to get 50, count on pennies by 1s to get 55.**

At Home Write 70¢. Have your child use coins to show that amount. Repeat the activity with other amounts.

Go on

396 three hundred ninety-six

Daily Test Prep

Which of these is equal to 27¢?

○ 1 dime, 2 nickels, 2 pennies
● 2 dimes, 1 nickel, 2 pennies
○ 4 nickels, 2 pennies
○ 2 dimes, 2 nickels, 2 pennies

Activity

Or use Intervention CD-ROM Lesson 14.4

Lesson Intervention

Identifying and Counting Coins

| 👥 Small Group | 🕐 5–10 minutes | Auditory, Tactile |

Materials: *coin sets*

30 ¢
15 ¢
3 ¢

1. Give each child in the group 3 dimes, 3 nickels, and 3 pennies.

2. Begin by counting the dimes, counting by 10s. (30¢) **Then count the nickels, counting by 5s,** (15¢) **and now count the pennies, counting by 1s.** (3¢)

3. Put the dimes and nickels together and count, **10, 20, 30, 35, 40, 45. What is the value of the group of dimes and nickels?** (45¢) Then put all the coins together and count, **10, 20, 30, 35, 40, 45, 46, 47, 48. What is the value of the group of dimes, nickels, and pennies?** (48¢)

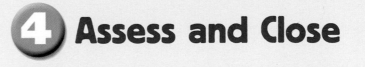

3 Practice

Independent Practice

Children complete **Exercises 1–4** independently.

Problem Solving

Remind children how to read a graph using the labels, bars, and numbers. After children complete **Exercise 5,** call on volunteers to share their solutions. Use the **Talk About It** question in **Exercise 6** to generate discussion of the answers.

Common Error

Counting Incorrectly When Changing Coins
Children may lose track of the value from which to count on when changing from counting one kind of coin to another. Tell children to write the value of one kind of coin they are counting before beginning to count a different kind of coin.

4 Assess and Close

Explain how to count a group of 3 dimes, 2 nickels, and 5 pennies. (Start with counting the dimes and count 10, 20, 30, 35, 40, 41, 42, 43, 44, 45¢)

Suppose you have 2 dimes, 3 nickels, and 4 pennies. Would you begin counting by 1s, 5s, or 10s? (tens)

✏️ Keeping a Journal

Draw a group of dimes, nickels, and pennies. Use words and pictures to show how to find the total value.

Lesson continues ➤

Fun with Coins

Purpose This game provides practice with comparing money amounts and trading coins.

Materials: *paper clips, pencils, coin sets*

How to Play

- Pair children with a partner. Then give each pair a set of materials.

- Tell children that in this game the winner is the player who has 60¢ with the fewest coins, or 6 dimes.

- Show children how to work together with a pencil and paper clip to make the spinner.

- Have children take turns spinning the spinner and taking coins that match the amounts shown.

- Remind them to trade pennies or nickels for coins of greater value as they play.

Other Ways to Play

Children may continue to play during the same session or these alternate versions of the Practice Game could be used in the Math Center at a later date.

A. The first player to have 60¢ with the most coins wins. Children trade nickels and dimes for pennies.

B. The first player to have 60¢ with only dimes and nickels wins.

Name_____

Fun With Coins

2 Players

What You Need: paper clip, pencil, pennies, nickels, and dimes

How to Play

1. Take turns. Spin the spinner.

2. Take coins that match the coins where the spinner lands.

3. Trade pennies for nickels. Trade nickels for dimes.

4. Continue playing until a player has 60¢ with the fewest coins.

Other Ways to Play

A. Play without trading. The first player to have 60¢ with the most coins wins.

B. The first player to have 60¢ with only dimes and nickels wins.

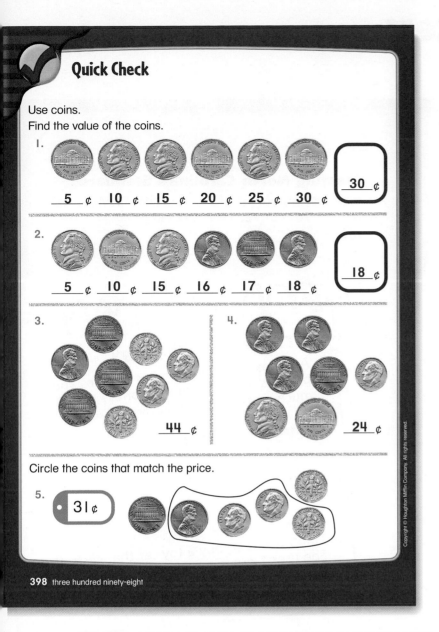

Use coins.
Find the value of the coins.

1.   5 ¢   10 ¢   15 ¢   20 ¢   25 ¢   30 ¢   30 ¢

2.   5 ¢   10 ¢   15 ¢   16 ¢   17 ¢   18 ¢   18 ¢

3.   44 ¢   4.   24 ¢

Circle the coins that match the price.

5.   31¢

Quick Check

Have children complete the Quick Check exercises independently to assess their understanding of concepts and skills taught in **Lessons 1–4**.

Item	Lesson	Error Analysis	Intervention
1	14.1	Children may have difficulty remembering the values of coins.	Reteach Resource 14.1 *Ways to Success* 14.1
2	14.2	Children may be unable to switch from 5s to 1s in counting.	Reteach Resource 14.2 *Ways to Success* 14.2
3, 5	14.3	Children may miscount the coins in a mixed set.	Reteach Resource 14.3 *Ways to Success* 14.3
4	14.4	Children may count incorrectly when changing from counting one kind of coin to another.	Reteach Resource 14.4 *Ways to Success* 14.4

Art Connection

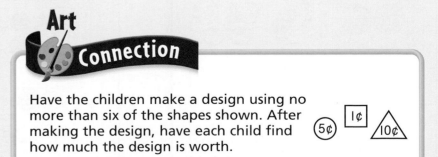

Have the children make a design using no more than six of the shapes shown. After making the design, have each child find how much the design is worth.

Hands-On: Quarters

Lesson 14.5

PLANNING THE LESSON

MATHEMATICS OBJECTIVE
Identify and count with quarters. Make 25 cents with pennies, nickels, and dimes.

Use Lesson Planner CD-ROM for Lesson 14.5.

Meeting North Carolina's Standards
1.02 Use groupings of 2's, 5's, and 10's with models and pictures to count collections of objects.
Also 1.01

Daily Routines

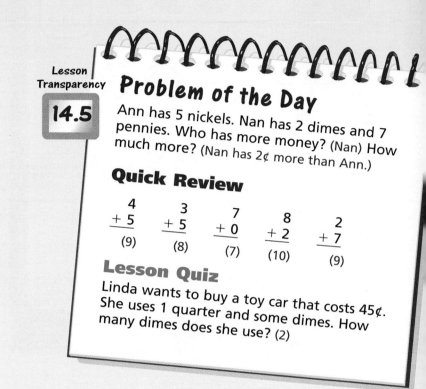

Lesson Transparency 14.5

Problem of the Day
Ann has 5 nickels. Nan has 2 dimes and 7 pennies. Who has more money? (Nan) How much more? (Nan has 2¢ more than Ann.)

Quick Review

$$\begin{array}{c} 4 \\ +5 \\ \hline (9) \end{array} \quad \begin{array}{c} 3 \\ +5 \\ \hline (8) \end{array} \quad \begin{array}{c} 7 \\ +0 \\ \hline (7) \end{array} \quad \begin{array}{c} 8 \\ +2 \\ \hline (10) \end{array} \quad \begin{array}{c} 2 \\ +7 \\ \hline (9) \end{array}$$

Lesson Quiz
Linda wants to buy a toy car that costs 45¢. She uses 1 quarter and some dimes. How many dimes does she use? (2)

Calendar
Have children take turns finding, naming, and circling dates on the calendar that have either of the digits in 25, a 2 or 5. (2nd, 5th, 12th, 15th, 20th, 21st, 22nd, 23rd, 24th, 25th, 26th, 27th, 28th, 29th)

Sunday	Monday	Tuesday	Wednesday	Thursday	Friday	Saturday
			1	2	3	4
5	6	7	8	9	10	11
12	13	14	15	16	17	18
19	20	21	22	23	24	25
26	27	28	29	30	31	

Vocabulary
Display and describe a **quarter**. Show children how to write its value as 25 cents and 25¢. Relate the coin to **dimes**, **nickels**, and **pennies**. Show single coins in random order and have children say the name of the coin.

Vocabulary Cards

LEVELED PRACTICE

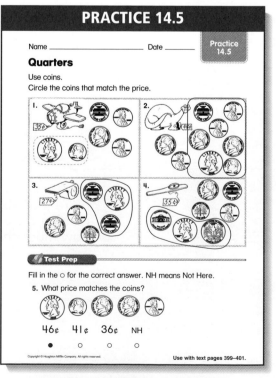

RETEACH 14.5

Name _____ Date _____ **Reteach 14.5**

Quarters
A quarter is equal to 25¢.

quarter
25 cents
25¢

Use coins.
Circle the group of coins that makes 25¢.

Use with text pages 399–401.

PRACTICE 14.5

Name _____ Date _____ **Practice 14.5**

Quarters
Use coins.
Circle the coins that match the price.

Test Prep
Fill in the ○ for the correct answer. NH means Not Here.

5. What price matches the coins?

46¢   41¢   36¢   NH
●   ○   ○   ○

Use with text pages 399–401.

ENRICHMENT 14.5

Name _____ Date _____ **Enrichment 14.5**

Questions and Quarters
Read each clue.
Draw the coins.

1. Sally has 3 coins that equal 25¢.   10¢ 10¢ 5¢

2. William has 2 coins that equal 35¢.   25¢ 10¢

3. David has 4 coins that equal 46¢.   25¢ 10¢ 10¢ 1¢

4. Jim has 4 coins that equal 28¢.   25¢ 1¢ 1¢ 1¢

5. Enrique has 4 coins that equal 55¢.   25¢ 10¢ 10¢ 10¢

Write About It Do you think people like to pay with fewer coins of the same value or with more coins of different values? Why?
Answers will vary. Possible answer: People like to pay with fewer coins because they are easier to count.

Practice Workbook Page 95

Reaching All Learners

Differentiated Instruction

English Learners

To solve some problems involving money, English-language learners will need to understand the word *only*. Use Worksheet 14.5 to help develop understanding of this word.

Special Needs
VISUAL, TACTILE

Materials: *price tags, coin sets, small objects*

- Place prices on objects such as pencils, erasers, etc.
- Give the child coins. Have the child count and show the coins needed to "buy" each item.

Gifted and Talented
VISUAL, TACTILE

Materials: *coin sets, index cards*

- Prepare index cards with amounts, such as 28¢, 15¢, 41¢, etc.
- Have one child choose a card. Have a partner find different ways to show the amount.
- Children record their combinations and then switch roles.

TECHNOLOGY

Spiral Review

You can prepare students for standardized tests with **customized** spiral review on key skills using the *Ways to Assess* CD-ROM.

eBook

eMathBook allows students to review lessons and do homework without carrying their textbooks home.

Manipulatives

Interactive **Coins and Bills** tool is available on the *Ways to Success* CD-ROM.

Social Studies Connection

Tell children that people sometimes use paper rolls, or penny wrappers, to group 50 pennies and make them easier to count. Challenge children to find how many quarters, dimes, and nickels make 50¢.

MATH CENTER

Real-Life Activity

Help children understand the usefulness of mathematics. This activity makes math come alive by connecting the lesson skills to a real-life situation.

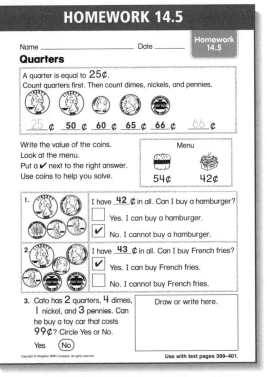

PROBLEM SOLVING 14.5

Name _____ Date _____

Quarters

Read each problem. Write the answer. Use coins to find the answer.

Dan trades 4 dimes and 2 nickels for quarters. How many quarters does he get?
___2___ quarters

1. Maria trades 5 dimes, 4 nickels, and 5 pennies for quarters. How many quarters does she get?
   Draw or write to explain.
   ___3___ quarters

2. Tina trades 15 pennies and 2 nickels for quarters. How many quarters does she get?
   ___1___ quarter

3. Jim trades 6 dimes, 2 nickels, and 5 pennies for quarters. How many quarters does he get?
   ___3___ quarters

Use with text pages 399–401.

HOMEWORK 14.5

Name _____ Date _____

Quarters

A quarter is equal to 25¢.
Count quarters first. Then count dimes, nickels, and pennies.
_25_ ¢ _50_ ¢ _60_ ¢ _65_ ¢ _66_ ¢ _66_ ¢

Write the value of the coins. Look at the menu. Put a ✔ next to the right answer. Use coins to help you solve.

Menu
54¢   42¢

1. I have _42_ ¢ in all. Can I buy a hamburger?
   ☐ Yes. I can buy a hamburger.
   ✔ No. I cannot buy a hamburger.

2. I have _43_ ¢ in all. Can I buy French fries?
   ✔ Yes. I can buy French fries.
   ☐ No. I cannot buy French fries.

3. Cato has 2 quarters, 4 dimes, 1 nickel, and 3 pennies. Can he buy a toy car that costs 99¢? Circle Yes or No.
   Yes   (No)
   Draw or write here.

Use with text pages 399–401.

Homework Workbook Page 95

ENGLISH LEARNERS 14.5

Name _____ Date _____

Quarters

only cats   not only cats

Draw pictures.

1. Drawing of pencils
   only pencils

2. Drawing of pencils and other things
   not only pencils

3. Drawing of hats
   only hats

4. Drawing of hats and other things
   not only hats

To the Teacher: Use the example at the top of the page to help children understand the meaning of the word only. Then read the labels with children and have them draw pictures to illustrate them.

Use with text pages 399–402.

TEACHING LESSON 14.5

LESSON ORGANIZER

Objective Identify and count with quarters. Make 25 cents with pennies, nickels, and dimes.

Resources Reteach, Practice, Enrichment, Problem Solving, Homework, English Learners, Transparencies, Math Center

Materials Coin sets, overhead coins, blank transparency

Activity

Warm-Up Activity
Identify and Trade Coins

| **Whole Group** | **5 minutes** | **Auditory, Tactile** |

Materials: *coin sets, overhead coins*

1. Display 1 dime, 1 nickel, and 1 penny on the overhead in random order. Have volunteers name and describe each coin. Compare the size, shape, color, and markings of the coins.

2. Discuss and model ways to use coins of lesser value to trade for a dime. (2 nickels, 1 nickel and 5 pennies, 10 pennies)

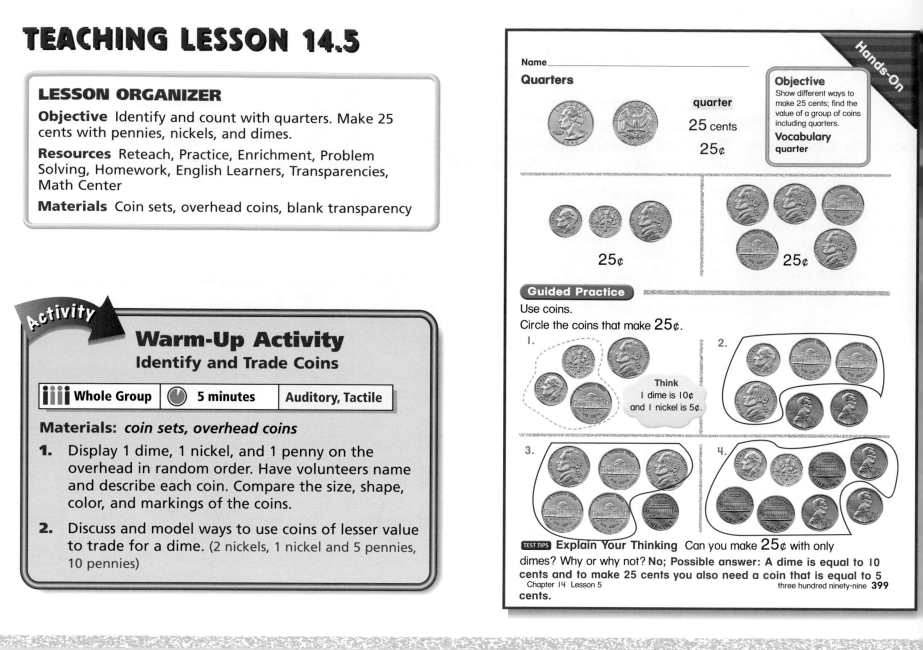

Name _____

Quarters

quarter
25 cents
25¢

Objective
Show different ways to make 25 cents; find the value of a group of coins including quarters.

Vocabulary
quarter

25¢   25¢

Guided Practice

Use coins.
Circle the coins that make 25¢.

1.

Think
1 dime is 10¢
and 1 nickel is 5¢.

2.

3.   4.

TEST TIPS **Explain Your Thinking** Can you make 25¢ with only dimes? Why or why not? **No; Possible answer: A dime is equal to 10 cents and to make 25 cents you also need a coin that is equal to 5 cents.**

Chapter 14 Lesson 5   three hundred ninety-nine **399**

---

1 Introduce

Model Ways to Make 25¢

| **Whole Group** | **10–15 minutes** | **Visual, Tactile** |

Materials: *coin sets, overhead coins, blank transparency*

1. Display a dime, nickel, and penny on the blank transparency. Review the name and value of each coin. Add a quarter to the display and identify it and its value. **How does the quarter compare to the other coins?** (bigger, greatest value)

2. Discuss mixed coins that equal 25¢. Display 2 dimes and a nickel and ask a volunteer to count the coins. Remind the child to count the coins with the greater value first. Write the cumulative value under the coins as the child counts. (10¢, 20¢, 25¢) **How much in all?** (25¢)

3. If I remove 1 dime, what 2 coins can I replace it with so that the coins still equal 25¢? (2 nickels) Continue trading coins to show different ways to make 25¢.

2 Develop

Guided Learning

Teaching Example Introduce the objective and vocabulary to children. Guide them through the example by having them place coins on the pictured coins to model how to show coins with a total value of 25¢. Discuss state quarters and display as many as possible. Emphasize that George Washington appears on both old and new quarters. The new quarters have a different design on the tails for each state.

Guided Practice

Have children complete **Exercises 1–4** as you observe. Remind students to circle the group of coins not individual ones. Give children the opportunity to answer the Explain Your Thinking question. Then discuss their responses with the class.

There are different ways to make 25¢.
Use coins to help you complete the chart.

Make sure each row shows a different way to make 25¢.

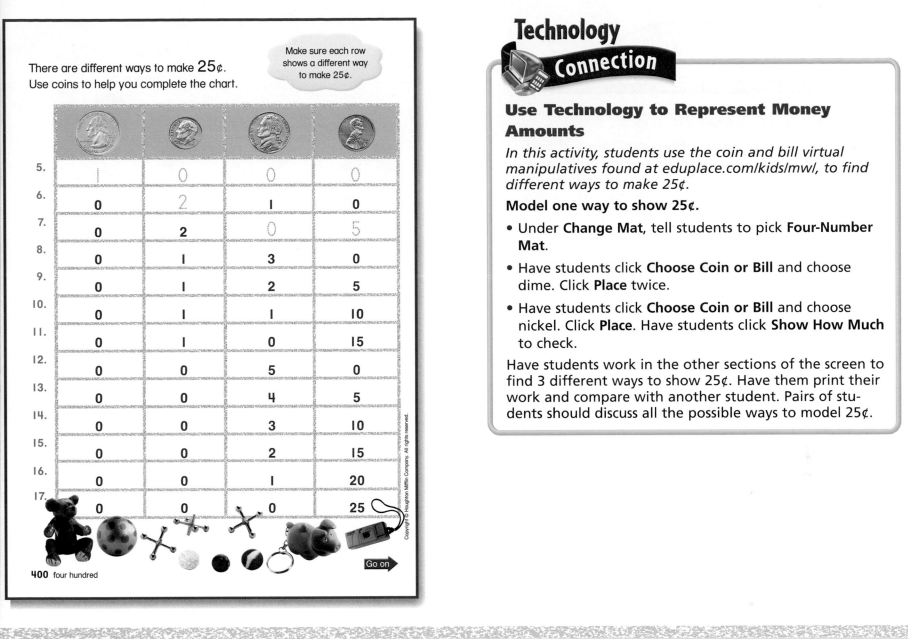

	(quarter)	(dime)	(nickel)	(penny)
5.	1	0	0	0
6.	0	2	1	0
7.	0	2	0	5
8.	0	1	3	0
9.	0	1	2	5
10.	0	1	1	10
11.	0	1	0	15
12.	0	0	5	0
13.	0	0	4	5
14.	0	0	3	10
15.	0	0	2	15
16.	0	0	1	20
17.	0	0	0	25

400 four hundred

Go on

Use Technology to Represent Money Amounts

In this activity, students use the coin and bill virtual manipulatives found at eduplace.com/kids/mwl, to find different ways to make 25¢.

Model one way to show 25¢.

- Under **Change Mat**, tell students to pick **Four-Number Mat**.

- Have students click **Choose Coin or Bill** and choose dime. Click **Place** twice.

- Have students click **Choose Coin or Bill** and choose nickel. Click **Place**. Have students click **Show How Much** to check.

Have students work in the other sections of the screen to find 3 different ways to show 25¢. Have them print their work and compare with another student. Pairs of students should discuss all the possible ways to model 25¢.

2 Develop

Guided Practice

Have children complete **Exercises 5–17** on page 400 as you observe. Students should work in pairs to complete the chart. Encourage children to look for patterns to find all the ways to show 25¢.

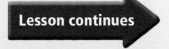
Lesson continues

What Is Good Practice?

Studies indicate that one of the best forms of practice has children use previously-learned skills while learning new concepts and skills. By practicing skills in a parallel manner, rather than in a serial manner, practice does not seem repetitive to children.

In this chapter on money, children consistently practice "old" skills as they learn new ones. They practice counting, counting on, skip counting, and basic addition in the process of learning to find the value of collections of pennies, nickels, dimes, quarters, and half-dollars.

Practice that is embedded in problem solving is also desirable. Children immediately understand the need to solve the problem "How much money is this?" Practicing basic skills while introducing money concepts is motivating because it connects to the children's world.

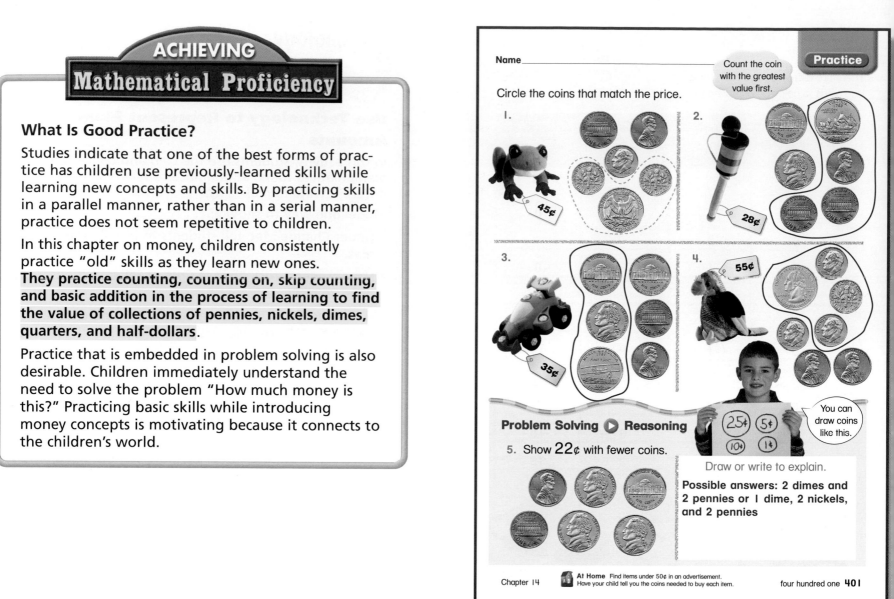

Name _____

Count the coin with the greatest value first.

Practice

Circle the coins that match the price.

1. 45¢

2. 28¢

3. 35¢

4. 55¢

Problem Solving ▶ Reasoning

5. Show 22¢ with fewer coins.

You can draw coins like this.

Draw or write to explain.

Possible answers: 2 dimes and 2 pennies or 1 dime, 2 nickels, and 2 pennies

Chapter 14

At Home Find items under 50¢ in an advertisement. Have your child tell you the coins needed to buy each item.

four hundred one 401

3 Practice

Independent Practice

Children complete **Exercises 1–4** on page 401 independently. Some students may want to use coins to complete the exercises.

Problem Solving

After children complete **Exercise 5,** call on volunteers to share their solutions and discuss why there is more than one possible answer.

Common Error

Showing Incorrect Combinations of Coins

Some children may write incorrect numbers for coins in the chart on page 400. Remind children to use coins to model ways to make 25¢ when filling in the chart, then count and record carefully.

4 Assess and Close

Sal has 2 dimes and 5 pennies. Rob has 4 nickels. Which boy has 25¢? (Sal)

Suppose you have 2 dimes and 1 nickel. If the price of a pen is 25¢, can you buy it? (yes)

Keeping a Journal

Draw coins to show 3 different ways to make 25¢.

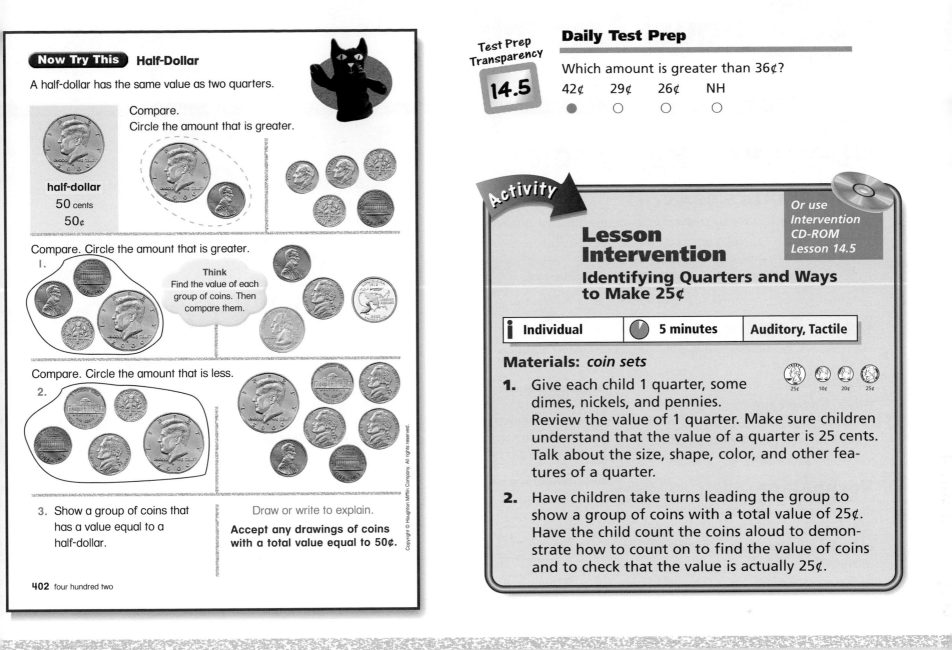

Now Try This Half-Dollar

A half-dollar has the same value as two quarters.

Compare.
Circle the amount that is greater.

half-dollar
50 cents
50¢

Compare. Circle the amount that is greater.

1.

Think
Find the value of each group of coins. Then compare them.

Compare. Circle the amount that is less.

2.

3. Show a group of coins that has a value equal to a half-dollar.

Draw or write to explain.

Accept any drawings of coins with a total value equal to 50¢.

402 four hundred two

Daily Test Prep

Which amount is greater than 36¢?

42¢   29¢   26¢   NH
●   ○   ○   ○

Activity

Or use Intervention CD-ROM Lesson 14.5

Lesson Intervention
Identifying Quarters and Ways to Make 25¢

| Individual | 5 minutes | Auditory, Tactile |

Materials: *coin sets*

1. Give each child 1 quarter, some dimes, nickels, and pennies. Review the value of 1 quarter. Make sure children understand that the value of a quarter is 25 cents. Talk about the size, shape, color, and other features of a quarter.

    25¢ 10¢ 20¢ 25¢

2. Have children take turns leading the group to show a group of coins with a total value of 25¢. Have the child count the coins aloud to demonstrate how to count on to find the value of coins and to check that the value is actually 25¢.

Now Try This

Materials: *coin set, overhead coins, blank transparency*

Introduce Display a quarter, dime, nickel, and penny on the transparency. Review the name and value of each coin. Add a half-dollar and write its value. *What is the value of a half-dollar?* (50 cents) Tell children that the half-dollar has the same value as 2 quarters, 5 dimes, 10 nickels, or 50 pennies.

Develop Guide children through **Exercise 1**. Discuss different ways to combine coins to make a half-dollar. Model how to compare amounts of money and circle the amount that is greater.

Practice Have children complete **Exercises 2** and **3** as you observe. Remind students to count the coins in each group to find the value before comparing.

Equal Amounts

PLANNING THE LESSON

MATHEMATICS OBJECTIVE
Find different ways to show the same amount of money.

Use Lesson Planner CD-ROM for Lesson 14.6.

Daily Routines

Calendar
Have children find pairs of numbers on the calendar that have the same sum. For example 1 and 5 have the same sum as 2 and 4.

Sunday	Monday	Tuesday	Wednesday	Thursday	Friday	Saturday
			1	2	3	4
5	6	7	8	9	10	11
12	13	14	15	16	17	18
19	20	21	22	23	24	25
26	27	28	29	30	31	

Vocabulary
Review **same** *amount*. Call on volunteers to give examples, such as 1 dime is the same amount of money as 2 nickels.

Vocabulary Cards

Meeting North Carolina's Standards
1.01 Develop number sense for whole numbers through 99.

• Connect the model, number word, and number using a variety of representations.

Lesson Transparency 14.6

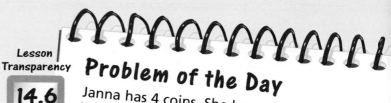

Problem of the Day
Janna has 4 coins. She has a total of 26¢. Which 4 coins does she have? (2 dimes, 1 nickel, 1 penny)

Quick Review
Lucy plays ball on Saturday starting at 5:30. How long does the game last? (2 hours)
Start: 5:30   End: 7:30

Lesson Quiz
Andy buys a stamp for 37¢. He pays for it with 3 dimes, a nickel, and some pennies. How many pennies does he use? (2 pennies)

LEVELED PRACTICE

RETEACH 14.6

Name _____ Date _____
Reteach 14.6

Equal Amounts

You can use different coins to show the same amount.

Both ways show 32¢.

Use coins.
Complete the chart. **Possible answers given.**

Show these coins.	Write the amount.	Show another way.
1.	24 ¢	10¢ 10¢ 1¢ / 1¢ 1¢ 1¢
2.	40 ¢	10¢ 10¢ 10¢ / 5¢ 5¢

Copyright © Houghton Mifflin Company. All rights reserved.
Use with text pages 403–404.

PRACTICE 14.6

Name _____ Date _____
Practice 14.6

Equal Amounts

Use coins.
Complete the chart.

Answers will vary. Possible answers are given.

	Show the amount with coins.	Show another way.
12¢	5¢ 5¢ 1¢ 1¢	10¢ 1¢ 1¢
32¢	10¢ 10¢ 10¢ 1¢ 1¢	25¢ 5¢ 1¢ 1¢
27¢	25¢ 1¢ 1¢	10¢ 10¢ 5¢ 1¢ 1¢
45¢	25¢ 10¢ 10¢	10¢ 10¢ 10¢ 10¢ 5¢

Test Prep

Fill in the ○ for the correct answer. NH means Not Here.
What is one way to show 25¢?

○   ●   ○   NH ○

Copyright © Houghton Mifflin Company. All rights reserved.
Use with text pages 403–404.

ENRICHMENT 14.6

Name _____ Date _____
Enrichment 14.6

Matching Money

Draw a line to match the banks that have the same amount of money.

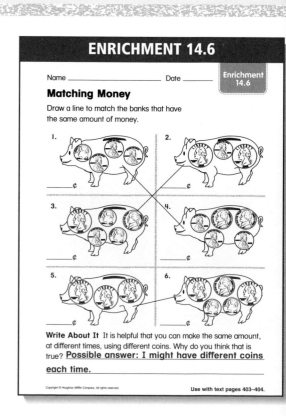

Write About It It is helpful that you can make the same amount, at different times, using different coins. Why do you think that is true? **Possible answer: I might have different coins each time.**

Copyright © Houghton Mifflin Company. All rights reserved.
Use with text pages 403–404.

Practice Workbook Page 96

Reaching All Learners

Differentiated Instruction

English Learners

English-language learners will need to have an understanding of the term *amount* in order to find different ways to show the same amount of money. Use Worksheet 14.6 to develop children's ability to understand and use this term.

Inclusion
VISUAL, TACTILE

Materials: *price tags, coin sets*

- Display a price tag of 8¢. Guide the child to use 8 pennies to match the amount.
- Tell the child to show the same amount a different way. Prompt the child to trade 5 pennies for a nickel. Continue with similar amounts.

Early Finishers
VISUAL, TACTILE

Materials: *coin sets, number cube*

- One child in a pair rolls the number cube, places that many coins on the desk, and says the value.
- The partner rolls for the number of coins and tries to match the first amount. Score 1 point for a match.

TECHNOLOGY

Spiral Review

Create **customized** spiral review worksheets for individual students using the *Ways to Assess* CD-ROM.

Education Place

You can visit **Education Place** at **eduplace.com/math/mw/** for teacher support materials.

Manipulatives

Interactive **Coins and Bills** tool is available on the *Ways to Success* CD-ROM.

Art Connection

Show children some state quarters. Discuss the pictures on each coin. Tell children that the U.S. Mint and other government groups sometimes hold competitions for coin designs. Have children design a quarter.

MATH CENTER

Cross-Curricular Activity

As you use this activity to relate the mathematics of this lesson to another curriculum area, children will see how math can help them with other subjects.

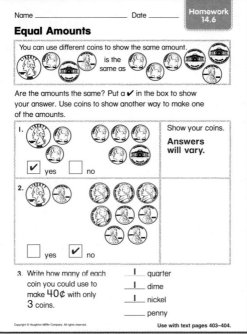

PROBLEM SOLVING 14.6

Name _____ Date _____ | Problem Solving 14.6

Equal Amounts

Read each problem.
Write the missing number to make both amounts the same.
Use coins to find the answer.

| Craig has 1 quarter, 1 dime and 2 pennies. | (25¢) (10¢) (1¢) (1¢) |
| John has 3 dimes, __1__ nickel, and 2 pennies. | (10¢)(10¢)(10¢)(5¢)(1¢)(1¢) |

1. Liz has 3 quarters.

   Melissa has 2 quarters, __2__ dimes, and 5 pennies.

   Draw or write to explain.

2. Paul has 2 quarters, 3 dimes, 1 nickel, and 2 pennies.

   Peter has __3__ quarters, 1 dime, and 2 pennies.

Use with text pages 403–404.

HOMEWORK 14.6

Name _____ Date _____ | Homework 14.6

Equal Amounts

You can use different coins to show the same amount.

... is the same as ...

Are the amounts the same? Put a ✔ in the box to show your answer. Use coins to show another way to make one of the amounts.

1.
   Show your coins.
   Answers will vary.
   ✔ yes ☐ no

2.
   ☐ yes ✔ no

3. Write how many of each coin you could use to make 40¢ with only 3 coins.
   __1__ quarter
   __1__ dime
   __1__ nickel
   ____ penny

Use with text pages 403–404.

ENGLISH LEARNERS 14.6

Name _____ Date _____ | English Learners 14.6

Equal Amounts

These coins show 10¢.
The **amount** is 10¢.

Write the amount.

1.
   The coins show __12¢__.
   The amount is __12¢__.

2.
   The coins show __9¢__.
   The amount is __9¢__.

3.
   The coins show __16¢__.
   The amount is __16¢__.

4.
   The coins show __3¢__.
   The amount is __3¢__.

To the Teacher: Use the example at the top of the page to teach children the concept of amount. Then have children count the coins and complete the sentences about them.

Use with text pages 403–404.

Homework Workbook Page 96

TEACHING LESSON 14.6

LESSON ORGANIZER

Objective Find different ways to show the same amount of money.

Resources Reteach, Practice, Enrichment, Problem Solving, Homework, English Learners, Transparencies, Math Center

Materials Coin sets, overhead coins, blank transparency

Warm-Up Activity
Model Ways to Make Prices

iiii Whole Group	5 minutes	Auditory, Tactile

Materials: *coin sets, overhead coins, blank transparency*

1. Draw a price tag showing 7¢ on the transparency. Have volunteers name and display on the overhead coins that can be used to show the price. (1 nickel, 2 pennies)

2. Discuss and model another group of coins equal to the price. (7 pennies)

3. Repeat with other prices 6¢–10¢. Have children display coins on the overhead to show 2 ways to make the prices.

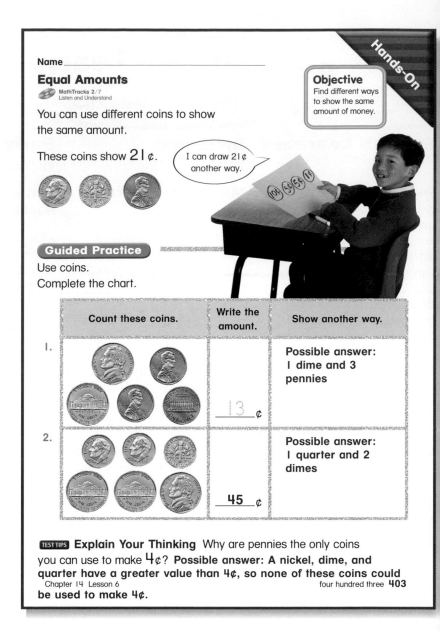

Equal Amounts

MathTracks 2/7
Listen and Understand

Objective Find different ways to show the same amount of money.

You can use different coins to show the same amount.

These coins show 21¢.

I can draw 21¢ another way.

Guided Practice

Use coins.
Complete the chart.

Count these coins.	Write the amount.	Show another way.
1.	13 ¢	Possible answer: 1 dime and 3 pennies
2.	45 ¢	Possible answer: 1 quarter and 2 dimes

TEST TIPS **Explain Your Thinking** Why are pennies the only coins you can use to make 4¢? **Possible answer: A nickel, dime, and quarter have a greater value than 4¢, so none of these coins could be used to make 4¢.**

Chapter 14 Lesson 6   four hundred three **403**

---

1 Introduce

Model Equal Amounts

iiii Whole Group	10–15 minutes	Visual, Tactile

Materials: *coin sets, overhead coins, blank transparency*

1. Discuss how to use different coins to show 11¢ in different ways. Display a dime and penny on the transparency. **How many coins?** (2 coins) **What are they?** (dime, penny) **How much are they worth?** (11¢)

2. Explain that different coins can be used to show the same amount of money. Discuss other coins that together make 11¢. Display 2 nickels and a penny on the transparency and ask a volunteer to count the coins. **How many coins?** (3 coins) **How much are they worth?** (11¢)

3. **How are the two groups of coins alike?** (both show 11¢) **How are they different?** (different number and kinds of coins)

2 Develop

Guided Learning

Teaching Example Introduce the objective to children. Guide them through the example to model how to show the same amount of money in a different way and how to draw the coins.

Guided Practice

Have children complete **Exercises 1–2** as you observe. Give children the opportunity to answer the Explain Your Thinking question. Then discuss their responses with the class.

Use coins.
Complete the chart.

Remember to use different coins to show the same amount.

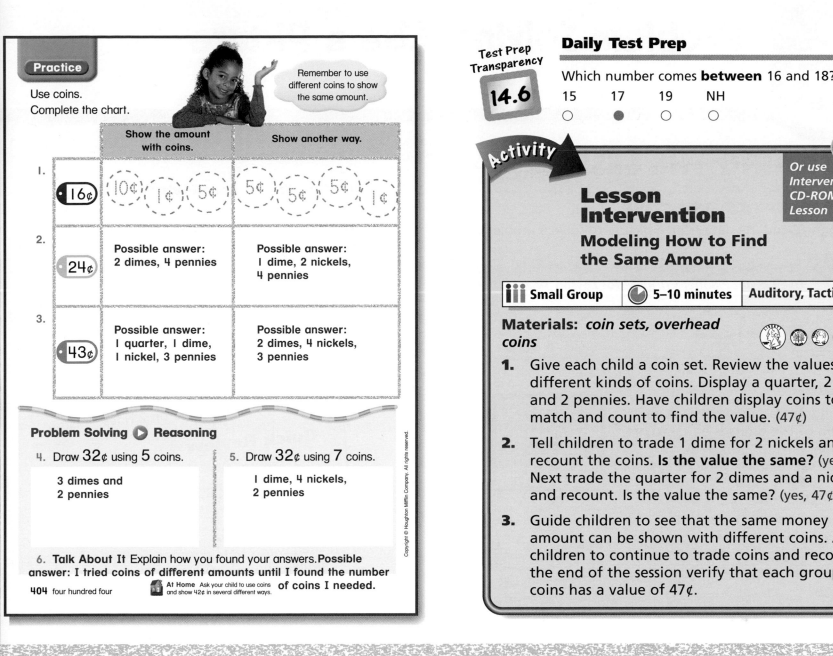

	Show the amount with coins.	Show another way.
1. 16¢	10¢ 1¢ 5¢	5¢ 5¢ 5¢ 1¢
2. 24¢	Possible answer: 2 dimes, 4 pennies	Possible answer: 1 dime, 2 nickels, 4 pennies
3. 43¢	Possible answer: 1 quarter, 1 dime, 1 nickel, 3 pennies	Possible answer: 2 dimes, 4 nickels, 3 pennies

Problem Solving ▶ Reasoning

4. Draw 32¢ using 5 coins.

   3 dimes and
   2 pennies

5. Draw 32¢ using 7 coins.

   1 dime, 4 nickels,
   2 pennies

6. **Talk About It** Explain how you found your answers. **Possible answer: I tried coins of different amounts until I found the number of coins I needed.**

At Home Ask your child to use coins and show 42¢ in several different ways.

404 four hundred four

Daily Test Prep

Which number comes **between** 16 and 18?

15   17   19   NH
○   ●   ○   ○

Activity

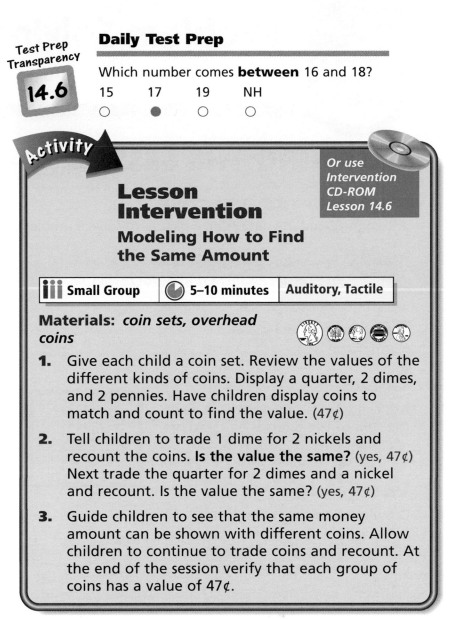

Lesson Intervention

Or use Intervention CD-ROM Lesson 14.6

Modeling How to Find the Same Amount

👤👤👤 Small Group	🕐 5–10 minutes	Auditory, Tactile

Materials: *coin sets, overhead coins*

1. Give each child a coin set. Review the values of the different kinds of coins. Display a quarter, 2 dimes, and 2 pennies. Have children display coins to match and count to find the value. (47¢)

2. Tell children to trade 1 dime for 2 nickels and recount the coins. **Is the value the same?** (yes, 47¢) Next trade the quarter for 2 dimes and a nickel and recount. Is the value the same? (yes, 47¢)

3. Guide children to see that the same money amount can be shown with different coins. Allow children to continue to trade coins and recount. At the end of the session verify that each group of coins has a value of 47¢.

---

3 Practice

Independent Practice

Children complete **Exercises 1–3** independently.

Problem Solving

In **Exercises 4–5** some students may continue to need to use coins to answer these problems. After children complete the exercises, call on volunteers to share their answers. Use the **Talk About It** in **Exercise 7** to guide the discussion of answers.

Common Error

Showing Different Amounts of Money

Some children may show different amounts of money. Have children show the same amount the same way first and then trade coins in one of the groups for different coins.

4 Assess and Close

Lee has 3 nickels and 3 pennies. Brett has 1 dime and 8 pennies. Do they have the same amount of money? (yes)

Describe two groups of coins worth 42 cents. (Possible answer: 1 quarter, 1 dime, 1 nickel, 2 pennies; 2 dimes, 4 nickels, 2 pennies.)

Keeping a Journal

Draw a price tag. Write a price between 10¢ and 65¢. Draw coins to show two different ways to make the price.

Problem Solving: Use a Picture

PLANNING THE LESSON

MATHEMATICS OBJECTIVE
Recognize and use data from a picture to solve a problem.

Use Lesson Planner CD-ROM for Lesson 14.7.

Daily Routines

Calendar
Ask children to name dates in which the sum of the digits is equal to or less than 5. (10th, 11th, 12th, 13th, 14th, 20th, 21st, 22nd, 23rd, 30th, 31st)

Sunday	Monday	Tuesday	Wednesday	Thursday	Friday	Saturday
			1	2	3	4
5	6	7	8	9	10	11
12	13	14	15	16	17	18
19	20	21	22	23	24	25
26	27	28	29	30	31	

Vocabulary
Draw a toy car with a price tag showing 10¢. Tell children that they can use *data*, or *information* from a picture like this one to solve problems.

Vocabulary Cards

Meeting North Carolina's Standards
1.04 Create, model, and solve problems that use addition, subtraction, and fair shares (between two or three).

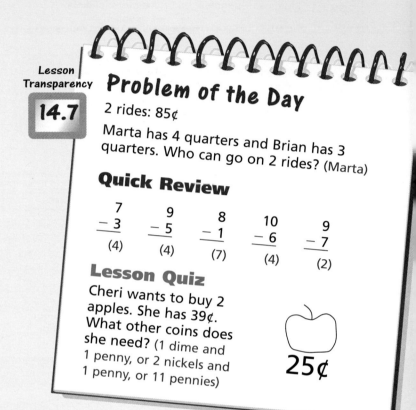

Lesson Transparency 14.7

Problem of the Day
2 rides: 85¢
Marta has 4 quarters and Brian has 3 quarters. Who can go on 2 rides? (Marta)

Quick Review

$$\begin{array}{c}7\\-3\\\hline(4)\end{array}\qquad\begin{array}{c}9\\-5\\\hline(4)\end{array}\qquad\begin{array}{c}8\\-1\\\hline(7)\end{array}\qquad\begin{array}{c}10\\-6\\\hline(4)\end{array}\qquad\begin{array}{c}9\\-7\\\hline(2)\end{array}$$

Lesson Quiz
Cheri wants to buy 2 apples. She has 39¢. What other coins does she need? (1 dime and 1 penny, or 2 nickels and 1 penny, or 11 pennies)

25¢

LEVELED PRACTICE

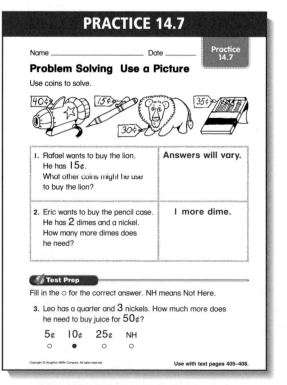

RETEACH 14.7

Name _____ Date _____ Reteach 14.7

Problem Solving: Use a Picture

The School Store
10¢ (pencil) 30¢ (pig eraser) 20¢ (stars)

Read It
Benji wants to buy the pig eraser.
He has 3 nickels, 1 dime, and 2 pennies.
What other coins does he need?

Picture It
Use the picture. The pig eraser costs __30__ ¢.

Solve It
Benji has 27¢. The eraser costs 30¢.

Does Benji need more nickels? __No__

Does Benji need more dimes? __No__

Does Benji need more pennies? __Yes__

How many coins does Benji need? __3 pennies__

Explain how the picture helped you know how many coins Benji needed.
__I know what coins Benji has and the picture__
__tells me how much the eraser costs.__

Copyright © Houghton Mifflin Company. All rights reserved. Use with text pages 405–408.

PRACTICE 14.7

Name _____ Date _____ Practice 14.7

Problem Solving Use a Picture
Use coins to solve.

40¢ 15¢ 30¢ 35¢

1. Rafael wants to buy the lion. He has 15¢. What other coins might he use to buy the lion?	**Answers will vary.**
2. Eric wants to buy the pencil case. He has 2 dimes and a nickel. How many more dimes does he need?	**1 more dime.**

Test Prep

Fill in the ○ for the correct answer. NH means Not Here.

3. Leo has a quarter and 3 nickels. How much more does he need to buy juice for 50¢?

5¢ 10¢ 25¢ NH
○ ● ○ ○

Copyright © Houghton Mifflin Company. All rights reserved. Use with text pages 405–408.

ENRICHMENT 14.7

Name _____ Date _____ Enrichment 14.7

Problem Solving Picture This

30¢ 20¢ 35¢

1. Read the Problem
Linda wants to buy a kazoo.
She has a quarter and 2 pennies.
What other coins does she need?

Think
How much money does Linda have now? __27__ ¢

Use the picture to find out how much money Linda needs.

Linda needs __30__ ¢

Now write your answer.

She needs __3__ pennies more.

2. Use the picture to write your own problem. _____
_____
_____

Write the answer to your problem. _____

Talk About It Would it also be helpful to draw a picture of the coins Linda has? Why? __Answers will vary.__

Copyright © Houghton Mifflin Company. All rights reserved. Use with text pages 405–408.

Practice Workbook Page 97

Reaching All Learners

Differentiated Instruction

English Learners

Worksheet 14.7 develops understanding of the word *need*. Children will need to understand this word in order to solve word problems about coins.

Inclusion
TACTILE, AUDITORY

Materials: *price tags, coin sets*

Display a price tag for 20¢ and have the child show 1 dime and 7 pennies. Ask how much more money is needed. Help the child show both money amounts and then add coins to the lesser amount until the amount needed is reached. Repeat with similar problems.

Gifted and Talented
TACTILE, AUDITORY

Materials: *paper plates or LT 38, coin sets*

- Make a paper plate spinner.
- Have pairs of children take turns spinning 3 times and taking the amount of money shown.
- The child with the most money wins the round.

TECHNOLOGY

Spiral Review

Using the *Ways to Assess* CD-ROM, you can create **customized** spiral review worksheets covering any lessons you choose.

Lesson Planner

Use the **Lesson Planner CD-ROM** to see how lesson objectives for this chapter are correlated to standards.

Intervention

Use the *Ways to Success* intervention software to support students who need more help in understanding the concepts and skills taught in this chapter.

Ways to Success

Literature Connection

Read *A Quarter From the Tooth Fairy* by Caren Holtzman. Display all the different coin combinations. Have children find the values. Summarize that more coins does not always mean the greater value.

MATH CENTER

Number of the Week Activity

Display the Number of the Week to motivate children to use their problem-solving skills. The exercises cover topics across all math strands.

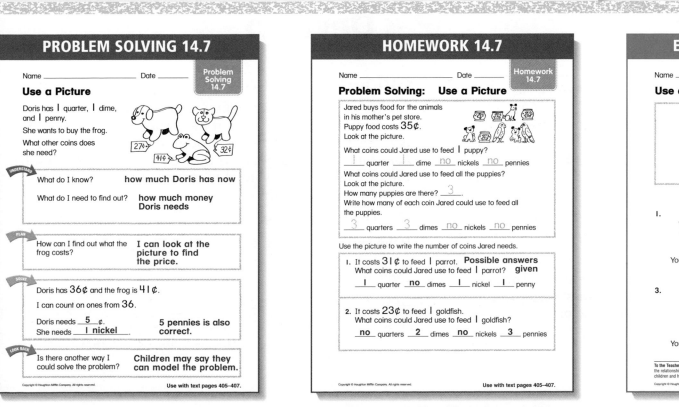

TEACHING LESSON 14.7

LESSON ORGANIZER

Objective Recognize and use data from a picture to solve a problem.

Resources Reteach, Practice, Enrichment, Problem Solving, Homework, English Learners, Transparencies, Math Center

Materials Coin sets, overhead coins, blank transparency, paper bags

Activity

Warm-Up Activity
Discuss Using a Picture

👤👤👤👤 Whole Group	🕐 10 minutes	Visual, Auditory

Materials: *coin sets, overhead coins, blank transparency*

35¢

1. Draw an orange on the transparency. Write 35¢ beneath it. **Danny has 1 quarter and 1 nickel. Can he buy an orange?** (no) Discuss why 30¢ is not enough to buy something that costs 35¢.

2. **Sharon wants to buy an orange. What coins can she use?** (1 quarter and 1 dime; 3 dimes and 1 nickel; and so on.) Call on volunteers to show 35¢ using different coin combinations.

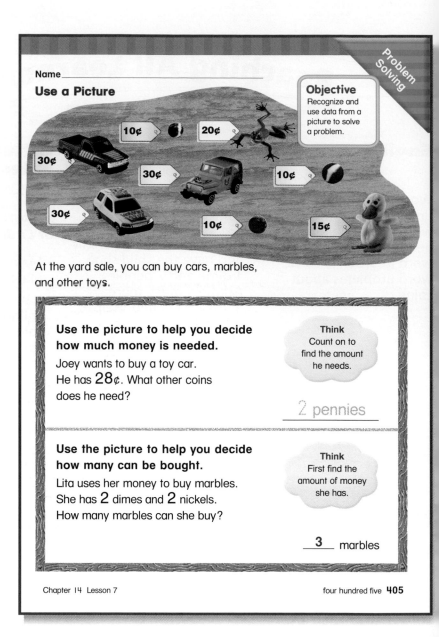

Name_____

Use a Picture

Objective Recognize and use data from a picture to solve a problem.

At the yard sale, you can buy cars, marbles, and other toys.

Use the picture to help you decide how much money is needed.

Joey wants to buy a toy car. He has 28¢. What other coins does he need?

Think Count on to find the amount he needs.

<u>2 pennies</u>

Use the picture to help you decide how many can be bought.

Lita uses her money to buy marbles. She has 2 dimes and 2 nickels. How many marbles can she buy?

Think First find the amount of money she has.

<u>3</u> marbles

Chapter 14 Lesson 7   four hundred five **405**

1 Introduce
Modeling Using a Picture

👤👤👤👤 Whole Group	🕐 10–15 minutes	Visual, Auditory

1. Draw a picture of a whistle with a price tag of 20¢. Write this problem on the board and read it aloud. **Kim wants to buy this whistle. She has 18¢. What other coins does she need?**

2. **How can you find the amount she needs?** (Count on from 18¢ until you get to 20¢; 2 pennies.) Ask a volunteer to show the coins Kim needs and explain how to solve the problem.

3. Present this problem: **Pete has 3 dimes and 2 nickels. How many whistles can he buy?** (2 whistles) Call on volunteers to explain how they got the answer.

2 Develop

Guided Learning

Teaching Example Have coin sets available for children to use to model the problems if necessary. Read the objective with children. Guide them through the example problems. Ask children to explain how they used the picture to solve the problems. Make sure students answer the questions using number of coins not cents.

Guided Practice

Have children complete **Exercises 1–2** on page 406 as you observe. Encourage children to explain how they found their answers.

Use coins and the picture to solve.

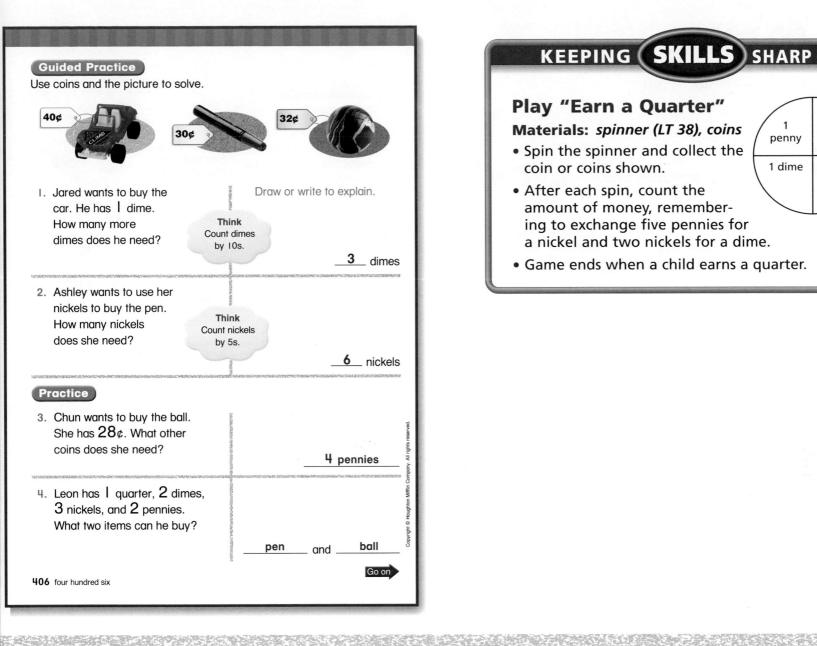

40¢
30¢
32¢

1. Jared wants to buy the car. He has 1 dime. How many more dimes does he need?

Draw or write to explain.

Think
Count dimes by 10s.

3 dimes

2. Ashley wants to use her nickels to buy the pen. How many nickels does she need?

Think
Count nickels by 5s.

6 nickels

Practice

3. Chun wants to buy the ball. She has 28¢. What other coins does she need?

4 pennies

4. Leon has 1 quarter, 2 dimes, 3 nickels, and 2 pennies. What two items can he buy?

pen and **ball**

Go on ▶

406 four hundred six

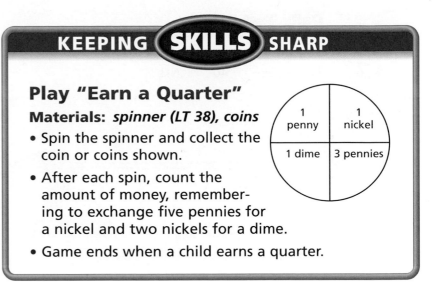

KEEPING SKILLS SHARP

Play "Earn a Quarter"

Materials: *spinner (LT 38), coins*

1 penny	1 nickel
1 dime	3 pennies

• Spin the spinner and collect the coin or coins shown.

• After each spin, count the amount of money, remembering to exchange five pennies for a nickel and two nickels for a dime.

• Game ends when a child earns a quarter.

Practice

Independent Practice

Children complete **Exercises 3–4** on page 406 independently.

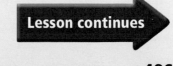

Lesson continues

Daily Test Prep

Which number comes **after** 39?

37   38   40   NH
○   ○   ●   ○

Activity

Or use
Intervention
CD-ROM
Lesson 14.7

Lesson Intervention
Finding the Value of Coins

| iii Small Group | ⏱ 5–10 minutes | Auditory, Tactile |

Materials: *coin sets, paper bags*

1. Prepare paper bags with various coins. Give each group a bag. Have a child from each group grab a small handful of coins from the bag and count to find their total value. Remind them to arrange the coins in order from greatest to least value before counting.

2. Have all children check to see that the amount is correct. The child returns the coins to the bag and gives it to someone else in the group to have a turn.

3. Continue until every child has had a turn.

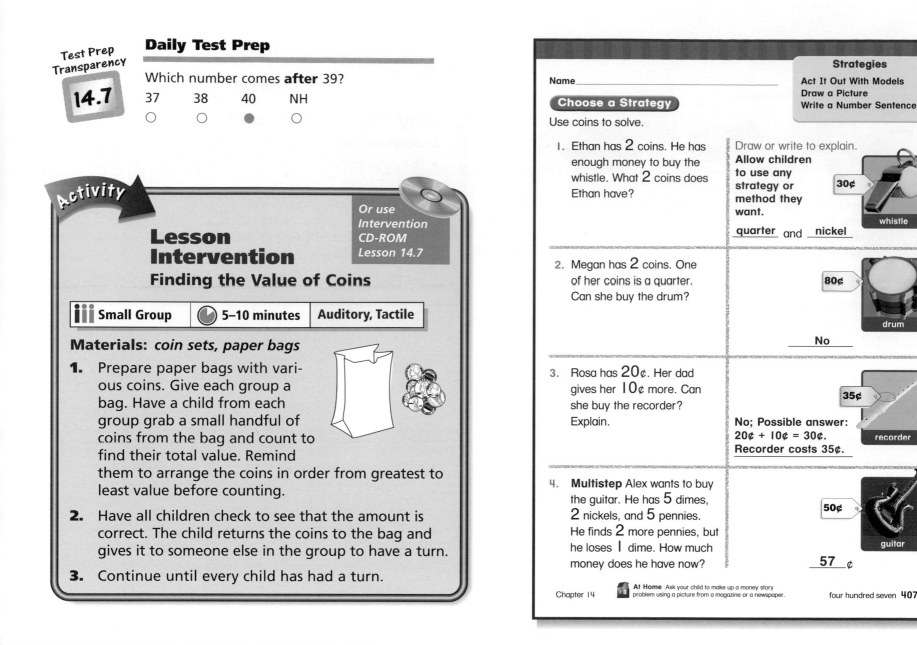

Strategies
Act It Out With Models
Draw a Picture
Write a Number Sentence

Name_____

Choose a Strategy

Use coins to solve.

Draw or write to explain.
Allow children to use any strategy or method they want.

1. Ethan has 2 coins. He has enough money to buy the whistle. What 2 coins does Ethan have?

  quarter and nickel

  30¢ whistle

2. Megan has 2 coins. One of her coins is a quarter. Can she buy the drum?

  80¢ drum

  No

3. Rosa has 20¢. Her dad gives her 10¢ more. Can she buy the recorder? Explain.

  No; Possible answer: 20¢ + 10¢ = 30¢. Recorder costs 35¢.

  35¢ recorder

4. **Multistep** Alex wants to buy the guitar. He has 5 dimes, 2 nickels, and 5 pennies. He finds 2 more pennies, but he loses 1 dime. How much money does he have now?

  57 ¢

  50¢ guitar

Chapter 14

At Home Ask your child to make up a money story problem using a picture from a magazine or a newspaper.

four hundred seven **407**

---

3 Practice

Mixed Strategy Practice

Read the problem-solving strategies with children. Make sure children can read and comprehend the problems in **Exercises 1–4** on page 407. If necessary, pair more proficient readers with less proficient readers. Encourage them to discuss the problems before solving.

Common Error

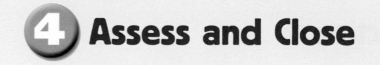

Comparing Incorrectly
Some children may incorrectly interpret that a price is the number of coins rather than the value. Have children show both amounts with coins and compare, then continue to solve the problem.

Some children may reverse the numbers in the prices. Have these children read the prices and identify the tens and ones. Ask for the amount in dimes and pennies.

4 Assess and Close

What information did the pictures in the problems give you? (items for sale and the prices) **How can you use a picture to help you solve a problem?** (Possible answer: a picture can show what the item costs. You can read the price tag and find out if there is enough money or how much more is needed to buy the item.)

Keeping a Journal

Draw a picture of a toy. Give it a price. Draw the coins you could use to buy it.

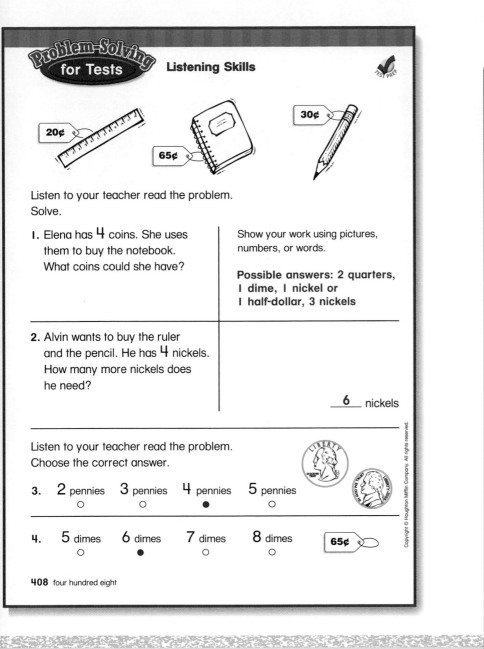

Problem-Solving for Tests

Listening Skills

20¢ **65¢** **30¢**

Listen to your teacher read the problem. Solve.

1. Elena has 4 coins. She uses them to buy the notebook. What coins could she have?

Show your work using pictures, numbers, or words.

Possible answers: 2 quarters, 1 dime, 1 nickel or 1 half-dollar, 3 nickels

2. Alvin wants to buy the ruler and the pencil. He has 4 nickels. How many more nickels does he need?

_____6_____ nickels

Listen to your teacher read the problem. Choose the correct answer.

3. 2 pennies ○   3 pennies ○   4 pennies ●   5 pennies ○

4. 5 dimes ○   6 dimes ●   7 dimes ○   8 dimes ○   **65¢**

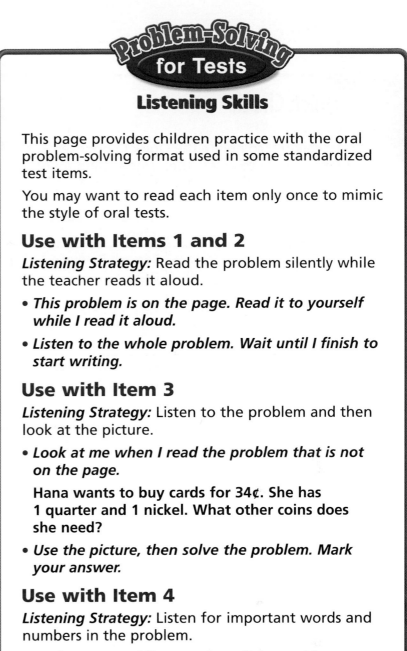

Problem-Solving for Tests

Listening Skills

This page provides children practice with the oral problem-solving format used in some standardized test items.

You may want to read each item only once to mimic the style of oral tests.

Use with Items 1 and 2

Listening Strategy: Read the problem silently while the teacher reads it aloud.

- *This problem is on the page. Read it to yourself while I read it aloud.*
- *Listen to the whole problem. Wait until I finish to start writing.*

Use with Item 3

Listening Strategy: Listen to the problem and then look at the picture.

- *Look at me when I read the problem that is not on the page.*

  Hana wants to buy cards for 34¢. She has 1 quarter and 1 nickel. What other coins does she need?

- *Use the picture, then solve the problem. Mark your answer.*

Use with Item 4

Listening Strategy: Listen for important words and numbers in the problem.

- *Look at me and listen as I read the problem.*

  Andre buys a toy that costs 65¢. He uses 1 nickel and some dimes. How many dimes does he use?

- *Use the picture to help you solve the problem. Then mark your answer.*

Quick Check

Have children complete the Quick Check exercises independently to assess their understanding of concepts and skills taught in **Lessons 5–7**.

Item	Lesson	Error Analysis	Intervention
1–2	14.5	Children may show an Incorrect combination of coins.	Reteach Resource 14.5 *Ways to Success* 14.5
3–4	14.6	Children may show different amounts of money.	Reteach Resource 14.6 *Ways to Success* 14.6
5	14.7	Children may compare incorrectly.	Reteach Resource 14.7 *Ways to Success* 14.7

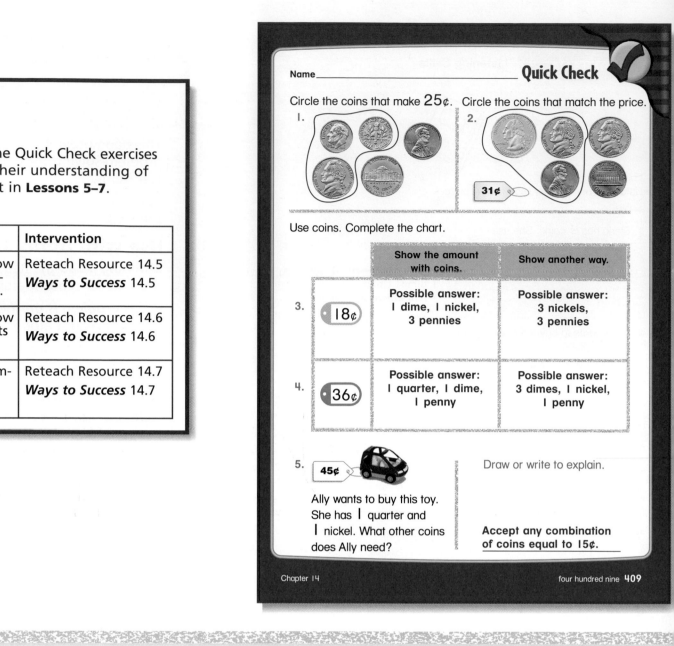

Name_____

Quick Check

Circle the coins that make 25¢.   Circle the coins that match the price.

1.

2.   31¢

Use coins. Complete the chart.

	Show the amount with coins.	Show another way.
3. 18¢	Possible answer: I dime, I nickel, 3 pennies	Possible answer: 3 nickels, 3 pennies
4. 36¢	Possible answer: I quarter, I dime, I penny	Possible answer: 3 dimes, I nickel, I penny

5. 45¢

Ally wants to buy this toy. She has I quarter and I nickel. What other coins does Ally need?

Draw or write to explain.

Accept any combination of coins equal to 15¢. _____

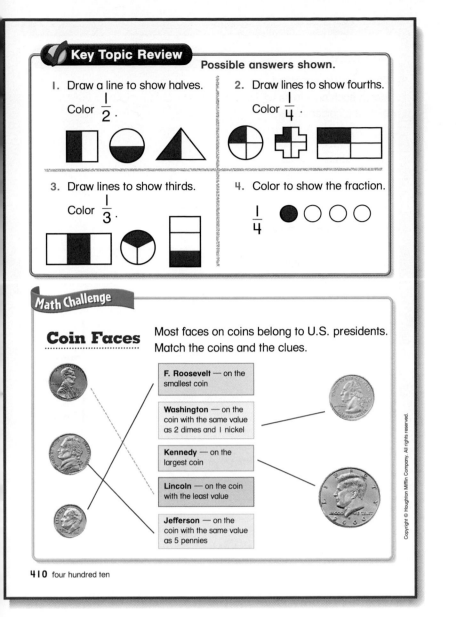

Possible answers shown.

1. Draw a line to show halves.
   Color $\frac{1}{2}$.

2. Draw lines to show fourths.
   Color $\frac{1}{4}$.

3. Draw lines to show thirds.
   Color $\frac{1}{3}$.

4. Color to show the fraction.
   $\frac{1}{4}$

Math Challenge

Coin Faces   Most faces on coins belong to U.S. presidents. Match the coins and the clues.

F. Roosevelt — on the smallest coin

Washington — on the coin with the same value as 2 dimes and 1 nickel

Kennedy — on the largest coin

Lincoln — on the coin with the least value

Jefferson — on the coin with the same value as 5 pennies

410 four hundred ten

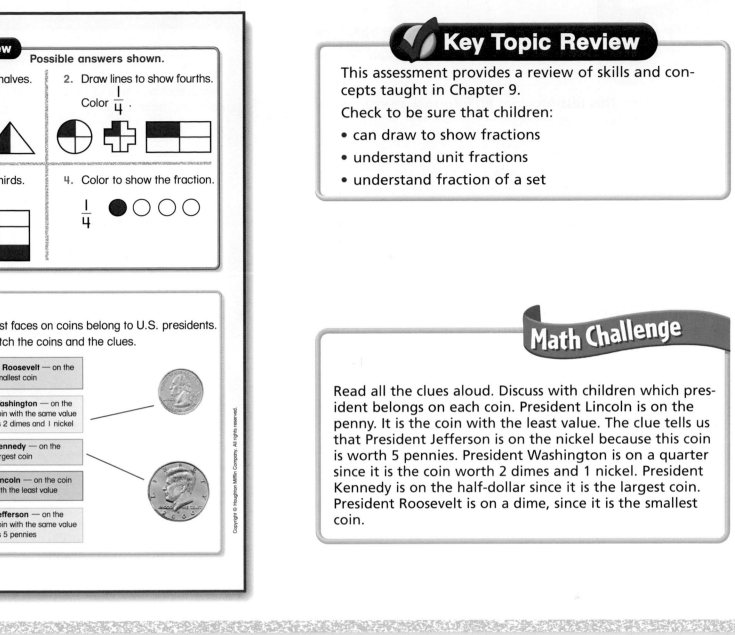

Key Topic Review

This assessment provides a review of skills and concepts taught in Chapter 9.

Check to be sure that children:

• can draw to show fractions

• understand unit fractions

• understand fraction of a set

Math Challenge

Read all the clues aloud. Discuss with children which president belongs on each coin. President Lincoln is on the penny. It is the coin with the least value. The clue tells us that President Jefferson is on the nickel because this coin is worth 5 pennies. President Washington is on a quarter since it is the coin worth 2 dimes and 1 nickel. President Kennedy is on the half-dollar since it is the largest coin. President Roosevelt is on a dime, since it is the smallest coin.

Chapter Review/Test

Purpose: This test provides an informal assessment of the Chapter 14 objectives.

Chapter Test Items 1–15

To assign a numerical grade for this Chapter Test, use 6 points for each test item and add 10 to the score.

Check Understanding

Use children's work on word problems to informally assess progress on chapter content.

Customizing Your Instruction

For children who have not yet mastered these objectives, you can use the reteaching resources listed in the chart below.

✔ **Assessment Options**

A summary test in this chapter is also provided in the Unit Resource Folder.

Reteaching Support

Chapter Test Items	Summary Test Items	Chapter Objectives Tested	TE Pages	Use These Reteaching Resources
1–5	1–3	**14A** Develop and use math vocabulary relating to money.	389A–390	Reteach Resource and *Ways to Success* CD: 14.1 Skillsheet 100
6–7	4–6	**14B** Identify coins including penny, nickel, and dime.	389A–396	Reteach Resources and *Ways to Success* CD: 14.1–14.4 Skillsheet 100
8–13	7–8	**14C** Find the value of a group of coins including pennies, nickels, dimes, and quarters and show different ways to the same amount.	391A–396, 399A–401, 403A–404	Reteach Resources and *Ways to Success* CD: 14.2–14.6 Skillsheets 101–104
14–15	9–10	**14D** Recognize and use data from a picture to solve a problem.	405A–408	Reteach Resource and *Ways to Success* CD: 14.7 Skillsheet 105

Complete the chart.

	Show the amount with coins.	Show another way.
10. **18¢**	Possible answer: I dime, 8 pennies	Possible answer: I dime, I nickel, 3 pennies
11. **25¢**	Possible answer: 2 dimes, 5 pennies	Possible answer: I quarter
12. **32¢**	Possible answer: I quarter, I nickel, 2 pennies	Possible answer: 3 dimes, 2 pennies
13. **50¢**	Possible answer: 5 dimes	Possible answer: 2 quarters

Problem Solving

Use the picture to solve.

25¢   50¢

Draw or write to explain.

14. Jed wants to buy the whistle. He has I dime. How many more dimes does he need?

___4___ more dimes

15. Ann wants to use her nickels to buy the pen. How many nickels does she need?

___5___ nickels

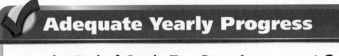

Adequate Yearly Progress

Use the End of Grade Test Prep Assessment Guide to help familiarize your children with the format of standardized tests.

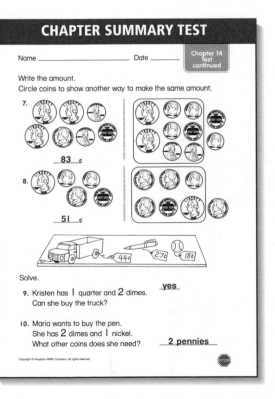

CHAPTER SUMMARY TEST

Name _____ Date _____

Chapter 14 Test continued

Write the amount.
Circle coins to show another way to make the same amount.

7. ___83___ ¢

8. ___51___ ¢

Solve.

9. Kristen has I quarter and 2 dimes. Can she buy the truck? ___yes___

10. Maria wants to buy the pen. She has 2 dimes and I nickel. What other coins does she need? ___2 pennies___

Science Connection

PURPOSE

To use a calendar to solve problems.

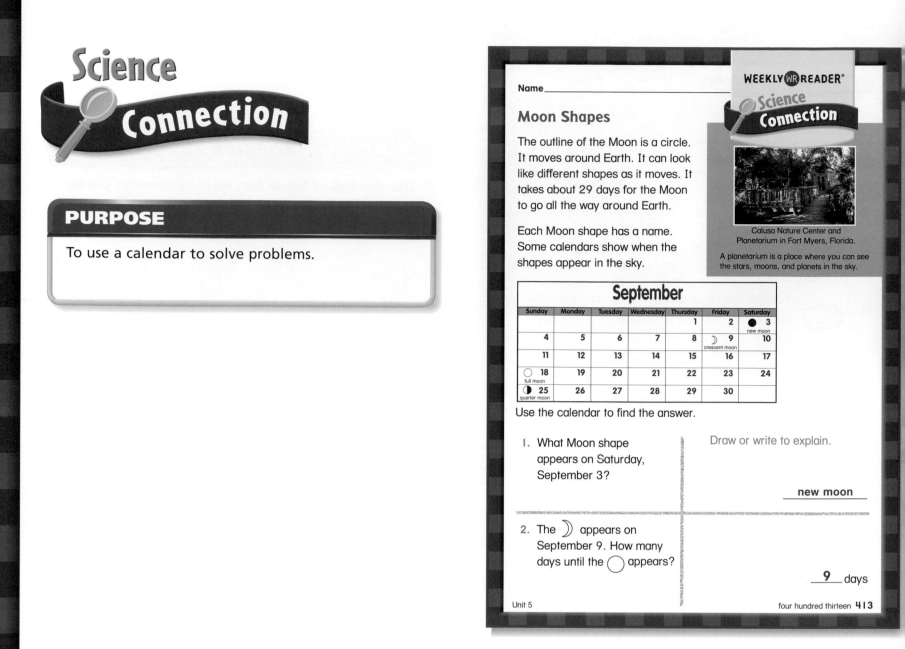

Name_____

Moon Shapes

The outline of the Moon is a circle. It moves around Earth. It can look like different shapes as it moves. It takes about 29 days for the Moon to go all the way around Earth.

Each Moon shape has a name. Some calendars show when the shapes appear in the sky.

Calusa Nature Center and Planetarium in Fort Myers, Florida.

A planetarium is a place where you can see the stars, moons, and planets in the sky.

September

Sunday	Monday	Tuesday	Wednesday	Thursday	Friday	Saturday
				1	2	● 3 new moon
4	5	6	7	8	9 crescent moon	10
11	12	13	14	15	16	17
18 full moon	19	20	21	22	23	24
25 quarter moon	26	27	28	29	30	

Use the calendar to find the answer.

1. What Moon shape appears on Saturday, September 3?

   Draw or write to explain.

   new moon

2. The 🌙 appears on September 9. How many days until the ○ appears?

   9 days

Unit 5   four hundred thirteen **413**

Using These Pages

Discussion Topics

- Tell children that people in China sometimes use a lunar calendar, which is based on the phases of the moon. Each month begins with a new moon.

- **Look at the September calendar. Which date would begin a new month on a lunar calendar?** (September 3)

- **Look at the May calendar. Which date would begin a new month on a lunar calendar?** (May 8)

- Refer children to the May calendar. **How many days are there from the new moon until the next crescent moon?** (4 days) Practice counting the days and tell children that we do not include the first day when counting. Begin counting with May 9.

May

Sun.	Mon.	Tues.	Wed.	Thurs.	Fri.	Sat.
1	2	3	☾ 4 crescent moon	5	6	7
● 8 new moon	9	10	11	☽ 12 crescent moon	13	14
15	◐ 16 quarter moon	17	18	19	20	21
22	○ 23 full moon	24	25	26	27	28
29	◑ 30 quarter moon	31				

Calendars help people follow the different shapes of the Moon each month.

Use the calendar to find the answer.

Draw or write to explain.

1. What day of the week is the ● ?

Sun. or Sunday

2. What Moon shape appears on May 23?

full moon

3. What Moon shape appears on the second Thursday of the month?

crescent moon

🖥 **Technology**
Visit *Education Place* at **eduplace.com/kids/mw/** to learn more about this topic.

414 four hundred fourteen

Wrap Up the Unit Project

- List scores for the coin toss. Make a table to show how many children got each score listed.

- Display the list of names and guesses. Discuss the guesses that came closest to the actual amount, and invite children to share their guessing strategies.

Charlotte	30
Aaron	32
Joy	25
Micah	42
Omar	35
Kim	15
Mike	20

- As children observe the clay shapes, point out different ways children made the same shapes.

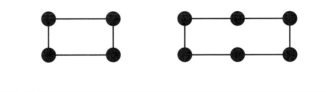

Unit 5 Test

PURPOSE

This test provides an informal assessment of the Unit 5 objectives.

Unit Test Items 1–15

To assign a numerical grade for this Unit Test, use 6 points for each test item and add 10 to the score.

Customizing Your Instruction

For children who have not yet mastered these objectives, you can use the **Reteaching Resources** listed in the chart below. *Ways to Success* is Houghton Mifflin's Intervention program available in CD-ROM and blackline master formats.

Name_____

Unit 5 Test

Vocabulary *e Glossary*
Complete the sentence.

| minute |
| half-hour |
| nickel |
| quarter |

1. 25¢ is equal to 1 ___quarter___.
2. A ___half-hour___ is 30 minutes long.
3. There are 60 seconds in 1 ___minute___.
4. A ___nickel___ is equal to 5¢.

Concepts and Skills
Read the clock.
Write the time two ways.

5. [clock] 4:00
___4___ o'clock

6. [clock] 7:30
half past ___7___

Write how long the activity takes.

7. Start End
2:00 3:00
___1___ hour

8. Start End
8:00 11:00
___3___ hours

Find the value of the coins.

9. [coins] ___28___ ¢

Reteaching Support

Unit Test Item			Unit Objectives Tested	TE Pages	Use These Reteaching Resources
p.415–416 2, 5–6	Tests A & B 2–7	5A	Tell time to the hour and half-hour using analog and digital clocks.	363A–367, 373A–374	Reteach Resources and *Ways to Success*, 13.3, 13.4, 13.6
3, 7–8	1, 9, 18–21	5B	Compare time, order events, and determine elapsed time.	369A–371	Reteach Resource and *Ways to Success*, 13.5
11–13	8–9	5C	Use a calendar.	375A–378	Reteach Resources and *Ways to Success*, 13.7, 13.8
4, 9–10	14, 16, 22–25	5D	Find the value of a group of coins including pennies, nickels, and dimes.	389A–396	Reteach Resources and *Ways to Success*, 14.1–14.4
1, 14	15, 17	5E	Show the same amount in different ways including ways to make $0.25.	399A–401, 403A–404	Reteach Resources and *Ways to Success*, 14.5, 14.6
15	18–25	5F	Apply skills and strategies to solve problems.	405A–408	Reteach Resource and *Ways to Success*, 14.7

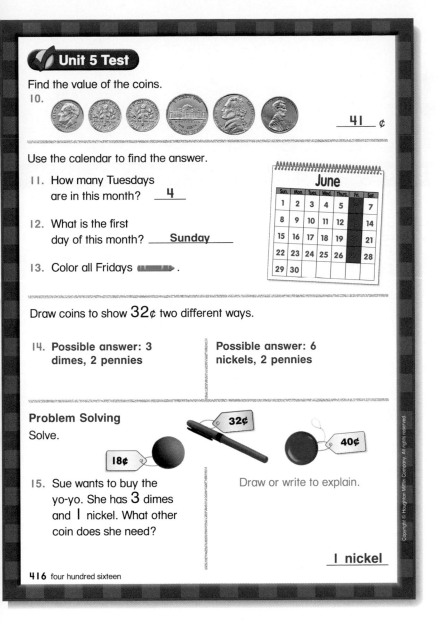

Unit 5 Test

Find the value of the coins.

10. _____41_____ ¢

Use the calendar to find the answer.

11. How many Tuesdays are in this month? ___4___

12. What is the first day of this month? ___Sunday___

13. Color all Fridays .

June

Sun.	Mon.	Tues.	Wed.	Thurs.	Fri.	Sat.
1	2	3	4	5	6	7
8	9	10	11	12	13	14
15	16	17	18	19	20	21
22	23	24	25	26	27	28
29	30					

Draw coins to show 32¢ two different ways.

14. Possible answer: 3 dimes, 2 pennies

Possible answer: 6 nickels, 2 pennies

Problem Solving
Solve.

18¢   32¢   40¢

15. Sue wants to buy the yo-yo. She has 3 dimes and 1 nickel. What other coin does she need?

Draw or write to explain.

_____I nickel_____

416 four hundred sixteen

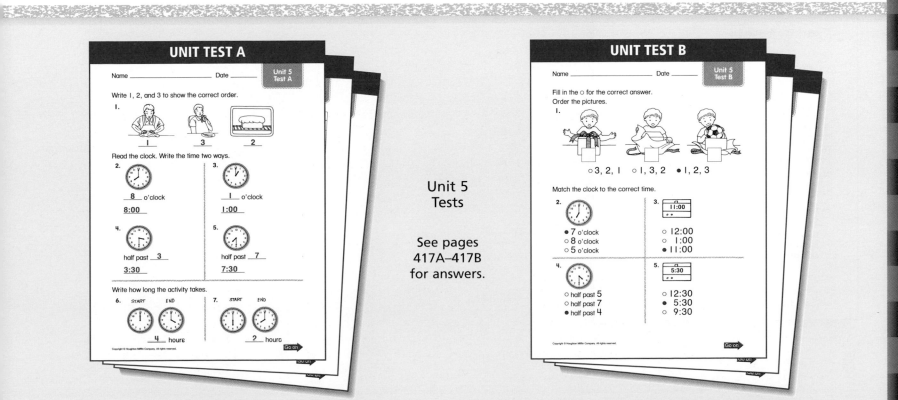

Assessment Options

Formal Tests for this unit are also provided in the Unit Resource Folder.

- **Unit 5 Test A (Open Response)**
- **Unit 5 Test B (Multiple Choice)**

Performance Assessment

You may want to use the Performance Assessment instead of, or in addition to, the Unit Test. Three Performance Assessment tasks can be found on Student Book pages 265–266.

Adequate Yearly Progress

Use the **End of Grade Test Prep Assessment Guide** to help familiarize your children with the format of standardized tests.

Unit 5 Tests

See pages 417A–417B for answers.

Unit Test Answers: Form A

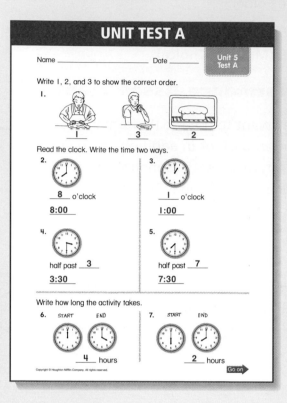

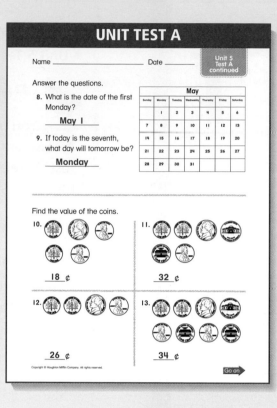

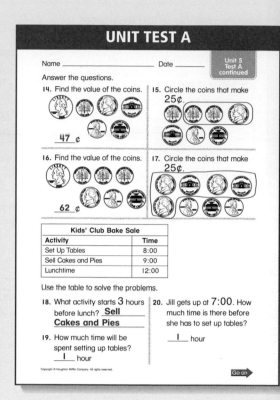

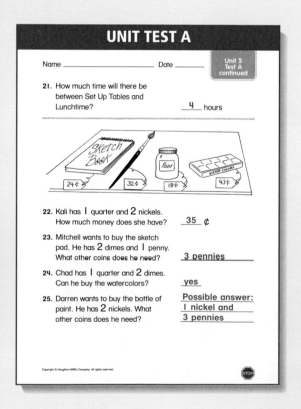

Unit Test Answers: Form B

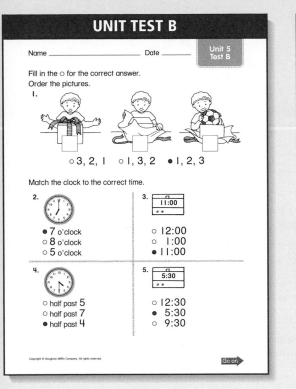

UNIT TEST B

Name _____ Date _____ Unit 5 Test B

Fill in the ○ for the correct answer.
Order the pictures.

1.

○ 3, 2, 1   ○ 1, 3, 2   ● 1, 2, 3

Match the clock to the correct time.

2.
● 7 o'clock
○ 8 o'clock
○ 5 o'clock

3. 11:00
○ 12:00
○ 1:00
● 11:00

4.
○ half past 5
○ half past 7
● half past 4

5. 5:30
○ 12:30
● 5:30
○ 9:30

Go on

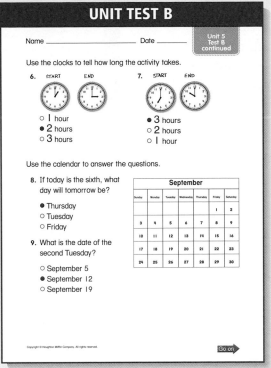

UNIT TEST B

Name _____ Date _____ Unit 5 Test B continued

Use the clocks to tell how long the activity takes.

6. START   END
○ 1 hour
● 2 hours
○ 3 hours

7. START   END
● 3 hours
○ 2 hours
○ 1 hour

Use the calendar to answer the questions.

8. If today is the sixth, what day will tomorrow be?
● Thursday
○ Tuesday
○ Friday

September						
Sunday	Monday	Tuesday	Wednesday	Thursday	Friday	Saturday
					1	2
3	4	5	6	7	8	9
10	11	12	13	14	15	16
17	18	19	20	21	22	23
24	25	26	27	28	29	30

9. What is the date of the second Tuesday?
○ September 5
● September 12
○ September 19

Go on

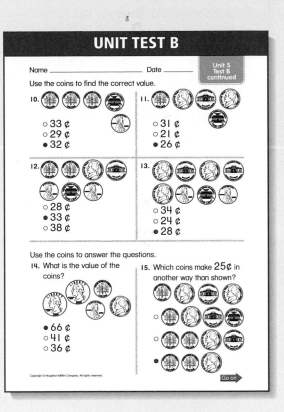

UNIT TEST B

Name _____ Date _____ Unit 5 Test B continued

Use the coins to find the correct value.

10.
○ 33 ¢
○ 29 ¢
● 32 ¢

11.
○ 31 ¢
○ 21 ¢
● 26 ¢

12.
○ 28 ¢
● 33 ¢
○ 38 ¢

13.
● 34 ¢
○ 24 ¢
○ 28 ¢

Use the coins to answer the questions.

14. What is the value of the coins?
● 66 ¢
○ 41 ¢
○ 36 ¢

15. Which coins make 25¢ in another way than shown?
○
○
●

Go on

UNIT TEST B

Name _____ Date _____ Unit 5 Test B continued

16. What is the value of the coins?
○ 48 ¢
● 58 ¢
○ 53 ¢

17. Which coins make 25¢ in another way than shown?
○
○
●

Use the table to solve the problems.

18. What activity starts 3 hours before lunch?
○ How to Use a Camera
● How to Take Great Photos
○ How to Smile for the Camera

Photo Club Schedule	
Activity	Time
How to Use a Camera	8:00
How to Take Great Photos	9:00
Lunchtime	12:00

19. How much time will be spent learning how to use a camera?
○ 2 hours   ● 1 hour   ○ 3 hours

Go on

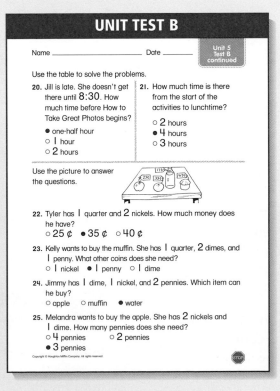

UNIT TEST B

Name _____ Date _____ Unit 5 Test B continued

Use the table to solve the problems.

20. Jill is late. She doesn't get there until 8:30. How much time before How to Take Great Photos begins?
● one-half hour
○ 1 hour
○ 2 hours

21. How much time is there from the start of the activities to lunchtime?
○ 2 hours
● 4 hours
○ 3 hours

Use the picture to answer the questions.

22. Tyler has 1 quarter and 2 nickels. How much money does he have?
○ 25 ¢   ● 35 ¢   ○ 40 ¢

23. Kelly wants to buy the muffin. She has 1 quarter, 2 dimes, and 1 penny. What other coins does she need?
○ 1 nickel   ● 1 penny   ○ 1 dime

24. Jimmy has 1 dime, 1 nickel, and 2 pennies. Which item can he buy?
○ apple   ○ muffin   ● water

25. Melandra wants to buy the apple. She has 2 nickels and 1 dime. How many pennies does she need?
○ 4 pennies   ○ 2 pennies
● 3 pennies

STOP

Performance Assessment

PURPOSE

This assessment focuses on time and money. Children should be able to tell time to the hour and half-hour using analog and digital clocks. They should be able to find the value of a group of coins and apply skills and strategies to solve problems.

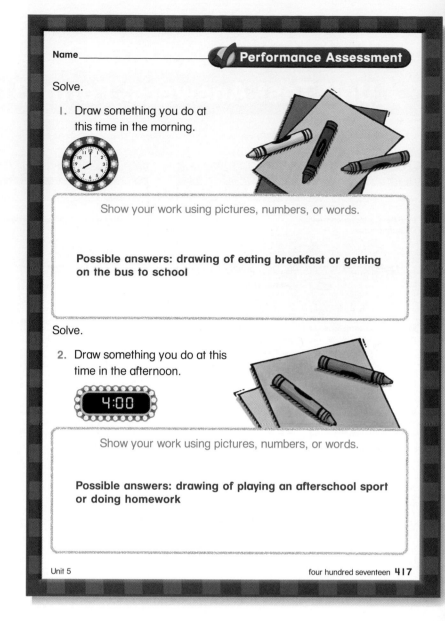

Solve.

1. Draw something you do at this time in the morning.

Show your work using pictures, numbers, or words.

Possible answers: drawing of eating breakfast or getting on the bus to school

Solve.

2. Draw something you do at this time in the afternoon.

Show your work using pictures, numbers, or words.

Possible answers: drawing of playing an afterschool sport or doing homework

Unit 5   four hundred seventeen **417**

Using These Pages

- Show a display clock and have children take turns moving the clock hands on an analog clock (LT 33) to show 10 o'clock, 12 o'clock, 3:30 and so on. **What time is it? How do you know?** (Children should be able to read the clock and tell where the short hand and long hand points.) Write each time on the board as it would appear on a digital clock and have the children read it aloud.

- Display 2 quarters and 1 dime. **How much money do I have?** (60 cents) **What other coins could I use to show 60 cents?** Allow children to work in small groups with coin sets to show 60 cents in at least 5 different ways.

- Direct children's attention to assessment tasks. You may wish to read the directions aloud to the children.

- Observe children as they work to complete the tasks.

Exercise One

In Exercise 1, children should be able to tell time to the hour on an analog clock and know the time it shows. (8 o'clock) They should be able to associate 8:00 with a certain time of day (in the Morning) and think of something they do at that time.

Solve.

3. Julie wants to buy a box of chalk. She has **2** dimes. How many more dimes does she need?

40¢

CHALK

Show your work using pictures, numbers, or words.

Possible answers: She has 2 dimes or 20¢.
She needs 2 more dimes to have 40¢; drawing of 4 dimes.

__2__ more dimes

Assessing Student Work

Use the **Scoring Rubric** to evaluate children's performance on these tasks.

Scoring Rubric

4 EXEMPLARY

Tells time on analog and digital clocks correctly and applies skills and strategies to solve problems involving money correctly.

3 PROFICIENT

Tells time on analog and digital clocks correctly. Solution to problems demonstrate mathematical reasoning, although the reasoning is faulty.

2 ACCEPTABLE

Tells time on analog and digital clocks correctly. Solution to problems is incomplete.

I LIMITED

Tells time on analog or digital clock incorrectly. Solution to problems shows no mathematical reasoning.

Exercise Two

In Exercise 2, children should be able to read a digital clock. (4 o'clock) They should also be able to think about 4 o'clock as a time of day in the afternoon and tell about something they typically do at that time.

Exercise Three

In Exercise 3, children should be able to use dimes to show the given value and solve the problem.
(2 more dimes)

UNIT 5

Enrichment

▶ Dollar

PURPOSE

This page provides an opportunity for children to apply their understanding of the value of coins to one dollar.

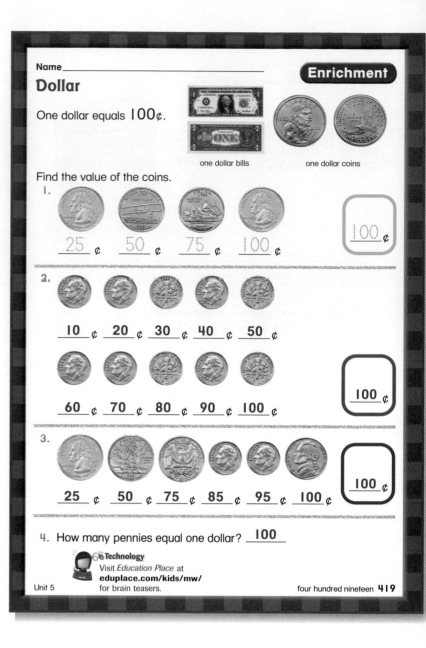

Using This Page

Discussion Topics

- This page extends Chapter 14, Lessons 4 and 5, by having children find different ways to make one dollar.

- Explain to children that there are many different combinations of coins that equal 100 cents, or one dollar.

- You may want to review coin names and values by holding up different coins, and having volunteers name the coins and their values.

- Point out that children will be using mental math to find the value of the coins. **What strategies can you use?** (Count on by 25, 10, 5, or 1.)

- Have children work individually or in pairs to complete the page. In pairs, children take turns solving the exercises and then check each other's work. Provide coins for those students who may need to use them.

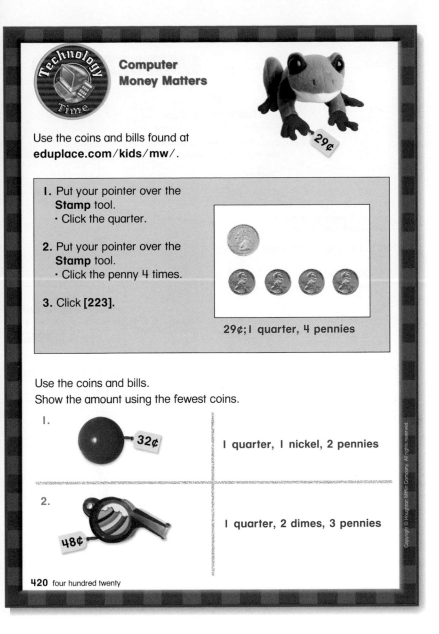

Computer
Money Matters

Use the coins and bills found at
eduplace.com/kids/mw/.

1. Put your pointer over the
Stamp tool.
· Click the quarter.

2. Put your pointer over the
Stamp tool.
· Click the penny 4 times.

3. Click **[223]**.

29¢; 1 quarter, 4 pennies

Use the coins and bills.
Show the amount using the fewest coins.

1.
32¢ | 1 quarter, 1 nickel, 2 pennies

2.
48¢ | 1 quarter, 2 dimes, 3 pennies

420 four hundred twenty

MONEY MATTERS

PURPOSE

To provide an opportunity for children to use a
computer when working with money.

Using This Page

Discussion Topics

● This is another way for the children to work with
the value of coins and counting money.

● You may want to review how to move the cursor.

● Work through the example with the children. **How
many pennies are in one quarter?** (25 pennies) **How
many nickels equal one dime?** (2 nickels) **What
other coins equal one dime?** (2 nickels; 10 pennies; 1
nickel and 5 pennies)

● Read the remaining questions and allow time
for the children to complete. When the page is
complete, have children share answers with
a partner.

Cumulative Test Prep

▶ Practice Test

PURPOSE

This page will familiarize children with the multiple-choice and open-response formats of many standardized state tests. Children can mark their responses directly on these pages. You may wish to read each multiple-choice test item and the answer choices aloud to the children.

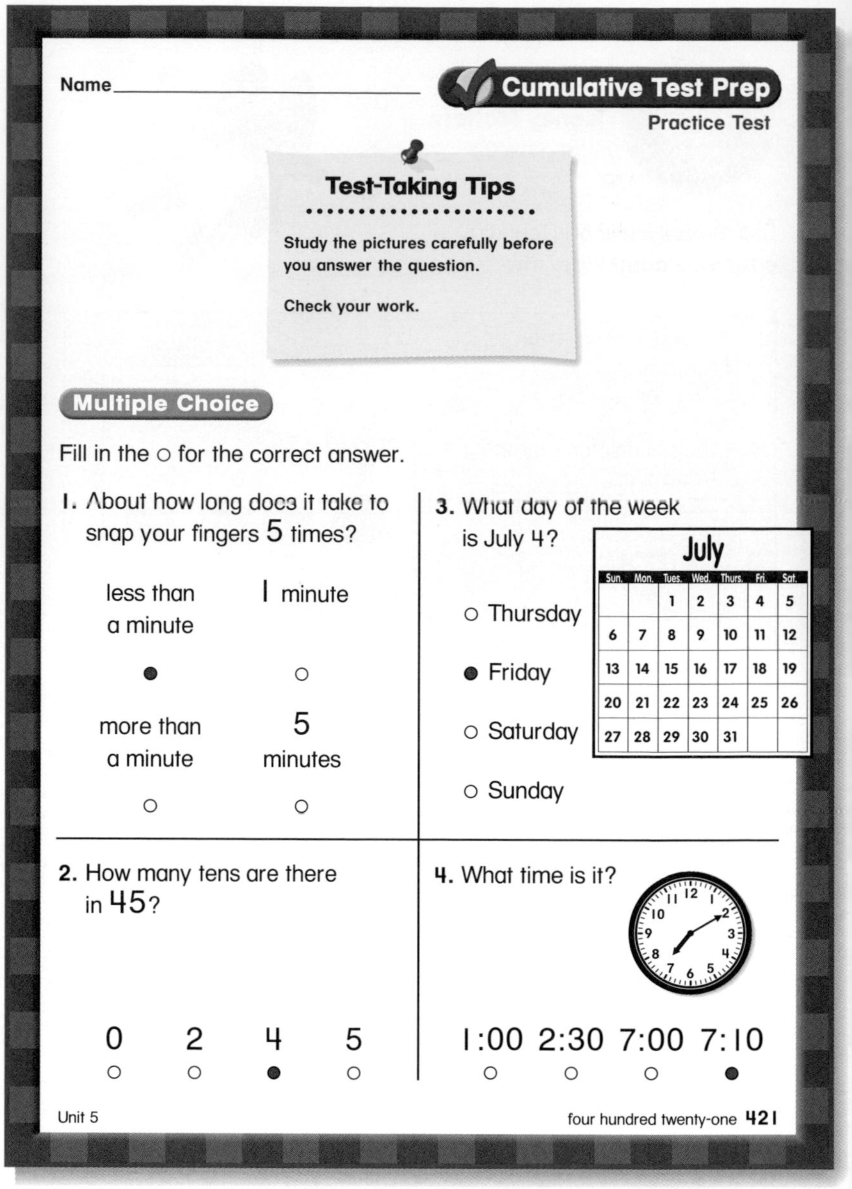

Name_____

Cumulative Test Prep
Practice Test

Test-Taking Tips
· ·
Study the pictures carefully before you answer the question.

Check your work.

Multiple Choice

Fill in the ○ for the correct answer.

1. About how long does it take to snap your fingers 5 times?

less than a minute	1 minute
●	○

more than a minute	5 minutes
○	○

3. What day of the week is July 4?

July						
Sun.	Mon.	Tues.	Wed.	Thurs.	Fri.	Sat.
		1	2	3	4	5
6	7	8	9	10	11	12
13	14	15	16	17	18	19
20	21	22	23	24	25	26
27	28	29	30	31		

○ Thursday

● Friday

○ Saturday

○ Sunday

2. How many tens are there in 45?

0	2	4	5
○	○	●	○

4. What time is it?

1:00	2:30	7:00	7:10
○	○	○	●

Unit 5   four hundred twenty-one **421**

Test-Taking TIPS

Review the test-taking tips with children before they begin the test. Remind children to look at each picture carefully before they fill in their answer.

- Encourage children to rule out unreasonable answers first.
- Review words that provide important information in test items, such as *more than, less than, most, in all*.

- Discuss with children some of the ways they can check their work.
- Remind children to answer every question on a test, even if they are unsure of the correct answer.

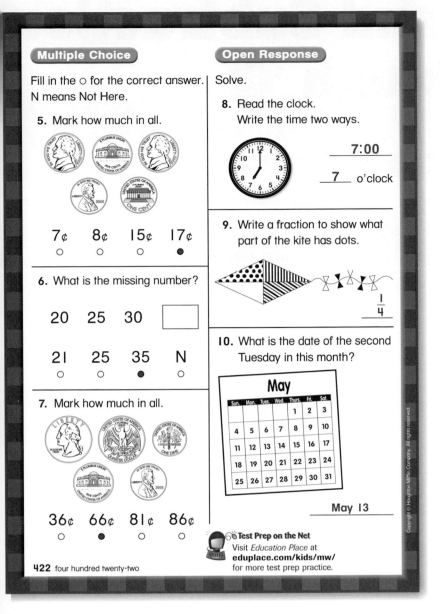

Multiple Choice

Fill in the ○ for the correct answer.
N means Not Here.

5. Mark how much in all.

    7¢   8¢   15¢   17¢
    ○   ○   ○   ●

6. What is the missing number?

20   25   30 ☐

21   25   35   N
○   ○   ●   ○

7. Mark how much in all.

36¢   66¢   81¢   86¢
○   ●   ○   ○

Open Response

Solve.

8. Read the clock.
Write the time two ways.

    <u> 7:00 </u>

    <u> 7 </u> o'clock

9. Write a fraction to show what part of the kite has dots.

$\frac{1}{4}$

10. What is the date of the second Tuesday in this month?

May

Sun.	Mon.	Tues.	Wed.	Thurs.	Fri.	Sat.
					1	2
3						
4	5	6	7	8	9	10
11	12	13	14	15	16	17
18	19	20	21	22	23	24
25	26	27	28	29	30	31

<u> May 13 </u>

Test Prep on the Net
Visit *Education Place* at
eduplace.com/kids/mw/
for more test prep practice.

Test-Taking Vocabulary

- Have a volunteer point out *minute hand* and *hour hand* on a clock. Discuss activities that take about a minute or about an hour.

- Have one volunteer name the months of the year and another tell the days of the week. **What is today's date? What was yesterday's date? What will the date be tomorrow?**

- Review coin names with children. Have volunteers identify and tell the value of *penny, nickel, dime,* and *quarter.*

National and state tests may use these words when talking about finding the value of a group of coins:

- *altogether*
- *together*
- *all together*

UNIT 6

Addition and Subtraction Facts Through 12

Unit at a Glance

Assessment System

Assessing Prior Knowledge

Check whether children understand the prerequisite concepts and skills.

- **CHAPTER PRETEST** (Unit Resource Folder or *Ways to Success* Intervention CD-ROM)
- **WARM-UP ACTIVITY:** Every TE Lesson
- **UNIT LITERATURE ACTIVITY:** PE p. 424

Ongoing Assessment

Monitor whether children are acquiring new concepts and skills.

- **PROBLEM OF THE DAY:** First page of every TE lesson
- **QUICK REVIEW:** First page of every TE lesson
- **LESSON QUIZ:** First page of every TE lesson
- **COMMON ERROR:** Every TE Lesson
- **QUICK CHECK:** PE pp. 438, 451, 464, 477
- **KEY TOPIC REVIEW:** PE pp. 452, 478

 Test Prep and Practice

Help children prepare for state and standardized tests.

- **DAILY TEST PREP:** Every TE Lesson
- **CUMULATIVE TEST PREP:** PE pp. 491–492
- **PROBLEM SOLVING FOR TESTS:** PE pp. 450, 476
- **TEST PREP ON THE NET:** eduplace.com/kids/mw
- **TEST-TAKING STRATEGIES:** eduplace.com/math/mw

Summary Assessment

Assess children's mastery of new concepts and skills.

- **CHAPTER TEST:**
    - ✔ PE pp. 453–454, 479–480
    - ✔ Unit Resource Folder
- **UNIT TEST:**
    - ✔ PE pp. 485–486
    - ✔ Test A, Unit Resource Folder
    - ✔ Test B, Unit Resource Folder

TEST TIPS Student Self-Assessment

Allow children to evaluate their own understanding.

- **EXPLAIN YOUR THINKING:** PE pp. 429, 431, 433, 435, 439, 443, 445, 457, 459, 461, 465, 467, 469, 471

Performance Assessment

Evaluate children's ability to use mathematics in real-world situations.

PERFORMANCE ASSESSMENT: PE pp. 487–488
WRITE ABOUT IT OR TALK ABOUT IT: in Hands-On lessons
WRITING MATH: CREATE AND SOLVE: PE p. 437

Technology Options

Use computer-based assessment to make testing and reporting easier.

- **WAYS TO ASSESS** (CD-ROM, LAN, or Web spiral review and test creation, administration, scoring, and report generation)
- **LEARNER PROFILE** (observations, evaluations, and reports from your handheld or desktop computer)

Reaching All Learners

Resources	On Level Students	Extra Support Students	English Learners	Inclusion/ Special Needs	Advanced Learners	Mathematically Promising
Student Editions						
Building Vocabulary	●	●	●	●	●	●
Guided Practice ✱	●	●	●	●	●	●
MathTracks MP3 Audio CD	●	●	○	○		
Teacher's Editions						
Building Vocabulary Strategies	●	●	○	○	●	○
Teacher Support	●	○	●		○	○
Intervention Activities	○	●	●	●		
Other Resources						
Chapter Challenges	○				●	●
Combination Classroom Guide	●	●	●	●	●	●
English Learners Handbook	○	○	●	○		
Ways to Success CD-ROM	○	●	●	●		

KEY   ● **Highly Appropriate**   ○ **Appropriate**   ✱ **Scaffolded Instruction**

Documenting Adequate Yearly Progress
National Test Correlations

UNIT 6 Objectives		ITBS	Terra Nova (CTBS)	CAT	SAT	MAT
6A	Use addition strategies to find sums through 12 and to add three addends.	●	●	●	●	●
6B	Find a missing addend.	●		●	●	●
6C	Use subtraction strategies to subtract from 12 or less.	●	●	●	●	●
6D	Use related facts and fact families to solve addition and subtraction problems.	●	●	●	●	●
6E	Apply skills and strategies to solve problems.	●	●	●	●	●

Activities for Reaching All Learners

Home-School Activity

Fact Family Fishing

Materials: fact family cards: one fact per card (different fact family for each player)

Shuffle and distribute 4 cards to each player. Players try to collect all 4 cards in one fact family. One player begins by asking any player for a specific fact. If the player has the fact, he or she gives it up and receives any card in return. Play continues until one player has a full fact family.

Unit Vocabulary Activity

Sum or Difference Spin

Materials: 2 sets of number cards 1–9; 2-part spinner labeled: sum, difference

Each child picks 2 cards. One child spins the spinner. If the word "sum" is spun, the child adds the 2 cards. If the word "difference" is spun, each child subtracts the 2 cards. Children compare the results. The child with the greatest sum or difference wins the round.

Remediation

MathTracks Lessons 15.1, 15.6, 15.7, 16.1, 16.4, 16.7, 16.8

Use the MathTracks CD-ROM to help children who need a quick review or extra support for the lesson, to provide children who were absent with complete lesson presentation, or to assist children with reading difficulties.

Intervention

Ways to Success CD-ROM

Use the Ways to Success CD-ROM to help children who need extra help with lessons. This software is designed to reteach the lesson objective, provide extra guided and independent practice, and if needed, reteach a key prerequisite skill.

Unit Project

Around the World Math Games

Math Topics:

- use addition strategies to find sums through 12
- find the sum of three one-digit numbers
- count back to subtract
- solve subtraction facts from 12

To Begin

- Children will play two different games from around the world. They will use their addition and subtraction skills as they play each game.

Ongoing

- Explain to children that one game they will learn to play is from West Africa. It is called Haba Gaba. For instructions on how to play this addition game, see page 427D, Chapter 15, for Connecting to the Unit Project.
- The other game children will learn to play is originally from Egypt. It is a bowling game. For instructions on how to play this subtraction game, see page 455D, Chapter 16, for Connecting to the Unit Project.

To Finish

- Discuss the responses to these questions: Could you have played Haba Gaba if you didn't know how to add? Could you have played the bowling game if you didn't know how to subtract?
- See page 484 to Wrap Up the Unit Project.

Starting Unit 6
Accessing Prior Knowledge

UNIT 6

Addition and Subtraction Facts Through 12

From the Read-Aloud Anthology

Twenty Is Too Many

Kate Duke

Access Prior Knowledge
This story will help you review
· Addition facts
· Subtraction facts

423a

Nine waving guinea pigs
minus one swinging guinea pig

423b from *Twenty Is Too Many*

Accessing Prior Knowledge

In Unit 2, children:

• understand addition and subtraction facts through 10

• use addition strategies

• use subtraction strategies

This selection from the Unit Opener gives you the opportunity to review some of these prerequisite skills.

• You may wish to review addition facts through 10 by saying a number and having volunteers tell the different ways to make the number.

• You may also wish to review subtraction facts by calling out facts and having volunteers solve them.

Story Summary

Today you will be reading a story about guinea pigs. The title of the story is *Twenty Is Too Many*. The author is Kate Duke.

Reading the Story

You can find the entire text of the book at the end of the Teacher's Edition on page T56.
Read the selection aloud to the children. Then read it again, having children raise their hands when you come to the word that tells which operation they should use.

This story is available in the Read-Aloud Anthology, Volume 3

leaves eight seasick guinea pigs.
9 – 1 = 8

423c

Literature Activity

Name _____

Use the pictures on pages 423b and 423c.
Count.

1. How many guinea pigs are in the boat?

    7 guinea pigs

2. How many guinea pigs are outside the boat?

    2 guinea pigs

3. How many guinea pigs are there in all?

    7 + **2** = **9**

    9 guinea pigs

Complete the sentence.

4. One swinging guinea pig is looking at 8 waving guinea pigs. How many guinea pigs are there altogether?

    1 + **8** = **9**

    9 guinea pigs

5. Eight waving guinea pigs are looking at 1 swinging guinea pig. How many guinea pigs are there in all?

    8 + **1** = **9**

    9 guinea pigs

6. How many guinea pigs are left when the one guinea pig swings away?

    9 – **1** = **8**

    8 guinea pigs

424

Unit Bibliography

The Eentsy, Weentsy, Spider: Fingerplays and Action Rhymes
by Joanna Cole and Stephanie Calmenson

The Grapes of Math by Greg Tang

one less fish
by Kim Michelle Toft and Allan Sheather

Sea Sums by Joy N. Hulme

So Many Cats! by Beatrice Schenk de Regniers

12 Ways to Get to 11 by Eve Merriam

Twenty Is Too Many by Kate Duke

See also the **Math and Literature Bibliography** in the Teacher Support Handbook at the back of this Teacher's Edition.

Literature Activity

Purpose: This activity provides an opportunity to informally assess children's understanding of addition and subtraction facts through 12.

Using This Page
- Observe children as they work to complete Exercises 1–3. **What operation do we use to find how many in all?** (addition)
- After children complete Exercises 4–6, discuss what they noticed about the numbers. **How are the number sentences alike?** (They use the same three numbers.) **How are they different?** (The order of the numbers and the operations are different.)

Math At Home

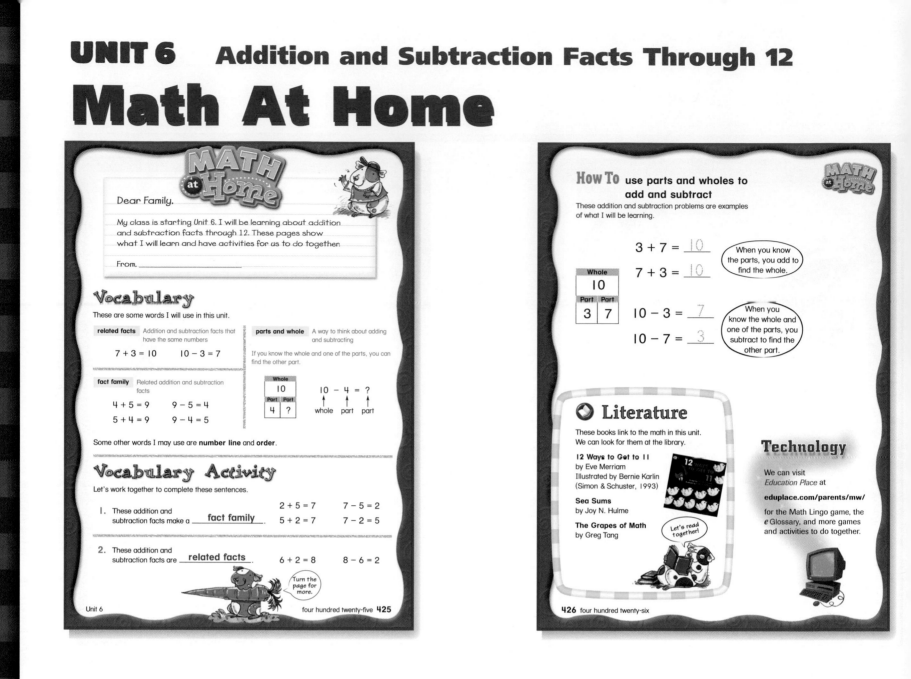

Math at Home

Dear Family,

My class is starting Unit 6. I will be learning about addition and subtraction facts through 12. These pages show what I will learn and have activities for us to do together.

From. _____

Vocabulary

These are some words I will use in this unit.

related facts Addition and subtraction facts that have the same numbers

$7 + 3 = 10$ $10 - 3 = 7$

parts and whole A way to think about adding and subtracting

If you know the whole and one of the parts, you can find the other part.

Whole	
10	
Part	Part
4	?

$10 - 4 = ?$
whole part part

fact family Related addition and subtraction facts

$4 + 5 = 9$ $9 - 5 = 4$
$5 + 4 = 9$ $9 - 4 = 5$

Some other words I may use are **number line** and **order**.

Vocabulary Activity

Let's work together to complete these sentences.

1. These addition and subtraction facts make a ___**fact family**___

   $2 + 5 = 7$ $7 - 5 = 2$
   $5 + 2 = 7$ $7 - 2 = 5$

2. These addition and subtraction facts are ___**related facts**___

   $6 + 2 = 8$ $8 - 6 = 2$

Turn the page for more.

Unit 6   four hundred twenty-five **425**

How To use parts and wholes to add and subtract

These addition and subtraction problems are examples of what I will be learning.

$3 + 7 = \underline{10}$

$7 + 3 = \underline{10}$

When you know the parts, you add to find the whole.

Whole	
10	
Part	Part
3	7

$10 - 3 = \underline{7}$

$10 - 7 = \underline{3}$

When you know the whole and one of the parts, you subtract to find the other part.

Literature

These books link to the math in this unit. We can look for them at the library.

12 Ways to Get to 11
by Eve Merriam
Illustrated by Bernie Karlin
(Simon & Schuster, 1993)

Sea Sums
by Joy N. Hulme

The Grapes of Math
by Greg Tang

Let's read together!

Technology

We can visit *Education Place* at

eduplace.com/parents/mw/

for the Math Lingo game, the *e* Glossary, and more games and activities to do together.

426 four hundred twenty-six

MATH at Home

Discuss the letter to the family with children. You may want to use this letter as an introduction to the unit. Highlight for children what they will be learning in the unit. Tell children that as they go through the unit they will be able to answer the questions on these pages.

Math at Home is available in Spanish and other languages on Education Place. www.eduplace.com/math/mw/

Literature

Encourage parents to find the suggested books and read them with their children.

Technology

Education Place is an award-winning website with engaging activities for students and helpful information for parents. Look for the eGlossary, the Math Lingo Game, and more.

Building Vocabulary

Strategies for Building Vocabulary

Understanding the Term Fact Family

Ask children what the term **fact family** means. Explain that seeing a picture or example can help them figure out the meaning.

Remind children that there is a glossary at the back of their books. Turn to the glossary and ask children what they notice. If necessary, point out that the words are in alphabetical order and the pictures show the meanings of the words. Have children find the term **fact family** and invite them to follow along as you describe the entry. Ask volunteers to describe a fact family in their own words and record their responses on a chart.

Graphic Organizer: Chart

What is a Fact Family?
Numbers that are related
Parts and wholes
Number sentences that use the same numbers in a different order
Two sums and two differences, except for doubles and zero

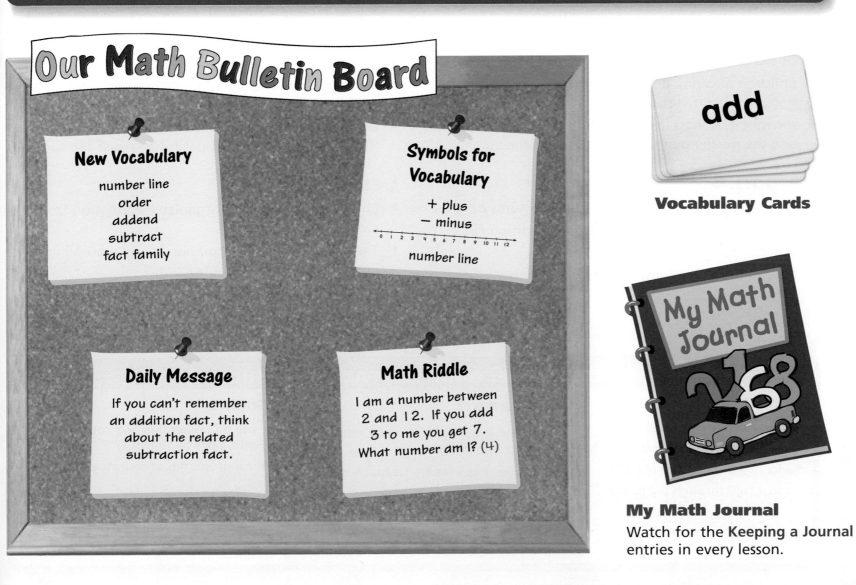

Our Math Bulletin Board

New Vocabulary
number line
order
addend
subtract
fact family

Symbols for Vocabulary
+ plus
− minus

0 1 2 3 4 5 6 7 8 9 10 11 12

number line

Daily Message
If you can't remember an addition fact, think about the related subtraction fact.

Math Riddle
I am a number between 2 and 12. If you add 3 to me you get 7. What number am I? (4)

add

Vocabulary Cards

My Math Journal

My Math Journal
Watch for the **Keeping a Journal** entries in every lesson.

Lesson by Lesson Overview
Addition Facts Through 12

Lesson 1

- Using a number line to count on to add reappears. Children begin to learn facts for 11 and 12 while reviewing facts to 10.
- Sums of 11 and 12 are covered again in later lessons.
- The order property is reviewed as children are instructed to start with the greater number.

Lesson 2

- This lesson focuses on making a ten as children find missing addends. Using a ten frame helps children find all the facts for 10.
- Children apply what they learned to solve a story problem.

Lesson 3

- A ten frame is also used in this lesson as children find missing addends to make sums of 11.
- Eleven is presented as 10 and 1 more through the use of the ten frame.
- Children also practice finding sums through 11 in horizontal and vertical exercises.
- Algebra Readiness exercises reinforce number sentences and the meaning of the equal sign as *is the same as*.

Lesson 4

- Order property is used as children find sums of 12.
- One set of counters is used for two addition facts.

  $8 + 4 = 12$ $4 + 8 = 12$

- Children practice sums through 12 in horizontal and vertical form.

- Children write an addition story problem and an addition sentence based on a picture.
- Next children write a story problem for a number sentence and then illustrate it.

Lesson 5

- Children practice addition facts through 12 using previously taught strategies.
- They count on, use doubles, use doubles plus one, and use a ten frame.

Lesson 6

- Children use addition strategies to add 3 numbers.
- Adding in any order is a practical strategy. Children start by looking for a fact they know.
- They add the sum of the first 2 numbers to the remaining number.

Lesson 7

- Missing addends are found for sums through 12.
- Previous work finding addends to make sums of 10 and sums of 11 form the ground work for this lesson.
- Children use cubes to model the known addend and then add on more cubes until they reach the sum.

Lesson 8

- Children are taught to organize information from a picture in a table.
- Then they use the information to solve problems that involve addition and subtraction.
- Children choose a strategy to practice previously learned problem-solving strategies.

SKILLS TRACE: ADDITION FACTS THROUGH 12

Grade K	Grade 1	Grade 2
• model addition (ch. 13)	• **use a number line and count on to add, facts to 12**	• use a number line and count on to add, facts to 18 (ch. 2)
• complete addition sentences (ch. 13)	• **use a ten frame to make sums of 10 and 11**	• use properties and strategies to add (ch. 2)
• add 1 to 0 through 9 (ch. 13)	• **find the sum of three numbers**	• make a 10 to add 7, 8, or 9 (ch. 2)
• add 2 to 0 through 8 (ch. 13)	• **find missing addends**	• find the sum of three one-digit numbers (ch. 2)

Chapter Planner

Lesson	Objective	Vocabulary	Materials	✓ NCTM Standards
15.1 **Count On to Add** p. 429A	Write sums through 12 by counting on 1, 2, or 3.	number line	counters, blank transparency, number cards 0–9 (Learning Tool (LT) 14)	Develop and use strategies for whole-number computations, with a focus on addition and subtraction.
15.2 **Sums of 10** **(Hands-On)** p. 431A	Use a ten frame to make sums of 10.	ten frame	Workmat 1, counters, yellow crayon, ten frame transparency, overhead two-color counters, sets of 10 cubes in three colors (red, yellow, blue) for each pair	Develop and use strategies for whole-number computations, with a focus on addition and subtraction.
15.3 **Sums of 11** **(Hands-On)** p. 433A	Use a ten frame to make sums of 11.		Workmat 1, two-color counters, ten-frame transparency, overhead two-color counters, yellow crayon, blank transparency, Workmat 2	Develop and use strategies for whole-number computations, with a focus on addition and subtraction.
15.4 **Sums of 12** p. 435A	Identify equivalent forms of the same number and write sums through 12.	order	Workmat 3, counters, red and blue cubes	Develop and use strategies for whole-number computations, with a focus on addition and subtraction.
15.5 **Addition Facts Practice** p. 439A	Use addition strategies to find sums through 12.		teacher-made addition fact cards for sums through 12, number cards 1–12 (LT 14 and 15)	Develop and use strategies for whole-number computations, with a focus on addition and subtraction.
15.6 **Add Three Numbers** p. 443A	Find the sum of three one-digit numbers.		cubes, blank transparency	Develop and use strategies for whole-number computations, with a focus on addition and subtraction.
15.7 **(Algebra Readiness)** **Missing Addends** p. 445A	Write missing addends to solve addition problems.	addend	two-color counters, Workmat 3, cubes, number cards 2–12 (LT 14 and 15), blank transparency, part-part-whole transparency, overhead counters	Develop and use strategies for whole-number computations, with a focus on addition and subtraction.
15.8 **Problem Solving:** **Make a Table** p. 447A	Make a table to solve problems.		cubes, paper lunch bags, blank transparency	Apply and adapt a variety of appropriate strategies to solve problems.

Resources For Reaching All Learners

LESSON RESOURCES: Reteach, Practice, Enrichment, Problem Solving, Homework, English Learners, Daily Routines, Transparencies, Math Center.

ADDITIONAL RESOURCES FROM HOUGHTON MIFFLIN: Chapter Challenges, Combination Classroom Planning Guide, Every Day Counts, Math to Learn (Student Handbook)

Every Day Counts
The Totally Ten Count and Daily Depositor activities in **Every Day Counts** support the math in this chapter.

Assessing Prior Knowledge

Monitoring Student Progress

Before beginning the chapter, you can assess student understandings in order to assist you in differentiating instruction.

Complete Chapter Pretest in Unit Resource Folder

Use this test to assess both prerequisite skills (**Are You Ready?** — one page) and chapter content (**Check What You Know** — two pages).

Chapter 15 Prerequisite Skills Pretest

Chapter 15 New Content Pretest

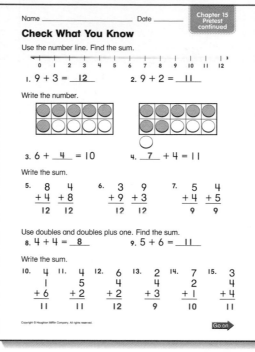

Customizing Instruction

For Students Having Difficulty

Items	Prerequisites	Ways to Success
1–3	Use a ten frame to add.	Skillsheet 106
4–6	Understand how to add in any order.	CD: 2.5 Skillsheet 107

Ways to Success: Intervention for every concept and skill (CD-ROM or Chapter Intervention Skillsheets).

For Students Having Success

Items	Objectives	Resources
1–2 16–18	15A Use vocabulary for addition facts through 12.	Enrichment 15.1, 15.2
5–9	15B Use strategies to find sums through 12.	Enrichment 15.1, 15.4
3–4	15C Use a ten frame to make sums of 10, 11.	Enrichment 15.2, 15.3
10–18	15D Add 3 numbers; find a missing addend.	Enrichment 15.6, 15.7
19–20	15E Make tables to solve problems.	Enrichment 15.8

Use **Chapter Challenges** with any students who have success with all new chapter content.

Other Pretest Options

Informal Pretest

The pretest assesses vocabulary and prerequisite skills needed for success in this chapter.

Ways to Success CD-ROM

The *Ways to Success* chapter pretest has automatic assignment of appropriate review lessons.

Chapter Resources

Assessing Prior Knowledge

Make Addition Flash Cards (find sums to 10)

- Have each child write addition facts showing sums to 5, 6, 7, 8, 9, and 10 on drawing paper. Instruct them to write the answers on the back.
- Have children cut out items from mail order catalogs and paste them below the facts to illustrate each fact they write.
- Use the pictures and facts as flash cards.

Ongoing Skill Activity

Moon Math Mobiles (find the sum of three one-digit numbers)

- Provide children moon shapes and star shapes.
- Have children write the numbers 8, 9, 10, 11, or 12 on a moon. Then have them write numbers that add up to that number on three stars.
- Have them tape the moon and stars together to make mobiles to hang in the classroom.

Connecting to the Unit Project

- Tell children that Haba Gaba is an addition game from West Africa.
- Draw a picture of a Haba Gaba game on the board.
- You may want to change the numbers next to the circles periodically to vary the addition.
- Have children solve this word problem: Omar threw 2 bean bags into each circle. How many points does he have? (12)

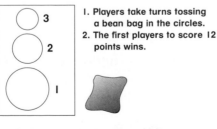

1. Players take turns tossing a bean bag in the circles.
2. The first players to score 12 points wins.

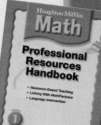

Professional Resources Handbook
- Research-Based Teaching
- Linking With MathPractices
- Language Intervention

Professional Resources Handbook

Research, Mathematics Content, and Language Intervention

Research-Based Teaching

Teachers should utilize children's informal knowledge to help them identify and appreciate the concepts and properties of each operation. For example, when teaching addition and subtraction, use problems in which the children are able to identify patterns and fact families as a way of building their experiences with early formal concepts. These patterns should also suggest to the child that subtraction is a complement to addition and that addition is commutative (Baroody, 1987; Baroody & Wilkins, 1999; Steffe & Cobb, 1988). See *Professional Resources Handbook, Grade 1,* Unit 6.

For more ideas relating to Unit 6, see the Teacher Support Handbook at the back of this Teacher's Edition.

Language Intervention

In China, the basic addition facts are taught using an approach that reinforces the importance of 10 as a special organizer of our number system. For further explanation, see "Mathematical Language and Addition Facts" in the *Professional Resources Handbook Grade 1.*

Technology

Time-Saving Technology Support

Ways to Assess Customized Spiral Review
  Test Generator CD
Lesson Planner CD-ROM
Ways to Success Intervention CD-ROM
MathTracks CD-ROM
Education Place: www.eduplace.com/math/mw
Houghton Mifflin Math eBook CD-ROM
eManipulatives
eGames

Starting Chapter 15
Addition Facts Through 12

CHAPTER OBJECTIVES

15A Develop and use math vocabulary relating to addition facts through 12.

15B Use strategies to solve addition problems through 12, including counting on, number line, doubles, and doubles plus one.

15C Use a ten frame to make sums of 10 and 11.

15D Add three numbers and find a missing addend.

15E Make tables to solve problems.

Math Background

Addition Facts Through 12

This chapter continues the work of addition from earlier chapters. Different ways to make sums of 10, 11, and 12 are explored. The use of the number line provides a concrete model for counting on. For example, children start at 8 and count on 4.

8 + 4

Children practice addition facts using strategies they have already learned. The strategies include counting on, using doubles and doubles plus one, and making a ten. Children also learn how to add three numbers. As children learn to add three numbers, they learn to look for facts they already know. This strategy is possible because of the Associative Property of Addition and the Commutative Property of Addition. The Associative Property of Addition states that when numbers are added, the addends can be grouped in different ways without changing the result. The Commutative Property of Addition states that when numbers or variables are added, the order of the addends can be changed without changing the results.

Children are also introduced to the missing addend concept through exercises such as 8 + □ = 11 and through relating addition and subtraction through fact families.

Using The Investigation

- Review the symbols used in addition sentences with children.

- Discuss addition strategies that children could use to find the sum. Encourage children to use doubles plus one or counting on.

- **Look at the picture. How many bears are there?** (4 bears) **How many pigs are there?** (5 pigs) **How many bears and pigs are there altogether?** (4 + 5 = 9)

- Discuss what strategies children used to find the sum.

- Have children work in small groups. Have them choose a place they like to visit and create problems about that place.

For more information about projects and investigations, visit Education Place. eduplace.com/math/mw/

Beach Party

Listen to your teacher.

CHAPTER CHALLENGES

For Mathematically Promising Students

The *Chapter Challenges* resource book provides blackline masters for activities that explore, extend, and connect the mathematics in every chapter. To support this independent work, see the Teacher Notes for each activity.

Explore: Counting On Patterns, page 85, after Lesson 1
Extend: Addition Puzzles, page 87, after Lesson 3
Connect: More Pesos, page 89, after Lesson 5

Using This Page

- Read these beach addition stories to the children.
- Have children model each story with counters and the workmat on the page. *Minnie found 5 shells on the beach and 5 in the water when she was wading. How many shells did she find altogether?*
- Have children place 5 counters on beach side of mat and 5 counters on water side. How many shells are there altogether? (10 shells)

Manuel saw 7 starfish on the beach and 2 starfish in the water. How many starfish did he see altogether?

- Have children explain how they used counters to solve the problem. How many starfish altogether? (9 starfish)
- Create other beach addition stories and have children model.

NSF Children's Math Worlds

Using lessons from the *Children's Math Worlds* is a good way to ensure that your students will develop a deep understanding of addition facts through 12. The most effective approach is to use the *Children's Math Worlds* lessons along with the lessons in the chapter.

Addition Facts Through 12   **428**

Count On to Add

Lesson 15.1

PLANNING THE LESSON

MATHEMATICS OBJECTIVE

Write sums through 12 by counting on 1, 2, or 3.

Use Lesson Planner CD-ROM for Lesson 15.1.

Meeting North Carolina's Standards

1.03 Develop fluency with single-digit addition and corresponding differences using strategies such as modeling, composing and decomposing quantities, using doubles, and making tens.

Also 1.04

Daily Routines

Calendar

Say a date and have children count forward and back from that date to find the date that is 3 days later and before.

Sunday	Monday	Tuesday	Wednesday	Thursday	Friday	Saturday
				1	2	3	4
5	6	7	8	9	10	11
12	13	14	15	16	17	18
19	20	21	22	23	24	25
26	27	28	29	30	31	

Vocabulary

Review **number line** by displaying a number line and asking children to hold up their Vocabulary Card that names this diagram or tool.

Vocabulary Cards

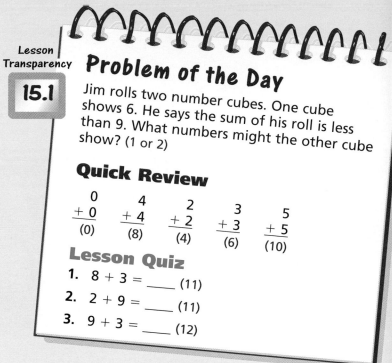

Lesson Transparency **15.1**

Problem of the Day

Jim rolls two number cubes. One cube shows 6. He says the sum of his roll is less than 9. What numbers might the other cube show? (1 or 2)

Quick Review

$$\begin{array}{ccccc} 0 & 4 & 2 & 3 & 5 \\ +0 & +4 & +2 & +3 & +5 \\ \hline (0) & (8) & (4) & (6) & (10) \end{array}$$

Lesson Quiz

1. $8 + 3 =$ ___ (11)
2. $2 + 9 =$ ___ (11)
3. $9 + 3 =$ ___ (12)

LEVELED PRACTICE

RETEACH 15.1

Name _____ Date _____

Reteach 15.1

Count On to Add

A number line can help you count on to add.

You can count on to add. Start with the greater number.

$7 + 2 = \underline{9}$

Start with the greater number.
Write the sum.

1. $\begin{array}{r} 1 \\ +9 \\ \hline 10 \end{array}$	2. $\begin{array}{r} 7 \\ +3 \\ \hline 10 \end{array}$	3. $\begin{array}{r} 2 \\ +4 \\ \hline 6 \end{array}$	4. $\begin{array}{r} 8 \\ +3 \\ \hline 11 \end{array}$	5. $\begin{array}{r} 5 \\ +3 \\ \hline 8 \end{array}$
6. $\begin{array}{r} 6 \\ +1 \\ \hline 7 \end{array}$	7. $\begin{array}{r} 4 \\ +3 \\ \hline 7 \end{array}$	8. $\begin{array}{r} 7 \\ +1 \\ \hline 8 \end{array}$	9. $\begin{array}{r} 2 \\ +6 \\ \hline 8 \end{array}$	10. $\begin{array}{r} 9 \\ +3 \\ \hline 12 \end{array}$

11. $2 + 8 = \underline{10}$ 12. $5 + 1 = \underline{6}$ 13. $4 + 6 = \underline{10}$

14. $7 + 5 = \underline{12}$ 15. $5 + 2 = \underline{7}$ 16. $9 + 1 = \underline{10}$

Copyright © Houghton Mifflin Company. All rights reserved.

Use with text pages 429–430.

PRACTICE 15.1

Name _____ Date _____

Practice 15.1

Count On to Add

Use the number line.
Write the sum.

0 1 2 3 4 5 6 7 8 9 10 11 12

1. $5 + 3 = \underline{8}$ 2. $9 + 2 = \underline{11}$ 3. $8 + 4 = \underline{12}$

4. $4 + 1 = \underline{5}$ 5. $7 + 5 = \underline{12}$ 6. $3 + 8 = \underline{11}$

7. $6 + 2 = \underline{8}$ 8. $9 + 1 = \underline{10}$ 9. $7 + 1 = \underline{8}$

10. $8 + 2 = \underline{10}$ 11. $5 + 4 = \underline{9}$ 12. $9 + 3 = \underline{12}$

13. $2 + 7 = \underline{9}$ 14. $3 + 4 = \underline{7}$ 15. $4 + 6 = \underline{10}$

Test Prep

Fill in the ○ for the correct answer. NH means Not Here.

16. Shawn had 6 pennies. He found 4 more pennies. How many pennies did he have in all?

8   10   12   NH
○   ●   ○   ○

Explain your answer.

Copyright © Houghton Mifflin Company. All rights reserved.

Use with text pages 429–430.

ENRICHMENT 15.1

Name _____ Date _____

Enrichment 15.1

More, More, More

Answer the question.

1. Who has more? Todd has 5 chicks. He buys 3 more. Sara has 2 chicks. She buys 7 more.

__Sara__ has more chicks than __Todd__

2. Who ran more? Greta runs 2 blocks. Then she runs 5 more blocks. Kim runs 3 blocks. Then she runs 6 more blocks.

__Kim__ ran more blocks than __Greta__

3. Who has more? Samuel has 3 action toys. His mother gives him 7 more. Daniel has 4 action toys. His father gives him 2 more.

__Samuel__ has more action toys than __Daniel__

4. Who has more? Muhammed went to the library and took out 4 books. Then he took out 6 more. Josef took out 5 books. Then he took out 3 more.

__Muhammed__ has more books than __Josef__

5. Who sold more? Phoebe sold 7 cups of lemonade. Then she sold 1 more. Washington sold 3 cups of lemonade. Then he sold 4 more.

__Phoebe__ sold more cups than __Washington__

Copyright © Houghton Mifflin Company. All rights reserved.

Use with text pages 429–430.

Practice Workbook Page 98

429A   CHAPTER 15   Lesson 1

Reaching All Learners

Differentiated Instruction

English Learners

English-language learners may not have the language skills to explain the process behind their thinking. Use Worksheet 15.1 to provide children with sentence frames they can use to complete the Explain Your Thinking activity.

Special Needs
VISUAL, TACTILE

Materials: *paper cup, counters*

- Have the child place up to 9 counters in the cup as he or she counts. Write the number on the cup.
- Show 1, 2, or 3 counters beside the cup. Ask the child to find how many counters there are in all by counting on from the number on the cup.

Early Finishers
TACTILE, AUDITORY

- Have children work in pairs.
- Have one child name a number and tell how many he or she counted on to get to that number. For example, "My number is 12. I got there by counting on 3." The partner then says from what number the first child started, 9.

Literature Connection

Teach children different finger plays or action rhymes that involve counting. *The Eentsy, Weentsy Spider Fingerplays and Action Rhymes* by Joanna Cole and Stephanie Calmenson is a good resource.

MATH CENTER

Basic Skills Activity

Motivate children to build basic skills. Use this activity to address multiple learning styles using hands-on activities related to the skills of this lesson.

PROBLEM SOLVING 15.1

Name _____ Date _____ Problem Solving 15.1

Count On to Add

Read each problem.
Count on to add.
Write the answer.

0 1 2 3 4 5 6 7 8 9 10 11 12

1. Marie saw 8 butterflies. Then she saw 3 more. How many butterflies did she see in all?

   Draw or write to explain.

   __11__ butterflies

2. Tim saw 6 bluebirds. He saw 2 robins. How many birds did Tim see in all?

   __8__ birds

3. Brett saw 9 frogs in the pond. He saw 3 frogs on a log. How many frogs did he see in all?

   __12__ frogs

Use with text pages 429–430.

HOMEWORK 15.1

Name _____ Date _____ Homework 15.1

Count On to Add

Find $3 + 6$.
Start with the greater number, 6.
Count on 3 to find the sum.

0 1 2 3 4 5 6 7 8 9 10 11 12

$3 + 6 = 9$

Use the number line. Write the sum.

0 1 2 3 4 5 6 7 8 9 10 11 12

1. $\begin{array}{r} 5 \\ +3 \\ \hline 8 \end{array}$
2. $\begin{array}{r} 2 \\ +8 \\ \hline 10 \end{array}$
3. $\begin{array}{r} 7 \\ +3 \\ \hline 10 \end{array}$
4. $\begin{array}{r} 6 \\ +2 \\ \hline 8 \end{array}$

5. $10 + 2 = \underline{12}$
6. $7 + 2 = \underline{9}$
7. $4 + 1 = \underline{5}$
8. $9 + 3 = \underline{12}$

9. Maia and Tina find shells on the beach. Maia find 6 shells. Tina finds 4 shells. How many shells did the girls find in all?

   __10__ shells in all

   Draw or write.

Use with text pages 429–430.

ENGLISH LEARNERS 15.1

Name _____ Date _____ English Learners 15.1

Count On to Add

0 1 2 3 4 5 6 7 8 9 10 11 12

Start with 7.
Count on 2.
The sum is 9.

When you add $9 + 2$, will the sum be greater than 9?

I start with __9__ .

I count on __2__ .

The sum is __11__ .

__11__ is greater than 9.

Use with text pages 429–430.

Homework Workbook Page 98

TEACHING LESSON 15.1

LESSON ORGANIZER

Objective Write sums through 12 by counting on 1, 2, or 3.

Resources Reteach, Practice, Enrichment, Problem Solving, Homework, English Learners, Transparencies, Math Center

Materials Blank transparency, counters, number cards 0–9 (Learning Tool (LT) 14)

Activity

Warm-Up Activity
Model Counting On Using a Number Line

| iiii Small Group | ⏱ 5–10 minutes | Auditory, Visual |

Materials: *blank transparency, counters*

1. Draw a number line from 0 to 10 on the transparency. Place a counter on 4. Write 4 + 2 = ____. Review how to count on using the number line. Move the counter as you count on 2: **Begin with 4. Count on 5, 6. What is the sum?** (6)

2. Write 2 + 4 = ____. Place a counter on 2. **Will the sum be the same or different?** (same) Model counting on 4 from 2 to check. **Is it faster to begin at 2 or 4?** (4) **Why?** (You had to count on fewer numbers.) Explain that the order in which you add numbers does not matter; therefore, they should count on from the greater number.

Name_____

Count On to Add

MathTracks 2/8
Listen to Understand

A **number line** can help you count on to add.

Objective
Write sums through 12 by counting on 1, 2, or 3.

Vocabulary
number line

```
←———————————————————————————→
  0  1  2  3  4  5  6  7  8  9  10  11  12
```

$\begin{array}{r} 8 \\ +3 \\ \hline 11 \end{array}$ Start with 8. Count on 3. *(Say 8. Count 9, 10, 11.)*

$\begin{array}{r} 9 \\ +2 \\ \hline 11 \end{array}$ Start with 9. Count on 2.

$\begin{array}{r} 9 \\ +3 \\ \hline 12 \end{array}$ Start with 9. Count on 3.

Guided Practice
Start with the greater number.
Write the sum.

1. $\begin{array}{r} 3 \\ +9 \\ \hline 12 \end{array}$ **Think** Count on 3 from 9. Say 9. Count 10, 11, 12.

2. $\begin{array}{r} 1 \\ +8 \\ \hline 9 \end{array}$

3. $\begin{array}{r} 9 \\ +2 \\ \hline 11 \end{array}$

4. $\begin{array}{r} 7 \\ +3 \\ \hline 10 \end{array}$

5. $\begin{array}{r} 6 \\ +3 \\ \hline 9 \end{array}$

6. $\begin{array}{r} 9 \\ +1 \\ \hline 10 \end{array}$

7. $\begin{array}{r} 2 \\ +6 \\ \hline 8 \end{array}$

8. $\begin{array}{r} 3 \\ +8 \\ \hline 11 \end{array}$

9. $\begin{array}{r} 4 \\ +3 \\ \hline 7 \end{array}$

10. $\begin{array}{r} 8 \\ +1 \\ \hline 9 \end{array}$

11. $7 + 2 = \underline{9}$ 12. $2 + 9 = \underline{11}$ 13. $5 + 3 = \underline{8}$

14. $3 + 7 = \underline{10}$ 15. $8 + 2 = \underline{10}$ 16. $1 + 9 = \underline{10}$

TEST TIPS **Explain Your Thinking** When you add $9 + 2$, will the sum be greater than 9? Why? **Yes; Possible answer: Because you are starting with 9 and adding 2 more.**

Chapter 15 Lesson 1   four hundred twenty-nine **429**

---

1 Introduce
Discuss Counting On to Add

| iiii Whole Group | ⏱ 10–15 minutes | Visual, Auditory |

Materials: *blank transparency*

1. Draw a number line from 0 to 12 on the transparency. Write 2 + 9 = ____. **What two numbers are being added?** (2 and 9) **Which is the greater number?** (9) Place a counter on 9. **How much is being added to 9?** (2) Have a volunteer move the counter as you count on 2: **10, 11.**

2. **If I start at 2 and count on 9, will I get the same sum?** (yes) Model counting on 9 from 2 to reinforce that the order you add numbers does not change the sum. **Why should you count on from the greater number?** (It is faster because you have to count on fewer numbers.)

3. Repeat the activity with other facts through 12 with an addend of 1, 2, or 3. Write the addition vertically and horizontally to review both forms.

2 Develop

Guided Learning

Teaching Example Read the objective and vocabulary with the children. Guide them through the example, reminding them that they should start with the greater number when they count on.

Guided Practice

Have children complete **Exercises 1–16** as you observe. Give children the opportunity to answer the Explain Your Thinking question. Then discuss their responses with the class.

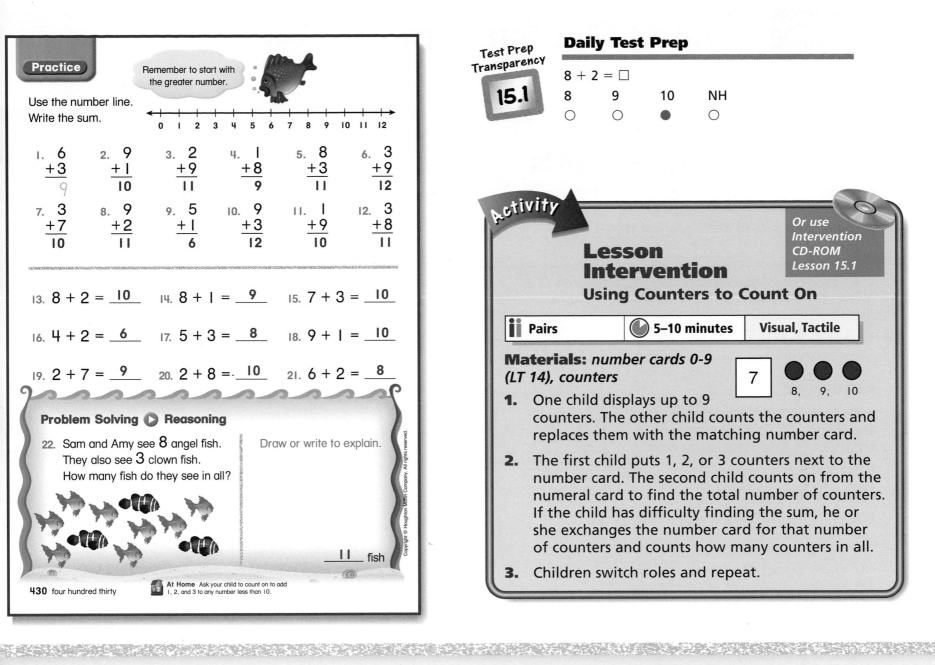

Practice

Remember to start with the greater number.

Use the number line.
Write the sum.

$$0\ 1\ 2\ 3\ 4\ 5\ 6\ 7\ 8\ 9\ 10\ 11\ 12$$

1. $6 + 3 = 9$
2. $9 + 1 = 10$
3. $2 + 9 = 11$
4. $1 + 8 = 9$
5. $8 + 3 = 11$
6. $3 + 9 = 12$

7. $3 + 7 = 10$
8. $9 + 2 = 11$
9. $5 + 1 = 6$
10. $9 + 3 = 12$
11. $1 + 9 = 10$
12. $3 + 8 = 11$

13. $8 + 2 = \underline{10}$
14. $8 + 1 = \underline{9}$
15. $7 + 3 = \underline{10}$

16. $4 + 2 = \underline{6}$
17. $5 + 3 = \underline{8}$
18. $9 + 1 = \underline{10}$

19. $2 + 7 = \underline{9}$
20. $2 + 8 = \underline{10}$
21. $6 + 2 = \underline{8}$

Problem Solving ▶ Reasoning

22. Sam and Amy see 8 angel fish. They also see 3 clown fish. How many fish do they see in all?

Draw or write to explain.

$\underline{11}$ fish

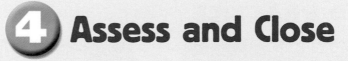

430 four hundred thirty

At Home Ask your child to count on to add 1, 2, and 3 to any number less than 10.

Daily Test Prep

$8 + 2 = \square$

8   9   10   NH
○   ○   ●   ○

Activity

Lesson Intervention
Using Counters to Count On

Or use Intervention CD-ROM Lesson 15.1

ii Pairs	🕐 5–10 minutes	Visual, Tactile

Materials: *number cards 0-9 (LT 14), counters*

7   ● ● ●   8, 9, 10

1. One child displays up to 9 counters. The other child counts the counters and replaces them with the matching number card.

2. The first child puts 1, 2, or 3 counters next to the number card. The second child counts on from the numeral card to find the total number of counters. If the child has difficulty finding the sum, he or she exchanges the number card for that number of counters and counts how many counters in all.

3. Children switch roles and repeat.

---

③ Practice

Independent Practice

Children complete **Exercises 1–21** independently.

Problem Solving

After children complete **Exercise 22**, call on volunteers to share their solutions. Then ask, **If Sam and Amy see the 3 clown fish first then the 8 angel fish, will they still see 11 fish in all?** (Yes, because changing the order of the addends does not change the sum.)

Common Error

Counting the Addend When Counting On
Tell children to put their finger on the number that they are counting on from and to begin counting from the next number.

④ Assess and Close

Write $9 + 2 = \underline{\quad}$.

How can you count on to find the sum? (Begin with 9, then count on 2: 10, 11.)

Keeping a Journal

Draw a 0 to 12 number line. Write or draw how to find the sum of $3 + 8$ using the number line.

Hands On: Sums of 10

PLANNING THE LESSON

MATHEMATICS OBJECTIVE
Use a ten frame to make sums of 10.

Use Lesson Planner CD-ROM for Lesson 15.2.

Meeting North Carolina's Standards

1.03 Develop fluency with single-digit addition and corresponding differences using strategies such as modeling, composing and decomposing quantities, using doubles, and making tens.

Also 1.04

Daily Routines

Calendar
Choose a date before the 10th of the month. Then have children count on to find how many days until the 10th.

Sunday	Monday	Tuesday	Wednesday	Thursday	Friday	Saturday
				1	2	3	4
5	6	7	8	9	10	11
12	13	14	15	16	17	18
19	20	21	22	23	24	25
26	27	28	29	30	31	

Vocabulary
Display a **ten frame** and ask children why it is called a ten frame. (There are 10 boxes.) Count the boxes with the children starting from the top row of the ten frame, then moving from left to right, then to the bottom row.

Vocabulary Cards

Lesson Transparency **15.2**

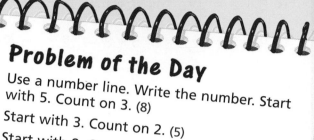

Problem of the Day
Use a number line. Write the number. Start with 5. Count on 3. (8)

Start with 3. Count on 2. (5)

Start with 8. Count on 2. (10)

Quick Review
Write the missing numbers. Skip count by 5s.

10, ___ (15), 20, ___ (25), 30

70, 75, ___ (80), ___ (85), 90

25, ___ (30), ___ (35), 40, 45

Lesson Quiz
Complete the number sentence.

1. 6 + 4 = ___ (10)

2. 5 + ___ (5) = 10

3. 3 + ___ (7) = 10

LEVELED PRACTICE

RETEACH 15.2

Name _____ Date _____   Reteach 15.2

Sums of 10

There are different ways to make the sum of 10 on a ten frame.

   6 + 4 = 10

Use Workmat 1 and ⬭ to make 10.
Draw counters.
Complete.

1. 9 + _1_ = 10

2. 4 + _6_ = _10_

3. 5 + _5_ = _10_

4. 2 + _8_ = _10_

5. 6 + _4_ = _10_

6. 9 + _1_ = _10_

Use with text pages 431–432.

PRACTICE 15.2

Name _____ Date _____   Practice 15.2

Sums of 10

Use Workmat 1 and ◯ to make 10.
Draw counters to fill the ten frame.
Complete the addition sentence.

1. 6 + _4_ = 10   **2.** 5 + _5_ = 10

Write the sum.

3. 3 + 7 = _10_   4. 0 + 9 = _9_   5. 6 + 2 = _8_

6. 3 + 3 = _6_   7. 8 + 1 = _9_   8. 4 + 5 = _9_

Test Prep

Fill in the ○ for the correct answer. NH means Not Here.

9. There are 10 spaces on a game board. Ben has moved 7 spaces. How many spaces does he still have to move?

Explain your answer.

7 ○   5 ○   3 ●   NH ○

Use with text pages 431–432.

ENRICHMENT 15.2

Name _____ Date _____   Enrichment 15.2

Ten Trains

Look at each 10 train.
Color some cubes ▭ Blue ▭.
Color some cubes ▭ Yellow ▭.
Then write a number sentence.

Answers will vary. Check children's work.

1. ___ + ___ = 10   **2.** ___ + ___ = 10

3. ___ + ___ = 10   **4.** ___ + ___ = 10

5. ___ + ___ = 10   **6.** ___ + ___ = 10

Write About It How could you show a friend that 8 + 2 = 10?

I could use 8 red counters and 2 yellow counters to model the problem.

Use with text pages 431–432.

Practice Workbook Page 99

Reaching All Learners

Differentiated Instruction

English Learners

Worksheet 15.2 develops an understanding of noun and verb forms with the endings *-er* and *-ing*. English-language learners will need to understand these forms in order to solve some word problems.

Inclusion
TACTILE, VISUAL

Materials: *two-color counters, cup*

- Have the child place 10 counters in the cup as he or she counts.
- Have the child gently shake and spill out the counters from the cup and record an addend for each color and write the sum.

Early Finishers
AUDITORY

Materials: *number line 0–10 (LT 8)*

- Have one child point to and say a number on a number line.
- The partner tells how many jumps are needed to get to 10 from that number. Then he or she counts on using the number line to check.
- Children switch roles and repeat.

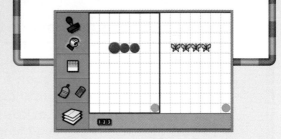
Art Connection

Provide children with 10 toothpicks or other small items and have them glue their items on paper in a 2-part design. Have children write a number sentence that describes their design.

MATH CENTER

Basic Skills Activity

Motivate children to build basic skills. Use this activity to address multiple learning styles using hands-on activities related to the skills of this lesson.

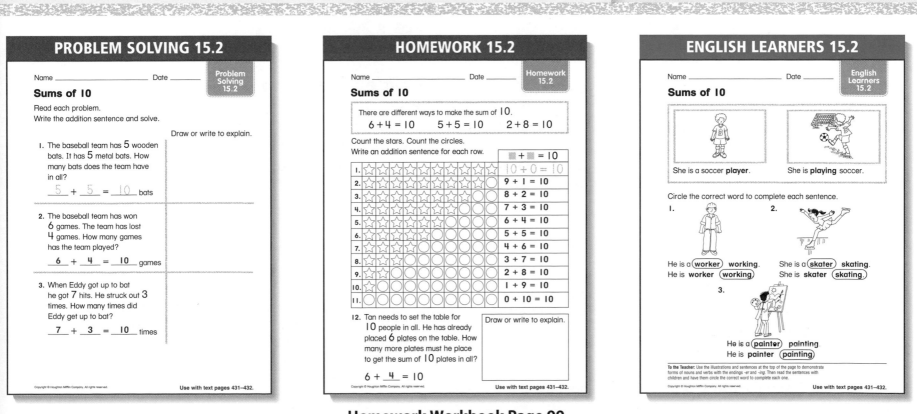

Homework Workbook Page 99

TEACHING LESSON 15.2

LESSON ORGANIZER

Objective Use a ten frame to make sums of 10.

Resources Reteach, Practice, Enrichment, Problem Solving, Homework, English Learners, Transparencies, Math Center

Materials Workmat 1, counters, yellow crayon, ten frame transparency, overhead two-color counters, sets of ten cubes in red, yellow, and blue

Activity

Warm-Up Activity

Modeling Numbers on a Ten Frame

| iiii Small Group | 🕐 5–10 minutes | Visual, Tactile |

Materials: *Workmat 1, counters*

1. Display a ten frame. **Why is this called a ten frame?** (There are 10 boxes.)

2. Display 7 counters randomly on a surface as children count. **How many counters?** (7) Place the counters in the ten frame starting from the top row moving left to right, then to the bottom row. **How many counters?** (7) **How does the ten frame help you see the number of counters more easily?** (It shows that there are 5 and 2 more.)

3. Repeat with other numbers up to 10.

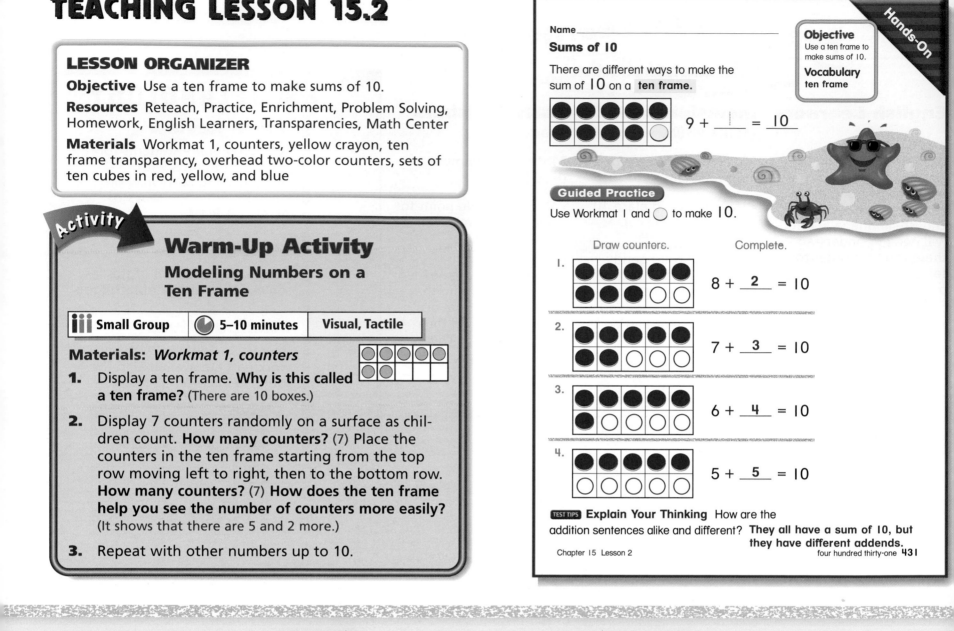

Name _____

Sums of 10

Objective Use a ten frame to make sums of 10.

Vocabulary ten frame

There are different ways to make the sum of 10 on a **ten frame**.

$9 + \underline{1} = 10$

Guided Practice

Use Workmat 1 and ◯ to make 10.

Draw counters.   Complete.

1. $8 + \underline{2} = 10$

2. $7 + \underline{3} = 10$

3. $6 + \underline{4} = 10$

4. $5 + \underline{5} = 10$

TEST TIPS **Explain Your Thinking** How are the addition sentences alike and different? **They all have a sum of 10, but they have different addends.**

Chapter 15 Lesson 2   four hundred thirty-one **431**

---

1 Introduce

Discuss Sums of 10

| iiii Whole Group | 🕐 10–15 minutes | Visual, Auditory |

Materials: *ten frame transparency, overhead two-color counters, Workmat 1, counters*

1. Display the ten frame transparency. **If I put one counter in each box, how many counters will I use?** (10) Place 3 red counters in the frame. **How many counters?** (3) Write $3 + \underline{\hspace{1cm}} = 10$ beneath the ten frame. **How many more counters do I need to make 10?** (7) Place yellow counters in each remaining box of the ten frame as children count.

2. Complete the number sentence. Have a volunteer explain how the counters in the ten frame relate to the number sentence. (They show $3 + 7 = 10$.)

3. Repeat with different sums for 10. Invite volunteers to complete the number sentences. Children can use Workmat 1 and counters to model the problems.

2 Develop

Guided Learning

Teaching Example Read the objective and vocabulary with children. Model the example using Workmat 1 and two-color counters as children follow along at their desks.

Ask a volunteer to explain how each number in the number sentence relates to the counters on the ten frame.

Guided Practice

Have children complete **Exercises 1–4** as you observe.

First, have them place the number of counters shown on their workmats (red side up). Next, have them place the yellow counters needed to make 10 on their workmats. They then use a yellow crayon to draw those counters to fill the frame as they count. Have children complete the number sentence. Give children the opportunity to answer the Explain Your Thinking question. Then discuss their responses with the class.

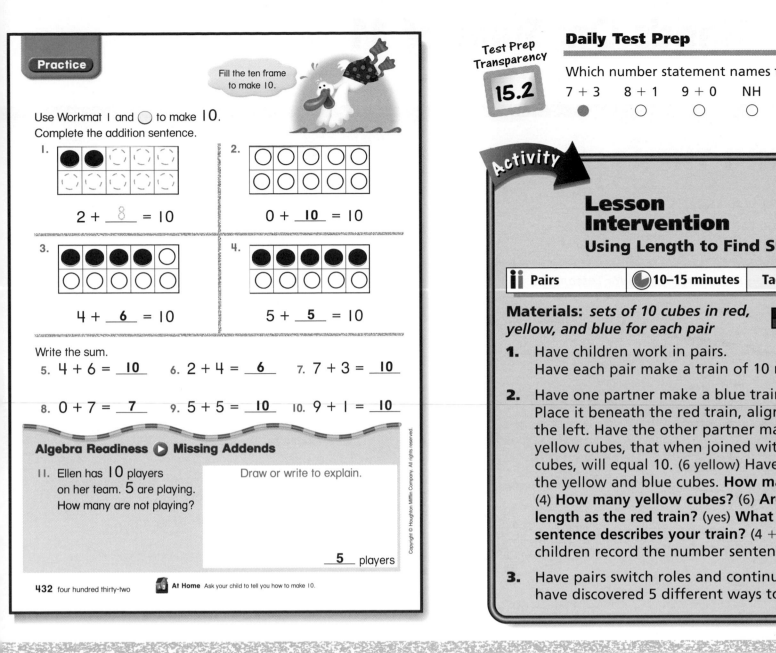

Practice

Fill the ten frame to make 10.

Use Workmat 1 and ○ to make 10.
Complete the addition sentence.

1.
2 + _8_ = 10

2.
0 + _10_ = 10

3.
4 + _6_ = 10

4.
5 + _5_ = 10

Write the sum.

5. 4 + 6 = _10_   6. 2 + 4 = _6_   7. 7 + 3 = _10_

8. 0 + 7 = _7_   9. 5 + 5 = _10_   10. 9 + 1 = _10_

Algebra Readiness ▶ Missing Addends

11. Ellen has 10 players on her team. 5 are playing. How many are not playing?

Draw or write to explain.

_5_ players

432 four hundred thirty-two

At Home Ask your child to tell you how to make 10.

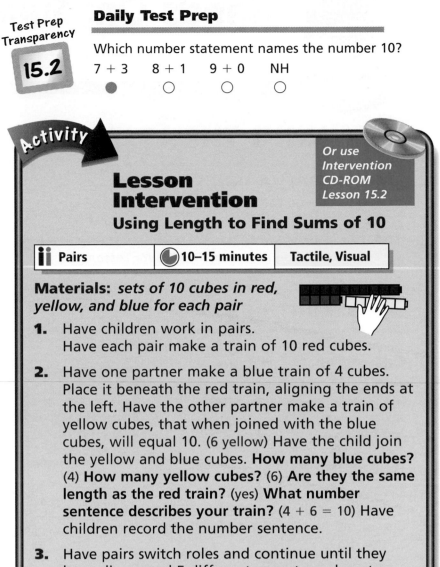

Daily Test Prep

Which number statement names the number 10?

7 + 3   8 + 1   9 + 0   NH
●   ○   ○   ○

Activity

Or use Intervention CD-ROM Lesson 15.2

Lesson Intervention
Using Length to Find Sums of 10

| ⚁ Pairs | ⏱ 10–15 minutes | Tactile, Visual |

Materials: *sets of 10 cubes in red, yellow, and blue for each pair*

1. Have children work in pairs. Have each pair make a train of 10 red cubes.

2. Have one partner make a blue train of 4 cubes. Place it beneath the red train, aligning the ends at the left. Have the other partner make a train of yellow cubes, that when joined with the blue cubes, will equal 10. (6 yellow) Have the child join the yellow and blue cubes. **How many blue cubes?** (4) **How many yellow cubes?** (6) **Are they the same length as the red train?** (yes) **What number sentence describes your train?** (4 + 6 = 10) Have children record the number sentence.

3. Have pairs switch roles and continue until they have discovered 5 different ways to make a ten.

③ Practice

Independent Practice

Children complete **Exercises 1–10** independently.

Algebra Readiness

After children complete **Exercise 11**, call on volunteers to share their solutions. **What addition sentence matches the problem?** (5 + 5 = 10)

Common Error

Guessing Sums
Children may guess sums they do not recall. Provide additional practice with a variety of models.

④ Assess and Close

• Write three number sentences that have a sum of 10.

Keeping a Journal

Draw a ten frame. Draw red and yellow counters on the ten frame to show the number sentence 3 + 7 = 10.

Hands On: Sums of 11

PLANNING THE LESSON

MATHEMATICS OBJECTIVE
Use a ten frame to make sums of 11.

Use Lesson Planner CD-ROM for Lesson 15.3.

Daily Routines

Calendar
Choose a date before the 11th of the month. Then have children count on to find how many days until the 11th.

Vocabulary
Review **sum** by writing number sentences on the board. Have a volunteer read the sentences and point to the sums.

Vocabulary Cards

Meeting North Carolina's Standards

1.03 Develop fluency with single-digit addition and corresponding differences using strategies such as modeling, composing and decomposing quantities, using doubles, and making tens.

Also 1.04

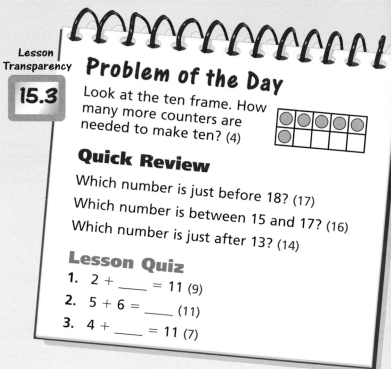

Lesson Transparency

15.3

Problem of the Day
Look at the ten frame. How many more counters are needed to make ten? (4)

Quick Review
Which number is just before 18? (17)

Which number is between 15 and 17? (16)

Which number is just after 13? (14)

Lesson Quiz
1. 2 + ____ = 11 (9)
2. 5 + 6 = ____ (11)
3. 4 + ____ = 11 (7)

LEVELED PRACTICE

RETEACH 15.3

Name _____ Date _____

Reteach 15.3

Sums of 11

There are different ways to make the sum of 11.

7 + 4 = 11

Use Workmat 1 and ⬭ to make 11.
Draw counters.
Complete.

1. 3 + 8 = 11
2. 9 + 2 = 11
3. 7 + 4 = 11
4. 6 + 5 = 11
5. 2 + 9 = 11
6. 3 + 8 = 11

Use with text pages 433–434.

PRACTICE 15.3

Name _____ Date _____

Practice 15.3

Sums of 11

Use Workmat 1 and ◯ to make 11.
Complete the addition sentence.

1. 6 + 5 = 11
2. 8 + 3 = 11

Write the sum.

3. 7 + 4 = 11
4. 5 + 6 = 11
5. 3 + 8 = 11
6. 9 + 2 = 11
7. 4 + 7 = 11
8. 2 + 9 = 11

9.
```
  6    5
 +5   +6
 11   11
```
10.
```
  8    2
 +2   +8
 10   10
```
11.
```
  7    4
 +4   +7
 11   11
```

Test Prep
Fill in the ○ for the correct answer. NH means Not Here.

12. Adam has 5 books about sports. He has 6 books about animals. How many books does he have in all?

8   9   10   NH
○   ○   ○   ●

Explain your answer.

Use with text pages 433–434.

ENRICHMENT 15.3

Name _____ Date _____

Enrichment 15.3

And Then There Was 1

Draw the missing objects.
Complete the number sentence.

1. 8 + 3 = 11
2. 6 + 5 = 11
3. 5 + 6 = 11
4. 7 + 4 = 11
5. 9 + 2 = 11
6. 4 + 7 = 11

Explain how the ten frame helps you add numbers.

I can make a ten and then count on with counters to find the sum.

Use with text pages 433–434.

Practice Workbook Page 100

Reaching All Learners

Differentiated Instruction

English Learners

To use ten frames to solve addition sentences with larger sums, English-language learners will need to understand the meaning of the word *outside*. Use Worksheet 15.3 to develop understanding of this word.

Inclusion
VISUAL, TACTILE

Materials: *cubes*

- Have the child make an 11-cube train out of red cubes. Now guide him or her to make a 9-cube train out of blue cubes.
- Ask the child to add yellow cubes to the blue cubes until the train is as long as the red train. Write 9 + 2 = 11.

Early Finishers
AUDITORY, VISUAL

Materials: *timer, number cards 7–11 (LT 14)*

- Have one child choose a card and set the timer. Children write number sentences using the number as the sum.
- After a minute, the child with the most correct number of sentences keeps the card.
- Children repeat until there are no cards remaining.

Literature Connection

Read the *12 Ways to Get to 11* by Eve Merriam. Pause before turning each page to let a volunteer write the number sentence that describes both the pictures and words.

MATH CENTER

Basic Skills Activity

Motivate children to build basic skills. Use this activity to address multiple learning styles using hands-on activities related to the skills of this lesson.

TECHNOLOGY

Spiral Review

Create **customized** spiral review worksheets for individual students using the *Ways to Assess* CD-ROM.

Lesson Planner

You can use the **Lesson Planner CD-ROM** to create a report of the lessons and standards you have taught.

eBook

eMathBook allows students to review lessons and do homework without carrying their textbooks home.

Manipulatives

Interactive Counters with several workmats are available on the *Ways to Success* CD-ROM.

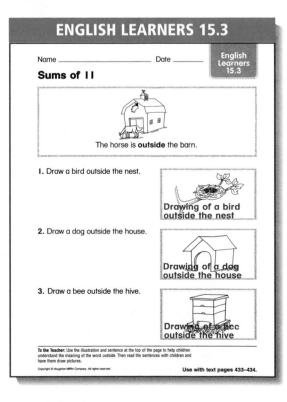

TEACHING LESSON 15.3

LESSON ORGANIZER

Objective Use a ten frame to make sums of 11.

Resources Reteach, Practice, Enrichment, Problem Solving, Homework, English Learners, Transparencies, Math Center

Materials Workmat 1, Workmat 2, two-color counters, ten frame transparency, overhead two-color counters, yellow crayon, blank transparency

Activity

Warm-Up Activity
Modeling Adding in Any Order

| 👥 Small Group | 🕐 5–10 minutes | Visual, Tactile |

Materials: *Workmat 2, two-color counters*

$$4 + 6 = 10 \qquad 6 + 4 = 10$$

1. Ask children to fill their ten frames with 4 counters, red side up, then 6 counters, yellow side up. **What addition sentence describes the counters?** (4 + 6 = 10) Write it on the board.

2. Now have children carefully turn their workmat so the yellow counters come first. **What addition sentence describes the counters now?** (6 + 4 = 10) Write it on the board beneath the other sentence.

3. Review how the sum stays the same even when numbers are added in a different order.

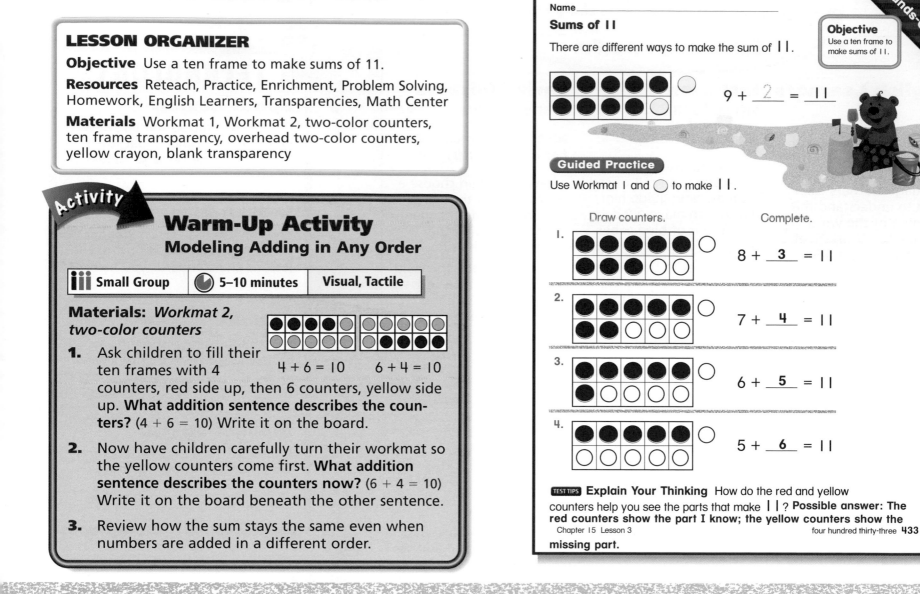

Name _____

Sums of 11

There are different ways to make the sum of 11.

Objective Use a ten frame to make sums of 11.

$$9 + \underline{2} = \underline{11}$$

Guided Practice

Use Workmat 1 and ○ to make 11.

Draw counters.   Complete.

1. $$8 + \underline{3} = 11$$

2. $$7 + \underline{4} = 11$$

3. $$6 + \underline{5} = 11$$

4. $$5 + \underline{6} = 11$$

TEST TIPS **Explain Your Thinking** How do the red and yellow counters help you see the parts that make 11? **Possible answer: The red counters show the part I know; the yellow counters show the missing part.**

---

① Introduce Activity
Discuss Sums of 11

| 👥 Whole Group | 🕐 10–15 minutes | Visual, Auditory |

Materials: *ten frame transparency, overhead two-color counters, Workmat 1, counters*

1. Display the ten frame. **If I put one counter in each box, how many counters do I use?** (10) **If I add one more counter, how many do I have?** (11) Place 5 red counters in the frame. Write 5 + ____ = 11 beneath the ten frame. **How many more counters do I need to make 11?** (6) Place yellow counters in each empty box plus one more outside the ten frame as children count with you.

2. Complete the number sentence. Repeat to develop 6 + 5. Review how the sum stays the same even when numbers are added in a different order.

3. Repeat a similar process with different sums for 11. Have children use Workmat 1 and counters to find the sums.

② Develop

Guided Learning

Teaching Example Read the objective with children. Model the example using Workmat 1 and two-color counters as children follow along at their desks.

Ask a volunteer to explain how each number in the number sentence relates to the counters.

Guided Practice

Have children complete **Exercises 1–4** as you observe.

Children can use a yellow crayon to record the number of counters they add and then complete the number sentence. Give children the opportunity to answer the Explain Your Thinking question. Then discuss their responses with the class.

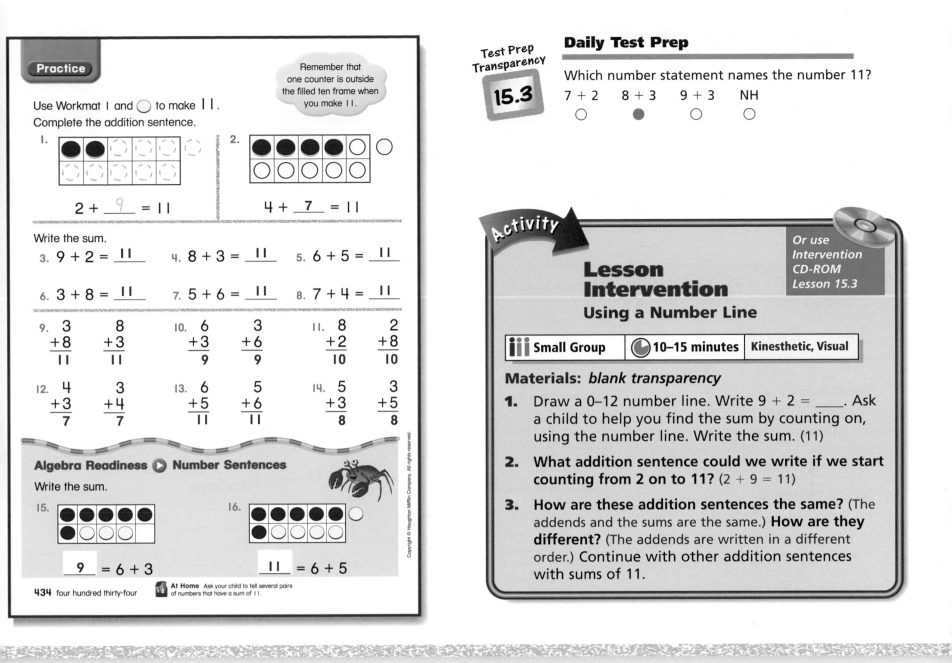

Practice

Remember that one counter is outside the filled ten frame when you make 11.

Use Workmat 1 and ⬤ to make 11.
Complete the addition sentence.

1.
$2 + \underline{9} = 11$

2.
$4 + \underline{7} = 11$

Write the sum.

3. $9 + 2 = \underline{11}$ 4. $8 + 3 = \underline{11}$ 5. $6 + 5 = \underline{11}$

6. $3 + 8 = \underline{11}$ 7. $5 + 6 = \underline{11}$ 8. $7 + 4 = \underline{11}$

9. $\begin{array}{r} 3 \\ +8 \\ \hline 11 \end{array}$ $\begin{array}{r} 8 \\ +3 \\ \hline 11 \end{array}$ 10. $\begin{array}{r} 6 \\ +3 \\ \hline 9 \end{array}$ $\begin{array}{r} 3 \\ +6 \\ \hline 9 \end{array}$ 11. $\begin{array}{r} 8 \\ +2 \\ \hline 10 \end{array}$ $\begin{array}{r} 2 \\ +8 \\ \hline 10 \end{array}$

12. $\begin{array}{r} 4 \\ +3 \\ \hline 7 \end{array}$ $\begin{array}{r} 3 \\ +4 \\ \hline 7 \end{array}$ 13. $\begin{array}{r} 6 \\ +5 \\ \hline 11 \end{array}$ $\begin{array}{r} 5 \\ +6 \\ \hline 11 \end{array}$ 14. $\begin{array}{r} 5 \\ +3 \\ \hline 8 \end{array}$ $\begin{array}{r} 3 \\ +5 \\ \hline 8 \end{array}$

Algebra Readiness ▶ Number Sentences

Write the sum.

15.
$\underline{9} = 6 + 3$

16.
$\underline{11} = 6 + 5$

At Home Ask your child to tell several pairs of numbers that have a sum of 11.

Daily Test Prep

Which number statement names the number 11?

7 + 2   ● 8 + 3   9 + 3   NH
○   ●   ○   ○

Activity

Or use Intervention CD-ROM Lesson 15.3

Lesson Intervention

Using a Number Line

| 👥 Small Group | ⏱ 10–15 minutes | Kinesthetic, Visual |

Materials: *blank transparency*

1. Draw a 0–12 number line. Write $9 + 2 = \underline{}$. Ask a child to help you find the sum by counting on, using the number line. Write the sum. (11)

2. **What addition sentence could we write if we start counting from 2 on to 11?** (2 + 9 = 11)

3. **How are these addition sentences the same?** (The addends and the sums are the same.) **How are they different?** (The addends are written in a different order.) Continue with other addition sentences with sums of 11.

③ Practice

Independent Practice

Children complete **Exercises 1–14** independently. Point out that **Exercises 9–14** reinforce that the order of addends will not change the sum.

Algebra Readiness

Explain that the sum will be written at the beginning of each addition sentence in **Exercises 15–16**. After children complete **Exercises 15–16**, call on volunteers to share their solutions. **How are these number sentences different from the other number sentences on the page?** (The sum comes first.) **Does this change the sum?** (no) **9 is the same as 6 plus 3, 11 is the same as 6 plus 5.**

Common Error

Making Fact Errors
Children may be unable to find sums without counters or a number line. Provide practice with counters and then flash cards.

④ Assess and Close

• **Write three number sentences that have a sum of 11.**
(Possible answers: 5 + 6 = 11, 2 + 9 = 11, 8 + 3 =11)

Keeping a Journal

Draw a ten frame with 4 counters in it.

Write how many more counters you would need to make 11. (7) Explain how the ten frame helps you see the answer without counting.

Sums of 12

Lesson 15.4

PLANNING THE LESSON

MATHEMATICS OBJECTIVE

Identify equivalent forms of the same number and write sums through 12.

Use Lesson Planner CD-ROM for Lesson 15.4.

Meeting North Carolina's Standards

1.03 Develop fluency with single-digit addition and corresponding differences using strategies such as modeling, composing and decomposing quantities, using doubles, and making tens.

Also 1.04

Daily Routines

Calendar

Ask children to find two dates on the calendar with sums of 12. Examples: 1st and 11th; 2nd and 10th; 3rd and 9th.

Sunday	Monday	Tuesday	Wednesday	Thursday	Friday	Saturday
				1	2	3	4
5	6	7	8	9	10	11
12	13	14	15	16	17	18
19	20	21	22	23	24	25
26	27	28	29	30	31	

Vocabulary

To review **order**, write 13, 8, 25 on the board. Ask children to arrange these numbers from least to greatest. (8, 13, 25) Then ask them to hold up the Vocabulary Card with the word that shows what they did to the numbers. (order)

Vocabulary Cards

Lesson Transparency 15.4

Problem of the Day

Ben had 5 crayons in his crayon box. There are 3 crayons on his desk. Write a number sentence for how many crayons Ben has altogether. ($5 + 3 = 8$)

Quick Review

Draw pairs of dots to show the number. Is the number odd or even?

11 (odd)   7 (odd)   12 (even)

Lesson Quiz

1. $3 + 9 =$ ____ (12) $9 + 3 =$ ____ (12)
2. $6 + 6 =$ ____ (12) $5 + 7 =$ ____ (12)
3. $8 + 3 =$ ____ (11) $3 + 8 =$ ____ (11)

LEVELED PRACTICE

RETEACH 15.4

Name _____ Date _____   **Reteach 15.4**

Sums of 12

You can add numbers in any order and get the same sum.

$7 + 5 = 12$

$5 + 7 = 12$

Write the sum.

1. $8 + 4 = 12$
   $4 + 8 = 12$

2. $9 + 3 = 12$
   $3 + 9 = 12$

3. $\begin{array}{r} 7 \\ +5 \\ \hline 12 \end{array}$ $\begin{array}{r} 5 \\ +7 \\ \hline 12 \end{array}$

4. $\begin{array}{r} 9 \\ +3 \\ \hline 12 \end{array}$ $\begin{array}{r} 3 \\ +9 \\ \hline 12 \end{array}$

5. $\begin{array}{r} 6 \\ +6 \\ \hline 12 \end{array}$

Talk About It Which double has a sum of 12?

Copyright © Houghton Mifflin Company. All rights reserved.   Use with text pages 435–436.

PRACTICE 15.4

Name _____ Date _____   **Practice 15.4**

Sums of 12

Write the sum.

1. $\begin{array}{r} 7 \\ +5 \\ \hline 12 \end{array}$ $\begin{array}{r} 5 \\ +7 \\ \hline 12 \end{array}$
2. $\begin{array}{r} 6 \\ +2 \\ \hline 8 \end{array}$ $\begin{array}{r} 2 \\ +6 \\ \hline 8 \end{array}$
3. $\begin{array}{r} 4 \\ +6 \\ \hline 10 \end{array}$ $\begin{array}{r} 6 \\ +4 \\ \hline 10 \end{array}$

4. $\begin{array}{r} 8 \\ +3 \\ \hline 11 \end{array}$ $\begin{array}{r} 3 \\ +8 \\ \hline 11 \end{array}$
5. $\begin{array}{r} 3 \\ +4 \\ \hline 7 \end{array}$ $\begin{array}{r} 4 \\ +3 \\ \hline 7 \end{array}$
6. $\begin{array}{r} 7 \\ +3 \\ \hline 10 \end{array}$ $\begin{array}{r} 3 \\ +7 \\ \hline 10 \end{array}$

7. $\begin{array}{r} 3 \\ +5 \\ \hline 8 \end{array}$ $\begin{array}{r} 5 \\ +3 \\ \hline 8 \end{array}$
8. $\begin{array}{r} 8 \\ +4 \\ \hline 12 \end{array}$ $\begin{array}{r} 4 \\ +8 \\ \hline 12 \end{array}$
9. $\begin{array}{r} 6 \\ +5 \\ \hline 11 \end{array}$ $\begin{array}{r} 5 \\ +6 \\ \hline 11 \end{array}$

10. $4 + 3 = 7$
11. $1 + 8 = 9$
12. $9 + 0 = 9$

$3 + 4 = 7$ $8 + 1 = 9$ $0 + 9 = 9$

Test Prep

Fill in the ○ for the correct answer. NH means Not Here.

13. Brendan needs 12 nails for a project. He has 9 nails. How many more nails does he need?

    5   4   3   NH
    ○   ○   ●   ○

Copyright © Houghton Mifflin Company. All rights reserved.   Use with text pages 435–436.

ENRICHMENT 15.4

Name _____ Date _____   **Enrichment 15.4**

Mixed-Up 12s

Look at the numbers in the squares. Add across. Add down.

3	9	12
9	3	12
12	12	24

1. Katie bought 3 goldfish. Then she bought 9 more. How many goldfish does she have?

   __12__ goldfish

2. Michael bought 9 goldfish. Then he bought 3 more. How many goldfish does he have?

   __12__ goldfish

Answer each question.

3. Zinta painted 5 masks. Then she painted 7 more. How many masks did she paint?

   __12__ masks

4. Adam painted 7 masks. Then he painted 5 more. How many masks did he paint?

   __12__ masks

5. Corinne watched 4 ants. Then she watched 8 more. How many ants did she watch?

   __12__ ants

6. Elijah watched 8 ants. Then he watched 4 more. How many ants did he watch?

   __12__ ants

Explain why $6 + 5$ and $5 + 6$ have the same sum.
Changing the order of the addends does not change the sum.

Copyright © Houghton Mifflin Company. All rights reserved.   Use with text pages 435–436.

Practice Workbook Page 101

Reaching All Learners

Differentiated Instruction

English Learners

English-language learners may not have the language skills to explain the process behind their thinking. Use Worksheets 15.4 to provide children with sentence frames they can use to complete the Explain Your Thinking activity.

Inclusion
TACTILE, VISUAL

Materials: *cubes*

- Have the child make a cube train that shows 5 + 7 and record the number sentence.

- Have the child turn the train around to show 7 + 5 and write the number sentence. Note that the sum is the same.

Gifted and Talented
AUDITORY, VISUAL

Materials: *cm graph paper (LT 30), crayons*

- Have each child in the group choose two different colors to color squares on the grid. Relate the rows on the grid to the cube trains children have made.

- Have them color to show all the different ways to make 12.

Literature Connection

Read the story *So Many Cats!* by Beatrice Schenk de Regniers. Then work with children to write a matching number sentence that shows how the narrator ended up with a dozen cats.
(1 + 1 + 3 + 1 + 1 + 3 + 2)

MATH CENTER

Real-Life Activity

Help children understand the usefulness of mathematics. This activity makes math come alive by connecting the lesson skills to a real-life situation.

TECHNOLOGY

Spiral Review

Using the *Ways to Assess* CD-ROM, you can create **customized** spiral review worksheets covering any lessons you choose.

Education Place

You can visit **Education Place** at eduplace.com/math/mw/ for teacher support materials.

Games

Students can practice their skills using the **Rock Hopper** math game, available on the *Ways to Success* CD-ROM.

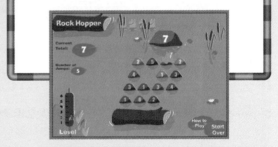

TEACHING LESSON 15.4

LESSON ORGANIZER

Objective Identify equivalent forms of the same number and write sums through 12.

Resources Reteach, Practice, Enrichment, Problem Solving, Homework, English Learners, Transparencies, Math Center

Materials Red and blue cubes, Workmat 3, counters

Activity

Warm-Up Activity
Modeling Adding in Any Order Vertically

| **Small Group** | **5–10 minutes** | **Visual, Tactile** |

Materials: *red and blue cubes*

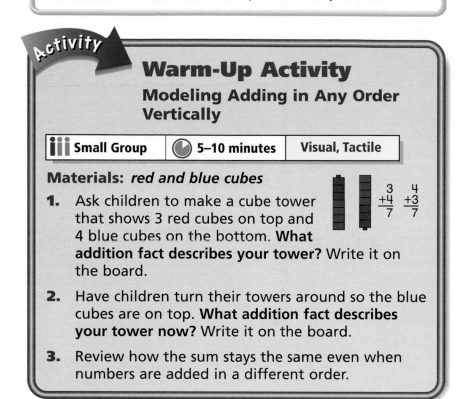

1. Ask children to make a cube tower that shows 3 red cubes on top and 4 blue cubes on the bottom. **What addition fact describes your tower?** Write it on the board.

$$\begin{array}{r} 3 \\ +4 \\ \hline 7 \end{array} \quad \begin{array}{r} 4 \\ +3 \\ \hline 7 \end{array}$$

2. Have children turn their towers around so the blue cubes are on top. **What addition fact describes your tower now?** Write it on the board.

3. Review how the sum stays the same even when numbers are added in a different order.

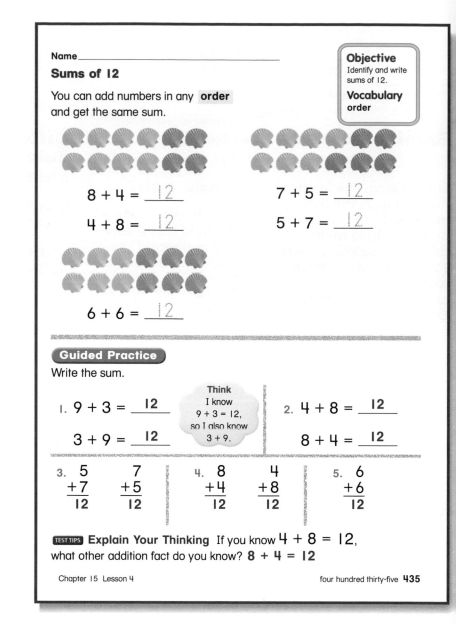

Name _____

Sums of 12

You can add numbers in any **order** and get the same sum.

Objective
Identify and write sums of 12.

Vocabulary
order

$8 + 4 = \underline{12}$ $7 + 5 = \underline{12}$

$4 + 8 = \underline{12}$ $5 + 7 = \underline{12}$

$6 + 6 = \underline{12}$

Guided Practice

Write the sum.

1. $9 + 3 = \underline{12}$

   $3 + 9 = \underline{12}$

   Think
   I know
   $9 + 3 = 12$,
   so I also know
   $3 + 9$.

2. $4 + 8 = \underline{12}$

   $8 + 4 = \underline{12}$

3. $\begin{array}{r} 5 \\ +7 \\ \hline 12 \end{array} \quad \begin{array}{r} 7 \\ +5 \\ \hline 12 \end{array}$
4. $\begin{array}{r} 8 \\ +4 \\ \hline 12 \end{array} \quad \begin{array}{r} 4 \\ +8 \\ \hline 12 \end{array}$
5. $\begin{array}{r} 6 \\ +6 \\ \hline 12 \end{array}$

TEST TIPS **Explain Your Thinking** If you know $4 + 8 = 12$, what other addition fact do you know? $8 + 4 = 12$

---

1 Introduce   Activity
Model Sums of 12

| **Whole Group** | **10–15 minutes** | **Visual, Auditory** |

Materials: *Workmat 3, counters*

1. Tell children to place 9 counters on the bottom left part of their workmat. Then have them place 3 counters on the bottom right part.

2. **How many counters are in the first part?** (9) **In the second part?** (3) **Find the whole. How many counters in all?** (12) **What is the number sentence that describes a part with 9 and a part with 3?** (9 + 3 = 12)

3. Reverse the addends and ask the same questions as above reversing the last question. (3, 9, 12; 3 + 9 = 12) **Does the sum change if you change the order and add 9 plus 3 instead of 3 plus 9?** (no) Repeat the activity with other addends whose sum equals 12.

2 Develop

Guided Learning

Teaching Example Read the objective and vocabulary with children. Guide them through each example, reinforcing how the sum stays the same even when numbers are added in a different order.

Guided Practice

Have children complete **Exercises 1–5** as you observe. Give children the opportunity to answer the Explain Your Thinking question. Then discuss their responses with the class.

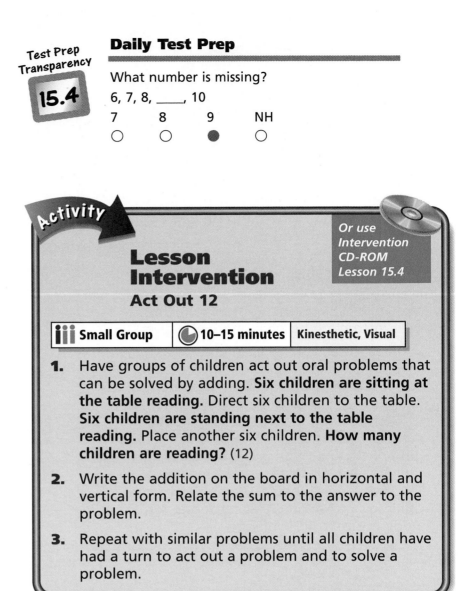

Practice

Changing the order of the addends does not change the sum.

Write the sum.

1. $3 + 2 = \underline{5}$ 2. $9 + 1 = \underline{10}$ 3. $2 + 9 = \underline{11}$

   $2 + 3 = \underline{5}$ $1 + 9 = \underline{10}$ $9 + 2 = \underline{11}$

4. $\begin{array}{r} 5 \\ +7 \\ \hline 12 \end{array}$ $\begin{array}{r} 7 \\ +5 \\ \hline 12 \end{array}$ 5. $\begin{array}{r} 8 \\ +3 \\ \hline 11 \end{array}$ $\begin{array}{r} 3 \\ +8 \\ \hline 11 \end{array}$ 6. $\begin{array}{r} 5 \\ +4 \\ \hline 9 \end{array}$ $\begin{array}{r} 4 \\ +5 \\ \hline 9 \end{array}$

7. $\begin{array}{r} 4 \\ +3 \\ \hline 7 \end{array}$ $\begin{array}{r} 3 \\ +4 \\ \hline 7 \end{array}$ 8. $\begin{array}{r} 4 \\ +6 \\ \hline 10 \end{array}$ $\begin{array}{r} 6 \\ +4 \\ \hline 10 \end{array}$ 9. $\begin{array}{r} 9 \\ +3 \\ \hline 12 \end{array}$ $\begin{array}{r} 3 \\ +9 \\ \hline 12 \end{array}$

10. $\begin{array}{r} 5 \\ +2 \\ \hline 7 \end{array}$ $\begin{array}{r} 2 \\ +5 \\ \hline 7 \end{array}$ 11. $\begin{array}{r} 4 \\ +8 \\ \hline 12 \end{array}$ $\begin{array}{r} 8 \\ +4 \\ \hline 12 \end{array}$ 12. $\begin{array}{r} 6 \\ +2 \\ \hline 8 \end{array}$ $\begin{array}{r} 2 \\ +6 \\ \hline 8 \end{array}$

13. $\begin{array}{r} 2 \\ +8 \\ \hline 10 \end{array}$ $\begin{array}{r} 8 \\ +2 \\ \hline 10 \end{array}$ 14. $\begin{array}{r} 2 \\ +7 \\ \hline 9 \end{array}$ $\begin{array}{r} 7 \\ +2 \\ \hline 9 \end{array}$ 15. $\begin{array}{r} 5 \\ +6 \\ \hline 11 \end{array}$ $\begin{array}{r} 6 \\ +5 \\ \hline 11 \end{array}$

Problem Solving ▶ Reasoning

16. The game starts at 1 o'clock. It ends two hours later. What time does the game end?

    Draw or write to explain.

    $\underline{3}$ o'clock

 **436** four hundred thirty-six   **At Home** Ask your child to solve $8 + 4$ and $4 + 8$ and tell how he or she found the sum.   **Go on**

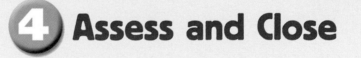

 Copyright © Houghton Mifflin Company. All rights reserved.

Test Prep Transparency 15.4

Daily Test Prep

What number is missing?

6, 7, 8, _____, 10

7 ○   8 ○   9 ●   NH ○

Activity

Lesson Intervention

Act Out 12

Or use Intervention CD-ROM Lesson 15.4

👤👤👤 Small Group	🕐 10–15 minutes	Kinesthetic, Visual

1. Have groups of children act out oral problems that can be solved by adding. **Six children are sitting at the table reading.** Direct six children to the table. **Six children are standing next to the table reading.** Place another six children. **How many children are reading?** (12)

2. Write the addition on the board in horizontal and vertical form. Relate the sum to the answer to the problem.

3. Repeat with similar problems until all children have had a turn to act out a problem and to solve a problem.

---

3 Practice

Independent Practice

Children complete **Exercises 1–15** independently.

Problem Solving

After children complete **Exercise 16**, call on volunteers to share their solutions. **Is 1 o'clock a time to the hour or a time to the half-hour?** (hour)

Common Error

Not Recognizing the Order Property

Children may not recognize that $8 + 4$ and $4 + 8$ have the same sum. Use cube trains to show them how you can turn them around and not change the sum.

4 Assess and Close

- **Write two addition sentences with a sum of 12 using the same addends.** (Answers will vary. Possible answers: $5 + 7 = 12$; $7 + 5 = 12$)

Keeping a Journal

Write all the different ways you can make a sum of 12 with two addends. ($0 + 12$; $1 + 11$; $2 + 10$; $3 + 9$; $4 + 8$; $5 + 7$; $6 + 6$ and the reverse addends)

Lesson continues →

 **CHAPTER 15   Lesson 4   436**

ACHIEVING Mathematical Proficiency

How Can Assessment Inform Instruction?

Assessment provides information about childrens' current level of understanding and skills. **This information helps teachers plan instruction that focuses on appropriate skills, tasks, and lessons.**

Research indicates that when teachers ask questions and make observations during lessons, they can use the information they receive to redirect their instruction. Thus, their instruction becomes more effective.

In this chapter, teachers can observe as children do guided practice and practice activities related to addition facts through 12. The chapter also provides **opportunities for children to explain their thinking about processes and skills involved in adding facts through 12 and to demonstrate problem-solving strategies and algebra readiness.** Teachers can use their assessments of children's oral and written responses to guide future instruction.

Name ______________________

Writing Math: Create and Solve

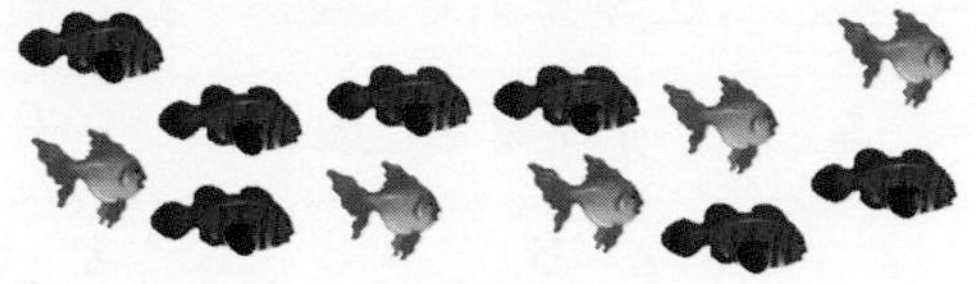

Write an addition story about the fish.

1. **Answers may vary. Possible answer: There are 5 yellow fish and 7 red fish. How many fish are there in all?**

Write the addition sentence.

2. **5** (+) **7** (=) **12**

Tell a story for the number sentence $8 + 3 = 11$.
Draw a picture to show your story.

3. **Stories and pictures may vary, but they should relate to 8 + 3 = 11.**

Chapter 15 Lesson 4 four hundred thirty-seven 437

Writing Math: Create and Solve

Discuss the picture for **Exercise 1** to be sure children understand that there are 5 yellow fish and 7 red fish. After children write their story, have them write an addition sentence for **Exercise 2**. You may want to have some children share their addition stories verbally.

Explain that for **Exercise 3,** children will tell an addition story to a partner for the number sentence $8 + 3 = 11$. Then they draw a picture to show the story.

Write the sum.

1. 8 + 2 = __10__   2. 9 + 3 = __12__   3. 2 + 9 = __11__

4. 4 + 6 = __10__   5. 3 + 7 = __10__   6. 5 + 5 = __10__

7. 9 + 2 = __11__   8. 8 + 3 = __11__   9. 6 + 5 = __11__

10.
$$\begin{array}{r} 5 \\ +2 \\ \hline 7 \end{array} \qquad \begin{array}{r} 2 \\ +5 \\ \hline 7 \end{array}$$
11.
$$\begin{array}{r} 4 \\ +8 \\ \hline 12 \end{array} \qquad \begin{array}{r} 8 \\ +4 \\ \hline 12 \end{array}$$
12.
$$\begin{array}{r} 6 \\ +2 \\ \hline 8 \end{array} \qquad \begin{array}{r} 2 \\ +6 \\ \hline 8 \end{array}$$

13.
$$\begin{array}{r} 2 \\ +8 \\ \hline 10 \end{array} \qquad \begin{array}{r} 8 \\ +2 \\ \hline 10 \end{array}$$
14.
$$\begin{array}{r} 2 \\ +7 \\ \hline 9 \end{array} \qquad \begin{array}{r} 7 \\ +2 \\ \hline 9 \end{array}$$
15.
$$\begin{array}{r} 5 \\ +6 \\ \hline 11 \end{array} \qquad \begin{array}{r} 6 \\ +5 \\ \hline 11 \end{array}$$

Science Connection

Egg to Tadpole to Frog

First there is an egg.
Then a tadpole hatches.
The tadpole grows legs.
Its tail shrinks.
Then it is a frog!

Show the order from egg to frog.
Number the pictures from 1 to 5.

__3__   __4__   __1__   __2__   __5__

WEEKLY WR READER eduplace.com/kids/mw/

Quick Check

Have children complete the Quick Check exercises independently to assess their understanding of concepts and skills taught in **Lessons 1–4.**

Item	Lesson	Error Analysis	Intervention
1–3	15.1	Children may count the addend when counting on.	Reteach Resource 15.1 *Ways to Success* 15.1
4–6	15.2	Children may guess sums they do not recall.	Reteach Resource 15.2 *Ways to Success* 15.2
7–9	15.3	Children may make fact errors.	Reteach Resource 15.3 *Ways to Success* 15.3
10–15	15.4	Children may not recognize the order property.	Reteach Resource 15.4 *Ways to Success* 15.4

Science Connection

Provide pictures or posters that show changes in nature, such as tadpoles to frogs, changing seasons, seeds growing into pumpkins, or the metamorphoses of caterpillars to butterflies. Children also may enjoy looking at picture books such as the following that show changes over time:

- *Tadpole and Frog* by Christine Back
- *The Very Hungry Caterpillar* by Eric Carle
- *Pumpkin, Pumpkin* by Jeanne Titherington
- *The Caterpillar and the Pollywog* by Jack Kent

Addition Facts Practice

PLANNING THE LESSON

MATHEMATICS OBJECTIVE
Use addition strategies to find sums through 12.

Use Lesson Planner CD-ROM for Lesson 15.5.

Daily Routines

Calendar
Ask children to find the date on the calendar whose sum of digits is 11. (The 29th day of the month unless it is February in a non-leap year.)

Sunday	Monday	Tuesday	Wednesday	Thursday	Friday	Saturday
				1	2	3	4
5	6	7	8	9	10	11
12	13	14	15	16	17	18
19	20	21	22	23	24	25
26	27	28	29	30	31	

Vocabulary
Review **plus sign** and **equal sign** by writing addition sentences, leaving out the operation symbols. Have children name the symbols as you complete the sentences. Then have them read the completed sentences aloud.

Vocabulary Cards

Meeting North Carolina's Standards
1.03 Develop fluency with single-digit addition and corresponding differences using strategies such as modeling, composing and decomposing quantities, using doubles, and making tens.

Also 1.04

Lesson Transparency **15.5**

Problem of the Day
Write two subtraction sentences using 2, 3, and 5. ($5 - 3 = 2$ and $5 - 2 = 3$)

Quick Review

$$\begin{array}{ccccc} 6 & 8 & 9 & 10 & 5 \\ -0 & -2 & -2 & -2 & -2 \\ \hline (6) & (6) & (7) & (8) & (3) \end{array}$$

Lesson Quiz
Write the sum. Write your strategy. (Possible strategies given.)

1. $3 + 6 =$ ___ (9) Strategy: ___ (count on)
2. $4 + 4 =$ ___ (8) Strategy: ___ (doubles)
3. $8 + 4 =$ ___ (12) Strategy: ___ (use a ten frame)

LEVELED PRACTICE

RETEACH 15.5

Name _____ Date _____ Reteach 15.5

Addition Facts Practice

Use these strategies to find the sum.

Count on.	Use a ten frame.
$8 + 2 = \underline{10}$ Say 8. Count 9, 10.	$7 + 3 = \underline{10}$
Use doubles. $5 + 5 = \underline{10}$ The addends are the same.	**Use doubles plus 1.** $5 + 6 = \underline{11}$ 5 + 5 and 1 more.

Use any strategy.
Find the sum.

1. $6 + 6 = \underline{12}$ 2. $4 + 7 = \underline{11}$ 3. $3 + 5 = \underline{8}$

4. $2 + 9 = \underline{11}$ 5. $3 + 6 = \underline{9}$ 6. $4 + 3 = \underline{7}$

7.	8.	9.	10.	11.	12.
1 +6 = 7	3 +3 = 6	7 +3 = 10	6 +4 = 10	8 +3 = 11	7 +2 = 9

13.	14.	15.	16.	17.	18.
2 +5 = 7	5 +5 = 10	6 +3 = 9	4 +4 = 8	5 +6 = 11	2 +3 = 5

Copyright © Houghton Mifflin Company. All rights reserved. Use with text pages 439–442.

PRACTICE 15.5

Name _____ Date _____ Practice 15.5

Addition Facts Practice

Use any strategy.
Find the sum.

1. $6 + 6 = \underline{12}$ 2. $3 + 7 = \underline{10}$ 3. $2 + 5 = \underline{7}$

4. $1 + 9 = \underline{10}$ 5. $4 + 6 = \underline{10}$ 6. $5 + 3 = \underline{8}$

7.	8.	9.	10.	11.	12.
1 +5 = 6	3 +2 = 5	7 +2 = 9	8 +4 = 12	9 +3 = 12	8 +2 = 10

13.	14.	15.	16.	17.	18.
2 +4 = 6	5 +6 = 11	7 +3 = 10	4 +5 = 9	5 +5 = 10	6 +3 = 9

⬤ **Test Prep**

Fill in the ○ for the correct answer. NH means Not Here.

19. Pat has 5 pencils. Doug has twice as many pencils. How many pencils does Doug have?

1 10 8 NH
○ ⬤ ○ ○

Copyright © Houghton Mifflin Company. All rights reserved. Use with text pages 439–442.

ENRICHMENT 15.5

Name _____ Date _____ Enrichment 15.5

I Can Use This and That

Find the sum.
Circle the strategy you used. **Strategies will vary.**

1.	8 +3 / 11	Count on. Use doubles. Use doubles plus one. Use a ten frame.	2.	5 +4 / 9	Count on. Use doubles. Use doubles plus one. Use a ten frame.
3.	2 +9 / 11	Count on. Use doubles. Use doubles plus one. Use a ten frame.	4.	6 +6 / 12	Count on. Use doubles. Use doubles plus one. Use a ten frame.
5.	4 +4 / 8	Count on. Use doubles. Use doubles plus one. Use a ten frame.	6.	7 +3 / 10	Count on. Use doubles. Use doubles plus one. Use a ten frame.
7.	5 +6 / 11	Count on. Use doubles. Use doubles plus one. Use a ten frame.	8.	8 +1 / 9	Count on. Use doubles. Use doubles plus one. Use a ten frame.

Talk About It What two strategies could you use to solve problem 1?
I could use a ten frame or I could count on to solve the problem.

Copyright © Houghton Mifflin Company. All rights reserved. Use with text pages 439–442.

Practice Workbook Page 102

Reaching All Learners
Differentiated Instruction

English Learners

Children will need to understand the concept of *doubles* in order to successfully use some addition strategies. Use Worksheet 15.5 to build familiarity with this concept.

Special Needs
VISUAL, TACTILE

Materials: *dot cards (LT 17)*

- Place the cards in an array face up on the table. Tell the child to find sums of 12.
- Have the child choose a card and record the number as the first addend.
- Now have the child find the dot card that completes a sum of 12 and complete the addition sentence.

Early Finishers
VISUAL, AUDITORY

Materials: *two number cubes labeled 1–6*

- In turn, one child in a group rolls the number cubes and says the 2 numbers.
- All children write an addition sentence with the 2 numbers and find the sum. They check each other's work.

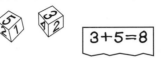

$3+5=8$

TECHNOLOGY

Spiral Review
To reinforce skills on lessons taught earlier, create **customized** spiral review worksheets using the *Ways to Assess* CD-ROM.

eBook
eMathBook allows students to review lessons and do homework without carrying their textbooks home.

Education Place
Recommend that parents visit **Education Place** at **eduplace.com/parents/mw/** for parent support activities.

Art Connection
Explain that print-making is an art form. Provide items that children can use to print. Children write addition sentences for their prints.

$4 + 6 = 10$

MATH CENTER

Basic Skills Activity
Motivate children to build basic skills. Use this activity to address multiple learning styles using hands-on activities related to the skills of this lesson.

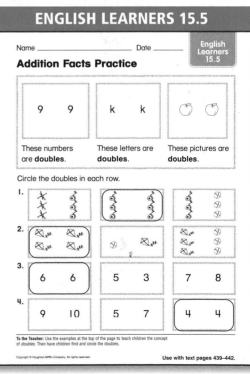

PROBLEM SOLVING 15.5

Name _____ Date _____

Problem Solving 15.5

Addition Facts Practice

Read and solve.
Think about addition strategies to help you.

Count on	Use doubles
Use a ten frame	Use doubles plus one

Draw or write to explain.

1. Enrique has 5 action figures. He gets 3 more for his birthday. How many action figures does he have in all?

   __8__ action figures

2. Marcia has 5 bears on her bed. She has 6 more bears on a shelf. How many bears does Marcia have in all?

   __11__ stuffed bears

3. Terry has 4 dog statues. She has 8 cat statues. How many statues does Terry have in all?

   __12__ statues

Use with text pages 439–442.

HOMEWORK 15.5

Name _____ Date _____

Homework 15.5

Addition Facts Practice

You can use different strategies to find sums.

Count on $6 + 2 = 8$	Say 6. Count 7, 8.	
Use doubles $3 + 3 = 6$	The addends are the same.	
Use doubles plus one $5 + 6 = 11$	$5 + 5$ and 1 more.	
Use a ten frame $3 + 7 = 10$		

Find the sum.

1. $2 + 3 = $ __5__   2. $6 + 3 = $ __9__

3. $3 + 4 = $ __7__   4. $5 + 3 = $ __8__

5. $4 + 4 = $ __8__   6. $4 + 6 = $ __10__

7. $\begin{array}{r} 5 \\ +3 \\ \hline 8 \end{array}$ 8. $\begin{array}{r} 8 \\ +4 \\ \hline 12 \end{array}$ 9. $\begin{array}{r} 6 \\ +6 \\ \hline 12 \end{array}$

10. Cindy has 5 marbles. She buys 4 more marbles. How many marbles does she have in all? Tell what strategies you used to find the sum.

    __9__ marbles

Draw or write to explain.

Use with text pages 439–442.

ENGLISH LEARNERS 15.5

Name _____ Date _____

English Learners 15.5

Addition Facts Practice

9 9	k k	🍎 🍎
These numbers are **doubles**.	These letters are **doubles**.	These pictures are **doubles**.

Circle the doubles in each row.

1.
2.
3.
   | 6 6 | 5 3 | 7 8 |
4.
   | 9 10 | 5 7 | 4 4 |

To the Teacher: Use the examples at the top of the page to teach children the concept of *doubles*. Then have children find and circle the doubles.

Use with text pages 439–442.

Homework Workbook Page 102

TEACHING LESSON 15.5

LESSON ORGANIZER

Objective Use addition strategies to find sums through 12.

Resources Reteach, Practice, Enrichment, Problem Solving, Homework, English Learners, Transparencies, Math Center

Materials Teacher-made addition fact cards for sums through 12, number cards 1–12 (LT 14 and 15)

Activity

Warm-Up Activity
Model Strategies Learned

iiii Whole Group	⏱ 5 minutes	Visual, Auditory

1. Write digits 1 to 9 (not in sequence) on the board.

2. Have a child come up and circle two digits that equal 10 when added together. Write the number sentence on the board without the addends and have the child fill in the circled digits.

3. Repeat for sums of 12.

Name_____

Addition Facts Practice

You can use these strategies to find sums.

Count on	$9 + 3 = \underline{12}$	Say 9. Count 10, 11, 12.
Use doubles	$4 + 4 = \underline{8}$	The addends are the same.
Use doubles plus one	$4 + 5 = \underline{9}$	4 + 4 and 1 more.
Use a ten frame	$4 + 7 = \underline{11}$	

Guided Practice

Use any strategy.
Find the sum.

Think I know 5 + 5 = 10. The sum of 6 + 5 is one more.

1. $6 + 5 = \underline{11}$ 2. $2 + 3 = \underline{5}$

3. $3 + 5 = \underline{8}$ 4. $4 + 2 = \underline{6}$ 5. $3 + 3 = \underline{6}$

6. $3 + 6 = \underline{9}$ 7. $5 + 5 = \underline{10}$ 8. $4 + 8 = \underline{12}$

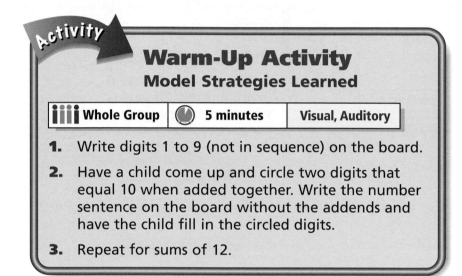

9. $\begin{array}{r} 4 \\ +7 \\ \hline 11 \end{array}$ 10. $\begin{array}{r} 1 \\ +1 \\ \hline 2 \end{array}$ 11. $\begin{array}{r} 6 \\ +4 \\ \hline 10 \end{array}$ 12. $\begin{array}{r} 9 \\ +1 \\ \hline 10 \end{array}$ 13. $\begin{array}{r} 3 \\ +8 \\ \hline 11 \end{array}$ 14. $\begin{array}{r} 7 \\ +2 \\ \hline 9 \end{array}$

TEST TIPS **Explain Your Thinking** Which strategy can help you find the sum of $4 + 5$? Tell why. **I can use doubles plus one. I know the double 4 + 4 = 8. I add 1 to find that 4 + 5 = 9.**

Chapter 15 Lesson 5   four hundred thirty-nine **439**

---

1 Introduce *Activity*
Discuss Addition Facts Practice

iiii Whole Group	⏱ 10–15 minutes	Visual, Auditory

Materials: *teacher-made addition fact cards for sums through 12, number cards 1 to 12 (LT 14 and 15)*

1. Prepare number cards 1–12 for each child.

2. Display an addition card. Ask children to hold up the number card that states the sum.

3. Review the strategy that might work best to find the sum. For example, if many children do not find the correct sum for 5 + 7, you might want to ask a volunteer to use counters on a ten frame to show how to find the sum.

2 Develop

Guided Learning

Teaching Example Read the objective with children. Guide them through each fact strategy. Remind children that they can add in any order.

Guided Practice

Have children complete **Exercises 1–14** as you observe. Give children the opportunity to answer the Explain Your Thinking question. Then discuss their responses with the class.

Practice

Remember to think about which strategy will work best.

Use any strategy.
Find the sum.

1. $4 + 6 = \underline{10}$ 2. $5 + 3 = \underline{8}$ 3. $9 + 1 = \underline{10}$

4. $6 + 2 = \underline{8}$ 5. $1 + 8 = \underline{9}$ 6. $7 + 2 = \underline{9}$

7. $4 + 5 = \underline{9}$ 8. $7 + 3 = \underline{10}$ 9. $5 + 2 = \underline{7}$

10. $\begin{array}{r} 3 \\ +7 \\ \hline 10 \end{array}$
11. $\begin{array}{r} 2 \\ +3 \\ \hline 5 \end{array}$
12. $\begin{array}{r} 4 \\ +3 \\ \hline 7 \end{array}$
13. $\begin{array}{r} 2 \\ +2 \\ \hline 4 \end{array}$
14. $\begin{array}{r} 2 \\ +8 \\ \hline 10 \end{array}$
15. $\begin{array}{r} 7 \\ +5 \\ \hline 12 \end{array}$

16. $\begin{array}{r} 3 \\ +2 \\ \hline 5 \end{array}$
17. $\begin{array}{r} 3 \\ +6 \\ \hline 9 \end{array}$
18. $\begin{array}{r} 5 \\ +6 \\ \hline 11 \end{array}$
19. $\begin{array}{r} 4 \\ +4 \\ \hline 8 \end{array}$
20. $\begin{array}{r} 6 \\ +6 \\ \hline 12 \end{array}$
21. $\begin{array}{r} 8 \\ +3 \\ \hline 11 \end{array}$

22. $\begin{array}{r} 7 \\ +1 \\ \hline 8 \end{array}$
23. $\begin{array}{r} 2 \\ +7 \\ \hline 9 \end{array}$
24. $\begin{array}{r} 6 \\ +5 \\ \hline 11 \end{array}$
25. $\begin{array}{r} 8 \\ +2 \\ \hline 10 \end{array}$
26. $\begin{array}{r} 4 \\ +7 \\ \hline 11 \end{array}$
27. $\begin{array}{r} 3 \\ +4 \\ \hline 7 \end{array}$

28. $\begin{array}{r} 2 \\ +9 \\ \hline 11 \end{array}$
29. $\begin{array}{r} 2 \\ +6 \\ \hline 8 \end{array}$
30. $\begin{array}{r} 3 \\ +8 \\ \hline 11 \end{array}$
31. $\begin{array}{r} 2 \\ +4 \\ \hline 6 \end{array}$
32. $\begin{array}{r} 8 \\ +4 \\ \hline 12 \end{array}$
33. $\begin{array}{r} 7 \\ +4 \\ \hline 11 \end{array}$

Go on

Literature Connection

Refer back to the unit story *Twenty Is Too Many!* by Kate Duke, on student book pages 423b and 423c. Reread the pages with children and talk about how the picture matches the words and the number sentence. Then write the following sentence frame on the board:

____ waving guinea pigs plus ____ swinging guinea pigs makes how many guinea pigs in all?

Have different volunteers complete the question using the following pairs of number words.

- Eight, two
- Seven, three
- Six, four
- Five, five

Have children use whatever strategies they choose to find the sums. Then have them write the matching number sentences.

- Eight, two ($8 + 2 = 10$)
- Seven, three ($7 + 3 = 10$)
- Six, four ($6 + 4 = 10$)
- Five, five ($5 + 5 = 10$)

How are your number sentences alike? (They all have a sum of 10.) **Do you see any patterns?** (First addend decreases as second addend increases.)

If time allows, create a class book using the new questions and number sentences. Let groups of children illustrate different pages to match the text.

3 Practice

Independent Practice

Children complete **Exercises 1–33** independently.

Lesson continues

Technology Connection
Use a Calculator to Practice Addition

In this activity, students use their calculator's constant function to check their mastery of addition facts.

Explain that the constant function allows you to repeatedly add or subtract a number. Show students how to set the constant to add 1. Then have them complete the activity.

- Have students press [+] [1] [=]. Tell them that each time they press [=], the calculator will add one.

- Have students work in pairs. Tell one student to enter a number from 1–9 and give the calculator to their partner. That student predicts how many times they must press [=] to get a sum of 12. Students use the calculator to check.

- Have students record the addition sentence that they created using the calculator. Then have them repeat the activity with different starting numbers and different target sums.

Find the sum.

1. $\begin{array}{r} 1 \\ +4 \\ \hline 5 \end{array}$	2. $\begin{array}{r} 3 \\ +5 \\ \hline 8 \end{array}$	3. $\begin{array}{r} 2 \\ +9 \\ \hline 11 \end{array}$	4. $\begin{array}{r} 5 \\ +7 \\ \hline 12 \end{array}$	5. $\begin{array}{r} 4 \\ +8 \\ \hline 12 \end{array}$	6. $\begin{array}{r} 4 \\ +6 \\ \hline 10 \end{array}$
7. $\begin{array}{r} 9 \\ +3 \\ \hline 12 \end{array}$	8. $\begin{array}{r} 2 \\ +7 \\ \hline 9 \end{array}$	9. $\begin{array}{r} 6 \\ +5 \\ \hline 11 \end{array}$	10. $\begin{array}{r} 2 \\ +8 \\ \hline 10 \end{array}$	11. $\begin{array}{r} 3 \\ +4 \\ \hline 7 \end{array}$	12. $\begin{array}{r} 5 \\ +5 \\ \hline 10 \end{array}$
13. $\begin{array}{r} 4 \\ +5 \\ \hline 9 \end{array}$	14. $\begin{array}{r} 6 \\ +3 \\ \hline 9 \end{array}$	15. $\begin{array}{r} 7 \\ +3 \\ \hline 10 \end{array}$	16. $\begin{array}{r} 9 \\ +1 \\ \hline 10 \end{array}$	17. $\begin{array}{r} 8 \\ +4 \\ \hline 12 \end{array}$	18. $\begin{array}{r} 6 \\ +2 \\ \hline 8 \end{array}$
19. $\begin{array}{r} 2 \\ +7 \\ \hline 9 \end{array}$	20. $\begin{array}{r} 2 \\ +5 \\ \hline 7 \end{array}$	21. $\begin{array}{r} 5 \\ +6 \\ \hline 11 \end{array}$	22. $\begin{array}{r} 4 \\ +6 \\ \hline 10 \end{array}$	23. $\begin{array}{r} 9 \\ +2 \\ \hline 11 \end{array}$	24. $\begin{array}{r} 8 \\ +3 \\ \hline 11 \end{array}$
25. $\begin{array}{r} 1 \\ +7 \\ \hline 8 \end{array}$	26. $\begin{array}{r} 3 \\ +5 \\ \hline 8 \end{array}$	27. $\begin{array}{r} 6 \\ +4 \\ \hline 10 \end{array}$	28. $\begin{array}{r} 6 \\ +6 \\ \hline 12 \end{array}$	29. $\begin{array}{r} 8 \\ +2 \\ \hline 10 \end{array}$	30. $\begin{array}{r} 1 \\ +8 \\ \hline 9 \end{array}$
31. $\begin{array}{r} 5 \\ +4 \\ \hline 9 \end{array}$	32. $\begin{array}{r} 1 \\ +9 \\ \hline 10 \end{array}$	33. $\begin{array}{r} 5 \\ +7 \\ \hline 12 \end{array}$	34. $\begin{array}{r} 4 \\ +7 \\ \hline 11 \end{array}$	35. $\begin{array}{r} 3 \\ +9 \\ \hline 12 \end{array}$	36. $\begin{array}{r} 7 \\ +4 \\ \hline 11 \end{array}$
37. $\begin{array}{r} 2 \\ +9 \\ \hline 11 \end{array}$	38. $\begin{array}{r} 2 \\ +6 \\ \hline 8 \end{array}$	39. $\begin{array}{r} 1 \\ +6 \\ \hline 7 \end{array}$	40. $\begin{array}{r} 3 \\ +5 \\ \hline 8 \end{array}$	41. $\begin{array}{r} 6 \\ +5 \\ \hline 11 \end{array}$	42. $\begin{array}{r} 3 \\ +6 \\ \hline 9 \end{array}$

Chapter 15   four hundred forty-one **441**

---

3 Practice

Independent Practice

Children complete **Exercises 1–66** on pages 441 and 442 independently.

Problem Solving

After children complete the **Talk About It** question in **Exercise 67** on page 442, call on volunteers to share their questions and solutions. Discuss responses with the class.

Common Error

Guessing to Find the Sum

Children may be guessing to find a sum. Allow children time to work with concrete materials and strategies for finding unknown sums.

Practice

Find the sum.

43. 4 +8 12	44. 5 +6 11	45. 9 +2 11	46. 4 +3 7	47. 2 +7 9	48. 8 +1 9
49. 3 +3 6	50. 5 +2 7	51. 6 +4 10	52. 3 +7 10	53. 4 +7 11	54. 6 +3 9
55. 2 +3 5	56. 7 +4 11	57. 5 +5 10	58. 7 +5 12	59. 8 +3 11	60. 4 +2 6
61. 4 +4 8	62. 6 +2 8	63. 6 +5 11	64. 5 +4 9	65. 4 +6 10	66. 6 +6 12

Problem Solving ▶ Data Sense

67. **Talk About It** Tell a question about the graph that you can answer by adding.

Animals Seen at the Beach

Types of Animals: Bird, Crab, Starfish
Number of Animals: 0 1 2 3 4 5 6 7 8 9 10

At Home Ask questions about the bar graph that require your child to add to find the answers.

442 four hundred forty-two

---

5 + 2 = ☐

2   5   6   NH
○   ○   ○   ●

Activity

Lesson Intervention

Or use Intervention CD-ROM Lesson 15.5

Discussing and Modeling Strategies

Small Group	5–10 minutes	Visual, Auditory

Materials: *teacher-made addition fact cards with sums through 12*

1. Display a variety of addition cards.

2. Which problems would you solve by using doubles? Which problems would you solve by using a ten frame?

3. Have volunteers choose a card to answer your question and then model finding the sum.

7 +3
9 +2
8 +4

---

4 Assess and Close

Which have the same sum?

- 8 + 3   3 + 9   6 + 6
  (3 + 9 and 6 + 6)

- 2 + 9   7 + 4   6 + 5
  (all of them)

Keeping a Journal

List some addition facts you know. List some with which you need more practice.

Add Three Numbers

PLANNING THE LESSON

MATHEMATICS OBJECTIVE
Find the sum of three one-digit numbers.

Use Lesson Planner CD-ROM for Lesson 15.6.

Meeting North Carolina's Standards
1.03 Develop fluency with single-digit addition and corresponding differences using strategies such as modeling, composing and decomposing quantities, using doubles, and making tens.

Also 1.04

Daily Routines

Calendar
Point to the 12th on the calendar. Have children name the numbers of three dates in a row whose sum equals the number 12. (3, 4, 5)

Sunday	Monday	Tuesday	Wednesday	Thursday	Friday	Saturday
				1	2	3	4
5	6	7	8	9	10	11
12	13	14	15	16	17	18
19	20	21	22	23	24	25
26	27	28	29	30	31	

Vocabulary
Review **add** by writing *d, d, a* on the board and asking children to unscramble the letters to name a word that means "find the sum." (add) Review other math vocabulary such as **addend** and **sum** in the same way.

Vocabulary Cards

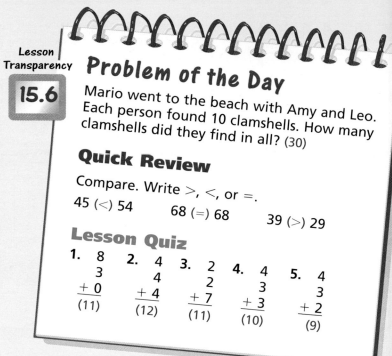

Lesson Transparency
15.6

Problem of the Day
Mario went to the beach with Amy and Leo. Each person found 10 clamshells. How many clamshells did they find in all? (30)

Quick Review
Compare. Write >, <, or =.
45 (<) 54   68 (=) 68   39 (>) 29

Lesson Quiz

1.	2.	3.	4.	5.
8	4	2	4	4
3	4	2	3	3
+ 0	+ 4	+ 7	+ 3	+ 2
(11)	(12)	(11)	(10)	(9)

LEVELED PRACTICE

RETEACH 15.6

Name _____ Date _____   Reteach 15.6

Add Three Numbers

Three numbers can be added in any order. Look for facts you know.

$$\begin{array}{c} 4 \\ 3 \\ +2 \end{array} \boxed{7} \quad \begin{array}{c} 4 \\ 3 \\ +2 \end{array} \quad \begin{array}{c} 4 \\ 3 \\ +2 \end{array} \boxed{5} \quad \begin{array}{c} 4 \\ 3 \\ +2 \end{array} \quad \begin{array}{c} 3 \\ +\boxed{6} \end{array}$$
9   9   9

Think 7 + 2.   Think 4 + 5.   Think 3 + 6.

The sum is the same each way.

Write the sum.

1.	2.	3.
2	2	6 1
4 6	5 9	1
+ 1 + 1	+ 4 + 2	+ 3 + 9
7	11	10

4.	5.	6.	7.
2	2	5	1
8	5	1	9
+ 1	+ 1	+ 4	+ 1
11	8	10	11

8. 7 + 3 + 2 = 12   9. 6 + 2 + 1 = 9

Copyright © Houghton Mifflin Company. All rights reserved.   Use with text pages 443–444.

PRACTICE 15.6

Name _____ Date _____   Practice 15.6

Add Three Numbers

Write the sum.

1.	2.	3.	4.	5.	6.
1	3	7	6	5	4
3	5	0	1	2	1
+ 4	+ 4	+ 4	+ 4	+ 3	+ 5
8	12	11	11	10	10

7.	8.	9.	10.	11.	12.
2	3	7	2	3	6
4	5	1	9	3	2
+ 4	+ 1	+ 3	+ 0	+ 5	+ 1
10	9	11	11	11	9

13. 7 + 2 + 2 = 11   14. 2 + 7 + 1 = 10

15. 2 + 3 + 1 = 6   16. 4 + 2 + 1 = 7

Test Prep

Fill in the ○ for the correct answer. NH means Not Here.

17. Hans has 5 stamps. He buys 2 more stamps. His mother gives him 4 more stamps. How many stamps does he have now?

Explain your answer.

9   11   7   NH
○   ●   ○   ○

Copyright © Houghton Mifflin Company. All rights reserved.   Use with text pages 443–444.

ENRICHMENT 15.6

Name _____ Date _____   Enrichment 15.6

Now I'm Up to 3

Write the numbers in the picture. Circle the two numbers that make 10, or circle the doubles. Then add to find the sum.

1. (4) (4) (2)
    + 2
    12

2. (4) (4)
    + 1
    9

3. (3) (4) (3)
    + 3
    10

4. (4) (1) (6)
    + 6
    11

5. (5) (2) (2)
    + 2
    9

6. (8) (1) (2)
    + 2
    11

Talk About It How did you decide which two numbers to add first?

Copyright © Houghton Mifflin Company. All rights reserved.   Use with text pages 443–444.

Practice Workbook Page 103

Reaching All Learners

Differentiated Instruction

English Learners

Worksheet 15.6 develops children's understanding of the words *first* and *then*. Children will need to understand these words as they learn the process for adding three numbers.

Special Needs
VISUAL, TACTILE

Materials: *number dot cards 1–12 (LT 12)*

- Show the child 3 dot cards with a sum through 12 and have him or her use the dots to help find the sum.

$$2 + 3 + 5$$
$$5 + 5 = 10$$

Gifted and Talented
VISUAL, TACTILE

- Have children work in pairs. Guide one child to write a vertical addition problem with 3 addends. Have the child leave a blank for one of the addends.

$$\begin{array}{r} 7 \\ \Box \\ +\ 1 \\ \hline 12 \end{array}$$

- Have the partner fill in the missing addend.

TECHNOLOGY

Spiral Review

Help students remember skills they learned earlier by creating **customized** spiral review worksheets using the *Ways to Assess* CD-ROM.

eBook

An electronic version of this lesson can be found in **eMathBook**, featuring an animated teaching model.

Education Place

Visit **Data Place** at **eduplace.com/dataplace/** to take a survey and see graphs of the results.

Music Connection

Discuss brass instruments. Explain that with most brass instruments notes are made by pressing valves. Create addition problems such as: There are 3 trumpets in a band and each trumpet has 3 valves. How many valves in all?

MATH CENTER

Basic Skills Activity

Motivate children to build basic skills. Use this activity to address multiple learning styles using hands-on activities related to the skills of this lesson.

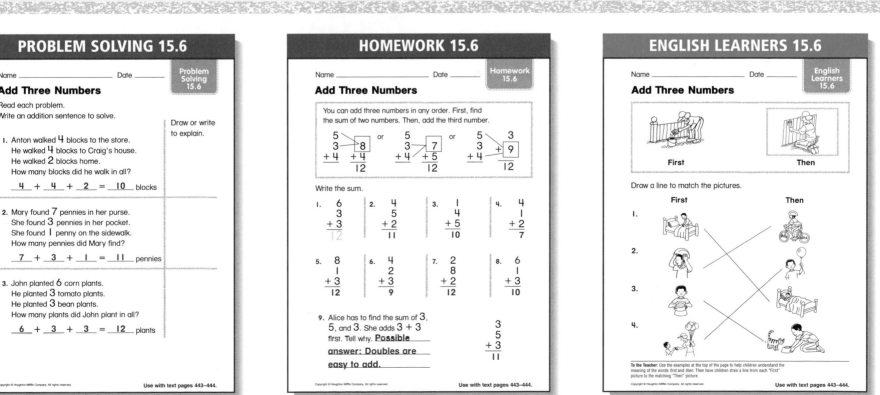

PROBLEM SOLVING 15.6

Name _____ Date _____
Problem Solving 15.6

Add Three Numbers

Read each problem.
Write an addition sentence to solve.

Draw or write to explain.

1. Anton walked 4 blocks to the store.
   He walked 4 blocks to Craig's house.
   He walked 2 blocks home.
   How many blocks did he walk in all?

   __4__ + __4__ + __2__ = __10__ blocks

2. Mary found 7 pennies in her purse.
   She found 3 pennies in her pocket.
   She found 1 penny on the sidewalk.
   How many pennies did Mary find?

   __7__ + __3__ + __1__ = __11__ pennies

3. John planted 6 corn plants.
   He planted 3 tomato plants.
   He planted 3 bean plants.
   How many plants did John plant in all?

   __6__ + __3__ + __3__ = __12__ plants

Use with text pages 443–444.

HOMEWORK 15.6

Name _____ Date _____
Homework 15.6

Add Three Numbers

You can add three numbers in any order. First, find the sum of two numbers. Then, add the third number.

$$\begin{array}{r} 5 \\ 3 \\ +4 \\ \hline \end{array} \begin{array}{r} 8 \\ +4 \\ \hline 12 \end{array} \text{ or } \begin{array}{r} 5 \\ 3 \\ +4 \\ \hline \end{array} \begin{array}{r} 7 \\ +5 \\ \hline 12 \end{array} \text{ or } \begin{array}{r} 5 \\ 3 \\ +4 \\ \hline \end{array} \begin{array}{r} 3 \\ 9 \\ \hline 12 \end{array}$$

Write the sum.

1. $$\begin{array}{r} 6 \\ 3 \\ +3 \\ \hline 12 \end{array}$$
2. $$\begin{array}{r} 4 \\ 5 \\ +2 \\ \hline 11 \end{array}$$
3. $$\begin{array}{r} 1 \\ 4 \\ +5 \\ \hline 10 \end{array}$$
4. $$\begin{array}{r} 4 \\ 1 \\ +2 \\ \hline 7 \end{array}$$

5. $$\begin{array}{r} 8 \\ 1 \\ +3 \\ \hline 12 \end{array}$$
6. $$\begin{array}{r} 4 \\ 2 \\ +3 \\ \hline 9 \end{array}$$
7. $$\begin{array}{r} 2 \\ 8 \\ +2 \\ \hline 12 \end{array}$$
8. $$\begin{array}{r} 6 \\ 1 \\ +3 \\ \hline 10 \end{array}$$

9. Alice has to find the sum of 3, 5, and 3. She adds 3 + 3 first. Tell why. **Possible answer: Doubles are easy to add.**

$$\begin{array}{r} 3 \\ 5 \\ +3 \\ \hline 11 \end{array}$$

Use with text pages 443–444.

Homework Workbook Page 103

ENGLISH LEARNERS 15.6

Name _____ Date _____
English Learners 15.6

Add Three Numbers

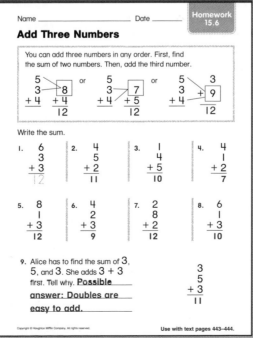

First   Then

Draw a line to match the pictures.

First   Then

1.

2.

3.

4.

To the Teacher: Use the examples at the top of the page to help children understand the meaning of the words *first* and *then*. Then have children draw a line from each "First" picture to the matching "Then" picture.

Use with text pages 443–444.

TEACHING LESSON 15.6

LESSON ORGANIZER

Objective Find the sum of three one-digit numbers.

Resources Reteach, Practice, Enrichment, Problem Solving, Homework, English Learners, Transparencies, Math Center

Materials Cubes, blank transparency

Activity
Warm-Up Activity
Model the Order Property

| 👤👤👤 Small Group | 🕐 5–10 minutes | Auditory, Visual |

Materials: *cubes*

1. Use cubes to review the order property. Display 4 red cubes and 5 blue cubes in a cube tower. Write the matching addition fact vertically on the board. Have a volunteer read the fact aloud.

$$\begin{array}{r} 4 \\ + 5 \\ \hline 9 \end{array} \qquad \begin{array}{r} 5 \\ + 4 \\ \hline 9 \end{array}$$

2. Then switch the tower so the blue cubes are on top. Have a child write the matching fact vertically and read it aloud.

3. Ask volunteers to explain the order property in their own words.

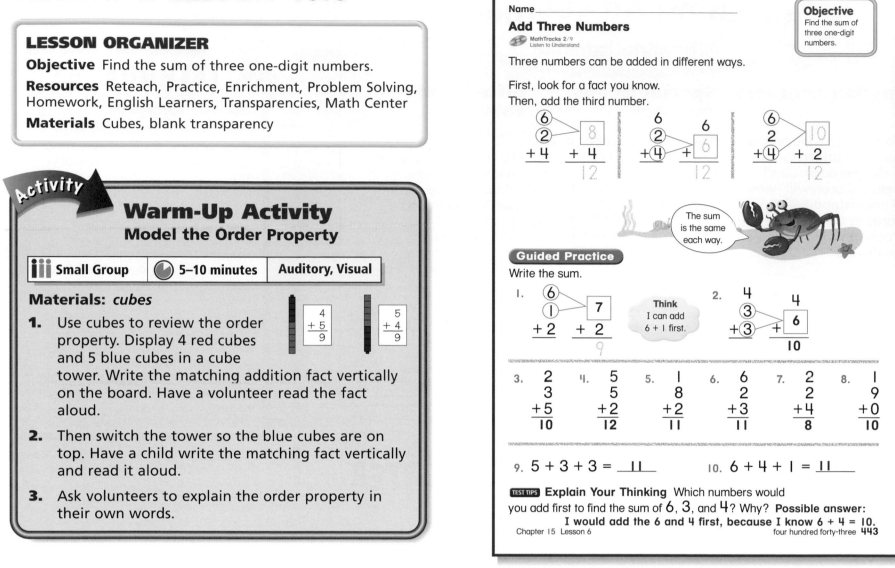

Name _____

Add Three Numbers

MathTracks 2/9
Listen to Understand

Objective Find the sum of three one-digit numbers.

Three numbers can be added in different ways.

First, look for a fact you know.
Then, add the third number.

The sum is the same each way.

Guided Practice

Write the sum.

9. $5 + 3 + 3 = \underline{11}$ 10. $6 + 4 + 1 = \underline{11}$

TEST TIPS **Explain Your Thinking** Which numbers would you add first to find the sum of 6, 3, and 4? Why? **Possible answer: I would add the 6 and 4 first, because I know 6 + 4 = 10.**

Chapter 15 Lesson 6   four hundred forty-three **443**

---

① Introduce
Activity
Discuss Adding Three Numbers

| 👤👤👤👤 Whole Group | 🕐 10–15 minutes | Visual, Auditory |

Materials: *cubes*

1. Have children make a red 2-cube tower, a green 3-cube tower, and a blue 5-cube tower.

2. **How many red cubes are there?** (2) **Green cubes?** (3) **Blue cubes?** (5) **How many cubes in all?** (10) Write $2 + 3 + 5 = 10$ vertically on the board and read the addition as you relate the towers to the addends.

3. Then have children connect the red and green towers. **How many cubes are in the new tower?** (5) Next, have them add the blue cubes to their tower. **How many cubes are in the tower now?** (10) **How is 2 + 3 + 5 similar to 5 + 5?** (Both have a sum of 10.)

4. Continue the activity focusing on grouping addends.

② Develop

Guided Learning

Teaching Example This lesson develops algebraic thinking. Both the associative and commutative property are used. Read the objective with the children. Guide them through the example to show that there are 3 ways to arrive at the same sum.

Guided Practice

Have children complete **Exercises 1–10** as you observe. Give children the opportunity to answer the Explain Your Thinking question. Then discuss their responses with the class.

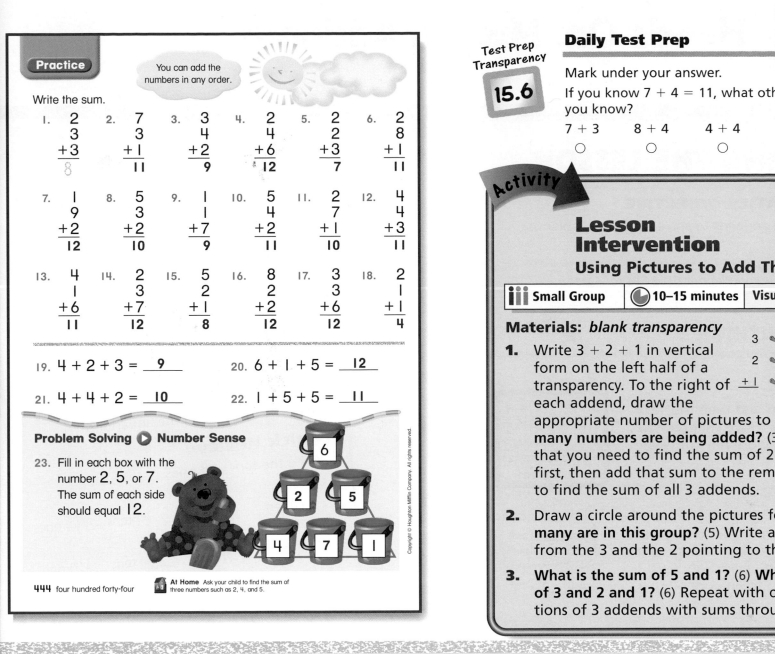

Practice

You can add the numbers in any order.

Write the sum.

1. 2
   3
   +3
   ‾8‾

2. 7
   3
   +1
   ‾11‾

3. 3
   4
   +2
   ‾9‾

4. 2
   4
   +6
   ‾12‾

5. 2
   2
   +3
   ‾7‾

6. 2
   8
   +1
   ‾11‾

7. 1
   9
   +2
   ‾12‾

8. 5
   3
   +2
   ‾10‾

9. 1
   1
   +7
   ‾9‾

10. 5
    4
    +2
    ‾11‾

11. 2
    7
    +1
    ‾10‾

12. 4
    4
    +3
    ‾11‾

13. 4
    1
    +6
    ‾11‾

14. 2
    3
    +7
    ‾12‾

15. 5
    2
    +1
    ‾8‾

16. 8
    2
    +2
    ‾12‾

17. 3
    3
    +6
    ‾12‾

18. 2
    1
    +1
    ‾4‾

19. 4 + 2 + 3 = __9__

20. 6 + 1 + 5 = __12__

21. 4 + 4 + 2 = __10__

22. 1 + 5 + 5 = __11__

Problem Solving ▶ Number Sense

23. Fill in each box with the number 2, 5, or 7. The sum of each side should equal 12.

6 / 2 / 5 / 4 / 7 / 1

444 four hundred forty-four

At Home Ask your child to find the sum of three numbers such as 2, 4, and 5.

Daily Test Prep

Mark under your answer.

If you know 7 + 4 = 11, what other addition fact do you know?

7 + 3 ○   8 + 4 ○   4 + 4 ○   NH ●

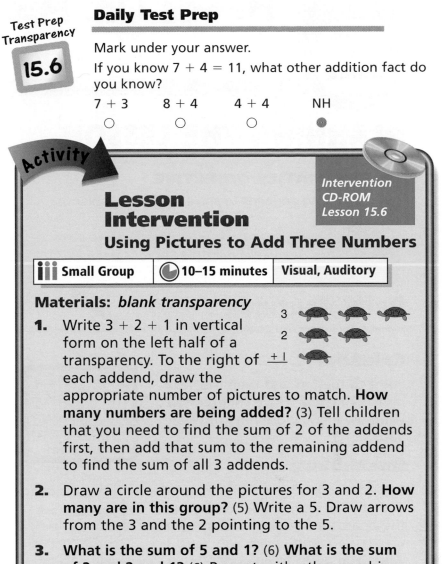

Activity

Lesson Intervention

Intervention CD-ROM Lesson 15.6

Using Pictures to Add Three Numbers

| 👥 Small Group | 🕐 10–15 minutes | Visual, Auditory |

Materials: *blank transparency*

1. Write 3 + 2 + 1 in vertical form on the left half of a transparency. To the right of each addend, draw the appropriate number of pictures to match. **How many numbers are being added?** (3) Tell children that you need to find the sum of 2 of the addends first, then add that sum to the remaining addend to find the sum of all 3 addends.

2. Draw a circle around the pictures for 3 and 2. **How many are in this group?** (5) Write a 5. Draw arrows from the 3 and the 2 pointing to the 5.

3. **What is the sum of 5 and 1?** (6) **What is the sum of 3 and 2 and 1?** (6) Repeat with other combinations of 3 addends with sums through 12.

---

③ Practice

Independent Practice

Children complete **Exercises 1–22** independently.

Problem Solving

After children complete **Exercise 23**, call on volunteers to share their solutions. **How did you find the number that belongs between 6 and 1?** (Possible answer: I added 6 + 1 to get 7. Then I tried 5 to see if the sum is 12.)

Common Error

Adding One Addend Twice
Have children check off the 2 addends they use first and write their sum next to or above them.

④ Assess and Close

- **Find the sum of 3 + 4 + 3.** (10)
- **Now find the sum of 6 + 1 + 4.** (11)

✏️ Keeping a Journal

Draw a picture to show how you would find the sum of 6, 2, and 4. Write the addition sentence.

Hands On: Missing Addends

Lesson 15.7

PLANNING THE LESSON

MATHEMATICS OBJECTIVE
Write missing addends to solve addition problems.

Use Lesson Planner CD-ROM for Lesson 15.7.

Daily Routines

Calendar

Point to the 5th and then the 12th on the calendar. Have children tell you how many more days until the 12th.

Sunday	Monday	Tuesday	Wednesday	Thursday	Friday	Saturday
			1	2	3	4
5	6	7	8	9	10	11
12	13	14	15	16	17	18
19	20	21	22	23	24	25
26	27	28	29	30	31	

Vocabulary

Review **addend** by writing horizontal and vertical addition sentences on the board. Then ask children to hold up their *addend* Vocabulary Card when you point to an addend in a sentence.

Vocabulary Cards

Meeting North Carolina's Standards

1.03 Develop fluency with single-digit addition and corresponding differences using strategies such as modeling, composing and decomposing quantities, using doubles, and making tens.

Also 1.04

Lesson Transparency 15.7

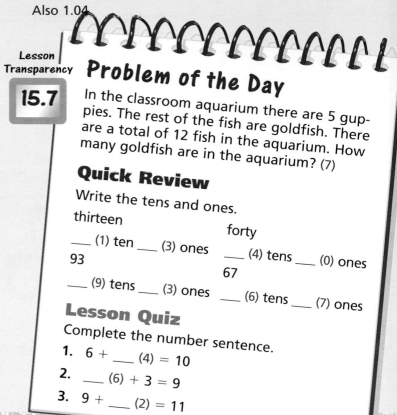

Problem of the Day
In the classroom aquarium there are 5 guppies. The rest of the fish are goldfish. There are a total of 12 fish in the aquarium. How many goldfish are in the aquarium? (7)

Quick Review
Write the tens and ones.

thirteen
___ (1) ten ___ (3) ones

93
___ (9) tens ___ (3) ones

forty
___ (4) tens ___ (0) ones

67
___ (6) tens ___ (7) ones

Lesson Quiz
Complete the number sentence.
1. 6 + ___ (4) = 10
2. ___ (6) + 3 = 9
3. 9 + ___ (2) = 11

LEVELED PRACTICE

RETEACH 15.7

Name _____ Date _____ Reteach 15.7

Missing Addends

Sometimes you know one addend and the sum.
Find the missing addend.

One addend is 3.
What is the missing addend?

3 + [5] = 8

Use cubes.
Find the missing addend.

1. [5] + 4 = 9
2. 5 + [6] = 11

3. 6 + [3] = 9   4. 2 + [5] = 7   5. 3 + [8] = 11

6. 1
   +[8]
   ___
    9

7. 4
   +[3]
   ___
    7

8. [7]
   + 4
   ___
    11

9. 6
   +[2]
   ___
    8

Copyright © Houghton Mifflin Company. All rights reserved.   Use with text pages 445–446.

PRACTICE 15.7

Name _____ Date _____ Practice 15.7

Missing Addends

Use cubes.
Find the missing addend.

1.  [3] + 4 = 7
2. [2] + 6 = 8

3. 5 + [3] = 8   4. 2 + [8] = 10   5. 3 + [8] = 11

6. 1
   +[7]
   ___
    8

7. 4
   +[2]
   ___
    6

8. [7]
   + 3
   ___
    10

9. 6
   +[3]
   ___
    9

10. [9]
   + 2
   ___
    11

11. [3]
   + 4
   ___
    7

12. [6]
   + 6
   ___
    12

13. [2]
   + 3
   ___
    5

14. [5]
   + 5
   ___
    10

15. 2
   +[5]
   ___
    7

Test Prep

Fill in the ○ for the correct answer. NH means Not Here.

16. Ethan has 10 model cars. 4 cars are red. How many cars are not red?

4 ○   6 ●   14 ○   NH ○

Explain your answer.

Copyright © Houghton Mifflin Company. All rights reserved.   Use with text pages 445–446.

ENRICHMENT 15.7

Name _____ Date _____ Enrichment 15.7

The Number Game

There will be 12 children at Jenny's party. Complete each number sentence. Write how many more of each thing Jenny needs. Use cubes if you need help.

1. Jenny has 7 party hats. How many more hats does she need?
   7 + 5 = 12
   She needs 5 more party hats.

2. Jenny has 6 balloons. How many more balloons does she need?
   6 + 6 = 12
   She needs 6 more balloons.

3. Jenny has 4 party bags. How many more bags does she need?
   4 + 8 = 12
   She needs 8 more party bags.

4. Jenny has 9 noisemakers. How many more noisemakers does she need?
   9 + 3 = 12
   She needs 3 more noisemakers.

5. Jenny has 10 cups. How many more cups does she need?
   10 + 2 = 12
   She needs 2 more cups.

6. Jenny has 5 cupcakes. How many more cupcakes does she need?
   5 + 7 = 12
   She needs 7 more cupcakes.

Copyright © Houghton Mifflin Company. All rights reserved.   Use with text pages 445–446.

Practice Workbook Page 104

445A   CHAPTER 15   Lesson 7

Reaching All Learners

Differentiated Instruction

English Learners

English-language learners will need to have an understanding of the word *missing* in order to find missing addends in addition problems. Use Worksheet 15.7 to develop children's ability to understand this word.

Special Needs
VISUAL, TACTILE

Materials: *paper cup, counters*

- Place 12 counters in a cup and label it.
- Have the child spill out some of the counters and tell how many, such as 7. Write the sentence. $7 + \_\_\_ = 12$
- Let the child count the counters still in the cup to find the missing addend.

Early Finishers
VISUAL, AUDITORY

Materials: *number cubes*

- Give each pair a number cube for 1–6 and a cube for 7–12.
- Children take turns rolling the cubes and using the greater number as the sum and the lesser number as the known addend in a missing addend sentence.
- The partner finds and writes the missing addend.

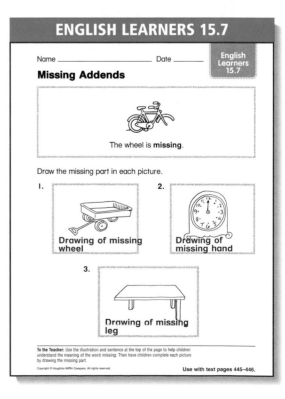

TECHNOLOGY

Spiral Review

You can prepare students for standardized tests with **customized** spiral review on key skills using the *Ways to Assess* CD-ROM.

Lesson Planner

You can customize your teaching plan or meet your curriculum requirements with the **Lesson Planner CD-ROM**.

Education Place

Encourage students to visit **Education Place** at **eduplace.com/kids/mw/** for more student activities.

Manipulatives

Interactive Connecting Cubes with several workmats are available on the *Ways to Success* CD-ROM.

Science Connection

Use a balance and cubes to find missing addends. Place 12 cubes on one pan for the sum, and 4 on the other pan for an addend. Have children count as they add cubes to the pan with 4 until the pans are level.

MATH CENTER

Basic Skills Activity

Motivate children to build basic skills. Use this activity to address multiple learning styles using hands-on activities related to the skills of this lesson.

PROBLEM SOLVING 15.7

Name _____ Date _____

Problem Solving 15.7

Missing Addends

Read each problem.
Complete the number sentence and solve.
Use ⬚ ⬚, if you wish.

1. There are 12 players on the soccer team. 8 players are at soccer practice. Other players are late. How many children are late?

    $8 + \underline{4} = 12$ players

    $\underline{4}$ players are late.

    Draw or write to explain.

2. Dan has kicked the ball for a goal 11 times. He missed 6 times. How many goals did he make?

    $\underline{5} + 6 = 11$ times

    He made $\underline{5}$ goals.

3. Two soccer teams scored 8 goals in all. One team scored 5 goals. How many goals did the other team score?

    $5 + \underline{3} = 8$

    The other team scored $\underline{3}$ goals.

Use with text pages 445–446.

HOMEWORK 15.7

Name _____ Date _____

Homework 15.7

Missing Addends

Sometimes you know one addend and the sum.

$4 + \underline{3} = 7$

Use objects.
Find the missing addend.

1. $6 + \underline{6} = 12$

2. $7 + \underline{2} = 9$

3. $\underline{7} + 5 = 12$

4. $\underline{6} + 5 = 11$

5. $\underline{5} + 3 = 8$

6. $\underline{7} + 4 = 11$

7. Beth needs 6 hats for her party. She already has 3. Find the missing addend.

    $3 + \underline{3} = 6$

    Draw or write to explain.

Use with text pages 445–446.

ENGLISH LEARNERS 15.7

Name _____ Date _____

English Learners 15.7

Missing Addends

The wheel is **missing**.

Draw the missing part in each picture.

1. Drawing of missing wheel

2. Drawing of missing hand

3. Drawing of missing leg

To the Teacher: Use the illustration and sentence at the top of the page to help children understand the meaning of the word *missing*. Then have children complete each picture by drawing the missing part.

Use with text pages 445–446.

Homework Workbook Page 104

TEACHING LESSON 15.7

LESSON ORGANIZER

Objective Write missing addends to solve addition problems.

Resources Reteach, Practice, Enrichment, Problem Solving, Homework, English Learners, Transparencies, Math Center

Materials Cubes, Workmat 3, number cards 2–12 (LT 14 and 15), blank transparency, part-part-whole transparency, overhead counters, 2-color counters

Activity

Warm-Up Activity
Model Names for Numbers

👥 Small Group	🕐 10–15 minutes	Tactile, Visual

Materials: *cubes, Workmat 3, number cards 2–12 (LT 14 and 15)*

1. Have children sit in a circle. Shuffle cards and place them face down in a stack. Ask one child to choose the top card and display it.

2. Ask children to show that number with cubes in the *whole* section of their mats. Then have children show two parts that equal the number by moving the cubes down into the two *part* sections of their mats. Have each child state the 2 parts. Record the different names for the number.

3. Continue similarly until each child has drawn a card.

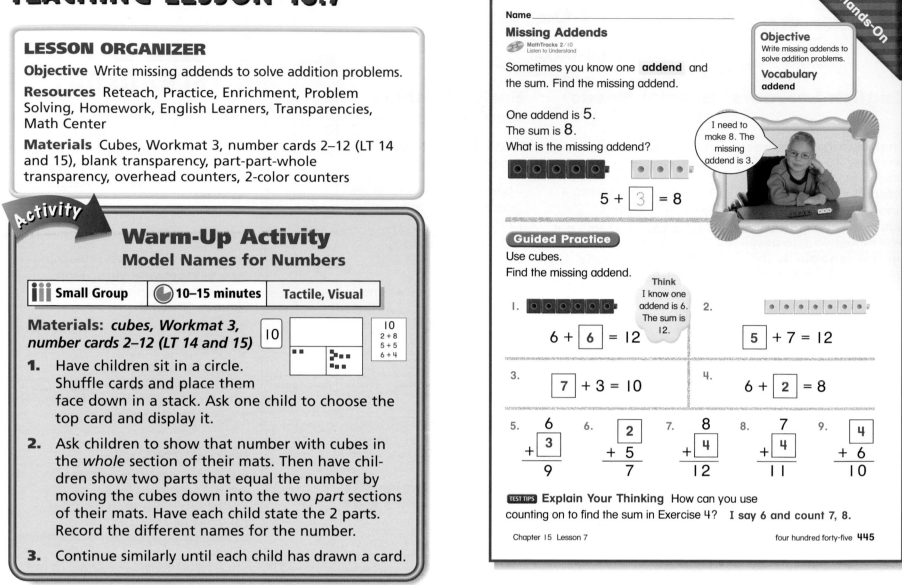

Name _____

Missing Addends
MathTracks 2 / 10
Listen to Understand

Objective
Write missing addends to solve addition problems.

Vocabulary
addend

Sometimes you know one **addend** and the sum. Find the missing addend.

One addend is 5.
The sum is 8.
What is the missing addend?

I need to make 8. The missing addend is 3.

$5 + \boxed{3} = 8$

Guided Practice
Use cubes.
Find the missing addend.

Think I know one addend is 6. The sum is 12.

1. $6 + \boxed{6} = 12$

2. $\boxed{5} + 7 = 12$

3. $\boxed{7} + 3 = 10$

4. $6 + \boxed{2} = 8$

5. $\begin{array}{r} 6 \\ + \boxed{3} \\ \hline 9 \end{array}$
6. $\begin{array}{r} \boxed{2} \\ + 5 \\ \hline 7 \end{array}$
7. $\begin{array}{r} 8 \\ + \boxed{4} \\ \hline 12 \end{array}$
8. $\begin{array}{r} 7 \\ + \boxed{4} \\ \hline 11 \end{array}$
9. $\begin{array}{r} \boxed{4} \\ + 6 \\ \hline 10 \end{array}$

TEST TIPS Explain Your Thinking How can you use counting on to find the sum in Exercise 4? **I say 6 and count 7, 8.**

Chapter 15 Lesson 7   four hundred forty-five **445**

---

1 Introduce
Discuss Missing Addends

👥 Whole Group	🕐 10–15 minutes	Visual, Auditory

Materials: *cubes, blank transparency*

1. Write $4 + \_\_\_ = 9$ on the transparency.

2. Display a yellow 4-cube train. **How many cubes are in the train?** (4) **How many more cubes do you need to make 9?** Have children count on from 4, as you add blue cubes one at a time. **How many blue cubes did I add to make 9?** (5) **5 is the missing addend.**

3. Continue similarly with other missing addend sentences with sums to 12. Allow children to share their own strategies for finding the missing addend.

2 Develop

Guided Learning

Teaching Example Read the objective and vocabulary with children. Guide them through the example as children follow along with cubes at their desks. Show a red 5-cube train, and then count on from 5 to 8 as you add yellow cubes one at a time to the train: **6, 7, 8. How many yellow cubes did you add to 5 to equal 8?** (3) **What is the missing addend?** (3)

Guided Practice

Have children complete **Exercises 1–9** as you observe. Give children the opportunity to answer the Explain Your Thinking question. Then discuss their responses with the class.

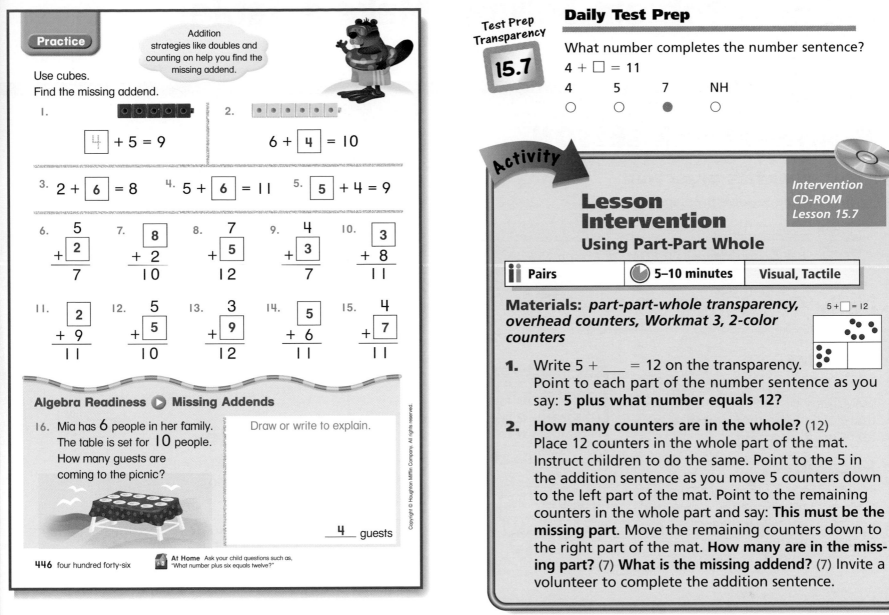

Practice

Addition strategies like doubles and counting on help you find the missing addend.

Use cubes.
Find the missing addend.

1. $\boxed{4} + 5 = 9$

2. $6 + \boxed{4} = 10$

3. $2 + \boxed{6} = 8$

4. $5 + \boxed{6} = 11$

5. $\boxed{5} + 4 = 9$

6. $\begin{array}{r} 5 \\ + \boxed{2} \\ \hline 7 \end{array}$

7. $\begin{array}{r} \boxed{8} \\ + 2 \\ \hline 10 \end{array}$

8. $\begin{array}{r} 7 \\ + \boxed{5} \\ \hline 12 \end{array}$

9. $\begin{array}{r} 4 \\ + \boxed{3} \\ \hline 7 \end{array}$

10. $\begin{array}{r} \boxed{3} \\ + 8 \\ \hline 11 \end{array}$

11. $\begin{array}{r} \boxed{2} \\ + 9 \\ \hline 11 \end{array}$

12. $\begin{array}{r} 5 \\ + \boxed{5} \\ \hline 10 \end{array}$

13. $\begin{array}{r} 3 \\ + \boxed{9} \\ \hline 12 \end{array}$

14. $\begin{array}{r} \boxed{5} \\ + 6 \\ \hline 11 \end{array}$

15. $\begin{array}{r} 4 \\ + \boxed{7} \\ \hline 11 \end{array}$

Algebra Readiness ▶ **Missing Addends**

16. Mia has 6 people in her family. The table is set for 10 people. How many guests are coming to the picnic?

Draw or write to explain.

$\underline{\hspace{1em}4\hspace{1em}}$ guests

At Home Ask your child questions such as, "What number plus six equals twelve?"

Daily Test Prep

What number completes the number sentence?

$4 + \square = 11$

4   5   7   NH
○   ○   ●   ○

Activity

Lesson Intervention

Using Part-Part Whole

Intervention CD-ROM Lesson 15.7

| 👥 Pairs | ⏱ 5–10 minutes | Visual, Tactile |

Materials: *part-part-whole transparency, overhead counters, Workmat 3, 2-color counters*

$5 + \square = 12$

1. Write $5 + \underline{\hspace{1em}} = 12$ on the transparency. Point to each part of the number sentence as you say: **5 plus what number equals 12?**

2. **How many counters are in the whole?** (12) Place 12 counters in the whole part of the mat. Instruct children to do the same. Point to the 5 in the addition sentence as you move 5 counters down to the left part of the mat. Point to the remaining counters in the whole part and say: **This must be the missing part.** Move the remaining counters down to the right part of the mat. **How many are in the missing part?** (7) **What is the missing addend?** (7) Invite a volunteer to complete the addition sentence.

3 Practice

Independent Practice

Children complete **Exercises 1–15** independently.

Algebra Readiness

After children complete **Exercise 16**, call on volunteers to share their solutions.

Common Error

Finding the Sum of the 2 Numbers
Remind children that the number they write cannot be greater than the sum. Have children model missing addend exercises with counters on a part-part-whole mat.

4 Assess and Close

Find the missing addend.

- $4 + \underline{\hspace{1em}} = 7$ (3)
- $\underline{\hspace{1em}} + 8 = 12$ (4)
- $6 + \underline{\hspace{1em}} = 10$ (4)

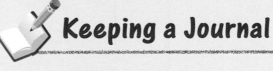

Keeping a Journal

Write $6 + \underline{\hspace{1em}} = 12$.

Write a story or draw a picture to match the missing addend sentence.

Problem Solving: Make a Table

PLANNING THE LESSON

MATHEMATICS OBJECTIVE
Make a table to solve problems.

Use Lesson Planner CD-ROM for Lesson 15.8.

Daily Routines

Calendar
Have children count and record how many of each day of the week there are in the month. Make a table using the data.

Vocabulary
Review *table* by displaying a simple table and asking volunteers to tell how the table makes the data easy to read.

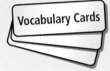

Vocabulary Cards

Meeting North Carolina's Standards
1.04 Create, model, and solve problems that use addition, subtraction, and fair shares (between two or three).

Also 1.03

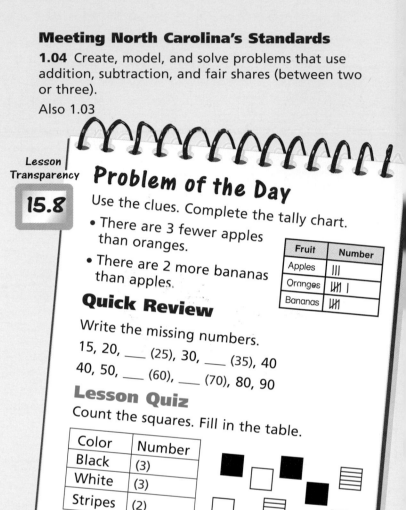

Lesson Transparency **15.8**

Problem of the Day
Use the clues. Complete the tally chart.
- There are 3 fewer apples than oranges.
- There are 2 more bananas than apples.

Fruit	Number
Apples	III
Oranges	IIII I
Bananas	IIII

Quick Review
Write the missing numbers.
15, 20, ___ (25), 30, ___ (35), 40
40, 50, ___ (60), ___ (70), 80, 90

Lesson Quiz
Count the squares. Fill in the table.

Color	Number
Black	(3)
White	(3)
Stripes	(2)

LEVELED PRACTICE

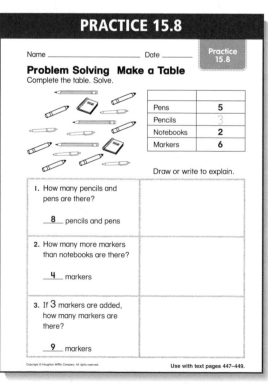

RETEACH 15.8

Name _____ Date _____ Reteach 15.8

Problem Solving Make a Table

Read It. Look for information.
Lee has 2 cars.
Lee has 7 airplanes.
He has 2 fewer dinosaurs than airplanes.
How many dinosaurs does Lee have?

Picture It.

Make a table with the information you have.

Toys	Number
Cars	2
Airplanes	7
Dinosaurs	5

Solve It. Use the table to solve the problem.

1. Use the table to write a subtraction sentence.

   7 airplanes − 2 = __5__ dinosaurs

2. Check your answer by writing an addition sentence.

   __5__ dinosaurs + 2 cars = 7 airplanes

The number of dinosaurs should be the same in each sentence.

Use with text pages 447–449.

PRACTICE 15.8

Name _____ Date _____ Practice 15.8

Problem Solving Make a Table
Complete the table. Solve.

Pens	5
Pencils	3
Notebooks	2
Markers	6

Draw or write to explain.

1. How many pencils and pens are there?

   __8__ pencils and pens

2. How many more markers than notebooks are there?

   __4__ markers

3. If 3 markers are added, how many markers are there?

   __9__ markers

Use with text pages 447–449.

ENRICHMENT 15.8

Name _____ Date _____ Enrichment 15.8

Snack Time

Complete the table.
Solve.

Snack	Numbers
apple	4
orange	3
banana	6

1. How many more bananas than oranges are there?

   __3__ more bananas

2. Write a problem that can be answered using the table.
   Problems and answers will vary.

   _____

   Use the table to answer your problem. Write the answer.

   _____

3. Look back at the problem.
   How could you check your answer?
   Answers will vary.

Use with text pages 447–449.

Practice Workbook Page 105

Reaching All Learners
Differentiated Instruction

English Learners

There are several meanings of the word *table* in English. English-language learners will have to understand the word in the context of mathematics in order to solve problems that require the use of tables.

Inclusion
VISUAL, AUDITORY

Materials: *cubes (red, blue, green)*

- Provide this table.

Color	Number
Red	
Blue	
Green	

- Have the child take a handful of cubes, sort, and record the numbers on the table. **What color cubes do you have the most of?**

Early Finishers
VISUAL, AUDITORY

Materials: *teacher-made chart*

- Have children count and record what pets each child has in the class. Then have them make a table using their data.
- Have children write questions that can be answered using the table.

Kind of Pets	Number of Children
dogs	5
fish	3
birds	6
cats	8

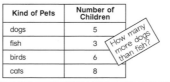

How many more dogs than fish?

TECHNOLOGY

Spiral Review
Create **customized** spiral review worksheets for individual students using the *Ways to Assess* CD-ROM.

Intervention
Use the *Ways to Success* CD-ROM intervention software to support students who need more help in understanding the concepts and skills taught in this chapter.

Lesson Planner
Use the **Lesson Planner** CD-ROM to see how lesson objectives for this chapter are correlated to standards.

Social Studies Connection
Talk about when and why people vote. Then, have the children "vote" for their favorite colors. Record the data in a table. How many more children like blue than orange? How many children like yellow? Which color do most of the children like?

MATH CENTER

Number of the Week Activity
Display the Number of the Week to motivate children to use their problem-solving skills. The exercises cover topics across all math strands.

PROBLEM SOLVING 15.8

Name _____ Date _____

Problem Solving 15.8

Make a Table

Noah saves 2 dimes each week. How much money will he have saved at the end of 3 weeks.

Week	Saved
1	20¢
2	40¢
3	60¢

UNDERSTAND

What do I need to find out? | the amount saved at the end of 3 weeks
What do I know? | the number of weeks; how much is saved each week

PLAN

How can a table help me find the answer? | I will write how much is saved altogether at the end of each week in the table.

SOLVE

The last amount in the table is the answer. | 60¢ is the answer.

LOOK BACK

How can I check my answer? | I can use real dimes to count and add.

Copyright © Houghton Mifflin Company. All rights reserved. — Use with text pages 447–449.

HOMEWORK 15.8

Name _____ Date _____

Homework 15.8

Problem Solving Make a Table

You can make a table to solve problems. Complete the table and solve.

1.

Kind of Sandwich	Number
Cheese	4
Peanut butter	7
Turkey	2

2. How many turkey sandwiches are there?
   2

3. How many peanut butter sandwiches and cheese sandwiches are there?
   11

4. How many more cheese sandwiches than turkey are there?
   2

5. How many sandwiches are there in all?
   13

Copyright © Houghton Mifflin Company. All rights reserved. — Use with text pages 447–449.

Homework Workbook Page 105

ENGLISH LEARNERS 15.8

Name _____ Date _____

English Learners 15.8

Make a Table

You can put food on a table.

Favorite Fruits	Number of Children
apple	6
banana	8
orange	4

You can make a table to help you solve problems.

Make a table to show how many boys and girls are in your class.

Children	Number of Children
Boys	Number of boys in class
Girls	Number of girls in class

To the Teacher: Use the examples at the top of the page to help children understand the different meanings of the word *table*. Then have children count the number of boys and girls in the class, and enter the information in the table.

Copyright © Houghton Mifflin Company. All rights reserved. — Use with text pages 447–449.

TEACHING LESSON 15.8

LESSON ORGANIZER

Objective Make a table to solve problems.

Resources Reteach, Practice, Enrichment, Problem Solving, Homework, English Learners, Transparencies, Math Center

Materials Cubes, paper lunch bags, blank transparency

Activity

Warm-Up Activity
Modeling Organizing Information

iii Small Group	🕐 5–10 minutes	Visual, Tactile

Materials: *cubes, paper lunch bags*

1. Tell children that you often need to organize information in order to solve problems.

2. Provide each group with a different number of red, blue, and yellow cubes in a bag.

3. **Which color do you have the most of? Are there more red cubes or blue cubes? How can you arrange the cubes so you can compare how many of each color without counting?** Guide children to connect the cubes of like colors in rows and align the rows.

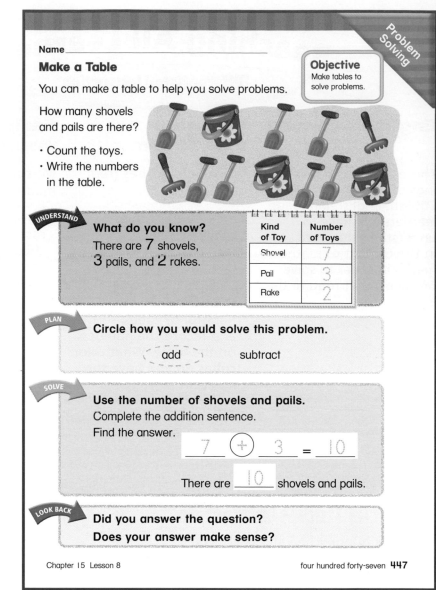

Name_____

Make a Table

Objective Make tables to solve problems.

You can make a table to help you solve problems.

How many shovels and pails are there?

- Count the toys.
- Write the numbers in the table.

UNDERSTAND

What do you know?
There are 7 shovels, 3 pails, and 2 rakes.

Kind of Toy	Number of Toys
Shovel	7
Pail	3
Rake	2

PLAN

Circle how you would solve this problem.

(add)   subtract

SOLVE

Use the number of shovels and pails.
Complete the addition sentence.
Find the answer.

$$7 \ (+) \ 3 \ = \ 10$$

There are ___10___ shovels and pails.

LOOK BACK

Did you answer the question?
Does your answer make sense?

Chapter 15 Lesson 8   four hundred forty-seven **447**

---

1 Introduce

Discuss Making a Table

iiii Whole Group	🕐 10–15 minutes	Visual, Auditory

Materials: *blank transparency*

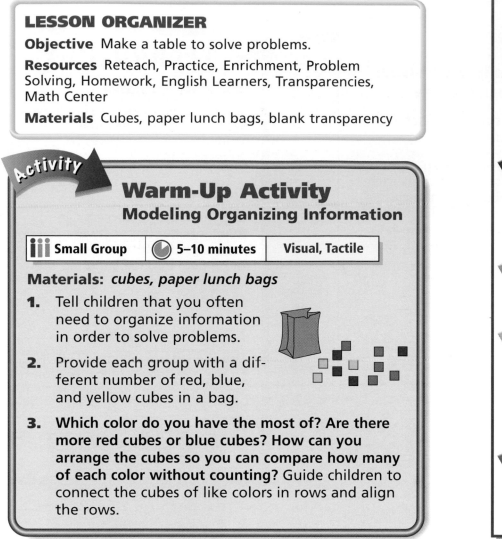

1. *Make a table to solve a problem.* Draw a group of 10 triangles, 7 circles, and 3 squares randomly arranged on the top half of the transparency. **How many more circles than squares are there?**

2. **You can make a table to organize the information.** Draw a two-column table. Label the columns "Shape" and "Number." Label the rows "Triangle", "Circle," "Square." Have children count with you as you complete the table.

3. **Which numbers will you use to find out how many more circles there are than squares?** (7 and 3) **Will you add or subtract?** (subtract) **What subtraction sentence can you write?** (7 – 3 = 4) **There are 4 more circles than squares.**

2 Develop

Guided Learning

Teaching Example Introduce the objective to children. Then read the problem at the top of the page with the children.

UNDERSTAND **What do you know?** (There are 7 shovels, 3 pails, and 2 rakes.) **What do you need to find?** (how many shovels and pails)

PLAN **Do you add or subtract to solve this problem?** (add)

SOLVE **Which numbers will you add to find how many shovels and pails?** (7 and 3) Have children trace 7 + 3 = 10.

What is the answer to the question? (10 shovels and pails)

LOOK BACK **Does 7 plus 3 match the groups in the picture?** (yes) **Does 10 show how many shovels and pails in all?** (yes)

Guided Practice

Have children complete **Exercise 1** on page 448 as you observe.

447   CHAPTER 15   Lesson 8

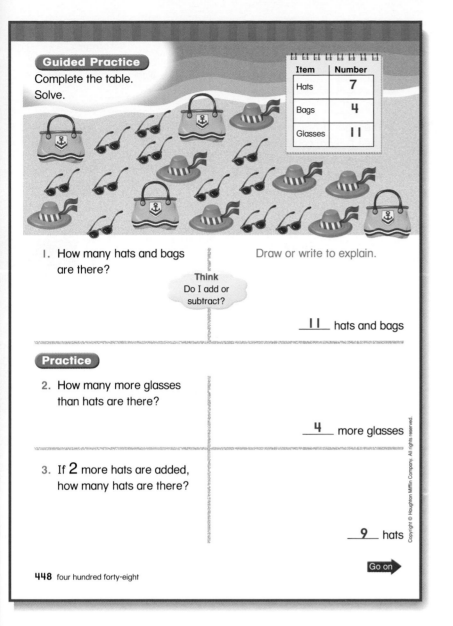

Guided Practice

Complete the table.
Solve.

Item	Number
Hats	7
Bags	4
Glasses	11

1. How many hats and bags are there?

   Draw or write to explain.

   Think
   Do I add or subtract?

   __11__ hats and bags

Practice

2. How many more glasses than hats are there?

   __4__ more glasses

3. If 2 more hats are added, how many hats are there?

   __9__ hats

Go on▶

448 four hundred forty-eight

Play "Make a Table."

Separate the class into two teams and decide which team goes first. Place a different number of cubes in three colors in a bag. Ask a question about the cubes; for example: **How many more red than yellow cubes?**

A child from the first team uses the cubes to make a table and states the answer. If the table and answer are correct, the team gets 1 point. If not, the other team gets a chance to edit the table and state the answer.

Now change the number of cubes in the bag and ask another question about the cubes, having a child from the second team edit the table and state the answer.

Continue as time allows.

ACHIEVING
Mathematical Proficiency

What Is Mathematical Proficiency?

Learning number combinations is a key element in developing mathematics proficiency. **Children often use number combinations with which they are familiar to find number combinations they do not know.**

Research has shown that some number combinations are learned earlier than others. For example, children frequently learn doubles and sums to 10 earlier than they learn other combinations. Once they have mastered these, they use this knowledge to learn other combinations.

In this chapter, children **practice using a ten frame to make sums of 10, and build on this learning to make sums of 11 and 12. They also apply this learning when they solve addition problems with three addends.** Mastering number combinations is an important first step in achieving math proficiency.

3 Practice

Independent Practice

Children complete **Exercises 2–3** on page 448 independently.

Lesson continues

Daily Test Prep

How many cats and dogs are there in all?

Pets	Number
Dog	7
Cat	4
Bird	6

3   10   11   NH
○   ○   ●   ○

Activity

Or use Intervention CD-ROM Lesson 15.8

Lesson Intervention

Using Models to Make a Table

iii Small Group	⏱ 5–10 minutes	Tactile, Visual

Materials: *cubes*

1. Have 11 cubes of three different colors (red, blue, green) on display. Draw two columns side by side. As the children answer the questions below, draw the rows across both columns and label them.

2. How many rows will be needed to chart the 11 cubes? (3) What will be written on each row? (red, blue, green) What will be the title above the color names? (Colors of Cubes)

3. Write the title "Number," above the second column. Hold up a cube and have a child write a tally in the correct place. Once a cube has been tallied, remove it from display.

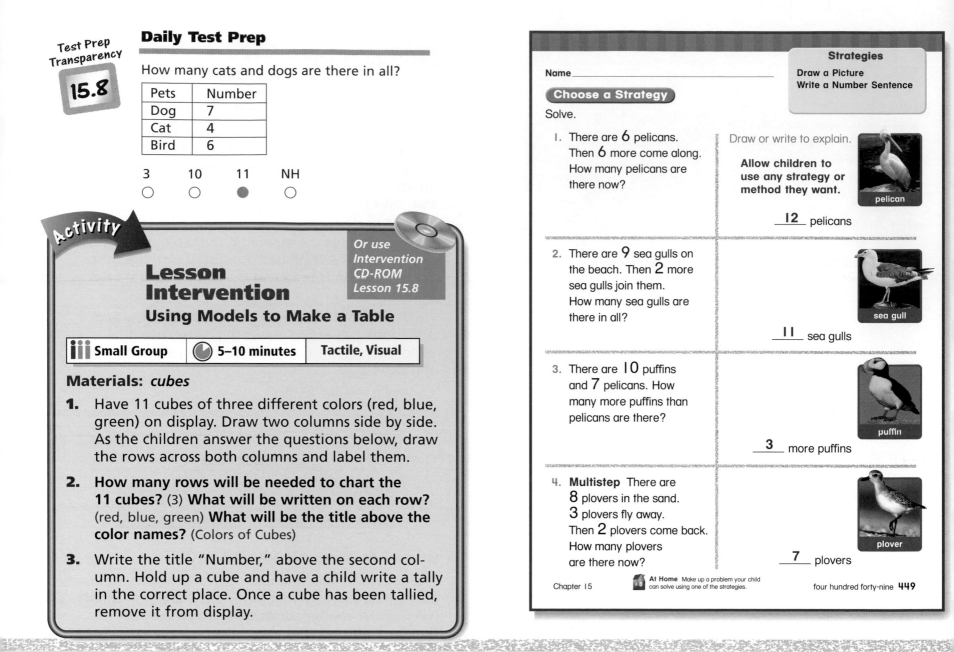

Strategies
Draw a Picture
Write a Number Sentence

Name_____

Choose a Strategy
Solve.

Draw or write to explain.
Allow children to use any strategy or method they want.

1. There are 6 pelicans. Then 6 more come along. How many pelicans are there now?

   __12__ pelicans

2. There are 9 sea gulls on the beach. Then 2 more sea gulls join them. How many sea gulls are there in all?

   __11__ sea gulls

3. There are 10 puffins and 7 pelicans. How many more puffins than pelicans are there?

   __3__ more puffins

4. **Multistep** There are 8 plovers in the sand. 3 plovers fly away. Then 2 plovers come back. How many plovers are there now?

   __7__ plovers

Chapter 15

At Home Make up a problem your child can solve using one of the strategies.

four hundred forty-nine **449**

③ Practice

Mixed Strategy Practice

Read the problem-solving strategies with children. Make sure children can read and comprehend the problems in **Exercises 1–4** on page 449. If necessary, pair more proficient readers with less proficient readers. Encourage them to discuss the problems before solving.

Common Error

Using the Wrong Information
Have children decide what numbers they will use to solve the problem before they decide whether to add or subtract to find the answer.

④ Assess and Close

Shapes	Number
Triangles	6
Circles	8
Squares	4

- **How many more triangles than squares?** (2)
- **Did you add or subtract?** (subtract)

Keeping a Journal

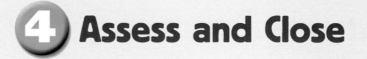

Draw a table about 3 sets of data. Write a question you could answer using the table.

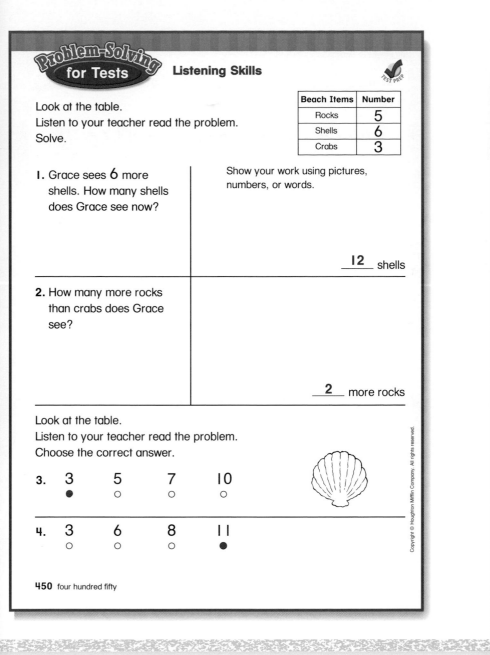

Problem-Solving for Tests — Listening Skills

Look at the table.
Listen to your teacher read the problem.
Solve.

Beach Items	Number
Rocks	5
Shells	6
Crabs	3

1. Grace sees 6 more shells. How many shells does Grace see now?

Show your work using pictures, numbers, or words.

12 shells

2. How many more rocks than crabs does Grace see?

2 more rocks

Look at the table.
Listen to your teacher read the problem.
Choose the correct answer.

3. 3 ●   5 ○   7 ○   10 ○

4. 3 ○   6 ○   8 ○   11 ●

450 four hundred fifty

Problem-Solving for Tests

Listening Skills

This page provides children practice with the oral problem-solving format used in some standardized test items.

You may want to read each item only once to mimic the style of oral tests.

Use with Items 1 and 2

Listening Strategy: Read the problem silently while the teacher reads it aloud.

- **This problem is on the page. Read it to yourself while I read it aloud.**
- **Listen to the whole problem. Wait until I finish before you start writing.**

Use with Item 3

Listening Strategy: Listen for important information.

- **Listen carefully for what the problem asks. Look at the table.**

  How many more shells than crabs does Grace see?

  Mark your answer. Does your answer match the question?

Use with Item 4

Listening Strategy: Listen for what information you will need from the table.

- **Listen carefully as I read the problem. You can mark the items in the table you will use to solve the problem.**

  Grace puts each rock and shell she finds in its own special box. How many boxes does Grace need?

- **Use the information from the table. Then mark your answer.**

Quick Check

Have children complete the Quick Check exercises independently to assess their understanding of concepts and skills taught in **Lessons 5–8.**

Item	Lesson	Error Analysis	Intervention
1–3	15.5	Children may guess to find the sum.	Reteach Resource 15.5 *Ways to Success* 15.5
4–9	15.6	Children may add one addend twice.	Reteach Resource 15.6 *Ways to Success* 15.6
10–14	15.7	Children may find the sum of the two numbers.	Reteach Resource 15.7 *Ways to Success* 15.7
15	15.8	Children may use the wrong information.	Reteach Resource 15.8 *Ways to Success* 15.8

Name_____

Quick Check

Use any strategy. Find the sum.

1. $6 + 2 =$ __8__   2. $3 + 4 =$ __7__   3. $4 + 7 =$ __11__

Write the sum.

4. $\begin{array}{r} 2 \\ 4 \\ +6 \\ \hline 12 \end{array}$
5. $\begin{array}{r} 5 \\ 3 \\ +2 \\ \hline 10 \end{array}$
6. $\begin{array}{r} 1 \\ 1 \\ +7 \\ \hline 9 \end{array}$
7. $\begin{array}{r} 5 \\ 4 \\ +2 \\ \hline 11 \end{array}$
8. $\begin{array}{r} 2 \\ 7 \\ +1 \\ \hline 10 \end{array}$
9. $\begin{array}{r} 2 \\ 8 \\ +1 \\ \hline 11 \end{array}$

Find the missing addend.

10. $\begin{array}{r} 8 \\ +\boxed{2} \\ \hline 10 \end{array}$
11. $\begin{array}{r} 7 \\ +\boxed{5} \\ \hline 12 \end{array}$
12. $\begin{array}{r} 3 \\ +\boxed{9} \\ \hline 12 \end{array}$
13. $\begin{array}{r} \boxed{5} \\ +6 \\ \hline 11 \end{array}$
14. $\begin{array}{r} 4 \\ +\boxed{7} \\ \hline 11 \end{array}$

Complete the table to solve.

Color	Number
Red	5
Blue	6
Green	8

15. How many more green balls than red balls are there?

Draw or write to explain.

____3____ more green balls

Write the tens and the ones.
Write the number.

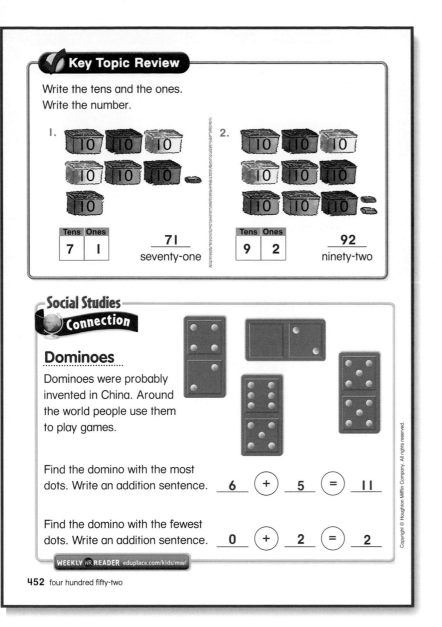

I.

Tens	Ones
7	1

71
seventy-one

2.

Tens	Ones
9	2

92
ninety-two

Social Studies
Connection

Dominoes

Dominoes were probably invented in China. Around the world people use them to play games.

Find the domino with the most dots. Write an addition sentence.

6 (+) 5 (=) 11

Find the domino with the fewest dots. Write an addition sentence.

0 (+) 2 (=) 2

WEEKLY WR READER eduplace.com/kids/mw/

Key Topic Review

This assessment provides a review of skills and concepts taught in Chapter 10.

Check to be sure that children:

• can count by tens then count on by ones to find the number.

• can identify tens and ones in a number.

Social Studies
Connection

Dominoes

Discuss the number sentences children have written. Ask if any children have played a game of dominoes or watched someone play dominoes. After a brief discussion, have children make number sentences for the two remaining dominoes shown. (4 + 2 = 6 and 5 + 5 = 10)

Chapter Review/Test

Purpose: This test provides an informal assessment of the Chapter 15 objectives.

Chapter Test Items 1–30

To assign a numerical grade for this Chapter Test, use 3 points for each test item and add 10 to the score.

Check Understanding

Use children's work on word problems to informally assess progress on chapter content.

Customizing Your Instruction

For children who have not yet mastered these objectives, you can use the reteaching resources listed in the chart below.

✔ Assessment Options

A summary test for this chapter is also provided in the Unit Resource Folder.

Reteaching Support

Chapter Test Items	Summary Test Items	Chapter Objectives Tested	TE Pages	Use These Reteaching Resources
1–3	1–2, 16–18	**15A** Develop and use math vocabulary relating to addition facts through 12.	429A–432	Reteach Resources and *Ways to Success* CD: 15.1, 15.2 Skillsheet 108
4–9, 12–23	5–9	**15B** Use strategies to solve addition problems through 12.	429A–430, 435A–436	Reteach Resources and *Ways to Success* CD: 15.1, 15.4 Skillsheet 109
10–11	3–4	**15C** Use a ten frame to make sums of 10 and 11.	431A–434	Reteach Resources and *Ways to Success* CD: 15.2, 15.3 Skillsheet 110
24–29	10–18	**15D** Add three numbers and find a missing addend.	443A–446	Reteach Resources and *Ways to Success* CD: 15.6, 15.7 Skillsheets 111–112
30	19–20	**15E** Make tables to solve problems.	447A–450	Reteach Resource and *Ways to Success* CD: 15.8 Skillsheet 113

Chapter Review/Test (student page)

Name _____

Vocabulary *e* Glossary
Draw lines to match.

1. **number line** ———— use this to help you add
2. **addend** ⟶ show a ten in this
3. **ten frame** ⟶ a number you are adding

Concepts and Skills
Use the number line.
Write the sum.

0 1 2 3 4 5 6 7 8 9 10 11 12

4. $\begin{array}{r} 3 \\ +6 \\ \hline 9 \end{array}$
5. $\begin{array}{r} 1 \\ +9 \\ \hline 10 \end{array}$
6. $\begin{array}{r} 1 \\ +5 \\ \hline 6 \end{array}$
7. $\begin{array}{r} 3 \\ +8 \\ \hline 11 \end{array}$
8. $\begin{array}{r} 9 \\ +3 \\ \hline 12 \end{array}$
9. $\begin{array}{r} 5 \\ +2 \\ \hline 7 \end{array}$

Use Workmat 1 and ⚪ to make 10.
Draw counters.
Complete the sentence.

10. $6 + \underline{4} = 10$

11. $2 + \underline{8} = 10$

Write the sum.

12. $8 + 3 = \underline{11}$

13. $2 + 9 = \underline{11}$

14. $5 + 6 = \underline{11}$

Chapter 15   four hundred fifty-three **453**

CHAPTER SUMMARY TEST

Name _____ Date _____
Chapter 15 Test

Use the number line. Find the sum.

0 1 2 3 4 5 6 7 8 9 10 11 12

1. $3 + 9 = \underline{12}$
2. $9 + 2 = \underline{11}$

Write the number.

3. $5 + \underline{5} = 10$
4. $6 + \underline{5} = 11$

Write the sum.

5. $\begin{array}{r} 5 \\ +7 \\ \hline 12 \end{array}\ \begin{array}{r} 7 \\ +5 \\ \hline 12 \end{array}$
6. $\begin{array}{r} 2 \\ +6 \\ \hline 8 \end{array}\ \begin{array}{r} 6 \\ +2 \\ \hline 8 \end{array}$
7. $\begin{array}{r} 4 \\ +8 \\ \hline 12 \end{array}\ \begin{array}{r} 8 \\ +4 \\ \hline 12 \end{array}$

Use doubles and doubles plus one. Find the sum.

8. $6 + 5 = \underline{11}$
9. $6 + 6 = \underline{12}$

Write the sum.

10. $\begin{array}{r} 2 \\ 8 \\ +2 \\ \hline 12 \end{array}$
11. $\begin{array}{r} 6 \\ 3 \\ +3 \\ \hline 12 \end{array}$
12. $\begin{array}{r} 3 \\ 5 \\ +2 \\ \hline 10 \end{array}$
13. $\begin{array}{r} 2 \\ 4 \\ +5 \\ \hline 11 \end{array}$
14. $\begin{array}{r} 3 \\ 4 \\ +2 \\ \hline 9 \end{array}$
15. $\begin{array}{r} 2 \\ 5 \\ +1 \\ \hline 8 \end{array}$

Copyright © Houghton Mifflin Company. All rights reserved.

Go on

Chapter Review/Test

Write the sum.

15.
$$\begin{array}{r} 8 \\ +4 \\ \hline 12 \end{array}$$
$$\begin{array}{r} 4 \\ +8 \\ \hline 12 \end{array}$$

16.
$$\begin{array}{r} 5 \\ +6 \\ \hline 11 \end{array}$$
$$\begin{array}{r} 6 \\ +5 \\ \hline 11 \end{array}$$

17.
$$\begin{array}{r} 9 \\ +3 \\ \hline 12 \end{array}$$
$$\begin{array}{r} 3 \\ +9 \\ \hline 12 \end{array}$$

18.
$$\begin{array}{r} 7 \\ +5 \\ \hline 12 \end{array}$$

19.
$$\begin{array}{r} 5 \\ +6 \\ \hline 11 \end{array}$$

20.
$$\begin{array}{r} 3 \\ +7 \\ \hline 10 \end{array}$$

21.
$$\begin{array}{r} 6 \\ +2 \\ \hline 8 \end{array}$$

22.
$$\begin{array}{r} 9 \\ +2 \\ \hline 11 \end{array}$$

23.
$$\begin{array}{r} 8 \\ +4 \\ \hline 12 \end{array}$$

24.
$$\begin{array}{r} 8 \\ 1 \\ +2 \\ \hline 11 \end{array}$$

25.
$$\begin{array}{r} 3 \\ 3 \\ +5 \\ \hline 11 \end{array}$$

26.
$$\begin{array}{r} 2 \\ 4 \\ +4 \\ \hline 10 \end{array}$$

Use cubes.
Find the missing addend.

27. $4 + \boxed{8} = 12$ 28. $5 + \boxed{6} = 11$ 29. $3 + \boxed{9} = 12$

Problem Solving
Complete the table.
Solve.

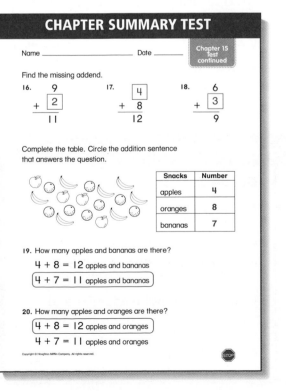

30. How many more pails than shovels are there?

Item	Number
Pails	7
Shovels	4
Rake	1

Draw or write to explain.

___3___ more pails

454 four hundred fifty-four

Adequate Yearly Progress

Use the End of Grade Test Prep Assessment Guide to help familiarize your children with the format of standardized tests.

CHAPTER SUMMARY TEST

Name _____ Date _____

Chapter 15 Test continued

Find the missing addend.

16.
$$\begin{array}{r} 9 \\ + \boxed{2} \\ \hline 11 \end{array}$$

17.
$$\begin{array}{r} \boxed{4} \\ + 8 \\ \hline 12 \end{array}$$

18.
$$\begin{array}{r} 6 \\ + \boxed{3} \\ \hline 9 \end{array}$$

Complete the table. Circle the addition sentence that answers the question.

Snacks	Number
apples	4
oranges	8
bananas	7

19. How many apples and bananas are there?

$4 + 8 = 12$ apples and bananas

$\boxed{4 + 7 = 11 \text{ apples and bananas}}$

20. How many apples and oranges are there?

$\boxed{4 + 8 = 12 \text{ apples and oranges}}$

$4 + 7 = 11$ apples and oranges

STOP

Addition Facts Through 12   **454**

CHAPTER 16

Lesson by Lesson Overview
Subtraction Facts Through 12

Lesson 1

- Use a number line to count back to subtract. Children begin to learn facts for 11 and 12.
- Problem solving has children write a subtraction question that can be answered using a bar graph.

Lesson 2

- This lesson focuses on subtracting from 11 or less.
- Children use a part-part-whole mat to find a missing part.
- Related subtraction facts help children see the relationship.

Lesson 3

- Children subtract from 12 or less.
- Children discuss how knowing one related fact helps to find the difference for the other fact.
- Children practice finding differences from 12 or less in horizontal and vertical exercises.
- Children complete function tables.
- A game provides more practice in subtracting from 12 or less.

Lesson 4

- Children relate addition and subtraction facts.
- Children use the addition fact to find the subtraction.
- Children choose three numbers from a larger set and write related addition and subtraction facts.

Lesson 5

- Children use part-part-whole to find fact families for 11.
- They complete addition and subtraction sentences for each part-part-whole model.
- Children use fact families to help them find unknown sums and differences.

Lesson 6

- Children write facts to complete families for 12.
- A part-part-whole model is shown and children complete the fact family.
- Children write a complete fact family using the numbers provided.

Lesson 7

- Names for numbers changes how children look at facts.
- Children use sums and differences, rather than parts and wholes, to determine relationships.
- Children find sums and differences and then identify the expressions that are names for a given number.
- Children extend a pattern to find names for 7.

Lesson 8

- Children choose an operation to solve a problem.
- Children use a part-part-whole model to help them determine if they need to find the whole or a part.
- Children choose a strategy to practice previously learned problem solving strategies.

SKILLS TRACE: SUBTRACTION FACTS THROUGH 12

Grade K	Grade 1	Grade 2
• model subtraction (ch. 14)	• use a number line and count back to subtract, facts to 12	• use a number line and count back to subtract, facts to 18 (ch. 3)
• complete subtraction sentences (ch. 14)	• subtract from 11 or less, 12 or less	• subtract to compare (ch. 3)
• subtract 1 from 1 through 10 (ch. 14)	• relate addition and subtraction, facts to 12	• use related addition facts to subtract; write fact families (ch. 3)
• subtract 2 from 2 through 10 (ch. 14)	• complete fact families for 11, 12	• identify and write addition and subtraction expressions that name the same number (ch. 3)
	• identify names for numbers	• find the missing number (ch. 3)

Chapter Planner

Lesson	Objective	Vocabulary	Materials	✓ NCTM Standards
16.1 **Count Back to Subtract** p. 457A	Solve subtraction facts.	number line	counters, 10-square number strip (Learning Tool (LT) 29), 0–12 number line (LT 8), blank transparency, cubes	Develop and use strategies for whole-number computations, with a focus on addition and subtraction.
16.2 **Subtract From 11 or Less** p. 459A	Solve subtraction facts from 11.		Workmat 3, cubes, counters, part-part-whole transparency	Develop and use strategies for whole-number computations, with a focus on addition and subtraction.
16.3 **Subtract From 12 or Less** p. 461A	Solve subtraction facts from 12.		counters, part-part-whole transparency, overhead counters, teacher-made triangle flash cards, number cube 6-12 (no 10), red crayon, blue crayon, game board	Develop fluency with basic number combinations for addition and subtraction.
16.4 **Relate Addition and Subtraction** p. 465A	Relate addition and subtraction facts to solve problems.	related facts	red and blue cubes, blank transparency, teacher-made cards with addition and subtraction facts through 12	Understand various meanings of addition and subtraction of whole numbers and the relationship between the two operations.
16.5 **Fact Families** **[Algebra Readiness] for 11** p. 467A	Write fact families for 11 using the inverse relationship.	fact family	part-part-whole transparency, cubes, Workmat 3	Understand various meanings of addition and subtraction of whole numbers...two operations.
16.6 **Fact Families** **[Algebra Readiness] for 12** p. 469A	Write fact families for 12 using the inverse relationship.		part-part-whole transparency, highlight markers (3 colors)	Understand various meanings of addition and subtraction of whole numbers...two operations.
16.7 **Names for Numbers** p. 471A	Recognize equivalent forms of the same number.		part-part-whole transparency, two-color counters	Develop fluency with basic number combinations for addition and subtraction.
16.8 **Problem Solving: Choose the Operation** p. 473A	Choose addition or subtraction to solve problems.			Understand the effects of adding and subtracting whole numbers.

Resources For Reaching All Learners

LESSON RESOURCES: Reteach, Practice, Enrichment, Problem Solving, Homework, English Learners, Daily Routines, Transparencies, Math Center.

ADDITIONAL RESOURCES FROM HOUGHTON MIFFLIN: Chapter Challenges, Combination Classroom Planning Guide, Every Day Counts, Math to Learn (Student Handbook)

> **Every Day Counts**
> *The Daily Depositor, Numbers Stories, and Daily Domino* activities in Every Day Counts support the math in this chapter.

Assessing Prior Knowledge

Before beginning the chapter, you can assess student understandings in order to assist you in differentiating instruction.

Complete Chapter Pretest in Unit Resource Folder

Use this test to assess both prerequisite skills (**Are You Ready?** — one page) and chapter content (**Check What You Know** — two pages).

Chapter 16 Prerequisite Skills Pretest

Name _____ Date _____   Chapter 16 Pretest

Are You Ready?

Write the number.

Whole
12

Part | Part
8 | 4

1. The numbers 8 and __4__ equal 12.

2. The numbers 4 and __8__ equal 12.

3. The number __12__ can be made with the numbers 8 and 4.

$$\begin{array}{r} 6 \\ + 5 \\ \hline 11 \end{array}$$

4. The numbers __6__ and 5 equal 11.

5. The numbers 5 and __6__ equal 11.

6. The number __11__ can be made with the numbers 6 and 5.

Go on

Chapter 16 New Content Pretest

Name _____ Date _____   Chapter 16 Pretest continued

Check What You Know

Count back. Find the difference.

0 1 2 3 4 5 6 7 8 9 10 11 12

1. $12 - 3 = $ __9__   2. $11 - 2 = $ __9__

Complete the related facts.

3. Whole
12
Part | Part
8

$12 - 8 = $ __4__
$12 - 4 = $ __8__

4. Whole
11
Part | Part
4

$11 - 4 = $ __7__
$11 - 7 = $ __4__

Go on

Name _____ Date _____   Chapter 16 Pretest continued

Complete the fact family.

5. Whole
11
Part | Part
3 | 8

$3 + 8 = $ __11__
$8 + 3 = $ 11
$11 - 8 = $ __3__
$11 - 3 = $ __8__

6. Whole
12
Part | Part
7 | 5

$7 + 5 = $ __12__
$5 + 7 = $ __12__
$12 - 7 = $ __5__
$12 - 5 = $ __7__

Circle the names for the number.

7. 10   (10 - 0)   6 + 3   (12 - 2)   (6 + 3 + 1)

8. 5   (11 - 6)   (3 + 2)   12 - 6   (4 + 0 + 1)

Choose the operation to solve the problem. Circle.

9. There are 12 bananas on a tree. A monkey eats 3 of them. How many bananas are still on the tree?

addition
(subtraction)

10. A horse eats 7 apples. The pony eats 4 apples How many apples do the animals eat?

(addition)
subtraction

STOP

Customizing Instruction

For Students Having Difficulty

Items	Prerequisites	Ways to Success
1–6	Order property of addition and basic addition facts through 12.	CD 15.4 Skillsheet 114

Ways to Success: Intervention for every concept and skill (CD-ROM or Chapter Intervention Skillsheets).

For Students Having Success

Items	Objectives	Resources
3–4	16A Use vocabulary for subtracting facts through 12.	Enrichment 16.1, 16.4
1–2	16B Subtract from 11 and 12 using strategies.	Enrichment 16.2, 16.3
5–8	16C Use related facts and fact families, through 12, to solve addition and subtraction problems, and find different names for the same number.	Enrichment 16.4, 16.7
9–10	16D Choose an operation to solve problems.	Enrichment 16.8

Other Pretest Options

Informal Pretest

The pretest assesses vocabulary and prerequisite skills needed for success in this chapter.

Ways to Success **CD-ROM**

The *Ways to Success* chapter pretest has automatic assignment of appropriate review lessons.

Use **Chapter Challenges** with any students who have success with all new chapter content.

Chapter Resources

Assessing Prior Knowledge

Puppet Stories (model subtraction from 8)

- Have child work with a partner to make 8 stick puppets by decorating craft sticks.
- Then have partners make up 2 or 3 subtraction stories that can be acted out with their puppets.
- Provide time for partners to share their stories with others.

Ongoing Skill Activity

Make Change for 12¢ (solve subtraction facts from 12)

- Use the items in the Class Store that were labeled with price tags from 1¢ to 11¢.
- Have shoppers choose an item and give the store clerk 12¢.
- Have the clerk model the whole and the part with pennies. The clerk then subtracts the price of the item from 12¢ and gives the shopper change.

Connecting to the Unit Project

- Tell children that bowling is a subtraction game originally from Egypt.
- Children take turns rolling a ball at the empty bottles. They count the number of bottles that are still standing. Then, they subtract that number from the total number of bottles to find their score.
- You may want to change the number of bottles periodically to vary the subtraction.
- Draw a picture of bottles knocked down and bottles still remaining in a bowling game.
- Have children solve this word problem: There were 11 bottles in a bowling game. Dina knocked over 7 bottles. How many bottles are still standing? (4)

Teacher Support

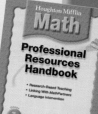

Houghton Mifflin
Math

Professional
Resources
Handbook

Professional Resources Handbook

Research, Mathematics Content, and Language Intervention

Research-Based Teaching

When introducing formal symbolism, teachers should be sensitive to the way they organize the problems they want the children to solve. Teachers should also convince children that their everyday mathematical activities are intimately associated with formal mathematical characteristics. Next, addition and subtraction curricula in the first grade should emphasize both external and internal factors in children's understanding. (Seo & Ginsburg, 2003). See *Professional Resources Handbook, Grade 1,* Unit 6.

For more ideas relating to Unit 6, see the Teacher Support Handbook at the back of this Teacher's Edition.

Language Intervention

In China, the basic subtraction facts are also taught using an approach that reinforces the importance of 10 as a special organizer of our number system. For further explanation, see "Mathematical Language and Subtraction Facts" in the *Professional Resources Handbook Grade 1.*

Technology

Time-Saving Technology Support

Ways to Assess Customized Spiral Review
  Test Generator CD
Lesson Planner CD-ROM
Ways to Success Intervention CD-ROM
MathTracks CD-ROM
Education Place: www.eduplace.com/math/mw
Houghton Mifflin Math eBook CD-ROM
eManipulatives
eGames

Starting Chapter 16
Subtraction Facts Through 12

CHAPTER OBJECTIVES

16A Develop and use math vocabulary relating to subtraction facts through 12.

16B Subtract from 12 using different strategies including counting back.

16C Use related facts and fact families, through 12, to solve addition and subtraction problems, and find different names for the same number.

16D Choose addition or subtraction to solve problems.

Math Background

Subtraction Facts Through 12

This chapter continues the work of subtraction from earlier chapters. Subtraction facts through 12 are explored.

The use of the number line provides a concrete model for counting back. For example, for $11 - 3$, children start at 11 and count back 3.

Children practice finding differences using the part-part-whole model. They also learn to relate addition and subtraction to find the answers to subtraction facts. It is important to remember that because addition and subtraction are inverse operations there are families of facts for addition and subtraction. Most fact families consist of four related facts.

For example, using the numbers 2, 4, and 6, four facts make a family.

$$6 - 2 = 4 \qquad 6 - 4 = 2$$
$$4 + 2 = 6 \qquad 2 + 4 = 6$$

Using variables, the four members of a fact family can be shown as

$$a - b = c \qquad a - c = b$$
$$c + b = a \qquad b + c = a$$

Chapter 16   four hundred fifty-five **455**

Using The Investigation

- Review the symbols used in subtraction sentences with children. Write $12 - 9 = $ _____ on the board. Ask volunteers to circle the minus sign and underline the equal sign.

- Discuss subtraction strategies children can use to find the difference. Encourage children to count back by 1s from 12 to find the difference.

- Read the question to children. **Look at the picture. How many more children are running than jumping rope? You need to subtract to find how many.** (3 children)

For more information about projects and investigations, visit Education Place.
eduplace.com/math/mw/

People Using Math

Wilma Rudolph

Wilma was a runner on the United States Olympic team in 1960. She was the first American woman to win 3 gold medals in one Olympics. She won them in the 100 meter dash, the 200 meter dash, and the 400 meter relay race. Wilma had to work harder than most athletes to achieve her goals.

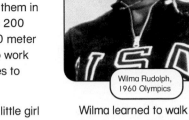
Wilma Rudolph, 1960 Olympics

When Wilma was a little girl she had a disease called polio. She couldn't walk. With help from her parents and a lot of hard work

Wilma learned to walk again. She became a basketball and track star and then won her Olympic medals.

1. Wilma got polio when she was about 5 years old. At 12 years old she could walk on her own. How many years passed from the time she got polio to when she could walk on her own?

   ___12___ – ___5___ = ___7___

   ___7___ years

2. Wilma ran 3 races. She ran 100 meters, 200 meters, and 100 meters in the relay race. How many meters did she run in all?

   100 + 200 + 100 =

   Hint: Just add the number of hundreds. 1 + 2 + 1 = 4

   ___400___ meters

456 four hundred fifty-six

CHAPTER CHALLENGES

For Mathematically Promising Students

The *Chapter Challenges* resource book provides blackline masters for activities that explore, extend, and connect the mathematics in every chapter. To support this independent work, see the Teacher Notes for each activity.

Explore: Count Back to Zero, page 91, after Lesson 1
Extend: How Much Is Left, page 93, after Lesson 3
Connect: Family Bowling, page 95, after Lesson 5

Using This Page

- Read about Wilma Rudolph to the children.
- Read the questions to children. Point out that in Exercise 2, they should add the numbers without the zeros, and then add the two zeros back to the sum. **Adding hundreds is just like adding ones, except there are two zeros after the hundreds digit.**
- Invite volunteers to talk about the sports they like to play. Ask them to tell how many years they have played.

NSF Children's Math Worlds

Children's Math Worlds focuses on the use of models to represent mathematical situations. Thus, using a *Children's Math Worlds* lesson helps students develop a general facility with drawing models to support their thinking that will transfer to all their mathematical work.

Count Back to Subtract

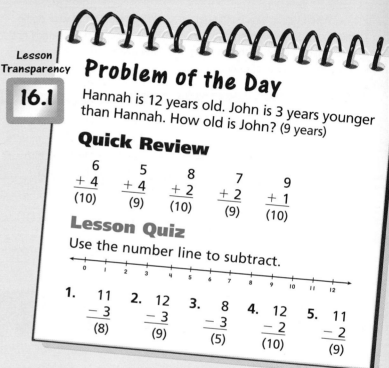

PLANNING THE LESSON

MATHEMATICS OBJECTIVE
Solve subtraction facts.

Use Lesson Planner CD-ROM for Lesson 16.1.

Meeting North Carolina's Standards
1.03 Develop fluency with single-digit addition and corresponding differences using strategies such as modeling, composing and decomposing quantities, using doubles, and making tens.

Also **1.04**

Daily Routines

Calendar

Name the dates for the first two Tuesdays in the month. Ask children to name the date that is one day before. Two days before. Continue with the second Tuesday of the month.

Sunday	Monday	Tuesday	Wednesday	Thursday	Friday	Saturday
			1	2	3	4
5	6	7	8	9	10	11
12	13	14	15	16	17	18
19	20	21	22	23	24	25
26	27	28	29	30	31	

Vocabulary

Draw a number line 0–12 on the board. Remind children that they learned to use a **number line** to **subtract**. Provide a subtraction example, such as 6 − 2, and model using the number line to start with 6 and **count back** 2.

Vocabulary Cards

Lesson Transparency 16.1

Problem of the Day
Hannah is 12 years old. John is 3 years younger than Hannah. How old is John? (9 years)

Quick Review

$$\begin{array}{ccccc} 6 & 5 & 8 & 7 & 9 \\ +4 & +4 & +2 & +2 & +1 \\ \hline (10) & (9) & (10) & (9) & (10) \end{array}$$

Lesson Quiz
Use the number line to subtract.

0 1 2 3 4 5 6 7 8 9 10 11 12

1. $\begin{array}{c} 11 \\ -3 \\ \hline (8) \end{array}$ **2.** $\begin{array}{c} 12 \\ -3 \\ \hline (9) \end{array}$ **3.** $\begin{array}{c} 8 \\ -3 \\ \hline (5) \end{array}$ **4.** $\begin{array}{c} 12 \\ -2 \\ \hline (10) \end{array}$ **5.** $\begin{array}{c} 11 \\ -2 \\ \hline (9) \end{array}$

LEVELED PRACTICE

RETEACH 16.1

Name _____ Date _____ **Reteach 16.1**

Count Back to Subtract

Count back on a number line to subtract.

0 1 2 3 4 5 6 7 8 9 10 11 12

| $\begin{array}{c} 11 \\ -3 \\ \hline 8 \end{array}$ Start with 11. Count back 3. | $\begin{array}{c} 12 \\ -2 \\ \hline 10 \end{array}$ Start with 12. Count back 2. |

Use the number line.
Subtract.

1. $\begin{array}{c} 9 \\ -2 \\ \hline 7 \end{array}$ 2. $\begin{array}{c} 12 \\ -2 \\ \hline 10 \end{array}$ 3. $\begin{array}{c} 8 \\ -3 \\ \hline 5 \end{array}$ 4. $\begin{array}{c} 9 \\ -2 \\ \hline 7 \end{array}$ 5. $\begin{array}{c} 11 \\ -3 \\ \hline 8 \end{array}$ 6. $\begin{array}{c} 10 \\ -1 \\ \hline 9 \end{array}$

7. $\begin{array}{c} 11 \\ -2 \\ \hline 9 \end{array}$ 8. $\begin{array}{c} 12 \\ -3 \\ \hline 9 \end{array}$ 9. $\begin{array}{c} 5 \\ -3 \\ \hline 2 \end{array}$ 10. $\begin{array}{c} 10 \\ -3 \\ \hline 7 \end{array}$ 11. $\begin{array}{c} 8 \\ -2 \\ \hline 6 \end{array}$ 12. $\begin{array}{c} 10 \\ -2 \\ \hline 8 \end{array}$

13. 11 − 1 = **10**   14. 9 − 3 = **6**

15. 8 − 1 = **7**   16. 8 − 3 = **5**

17. 4 − 3 = **1**   18. 7 − 3 = **4**

Use with text pages 457–458.

PRACTICE 16.1

Name _____ Date _____ **Practice 16.1**

Count Back to Subtract

0 1 2 3 4 5 6 7 8 9 10 11 12

Use the number line.
Subtract.

1. $\begin{array}{c} 9 \\ -1 \\ \hline 8 \end{array}$ 2. $\begin{array}{c} 7 \\ -2 \\ \hline 5 \end{array}$ 3. $\begin{array}{c} 10 \\ -3 \\ \hline 7 \end{array}$ 4. $\begin{array}{c} 6 \\ -2 \\ \hline 4 \end{array}$ 5. $\begin{array}{c} 11 \\ -3 \\ \hline 8 \end{array}$ 6. $\begin{array}{c} 8 \\ -1 \\ \hline 7 \end{array}$

7. $\begin{array}{c} 5 \\ -2 \\ \hline 3 \end{array}$ 8. $\begin{array}{c} 11 \\ -2 \\ \hline 9 \end{array}$ 9. $\begin{array}{c} 9 \\ -3 \\ \hline 6 \end{array}$ 10. $\begin{array}{c} 10 \\ -2 \\ \hline 8 \end{array}$ 11. $\begin{array}{c} 9 \\ -2 \\ \hline 7 \end{array}$ 12. $\begin{array}{c} 10 \\ -1 \\ \hline 9 \end{array}$

13. 8 − 3 = **5**   14. 7 − 1 = **6**   15. 11 − 1 = **10**

Test Prep

Fill in the ○ for the correct answer. NH means Not Here.

16. Subtract. $\begin{array}{c} 12 \\ -2 \end{array}$

Explain your answer.

9   **10**   11   NH
○   ●   ○   ○

Use with text pages 457–458.

ENRICHMENT 16.1

Name _____ Date _____ **Enrichment 16.1**

From Start to End

Write the missing numbers.
Then write the rule you used to count back.

1.

Start	→ End
8	6
5	3
9	7
7	5

Count back 2

2.

Start	→ End
9	8
7	6
1	0
5	4

Count back 1

3.

Start	→ End
11	8
5	2
7	4
10	7

Count back 3

4.

Start	→ End
1	1
3	3
5	5
7	7

Count back 0

Talk About It When you count back 3 from 10, what number do you say first?

I say 9 first.

Use with text pages 457–458.

Practice Workbook Page 106

Reaching All Learners
Differentiated Instruction

English Learners

English-language learners may not have the language skills to explain the process behind their thinking. Use Worksheet 16.1 to provide children with sentence frames they can use to complete the Explain Your Thinking activity.

Special Needs
TACTILE, AUDITORY

Materials: 0–10 number line (LT 8)

Write $7 - 3 =$ ___. Have the child point to the greater number and say it aloud. Then, guide him or her to count back 3 numbers. Reinforce that $7 - 3 = 4$.

Repeat the activity with other subtraction sentences.

Gifted and Talented
TACTILE, VISUAL

Materials: number cards 0–12 (LT 14 and 15)

Children work in pairs. One child places 2 number cards face up. Have children make as many number sentences as they can using these numbers.

Then have pairs compare their lists and check to see if they have written eight number sentences between them.

Repeat using another pair of numbers.

TECHNOLOGY

Spiral Review

Using the *Ways to Assess* CD-ROM, you can create **customized** spiral review worksheets covering any lessons you choose.

eBook

An electronic version of this lesson can be found in **eMathBook**.

Lesson Planner

Use the **Lesson Planner CD-ROM** to see how lesson objectives for this chapter are correlated to standards.

Science Connection

Read the literature selection *one less fish*, by Kim Michelle Toft and Allan Sheather. Invite children to count back from 12 to 0 as you go through the pages.

MATH CENTER

Basic Skills Activity

Motivate children to build basic skills. Use this activity to address multiple learning styles using hands-on activities related to the skills of this lesson.

PROBLEM SOLVING 16.1

Name _____ Date _____ Problem Solving 16.1

Count Back to Subtract

Read and solve.
Count back to subtract.

0 1 2 3 4 5 6 7 8 9 10 11 12

1. There are 11 clowns at the circus. 3 clowns ride bicycles. The others ride in a little car. How many clowns ride in the car?

   8 clowns

   Draw or write to explain.

2. The lion tamer has 10 lions and tigers. There are only 2 tigers. How many lions does the lion tamer have?

   8 lions

3. There are 8 elephants altogether. There are 3 elephant babies. How many of the elephants are adults?

   5 adult elephants

Copyright © Houghton Mifflin Company. All rights reserved. **Use with text pages 457–458.**

HOMEWORK 16.1

Name _____ Date _____ Homework 16.1

Count Back to Subtract

Count back on a number line to subtract.

Find $9 - 3$.

Start from 9. Count back 3.

0 1 2 3 4 5 6 7 8 9 10 11 12

$9 - 3 = 6$

0 1 2 3 4 5 6 7 8 9 10 11 12

Use the number line. Subtract.

1. $8 - 3 = \underline{5}$ 2. $10 - 2 = \underline{8}$
3. $12 - 2 = \underline{10}$ 4. $11 - 1 = \underline{10}$

5. $\begin{array}{r} 6 \\ -3 \\ \hline 3 \end{array}$ 6. $\begin{array}{r} 11 \\ -3 \\ \hline \end{array}$ 7. $\begin{array}{r} 7 \\ -2 \\ \hline \end{array}$ 8. $\begin{array}{r} 10 \\ -1 \\ \hline 9 \end{array}$

9. Put 12 buttons on a table. Take 3 away. How many are left?

   9 buttons

   Draw or explain here.

Copyright © Houghton Mifflin Company. All rights reserved. **Use with text pages 457–458.**

ENGLISH LEARNERS 16.1

Name _____ Date _____ English Learners 16.1

Count Back to Subtract

0 1 2 3 4 5 6 7 8 9 10 11 12

Start with 10.
Count back 3.
The difference is 7.

When you find $11 - 3$, is the difference greater than 11?

I start with **11**.

I count back **3**.

The difference is **8**.

8 is less than 11.

To the Teacher: Use the example at the top of the page to demonstrate the meaning of *count back.* Then read the sentences with children and have them complete each one.

Copyright © Houghton Mifflin Company. All rights reserved. **Use with text pages 457–458.**

Homework Workbook Page 106

TEACHING LESSON 16.1

LESSON ORGANIZER

Objective Solve subtraction facts.

Resources Reteach, Practice, Enrichment, Problem Solving, Homework, English Learners

Materials Counters, 10-square number strip (Learning Tool (LT) 29), blank transparency, 0–12 number line (LT 8), cubes

Activity

Warm-Up Activity
Modeling Counting Back

Whole Group	5 minutes	Visual, Tactile

Materials: *counters, 10-square number strip (LT 29)*

1. Help each child make a number strip 1–10. Tell them to fold the last two numbers back. **What number does your number strip model?** (8)

2. Count back 3 from 8 as children place a counter on each number. Model the counting: Say 8. Count 7, 6, 5. **What are you doing when you are counting back?** (subtracting)

3. **What number is just before the last covered counter?** (5) **How many counters do you have on your number strip?** (3) **What is the difference for 8 minus 3?** (5) Repeat the activity, changing the starting number.

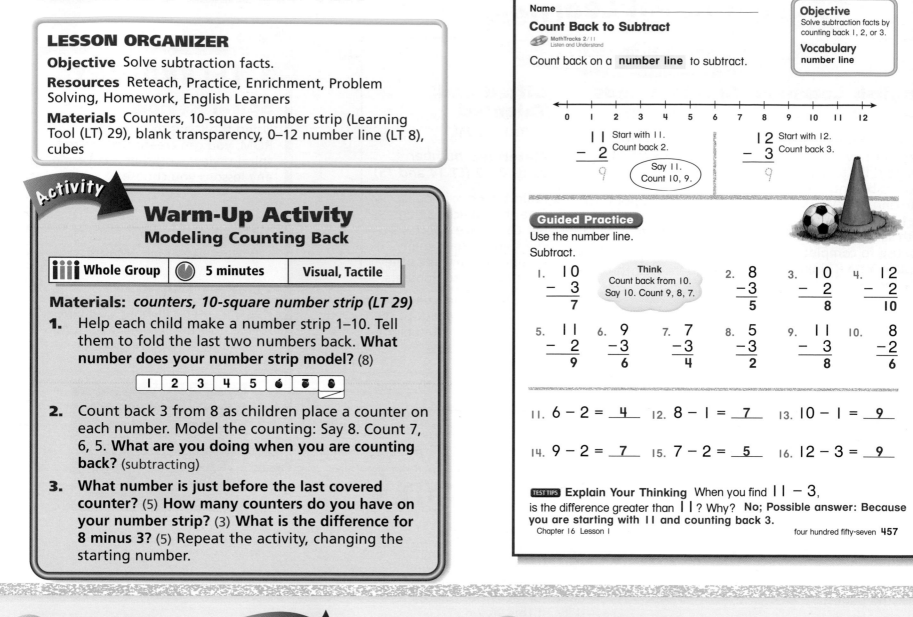

Name_____

Count Back to Subtract

MathTracks 2 / 11
Listen and Understand

Count back on a **number line** to subtract.

$$0 \quad 1 \quad 2 \quad 3 \quad 4 \quad 5 \quad 6 \quad 7 \quad 8 \quad 9 \quad 10 \quad 11 \quad 12$$

$$\begin{array}{r} 11 \\ -\ 2 \\ \hline 9 \end{array}$$ Start with 11. Count back 2. Say 11. Count 10, 9.

$$\begin{array}{r} 12 \\ -\ 3 \\ \hline 9 \end{array}$$ Start with 12. Count back 3.

Guided Practice

Use the number line. Subtract.

Think Count back from 10. Say 10. Count 9, 8, 7.

1. $\begin{array}{r} 10 \\ -\ 3 \\ \hline 7 \end{array}$ 2. $\begin{array}{r} 8 \\ -3 \\ \hline 5 \end{array}$ 3. $\begin{array}{r} 10 \\ -\ 2 \\ \hline 8 \end{array}$ 4. $\begin{array}{r} 12 \\ -\ 2 \\ \hline 10 \end{array}$

5. $\begin{array}{r} 11 \\ -\ 2 \\ \hline 9 \end{array}$ 6. $\begin{array}{r} 9 \\ -3 \\ \hline 6 \end{array}$ 7. $\begin{array}{r} 7 \\ -3 \\ \hline 4 \end{array}$ 8. $\begin{array}{r} 5 \\ -3 \\ \hline 2 \end{array}$ 9. $\begin{array}{r} 11 \\ -\ 3 \\ \hline 8 \end{array}$ 10. $\begin{array}{r} 8 \\ -2 \\ \hline 6 \end{array}$

11. $6 - 2 = \underline{4}$ 12. $8 - 1 = \underline{7}$ 13. $10 - 1 = \underline{9}$

14. $9 - 2 = \underline{7}$ 15. $7 - 2 = \underline{5}$ 16. $12 - 3 = \underline{9}$

TEST TIPS **Explain Your Thinking** When you find $11 - 3$, is the difference greater than 11? Why? **No; Possible answer: Because you are starting with 11 and counting back 3.**

Chapter 16 Lesson 1   four hundred fifty-seven **457**

---

1 Introduce

Activity

Discuss Counting Back with a Number Line

Whole Group	10–15 minutes	Visual, Auditory

Materials: *blank transparency*

1. Draw a 0–12 number line on the transparency. Count together with children forward and then backward.

2. Write $11 - 3$ in vertical form below the number line. Explain to children that you will use the number line to find the difference. **Which numbers on the number line are less than 11?** (the numbers to the left of 11: 10, 9, 8, . . ., 0) **Start at 11 and count back 3. Where do you land?** (8) **So, what is the difference for $11 - 3$?** (8)

3. Ask a volunteer to say the subtraction fact. **To find the difference, we start counting back from the greater number. Which number is greater?** (11) **How many spaces do we count back?** (the lesser number, 3) **What is the difference?** (8)

2 Develop

Guided Learning

Teaching Example Introduce the objective and vocabulary to the children. Remind children that they learned to count back on a number line in Chapter 6. Guide them through the example to show how to count back to subtract.

Guided Practice

You may want to provide Learning Tool 8 for children to use with this page.

Have children complete **Exercises 1–16** as you observe. Have children answer the Explain Your Thinking question. Then discuss their responses with the class.

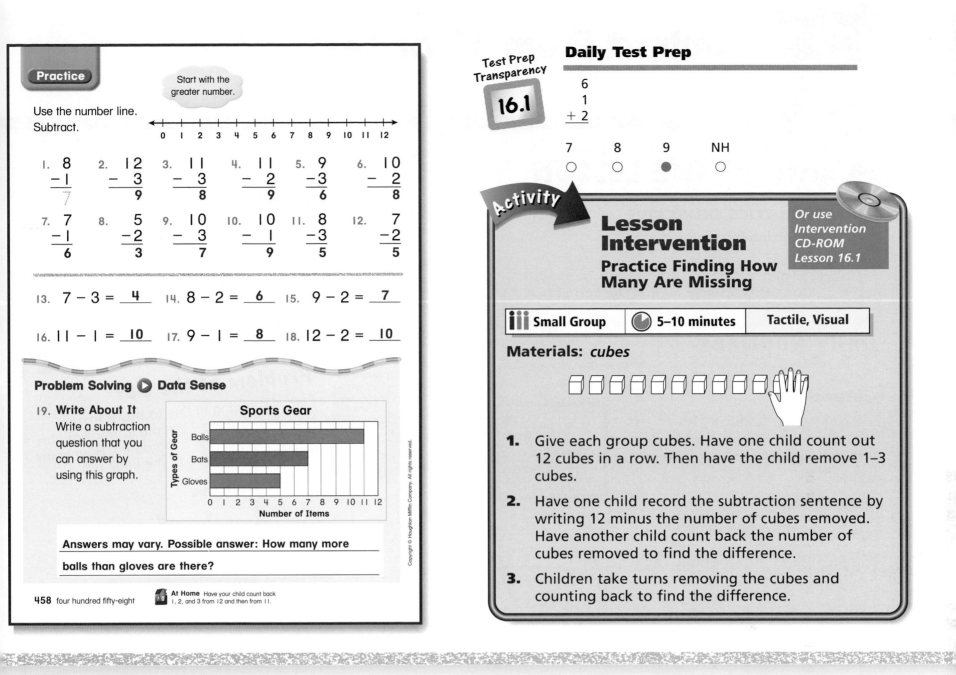

Practice

Start with the greater number.

Use the number line. Subtract.

0 1 2 3 4 5 6 7 8 9 10 11 12

1. 8
−1
7

2. 12
−3
9

3. 11
−3
8

4. 11
−2
9

5. 9
−3
6

6. 10
−2
8

7. 7
−1
6

8. 5
−2
3

9. 10
−3
7

10. 10
−1
9

11. 8
−3
5

12. 7
−2
5

13. 7 − 3 = **4**   14. 8 − 2 = **6**   15. 9 − 2 = **7**

16. 11 − 1 = **10**   17. 9 − 1 = **8**   18. 12 − 2 = **10**

Problem Solving ▶ Data Sense

19. **Write About It**
Write a subtraction question that you can answer by using this graph.

Sports Gear

Types of Gear: Balls, Bats, Gloves

Number of Items: 0 1 2 3 4 5 6 7 8 9 10 11 12

Answers may vary. Possible answer: How many more balls than gloves are there?

458 four hundred fifty-eight

At Home Have your child count back 1, 2, and 3 from 12 and then from 11.

Daily Test Prep

6
1
+ 2

7   8   9   NH
○   ○   ●   ○

Activity

Lesson Intervention
Practice Finding How Many Are Missing

Or use Intervention CD-ROM Lesson 16.1

| 👥 Small Group | ⏱ 5–10 minutes | Tactile, Visual |

Materials: *cubes*

1. Give each group cubes. Have one child count out 12 cubes in a row. Then have the child remove 1–3 cubes.

2. Have one child record the subtraction sentence by writing 12 minus the number of cubes removed. Have another child count back the number of cubes removed to find the difference.

3. Children take turns removing the cubes and counting back to find the difference.

③ Practice

Independent Practice

Children complete **Exercises 1–18** independently.

Problem Solving

After children complete the **Write About It** for **Exercise 19**, call on volunteers to share their questions and answers.

Common Error

Counting Back Incorrectly
Children may count back incorrectly. Have them cover their first number in the subtraction fact with a finger or counter before they count back.

④ Assess and Close

How can you tell that 8 − 2 = 10 is not correct? (Because the difference has to be 8 or less.)

How can you use a number line to subtract 12 − 2? (Start at 12 and count back 2. The difference is 10.)

✏ Keeping a Journal

Write a subtraction story problem with the numbers 12 and 3. Then write a number sentence to solve the problem.

Subtract From 11 or Less

PLANNING THE LESSON

MATHEMATICS OBJECTIVE
Solve subtraction facts from 11.

Use Lesson Planner CD-ROM for Lesson 16.2.

Meeting North Carolina's Standards
1.03 Develop fluency with single-digit addition and corresponding differences using strategies such as modeling, composing and decomposing quantities, using doubles, and making tens.

Also 1.04

Daily Routines

Calendar
Ask children to find the 11th on the calendar. Have them name the date that is 1 day, 2 days, 3 days, before the 11th.

Sunday	Monday	Tuesday	Wednesday	Thursday	Friday	Saturday
			1	2	3	4
5	6	7	8	9	10	11
12	13	14	15	16	17	18
19	20	21	22	23	24	25
26	27	28	29	30	31	

Vocabulary
Write the **subtraction sentence** $11 - 3 = 8$ on the board. Point to and identify 11 as the **whole**, and 3 and 8 as each **part**. Then write $11 - 8 = \underline{\quad}$ on the board and ask children to find the other **part**.

Vocabulary Cards

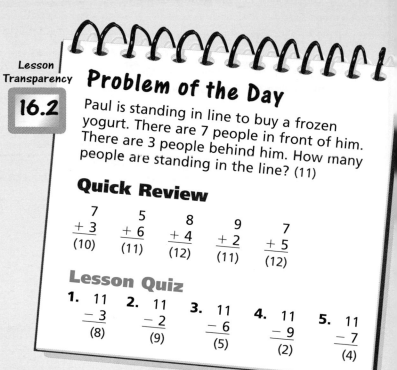

Lesson Transparency 16.2

Problem of the Day
Paul is standing in line to buy a frozen yogurt. There are 7 people in front of him. There are 3 people behind him. How many people are standing in the line? (11)

Quick Review
$$\begin{array}{c} 7 \\ +\ 3 \\ \hline (10) \end{array} \qquad \begin{array}{c} 5 \\ +\ 6 \\ \hline (11) \end{array} \qquad \begin{array}{c} 8 \\ +\ 4 \\ \hline (12) \end{array} \qquad \begin{array}{c} 9 \\ +\ 2 \\ \hline (11) \end{array} \qquad \begin{array}{c} 7 \\ +\ 5 \\ \hline (12) \end{array}$$

Lesson Quiz
$$\textbf{1.}\ \begin{array}{c} 11 \\ -\ 3 \\ \hline (8) \end{array} \qquad \textbf{2.}\ \begin{array}{c} 11 \\ -\ 2 \\ \hline (9) \end{array} \qquad \textbf{3.}\ \begin{array}{c} 11 \\ -\ 6 \\ \hline (5) \end{array} \qquad \textbf{4.}\ \begin{array}{c} 11 \\ -\ 9 \\ \hline (2) \end{array} \qquad \textbf{5.}\ \begin{array}{c} 11 \\ -\ 7 \\ \hline (4) \end{array}$$

LEVELED PRACTICE

RETEACH 16.2

Name _____ Date _____
Reteach 16.2

Subtract From 11 or Less

If you know the whole and one of the parts, you can find the other part.

Whole		Whole	
11		11	
Part	**Part**	**Part**	**Part**
3	?	2	?

$11 - 3 = \underline{8}$ $11 - 2 = \underline{9}$
$11 - 8 = \underline{3}$ $11 - 9 = \underline{2}$

Write the difference.

Whole		Whole		Whole	
11		11		10	
Part	**Part**	**Part**	**Part**	**Part**	**Part**
7	?	9	?	4	?

1. $11 - 7 = \underline{4}$ 2. $11 - 9 = \underline{2}$ 3. $10 - 4 = \underline{6}$
$11 - 4 = \underline{7}$ $11 - 2 = \underline{9}$ $10 - 6 = \underline{4}$

$$\textbf{4.}\ \begin{array}{cc} 11 & 11 \\ -\ 5 & -\ 6 \\ \hline 6 & 5 \end{array} \quad \textbf{5.}\ \begin{array}{cc} 11 & 11 \\ -\ 2 & -\ 9 \\ \hline 9 & 2 \end{array} \quad \textbf{6.}\ \begin{array}{cc} 10 & 10 \\ -\ 7 & -\ 3 \\ \hline 3 & 7 \end{array}$$

Copyright © Houghton Mifflin Company. All rights reserved.   Use with text pages 459–460.

PRACTICE 16.2

Name _____ Date _____
Practice 16.2

Subtract From 11 or Less

Write the difference.

Whole		Whole		Whole	
11		11		10	
Part	**Part**	**Part**	**Part**	**Part**	**Part**
9	?	5	?	2	?

1. $11 - 9 = \underline{2}$ 2. $11 - 5 = \underline{6}$ 3. $10 - 2 = \underline{8}$
$11 - 2 = \underline{9}$ $11 - 6 = \underline{5}$ $10 - 8 = \underline{2}$

$$\textbf{4.}\ \begin{array}{cc} 11 & 11 \\ -\ 2 & -\ 9 \\ \hline 9 & 2 \end{array} \quad \textbf{5.}\ \begin{array}{cc} 10 & 10 \\ -\ 7 & -\ 3 \\ \hline 3 & 7 \end{array} \quad \textbf{6.}\ \begin{array}{cc} 11 & 11 \\ -\ 7 & -\ 4 \\ \hline 4 & 7 \end{array}$$

$$\textbf{7.}\ \begin{array}{cc} 9 & 9 \\ -\ 3 & -\ 6 \\ \hline 6 & 3 \end{array} \quad \textbf{8.}\ \begin{array}{cc} 10 & 10 \\ -\ 6 & -\ 4 \\ \hline 4 & 6 \end{array} \quad \textbf{9.}\ \begin{array}{cc} 11 & 11 \\ -\ 3 & -\ 8 \\ \hline 8 & 3 \end{array}$$

Test Prep

Fill in the ○ for the correct answer. NH means Not Here.

10. Subtract.

$10 - 7$

1 ○   2 ○   3 ●   NH ○

Explain your answer.

Copyright © Houghton Mifflin Company. All rights reserved.   Use with text pages 459–460.

ENRICHMENT 16.2

Name _____ Date _____
Enrichment 16.2

What Happened to 11?

Look at the objects in each row.
Color some of the objects ⬛ Red
Color the rest of the objects ⬛ Blue
Then complete the subtraction sentence.

Answers will vary. Check children's coloring.

1.

$11 - \underline{\quad}$ red flowers = $\underline{\quad}$ blue flowers.

2.

$10 - \underline{\quad}$ blue butterflies = $\underline{\quad}$ red butterflies.

3.

$11 - \underline{\quad}$ red birds = $\underline{\quad}$ blue birds.

Write About It How could you show a friend that $11 - 2 = 9$?
I could use 11 counters and take away 2 of them to show 9.

Copyright © Houghton Mifflin Company. All rights reserved.   Use with text pages 459–460.

Practice Workbook Page 107

Reaching All Learners
Differentiated Instruction

English Learners

Review the words **part** and **whole**.

Children will need to understand that parts make a whole as they solve subtraction facts. Use Worksheet 16.2 to develop understanding of this concept.

Special Needs
TACTILE, AUDITORY

Materials: *Workmat 3*

Write $11 - 5 = $ ____. Have the child put 11 cubes in the whole part of the mat.

Now, have the child move 5 cubes to the left part of the mat. Have him or her count the remaining cubes and move them into the other part of the mat.

Have the child point to the numbers and read the sentence aloud. Continue using other examples.

Early Finishers
TACTILE, VISUAL

Materials: *number cards 0–11 (LT 14)*

- For each pair, make a pile of 0–5 cards (to use as a part), and a pile of 6–11 cards (to use as the whole). Children work in pairs. Have each child choose a card one from one pile, one from the other pile.

- Have children write a subtraction fact using the cards.

- Have partners return the cards to the pile and play again.

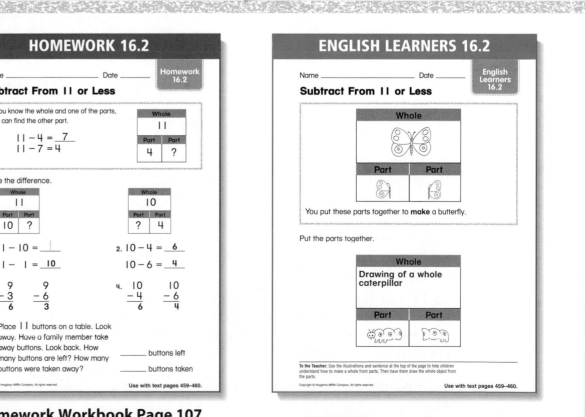

TECHNOLOGY

Spiral Review

To reinforce skills on lessons taught earlier, create **customized** spiral review worksheets using the *Ways to Assess* CD-ROM.

Lesson Planner

You can use the **Lesson Planner CD-ROM** to create a report of the lessons and standards you have taught.

Education Place

Encourage students to visit **Education Place** at **eduplace.com/kids/mw/** for more student activities.

Social Studies Connection

Point out that in a soccer game, there are 11 players for each team. Make up subtraction stories about numbers of soccer players. Have children solve them.

MATH CENTER

Basic Skills Activity

Motivate children to build basic skills. Use this activity to address multiple learning styles using hands-on activities related to the skills of this lesson.

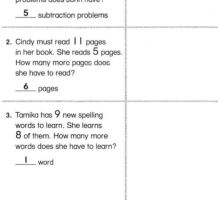

PROBLEM SOLVING 16.2

Name _____ Date _____ Problem Solving 16.2

Subtract From 11 or Less

Read and solve.
Write the difference.

1. John has 11 math problems. 6 are addition problems. The others are subtraction problems. How many subtraction problems does John have?

   __5__ subtraction problems

   Draw or write to explain.

2. Cindy must read 11 pages in her book. She reads 5 pages. How many more pages does she have to read?

   __6__ pages

3. Tamika has 9 new spelling words to learn. She learns 8 of them. How many more words does she have to learn?

   __1__ word

Copyright © Houghton Mifflin Company. All rights reserved. **Use with text pages 459–460.**

HOMEWORK 16.2

Name _____ Date _____ Homework 16.2

Subtract From 11 or Less

If you know the whole and one of the parts, you can find the other part.

Whole
11

Part	Part
4	?

$11 - 4 = \underline{7}$
$11 - 7 = 4$

Write the difference.

Whole
11

Part	Part
10	?

Whole
10

Part	Part
?	4

1. $11 - 10 = \underline{\quad}$
   $11 - 1 = \underline{10}$

2. $10 - 4 = \underline{6}$
   $10 - 6 = \underline{4}$

3. $\begin{array}{r} 9 \\ -3 \\ \hline 6 \end{array}$ $\begin{array}{r} 9 \\ -6 \\ \hline 3 \end{array}$

4. $\begin{array}{r} 10 \\ -4 \\ \hline 6 \end{array}$ $\begin{array}{r} 10 \\ -6 \\ \hline 4 \end{array}$

5. Place 11 buttons on a table. Look away. Have a family member take away buttons. Look back. How many buttons are left? How many buttons were taken away?

   ____ buttons left
   ____ buttons taken

Copyright © Houghton Mifflin Company. All rights reserved. **Use with text pages 459–460.**

ENGLISH LEARNERS 16.2

Name _____ Date _____ English Learners 16.2

Subtract From 11 or Less

Whole

Part	Part

You put these parts together to **make** a butterfly.

Put the parts together.

Whole
Drawing of a whole caterpillar

Part	Part

To the Teacher: Use the illustrations and sentence at the top of the page to help children understand how to make a whole from parts. Then have them draw the whole object from the parts.

Copyright © Houghton Mifflin Company. All rights reserved. **Use with text pages 459–460.**

Homework Workbook Page 107

CHAPTER 16   Lesson 2   459B

TEACHING LESSON 16.2

LESSON ORGANIZER

Objective Solve subtraction facts from 11.

Resources Reteach, Practice, Enrichment, Problem Solving, Homework, English Learners, Transparencies, Math Center

Materials Cubes, counters, part-part-whole transparency, Workmat 3

Warm-Up Activity
Model Subtracting From 10

👤 Small Group	🕐 5–10 minutes	Tactile, Auditory

Materials: *cubes*

1. Distribute cubes to each group. Ask children to make one train of 10 cubes. Tell them to break off 1 cube and count back to show the subtraction 10 − 1. **What is the difference for 10 − 1?** (9) **If 10 − 1 = 9, what is the difference for 10 − 9?** (1)

   $10 - 1 = 9$
   $10 - 9 = 1$

2. Have children repeat the activity, breaking off 2 cubes. **What is the difference for 10 − 2?** (8) **What is the difference for 10 − 8?** (2) **How are the number sentences the same?** (They both have the same numbers.) **How are they different?** (A different number is subtracted from 10, so the difference is not the same.)

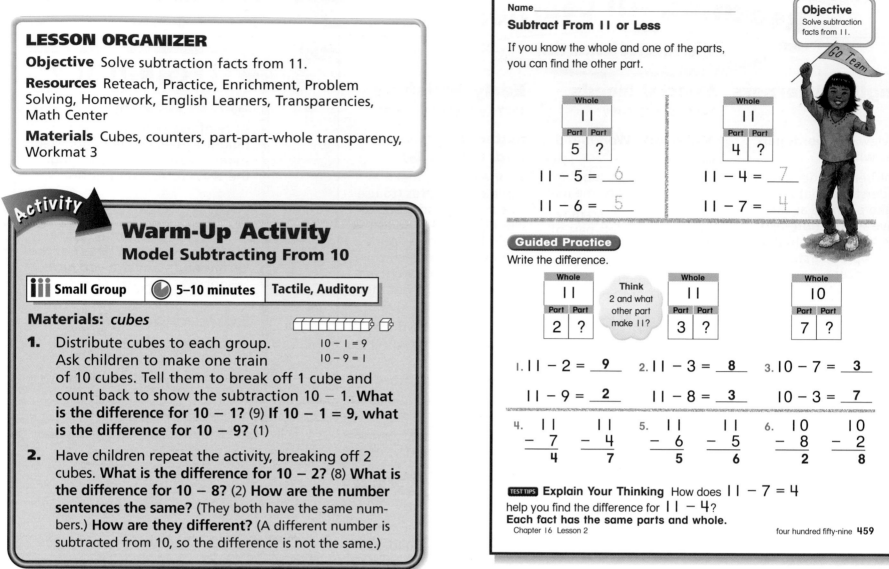

Name_____

Subtract From 11 or Less

Objective Solve subtraction facts from 11.

If you know the whole and one of the parts, you can find the other part.

Whole
11

Part	Part
5	?

$11 - 5 = \underline{6}$

$11 - 6 = \underline{5}$

Whole
11

Part	Part
4	?

$11 - 4 = \underline{7}$

$11 - 7 = \underline{4}$

Guided Practice

Write the difference.

Whole
11

Part	Part
2	?

Think 2 and what other part make 11?

Whole
11

Part	Part
3	?

Whole
10

Part	Part
7	?

1. $11 - 2 = \underline{9}$ 2. $11 - 3 = \underline{8}$ 3. $10 - 7 = \underline{3}$

   $11 - 9 = \underline{2}$ $11 - 8 = \underline{3}$ $10 - 3 = \underline{7}$

4. $\begin{array}{r} 11 \\ -7 \\ \hline 4 \end{array}$ $\begin{array}{r} 11 \\ -4 \\ \hline 7 \end{array}$ 5. $\begin{array}{r} 11 \\ -6 \\ \hline 5 \end{array}$ $\begin{array}{r} 11 \\ -5 \\ \hline 6 \end{array}$ 6. $\begin{array}{r} 10 \\ -8 \\ \hline 2 \end{array}$ $\begin{array}{r} 10 \\ -2 \\ \hline 8 \end{array}$

TEST TIPS **Explain Your Thinking** How does $11 - 7 = 4$ help you find the difference for $11 - 4$? **Each fact has the same parts and whole.**

Chapter 16 Lesson 2

four hundred fifty-nine **459**

---

① Introduce
Discuss the Whole and Parts

👤 Whole Group	🕐 10–15 minutes	Visual, Auditory

Materials: *counters, part-part-whole transparency*

1. Display a part-part-whole transparency. Write 11 − 3 = _____ . Put 11 counters in the whole section. Have children count the cubes. **How many counters?** (11) **What number describes the whole?** (11)

2. Move 3 counters to the part on the left. **How many counters are in this part?** (3) **If you know the whole and one of the parts, you can find the other part. What is the other part?** (8) **So, 11 − 3 = 8.**

3. Return the 11 counters to the whole section. Move 8 counters to the left part. **You know the whole is 11 and one of the parts is 8. What is the other part?** (3) Write the sentence on the transparency. (11 − 8 = 3) **How are the sentences the same?** (same whole and parts) **Different?** (The differences are different; a different number is being subtracted.)

② Develop

Guided Learning

Teaching Example Introduce the objective to the children. Guide them through the example. Explain that if they know the whole and one of the parts, then they can subtract to find the other part.

Guided Practice

Have children complete **Exercises 1–6** as you observe. Have children answer the Explain Your Thinking question. Then discuss their responses with the class.

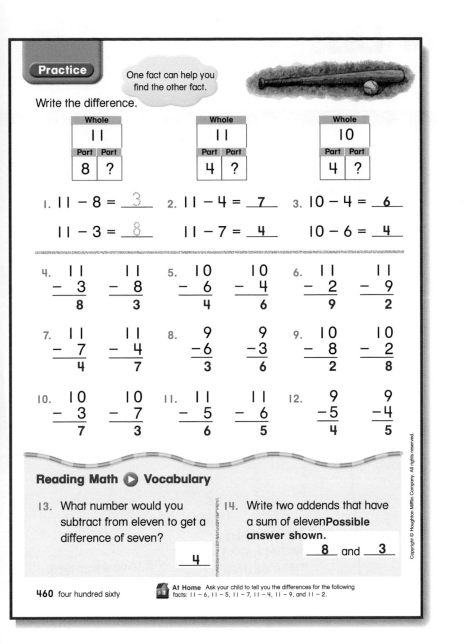

Practice

One fact can help you find the other fact.

Write the difference.

Whole			Whole			Whole	
11			11			10	
Part	Part		Part	Part		Part	Part
8	?		4	?		4	?

1. 11 − 8 = _3_   2. 11 − 4 = _7_   3. 10 − 4 = _6_

   11 − 3 = _8_   11 − 7 = _4_   10 − 6 = _4_

4.
$$\begin{array}{r}11\\-\ 3\\\hline 8\end{array}\quad\begin{array}{r}11\\-\ 8\\\hline 3\end{array}$$
5.
$$\begin{array}{r}10\\-\ 6\\\hline 4\end{array}\quad\begin{array}{r}10\\-\ 4\\\hline 6\end{array}$$
6.
$$\begin{array}{r}11\\-\ 2\\\hline 9\end{array}\quad\begin{array}{r}11\\-\ 9\\\hline 2\end{array}$$

7.
$$\begin{array}{r}11\\-\ 7\\\hline 4\end{array}\quad\begin{array}{r}11\\-\ 4\\\hline 7\end{array}$$
8.
$$\begin{array}{r}9\\-6\\\hline 3\end{array}\quad\begin{array}{r}9\\-3\\\hline 6\end{array}$$
9.
$$\begin{array}{r}10\\-\ 8\\\hline 2\end{array}\quad\begin{array}{r}10\\-\ 2\\\hline 8\end{array}$$

10.
$$\begin{array}{r}10\\-\ 3\\\hline 7\end{array}\quad\begin{array}{r}10\\-\ 7\\\hline 3\end{array}$$
11.
$$\begin{array}{r}11\\-\ 5\\\hline 6\end{array}\quad\begin{array}{r}11\\-\ 6\\\hline 5\end{array}$$
12.
$$\begin{array}{r}9\\-5\\\hline 4\end{array}\quad\begin{array}{r}9\\-4\\\hline 5\end{array}$$

Reading Math ▶ Vocabulary

13. What number would you subtract from eleven to get a difference of seven?

_4_

14. Write two addends that have a sum of eleven. **Possible answer shown.**

_8_ and _3_

460 four hundred sixty

At Home Ask your child to tell you the differences for the following facts: 11 − 6, 11 − 5, 11 − 7, 11 − 4, 11 − 9, and 11 − 2.

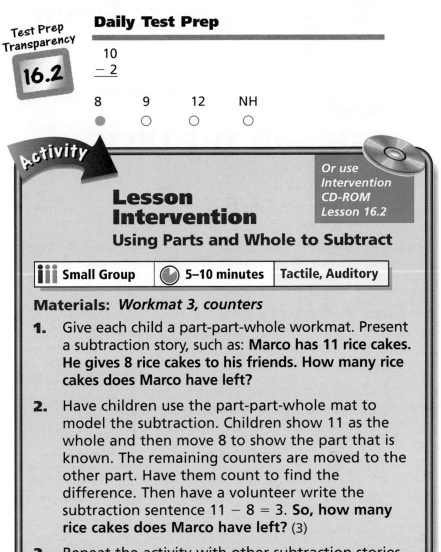

Test Prep Transparency 16.2

Daily Test Prep

$$\begin{array}{r}10\\-\ 2\\\hline\end{array}$$

8   9   12   NH
●   ○   ○   ○

Activity

Or use Intervention CD-ROM Lesson 16.2

Lesson Intervention
Using Parts and Whole to Subtract

👥 Small Group	🕐 5–10 minutes	Tactile, Auditory

Materials: *Workmat 3, counters*

1. Give each child a part-part-whole workmat. Present a subtraction story, such as: **Marco has 11 rice cakes. He gives 8 rice cakes to his friends. How many rice cakes does Marco have left?**

2. Have children use the part-part-whole mat to model the subtraction. Children show 11 as the whole and then move 8 to show the part that is known. The remaining counters are moved to the other part. Have them count to find the difference. Then have a volunteer write the subtraction sentence 11 − 8 = 3. **So, how many rice cakes does Marco have left?** (3)

3. Repeat the activity with other subtraction stories.

---

③ Practice

Independent Practice
Children complete **Exercises 1–12** independently.

Reading Math
After children complete **Exercises 13–14**, call on volunteers to share their responses.

Common Error

Writing the Wrong Difference
Children may make subtraction errors and write the wrong difference. Have children use counters on a part-part-whole workmat to model exercises before they write the differences.

④ Assess and Close

In the subtraction sentence 11 − 3 = 8, what is the whole? (11) **What are the parts?** (3 and 8)

What other fact do you know when you know that 11 − 2 = 9? (11 − 9 = 2)

Keeping a Journal

Write two subtraction sentences that include the numbers 11 and 5.

Subtract From 12 or Less

PLANNING THE LESSON

MATHEMATICS OBJECTIVE
Solve subtraction facts from 12.

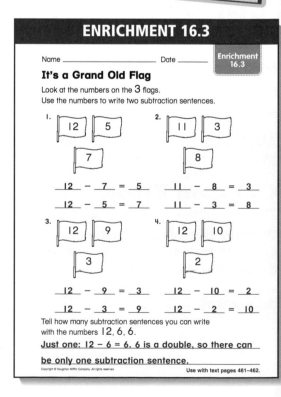

Use Lesson Planner CD-ROM for Lesson 16.3.

Meeting North Carolina's Standards

1.03 Develop fluency with single-digit addition and corresponding differences using strategies such as modeling, composing and decomposing quantities, using doubles, and making tens.

Also 1.04

Daily Routines

Calendar

Say numbers from 2 to 11 and have children name a date whose digits have that number as their sum. Give children examples to start: the digits of the 11th have a sum of 2, the digits of the 29th have a sum of 11.

Sunday	Monday	Tuesday	Wednesday	Thursday	Friday	Saturday
			1	2	3	4
5	6	7	8	9	10	11
12	13	14	15	16	17	18
19	20	21	22	23	24	25
26	27	28	29	30	31	

Vocabulary

Review the words **part** and **whole** by stating the whole and having children tell the parts. For example: the number 12, possible parts include 9 and 3, 8 and 4, 6 and 6, or 7 and 5.

Vocabulary Cards

Lesson Transparency 16.3

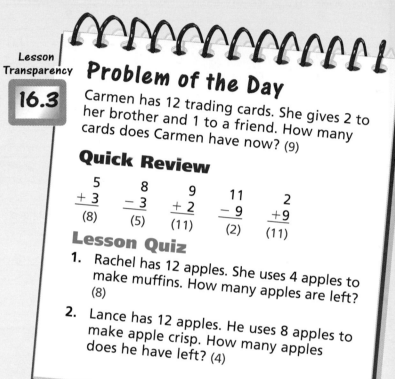

Problem of the Day
Carmen has 12 trading cards. She gives 2 to her brother and 1 to a friend. How many cards does Carmen have now? (9)

Quick Review

$$5 + 3 \quad (8)$$
$$8 - 3 \quad (5)$$
$$9 + 2 \quad (11)$$
$$11 - 9 \quad (2)$$
$$2 + 9 \quad (11)$$

Lesson Quiz

1. Rachel has 12 apples. She uses 4 apples to make muffins. How many apples are left? (8)

2. Lance has 12 apples. He uses 8 apples to make apple crisp. How many apples does he have left? (4)

LEVELED PRACTICE

RETEACH 16.3

Name _____ Date _____

Reteach 16.3

Subtract From 12 or Less

If you know the whole and one of the parts, you can find the other part.

Whole
12

Part	Part
3	?

$12 - 3 = \underline{9}$
$12 - 9 = \underline{3}$

Whole
12

Part	Part
8	?

$12 - 8 = \underline{4}$
$12 - 4 = \underline{8}$

Write the difference.

Whole
12

Part	Part
5	?

Whole
11

Part	Part
4	?

Whole
10

Part	Part
3	?

1. $12 - 5 = \underline{7}$
   $12 - 7 = \underline{5}$

2. $11 - 4 = \underline{7}$
   $11 - 7 = \underline{4}$

3. $10 - 3 = \underline{7}$
   $10 - 7 = \underline{3}$

4. $12 - 9 = 3$ $12 - 3 = 9$
5. $12 - 8 = 4$ $12 - 4 = 8$
6. $11 - 5 = 6$ $11 - 6 = 5$

Use with text pages 461–462.

PRACTICE 16.3

Name _____ Date _____

Practice 16.3

Subtract From 12 or Less

Write the difference.

Whole
9

Part	Part
3	?

Whole
10

Part	Part
9	?

Whole
12

Part	Part
5	?

1. $9 - 3 = \underline{6}$
   $9 - 6 = \underline{3}$

2. $10 - 9 = \underline{1}$
   $10 - 1 = \underline{9}$

3. $12 - 5 = \underline{7}$
   $12 - 7 = \underline{5}$

4. $12 - 4 = 8$ $12 - 8 = 4$
5. $11 - 8 = 3$ $11 - 3 = 8$
6. $9 - 7 = 2$ $9 - 2 = 7$

7. $12 - 3 = 9$ $12 - 9 = 3$
8. $10 - 8 = 2$ $10 - 2 = 8$
9. $11 - 5 = 6$ $11 - 6 = 5$

Test Prep

Fill in the ○ for the correct answer. NH means Not Here.

10. Subtract.

$12 - 5$

○ 6   ○ 5   ○ 4   ● NH

Explain your answer.

Use with text pages 461–462.

ENRICHMENT 16.3

Name _____ Date _____

Enrichment 16.3

It's a Grand Old Flag

Look at the numbers on the 3 flags.
Use the numbers to write two subtraction sentences.

1. 12 5 7

$12 - 7 = 5$
$12 - 5 = 7$

2. 11 3 8

$11 - 8 = 3$
$11 - 3 = 8$

3. 12 9 3

$12 - 9 = 3$
$12 - 3 = 9$

4. 12 10 2

$12 - 10 = 2$
$12 - 2 = 10$

Tell how many subtraction sentences you can write with the numbers 12, 6, 6.

<u>Just one: 12 – 6 = 6. 6 is a double, so there can</u>
<u>be only one subtraction sentence.</u>

Use with text pages 461–462.

Practice Workbook Page 108

Reaching All Learners
Differentiated Instruction

English Learners

Worksheet 16.3 develops understanding of the words *parts* and *wholes*. Children will need to understand this word as they complete some problems that involve subtraction facts.

Inclusion
TACTILE, AUDITORY

Materials: *12 straws*

Give the child 12 straws. Have the child count the straws and lay them down one at a time.

Ask the child to give you a number of straws, such as 4. Have the child tell you how many straws are left. Write $12 - 4 = 8$. Have the child read the subtraction sentence. Repeat the activity.

$12 - 4 = 8$

Gifted and Talented
TACTILE, VISUAL

Materials: *number cards 1–12 (LT 14 and 15)*

Have children work in pairs. Each child gets 6 cards.

Children use 12 as the whole. One child puts down a card (8). The partner tries to lay down the difference (4). If neither child has a 4, partners switch roles and continue.

TECHNOLOGY

Spiral Review

Help students remember skills they learned earlier by creating **customized** spiral review worksheets using the *Ways to Assess* CD-ROM.

Lesson Planner

You can customize your teaching plan or meet your curriculum requirements with the **Lesson Planner CD-ROM.**

Education Place

You can visit **Education Place** at **eduplace.com/math/mw/** for teacher support materials.

Art Connection

Have children make 5 small fish shapes. Have them write a subtraction sentence for 12 on each fish. Then color the fish and use string to attach them to a wire hanger to create a mobile.

MATH CENTER

Basic Skills Activity

Motivate children to build basic skills. Use this activity to address multiple learning styles using hands-on activities related to the skills of this lesson.

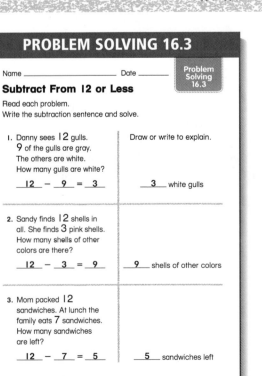

PROBLEM SOLVING 16.3

Name _____ Date _____   Problem Solving 16.3

Subtract From 12 or Less

Read each problem.
Write the subtraction sentence and solve.

1. Danny sees 12 gulls. 9 of the gulls are gray. The others are white. How many gulls are white?

   Draw or write to explain.

   $12 - 9 = 3$ 3 white gulls

2. Sandy finds 12 shells in all. She finds 3 pink shells. How many shells of other colors are there?

   $12 - 3 = 9$ 9 shells of other colors

3. Mom packed 12 sandwiches. At lunch the family eats 7 sandwiches. How many sandwiches are left?

   $12 - 7 = 5$ 5 sandwiches left

Use with text pages 461–462.

HOMEWORK 16.3

Name _____ Date _____   Homework 16.3

Subtract From 12 or Less

If you know the whole and one of the parts, you can find the other part.

$12 - 2 = \underline{10}$
$12 - 10 = 2$

Whole	
12	
Part	Part
2	?

Write the difference.

Whole	
12	
Part	Part
3	?

Whole	
8	
Part	Part
?	2

1. $12 - 3 = \underline{9}$
   $12 - 9 = \underline{3}$

2. $8 - 2 = \underline{6}$
   $8 - 6 = \underline{2}$

3. $\begin{array}{r} 12 \\ -7 \\ \hline 5 \end{array}$ $\begin{array}{r} 12 \\ -5 \\ \hline 7 \end{array}$

4. $\begin{array}{r} 12 \\ -4 \\ \hline 8 \end{array}$ $\begin{array}{r} 12 \\ -8 \\ \hline 4 \end{array}$

5. Place 12 buttons in a bag. Take buttons out of the bag. How many buttons did you take out? How many buttons are left in the bag? Complete the chart.

Whole	
12	
Part	Part

Use with text pages 461–462.

Homework Workbook Page 108

ENGLISH LEARNERS 16.3

Name _____ Date _____   English Learners 16.3

Subtract From 12 or Less

Whole	
Part	Part

You can make two **parts** from this **whole**.

Draw the two parts that make the whole.

Whole	
♡	
Part	Part

To the Teacher: Use the illustrations and sentence at the top of the page to help children understand how to make parts from a whole. Then have them draw the parts that make the whole.

Use with text pages 461–463.

TEACHING LESSON 16.3

LESSON ORGANIZER

Objective Solve subtraction facts from 12.

Resources Reteach, Practice, Enrichment, Problem Solving, Homework, English Learners, Transparencies, Math Center

Materials Counters, part-part-whole transparency, overhead counters, teacher-made triangle flash cards, number cube labeled 6, 7, 8, 9, 11, 12, red and blue crayon, gameboard

Activity

Warm-Up Activity
Modeling Subtraction Stories

| Whole Group | 10 minutes | Visual, Tactile |

Materials: *counters*

1. Give each child 10 counters. Say this number story aloud and have children model it. **Ten children ride the train at the zoo. Three children get off the train to go see the bears.** Tell children to take 3 counters away. **How many children are left on the train?** (7)

2. Have children collect the counters and begin again with 10. **What if 7 children went to see the bears?** Tell children to take 7 counters away. **How many children are left on the train?** (3) Discuss how knowing the whole and one part helps you find the other part.

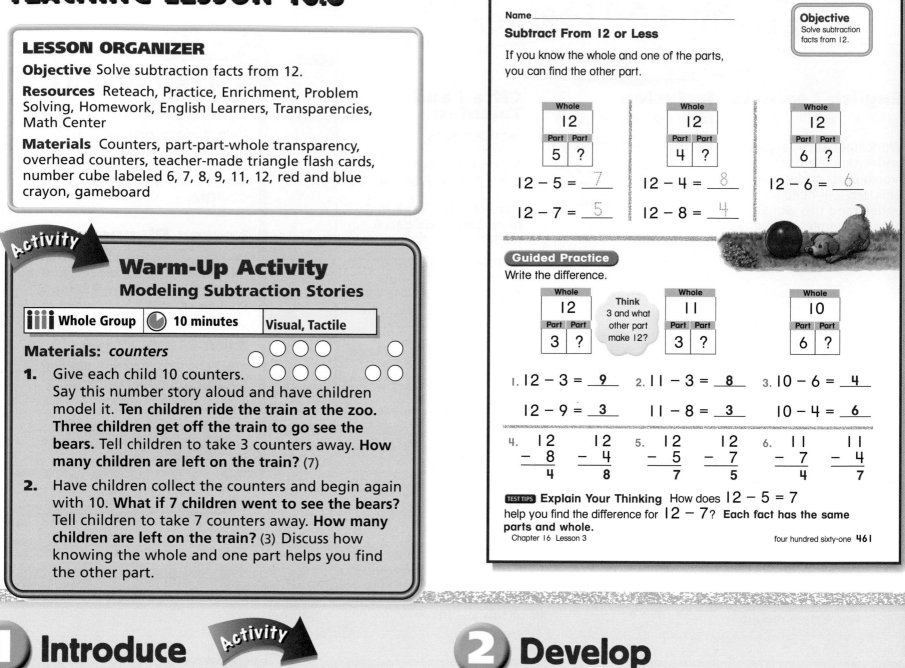

1 Introduce Activity
Discuss Subtracting From 12

| Whole Group | 10–15 minutes | Visual, Auditory |

Materials: *part-part-whole transparency, overhead counters*

1. Show a part-part-whole transparency. Place 12 counters in the whole section; 3 red and 9 yellow. Have a count the number of counters. Write 12 under the mat.

2. Move the 3 red counters to one part. **How many counters are in this part?** (3) **How can we show this as a subtraction sentence?** (12 − 3) Write − 3 next to the 12 under the mat.

3. Have a volunteer count out the remaining yellow counters. **How many counters are in the other part?** (9) Write = 9 to complete the subtraction sentence. Follow the same procedure for presenting the related fact 12 − 9 = 3. Discuss how the subtraction sentences are alike and different.

2 Develop

Guided Learning

Teaching Example Introduce the objective to the children. Guide them through the example and explain that if they know the whole and one of the parts, they can find the other part. Also focus on the pairs of facts and how to use the knowledge of one to find the difference for the other.

Guided Practice

Have children complete **Exercises 1–6** as you observe. Have children answer the Explain Your Thinking question. Then discuss their responses with the class.

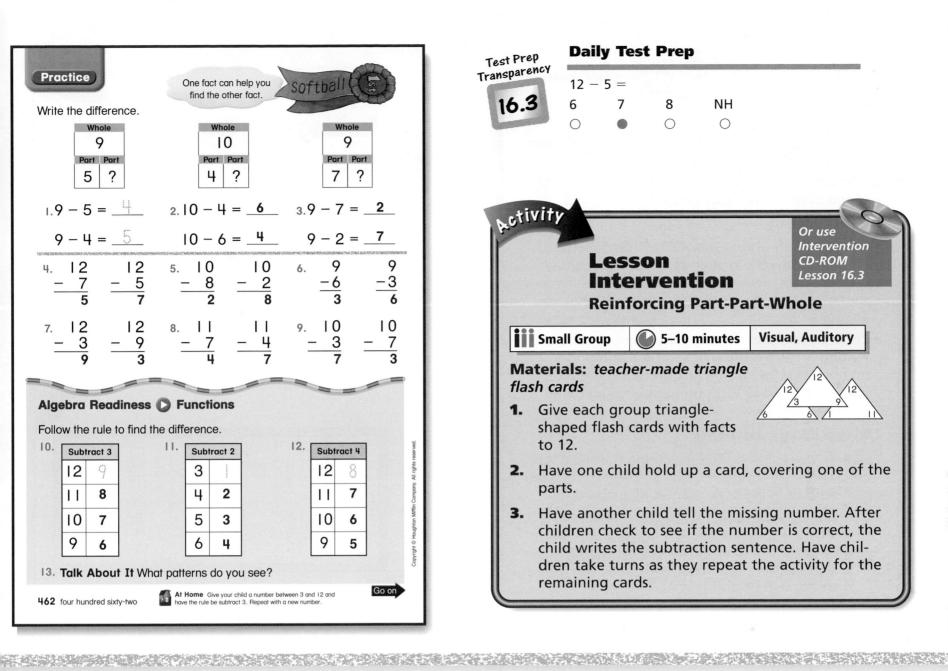

Practice

One fact can help you find the other fact. softball 1st

Write the difference.

Whole
9
Part	Part
5	?

Whole
10
Part	Part
4	?

Whole
9
Part	Part
7	?

1. $9 - 5 = \underline{4}$

$9 - 4 = \underline{5}$

2. $10 - 4 = \underline{6}$

$10 - 6 = \underline{4}$

3. $9 - 7 = \underline{2}$

$9 - 2 = \underline{7}$

4. $\begin{array}{r} 12 \\ -\ 7 \\ \hline 5 \end{array}$ $\begin{array}{r} 12 \\ -\ 5 \\ \hline 7 \end{array}$

5. $\begin{array}{r} 10 \\ -\ 8 \\ \hline 2 \end{array}$ $\begin{array}{r} 10 \\ -\ 2 \\ \hline 8 \end{array}$

6. $\begin{array}{r} 9 \\ -6 \\ \hline 3 \end{array}$ $\begin{array}{r} 9 \\ -3 \\ \hline 6 \end{array}$

7. $\begin{array}{r} 12 \\ -\ 3 \\ \hline 9 \end{array}$ $\begin{array}{r} 12 \\ -\ 9 \\ \hline 3 \end{array}$

8. $\begin{array}{r} 11 \\ -\ 7 \\ \hline 4 \end{array}$ $\begin{array}{r} 11 \\ -\ 4 \\ \hline 7 \end{array}$

9. $\begin{array}{r} 10 \\ -\ 3 \\ \hline 7 \end{array}$ $\begin{array}{r} 10 \\ -\ 7 \\ \hline 3 \end{array}$

Algebra Readiness ▶ Functions

Follow the rule to find the difference.

10.

Subtract 3	
12	9
11	8
10	7
9	6

11.

Subtract 2	
3	1
4	2
5	3
6	4

12.

Subtract 4	
12	8
11	7
10	6
9	5

13. **Talk About It** What patterns do you see?

At Home Give your child a number between 3 and 12 and have the rule be subtract 3. Repeat with a new number.

Go on ▶

Daily Test Prep

$12 - 5 = $

6 ○   7 ●   8 ○   NH ○

Activity

Lesson Intervention
Reinforcing Part-Part-Whole

Or use Intervention CD-ROM Lesson 16.3

👥 Small Group	⏱ 5–10 minutes	Visual, Auditory

Materials: *teacher-made triangle flash cards*

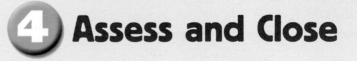

1. Give each group triangle-shaped flash cards with facts to 12.

2. Have one child hold up a card, covering one of the parts.

3. Have another child tell the missing number. After children check to see if the number is correct, the child writes the subtraction sentence. Have children take turns as they repeat the activity for the remaining cards.

---

3 Practice

Independent Practice

Children complete **Exercises 1–9** independently.

Algebra Readiness

After children complete **Exercises 10–12**, call on volunteers to share their responses. Use the **Talk About It** question in **Exercise 13** to discuss the patterns children see.

Common Error

Writing the Same Difference Twice

Children may write the same difference twice for related facts. Have children model each subtraction sentence with cubes or counters.

4 Assess and Close

In the subtraction sentence $12 - 7 = 5$, what is the whole? (12) **What are the parts?** (7 and 5)

If you know that $12 - 3 = 9$, what other fact do you know? ($12 - 9 = 3$)

📝 Keeping a Journal

Write two subtraction sentences that include the numbers 12 and 7.

Lesson continues ➡

Purpose: This game provides practice with addition and subtraction facts through 12.

Materials: *number cube labeled 6, 7, 8, 9, 11, 12, red and blue crayon, game board*

How to Play

- Have children play in pairs. Read the directions with children. The first child tosses the number cube and decides which fact has that number as a sum or difference. Then the child writes the answer in the box.

- Children take turns tossing the number cube and writing an answer in a box. If no box has the number as either a sum or difference, the child loses a turn. Children continue playing until all the boxes have correct answers.

Other Ways to Play

Children may continue to play during the same session, or these alternate versions of the Practice Game could be used in the Math Center at a later date.

A. Make a 6-part spinner with the numbers 6, 7, 8, 9, 11, 12. Children choose a box and spin until they get the sum or difference for that box. Children score 1 point for each spin. The child with the fewest points wins.

B. Prepare cards to match the boxes and place cards face down. Children take turns spinning to get a sum or difference. They pick a card, and if the number spun is the sum or difference then the card is kept. The player with the most cards wins.

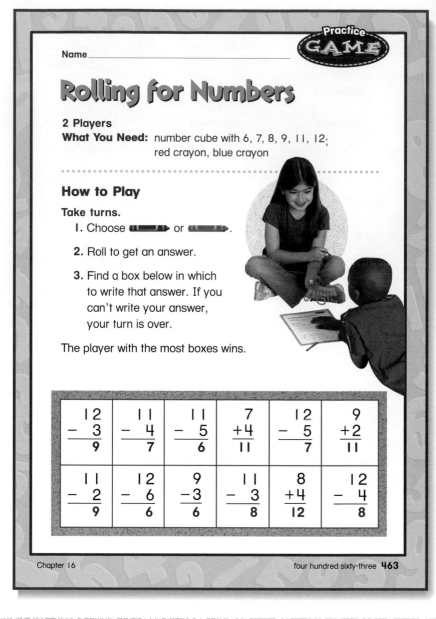

Name _____

Rolling for Numbers

2 Players
What You Need: number cube with 6, 7, 8, 9, 11, 12; red crayon, blue crayon

How to Play

Take turns.

1. Choose ▬▬▶ or ▬▬▶.

2. Roll to get an answer.

3. Find a box below in which to write that answer. If you can't write your answer, your turn is over.

The player with the most boxes wins.

$\begin{array}{r} 12 \\ -3 \\ \hline 9 \end{array}$	$\begin{array}{r} 11 \\ -4 \\ \hline 7 \end{array}$	$\begin{array}{r} 11 \\ -5 \\ \hline 6 \end{array}$	$\begin{array}{r} 7 \\ +4 \\ \hline 11 \end{array}$	$\begin{array}{r} 12 \\ -5 \\ \hline 7 \end{array}$	$\begin{array}{r} 9 \\ +2 \\ \hline 11 \end{array}$
$\begin{array}{r} 11 \\ -2 \\ \hline 9 \end{array}$	$\begin{array}{r} 12 \\ -6 \\ \hline 6 \end{array}$	$\begin{array}{r} 9 \\ -3 \\ \hline 6 \end{array}$	$\begin{array}{r} 11 \\ -3 \\ \hline 8 \end{array}$	$\begin{array}{r} 8 \\ +4 \\ \hline 12 \end{array}$	$\begin{array}{r} 12 \\ -4 \\ \hline 8 \end{array}$

Literature

Connection

Refer to the unit story *Twenty Is Too Many* by Kate Duke. Ask children these questions, based on the passage that appears on PE pages 423b and 423c.

- **How do you decide how many guinea pigs in all?** (Start with the 7 in the boat and add 2 more to get 9.)

- **If you know that 7 + 2 = 9, what other addition fact do you know?** (2 + 7 = 9)

- **If there are 9 guinea pigs and 8 walk away, how many guinea pigs are left?** (1)

Continue with similar questions.

Quick Check

Use the number line.
Subtract.

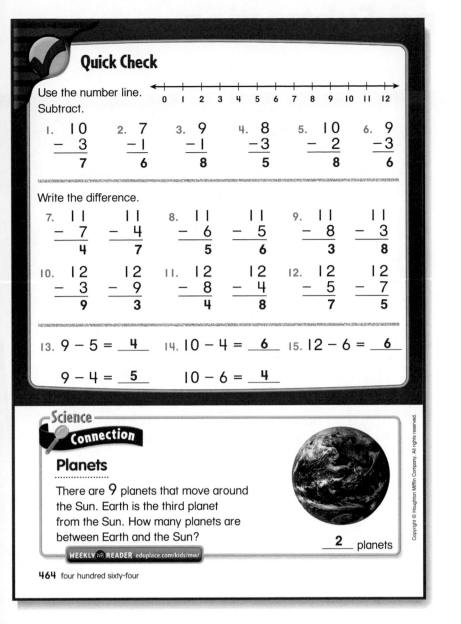

0 1 2 3 4 5 6 7 8 9 10 11 12

1.	2.	3.	4.	5.	6.
10 − 3 **7**	7 −1 **6**	9 −1 **8**	8 −3 **5**	10 − 2 **8**	9 −3 **6**

Write the difference.

7. 11   11   8. 11   11   9. 11   11
   − 7   − 4   − 6   − 5   − 8   − 3
    4   **7**   **5**   **6**   **3**   **8**

10. 12   12   11. 12   12   12. 12   12
    − 3   − 9   − 8   − 4   − 5   − 7
     9   **3**   **4**   **8**   **7**   **5**

13. 9 − 5 = __4__   14. 10 − 4 = __6__   15. 12 − 6 = __6__

    9 − 4 = __5__   10 − 6 = __4__

Science Connection

Planets

There are 9 planets that move around the Sun. Earth is the third planet from the Sun. How many planets are between Earth and the Sun?

__2__ planets

WEEKLY WR READER eduplace.com/kids/mw/

Quick Check

Have children complete the Quick Check exercises independently to assess their understanding of concepts and skills taught in **Lessons 1–3.**

Item	Lesson	Error Analysis	Intervention
1–6	16.1	Children count back incorrectly.	Reteach Resource 16.1 ***Ways to Success*** 16.1
7–9	16.2	Children may write the wrong difference.	Reteach Resource 16.2 ***Ways to Success*** 16.2
10–15	16.3	Children may write the same difference twice for related facts.	Reteach Resource 16.3 ***Ways to Success*** 16.3

Science Connection

Introduce the 9 planets to the children. Display a diagram. Then have children answer other questions about the position of planets relative to each other and to the sun.

Relate Addition and Subtraction

PLANNING THE LESSON

MATHEMATICS OBJECTIVE
Relate addition and subtraction facts to solve problems.

Use Lesson Planner CD-ROM for Lesson 16.4.

Meeting North Carolina's Standards

1.03 Develop fluency with single-digit addition and corresponding differences using strategies such as modeling, composing and decomposing quantities, using doubles, and making tens.

Also 1.04

Daily Routines

Calendar
Name an addition or subtraction fact through 12. Have children find the number of the date on the calendar that is the same as the sum or difference of the fact.

Sunday	Monday	Tuesday	Wednesday	Thursday	Friday	Saturday
				1	2	3 4
5	6	7	8	9	10	11
12	13	14	15	16	17	18
19	20	21	22	23	24	25
26	27	28	29	30	31	

Vocabulary
Write the addition sentence $8 + 2 = 10$ on the board. Have children identify the parts and the whole. Write the subtraction sentence $10 - 2 = 8$. Have children identify the parts and the whole. Demonstrate how these facts are **related facts**, since they have the same parts and same whole.

Vocabulary Cards

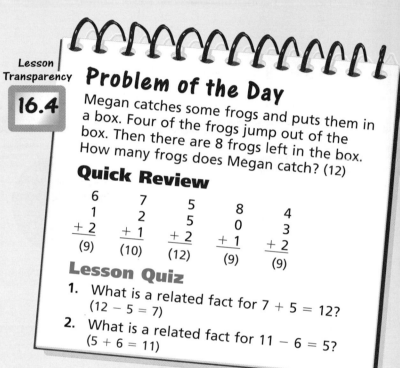

Lesson Transparency **16.4**

Problem of the Day
Megan catches some frogs and puts them in a box. Four of the frogs jump out of the box. Then there are 8 frogs left in the box. How many frogs does Megan catch? (12)

Quick Review

6	7	5	8	4
1	2	5	0	3
+ 2	+ 1	+ 2	+ 1	+ 2
(9)	(10)	(12)	(9)	(9)

Lesson Quiz
1. What is a related fact for $7 + 5 = 12$?
   ($12 - 5 = 7$)
2. What is a related fact for $11 - 6 = 5$?
   ($5 + 6 = 11$)

LEVELED PRACTICE

RETEACH 16.4

Name _____ Date _____ Reteach 16.4

Relate Addition and Subtraction

An addition fact and a subtraction fact that have the same numbers are related facts.

$$\begin{array}{cc} 3 & 9 \\ + 6 & - 6 \\ \hline 9 & 3 \end{array}$$

Use related facts to add and subtract.

1.	8 +4 = 12	12 −4 = 8	2.	3 +4 = 7	7 −4 = 3	3.	9 +2 = 11	11 −2 = 9
4.	5 +5 = 10	10 −5 = 5	5.	7 +5 = 12	12 −5 = 7	6.	6 +5 = 11	11 −5 = 6
7.	9 +3 = 12	12 −3 = 9	8.	2 +8 = 10	10 −8 = 2	9.	7 +4 = 11	11 −4 = 7

Use with text pages 465–466.

PRACTICE 16.4

Name _____ Date _____ Practice 16.4

Relate Addition and Subtraction

Use related facts to add and subtract.

1.	7 +4 = 11	11 −7 = 4	2.	6 +3 = 9	9 −6 = 3	3.	9 +3 = 12	12 −9 = 3
4.	6 +6 = 12	12 −6 = 6	5.	7 +5 = 12	12 −7 = 5	6.	6 +4 = 10	10 −4 = 6
7.	5 +4 = 9	9 −4 = 5	8.	2 +9 = 11	11 −2 = 9	9.	7 +2 = 9	9 −2 = 7
10.	7 +3 = 10	10 −7 = 3	11.	2 +8 = 10	10 −8 = 2	12.	8 +4 = 12	12 −4 = 8

Test Prep

Fill in the ○ for the correct answer. NH means Not Here.

13. Find the related subtraction sentence.

$7 + 5 = 12$

○ $12 - 6 = 6$ ● $12 - 5 = 7$ ○ $12 - 4 = 8$ ○ NH

Use with text pages 465–466.

ENRICHMENT 16.4

Name _____ Date _____ Enrichment 16.4

First Add, Then Subtract

Color some squares 🖍 Orange.
Color the rest of the squares 🖍 Purple.
Write one addition sentence and one subtraction sentence for the squares you colored. **Answers will vary.**

1.

_____ + _____ = **12**

12 − _____ = _____

2.

_____ + _____ = **11**

11 − _____ = _____

3.

_____ + _____ = **10**

10 − _____ = _____

Write About It How can knowing that $3 + 7 = 10$ help you find the difference of $10 - 7$?

I know that addition and subtraction are related.
So the answer has to be the other addend.

Use with text pages 465–466.

Practice Workbook Page 109

Reaching All Learners

Differentiated Instruction

English Learners

Children will need to understand the word *related* as they learn about related facts. Use Worksheet 16.4 to introduce the word to English-language learners.

Inclusion
TACTILE, VISUAL

Materials: *index cards*

- Give the child 6 blank cards. Ask him or her to write the numbers 7, 5, 12, and the signs $-$, $+$, $=$ on the cards.
- Make a number sentence, such as $7 + 5 = 12$, with the cards. Have the child use counters to model the sentence.
- Rearrange the cards to show the subtraction sentence $12 - 5 = 7$. Have the child model the sentence with counters.

Gifted and Talented
TACTILE, VISUAL

Materials: *number cards 1–9 (LT 14)*

- Children work in pairs. Give pairs number cards 1–9.
- Have pairs use all the cards to make related addition and subtraction sentences.
- Children may use numbers more than once. Partners check each other's work.

$$3+2=5 \qquad 5-3=2$$

TECHNOLOGY

Spiral Review
You can prepare students for standardized tests with **customized** spiral review on key skills using the *Ways to Assess* CD-ROM.

eBook
eMathBook allows students to review lessons and do homework without carrying their textbooks home.

Education Place
Recommend that parents visit **Education Place** at eduplace.com/parents/mw/ for parent support activities.

Literature Connection

Read the first 3 pages of *one less fish* by Kim Michelle Toft and Allan Sheather. Have children write a related subtraction and addition sentence to show how many fish were left after the divers came.
$(12 - 1 = 11 \quad 11 + 1 = 12)$

MATH CENTER

Cross-Curricular Activity
As you use this activity to relate the mathematics of this lesson to another curriculum area, children will see how math can help them with other subjects.

PROBLEM SOLVING 16.4

Name _____ Date _____ | Problem Solving 16.4

Relate Addition and Subtraction

Read each problem.
Write the number sentence and solve.

1. Mario has 9 potatoes. He gets 3 more from his garden. How many potatoes does he have in all?

   $\underline{9} + \underline{3} = \underline{12}$

   $\underline{12}$ potatoes

   Draw or write to explain.

2. Mindy has 12 tomatoes. She uses 9 tomatoes in a salad. How many tomatoes are left?

   $\underline{12} - \underline{9} = \underline{3}$

   $\underline{3}$ tomatoes

3. There are 12 carrot plants. The rabbits eat 7 carrot plants. How many carrot plants are left?

   $\underline{12} - \underline{7} = \underline{5}$

   $\underline{5}$ carrot plants

Use with text pages 465–466.

HOMEWORK 16.4

Name _____ Date _____ | Homework 16.4

Relate Addition and Subtraction

> An addition fact and a subtraction fact that have the same numbers are related facts.
>
> $$6 + 5 = 11$$
> $$11 - 5 = 6$$

Use related facts to add and subtract.

1. $\begin{array}{r} 4 \\ + 6 \\ \hline 10 \end{array}$ $\begin{array}{r} 10 \\ - 6 \\ \hline 4 \end{array}$
   2. $\begin{array}{r} 8 \\ + 3 \\ \hline 11 \end{array}$ $\begin{array}{r} 11 \\ - 3 \\ \hline 8 \end{array}$

3. $\begin{array}{r} 7 \\ + 5 \\ \hline 12 \end{array}$ $\begin{array}{r} 12 \\ - 5 \\ \hline 7 \end{array}$
   4. $\begin{array}{r} 1 \\ + 8 \\ \hline 9 \end{array}$ $\begin{array}{r} 9 \\ - 8 \\ \hline 1 \end{array}$

5. $\begin{array}{r} 7 \\ + 3 \\ \hline 10 \end{array}$ $\begin{array}{r} 10 \\ - 3 \\ \hline 7 \end{array}$
   6. $\begin{array}{r} 3 \\ + 9 \\ \hline 12 \end{array}$ $\begin{array}{r} 12 \\ - 9 \\ \hline 3 \end{array}$

7. Jennifer has 6 rings. She gets 2 more for her birthday. How many rings does she have in all?

   $\underline{8}$ rings

8. Then Jennifer gives 2 rings to her sister. How many rings does she have left?

   $\underline{6}$ rings

Use with text pages 465–466.

ENGLISH LEARNERS 16.4

Name _____ Date _____ | English Learners 16.4

Relate Addition and Subtraction

I am **related** to my father.

Draw members of your family.

1. I am related to my _____

   Drawing of person in family

2. I am related to my _____

   Drawing of person in family

To the Teacher: Use the example at the top of the page to help children understand the meaning of the word *related*. Then read the sentences with children and have them draw pictures.

Use with text pages 465–466.

Homework Workbook Page 109

TEACHING LESSON 16.4

LESSON ORGANIZER

Objective Relate addition and subtraction facts to solve problems.

Resources Reteach, Practice, Enrichment, Problem Solving, Homework, English Learners, Transparencies, Math Center

Materials Cubes, blank transparency

Activity

Warm-Up Activity
Modeling Related Facts

| Whole Group | 10–15 minutes | Visual, Tactile |

Materials: *red and blue cubes*

1. Have children make a train with 8 red cubes and 4 blue cubes. Then have them connect the trains. **How many red and blue cubes do you have altogether?** (12) **What addition sentence does this train show?** (8 + 4 = 12)

2. Now tell children to take away the 4 blue cubes. **What subtraction sentence does this show?** (12 − 4 = 8)

3. Explain to children that the sentences 8 + 4 = 12 and 12 − 4 = 8 are related because they use the same numbers.

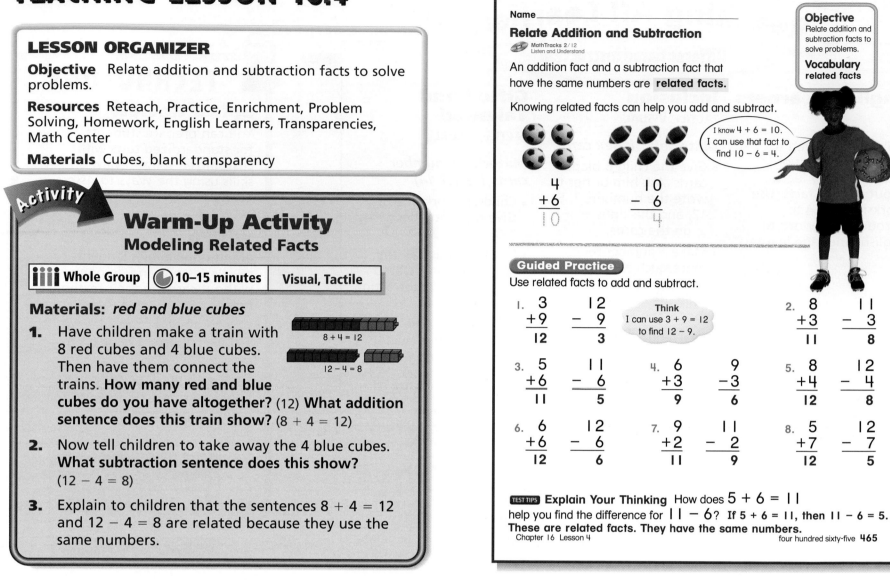

Name_____

Relate Addition and Subtraction

MathTracks 2/12
Listen and Understand

An addition fact and a subtraction fact that have the same numbers are **related facts**.

Objective
Relate addition and subtraction facts to solve problems.

Vocabulary
related facts

Knowing related facts can help you add and subtract.

I know 4 + 6 = 10.
I can use that fact to find 10 − 6 = 4.

$$\begin{array}{r} 4 \\ +6 \\ \hline 10 \end{array} \qquad \begin{array}{r} 10 \\ -6 \\ \hline 4 \end{array}$$

Guided Practice

Use related facts to add and subtract.

1.
$$\begin{array}{r} 3 \\ +9 \\ \hline 12 \end{array} \qquad \begin{array}{r} 12 \\ -9 \\ \hline 3 \end{array}$$

Think
I can use 3 + 9 = 12 to find 12 − 9.

2.
$$\begin{array}{r} 8 \\ +3 \\ \hline 11 \end{array} \qquad \begin{array}{r} 11 \\ -3 \\ \hline 8 \end{array}$$

3.
$$\begin{array}{r} 5 \\ +6 \\ \hline 11 \end{array} \qquad \begin{array}{r} 11 \\ -6 \\ \hline 5 \end{array}$$

4.
$$\begin{array}{r} 6 \\ +3 \\ \hline 9 \end{array} \qquad \begin{array}{r} 9 \\ -3 \\ \hline 6 \end{array}$$

5.
$$\begin{array}{r} 8 \\ +4 \\ \hline 12 \end{array} \qquad \begin{array}{r} 12 \\ -4 \\ \hline 8 \end{array}$$

6.
$$\begin{array}{r} 6 \\ +6 \\ \hline 12 \end{array} \qquad \begin{array}{r} 12 \\ -6 \\ \hline 6 \end{array}$$

7.
$$\begin{array}{r} 9 \\ +2 \\ \hline 11 \end{array} \qquad \begin{array}{r} 11 \\ -2 \\ \hline 9 \end{array}$$

8.
$$\begin{array}{r} 5 \\ +7 \\ \hline 12 \end{array} \qquad \begin{array}{r} 12 \\ -7 \\ \hline 5 \end{array}$$

TEST TIPS **Explain Your Thinking** How does 5 + 6 = 11 help you find the difference for 11 − 6? **If 5 + 6 = 11, then 11 − 6 = 5. These are related facts. They have the same numbers.**

Chapter 16 Lesson 4   four hundred sixty-five **465**

1 Introduce

Activity

Discuss Relating Addition and Subtraction

| Whole Group | 10–15 minutes | Visual, Auditory |

Materials: *blank transparency*

1. Write 7 + 5 in vertical form on the transparency. **What is the sum?** (12) Then write 12 − 5 in vertical form. **What is the difference?** (7)

2. Explain that these facts are related because they have the same parts and the same whole. **What other subtraction fact is related to 7 + 5 = 12?** (12 − 7 = 5) **How are these sentences alike?** (They both use the same numbers.) **How are they different?** (One is addition and one is subtraction.)

3. **If you know 7 + 5 = 12, then you know that 12 − 5 = 7 and 12 − 7 = 5.** Explain that when children know one fact, they can use it to find a related fact.

2 Develop

Guided Learning

Teaching Example Introduce the objective and vocabulary to the children. Guide them through the example to show the addition of 4 + 6 = 10. Then relate the subtraction to show the difference. Emphasize that when they know an addition fact, they know the related subtraction fact.

Guided Practice

Have children complete **Exercises 1–8** as you observe. Have children answer the Explain Your Thinking question. Then discuss their responses with the class.

Practice

Use the first fact to find the other fact.

Use related facts to add and subtract.

1. 3   11
   +8   − 8
   ‾11   ‾3

    2. 4   9
       +5   −5
       ‾9   ‾4

    3. 4   12
       +8   − 8
       ‾12 ‾4

4. 8   10
   +2   − 2
   ‾10 ‾8

    5. 9   12
       +3   − 3
       ‾12 ‾9

    6. 2   8
       +6   −6
       ‾8   ‾2

7. 7   12
   +5   − 5
   ‾12 ‾7

    8. 3   10
       +7   − 7
       ‾10 ‾3

    9. 4   11
       +7   − 7
       ‾11 ‾4

10. 6   10
    +4   − 4
    ‾10 ‾6

    11. 6   8
        +2   −2
        ‾8   ‾6

    12. 5   10
        +5   − 5
        ‾10 ‾5

13. 4   8
    +4   −4
    ‾8   ‾4

    14. 6   11
        +5   − 5
        ‾11 ‾6

    15. 2   9
        +7   −7
        ‾9   ‾2

Problem Solving ▶ Reasoning

Choose three of the numbers.
Write two related facts.

| 4 | 5 | 6 | 7 | 11 |

16. $\underline{5} + \underline{6} = \underline{11}$

$\underline{11} − \underline{6} = \underline{5}$

**Answers may vary.
Possible answers shown.**

At Home Say an addition fact such as 8 + 3 = 11. Ask your child to name a related subtraction fact such as 11 − 3 = 8 or 11 − 8 = 3.

Daily Test Prep

Which is a related fact for 11 − 6 = 5?

6 + 5 = 11   6 + 6 = 12   5 + 11 = 16   NH
   ●   ○   ○   ○

Activity

Lesson Intervention
Relate Addition and Subtraction

Or use Intervention CD-ROM Lesson 16.4

| 👥 Small Group | ⏱ 5–10 minutes | Visual, Tactile |

Materials: *teacher-made cards with addition and subtraction facts through 12*

12 − 5 = 7   7 + 5 = 12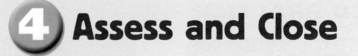

1. Prepare cards with addition and subtraction facts through 12. Give each child a set of cards.

2. Write an addition or subtraction fact through 12 on the board. Ask children to show a card with a related fact.

3. As children become comfortable with the activity, invite volunteers to write a fact on the board. Have other children show a related fact.

❸ Practice

Independent Practice

Children complete **Exercises 1–15** independently.

Problem Solving

After children complete **Exercise 16**, call on volunteers to share their solutions. Discuss why there may be more than two correct answers.

Common Error

Adding Instead of Subtracting
Children may add when they should subtract. Suggest that children circle the sign before they compute for each example.

❹ Assess and Close

What is a related subtraction fact for 7 + 4 = 11?
(11 − 4 = 7 or 11 − 7 = 4)

What is a related addition fact for 12 − 3 = 9? (9 + 3 = 12 or 3 + 9 = 12)

Keeping a Journal

Write a pair of related facts. Show how you know they are related.

Algebra Readiness: Fact Families for 11

PLANNING THE LESSON

MATHEMATICS OBJECTIVE
Write fact families for 11 using the inverse relationship.

Use Lesson Planner CD-ROM for Lesson 16.5.

Meeting North Carolina's Standards
1.03 Develop fluency with single-digit addition and corresponding differences using strategies such as modeling, composing and decomposing quantities, using doubles, and making tens.

Also 1.04

Daily Routines

Calendar
Name a date with 2 digits. Have children say an addition fact using the digits. For example, 23: $2 + 3 = 5$. Have them say the related subtraction fact, $5 - 3 = 2$

Sunday	Monday	Tuesday	Wednesday	Thursday	Friday	Saturday
			1	2	3	4
5	6	7	8	9	10	11
12	13	14	15	16	17	18
19	20	21	22	23	24	25
26	27	28	29	30	31	

Vocabulary
Write addition facts $6 + 5 = 11$ and $5 + 6 = 11$ and ask children to name the **related facts**. Write $11 - 5 = 6$ and $11 - 6 = 5$ and identify the four facts as a **fact family**.

Vocabulary Cards

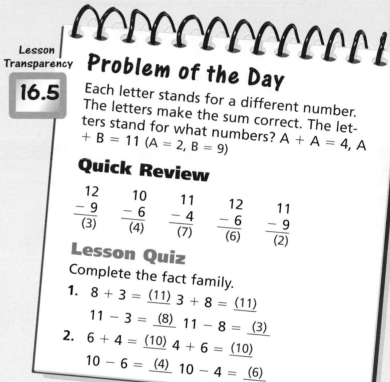

Lesson Transparency 16.5

Problem of the Day
Each letter stands for a different number. The letters make the sum correct. The letters stand for what numbers? $A + A = 4$, $A + B = 11$ ($A = 2$, $B = 9$)

Quick Review
$$\begin{array}{ccccc} 12 & 10 & 11 & 12 & 11 \\ -\ 9 & -\ 6 & -\ 4 & -\ 6 & -\ 9 \\ \hline (3) & (4) & (7) & (6) & (2) \end{array}$$

Lesson Quiz
Complete the fact family.
1. $8 + 3 = \underline{(11)}$ $3 + 8 = \underline{(11)}$
   $11 - 3 = \underline{(8)}$ $11 - 8 = \underline{(3)}$
2. $6 + 4 = \underline{(10)}$ $4 + 6 = \underline{(10)}$
   $10 - 6 = \underline{(4)}$ $10 - 4 = \underline{(6)}$

LEVELED PRACTICE

RETEACH 16.5

Name _____ Date _____ **Reteach 16.5**

Fact Families for 11

A fact family has the same numbers.

This fact family has the numbers 11, 9, and 2.

Whole	
11	
Part	**Part**
9	2

11 is the whole. 9 and 2 are the parts.

$9 + 2 = \underline{11}$ $11 - 9 = \underline{2}$
$2 + 9 = \underline{11}$ $11 - 2 = \underline{9}$

Complete the fact family.

1. | 11 | |
   |---|---|
   | 4 | 7 |

   $4 + 7 = \underline{11}$ $11 - 7 = \underline{4}$
   $7 + 4 = \underline{11}$ $11 - 4 = \underline{7}$

2. | 11 | |
   |---|---|
   | 5 | 6 |

   $5 + 6 = \underline{11}$ $11 - 5 = \underline{6}$
   $6 + 5 = \underline{11}$ $11 - 6 = \underline{5}$

3. | 11 | |
   |---|---|
   | 8 | 3 |

   $8 + 3 = \underline{11}$ $11 - 8 = \underline{3}$
   $3 + 8 = \underline{11}$ $11 - 3 = \underline{8}$

Use with text pages 467–468.

PRACTICE 16.5

Name _____ Date _____ **Practice 16.5**

Fact Families for 11

Complete the fact family.

1. | 11 | |
   |---|---|
   | 6 | 5 |

   $6 + 5 = \underline{11}$ $11 - 6 = \underline{5}$
   $5 + 6 = \underline{11}$ $11 - 5 = \underline{6}$

2. | 9 | |
   |---|---|
   | 3 | 6 |

   $3 + 6 = \underline{9}$ $9 - 3 = \underline{6}$
   $6 + 3 = \underline{9}$ $9 - 6 = \underline{3}$

3. | 11 | |
   |---|---|
   | 8 | 3 |

   $8 + 3 = \underline{11}$ $11 - 8 = \underline{3}$
   $3 + 8 = \underline{11}$ $11 - 3 = \underline{8}$

4. | 11 | |
   |---|---|
   | 2 | 9 |

   $2 + 9 = \underline{11}$ $11 - 2 = \underline{9}$
   $9 + 2 = \underline{11}$ $11 - 9 = \underline{2}$

Test Prep

Fill in the ○ for the correct answer. NH means Not Here.

5. Complete the fact family.

11	
7	4

$7 + 4 = 11$ $11 - 7 = 4$
$?$ $11 - 4 = 7$

○ $3 + 8 = 11$ ○ $2 + 9 = 11$ ● $4 + 7 = 11$ ○ NH

Use with text pages 467–468.

ENRICHMENT 16.5

Name _____ Date _____ **Enrichment 16.5**

3 Numbers, 4 Sentences

Complete the addition and subtraction sentences for each fact family.

1. $9 + 2 = 11$ $11 - 9 = 2$
   $2 + 9 = 11$ $11 - 2 = 9$

2. $7 + 4 = 11$ $11 - 7 = 4$
   $4 + 7 = 11$ $11 - 4 = 7$

3. $6 + 5 = 11$ $11 - 6 = 5$
   $5 + 6 = 11$ $11 - 5 = 6$

4. $8 + 3 = 11$ $11 - 8 = 3$
   $3 + 8 = 11$ $11 - 3 = 8$

Write About It How can you use $11 - 3 = 8$ to help you find $11 - 8$? If I know that $11 - 3 = 8$, then the 3 has to be the answer in $11 - 8$.

Use with text pages 467–468.

Practice Workbook Page 110

Reaching All Learners
Differentiated Instruction

English Learners

English-language learners may not have the language skills to explain the process behind their thinking. Use Worksheet 16.5 to provide children with sentence frames they can use to complete the Explain Your Thinking activity.

Special Needs
VISUAL, AUDITORY

Materials: *index cards*

- Write the numbers 5, 6, and 11 and the symbols + and = on individual index cards.
- Explain that you are going to make 4 facts with these numbers.
- Say 6 + 5 = 11. Have the child arrange the cards.
- Now, have the child rearrange the numbers to show the same sum of 11. Continue with 11 − 6 = 5.

Gifted and Talented
AUDITORY, TACTILE

- Have children work in pairs. One child names two numbers with a sum of 11 or less.
- The partner writes the other addition and the 2 subtraction facts in the fact family.
- Partners switch roles.

$$7 + 4 = 11$$

$$4 + 7 = 11$$
$$11 − 4 = 7$$
$$11 − 7 = 4$$

TECHNOLOGY

Spiral Review

Create **customized** spiral review worksheets for individual students using the *Ways to Assess* CD-ROM.

Education Place

Visit **Data Place** at **eduplace.com/dataplace/** to take a survey and see graphs of the results.

Lesson Planner

Use the **Lesson Planner CD-ROM** to see how lesson objectives for this chapter are correlated to standards.

ScienceConnection

Display a variety of rocks of different sizes and colors. Explain that minerals give rocks their colors. Have children count out 11 rocks and use them to model fact families for 11 as they write the addition and subtraction facts.

MATH CENTER

Basic Skills Activity

Motivate children to build basic skills. Use this activity to address multiple learning styles using hands-on activities related to the skills of this lesson.

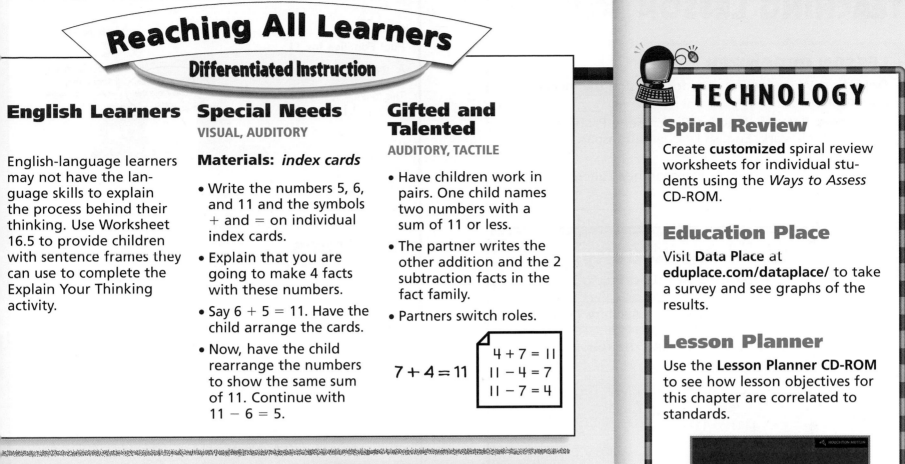

Homework Workbook Page 110

TEACHING LESSON 16.5

LESSON ORGANIZER

Objective Write fact families for 11 using the inverse relationship.

Resources Reteach, Practice, Enrichment, Problem Solving, Homework, English Learners, Transparencies, Math Center

Materials Part-part-whole transparency, cubes, Workmat 3

Activity

Warm-Up Activity
Identifying Related Facts

iiii Whole Group	⏱ 5 minutes	Auditory, Tactile

1. Review related facts by writing the following facts on the board:

$$\begin{array}{ccc} 7 & 9 & 11 \\ +\,4 & +\,2 & -\,7 \\ \hline (11) & (11) & (4) \end{array}$$

2. **Which of these are related facts?** (7 + 4 = 11 and 11 − 7 = 4) **Why?** (All the numbers in the facts are the same: 4, 7, 11.)

3. Continue by asking volunteers to write similar facts on the board using different numbers. Ask another volunteer to solve.

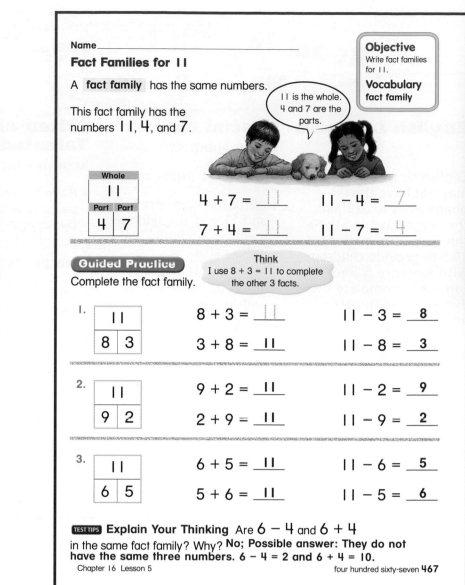

Name_____

Fact Families for 11

A fact family has the same numbers.

This fact family has the numbers 11, 4, and 7.

Objective
Write fact families for 11.
Vocabulary
fact family

11 is the whole. 4 and 7 are the parts.

Whole
11

Part	Part
4	7

$4 + 7 = \underline{11}$ $11 - 4 = \underline{7}$

$7 + 4 = \underline{11}$ $11 - 7 = \underline{4}$

Guided Practice
Complete the fact family.

Think
I use 8 + 3 = 11 to complete the other 3 facts.

1.

11	
8	3

$8 + 3 = \underline{11}$ $11 - 3 = \underline{8}$

$3 + 8 = \underline{11}$ $11 - 8 = \underline{3}$

2.

11	
9	2

$9 + 2 = \underline{11}$ $11 - 2 = \underline{9}$

$2 + 9 = \underline{11}$ $11 - 9 = \underline{2}$

3.

11	
6	5

$6 + 5 = \underline{11}$ $11 - 6 = \underline{5}$

$5 + 6 = \underline{11}$ $11 - 5 = \underline{6}$

TEST TIPS **Explain Your Thinking** Are $6 - 4$ and $6 + 4$ in the same fact family? Why? **No; Possible answer: They do not have the same three numbers. 6 − 4 = 2 and 6 + 4 = 10.**

Chapter 16 Lesson 5   four hundred sixty-seven **467**

---

1 Introduce
Discuss Fact Families

iiii Whole Group	⏱ 10–15 minutes	Visual, Auditory

Materials: *part-part-whole transparency*

1. Display the part-part-whole transparency. Write 11 in the whole section. Draw 3 triangles in one part and 8 triangles in the other part.

2. Write the number sentences 8 + 3 = 11, 3 + 8 = 11, 11 − 8 = 3, and 11 − 3 = 8 under the pictures. Explain how each fact relates to the pictures. Point to all the triangles in both halves and say: **11 is the whole**. Point to the groups of 8 triangles and 3 triangles and say: **8 and 3 are the parts**.

3. **How are the four number sentences alike?** (They all use the same numbers 3, 8, and 11.)

4. Explain that facts that use the same numbers are called a fact family. **This fact family uses the numbers 3, 8, and 11.**

2 Develop

Guided Learning

Teaching Example Introduce the objective and vocabulary to the children. Guide them through the example, explaining that only the numbers 11, 4, and 7 are used in the four addition and subtraction sentences, therefore, this is a fact family.

Guided Practice

Have children complete **Exercises 1–3** as you observe. Have children answer the Explain Your Thinking question. Then discuss their responses with the class.

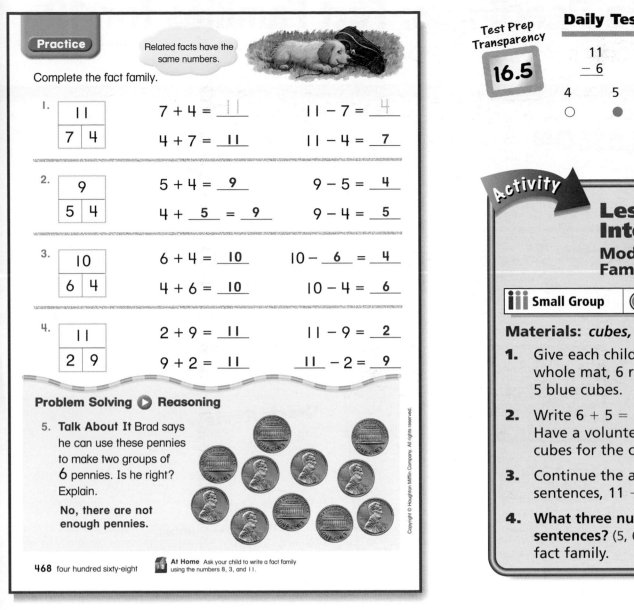

Practice

Related facts have the same numbers.

Complete the fact family.

1.
11
7	4

$7 + 4 = \underline{11}$ $11 - 7 = \underline{4}$

$4 + 7 = \underline{11}$ $11 - 4 = \underline{7}$

2.
9
5	4

$5 + 4 = \underline{9}$ $9 - 5 = \underline{4}$

$4 + \underline{5} = \underline{9}$ $9 - 4 = \underline{5}$

3.
10
6	4

$6 + 4 = \underline{10}$ $10 - \underline{6} = \underline{4}$

$4 + 6 = \underline{10}$ $10 - 4 = \underline{6}$

4.
11
2	9

$2 + 9 = \underline{11}$ $11 - 9 = \underline{2}$

$9 + 2 = \underline{11}$ $\underline{11} - 2 = \underline{9}$

Problem Solving ▶ Reasoning

5. **Talk About It** Brad says he can use these pennies to make two groups of 6 pennies. Is he right? Explain.

No, there are not enough pennies.

468 four hundred sixty-eight

At Home Ask your child to write a fact family using the numbers 8, 3, and 11.

Daily Test Prep

$$\begin{array}{r} 11 \\ -\ 6 \\ \hline \end{array}$$

4   5   6   7
○   ●   ○   ○

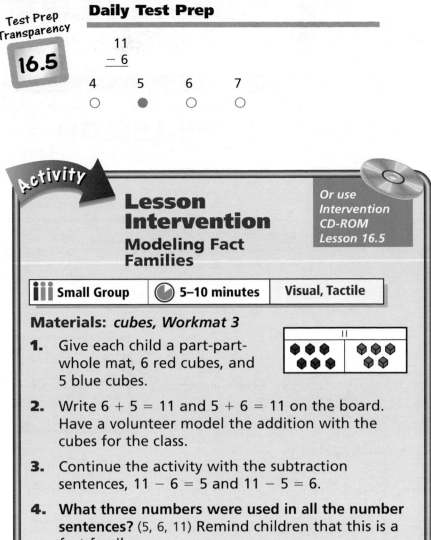

Activity

Lesson Intervention

Modeling Fact Families

Or use Intervention CD-ROM Lesson 16.5

| iii Small Group | 🕐 5–10 minutes | Visual, Tactile |

Materials: *cubes, Workmat 3*

1. Give each child a part-part-whole mat, 6 red cubes, and 5 blue cubes.

2. Write $6 + 5 = 11$ and $5 + 6 = 11$ on the board. Have a volunteer model the addition with the cubes for the class.

3. Continue the activity with the subtraction sentences, $11 - 6 = 5$ and $11 - 5 = 6$.

4. **What three numbers were used in all the number sentences?** (5, 6, 11) Remind children that this is a fact family.

---

3 Practice

Independent Practice

Children complete **Exercises 1–4** independently.

Problem Solving

Use the **Talk About It** in **Exercise 5** to discuss why the 11 pennies cannot make two groups of 6.

Common Error

Difficulty Identifying Fact Families

Children may have difficulty identifying fact families. Remind them that there are only 3 numbers in a fact family. One number is the number that tells how many are in the whole, the other 2 numbers tell how many are in the two parts.

4 Assess and Close

Complete this fact family.

$11 - 2 = \underline{}$ (9)

$11 - \underline{} = \underline{}$ (9, 2)

$2 + \underline{} = \underline{}$ (9, 11)

$\underline{} + \underline{} = 11$ (9, 2)

Keeping a Journal

Explain what a fact family is. Then write a fact family for 11.

Algebra Readiness: Fact Families for 12

PLANNING THE LESSON

MATHEMATICS OBJECTIVE
Write fact families for 12 using the inverse relationship.

Use Lesson Planner CD-ROM for Lesson 16.6.

Daily Routines

Calendar
Ask children to name the day of the week for the 12th. Now have them tell related facts using 12 as the whole.

Vocabulary
Review **fact family** by writing 6, 4, 10 on the board and having children write the 2 addition and 2 subtraction facts in the family.

Vocabulary Cards

Meeting North Carolina's Standards
1.03 Develop fluency with single-digit addition and corresponding differences using strategies such as modeling, composing and decomposing quantities, using doubles, and making tens.

Also 1.04

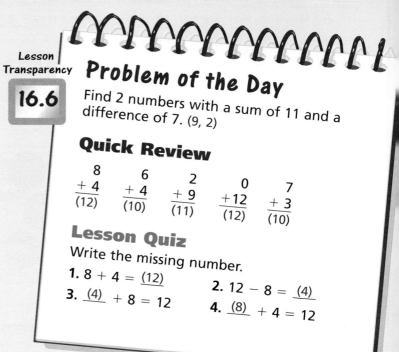

Lesson Transparency

16.6

Problem of the Day
Find 2 numbers with a sum of 11 and a difference of 7. (9, 2)

Quick Review

$$\begin{array}{ccccc} 8 & 6 & 2 & 0 & 7 \\ +4 & +4 & +9 & +12 & +3 \\ \hline (12) & (10) & (11) & (12) & (10) \end{array}$$

Lesson Quiz
Write the missing number.
1. $8 + 4 = \underline{(12)}$
2. $12 - 8 = \underline{(4)}$
3. $\underline{(4)} + 8 = 12$
4. $\underline{(8)} + 4 = 12$

LEVELED PRACTICE

RETEACH 16.6

Name _____ Date _____

Reteach 16.6

Fact Families for 12

The facts in a fact family are related.

The numbers 12, 5, and 7 make a fact family.

Whole	
12	
Part	Part
5	7

Fact families always use the same numbers.

$5 + 7 = \underline{12}$ $12 - 5 = \underline{7}$
$7 + 5 = \underline{12}$ $12 - 7 = \underline{5}$

Complete the fact family.

1. | 12 | |
   |---|---|
   | 8 | 4 |

$8 + 4 = \underline{12}$ $12 - 8 = \underline{4}$
$12 - 4 = \underline{8}$ $4 \; \boxed{+} \; 8 \; \boxed{=} \; 12$

2. | 12 | |
   |---|---|
   | 6 | 6 |

$6 + 6 = \underline{12}$ $12 \; \boxed{-} \; 6 \; \boxed{=} \; 6$

3. | 12 | |
   |---|---|
   | 3 | 9 |

$3 + 9 = \underline{12}$ $12 - 9 = \underline{3}$
$9 + 3 = \underline{12}$ $12 \; \boxed{-} \; 3 \; \boxed{=} \; 9$

Use with text pages 469–470.

PRACTICE 16.6

Name _____ Date _____

Practice 16.6

Fact Families for 12

Complete the fact family.

1. | 12 | |
   |---|---|
   | 9 | 3 |

$9 + 3 = \underline{12}$ $12 - 9 = \underline{3}$
$12 - 3 = \underline{9}$ $3 \; \boxed{+} \; 9 \; = 12$

2. | 12 | |
   |---|---|
   | 5 | 7 |

$5 + 7 = \underline{12}$ $12 - 5 = \underline{7}$
$7 + 5 = \underline{12}$ $12 \; \boxed{-} \; 7 \; = 5$

3. | 11 | |
   |---|---|
   | 6 | 5 |

$11 - 6 = \underline{5}$ $11 - 5 = \underline{6}$
$5 + 6 = \underline{11}$ $6 \; \boxed{+} \; 5 \; = 11$

Test Prep

Fill in the ○ for the correct answer. NH means Not Here.

4. Complete the fact family.

12	
8	4

$8 + 4 = 12$ $4 + 8 = 12$
$12 - 4 = 8$ $?$

$8 - 4 = 4$ $4 + 4 = 8$ $12 - 6 = 6$ NH
    ○   ○   ○   ●

Use with text pages 469–470.

ENRICHMENT 16.6

Name _____ Date _____

Enrichment 16.6

Fill In the Flag

Pick 3 numbers from the flags that can be used to write a fact family. Write the three numbers on the flags. Then complete the number sentences.   **Answers will vary.**

| 2 | 3 | 4 | 5 | 6 | 7 | 8 | 12 |

1. | 3 | 5 | 8 | 2. | 12 | 7 | 5 |

___ + ___ = ___   ___ + ___ = ___
___ + ___ = ___   ___ + ___ = ___
___ − ___ = ___   ___ − ___ = ___
___ − ___ = ___   ___ − ___ = ___

3. | 8 | 4 | 12 | 4. | 5 | 3 | 2 |

___ + ___ = ___   ___ + ___ = ___
___ + ___ = ___   ___ + ___ = ___
___ − ___ = ___   ___ − ___ = ___
___ − ___ = ___   ___ − ___ = ___

Use with text pages 469–470.

Practice Workbook Page 111

Reaching All Learners

Differentiated Instruction

English Learners

Children need to understand that fact families are made with parts and wholes. Use Worksheet 16.6 to develop familiarity with this concept.

Special Needs
VISUAL, TACTILE

Materials: *Workmat 3, counters*

- Write a 12 in the whole section of the mat.
- Have the child count out 12 counters and separate them into 2 parts on the mat.
- Have the child write the two addition and two subtraction facts for the fact family modeled.

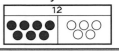

Early Finishers
AUDITORY, KINESTHETIC

- Have a small group sit in a circle, with one child in the center.
- The child in the center says an addition fact to another child.
- The child says a related subtraction fact back.
- If the fact is correct, children trade places. If incorrect, the child in the center continues.

TECHNOLOGY

Spiral Review

Using the *Ways to Assess* CD-ROM, you can create **customized** spiral review worksheets covering any lessons you choose.

eBook

An electronic version of this lesson can be found in **eMathBook**.

Games

Students can practice their skills using **Find a Friend** math game, available on the *Ways to Assess* CD-ROM.

Science Connection

Tell children that a wild horse family is called a *band*. A band consists of a number of adults and young foals. Suppose a band has 7 adults and 4 foals. Write 2 addition facts and 2 related subtraction facts.

MATH CENTER

Real-Life Activity

Help children understand the usefulness of mathematics. This activity makes math come alive by connecting the lesson skills to a real-life situation.

PROBLEM SOLVING 16.6

Name _____ Date _____ Problem Solving 16.6

Fact Families for 12

Read and solve.

1. Joe needs to write a number sentence that is part of this fact family. Write a number sentence that Joe might write.

   $3 + 9 = 12$

   Answers will vary.

   ___○___○___

2. Chris needs to write a number sentence that is part of this fact family. Write a number sentence Chris might write.

   $7 + 5 = 12$

   ___○___○___

3. Emma needs to write a number sentence that is part of this fact family. Write a number sentence Emma might write.

   $4 + 8 = 12$

   ___○___○___

Copyright © Houghton Mifflin Company. All rights reserved.   Use with text pages 469–470.

HOMEWORK 16.6

Name _____ Date _____ Homework 16.6

Fact Families for 12

A fact family is a group of facts that share the same numbers.

The facts in a fact family are related.
The numbers 12, 8, and 4 make a fact family.

Whole		
12	$4 + 8 = 12$	$12 - 4 = 8$
	$8 + 4 = 12$	$12 - 8 = 4$

Part	Part
4	8

Complete the fact family.

1. | 12 |
   | 5 | 7 |

   $5 + 7 = \underline{12}$ $12 - 5 = \underline{7}$
   $7 + 5 = \underline{12}$ $12 - 7 = \underline{5}$

2. | 12 |
   | 6 | 6 |

   $6 + 6 = \underline{12}$ $12 - 6 = \underline{6}$

3. | 12 |
   | 3 | 9 |

   $3 + 9 = \underline{12}$ $12 - 3 = \underline{9}$
   $9 + 3 = \underline{12}$ $12 - 9 = \underline{3}$

4. Write a fact family for these flowers.

   $\underline{5} + \underline{4} = \underline{9}$
   $\underline{4} + \underline{5} = \underline{9}$
   $\underline{9} - \underline{5} = \underline{4}$
   $\underline{9} - \underline{4} = \underline{5}$

Copyright © Houghton Mifflin Company. All rights reserved.   Use with text pages 469–470.

Homework Workbook Page 111

ENGLISH LEARNERS 16.6

Name _____ Date _____ English Learners 16.6

Fact Families for 12

$9 - 6 = 3$

Whole	
9	
Part	Part
6	3

Fact family: 9, 6, 3

$3 + 7 = 10$

Whole	
10	
Part	Part
3	7

Fact family: 10, 3, 7

Are $9 - 2$ and $9 + 2$ in the same fact family?

$9 - 2 = \underline{7}$

   $\underline{9}$ is the whole.

   $\underline{2}$ and $\underline{7}$ are the parts.

   The fact family has the numbers $\underline{9}$, $\underline{2}$, and $\underline{7}$.

$9 + 2 = \underline{11}$

   $\underline{11}$ is the whole.

   $\underline{9}$ and $\underline{2}$ are the parts.

   The fact family has the numbers $\underline{11}$, $\underline{9}$, and $\underline{2}$.

$9 - 2$ and $9 + 2$ are not in the same fact family.

To the Teacher: Use the examples at the top of the page to show how to determine fact families. Then read the sentences with children and have them complete each one.

Copyright © Houghton Mifflin Company. All rights reserved.   Use with text pages 469–470.

TEACHING LESSON 16.6

LESSON ORGANIZER

Objective Write fact families for 12 using the inverse relationship.

Resources Reteach, Practice, Enrichment, Problem Solving, Homework, English Learners, Transparencies, Math Center

Materials Part-part-whole transparency, highlight markers (3 colors)

Activity

Warm-Up Activity
Discuss Related Facts

👥 Whole Group	⏱ 5 minutes	Auditory, Visual

1. Review the concept of related facts by writing the following addition and subtraction sentences on the board.

7 + 4 = 11	7 − 3 = 4
4 + 7 = 11	11 − 7 = 4
7 − 4 = 3	11 − 4 = 7

2. Which 2 facts are not related to the other facts?
(7 − 4 = 3 and 7 − 3 = 4) **Why?** (They have a different whole and different parts.)

3. Have a volunteer write the addition facts to complete the family for 7, 3, and 4.

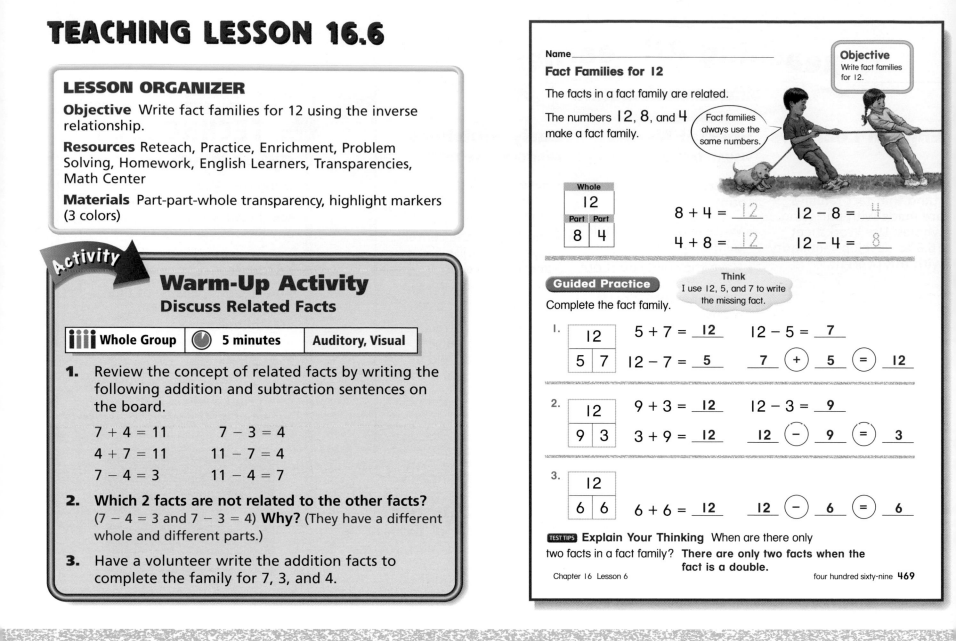

Name _____

Fact Families for 12

Objective Write fact families for 12.

The facts in a fact family are related.

The numbers 12, 8, and 4 make a fact family.

Fact families always use the same numbers.

Whole	
12	
Part	**Part**
8	4

$8 + 4 = 12$ $12 - 8 = 4$

$4 + 8 = 12$ $12 - 4 = 8$

Guided Practice

Think I use 12, 5, and 7 to write the missing fact.

Complete the fact family.

1.
12	
5	7

$5 + 7 = 12$ $12 - 5 = 7$

$12 - 7 = 5$ $7 \;(+)\; 5 \;(=)\; 12$

2.
12	
9	3

$9 + 3 = 12$ $12 - 3 = 9$

$3 + 9 = 12$ $12 \;(-)\; 9 \;(=)\; 3$

3.
12	
6	6

$6 + 6 = 12$ $12 \;(-)\; 6 \;(=)\; 6$

TEST TIPS **Explain Your Thinking** When are there only two facts in a fact family? **There are only two facts when the fact is a double.**

1 Introduce
Activity
Discuss Fact Families

👥 Whole Group	⏱ 10–15 minutes	Visual, Auditory

Materials: *part-part-whole transparency*

1. Display a part-part-whole transparency. Write a 12 in the whole section.

2. What 2 numbers can we put in the part sections that would have a sum of 12? Accept a possible answer, such as 9 + 3, and explain that other combinations of numbers would also work.

3. Invite 4 volunteers to say 1 addition or related subtraction fact that can be made using the three numbers in the frame. Write the sentences on the transparency.

4. How are these addition and subtraction sentences related? (They have the same whole and parts: 12, 9, and 3.)

2 Develop

Guided Learning

Teaching Example Introduce the objective to children. Guide them through the example. Discuss why the 12 is in the whole section and the 8 and 4 are in the part sections.

Guided Practice

Have children complete **Exercises 1–3** as you observe. Have children answer the Explain Your Thinking question. Then discuss their responses with the class.

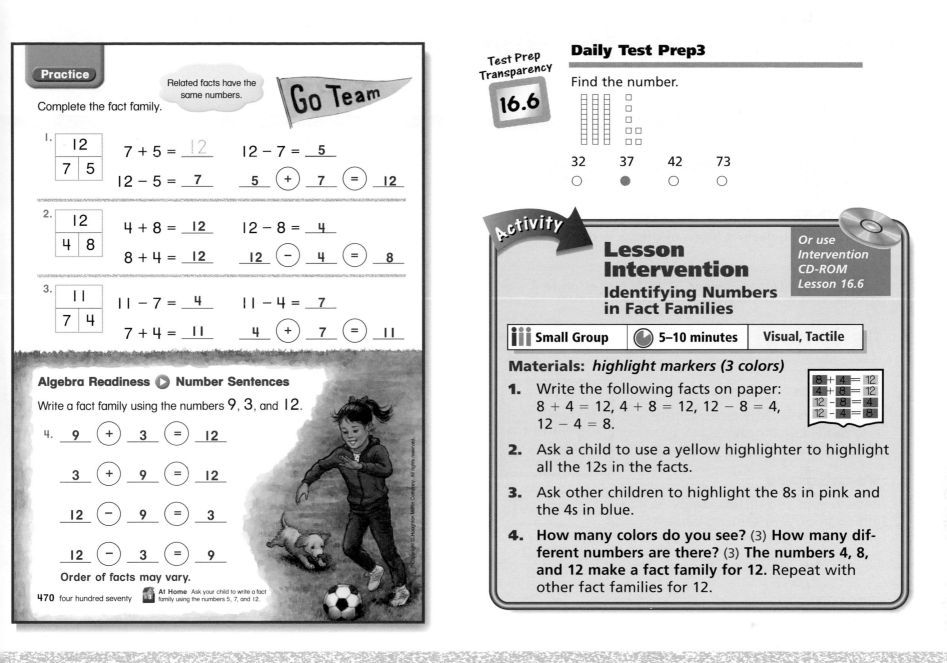

Practice

Practice

Related facts have the same numbers.

Go Team

Complete the fact family.

1.
12
7	5

$7 + 5 = 12$ $12 - 7 = 5$

$12 - 5 = 7$ $5 + 7 = 12$

2.
12
4	8

$4 + 8 = 12$ $12 - 8 = 4$

$8 + 4 = 12$ $12 - 4 = 8$

3.
11
7	4

$11 - 7 = 4$ $11 - 4 = 7$

$7 + 4 = 11$ $4 + 7 = 11$

Algebra Readiness ▶ Number Sentences

Write a fact family using the numbers 9, 3, and 12.

4. $9 + 3 = 12$

$3 + 9 = 12$

$12 - 9 = 3$

$12 - 3 = 9$

Order of facts may vary.

470 four hundred seventy

At Home Ask your child to write a fact family using the numbers 5, 7, and 12.

Test Prep Transparency **16.6**

Find the number.

32   37   42   73
○   ●   ○   ○

Activity

Lesson Intervention

Identifying Numbers in Fact Families

Or use Intervention CD-ROM Lesson 16.6

| 👤👤👤 Small Group | 🕐 5–10 minutes | Visual, Tactile |

Materials: *highlight markers (3 colors)*

| 8 + 4 = 12 |
| 4 + 8 = 12 |
| 12 – 8 = 4 |
| 12 – 4 = 8 |

1. Write the following facts on paper: 8 + 4 = 12, 4 + 8 = 12, 12 − 8 = 4, 12 − 4 = 8.

2. Ask a child to use a yellow highlighter to highlight all the 12s in the facts.

3. Ask other children to highlight the 8s in pink and the 4s in blue.

4. **How many colors do you see?** (3) **How many different numbers are there?** (3) **The numbers 4, 8, and 12 make a fact family for 12.** Repeat with other fact families for 12.

---

3 Practice

Independent Practice

Children complete **Exercises 1–3** independently.

Algebra Readiness

After children complete **Exercise 4**, call on volunteers to share their answers.

Common Error

Writing an Unrelated Fact
Children may think that all numbers that add up to the same sum are in a fact family. Remind them that only the same whole and the same 2 parts can be used in a fact family.

4 Assess and Close

Which 2 number sentences belong to the same fact family?
1 + 11 = 12, 8 + 4 = 12, 8 − 4 = 4, 12 − 8 = 4
(8 + 4 = 12 and 12 − 8 = 4)

What is the rest of the fact family? (4 + 8 = 12 and 12 − 4 = 8)

Keeping a Journal

Write a story about the numbers in this fact family: 3, 9, 12. Draw a picture to go with your story.

Names for Numbers

PLANNING THE LESSON

MATHEMATICS OBJECTIVE
Recognize equivalent forms of the same number.

Use Lesson Planner CD-ROM for Lesson 16.7.

Daily Routines

Calendar
Have children name dates whose two digits equal or have a difference of 4. (13, 22, 31; 15, 26)

Sunday	Monday	Tuesday	Wednesday	Thursday	Friday	Saturday
			1	2	3	4
5	6	7	8	9	10	11
12	13	14	15	16	17	18
19	20	21	22	23	24	25
26	27	28	29	30	31	

Vocabulary
Review **sum** and **difference** by reciting addition and subtraction facts and having children identify the sum or difference.

Vocabulary Cards

Meeting North Carolina's Standards
1.03 Develop fluency with single-digit addition and corresponding differences using strategies such as modeling, composing and decomposing quantities, using doubles, and making tens.

Also 5.03

Lesson Transparency **16.7**

Problem of the Day
Vera wants to put 10 pennies into 2 pockets. How many ways can she do this? (9 ways: 9,1; 1,9; 8,2; 2,8; 7,3; 3,7; 4,6; 6,4; 5,5)

Quick Review

$$\begin{array}{ccccc} 2 & 4 & 7 & 8 & 3 \\ 6 & 5 & 4 & 0 & 2 \\ +1 & +2 & +1 & +4 & +5 \\ \hline (9) & (11) & (12) & (12) & (10) \end{array}$$

Lesson Quiz
1. What is another name for 10? (Answers may include $5 + 5$, $6 + 4$, $7 + 3$, $12 - 2$, $11 - 1$, $10 - 0$.)
2. What is another name for 12? (Answers may include $11 + 1$, $10 + 2$, $9 + 3$, $8 + 4$, $7 + 5$, $6 + 6$.)

LEVELED PRACTICE

RETEACH 16.7

Name _____ Date _____ Reteach 16.7

Names for Numbers

You can get the same answer with different numbers. Circle the names for 7.

7	(3 + 4)	6 − 2	4 + 2	(11 − 4)
	7	4	6	7

$3 + 4$ and $11 - 4$ are names for 7.

Write the sums and differences. Circle the names for the number.

1. | 11 | 9 − 2 | (5 + 6) | (11 − 0) |
|---|---|---|---|
| | 7 | 11 | 11 |

2. | 5 | (2 + 3) | 9 5 | (10 − 5) |
|---|---|---|---|
| | 5 | 4 | 5 |

Circle the names for the number.

3. | 10 | (6 + 4) | 7 + 2 | (5 + 4 + 1) |

Copyright © Houghton Mifflin Company. All rights reserved. Use with text pages 471–472.

PRACTICE 16.7

Name _____ Date _____ Practice 16.7

Names for Numbers

Circle the names for the number.

1. | 7 | (5 + 2) | (3 + 4) | (4 + 2 + 1) |
|---|---|---|---|
| | 12 − 7 | 7 − 2 | 6 + 0 + 2 |

2. | 12 | (12 − 0) | 3 + 8 | (5 + 3 + 4) |
|---|---|---|---|
| | 2 + 9 | (7 + 5) | 9 + 1 + 1 |

3. | 6 | (2 + 4) | (12 − 6) | 6 + 0 + 1 |
|---|---|---|---|
| | (3 + 3) | 7 − 2 | (3 + 1 + 2) |

4. | 10 | 12 − 3 | (9 + 1) | 5 + 5 + 1 |
|---|---|---|---|
| | 3 + 8 | (11 − 1) | (4 + 1 + 5) |

Test Prep

Fill in the ○ for the correct answer. NH means Not Here.

5. Which choice does not name the number 11?

$8 + 3$ ○ $7 + 4$ ○ $12 - 2$ ●   NH ○

Copyright © Houghton Mifflin Company. All rights reserved. Use with text pages 471–472.

ENRICHMENT 16.7

Name _____ Date _____ Enrichment 16.7

Teams and T-Shirts

The children in Mrs. Roses's class are making up teams of three. Look at the number for each team. Match the names for the number. Circle the names of the children on the same team.

1. TEAM A 10
(Jenny)	Carey	Eric	(Andrea)
9 + 2	10 + 1	11 − 2	6 + 5

2. TEAM B 8
Kevin	(Sidney)	(Lynn)	Rose
9 − 1	11 − 3	2 + 6	4 + 3

3. TEAM C 10
Kwamo	(Erio)	Milko	Laura
12 − 2	11 − 1	6 + 4	6 + 5

Talk About It Why does each number have so many names? Each number has many names because there are many addition and subtraction combinations that can result in that number.

Copyright © Houghton Mifflin Company. All rights reserved. Use with text pages 471–472.

Practice Workbook Page 112

Reaching All Learners

Differentiated Instruction

English Learners

Children will need to understand the phrase *different ways* in order to understand that numbers can be represented in a variety of ways. Use Worksheet 16.7 to help English-language learners develop an understanding of this phrase.

Special Needs
VISUAL, TACTILE

Materials: *cubes*

Make two trains of 10 cubes.

Have the child break apart one train. Then write an addition sentence using the parts. Break apart the other train at a different place. Write another addition sentence.

Emphasize that each fact is a different name for 10.

$$2 + 8 = 10$$
$$4 + 6 = 10$$

Early Finishers
VISUAL, TACTILE

Materials: *number cards 0–12 (LT 14 and 15)*

Children work in pairs. Give each pair 2 sets of number cards.

Partners arrange cards face down in an array.

One child turns over 2 cards. The child keeps both cards if 12 is the sum. If not, both cards are returned. Partners take turns until all cards have been claimed.

Literature Connection

Read *one less fish* by Kim Michelle Toft and Allan Sheather. Choose one fish from the story. Have children count how many are in the story. Now have children write all the names for that number.

MATH CENTER

Vocabulary Activity

This vocabulary activity helps children understand and remember new words. Encourage children to use the words in math discussion.

TECHNOLOGY

Spiral Review

To reinforce skills on lessons taught earlier, create **customized** spiral review worksheets using the *Ways to Assess* CD-ROM.

Lesson Planner

You can use the **Lesson Planner CD-ROM** to create a report of the lessons and standards you have taught.

eBook

eMathBook allows students to review lessons and do homework without carrying their textbooks home.

Education Place

Encourage students to visit **Education Place** at **eduplace.com/kids/mw/** for more student activities.

PROBLEM SOLVING 16.7

Name _____ Date _____ | Problem Solving 16.7

Names for Numbers

Read each problem.
Circle the name for the number in the problem.

	Draw or write to explain.
1. Julia has a cat. She says the age of her cat is $9 + 2$. What is another name for $9 + 2$? $0 + 2$ ⟨$12 - 1$⟩	
2. Dan has a parrot that says words. The parrot says hello 6 times and good-bye 5 times. What is another name for $6 + 5$? ⟨$1 + 0$⟩ $12 - 6$	
3. Lee has fish. He says he has $12 - 2$ fish. What is another name for the number? ⟨$6 + 4$⟩ $7 + 5$	
4. Sarah has a dog. She says the dog can do $3 + 3$ tricks. What is another name for the number? $6 + 6$ ⟨$11 - 5$⟩	

Use with text pages 471–472.

HOMEWORK 16.7

Name _____ Date _____ | Homework 16.7

Names for Numbers

8	$2 + 6$	$5 + 7$	$10 - 4$	$9 - 1$
	$5 + 4$	$4 + 4$	$11 - 3$	$8 + 2$

Put an X on the name that does not belong in each box.

1. 6	$3 + 3$	$4 - 2$	$1 + 2 + 3$
	$2 + 4$	$5 + 1$	$3 + 3 + 1$

2. 7	$9 - 2$	$4 - 3$	$1 + 2 + 4$
	$5 - 2$	$7 - 0$	$5 + 2$

3. 10	$5 - 5$	$12 - 2$	$5 + 5 + 0$
	$6 - 4$	$1 + 9$	$3 + 3 + 4$

4. Leo has 6 marbles. Write three different names for the number of marbles.

Write here.
Answers will vary.

Use with text pages 471–472.

Homework Workbook Page 112

ENGLISH LEARNERS 16.7

Name _____ Date _____ | English Learners 16.7

Names for Numbers

Show the number 7 in *different ways*.

pictures	words	symbols
(7 circles)	seven	$1 + 6$ $4 + 3$

Show the number in different ways.

1. 5	Possible answer: (5 circles)	five	Possible answer: $3 + 2$ $6 - 1$
	pictures	words	symbols

Show the number in different ways.

2. 12	Possible answer: (12 circles)	twelve	Possible answer: $8 + 4$ $9 + 3$
	pictures	words	symbols

To the Teacher: Use the example at the top of the page to help children understand the different ways of representing numbers.

Use with text pages 471–472.

TEACHING LESSON 16.7

LESSON ORGANIZER

Objective Recognize equivalent forms of the same number.

Resources Reteach, Practice, Enrichment, Problem Solving, Homework, English Learners, Transparencies, Math Center

Materials Part-part-whole transparency, counters

Activity

Warm-Up Activity
Ways to Make Ten

iiii Whole Group	⏱ 5 minutes	Auditory, Visual

Materials: *part-part-whole transparency, counters*

1. Review facts for 10 on a part-part-whole transparency. Write a 10 in the whole section and a 6 and a 4 in the part sections.

10	
6	4

$6 + 4 = 10$

2. **Are 6 and 4 the only numbers that we can put in the part sections to make 10?** (no) **What other numbers could we put here?** Encourage children to use counters to find other facts. Write in other acceptable numbers that children suggest and keep a list of the combinations.

3. Count the listed combinations and ask: **How many ways did we find to make 10?**

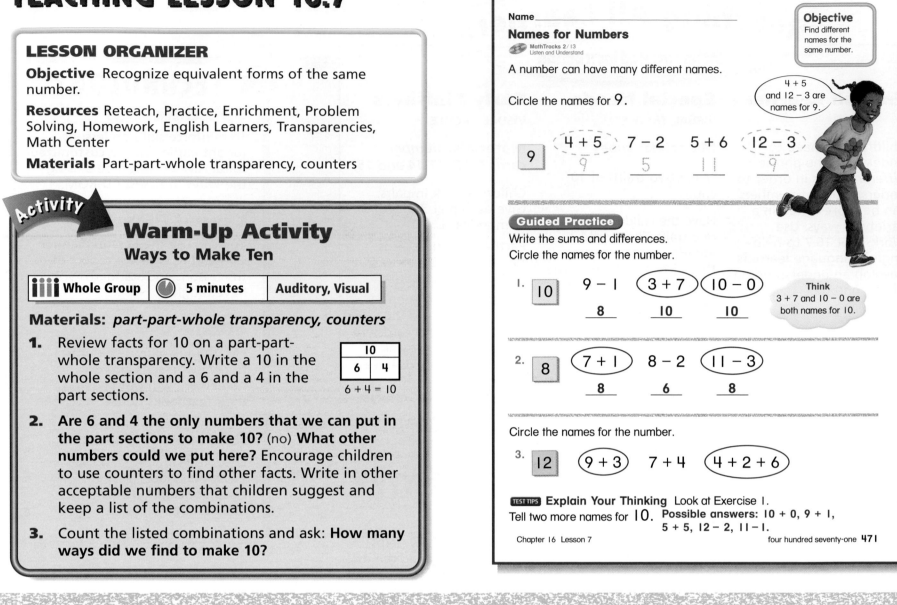

Name_____

Names for Numbers

MathTracks 2/13
Listen and Understand

Objective
Find different names for the same number.

A number can have many different names.

Circle the names for **9**.

4 + 5 and 12 − 3 are names for 9.

9	⟨4 + 5⟩	7 − 2	5 + 6	⟨12 − 3⟩
	9	5	11	9

Guided Practice

Write the sums and differences.
Circle the names for the number.

1. | 10 | 9 − 1 | ⟨3 + 7⟩ | ⟨10 − 0⟩ |
   |---|---|---|---|
   | | 8 | 10 | 10 |

Think
3 + 7 and 10 − 0 are both names for 10.

2. | 8 | ⟨7 + 1⟩ | 8 − 2 | ⟨11 − 3⟩ |
   |---|---|---|---|
   | | 8 | 6 | 8 |

Circle the names for the number.

3. | 12 | ⟨9 + 3⟩ | 7 + 4 | ⟨4 + 2 + 6⟩ |
   |---|---|---|---|

TEST TIPS Explain Your Thinking Look at Exercise 1.
Tell two more names for **10**. Possible answers: 10 + 0, 9 + 1, 5 + 5, 12 − 2, 11 − 1.

Chapter 16 Lesson 7   four hundred seventy-one **471**

---

① Introduce

Activity

Discuss Names for Numbers

iiii Whole Group	⏱ 10–15 minutes	Visual, Auditory

1. Write an 11 on the board. Under the 11, write the following expressions in vertical format:

   7 + 4   14 − 3   11 + 2   11 − 1   12 − 1

2. **Which of these facts has a sum or a difference of 11?** Invite children to find the sums and differences and identify the facts that equal 11. Identify these as names for 11. Erase the expressions that are not names for 11. (11 + 2 and 11 − 1)

3. Ask children to name other facts that have a sum of 11. Then ask them to name facts that have a difference of 11.

② Develop

Guided Learning

Teaching Example Introduce the objective to the children. Explain that 4 + 5 and 12 − 3 are two different names for 9. Point out that 7 − 2 is a name for 5 and 5 + 6 is a name for 11.

Guided Practice

Have children complete Exercises 1–3 as you observe. Have children share their responses for the Explain Your Thinking question.

Circle the names for the number.

1. **5**   (3 + 2)   5 + 2   (1 + 2 + 2)
   (11 − 6)   (9 − 4)   4 + 0 + 3

2. **11**   (11 − 0)   6 + 4   (1 + 7 + 3)
   (8 + 3)   (9 + 2)   4 + 0 + 3

3. **9**   (6 + 3)   (12 − 3)   5 + 3 + 2
   (11 − 2)   9 − 1   (7 + 1 + 1)

4. **8**   12 − 5   (5 + 3)   1 + 6 + 3
   8 − 3   (11 − 3)   (4 + 0 + 4)

5. **4**   (11 − 7)   (3 + 1)   2 + 2 + 4
   (9 − 5)   2 + 5   6 + 2 + 0

Algebra Readiness ▶ Patterns

Write the sums. Look for a pattern.
Write the facts likely to come next.

6.
0	1	2	3	4	5
+7	+6	+5	+4	+3	+2
7	7	7	7	7	7

At Home Say a number such as 8. Have your child tell you three or four names for 8, such as 6 + 2, 10 − 2, 3 + 5.

Daily Test Prep

Bill had 40¢. His uncle gave him 3 dimes. How much money does Bill have in all?

43¢   55¢   70¢   80¢
○   ○   ●   ○

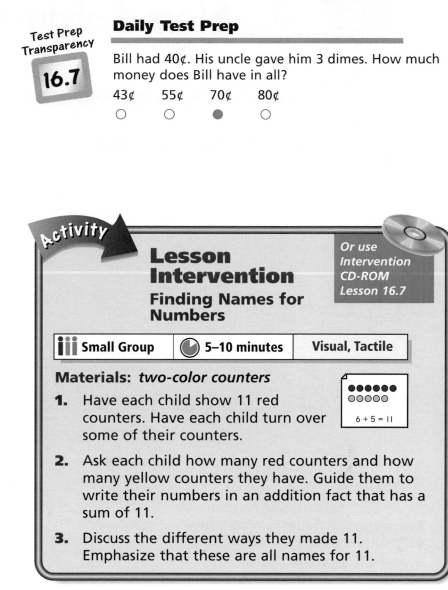

Activity

Lesson Intervention
Finding Names for Numbers

Or use Intervention CD-ROM Lesson 16.7

👥 Small Group	🕐 5–10 minutes	Visual, Tactile

Materials: *two-color counters*

1. Have each child show 11 red counters. Have each child turn over some of their counters.

   6 + 5 = 11

2. Ask each child how many red counters and how many yellow counters they have. Guide them to write their numbers in an addition fact that has a sum of 11.

3. Discuss the different ways they made 11. Emphasize that these are all names for 11.

---

③ Practice

Independent Practice

Children complete **Exercises 1–5** independently.

Algebra Readiness

After children complete **Exercise 6**, call on volunteers to share the pattern they found with the class.

Common Error

Circling the Wrong Fact

Children may forget that they are looking for names for the number on the left. Remind them to circle only those facts with sums or differences that match that number.

④ Assess and Close

Which of these are names for 9? 12 − 3,   9 − 6, 5 + 4, 9 + 2 (12 − 3, 5 + 4)

What are two names for 5? (Answers may include 1 + 4, 2 + 3, 10 − 5, 9 − 4, 8 − 3, 7 − 2, 6 − 1.)

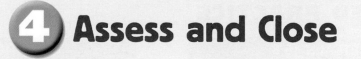

Keeping a Journal

Explain why 10 + 2 is a name for 12, and why 12 − 2 is not a name for 12.

Problem Solving: Choose the Operation

PLANNING THE LESSON

MATHEMATICS OBJECTIVE
Choose addition or subtraction to solve problems.

Use Lesson Planner CD-ROM for Lesson 16.8.

Daily Routines

Calendar
Have children find out how many names for 12 they can make by adding the digits of dates in the month, such as 1 + 11, 2 + 10, and 3 + 9.

Sunday	Monday	Tuesday	Wednesday	Thursday	Friday	Saturday
			1	2	3	4
5	6	7	8	9	10	11
12	13	14	15	16	17	18
19	20	21	22	23	24	25
26	27	28	29	30	31	

Vocabulary
Review the terms **addition** and **subtraction** by calling on volunteers to give examples of when you would use each to solve a problem.

Vocabulary Cards

Meeting North Carolina's Standards
1.03 Develop fluency with single-digit addition and corresponding differences using strategies such as modeling, composing and decomposing quantities, using doubles, and making tens.

Also 1.04

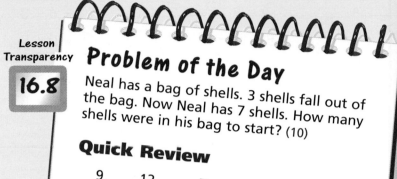

Lesson Transparency 16.8

Problem of the Day
Neal has a bag of shells. 3 shells fall out of the bag. Now Neal has 7 shells. How many shells were in his bag to start? (10)

Quick Review

$$\begin{array}{cc} 9 \\ -5 \\ \hline (4) \end{array} \quad \begin{array}{cc} 12 \\ -6 \\ \hline (6) \end{array} \quad \begin{array}{cc} 7 \\ -3 \\ \hline (4) \end{array} \quad \begin{array}{cc} 11 \\ -9 \\ \hline (2) \end{array} \quad \begin{array}{cc} 10 \\ -7 \\ \hline (3) \end{array}$$

Lesson Quiz
1. There are 12 cows in a barn. 4 cows get out. How many cows are in the barn now? (8)
2. There are 5 pigs in a puddle. 4 more pigs come. How many pigs are in the puddle now? (9)

LEVELED PRACTICE

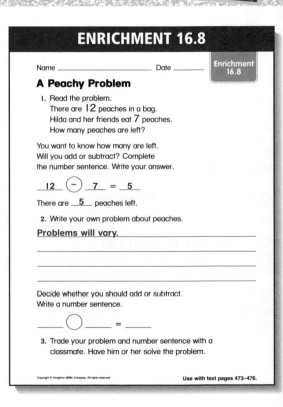

RETEACH 16.8

Name _____ Date _____ Reteach 16.8

Problem Solving Choose the Operation

Read It
Marta has 12 apples. Some of the apples are red. There are 8 green apples. How many apples are red?

Picture It

Whole
12

Part	Part
●●●●●	?

Solve It Look for clues.
1. I know that the whole is __12__ apples.
2. I know that one part is __8__ green apples.
3. I can't add __12__ and __8__ because __12__ is the whole.
4. I need to __subtract__ to find the missing part.
5. 12 − __8__ = __4__
6. Marta has __4__ red apples.

Explain. If you know both parts, do you add or subtract to get your answer? Why?
If I know the whole and 1 part, I need to subtract to find the missing part. If I know the two parts, I need to add to find the whole.

Use with text pages 473–476.

PRACTICE 16.8

Name _____ Date _____ Practice 16.8

Problem Solving Choose the Operation

Add or subtract to solve.

	Draw or write to explain.
1. There are 8 puppies asleep in the basket. Some of the puppies wake up. Now 5 puppies are still sleeping. How many puppies are awake? __3__ puppies are awake.	
2. There are 4 gray kittens in the yard. There are 4 orange kittens on the porch. How many kittens are there in both places? __8__ kittens in both places	

Test Prep

Fill in the ○ for the correct answer. NH means Not Here.

3. Ramón sees 9 kittens in the pet shop window. He sees 6 puppies there, too. How many fewer puppies than kittens does Ramón see in the pet shop window?

3 ●   4 ○   5 ○   NH ○

Use with text pages 473–476.

ENRICHMENT 16.8

Name _____ Date _____ Enrichment 16.8

A Peachy Problem

1. Read the problem.
There are 12 peaches in a bag. Hilda and her friends eat 7 peaches. How many peaches are left?

You want to know how many are left. Will you add or subtract? Complete the number sentence. Write your answer.

__12__ ⊝ __7__ = __5__

There are __5__ peaches left.

2. Write your own problem about peaches.

Problems will vary.
_____
_____

Decide whether you should add or subtract. Write a number sentence.

_____ ○ _____ = _____

3. Trade your problem and number sentence with a classmate. Have him or her solve the problem.

Use with text pages 473–476.

Practice Workbook Page 113

Reaching All Learners

Differentiated Instruction

English Learners

In order to understand some addition and subtraction word problems, children will need to understand the word *both*. Use Worksheet 16.8 to provide practice with the word.

Special Needs
AUDITORY, TACTILE

- Tell the child an addition story. Ask the child to model it with counters. For example: There are 6 frogs on a log. Two more frogs join them. Ask the child if there are more or fewer frogs on the log. (more)
- Then, ask if he or she will add or subtract to solve. (add)
- Continue with other addition and subtraction stories.

Gifted and Talented
TACTILE, AUDITORY

- Prepare incomplete number sentence cards such as 3 ○ □ = 7. Have children place 10 cards face down.
- One child chooses a card and tells the missing symbol and number.
- The partner models the sentence with counters to check.
- Play continues as children switch roles.

$$3 \bigcirc \square = 7 \qquad \circ\circ\circ + \circ\circ\circ\circ = 7$$

Art Connection

Have children draw a scene to use as a background for a story. Then have children place counters on their backgrounds and tell an addition or subtraction story.

MATH CENTER

Number of the Week Activity

Display the Number of the Week to motivate children to use their problem-solving skills. The exercises cover topics across all math strands.

TECHNOLOGY

Spiral Review

Help students remember skills they learned earlier by creating **customized** spiral review worksheets using the *Ways to Assess* CD-ROM.

Intervention

Use the *Ways to Success* CD-ROM intervention software to support students who need more help in understanding the concepts and skills taught in this chapter.

Education Place

You can visit **Education Place** at **eduplace.com/math/mw/** for teacher support materials.

PROBLEM SOLVING 16.8

Name _____ Date _____ | Problem Solving 16.8

Choose the Operation

Ann has 12 pennies.
She uses 7 of them to buy a pencil.
How many pennies does Ann have left?

UNDERSTAND
What do I need to find out?
What do I know that can help me?

> How many pennies Ann has left.
> I know she had 12.
> I know she used 7.

PLAN
Should I add or subtract?

> The question asks me to find how many are left. That means I must subtract.

SOLVE
I will write a subtraction sentence.

> 12 − 7 = 5
> Ann has 5 pennies left.

LOOK BACK
How can I check my answer?

> I can add 7 + 5 and get 12.

Copyright © Houghton Mifflin Company. All rights reserved.   Use with text pages 473–475.

HOMEWORK 16.8

Name _____ Date _____ | Homework 16.8

**Problem Solving
Choose the Operation**

You can use addition or subtraction to solve a problem.
There are 6 guinea pigs in a cage.
Gail buys 2 of them.
How many guinea pigs are left?

UNDERSTAND
What do I need to find out?

> I need to find out how many guinea pigs are ___left___.

What do I know?

> I know there are __6__ guinea pigs and Gail buys __2__ of them.

PLAN
What operation do I use?

> ___subtraction___

SOLVE
What number sentence can I write to solve the problem?

> __6__ (−) __2__ (=) __4__

LOOK BACK
Is there another way I could solve the problem?

> Answers might include: I knew to subtract because the problem said *are left*.

Copyright © Houghton Mifflin Company. All rights reserved.   Use with text pages 473–475.

Homework Workbook Page 113

ENGLISH LEARNERS 16.8

Name _____ Date _____ | English Learners 16.8

Choose the Operation

He has a hat.   They **both** have hats.

Circle **yes** or **no**.

1.
Do they both have coats?
yes (no)

2.
Do they both have boots?
(yes) no

3.
Do they both have dogs?
(yes) no

4.
Do they both have books?
yes (no)

To the Teacher: Use the illustrations and sentences at the top of the page to help children understand the meaning of the word *both*. Then read the questions with children and have them circle the correct response.

Copyright © Houghton Mifflin Company. All rights reserved.   Use with text pages 473–475.

TEACHING LESSON 16.8

LESSON ORGANIZER

Objective Choose addition or subtraction to solve problems.

Resources Reteach, Practice, Enrichment, Problem Solving, Homework, English Learners, Transparencies, Math Center

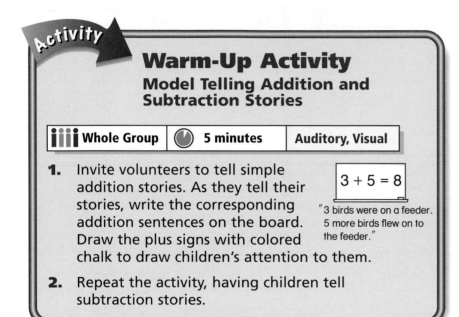

Warm-Up Activity

Model Telling Addition and Subtraction Stories

Whole Group	5 minutes	Auditory, Visual

1. Invite volunteers to tell simple addition stories. As they tell their stories, write the corresponding addition sentences on the board. Draw the plus signs with colored chalk to draw children's attention to them.

$3 + 5 = 8$

"3 birds were on a feeder. 5 more birds flew on to the feeder."

2. Repeat the activity, having children tell subtraction stories.

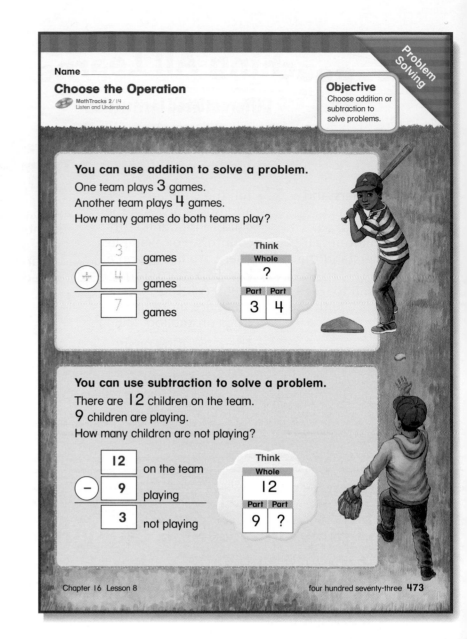

Choose the Operation

MathTracks 2/14
Listen and Understand

Objective Choose addition or subtraction to solve problems.

You can use addition to solve a problem.
One team plays 3 games.
Another team plays 4 games.
How many games do both teams play?

3 games
+ 4 games
——
7 games

Think
Whole
?
Part | Part
3 | 4

You can use subtraction to solve a problem.
There are 12 children on the team.
9 children are playing.
How many children are not playing?

12 on the team
− 9 playing
——
3 not playing

Think
Whole
12
Part | Part
9 | ?

Chapter 16 Lesson 8   four hundred seventy-three **473**

---

1 Introduce

Discuss Using Addition and Subtraction to Solve a Problem

Whole Group	10–15 minutes	Visual, Auditory

1. *Choose the operation to solve a problem.* Present the problem: **Jenna has 4 rabbits. Her brother has 7 rabbits. How many rabbits do they have in all?** (11)

2. **What numbers will you use to solve the problem?** (4 and 7) **Will you add or subtract to solve the problem?** (add) **Why?** (You have to add to find how many in all.)

3. Repeat the process using this problem. **José has 8 hamsters. He gives 3 of them to his sister. How many hamsters does José have now?** (5) **Will you add or subtract to solve the problem?** (subtract) **Why?** (You have to subtract to find how many are left.)

2 Develop

Guided Learning

Teaching Example Introduce the objective to children. Then call on a volunteer to read the first problem. **What numbers do we need to solve the problem?** (3 and 4) **Why do we add these numbers to solve the problem?** (We have to find out how many games both teams played.) Point out the Think cloud and relate the numbers in the problem to the parts. **What is the answer to the problem?** (7 games) Repeat the process for the subtraction problem. **How do we subtract to solve the problem?** (Subtract 9 from 12 to find the difference or missing part.) **What is the answer to the problem?** (3 children are not playing.)

Guided Practice

Have children complete **Exercises 1** and **2** on page 474 as you observe.

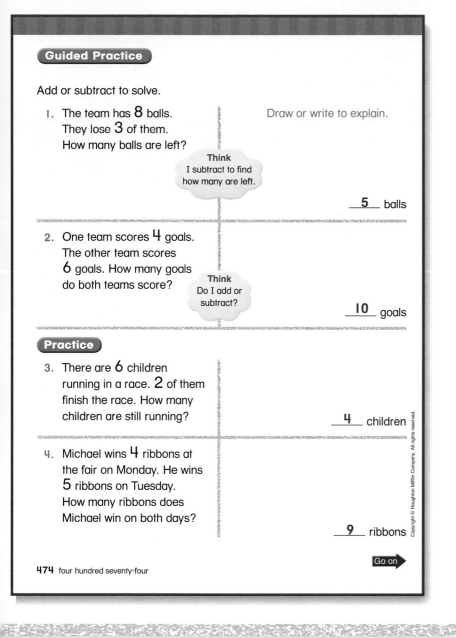

Guided Practice

Add or subtract to solve.

Draw or write to explain.

1. The team has 8 balls.
They lose 3 of them.
How many balls are left?

Think
I subtract to find
how many are left.

_____5_____ balls

2. One team scores 4 goals.
The other team scores
6 goals. How many goals
do both teams score?

Think
Do I add or
subtract?

_____10_____ goals

Practice

3. There are 6 children
running in a race. 2 of them
finish the race. How many
children are still running?

_____4_____ children

4. Michael wins 4 ribbons at
the fair on Monday. He wins
5 ribbons on Tuesday.
How many ribbons does
Michael win on both days?

_____9_____ ribbons

474 four hundred seventy-four

Go on

Play "Give Me a Sign"

Separate the class into two teams. Say an addition
or subtraction story aloud, for example:

There are 7 bugs on a leaf.

2 bugs crawl away.

How many bugs are still on the leaf?

A child from each team goes to the board and
decides if the problem is an addition or subtraction
problem. He or she writes the complete addition or
subtraction sentence on the board. If the child is
correct, their team gets a point. Continue with other
addition and subtraction stories. Have volunteers
use tally marks to keep score for each team.

ACHIEVING
Mathematical Proficiency

Understanding Algebraic Thinking

Current research and development in elementary
mathematics curriculum is exploring ways curriculum can be used to encourage the development of
algebraic thinking. Experts believe that students can
learn the basics of algebra in early elementary
school grades. In primary grades, one way to teach
subtraction facts is to use related addition facts.
Fact families and related facts provide practice as
well as introduce children to the algebraic concept
of equations.

In this chapter, children relate addition and
subtraction facts, and explain how knowing an
addition fact helps find the difference for a related
subtraction fact. They write fact families for 11
and 12, and explain how they know that specific
addition and subtraction facts are in the same fact
family. These types of practice activities serve as
stepping stones to algebraic thinking.

3 Practice

Independent Practice

Children complete **Exercises 3** and **4** on page 474
independently.

Lesson continues

Daily Test Prep

12 − ___ = 4

5	6	7	8
○	○	○	●

Activity

Lesson Intervention

Modeling Addition and Subtraction Stories

Or use Intervention CD-ROM Lesson 16.8

iii Small Group	⏱ 5–10 minutes	Auditory, Tactile

1. Have children draw a pond on a piece of paper.

2. Say: **There are 9 ducks in a pond.** Ask: **What number did you hear?** (9) Help children model this with their counters.

3. Continue the story: **3 ducks waddle away. What number did you hear in this part of the story?** (3)

4. **How can you show with counters how many ducks are still in the pond?** (take 3 away) **Are you adding or subtracting?** (subtracting) **How many ducks are still in the pond?** (6)

5. Repeat the activity with a similar addition story.

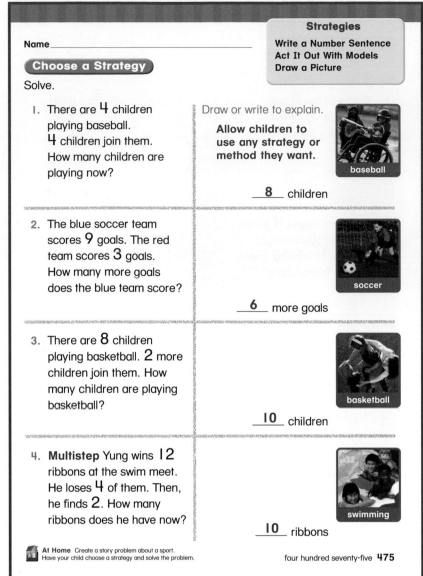

Name _____

Choose a Strategy

Solve.

Strategies
Write a Number Sentence
Act It Out With Models
Draw a Picture

1. There are 4 children playing baseball. 4 children join them. How many children are playing now?

   Draw or write to explain.
   Allow children to use any strategy or method they want.

   baseball

   ___8___ children

2. The blue soccer team scores 9 goals. The red team scores 3 goals. How many more goals does the blue team score?

   soccer

   ___6___ more goals

3. There are 8 children playing basketball. 2 more children join them. How many children are playing basketball?

   basketball

   ___10___ children

4. **Multistep** Yung wins 12 ribbons at the swim meet. He loses 4 of them. Then, he finds 2. How many ribbons does he have now?

   swimming

   ___10___ ribbons

At Home Create a story problem about a sport. Have your child choose a strategy and solve the problem.

③ Practice

Mixed Strategy Practice

Read the problem-solving strategies with children. Make sure children can read and comprehend the problems in **Exercises 1–4** on page 475. If necessary, pair more proficient readers with less proficient readers. Encourage them to discuss the problems before solving.

Common Error

Choosing the Wrong Operation

Children may choose the wrong operation to solve problems. Have them use counters to model the action in each problem. Then have them describe the action in their own words before they choose the operation.

④ Assess and Close

Would you add or subtract to find how many goals 2 players on a soccer team scored? (add)

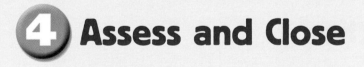 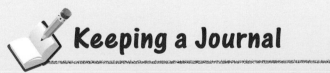

Keeping a Journal

Create a story about a day at the park. Choose a strategy and solve the problem. Write why you chose to add or subtract to solve the problem.

Problem-Solving for Tests **Listening Skills**

Listen to your teacher read the problem.
Solve.

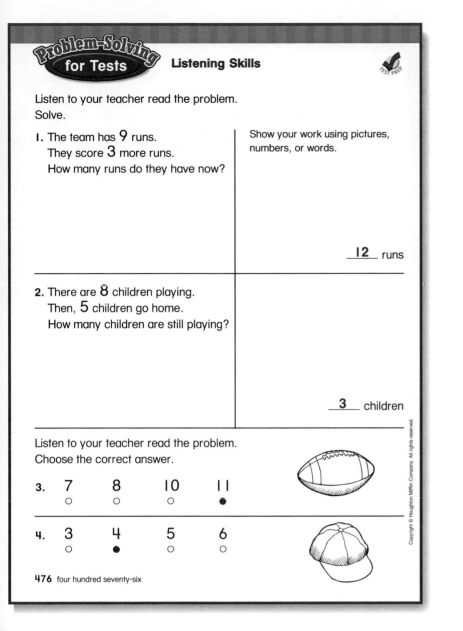

1. The team has 9 runs.
   They score 3 more runs.
   How many runs do they have now?

Show your work using pictures, numbers, or words.

_12_ runs

2. There are 8 children playing.
   Then, 5 children go home.
   How many children are still playing?

_3_ children

Listen to your teacher read the problem.
Choose the correct answer.

3. 7   8   10   11
    ○   ○   ○   ●

4. 3   4   5   6
    ○   ●   ○   ○

476 four hundred seventy-six

Problem-Solving for Tests

Listening Skills

This page provides children practice with the oral problem-solving format used in some standardized test items.

You may want to read each item only once to mimic the style of oral tests.

Use with Items 1 and 2

Listening Strategy: Read the problem while the teacher reads it aloud.

- *This problem is on the page. Read it to yourself while I read it aloud.*

- *Listen to the whole problem. Wait until I finish reading to start writing.*

Use with Item 3

Listening Strategy: Listen to the problem. Then draw a picture, if you want, to help you find the answer.

- *Look at me as I read the problem.*

  There are 8 children playing tag football.

  3 children join them.

  How many children are playing football now?

- *You can draw a picture now. Then mark your answer.*

Use with Item 4

Listening Strategy: Listen for important facts and numbers.

- *Listen for the question the problem asks.*

  There are 7 baseball hats.
  3 of them get lost.
  How many hats are left?

- *Use the numbers to solve the problem. Think about whether you need to add or subtract to solve the problem. Then mark your answer.*

Quick Check

Have children complete the Quick Check exercises independently to assess their understanding of concepts and skills taught in **Lessons 4–8**.

Item	Lesson	Error Analysis	Intervention
1–3	16.4	Children may add instead of subtract.	Reteach Resource 16.4 *Ways to Success 16.4*
4	16.5	Children may have difficulty identifying fact families.	Reteach Resource 16.5 *Ways to Success 16.5*
5	16.6	Children may write unrelated facts.	Reteach Resource 16.6 *Ways to Success 16.6*
6	16.7	Children may circle the wrong fact.	Reteach Resource 16.7 *Ways to Success 16.7*
7	16.8	Children may choose the wrong operation.	Reteach Resource 16.8 *Ways to Success 16.8*

Name_____ **Quick Check**

Use related facts to add and subtract.

1. $\begin{array}{r} 8 \\ +2 \\ \hline 10 \end{array}$ $\begin{array}{r} 10 \\ -\ 2 \\ \hline 8 \end{array}$
2. $\begin{array}{r} 9 \\ +3 \\ \hline 12 \end{array}$ $\begin{array}{r} 12 \\ -\ 3 \\ \hline 9 \end{array}$
3. $\begin{array}{r} 5 \\ +6 \\ \hline 11 \end{array}$ $\begin{array}{r} 11 \\ -\ 6 \\ \hline 5 \end{array}$

Complete the fact family.

4.
11	
8	3

$8 + 3 = \underline{11}$ $11 - 8 = \underline{3}$

$3 + 8 = \underline{11}$ $11 - 3 = \underline{8}$

Add or subtract. Write the missing fact.

5.
12	
7	5

$7 + 5 = \underline{12}$ $12 - 7 = \underline{5}$

$12 - 5 = \underline{7}$ $\underline{5} \ (+) \ \underline{7} \ (=) \ \underline{12}$

Circle the names for the number.

6. **11** $7 + 3$ $\boxed{10 + 1}$ $\boxed{1 + 6 + 4}$

7. There are 11 players. 9 of the players have hats. How many players do not have hats?

Draw or write to explain.

$\underline{2}$ players

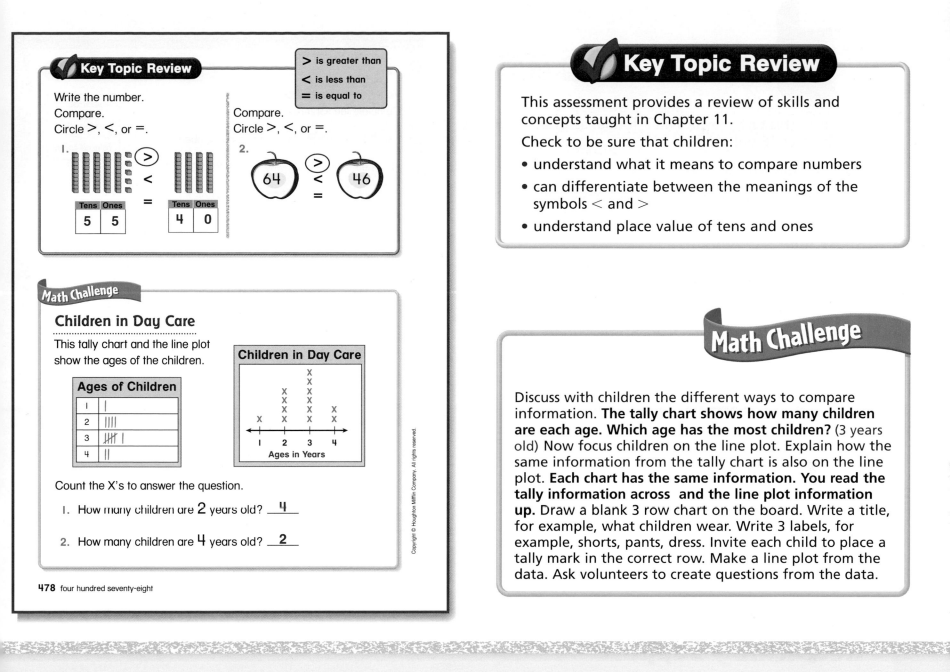

Key Topic Review

> is greater than
< is less than
= is equal to

Write the number.
Compare.
Circle >, <, or =.

1.

	Tens	Ones	
5	5

> < =

	Tens	Ones	
4	0

Compare.
Circle >, <, or =.

2.

64 > < = 46

Math Challenge

Children in Day Care

This tally chart and the line plot show the ages of the children.

Ages of Children

1		
2					
3						
4			

Children in Day Care

```
              X
              X
      X       X
      X   X   X
      X   X   X   X
  X   X   X   X
  ─────────────────
  1   2   3   4
     Ages in Years
```

Count the X's to answer the question.

1. How many children are 2 years old? __4__

2. How many children are 4 years old? __2__

Key Topic Review

This assessment provides a review of skills and concepts taught in Chapter 11.

Check to be sure that children:

• understand what it means to compare numbers

• can differentiate between the meanings of the symbols < and >

• understand place value of tens and ones

Math Challenge

Discuss with children the different ways to compare information. **The tally chart shows how many children are each age. Which age has the most children?** (3 years old) Now focus children on the line plot. Explain how the same information from the tally chart is also on the line plot. **Each chart has the same information. You read the tally information across and the line plot information up.** Draw a blank 3 row chart on the board. Write a title, for example, what children wear. Write 3 labels, for example, shorts, pants, dress. Invite each child to place a tally mark in the correct row. Make a line plot from the data. Ask volunteers to create questions from the data.

Chapter Review/Test

Purpose: This test provides an informal assessment of the Chapter 16 objectives.

Chapter Test Items 1–25

To assign a numerical grade for this Chapter Test, use 4 points for each test item.

Check Understanding

Use children's work on word problems to informally assess progress on chapter content.

Customizing Your Instruction

For children who have not yet mastered these objectives, you can use the reteaching resources listed in the chart below.

✓ Assessment Options

A summary test for this chapter is also provided in the Unit Resource Folder.

Name _____ ✓ **Chapter Review/Test**

Vocabulary *e* Glossary
Complete the sentence.

| subtract |
| number line |
| related facts |

1. __Related facts__ have the same numbers.

2. When I take some away I __subtract__.

3. A __number line__ can help me subtract.

Concepts and Skills
Use the number line.
Subtract.

0 1 2 3 4 5 6 7 8 9 10 11 12

| 4. $9 - 2 = 7$ | 5. $11 - 1 = 10$ | 6. $10 - 3 = 7$ | 7. $12 - 2 = 10$ | 8. $7 - 3 = 4$ | 9. $10 - 2 = 8$ |

Write the difference.

| 10. $9 - 6 = 3$ | $9 - 3 = 6$ | 11. $10 - 2 = 8$ | $10 - 8 = 2$ | 12. $11 - 7 = 4$ | $11 - 4 = 7$ |

| 13. $12 - 7 = 5$ | $12 - 5 = 7$ | 14. $9 - 5 = 4$ | $9 - 4 = 5$ | 15. $10 - 6 = 4$ | $10 - 4 = 6$ |

Chapter 16   four hundred seventy-nine **479**

Reteaching Support

Chapter Test Items	Summary Test Items	Chapter Objectives Tested	TE Pages	Use These Reteaching Resources
1–3	3–4	**16A** Develop and use math vocabulary relating to subtraction facts through 12.	457A–458, 465A–466	Reteach Resources and *Ways to Success* CD: 16.1, 16.4 Skillsheet 115
4–9	1–2	**16B** Subtract from 12 using different strategies including counting back.	459A–462	Reteach Resources and *Ways to Success* CD: 16.2, 16.3 Skillsheet 116
10–24	5–8	**16C** Use related facts and fact families, through 12, to solve addition and subtraction problems, and find different names for the same number.	465A–472	Reteach Resources and *Ways to Success* CD: 16.1–16.7 Skillsheets 117–118
25	9–10	**16D** Choose addition or subtraction to solve problems.	473A–476	Reteach Resource and *Ways to Success* CD: 16.8 Skillsheet 119

CHAPTER SUMMARY TEST

Name _____ Date _____   Chapter 16 Test

Count back. Find the difference.

0 1 2 3 4 5 6 7 8 9 10 11 12

1. $11 - 3 = $ __8__   2. $12 - 2 = $ __10__

Complete the related facts.

3. Whole 10 / Part 6 / Part
$10 - 6 = $ __4__
$10 - 4 = $ __6__

4. Whole 12 / Part 7 / Part
$12 - 7 = $ __5__
$12 - 5 = $ __7__

Go on ➤

Use related facts to add and subtract.

16.
```
  9      11
 +2    –  2
 ——    ——
 11       9
```

17.
```
  6      12
 +6    –  6
 ——    ——
 12       6
```

18.
```
  2      10
 +8    –  8
 ——    ——
 10       2
```

19.
```
  7      12
 +5    –  5
 ——    ——
 12       7
```

20.
```
  5      10
 +5    –  5
 ——    ——
 10       5
```

21.
```
  5       8
 +3    – 3
 ——    ——
  8       5
```

Complete the fact family.

22.

12	
4	8

$4 + 8 = \underline{12}$ $12 - 4 = \underline{8}$

$8 + 4 = \underline{12}$ $12 \; \bigcirc{-} \; \underline{8} \; \bigcirc{=} \; \underline{4}$

Circle the names for the number.

23. **12**   8 + 3   ⟨6 + 6⟩   ⟨5 + 5 + 2⟩

24. **9**   ⟨12 – 3⟩   ⟨8 + 1⟩   6 + 4

Problem Solving

Add or subtract to solve.

Draw or write to explain.

25. The team has 10 players.
4 players go home.
How many players are left?

    __6__ players

Adequate Yearly Progress

Use the End of Grade Test Prep Assessment Guide to help familiarize your children with the format of standardized tests.

CHAPTER SUMMARY TEST

Name _____ Date _____

Chapter 16 Test continued

Complete the fact family.

5.
Whole	
11	
Part	Part
9	2

$9 + 2 = \underline{11}$
$2 + \underline{9} = \underline{11}$
$11 - 9 = \underline{2}$
$11 - 2 = \underline{9}$

6.
Whole	
12	
Part	Part
4	8

$4 + 8 = \underline{11}$
$8 + 4 = \underline{12}$
$12 - 8 = \underline{4}$
$12 - \underline{4} = \underline{8}$

Circle the names for the number.

7. | 9 | ⟨9 – 0⟩   5 + 3   ⟨12 – 3⟩   ⟨5 + 3 + 1⟩

8. | 6 | ⟨11 – 5⟩   ⟨3 + 3⟩   12 – 5   ⟨4 + 0 + 2⟩

Choose the operation to solve the problem. Circle.

9. The team has 9 baseball players. Then 3 more children join the team. How many children are on the team now?

    ⟨addition⟩
    subtraction

10. There are 11 children on the Kick soccer team. There are 7 children on the Pass team. How many more players are there on the Kick team?

    addition
    ⟨subtraction⟩

Facts Practice ....

Name_____

Add.
Write the sum.

1.
4	3	8	0	1	9	6
+4	+5	+0	+0	+5	+2	+4
8	8	8	0	6	11	10

2.
4	2	0	2	9	3	8
+8	+5	+1	+3	+3	+2	+2
12	7	1	5	12	5	10

3.
7	5	9	6	3	1	7
+1	+2	+0	+4	+3	+4	+4
8	7	9	10	6	5	11

4.
3	6	2	9	0	3	5
+9	+5	+7	+1	+6	+8	+4
12	11	9	10	6	11	9

5.
2	5	5	8	1	5	3
+9	+7	+5	+1	+3	+3	+6
11	12	10	9	4	8	9

6.
2	4	8	6	4	4	6
+4	+0	+3	+2	+7	+5	+3
6	4	11	8	11	9	9

7.
7	2	4	3	7	6	3
+3	+6	+2	+4	+2	+6	+7
10	8	6	7	9	12	10

Chapter 16

four hundred eighty-one **481**

Facts Practice

Subtract.
Write the difference.

1.
$$\begin{array}{r} 8 \\ -6 \\ \hline 2 \end{array}$$ $$\begin{array}{r} 9 \\ -2 \\ \hline 7 \end{array}$$ $$\begin{array}{r} 10 \\ -3 \\ \hline 7 \end{array}$$ $$\begin{array}{r} 4 \\ -4 \\ \hline 0 \end{array}$$ $$\begin{array}{r} 6 \\ -2 \\ \hline 4 \end{array}$$ $$\begin{array}{r} 10 \\ -9 \\ \hline 1 \end{array}$$ $$\begin{array}{r} 12 \\ -3 \\ \hline 9 \end{array}$$

2.
$$\begin{array}{r} 9 \\ -7 \\ \hline 2 \end{array}$$ $$\begin{array}{r} 12 \\ -7 \\ \hline 5 \end{array}$$ $$\begin{array}{r} 6 \\ -3 \\ \hline 3 \end{array}$$ $$\begin{array}{r} 8 \\ -4 \\ \hline 4 \end{array}$$ $$\begin{array}{r} 11 \\ -5 \\ \hline 6 \end{array}$$ $$\begin{array}{r} 7 \\ -3 \\ \hline 4 \end{array}$$ $$\begin{array}{r} 4 \\ -3 \\ \hline 1 \end{array}$$

3.
$$\begin{array}{r} 5 \\ -2 \\ \hline 3 \end{array}$$ $$\begin{array}{r} 9 \\ -3 \\ \hline 6 \end{array}$$ $$\begin{array}{r} 10 \\ -8 \\ \hline 2 \end{array}$$ $$\begin{array}{r} 12 \\ -4 \\ \hline 8 \end{array}$$ $$\begin{array}{r} 5 \\ -4 \\ \hline 1 \end{array}$$ $$\begin{array}{r} 10 \\ -5 \\ \hline 5 \end{array}$$ $$\begin{array}{r} 11 \\ -2 \\ \hline 9 \end{array}$$

4.
$$\begin{array}{r} 11 \\ -6 \\ \hline 5 \end{array}$$ $$\begin{array}{r} 2 \\ -0 \\ \hline 2 \end{array}$$ $$\begin{array}{r} 12 \\ -6 \\ \hline 6 \end{array}$$ $$\begin{array}{r} 7 \\ -2 \\ \hline 5 \end{array}$$ $$\begin{array}{r} 8 \\ -1 \\ \hline 7 \end{array}$$ $$\begin{array}{r} 10 \\ -4 \\ \hline 6 \end{array}$$ $$\begin{array}{r} 12 \\ -8 \\ \hline 4 \end{array}$$

5.
$$\begin{array}{r} 12 \\ -5 \\ \hline 7 \end{array}$$ $$\begin{array}{r} 10 \\ -2 \\ \hline 8 \end{array}$$ $$\begin{array}{r} 7 \\ -1 \\ \hline 6 \end{array}$$ $$\begin{array}{r} 10 \\ -7 \\ \hline 3 \end{array}$$ $$\begin{array}{r} 9 \\ -4 \\ \hline 5 \end{array}$$ $$\begin{array}{r} 7 \\ -5 \\ \hline 2 \end{array}$$ $$\begin{array}{r} 11 \\ -4 \\ \hline 7 \end{array}$$

6.
$$\begin{array}{r} 7 \\ -6 \\ \hline 1 \end{array}$$ $$\begin{array}{r} 12 \\ -8 \\ \hline 4 \end{array}$$ $$\begin{array}{r} 8 \\ -3 \\ \hline 5 \end{array}$$ $$\begin{array}{r} 12 \\ -7 \\ \hline 5 \end{array}$$ $$\begin{array}{r} 9 \\ -6 \\ \hline 3 \end{array}$$ $$\begin{array}{r} 6 \\ -4 \\ \hline 2 \end{array}$$ $$\begin{array}{r} 11 \\ -5 \\ \hline 6 \end{array}$$

7.
$$\begin{array}{r} 12 \\ -4 \\ \hline 8 \end{array}$$ $$\begin{array}{r} 9 \\ -5 \\ \hline 4 \end{array}$$ $$\begin{array}{r} 11 \\ -9 \\ \hline 2 \end{array}$$ $$\begin{array}{r} 5 \\ -3 \\ \hline 2 \end{array}$$ $$\begin{array}{r} 7 \\ -4 \\ \hline 3 \end{array}$$ $$\begin{array}{r} 8 \\ -2 \\ \hline 6 \end{array}$$ $$\begin{array}{r} 10 \\ -6 \\ \hline 4 \end{array}$$

482 four hundred eighty-two

Science Connection

PURPOSE

To practice addition and subtraction facts through 12.

Name_____

The President's Challenge

Children at some schools take The President's Challenge. It tells them if they are fit. **Fit** means having a healthy body. Children who finish the Challenge earn a patch.

Gerry and Adra take the President's Challenge. The chart shows what they did on each test in the Challenge.

Test	Gerry	Adra
Curl-ups	4	5
Pull-ups	7	5
Distance run	12 minutes	8 minutes
Shuttle run	8 seconds	12 seconds
Sit and reach	8 inches	10 inches

The pull-up is one test in the President's Challenge.

Use the table to solve.

1. How many pull-ups do Gerry and Adra do in all?

   $\underline{7} + \underline{5} = \underline{12}$

   $\underline{12}$ pull-ups

2. Gerry wants to do 11 curl-ups in all. How many more does he need to do?

   $\underline{11} - \underline{4} = \underline{7}$

   $\underline{7}$ more curl-ups

3. How many more inches can Adra sit and reach than Gerry?

   $\underline{10} - \underline{8} = \underline{2}$

   $\underline{2}$ more inches

Unit 6   four hundred eighty-three **483**

Using These Pages

Discussion Topics

- Tell children that some schools take the Presidential Challenge. One test is the pull-ups. **If one child does 14 and another does 9, what is the difference?** (5)

- Refer children to the table. **Another classmate did the shuttle run in 9 seconds. How much faster was Adra than her classmate?** (3 seconds)

- **How much farther would Gerry have to stretch in his sit and reach to get to 12 inches?** (4 inches)

- You may want to tell children that the shuttle run helps total body coordination and that the distance run is also called the endurance run.

- Point out to children that Exercises 1 and 3 on page 484 are different problems with the same number sentences and answers.

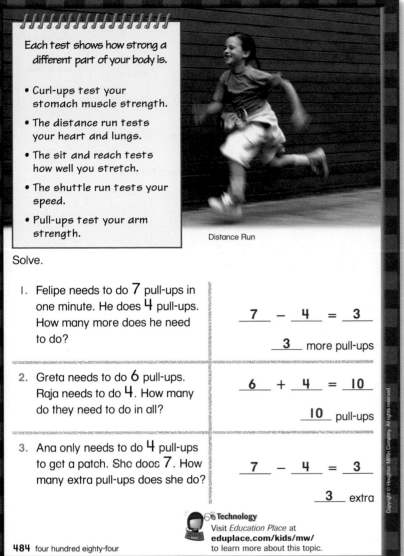

Each test shows how strong a different part of your body is.

- Curl-ups test your stomach muscle strength.
- The distance run tests your heart and lungs.
- The sit and reach tests how well you stretch.
- The shuttle run tests your speed.
- Pull-ups test your arm strength.

Distance Run

Solve.

1. Felipe needs to do 7 pull-ups in one minute. He does 4 pull-ups. How many more does he need to do?

    $\underline{\ 7\ } - \underline{\ 4\ } = \underline{\ 3\ }$

    $\underline{\ 3\ }$ more pull-ups

2. Greta needs to do 6 pull-ups. Raja needs to do 4. How many do they need to do in all?

    $\underline{\ 6\ } + \underline{\ 4\ } = \underline{\ 10\ }$

    $\underline{\ 10\ }$ pull-ups

3. Ana only needs to do 4 pull-ups to get a patch. She does 7. How many extra pull-ups does she do?

    $\underline{\ 7\ } - \underline{\ 4\ } = \underline{\ 3\ }$

    $\underline{\ 3\ }$ extra

⌨ **Technology**
Visit *Education Place* at
eduplace.com/kids/mw/
to learn more about this topic.

484 four hundred eighty-four

Wrap Up the Unit Project

- Have children vote to find out which game was the class favorite.

- Invite a volunteer to record children's votes with tally marks, then use the data to make a bar graph.

Unit 6 Test

PURPOSE

This test provides an informal assessment of the Unit 6 objectives.

Unit Test Items 1–30

To assign a numerical grade for this Unit Test, use 3 points for each test item and add 10 to the score.

Customizing Your Instruction

For children who have not yet mastered these objectives, you can use the **Reteaching Resources** listed in the chart below. *Ways to Success* is Houghton Mifflin's Intervention program available in CD-ROM and blackline master formats.

Name_____

Unit 6 Test

Vocabulary *e Glossary*

Complete the sentence.

| number line |
| ten frame |
| subtract |

1. You can use a __number line__ to help you add.

2. You can show ten in a __ten frame__.

3. You can __subtract__ to find the difference.

Concepts and Skills

Find the sum.

4. $\begin{array}{r} 5 \\ +6 \\ \hline 11 \end{array}$ 5. $\begin{array}{r} 6 \\ +5 \\ \hline 11 \end{array}$ 6. $\begin{array}{r} 8 \\ +4 \\ \hline 12 \end{array}$ 7. $\begin{array}{r} 4 \\ +8 \\ \hline 12 \end{array}$ 8. $\begin{array}{r} 2 \\ +8 \\ \hline 10 \end{array}$ 9. $\begin{array}{r} 8 \\ +2 \\ \hline 10 \end{array}$

10. $\begin{array}{r} 3 \\ 3 \\ +4 \\ \hline 10 \end{array}$ 11. $\begin{array}{r} 2 \\ 5 \\ +5 \\ \hline 12 \end{array}$ 12. $\begin{array}{r} 4 \\ 6 \\ +1 \\ \hline 11 \end{array}$ 13. $\begin{array}{r} 5 \\ 2 \\ +5 \\ \hline 12 \end{array}$ 14. $\begin{array}{r} 1 \\ 9 \\ +1 \\ \hline 11 \end{array}$ 15. $\begin{array}{r} 2 \\ 2 \\ +7 \\ \hline 11 \end{array}$

Use cubes.
Write the missing addend.

16. $5 + \boxed{6} = 11$ 17. $5 + \boxed{4} = 9$ 18. $2 + \boxed{10} = 12$

19. $3 + \boxed{9} = 12$ 20. $6 + \boxed{2} = 8$ 21. $3 + \boxed{8} = 11$

Unit 6   four hundred eighty-five **485**

Reteaching Support

Unit Test Item		Unit Objectives Tested	TE Pages	Use These Reteaching Resources
pp. 485–486 1–2, 4–15	Tests A & B 1–10	**6A** Use addition strategies to find sums through 12 and to add three addends.	429A–436, 439A–444	Reteach Resources and *Ways to Success*, 15.1–15.6
16–21	11–16	**6B** Find a missing addend.	445A–446	Reteach Resource and *Ways to Success*, 15.7
3, 22–24	17–20	**6C** Use subtraction strategies to subtract from 12 or less.	457A–462	Reteach Resources and *Ways to Success*, 16.1–16.3
25–29	21–22	**6D** Use related facts and fact families to solve addition and subtraction problems.	465A–470	Reteach Resources and *Ways to Success*, 16.4–16.6
30	23–25	**6E** Apply skills and strategies to solve problems.	473A–476	Reteach Resource and *Ways to Success*, 16.8

Unit 6 Test

Write the difference.

22. $\begin{array}{r}11\\-8\\\hline 3\end{array}$ $\begin{array}{r}11\\-3\\\hline 8\end{array}$ 23. $\begin{array}{r}9\\-2\\\hline 7\end{array}$ $\begin{array}{r}9\\-7\\\hline 2\end{array}$ 24. $\begin{array}{r}12\\-7\\\hline 5\end{array}$ $\begin{array}{r}12\\-5\\\hline 7\end{array}$

Use related facts to add and subtract.

25. $\begin{array}{r}8\\+2\\\hline 10\end{array}$ $\begin{array}{r}10\\-2\\\hline 8\end{array}$ 26. $\begin{array}{r}5\\+6\\\hline 11\end{array}$ $\begin{array}{r}11\\-6\\\hline 5\end{array}$ 27. $\begin{array}{r}2\\+7\\\hline 9\end{array}$ $\begin{array}{r}9\\-7\\\hline 2\end{array}$ 28. $\begin{array}{r}9\\+1\\\hline 10\end{array}$ $\begin{array}{r}10\\-1\\\hline 9\end{array}$

Complete the fact family.

29.
11	
2	9

$9 + 2 = \underline{11}$ $11 - 2 = \underline{9}$

$2 + 9 = \underline{11}$ $11 \; \bigcirc{-} \; 9 \; \bigcirc{=} \; 2$

Problem Solving

Add or subtract to solve.   Draw or write to explain.

30. There are 5 balls for gym.
Kyle brings 6 more. How
many balls are there now?

_____11_____ balls

Assessment Options

Formal Tests for this unit are also provided in the Unit Resource Folder.

- **Unit 1 Test A (Open Response)**
- **Unit 1 Test B (Multiple Choice)**

Performance Assessment

You may want to use the Performance Assessment instead of, or in addition to, the Unit Test. Three Performance Assessment tasks can be found on Student Book pages 487–488.

Adequate Yearly Progress

Use the *End of Grade Test Prep Assessment Guide* to help familiarize your children with the format of standardized tests.

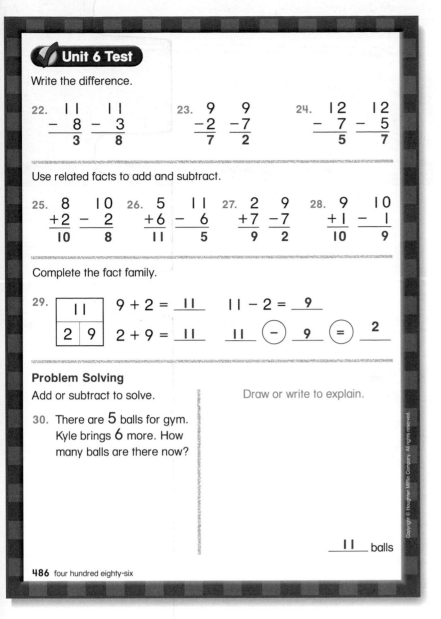

UNIT TEST A

Name _____ Date _____   Unit 6 Test A

Use the number line to find the sum.

0 1 2 3 4 5 6 7 8 9 10 11 12

1. $7 + 2 = \underline{9}$ 2. $9 + 3 = \underline{12}$

3. $1 + 10 = \underline{11}$ 4. $7 + 3 = \underline{10}$

Use doubles and doubles plus one to find the sum.
5. $6 + 6 = \underline{12}$ 6. $5 + 4 = \underline{9}$

Count on to add.
7. $9 + 1 = \underline{10}$ 8. $10 + 2 = \underline{12}$

Use the ten frame. Find the sum.

9.   10.

$5 + \underline{5} = 10$ $6 + \underline{5} = 11$

Unit 6 Tests

See pages 487A–487B for answers.

UNIT TEST B

Name _____ Date _____   Unit 6 Test B

Fill in the ○ for the correct answer.
Use the number line to find the sum.

0 1 2 3 4 5 6 7 8 9 10 11 12

1. $6 + 2 = \Box$ 2. $8 + 3 = \Box$
   ○7 ●8 ○9   ○12 ●11 ○10

3. $2 + 9 = \Box$ 4. $6 + 4 = \Box$
   ●11 ○10 ○9   ○8 ○9 ●10

Use doubles and doubles plus one to find the sum.

5. $5 + 5 = \Box$ 6. $4 + 5 = \Box$
   ○11 ○9 ●10   ○7 ●9 ○11

Count on to add.

7. $9 + 2 = \Box$ 8. $11 + 1 = \Box$
   ●11 ○10 ○9   ○11 ●12 ○10

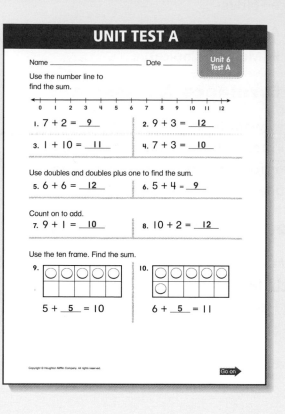

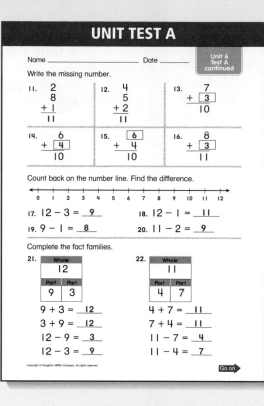

UNIT TEST A

Name _____ Date _____

Unit 6
Test A

Use the number line to find the sum.

0 1 2 3 4 5 6 7 8 9 10 11 12

1. 7 + 2 = __9__

2. 9 + 3 = __12__

3. 1 + 10 = __11__

4. 7 + 3 = __10__

Use doubles and doubles plus one to find the sum.

5. 6 + 6 = __12__

6. 5 + 4 = __9__

Count on to add.

7. 9 + 1 = __10__

8. 10 + 2 = __12__

Use the ten frame. Find the sum.

9.

5 + __5__ = 10

10.

6 + __5__ = 11

Go on

UNIT TEST A

Name _____ Date _____

Unit 6
Test A
continued

Write the missing number.

11.
$\begin{array}{r} 2 \\ 8 \\ +1 \\ \hline 11 \end{array}$

12.
$\begin{array}{r} 4 \\ 5 \\ +2 \\ \hline 11 \end{array}$

13.
$\begin{array}{r} 7 \\ +\boxed{3} \\ \hline 10 \end{array}$

14.
$\begin{array}{r} 6 \\ +\boxed{4} \\ \hline 10 \end{array}$

15.
$\begin{array}{r} \boxed{6} \\ +4 \\ \hline 10 \end{array}$

16.
$\begin{array}{r} 8 \\ +\boxed{3} \\ \hline 11 \end{array}$

Count back on the number line. Find the difference.

0 1 2 3 4 5 6 7 8 9 10 11 12

17. 12 − 3 = __9__

18. 12 − 1 = __11__

19. 9 − 1 = __8__

20. 11 − 2 = __9__

Complete the fact families.

21.
Whole
12

Part	Part
9	3

9 + 3 = __12__

3 + 9 = __12__

12 − 9 = __3__

12 − 3 = __9__

22.
Whole
11

Part	Part
4	7

4 + 7 = __11__

7 + 4 = __11__

11 − 7 = __4__

11 − 4 = __7__

Go on

UNIT TEST A

Name _____ Date _____

Unit 6
Test A
continued

Add or subtract to solve.

23. There are 9 bananas. The monkey eats 4 of them. How many bananas are left?

__5__ bananas

24. The giraffe eats 5 carrots on Wednesday and 2 on Thursday. How many carrots does the giraffe eat in 2 days?

__7__ carrots

25. There are 9 apples. The pony eats 6 of them. How many apples are left?

__3__ apples

STOP

Unit Test Answers: Form B

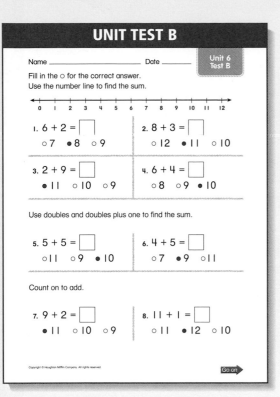

UNIT TEST B

Name _____ Date _____

Fill in the ○ for the correct answer.
Use the number line to find the sum.

0 1 2 3 4 5 6 7 8 9 10 11 12

1. 6 + 2 = ☐
   ○ 7   ● 8   ○ 9

2. 8 + 3 = ☐
   ○ 12   ● 11   ○ 10

3. 2 + 9 = ☐
   ● 11   ○ 10   ○ 9

4. 6 + 4 = ☐
   ○ 8   ○ 9   ● 10

Use doubles and doubles plus one to find the sum.

5. 5 + 5 = ☐
   ○ 11   ○ 9   ● 10

6. 4 + 5 = ☐
   ○ 7   ● 9   ○ 11

Count on to add.

7. 9 + 2 = ☐
   ● 11   ○ 10   ○ 9

8. 11 + 1 = ☐
   ○ 11   ● 12   ○ 10

Go on

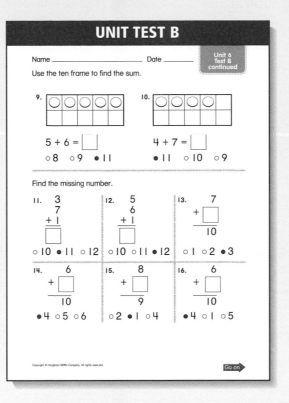

UNIT TEST B

Name _____ Date _____

Use the ten frame to find the sum.

9. 5 + 6 = ☐
   ○ 8   ○ 9   ● 11

10. 4 + 7 = ☐
    ● 11   ○ 10   ○ 9

Find the missing number.

11. 3
     7
   + 1
   ─────
   ○ 10   ● 11   ○ 12

12. 5
     6
   + 1
   ─────
   ○ 10   ○ 11   ● 12

13.   7
    + ☐
   ─────
     10
   ○ 1   ○ 2   ● 3

14.   6
    + ☐
   ─────
     10
   ● 4   ○ 5   ○ 6

15.   8
    + ☐
   ─────
      9
   ○ 2   ● 1   ○ 4

16.   6
    + ☐
   ─────
     10
   ● 4   ○ 1   ○ 5

Go on

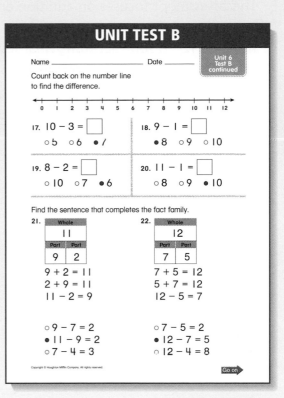

UNIT TEST B

Name _____ Date _____

Count back on the number line
to find the difference.

0 1 2 3 4 5 6 7 8 9 10 11 12

17. 10 − 3 = ☐
    ○ 5   ○ 6   ● 7

18. 9 − 1 = ☐
    ● 8   ○ 9   ○ 10

19. 8 − 2 = ☐
    ○ 10   ○ 7   ● 6

20. 11 − 1 = ☐
    ○ 8   ○ 9   ● 10

Find the sentence that completes the fact family.

21.
Whole
11

Part	Part
9	2

9 + 2 = 11
2 + 9 = 11
11 − 2 = 9

○ 9 − 7 = 2
● 11 − 9 = 2
○ 7 − 4 = 3

22.
Whole
12

Part	Part
7	5

7 + 5 = 12
5 + 7 = 12
12 − 5 = 7

○ 7 − 5 = 2
● 12 − 7 = 5
○ 12 − 4 = 8

Go on

UNIT TEST B

Name _____ Date _____

Find the correct answer.

23. There are 7 roses. Sandi cuts 6 of them. How many roses are left?
    ○ 3 roses
    ○ 2 roses
    ● 1 rose

24. Sami plants 4 rose bushes on Friday and 5 on Saturday. How many bushes does he plant in all?
    ● 9 bushes
    ○ 8 bushes
    ○ 1 bush

25. There are 9 daisies. Maria takes 4 of them. How many daisies are left?
    ○ 4 daisies
    ● 5 daisies
    ○ 6 daisies

STOP

Performance Assessment

PURPOSE

This assessment focuses on addition and subtraction strategies. Children should be able to find sums through 12, to subtract from 12 or less, and to apply skills and strategies to solve problems.

Choose a strategy. Solve.

1. There are 9 frogs in a pond. 5 frogs hop away. Then 3 frogs come. How many frogs are in the pond now?

Show your work using pictures, numbers, or words.

_____7_____ frogs

Choose a strategy. Solve.

2. There are 2 monkeys. Each monkey has 2 bananas. Then they each get 1 more banana. How many bananas do they have in all?

Show your work using pictures, numbers, or words.

_____6_____ bananas

Using These Pages

- Write 6 + 2 + 3 on the board and model the addition with counters. **How many counters do you have in all when you add 6 plus 2 plus 3?** (11 counters) **Explain how you added.** (Children should tell strategies including modeling and counting, counting on 2 from 6 to get 8 and then counting on from 8.)

- **If I take 8 counters away from the 11 counters, how many counters do I have left?** Demonstrate the subtraction with counters. (3 counters) **Explain how you subtracted.** (Children should tell strategies including modeling and counting and related facts.)

- Direct children's attention to assessment tasks. You may wish to read the directions aloud to the children.

- Observe children as they work to complete the tasks.

 Exercise One

In Exercise 1, children should be able to show how to solve a multistep addition and subtraction problem. (7 frogs)

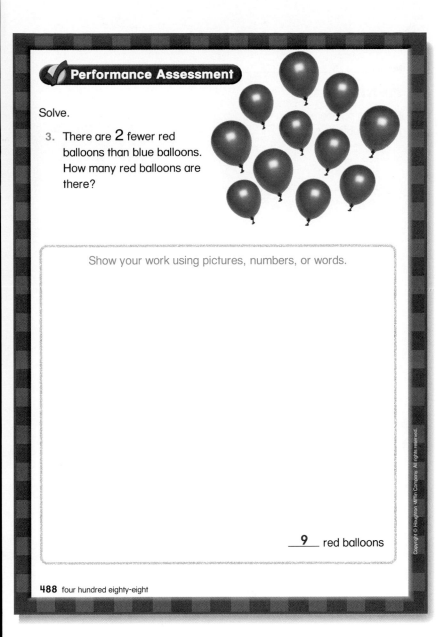

Performance Assessment

Solve.

3. There are 2 fewer red balloons than blue balloons. How many red balloons are there?

Show your work using pictures, numbers, or words.

_____**9**_____ red balloons

488 four hundred eighty-eight

Exercise Two

In Exercise 2, children may show the problem using three addends (2 + 2 + 2) to find the sum.
(6 bananas)

Exercise Three

In Exercise 3, children should be able to recognize, represent, and solve a subtraction problem.
(9 red balloons)

Assessing Student Work

Use the **Scoring Rubric** to evaluate children's performance on these tasks.

Scoring Rubric

4 EXEMPLARY

Represents the addition and subtraction correctly and finds the correct sum and difference, and applies skills and strategies to solve problems correctly.

3 PROFICIENT

Represents the addition and subtraction correctly and finds the correct sum and difference. Solution to problems demonstrates mathematical reasoning, although the picture or the number sentence is faulty.

2 ACCEPTABLE

Represents the addition and subtraction correctly and finds the correct sum and difference. Solution to problems is incorrect or incomplete.

I LIMITED

Represents the addition and subtraction incorrectly or finds the incorrect sum and difference. Solution to problems shows no mathematical reasoning.

UNIT 6

Enrichment

PURPOSE

This page provides an opportunity for children to apply their understanding of addition and subtraction concepts by using them in mental math.

Using This Page

Discussion Topics

- This page extends children's understanding of addition and subtraction facts through 12 by having them use mental math.

- Explain to children they will begin at START and move clockwise around the pond. Remind them to read the operation and number in each plant between the rocks carefully.

- Point out that children will be using mental math to fill in the numbers on the rocks. **What strategies can you use?** (Possible answer: count on)

- Have children work individually or in pairs to complete the page. In pairs, children can use strategies to fill in the numbers on the rocks.

AMAZING!

Calculator
Amazing!

Help the puppy find her way home.

1. Use a 🖩 to check each number sentence.

2. Circle the number sentences that are incorrect.

3. Follow the path in which all the number sentences are correct.

4. Color the correct path.

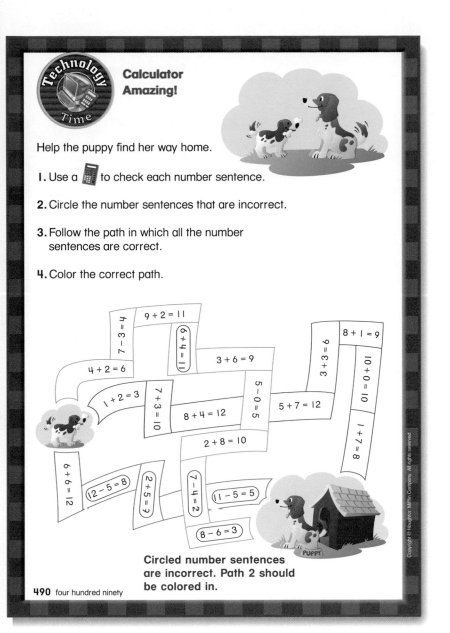

Circled number sentences
are incorrect. Path 2 should
be colored in.

PURPOSE

To provide an opportunity for children to use a calculator to check addition and subtraction facts.

Using This Page

Discussion Topics

- This is another way for the children to practice addition and subtraction by identifying correct and incorrect facts.

- You may want to remind children to note whether they are adding or subtracting.

- Read the directions and work through the first problem at the beginning of each path.

- Remind the children that they are to circle any incorrect problem. **Will the path you choose have any incorrect number sentences?** (no)

- After they complete the page, have children compare the paths they followed to see if everyone followed the same path.

Cumulative Test Prep

▶ Practice Test

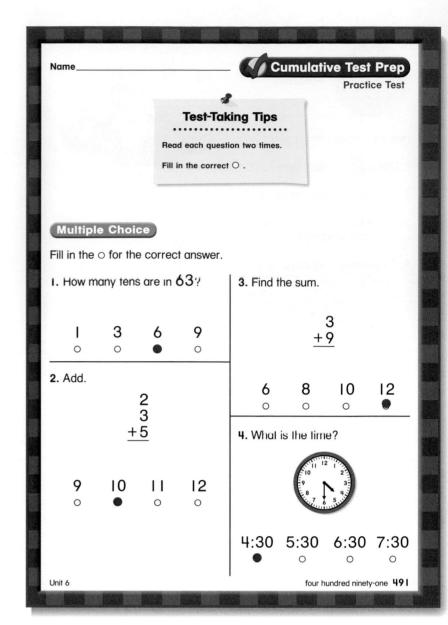

Name _____

Cumulative Test Prep

Practice Test

Test-Taking Tips
....
Read each question two times.

Fill in the correct ○ .

Multiple Choice

Fill in the ○ for the correct answer.

1. How many tens are in **63**?

1	3	6	9
○	○	●	○

2. Add.

$$\begin{array}{r} 2 \\ 3 \\ +5 \\ \hline \end{array}$$

9	10	11	12
○	●	○	○

3. Find the sum.

$$\begin{array}{r} 3 \\ +9 \\ \hline \end{array}$$

6	8	10	12
○	○	○	●

4. What is the time?

4:30	5:30	6:30	7:30
●	○	○	○

Unit 6

four hundred ninety-one **491**

Test-Taking TIPS

Review the test-taking tips with children before they begin the test. Remind children to read each question twice.

- Work with children to help them recognize mathematical actions like joining, separating, and comparing numbers.

- Remind children that they can draw sets or model numbers on scrap paper to help them solve problems.

- Discuss with children some of the ways they can check their work.

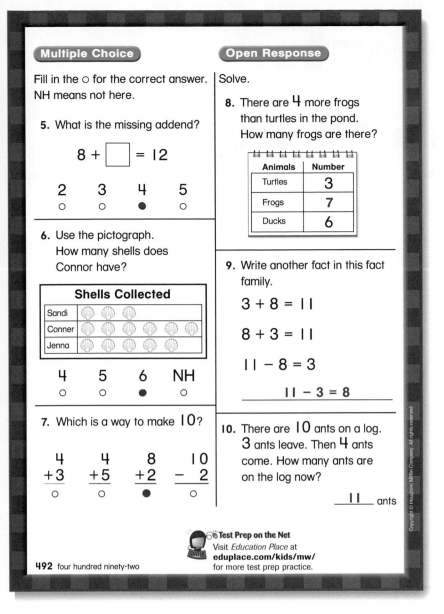

Fill in the ○ for the correct answer.
NH means not here.

5. What is the missing addend?

$8 + \boxed{} = 12$

2   3   4   5
○   ○   ●   ○

6. Use the pictograph.
How many shells does
Connor have?

Shells Collected

Sandi			
Conner				
Jenna				

4   5   6   NH
○   ○   ●   ○

7. Which is a way to make 10?

$\begin{array}{r} 4 \\ +3 \\ \hline \end{array}$ $\begin{array}{r} 4 \\ +5 \\ \hline \end{array}$ $\begin{array}{r} 8 \\ +2 \\ \hline \end{array}$ $\begin{array}{r} 10 \\ -\ 2 \\ \hline \end{array}$
○   ○   ●   ○

Open Response

Solve.

8. There are 4 more frogs
than turtles in the pond.
How many frogs are there?

Animals	Number
Turtles	3
Frogs	7
Ducks	6

9. Write another fact in this fact
family.

$3 + 8 = 11$

$8 + 3 = 11$

$11 - 8 = 3$

$\underline{\hspace{1cm}11 - 3 = 8}$

10. There are 10 ants on a log.
3 ants leave. Then 4 ants
come. How many ants are
on the log now?

$\underline{\hspace{0.6cm}11\hspace{0.2cm}}$ ants

Test Prep on the Net
Visit *Education Place* at
eduplace.com/kids/mw/
for more test prep practice.

Copyright © Houghton Mifflin Company. All rights reserved.

492 four hundred ninety-two

Test-Taking Vocabulary

- Write the addition fact 5 + 7 = 12 on
the board. Have a volunteer tell the
other facts in the *fact family*. Repeat
with the fact 11 − 2 = 9.

- Review addition and subtraction
vocabulary with children. Have
volunteers define *addend, sum,* and
difference.

- Discuss *related facts* with children.
Remind them that they can use what

they know about addition facts to
help them subtract. Demonstrate
with the related facts:

12 − 3 = 9 and 9 + 3 = 12.

**National and state tests may use these
words with subtraction problems:**

- left
- remaining
- how many more

Addition and Subtraction Facts Through 12   **492**

Measurement

Unit at a Glance

UNIT 7 MEASUREMENT

Assessment System

Assessing Prior Knowledge

Check whether children understand the prerequisite concepts and skills.

- **CHAPTER PRETEST** (Unit Resource Folder or Ways to Success Intervention CD-ROM)
- **WARM-UP ACTIVITY:** Every TE Lesson
- **UNIT LITERATURE ACTIVITY:** PE p. 494

Ongoing Assessment

Monitor whether children are acquiring new concepts and skills.

- **PROBLEM OF THE DAY:** First page of every TE lesson
- **QUICK REVIEW:** First page of every TE lesson
- **LESSON QUIZ:** First page of every TE lesson
- **COMMON ERROR:** Every TE Lesson
- **QUICK CHECK:** PE pp. 508, 517, 530, 535
- **KEY TOPIC REVIEW:** PE pp. 518, 536

Test Prep and Practice

Help children prepare for state and standardized tests.

- **DAILY TEST PREP:** Every TE Lesson
- **CUMULATIVE TEST PREP:** PE pp. 549–550
- **TEST PREP ON THE NET:** eduplace.com/kids/mw
- **TEST-TAKING STRATEGIES:** eduplace.com/math/mw

Summary Assessment

Assess children's mastery of new concepts and skills.

- **CHAPTER TEST:**
    - ✔ PE pp. 519–520, 537–538
    - ✔ Unit Resource Folder
- **UNIT TEST:**
    - ✔ PE pp. 543–544
    - ✔ Test A, Unit Resource Folder
    - ✔ Test B, Unit Resource Folder

TEST TIPS Student Self-Assessment

Allow children to evaluate their own understanding.

- **EXPLAIN YOUR THINKING:** PE pp. 501, 505, 531

Performance Assessment

Evaluate children's ability to use mathematics in real-world situations.

PERFORMANCE ASSESSMENT: PE pp. 545–546
WRITE ABOUT IT OR TALK ABOUT IT: in Hands-On lessons

Technology Options

Use computer-based assessment to make testing and reporting easier.

- **WAYS TO ASSESS** (CD-ROM, LAN, or Web spiral review and test creation, administration, scoring, and report generation)
- **LEARNER PROFILE** (observations, evaluations, and reports from your handheld or desktop computer)

Reaching All Learners

Resources	On Level Students	Extra Support Students	English Learners	Inclusion/ Special Needs	Advanced Learners	Mathematically Promising
Student Editions						
Building Vocabulary	●	●	●	●	●	●
Guided Practice ✱	●	●	●	●	●	●
MathTracks MP3 Audio CD	●	●	○	○		
Teacher's Editions						
Building Vocabulary Strategies	●	●	●	○	●	○
Teacher Support	●	○	●		○	○
Intervention Activities	○	●	●	●		
Other Resources						
Chapter Challenges	○				●	●
Combination Classroom Guide	●	●	●	●	●	●
English Learners Handbook	○	○	●	○		
Ways to Success CD-ROM	○	●	●	●		

KEY ● **Highly Appropriate** ○ **Appropriate** ✱ **Scaffolded Instruction**

Documenting Adequate Yearly Progress
National Test Correlation

UNIT 7 Objectives		ITBS	Terra Nova (CTBS)	CAT	SAT	MAT
7A	Estimate and measure length using nonstandard units, inches and centimeters.	●	●	●	●	●
7B	Compare and order objects using nonstandard weights, pounds, and kilograms.	●	●	●	●	
7C	Compare and order capacity of containers.	●	●	●	●	
7D	Understand hot and cold using a °F thermometer.			●		
7E	Choose an appropriate measuring tool.	●		●		●
7F	Apply skills and strategies to solve problems.	●	●	●	●	●

Activities for Reaching All Learners

Home-School Activity

Compare Units

Materials: toothpicks, paper clips, ruler, book, cereal box

Prepare a 4-column, 4-row chart. Label columns: Item, Inches, Toothpicks, Paper Clips. Label the rows: book, cereal box, kitchen table. Players take turns measuring the length of each item and recording the length in their chart. Compare how many of each measuring unit. Players can continue with other items.

Unit Vocabulary Activity

Measure It

Materials: vocabulary cards: inches, centimeters, pounds, kilometers, cup, pint, quart, liter, degrees

Shuffle the cards and place them facedown. One child turns over the top card and places it face up. All children write or draw one item that is measured with this unit. The first child to show a correct item scores 1 point. Play continues until all cards are turned over. The child with the most points wins.

Remediation

MathTracks Lessons 17.2, 17.5, 17.6, 17.7, 17.8, 18.2, 18.3

Use the MathTracks CD-ROM to help children who need a quick review or extra support for the lesson, to provide children who were absent with complete lesson presentation, or to assist children with reading difficulties.

Intervention

Ways to Success CD-ROM

Use the Ways to Success CD-ROM to help children who need extra help with lessons. This software is designed to reteach the lesson objective, provide extra guided and independent practice, and if needed, reteach a key prerequisite skill.

Unit Project

Bird Feeders

Math Topics:

- measure an object in inches using a ruler
- measure an object in centimeters using a ruler
- compare the capacity of pints, cups, and quarts

To Begin

- Ask children what they know about birds and bird feeders.
- Tell children that in this Unit Project they will be making bird feeders and measuring how much food the birds eat.

Ongoing

- Introduce the idea of making a bird feeder by using pint or quart containers tied with string to hang from trees or poles.
- Have children bring in clean pint and quart containers.
- For Connecting to the Unit Project see page 497D for Chapter 17 and page 521D for Chapter 18.

To Finish

- Maintain the bird feeders throughout the month. Discuss any changes or problems that occurred while working on the project.
- Encourage children to share ways to improve the feeders.
- See page 542 to Wrap Up the Unit Project.

Starting Unit 7
Accessing Prior Knowledge

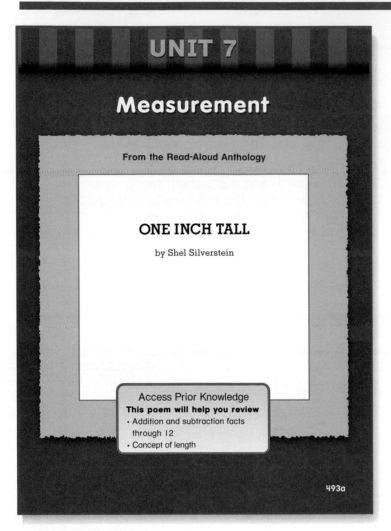

UNIT 7

Measurement

From the Read-Aloud Anthology

ONE INCH TALL

by Shel Silverstein

Access Prior Knowledge
This poem will help you review
- Addition and subtraction facts through 12
- Concept of length

493a

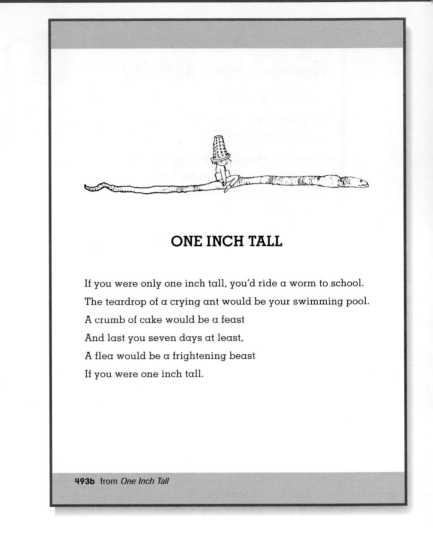

ONE INCH TALL

If you were only one inch tall, you'd ride a worm to school.
The teardrop of a crying ant would be your swimming pool.
A crumb of cake would be a feast
And last you seven days at least,
A flea would be a frightening beast
If you were one inch tall.

493b from *One Inch Tall*

Unit Bibliography

Inch by Inch by Leo Lionni

Just a Little Bit by Ann Tompert

Lulu's Lemonade by Barbara deRubertis

Measuring Penny by Loreen Leedy

Numbers (Math Counts) by Henry Arthur Pluckrose

Where the Sidewalk Ends (One Inch Tall)
by Shel Silverstein

See also the **Math and Literature Bibliography** in the Teacher Support Handbook at the back of this Teacher's Edition.

Poem Summary

Today you will read a poem about being very small. The title of the poem is *One Inch Tall*. The author is Shel Silverstein.

Reading the Poem

Read the selection aloud to the children. Show them an inch on a ruler, and have them imagine being one inch tall at school.

This story is available in the Read-Aloud Anthology, Volume 4

If you were only one inch tall, you'd walk beneath the door,

And it would take about a month to get down to the store.

A bit of fluff would be your bed,

You'd swing upon a spider's thread,

And wear a thimble on your head

If you were one inch tall.

You'd surf across the kitchen sink upon a stick of gum.

You couldn't hug your mama, you'd just have to hug her thumb.

You'd run from people's feet in fright,

To move a pen would take all night,

(This poem took fourteen years to write—

'Cause I'm just one inch tall).

493c

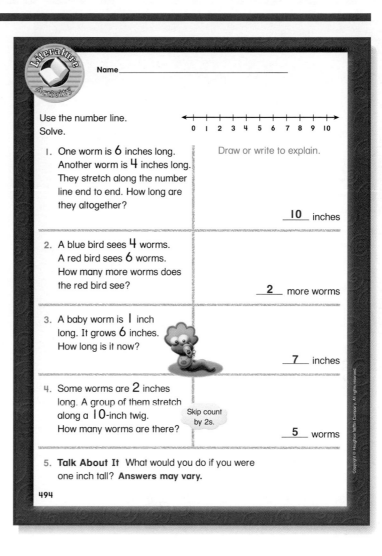

Name

Use the number line.
Solve.

0 1 2 3 4 5 6 7 8 9 10

1. One worm is 6 inches long. Another worm is 4 inches long. They stretch along the number line end to end. How long are they altogether?

Draw or write to explain.

_____10_____ inches

2. A blue bird sees 4 worms. A red bird sees 6 worms. How many more worms does the red bird see?

_____2_____ more worms

3. A baby worm is 1 inch long. It grows 6 inches. How long is it now?

_____7_____ inches

4. Some worms are 2 inches long. A group of them stretch along a 10-inch twig. How many worms are there?

Skip count by 2s.

_____5_____ worms

5. **Talk About It** What would you do if you were one inch tall? **Answers may vary.**

494

Unit Bibliography

Inch by Inch by Leo Lionni

Just a Little Bit by Ann Tompert

Lulu's Lemonade by Barbara deRubertis

Measuring Penny by Loreen Leedy

Numbers (Math Counts) by Henry Arthur Pluckrose

Where the Sidewalk Ends (One Inch Tall) by Shel Silverstein

See also the **Math and Literature Bibliography** in the Teacher Support Handbook at the back of this Teacher's Edition.

Literature Activity

Purpose: This activity provides an opportunity to informally assess children's understanding of addition and subtraction facts to 12.

Using This Page

- Observe children as they work to complete Exercises 1–3. **How do you know whether to add or subtract?** (Read the problem carefully to see whether it asks "in all" or "left.")
- After children complete Exercise 4, ask: **How many worms would cover a 12-inch twig?** (6 worms)
- Invite children to share their response to the Talk About It question in Exercise 5.

UNIT 7 Measurement
Math At Home

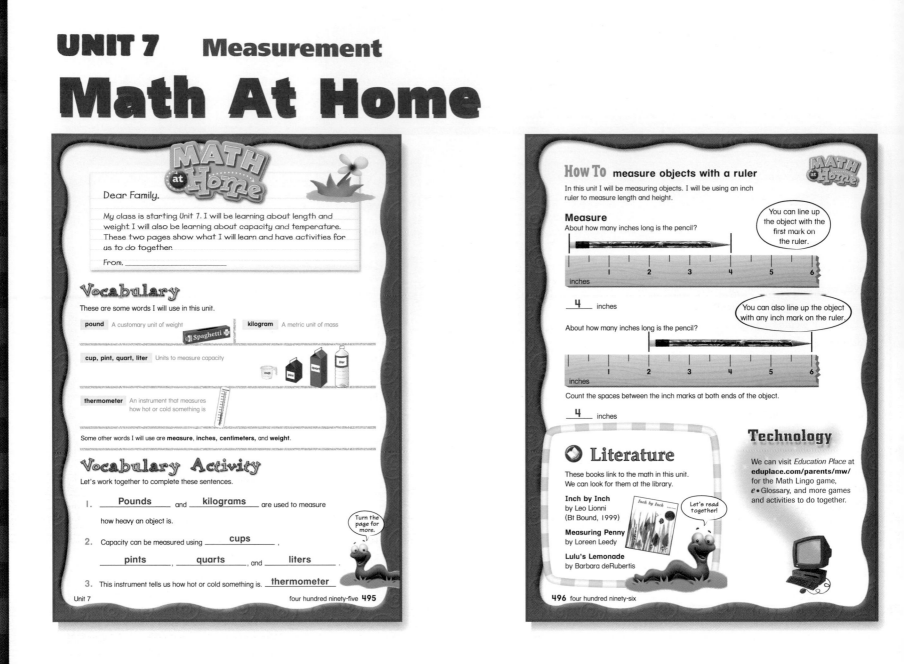

Dear Family,

My class is starting Unit 7. I will be learning about length and weight. I will also be learning about capacity and temperature. These two pages show what I will learn and have activities for us to do together.

From, _____

Vocabulary

These are some words I will use in this unit.

pound A customary unit of weight	**kilogram** A metric unit of mass

cup, pint, quart, liter Units to measure capacity

thermometer An instrument that measures how hot or cold something is

Some other words I will use are **measure, inches, centimeters,** and **weight**.

Vocabulary Activity

Let's work together to complete these sentences.

1. __Pounds__ and __kilograms__ are used to measure how heavy an object is.

2. Capacity can be measured using __cups__, __pints__, __quarts__, and __liters__.

3. This instrument tells us how hot or cold something is. __thermometer__

Turn the page for more.

Unit 7   four hundred ninety-five **495**

How To measure objects with a ruler

In this unit I will be measuring objects. I will be using an inch ruler to measure length and height.

Measure
About how many inches long is the pencil?

You can line up the object with the first mark on the ruler.

__4__ inches

About how many inches long is the pencil?

You can also line up the object with any inch mark on the ruler.

Count the spaces between the inch marks at both ends of the object.

__4__ inches

Literature

These books link to the math in this unit. We can look for them at the library.

Inch by Inch
by Leo Lionni
(Bt Bound, 1999)

Measuring Penny
by Loreen Leedy

Lulu's Lemonade
by Barbara deRubertis

Let's read together!

Technology

We can visit *Education Place* at **eduplace.com/parents/mw/** for the Math Lingo game, *e* • Glossary, and more games and activities to do together.

496 four hundred ninety-six

Discuss the letter to the family with children. You may want to use this letter as an introduction to the unit. Highlight for children what they will be learning in the unit. Tell children that as they go through the unit they will be able to answer the questions on these pages.

Math at Home is available in Spanish and other languages on Education Place. www.eduplace.com/math/mw/

Literature

Encourage parents to find the suggested books and read them with their children.

Technology

Education Place is an award-winning website with engaging activities for students and helpful information for parents. Look for the eGlossary, the Math Lingo Game, and more.

Building Vocabulary

Strategies for Building Vocabulary

Understanding Length and Weight

Write the words **one inch** on the board and create the table to the right. Ask children to list things that are longer and shorter than one inch.

Repeat this activity with things that are heavier and lighter than one pound.

Graphic Organizer: Table

ONE INCH	
SHORTER THAN	LONGER THAN
a penny	a pencil
a finger nail	a hand

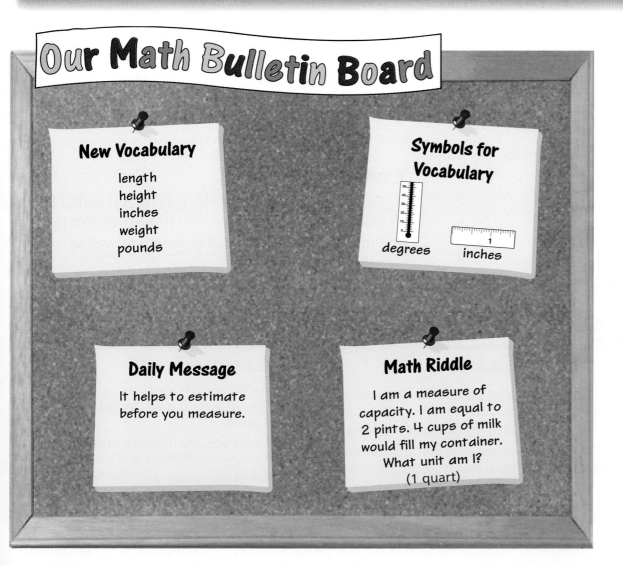

Our Math Bulletin Board

New Vocabulary

length
height
inches
weight
pounds

Symbols for Vocabulary

degrees   inches

Daily Message

It helps to estimate before you measure.

Math Riddle

I am a measure of capacity. I am equal to 2 pints. 4 cups of milk would fill my container. What unit am I?
(1 quart)

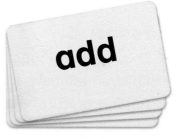

Vocabulary Cards

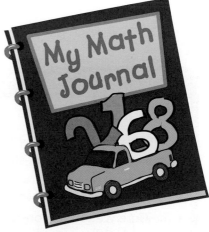

My Math Journal
Watch for **Keeping a Journal** entries in every lesson.

Lesson by Lesson Overview
Length and Weight

Lesson 1
- This lesson reviews comparing length and height.
- Children determine if real-life objects are taller or shorter than they are; and if objects are longer or shorter than their hands.
- Children also find the longest, tallest, and shortest object in a group and order objects by size.

Lesson 2
- Children measure length in nonstandard units.
- They measure real-life objects with both paper-clip and cube units.
- Then children choose a unit, measure, and record.

Lesson 3
- This lesson estimates and measures length in inches.
- Pictures show children how to correctly align a ruler and the objects being measured.
- Children also measure parts of a picture.

Lesson 4
- This lesson introduces centimeters as a unit of length.
- Children estimate and measure pictured objects.
- A game practices measuring in centimeters.

Lesson 5
- Children compare and order objects by weight.
- First children hold two objects to estimate which is heavier. Then they compare on a balance.
- Next children choose a nonstandard unit and measure real-life objects on a balance.

Lesson 6
- Introduces *pound* as a unit to measure weight.
- Children use a balance to compare real-life objects to a 1-pound weight and determine if the objects weigh more than, less than, or about 1 pound.
- Then children estimate if pictured objects are more than or less than 1 pound.

Lesson 7
- The focus of this lesson is on *kilograms* as a measure of how heavy an object is. The word *mass* is not used at this grade level, and the word *weight* is avoided.
- Children use a balance to compare real-life objects to 1-kilogram and determine if the object is more than, less than, or about 1 kilogram.
- Then children estimate if pictured objects are more than or less than 1 kilogram.

Lesson 8
- Decision making in problem solving is revisited as children use logical reasoning to solve problems.
- Problems involve comparing length as well as other attributes.

SKILLS TRACE: LENGTH AND WEIGHT

Grade K	Grade 1	Grade 2
• compare and order by length (ch. 11)	• **compare, order, estimate and measure length in nonstandard units, inches, and centimeters**	• estimate and measure length in nonstandard units, inches, feet, and yards (ch. 17)
• measure length in non-standard units (ch. 11)	• **compare, order and estimate objects using pounds and kilograms**	• estimate and measure length to the nearest centimeter and meter (ch. 17)
• compare and order by weight (ch. 12)		• find perimeter; area (ch. 17)
• measure weight in nonstandard units (ch. 12)		• estimate and measure using pounds and kilograms (ch. 18)

Chapter Planner

Lesson	Objective	Vocabulary	Materials	✔ NCTM Standards
17.1 **Compare and Order Length** (Hands-On) p. 499A	Compare and order length and height of objects.	longer, shorter, taller, length, height	paper strips, blank transparency, yarn, pencil, paper clip	Compare and order objects according to these attributes (length, volume, weight, area, and time).
17.2 **Nonstandard Units** (Hands-On) p. 501A	Estimate length using nonstandard units.	measure units	paper clips, cubes, paint brush, new crayons	Understand how to measure using nonstandard and standard units.
17.3 **Inches** (Hands-On) p. 503A	Measure an object in inches using a ruler.	inches	12-inch rulers (Learning Tool (LT) 37), cubes, ruler transparency, blank transparency, one-inch paper squares, 12-inch paper strips (use LT 28), paste	Understand how to measure using nonstandard and standard units.
17.4 **Centimeter** (Hands-On) p. 505A	Measure an object in centimeters using a ruler.	centimeters	large and small paper clips, unsharpened pencils, ruler transparency, rulers (LT 37), overhead pattern blocks, blank transparency, centimeter grid paper (LT 30), self-stick notes	Understand how to measure using nonstandard and standard units.
17.5 **Compare Weight** (Hands-On) p. 509A	Compare and order the weights of objects using nonstandard units and direct comparison.	weight heavier lighter	balance, paper clip, 6 objects of different weights, cubes, brown paper bags	Understand how to measure using nonstandard and standard units.
17.6 **Pounds** (Hands-On) p. 511A	Compare and order the weights of objects using nonstandard units and direct comparison.	pound	balance, 1-pound weight or object	Understand how to measure using nonstandard and standard units.
17.7 **Kilograms** (Hands-On) p. 513A	Compare objects to a kilogram.	kilogram	balance, 1-kilogram objects, cubes, paper bags, brown bags, objects including small heavy objects and larger light objects	Compare and order objects according to these attributes (length, volume, weight, area, and time).
17.8 **Problem Solving: Use Logical Reasoning** p. 515A	Use logical reasoning to solve word problems.		set of precut construction paper shapes (teacher-made), blank transparency	Select and use various types of reasoning and methods of proof.

Resources For Reaching All Learners

LESSON RESOURCES: Reteach, Practice, Enrichment, Problem Solving, Homework, English Learners, Daily Routines, Transparencies, Math Center.

ADDITIONAL RESOURCES FROM HOUGHTON MIFFLIN: Combination Classroom Planning Guide, Chapter Challenges, Every Day Counts, Math to Learn (Student Handbook)

Every Day Counts
The *Measurement* activities in **Every Day Counts** support the math in this chapter.

Assessing Prior Knowledge

Before beginning the chapter, you can assess student understandings in order to assist you in differentiating instruction.

Complete Chapter Pretest in Unit Resource Folder

Use this test to assess both prerequisite skills (**Are You Ready?** — one page) and chapter content (**Check What You Know** — two pages).

Chapter 17 Prerequisite Skills Pretest

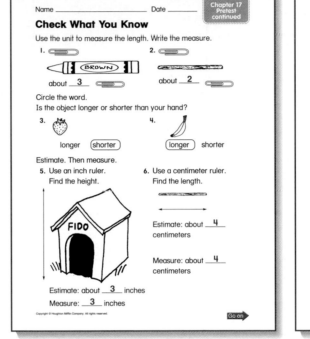

Chapter 17 New Content Pretest

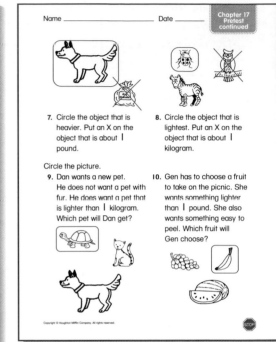

Customizing Instruction

For Students Having Difficulty

Items	Prerequisites	*Ways to Success*
1–3	Compare the height or length of objects.	CD: 17a Skillsheet 120
4–6	Compare the size or weight of objects.	CD: 17b Skillsheet 121

Ways to Success: Intervention for every concept and skill (CD-ROM or Chapter Intervention Skillsheets).

For Students Having Success

Items	Objectives	Resources
3–4 7–8	17A Use vocabulary for length and weight.	Enrichment 17.1, 17.4–17.6
1–6	17B Estimate, compare, and measure, using nonstandard units, inches, and centimeters.	Enrichment 17.1–17.4
7–8	17C Compare and order using nonstandard and standard units	Enrichment 17.5, 17.7
9–10	17D Use logical reasoning to solve problems.	Enrichment 17.8

Use **Chapter Challenges** with any students who have success with all new chapter content.

Other Pretest Options

Informal Pretest

The pretest assesses vocabulary and prerequisite skills needed for success in this chapter.

***Ways to Success* CD-ROM**

The *Ways to Success* chapter pretest has automatic assignment of appropriate review lessons.

Chapter Resources

Activity

Assessing Prior Knowledge

It's About This Long (estimate length)

- Each day, place a line of nonstandard measuring objects, such as paper clips or crayons, on a tray. (Have objects measure from 3 inches to 12 inches.)
- Have children search the classroom for items that are approximately the same length.
- Have children share their findings.

Activity

Ongoing Skill Activity

Compare Weights of Items in the Class Store (compare the weights/mass of objects to 1 pound/kilogram)

- Place a balance and a 1-pound weight in the class store.
- Have children use the balance to discover which items weigh more or less than 1 pound. Later, have children compare items to 1 kilogram.

Activity

Connecting to the Unit Project

- Tell children that they will begin work on the bird feeders.
- Have children draw a rectangle 10 cm in height and 8 cm in width on front of containers for an adult to cut.
- Have children measure various lengths of string using an inch ruler. This string will be tied to top of container for hanging the feeder outside.

Professional Resources Handbook

Research, Mathematics Content, and Language Intervention

Research-Based Teaching

Reeves (1999) recommends activities for teaching measurement as part of the mathematical education of school children in the United States and agrees that measurement activities should reflect a dynamic interaction between children and their environment. Moreover, children should begin to develop an understanding of the attributes of length, weight, and capacity by looking at, touching, and directly comparing objects in their immediate surroundings. See *Professional Resources Handbook, Grade 1,* Unit 7.

For more ideas relating to Unit 7, see the Teacher Support Handbook at the back of this Teacher's Edition.

Language Intervention

In East Asian countries, children learn that just as numbers can be composed and decomposed as sets and subsets, units of measurement can be composed and decomposed as well. For further explanation, see "Mathematical Language and Measurement" in the *Professional Resources Handbook Grade 1.*

Technology

Time-Saving Technology Support
Ways to Assess Customized Spiral Review
   Test Generator CD
Lesson Planner CD-ROM
Ways to Success Intervention CD-ROM
MathTracks CD-ROM
Education Place: www.eduplace.com/math/mw
Houghton Mifflin Math eBook CD-ROM
eManipulatives
eGames

Starting Chapter 17
Length and Weight

Math Background

Length and Weight

The basic idea of measurement is determining how many times a specific unit fits a specific object. To say that a table's width measures 5 units is to say that the unit of measurement fits 5 times along that side.

There are benefits to using standardized units. It was once common to use arm lengths to measure objects. However, different people have different arm lengths, resulting in different measurements for the same object. A standard unit of length ensures an object has the same dimensions no matter who measures it.

In Grade 1, length, height, weight, and mass are measured. Precision depends upon size of units used. The smaller the unit, the more precise the measurement.

There are two common measurement systems: customary and metric. The metric system is based on regular relationships using the number 10. It is helpful to remember that 1 liter is a little more than a quart, 1 kilogram is a little more than 2 pounds, 1 meter is a little more than a yard, and 1 centimeter is a little less than a half-inch – about the width of an adult's little finger.

Length and Weight

INVESTIGATION

In the picture find objects taller than a paper clip.

Using The Investigation

- Invite two children of different heights to stand back to back. Ask the class to tell who is *shorter* and who is *taller*.

- Tell children that height is usually measured in *units* called *inches, feet, centimeters,* or *meters.* Explain that they can also measure by comparing height with units like hands or pencils. Emphasize the measurement unit has to stay the same when two objects are compared.

- Read the directions to children. **Look at the picture. Think about the size of a paper clip. Find three objects that are taller than a paper clip.** (using a large paper clip: spool of thread, yellow thimble, watch, stamp, key, girl mouse, boy mouse)

For more information about projects and investigations, visit Education Place. **eduplace.com/math/mw/**

How Long Is It?

Use .
Find about how long the object is.

1.

about **6**

2.

about **8**

3.

about **4**

4.

about **2**

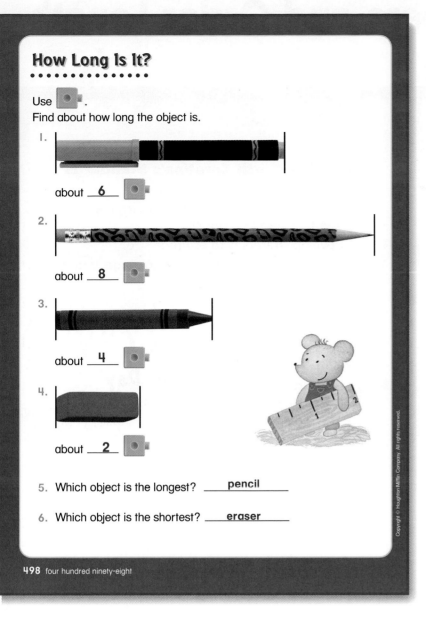

5. Which object is the longest? **pencil**

6. Which object is the shortest? **eraser**

CHAPTER CHALLENGES

For Mathematically Promising Students

The *Chapter Challenges* resource book provides blackline masters for activities that explore, extend, and connect the mathematics in every chapter. To support this independent work, see the Teacher Notes for each activity.

Explore: Compare with Cubits, page 97, after Lesson 1

Extend: Round About Measurement, page 99, after Lesson 3

Connect: Balance It, page 101, after Lesson 5

Using This Page

- Give each child a set of cubes.
- **Look at each picture. Use your cubes to measure each object. Then tell about how many cubes long each object is.**
- Direct children to compare the objects they measured to complete Exercises 5 and 6.
- After children have finished the exercises, have them measure objects around the classroom with their cubes.

NSF Children's Math Worlds

Build stronger conceptual understanding of length and weight with *Children's Math Worlds* lessons. The most effective approach is to use the *Children's Math Worlds* lessons along with the lessons in the chapter.

Hands-On: Compare and Order Length

Lesson 17.1

PLANNING THE LESSON

MATHEMATICS OBJECTIVE
Compare and order length and height of objects.

Use Lesson Planner CD-ROM for Lesson 17.1.

Meeting North Carolina's Standards

2.01 For given objects:
- Select an attribute (length, capacity, mass) to measure (use non-standard units).
- Develop strategies to estimate size.
- Compare, using appropriate language, with respect to the attribute selected.

Daily Routines

Calendar
Ask comparison questions about lengths of time on the calendar. Example: Which is a shorter amount of time—a school week or a weekend?

Sunday	Monday	Tuesday	Wednesday	Thursday	Friday	Saturday
			1	2	3	4
5	6	7	8	9	10	11
12	13	14	15	16	17	18
19	20	21	22	23	24	25
26	27	28	29	30	31	

Vocabulary
Have volunteers use the words **longer** and **shorter** in statements to compare **length**. Example: The teacher's desk is longer than my desk. Extend to include **taller**, **longest**, **shortest**, and **tallest**.

Vocabulary Cards

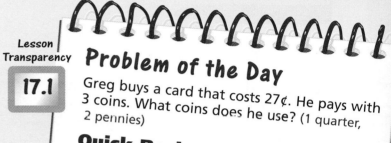

Lesson Transparency 17.1

Problem of the Day
Greg buys a card that costs 27¢. He pays with 3 coins. What coins does he use? (1 quarter, 2 pennies)

Quick Review

$$5 + 7 = (12) \qquad 7 + 5 = (12) \qquad 11 - 6 = (5) \qquad 11 - 5 = (6)$$

Lesson Quiz
1. Which is longer, your thumb or your foot? (foot)
2. Which is shorter, your hand or your arm? (hand)
3. Which is taller, your classmate or your classroom door? (classroom door)

LEVELED PRACTICE

RETEACH 17.1

Name _____ Date _____ **Reteach 17.1**

Activity: Compare and Order Length

Compare length and height.
Use the words longer, taller, and shorter.

Longer

Shorter

Taller   Shorter

Stand next to the object.
Is the object taller or shorter than you?
Circle. **Answers may vary.**

1.
taller   (shorter)

2.
taller   (shorter)

3.
(taller) shorter

4.
(taller) shorter

Copyright © Houghton Mifflin Company. All rights reserved.   Use with text pages 499–500.

PRACTICE 17.1

Name _____ Date _____ **Practice 17.1**

Compare and Order Length

Is the object longer or shorter than your hand?
Answers may vary.

1.
(longer) shorter

2.
longer (shorter)

3.
(longer) shorter

4.
longer (shorter)

Number the objects in order from shortest to longest.
Answers may vary.

5.
3   1   4   2

Test Prep

Fill in the ○ for the correct answer. NH means Not Here.

6. Which of these items is probably longer than your shoe?

pen   backpack   bar of soap   NH
○   ●   ○   ○

Copyright © Houghton Mifflin Company. All rights reserved.   Use with text pages 499–500.

ENRICHMENT 17.1

Name _____ Date _____ **Enrichment 17.1**

How Long? How High?

Compare length and height. Circle the correct answer. Answers may vary. Some suggested answers are given.

1. Is your teacher taller or shorter than you? (taller) shorter	2. Is your friend taller or shorter than you? taller shorter
3. Is the school bus taller or shorter than a car? (taller) shorter	4. Is the school bus longer or shorter than a car? (longer) shorter
5. Is your hand longer or shorter than your foot? longer (shorter)	6. Is your small finger longer or shorter than your pencil? longer (shorter)
7. Write the name of a person who is taller than you.	8. Write the name of an object that is longer than your pencil.

Talk About It How could you use string to compare the length of two objects? **I could use string to see how long each object is. Then I could see which string is longer.**

Copyright © Houghton Mifflin Company. All rights reserved.   Use with text pages 499–500.

Practice Workbook Page 114

Reaching All Learners
Differentiated Instruction

English Learners

In order to compare and order length and height, children will need to understand the vocabulary words associated with comparing and ordering. Use Worksheet 17.1 to help children understand the related words *length/long* and *height/tall/short*.

Special Needs
VISUAL, TACTILE

- Display a pencil and a crayon. Ask the child which is longer and which is shorter.
- Model aligning the left ends of the objects to compare.

Early Finishers
TACTILE, VISUAL

- Have children cut out paper strips that can be labeled **long, longer, longest**.
- Have them align the strips on the left and paste them onto a sheet of paper. Have them label each strip.
- Repeat for **short, shorter, shortest** and **tall, taller, tallest**.

TECHNOLOGY

Spiral Review

Using the *Ways to Assess* CD-ROM, you can create **customized** spiral review worksheets covering any lessons you choose.

Lesson Planner

Use the **Lesson Planner CD-ROM** to see how lesson objectives for this chapter are correlated to standards.

Games

Students can practice their math vocabulary using the Math Lingo game, available on the *Ways to Success* CD-ROM.

Social Studies Connection

Display a picture of a city skyline. Identify the city and state and one or two important buildings. Have volunteers make comparison statements about the heights of different buildings. Discuss why cities have so many tall buildings.

MATH CENTER

Cross-Curricular Activity

As you use this activity to relate the mathematics of this lesson to another curriculum area, children will see how math can help them with other subjects.

TEACHING LESSON 17.1

LESSON ORGANIZER

Objective Compare and order lengths and heights.

Resources Reteach, Practice, Enrichment, Problem Solving, Homework, English Learners, Transparencies, Math Center

Materials Paper strips, blank transparency, paper clip, ruler, pencil, yarn

Warm-Up Activity
Model Same and Different

Small Group	5 minutes	Visual, Auditory

Materials: *paper strips*

1. Cut 6 paper strips. 2 strips should be of equal length. Display the paper strips in random order but aligned at the left end. Ask volunteers to find two strips that are the same and two strips that are different.

    These two strips are the same.

2. Discuss with children how the strips are the same and different, focusing on length.

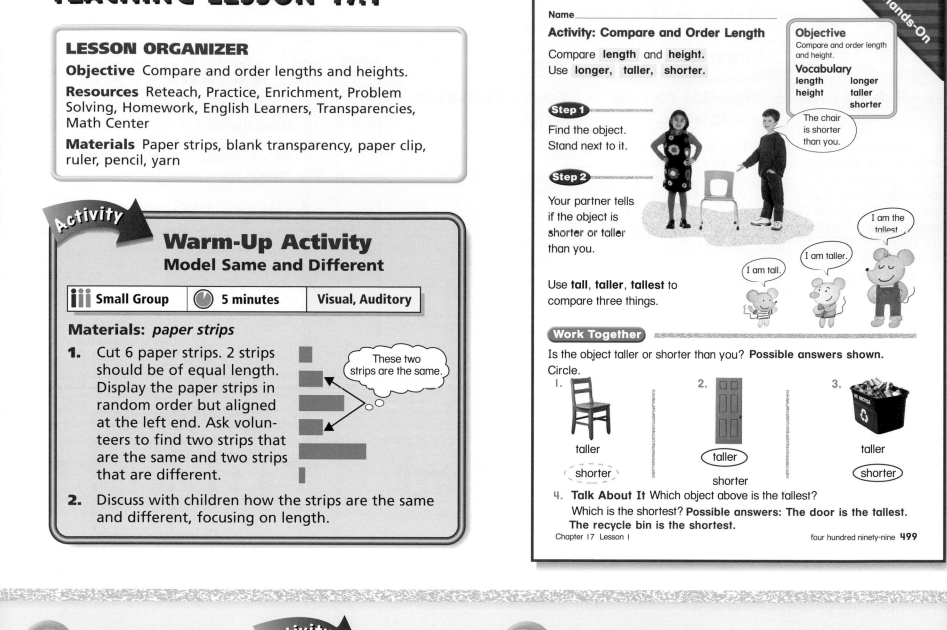

Name_____

Activity: Compare and Order Length

Compare **length** and **height**.
Use **longer**, **taller**, **shorter**.

Objective
Compare and order length and height.

Vocabulary
length   longer
height   taller
            shorter

Step 1
Find the object. Stand next to it.

The chair is shorter than you.

Step 2
Your partner tells if the object is shorter or taller than you.

Use **tall**, **taller**, **tallest** to compare three things.

I am tall.   I am taller.   I am the tallest

Work Together

Is the object taller or shorter than you? **Possible answers shown.** Circle.

1. taller (shorter)   2. (taller) shorter   3. taller (shorter)

4. **Talk About It** Which object above is the tallest? Which is the shortest? **Possible answers: The door is the tallest. The recycle bin is the shortest.**

Chapter 17 Lesson 1   four hundred ninety-nine **499**

---

① Introduce

Activity

Discuss Comparing and Ordering Length

Whole Group	10–15 minutes	Visual, Auditory

Materials: *blank transparency, paper clip, ruler*

1. Display a paper clip and a ruler on the overhead. **Compare the length of these two objects.** Emphasize the meaning of length. **Which is longer?** (ruler) **Which is shorter?** (paper clip)

2. Include a pencil. **Which is the longest object?** (ruler) **Which is the shortest object?** (paper clip) Ask a volunteer to come up and order the objects by length and then describe the order using the terms **long, longer, longest** or **short, shorter, shortest**.

3. Repeat the activity with other objects that you place vertically on the overhead to introduce **height** and the terms **tall, taller, tallest**.

② Develop

Guided Learning

Teaching Example Read the objective to children and introduce the vocabulary. Make sure children understand that the words **long, longer, longest** refer to objects that are placed horizontally and that the words **tall, taller, tallest** refer to things that stand vertically.

Guide pairs through the activity steps.

Work Together

Have pairs complete **Exercises 1–3** as you observe. Give several pairs the opportunity to answer the **Talk About It** question in **Exercise 4**. Then discuss their responses with the class.

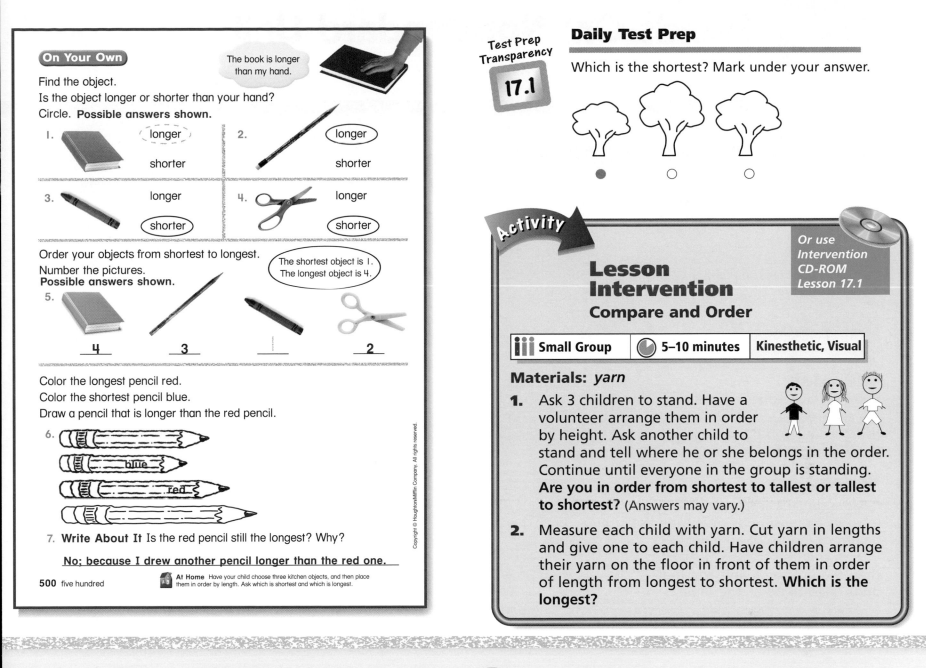

On Your Own

The book is longer than my hand.

Find the object.
Is the object longer or shorter than your hand?
Circle. **Possible answers shown.**

1. (longer)   2. longer
   shorter   shorter

3. longer   4. longer
   (shorter)   (shorter)

Order your objects from shortest to longest.
Number the pictures.
Possible answers shown.

The shortest object is 1.
The longest object is 4.

5.

   __4__   __3__   __1__   __2__

Color the longest pencil red.
Color the shortest pencil blue.
Draw a pencil that is longer than the red pencil.

6.

   blue
   red

7. **Write About It** Is the red pencil still the longest? Why?

No; because I drew another pencil longer than the red one.

500 five hundred

At Home Have your child choose three kitchen objects, and then place them in order by length. Ask which is shortest and which is longest.

Test Prep Transparency

17.1

Daily Test Prep

Which is the shortest? Mark under your answer.

●   ○   ○

Activity

Or use Intervention CD-ROM Lesson 17.1

Lesson Intervention

Compare and Order

| Small Group | 5–10 minutes | Kinesthetic, Visual |

Materials: *yarn*

1. Ask 3 children to stand. Have a volunteer arrange them in order by height. Ask another child to stand and tell where he or she belongs in the order. Continue until everyone in the group is standing. **Are you in order from shortest to tallest or tallest to shortest?** (Answers may vary.)

2. Measure each child with yarn. Cut yarn in lengths and give one to each child. Have children arrange their yarn on the floor in front of them in order of length from longest to shortest. **Which is the longest?**

---

3 Practice

On Your Own

Children complete **Exercises 1–4** independently. You may want to guide children through **Exercises 5–6** to be sure they understand the directions. Clarify that the objects used in Exercises 1–4 should be the same ones used in Exercise 5.

After children complete **Exercise 6**, call on several volunteers to share their drawings of the pencil and to answer the **Write About It** question in **Exercise 7**. Discuss children's responses.

Common Error

Comparing Wrong Dimension
Some children may compare the wrong dimension. Have children run their fingers along the length of each object to emphasize what is being compared.

4 Assess and Close

- **Is your teacher taller or shorter than you are?** (taller)
- **Is a cat taller or shorter than you are?** (shorter)

Keeping a Journal

Make a list of things in the classroom that are taller than you.

Hands-On: Nonstandard Units

PLANNING THE LESSON

MATHEMATICS OBJECTIVE
Estimate length using nonstandard units.

Use Lesson Planner CD-ROM for Lesson 17.2.

Daily Routines

Calendar
After naming today's day and date, ask children to count on 3 from today's date and name the day of the week and the new date.

Sunday	Monday	Tuesday	Wednesday	Thursday	Friday	Saturday
			1	2	3	4
5	6	7	8	9	10	11
12	13	14	15	16	17	18
19	20	21	22	23	24	25
26	27	28	29	30	31	

Vocabulary
Review **shorter** and **longer**. Introduce **measure** by discussing the **height** or **length** of an object. Inform children that to measure they need to use a **unit** and that **units** need to be all the same.

Vocabulary Cards

Meeting North Carolina's Standards
2.01 For given objects:
- Select an attribute (length, capacity, mass) to measure (use non-standard units).
- Develop strategies to estimate size.
- Compare, using appropriate language, with respect to the attribute selected.

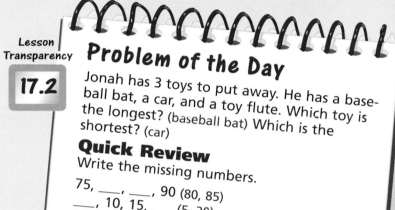

Lesson Transparency
17.2

Problem of the Day
Jonah has 3 toys to put away. He has a baseball bat, a car, and a toy flute. Which toy is the longest? (baseball bat) Which is the shortest? (car)

Quick Review
Write the missing numbers.

75, ___, ___, 90 (80, 85)
___, 10, 15, ___ (5, 20)
94, 96, ___, ___ (98, 100)

Lesson Quiz
Measure the length with paper clips.
1. desktop   about _____ paper clips
2. your shoe   about _____ paper clips
3. your thumb   about _____ paper clips

LEVELED PRACTICE

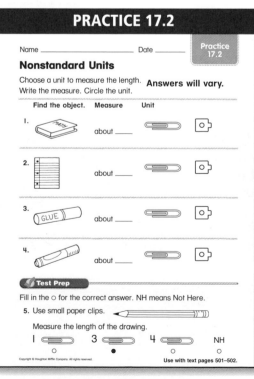

RETEACH 17.2

Name _____ Date _____   Reteach 17.2

Nonstandard Units

You can measure length with different units.

Green

about 2 [paper clip] long   about 2 [eraser] long

Complete the chart. **Answers may vary.**

Find the object.	Measure with [paper clip].	Measure with [eraser].
1. [shoe]	about _____	about _____
2. [box]	about _____	about _____
3. [book]	about _____	about _____
4. [scissors]	about _____	about _____

Copyright © Houghton Mifflin Company. All rights reserved.   Use with text pages 501–502.

PRACTICE 17.2

Name _____ Date _____   Practice 17.2

Nonstandard Units

Choose a unit to measure the length. **Answers will vary.**
Write the measure. Circle the unit.

Find the object.	Measure	Unit
1. [book]	about _____	[paper clip] [eraser]
2. [notebook]	about _____	[paper clip] [eraser]
3. [GLUE]	about _____	[paper clip] [eraser]
4. [marker]	about _____	[paper clip] [eraser]

Test Prep

Fill in the ○ for the correct answer. NH means Not Here.

5. Use small paper clips.

Measure the length of the drawing.

1 [paper clip]   3   4 [paper clip]   NH
○   ○   ●   ○

Copyright © Houghton Mifflin Company. All rights reserved.   Use with text pages 501–502.

ENRICHMENT 17.2

Name _____ Date _____   Enrichment 17.2

Measuring with Paper Clips

Look at each object below.
Estimate the length in [paper clip].
Then measure with [paper clip].

Estimates may vary. Suggested measurements are given.

1. [pencil]
Estimate: about _____ [paper clip]
Measure: about **3** [paper clip]

2. [paintbrush]
Estimate: about _____ [paper clip]
Measure: about **5** [paper clip]

3. [yarn]
Estimate: about _____ [paper clip]
Measure: about **4** [paper clip]

4. [crayon]
Estimate: about _____ [paper clip]
Measure: about **6** [paper clip]

Copyright © Houghton Mifflin Company. All rights reserved.   Use with text pages 501–502.

Practice Workbook Page 115

Reaching All Learners

Differentiated Instruction

English Learners

Worksheet 17.2 develops the concept of estimating numbers using the word *about*. Children will need to understand this word as they estimate length using nonstandard units.

Inclusion
VISUAL, TACTILE

Materials: *paper clips*

- Explain that you will use a paper clip as a unit to measure the length of the book.
- Show the child how to line the clips end to end. Have the child count the clips and say the measure. (The length of my book is about 7 clips.)
- Then have the child measure.

Gifted and Talented
TACTILE, VISUAL

- Ask children to use the same nonstandard unit of measurement to measure different objects and record the measurements.
- Then have children make a graph to show the different lengths.

How Many Markers Long

table												
shoe												
book												
window												

0 1 2 3 4 5 6 7 8 9 10 11 12
Number of Markers

TECHNOLOGY

Spiral Review

To reinforce skills on lessons taught earlier, create **customized** spiral review worksheets using the *Ways to Assess* CD-ROM.

Education Place

Encourage students to visit **Education Place** at **eduplace.com/kids/mw/** for more student activities.

Manipulatives

Interactive **Connecting Cubes** with several workmats are available on the *Ways to Success* CD-ROM.

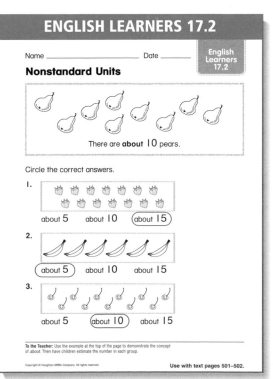

Literature Connection

Read *Measuring Penny* by Loreen Leedy. Help children recall the units the girl uses to measure the length of her dog's tail and ears. (dog biscuits and cotton swabs) Discuss what other units she could use.

MATH CENTER

Real-Life Activity

Help children understand the usefulness of mathematics. This activity makes math come alive by connecting the lesson skills to a real-life situation.

PROBLEM SOLVING 17.2

Name _____ Date _____

Problem Solving 17.2

Nonstandard Units

Draw a picture to solve.   **Check children's**
Use ⌇ and ▓ to help you.   **drawings.**

1. Dora wants to draw a picture of a snake that is about 5 ▓ long. Show her how you would draw the snake. Use ▓ to check your picture.

2. Larry wants to draw a bug that is about 1 ⌇ long. Show him how *you* would draw the bug. Use ⌇ to check your picture.

3. Judy wants to draw a bookmark that is about 6 ⌇ long. Show her how *you* would draw the bookmark. Use ⌇ to check your picture.

Copyright © Houghton Mifflin Company. All rights reserved.   **Use with text pages 501–502.**

HOMEWORK 17.2

Name _____ Date _____

Homework 17.2

Nonstandard Units

You can measure length with different units.

You can use ⌇ as units.

You can use ▭ as units.

The paintbrush is **6** paper clips long.

The paintbrush is **8** cubes long.

Write the number of units.   **Answers will vary.**

1. About how many teaspoons long is your kitchen table?	My kitchen table is about _____ teaspoons long.
2. About how many toothpicks long is a pen?	A pen is about _____ toothpicks long.
3. About how many footsteps long is your bed?	My bed is about _____ footsteps long.
4. Measure your bed with a teaspoon. Why is the length different than the length measured with your feet?	Explain here. **The units of measure are different lengths.**

Copyright © Houghton Mifflin Company. All rights reserved.   **Use with text pages 501–502.**

ENGLISH LEARNERS 17.2

Name _____ Date _____

English Learners 17.2

Nonstandard Units

There are **about** 10 pears.

Circle the correct answers.

1. about 5   about 10   (about 15)

2. (about 5)   about 10   about 15

3. about 5   (about 10)   about 15

To the Teacher: Use the example at the top of the page to demonstrate the concept of *about*. Then have children estimate the number in each group.

Copyright © Houghton Mifflin Company. All rights reserved.   **Use with text pages 501–502.**

Homework Workbook Page 115

TEACHING LESSON 17.2

LESSON ORGANIZER

Objective Estimate length using nonstandard units.

Resources Reteach, Practice, Enrichment, Problem Solving, Homework, English Learners, Transparencies, Math Center

Materials Cubes, paper clips, new crayons, paint brush

Activity

Warm-Up Activity
Modeling Comparing Lengths

iiii Small Group	5–10 minutes	Visual, Tactile

Materials: *cubes*

1. Display a train made of 6 cubes. Ask children to make a cube train that is the same length. **How do you know your train is the same length?** (Possible answers: both have 6 cubes; they line up end to end.)

2. Have children make two more trains, a train that is shorter and a train that is longer than the first train.

3. Let children check each other's work and explain how they know their trains are shorter and longer than the original train.

Nonstandard Units

MathTracks 2/15
Listen and Understand

Objective Estimate and measure length using nonstandard units.

Vocabulary measure units

Hands-On

You can **measure** length with different **units.**

About how many ⊂⊃ long is the pencil?

about __5__ ⊂⊃ long

About how many ▪ long is the pencil?

Line up the units. Make sure they touch end to end.

about __8__ ▪ long

Guided Practice
Complete the chart. **Answers may vary.**

Find the object.	Measure with ⊂⊃.	Measure with ▪.
1.	about _____ ⊂⊃	about _____ ▪
2.	about _____ ⊂⊃	about _____ ▪
3.	about _____ ⊂⊃	about _____ ▪

TEST TIPS **Explain Your Thinking** Can you mix cubes and paperclips when measuring an object? Why or why not? **No, you need to use the same unit when measuring an object.**

Chapter 17 Lesson 2

five hundred one **501**

---

1 Introduce → Activity
Discuss Nonstandard Units

iiiii Whole Group	10–15 minutes	Visual, Auditory

Materials: *paper clips, paint brush, new crayons*

1. Place a paint brush horizontally on the overhead. **You can measure the length of this brush using paper clips as a unit of measure.**

2. **About how many paper clips long is the brush?** Start to model placing the clips end to end to find the length. Have a volunteer come up and count as he or she finishes placing the clips. Record the measure, about _____ paper clips.

3. Have children repeat the activity using crayons as the unit of measure. First have students predict whether you will need more or fewer crayons than paper clips to measure the paint brush. **Why do you get a different number when you measure with crayons?** (Crayons are longer than clips, so you use fewer of them or the crayons and clips are different lengths so you use a different number of them.)

2 Develop

Guided Learning

Teaching Example Introduce the objective and vocabulary to the children. Guide them through the example. Have them place clips and cubes on top of the pictured units to reinforce how to line up units end to end. Now, have them count the number of units to find the measure. Discuss with students other nonstandard units (i.e. pennies) that could be used to measure the objects.

Guided Practice

Place the items pictured in **Exercises 1–3** in different areas of the classroom. Have small groups of children rotate to the different areas until each group has measured every item with clips and cubes. Observe children as they complete the exercises. Give children the opportunity to answer the Explain Your Thinking question. Then discuss their responses with the class.

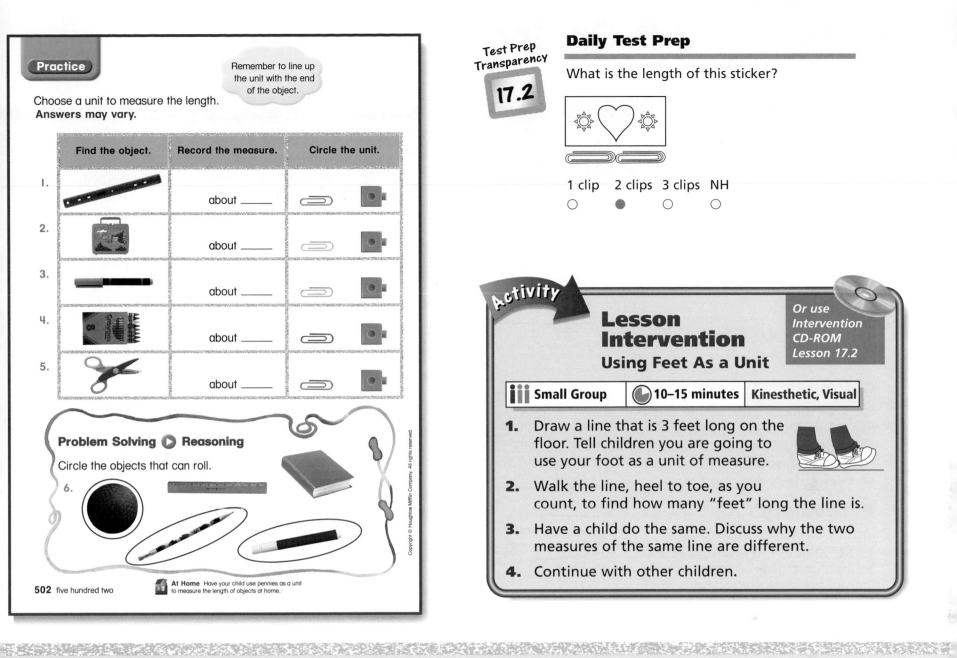

Practice

Remember to line up the unit with the end of the object.

Choose a unit to measure the length.
Answers may vary.

Find the object.	Record the measure.	Circle the unit.
1.	about ___	📎 ⬜
2.	about ___	📎 ⬜
3.	about ___	📎 ⬜
4.	about ___	📎 ⬜
5.	about ___	📎 ⬜

Problem Solving ▶ Reasoning

Circle the objects that can roll.

6.

502 five hundred two

At Home Have your child use pennies as a unit to measure the length of objects at home.

Daily Test Prep

Test Prep Transparency **17.2**

What is the length of this sticker?

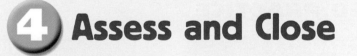

1 clip   2 clips   3 clips   NH
○   ●   ○   ○

Activity

Lesson Intervention
Using Feet As a Unit

Or use Intervention CD-ROM Lesson 17.2

👥 Small Group	⏱ 10–15 minutes	Kinesthetic, Visual

1. Draw a line that is 3 feet long on the floor. Tell children you are going to use your foot as a unit of measure.

2. Walk the line, heel to toe, as you count, to find how many "feet" long the line is.

3. Have a child do the same. Discuss why the two measures of the same line are different.

4. Continue with other children.

---

③ Practice

Independent Practice

Place the items pictured in **Exercises 1–5** in different areas of the classroom. Have small groups of children rotate to the different areas until each group has measured every item in either cubes or clips.

Problem Solving

After children complete **Exercise 6**, call on volunteers to share their solutions. **Why can't a book roll?** (The faces of a book are all flat.)

Common Error

Not Placing Units End to End
Remind children that the nonstandard units must be in a straight line touching end to end with no overlapping in order to get the correct measurement.

④ Assess and Close

Have children trace a hand on paper.

• **About how many paper clips long is your hand?**

• **About how many cubes long is your hand?**

(Answers will vary, but children should actually use cubes and clips to measure their hand lengths.) Discuss with students why the numbers are different when you measure using units of different lengths.

✏ Keeping a Journal

Write how to tell a friend to measure the length of a picture book with cubes.

Hands-On: Inches

PLANNING THE LESSON

MATHEMATICS OBJECTIVE
Measure an object in inches using a ruler.

Use Lesson Planner CD-ROM for Lesson 17.3.

Daily Routines

Calendar
Point to today's date on the calendar. After children tell you what day of the week and date it is, ask them to name tomorrow's day and date and yesterday's day and date.

Sunday	Monday	Tuesday	Wednesday	Thursday	Friday	Saturday
			1	2	3	4
5	6	7	8	9	10	11
12	13	14	15	16	17	18
19	20	21	22	23	24	25
26	27	28	29	30	31	

Vocabulary
Introduce **inch** by displaying a 1-inch square and identifying it as an inch unit. Then ask children to name objects that are about the same *length*, are *longer* than, and are *shorter* than an inch.

Vocabulary Cards

Meeting North Carolina's Standards
Prepare for Grade 2 Standard 2.01 Estimate and measure using appropriate units.

Lesson Transparency 17.3

Problem of the Day
Sally is using her hand as a unit for measuring. Her desk is 6 units long. Dan also is using his hand as a unit. He measured Sally's desk as 5 units long. Why are the lengths different? (The sizes of the hands are different.)

Quick Review
$$\begin{array}{r} 5 \\ +7 \\ \hline (12) \end{array} \qquad \begin{array}{r} 9 \\ +2 \\ \hline (11) \end{array} \qquad \begin{array}{r} 4 \\ +8 \\ \hline (12) \end{array} \qquad \begin{array}{r} 6 \\ +5 \\ \hline (11) \end{array}$$

Lesson Quiz
Find the object. Estimate. Then measure with an inch ruler.

1. crayon
   Estimate: about _____ inches
   Measure: about _____ inches

2. marker
   Estimate: about _____ inches
   Measure: about _____ inches

LEVELED PRACTICE

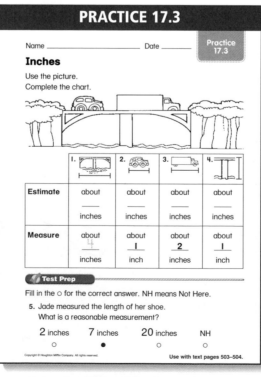

RETEACH 17.3
Name _____ Date _____ **Reteach 17.3**

Activity: Inches

You can estimate before you measure.
Estimate the length in inches.
Estimate: about __3__ inches.
Use an inch ruler to measure the length.

Red

Measure: The crayon is about __3__ inches.

Estimate. Write your answer.
Then use an inch ruler to measure.
Write your answer. **Estimates may vary.**

1. Estimate: about _____ inches   Measure: about __2__ inches

2. Estimate: about _____ inches   Measure: about __4__ inches

3. Estimate: about _____ inches   Measure: about __3__ inches

4. Estimate: about _____ inches   Measure: about __1__ inches

Copyright © Houghton Mifflin Company. All rights reserved.   Use with text pages 503–504.

PRACTICE 17.3
Name _____ Date _____ **Practice 17.3**

Inches

Use the picture.
Complete the chart.

	1.	2.	3.	4.
Estimate	about _____ inches	about _____ inches	about _____ inches	about _____ inches
Measure	about __4__ inches	about __1__ inch	about __2__ inches	about __1__ inch

Test Prep
Fill in the ○ for the correct answer. NH means Not Here.

5. Jade measured the length of her shoe.
   What is a reasonable measurement?

   ○ 2 inches   ● 7 inches   ○ 20 inches   ○ NH

Copyright © Houghton Mifflin Company. All rights reserved.   Use with text pages 503–504.

ENRICHMENT 17.3
Name _____ Date _____ **Enrichment 17.3**

Inch by Inch

Use a ruler to measure each length.
Then compare.   **Measurements will vary.**

1. Measure your pinky and your index finger.
   My pinky is _____ inches.   My index finger is _____ inches.
   Which is shorter? My __pinky__ is shorter.

2. Measure your hand and your foot.
   My hand is _____ inches.   My foot is _____ inches.
   Which is shorter? My __hand__ is shorter.

3. READING   MATH
   Measure your math book and your reading book.
   My math book is _____ inches.
   My reading book is _____ inches.
   Which is shorter? My _____ is shorter.

Copyright © Houghton Mifflin Company. All rights reserved.   Use with text pages 503–504.

Practice Workbook Page 116

Reaching All Learners
Differentiated Instruction

English Learners

Children will need to understand the difference between estimating and counting before they learn to measure objects. Use Worksheet 17.3 to build familiarity with these concepts.

Special Needs
TACTILE, VISUAL

Materials: *square pattern blocks*

- Hold up a square pattern block. Explain that it is 1 inch long. Help the child measure objects by placing blocks end to end. Have the child count the blocks to find the length in inches.

about 7 inches

Gifted and Talented
TACTILE, KINESTHETIC

Materials: *12-inch rulers, lengths of yarn*

- Prepare lengths of yarn cut to 2, 3, and 4 feet long.
- Explain to children that 12 inches equal 1 foot. Have pairs of children use a foot ruler to measure and record the lengths of each piece of yarn.

Literature Connection

Read *Inch by Inch* by Leo Lionni. Talk about how the inchworm finds the length of the robin's tail. Have each child use a one-inch piece of yarn to measure objects and share their strategies for measuring with a single unit.

MATH CENTER

Real-Life Activity

Help children understand the usefulness of mathematics. This activity makes math come alive by connecting the lesson skills to a real-life situation.

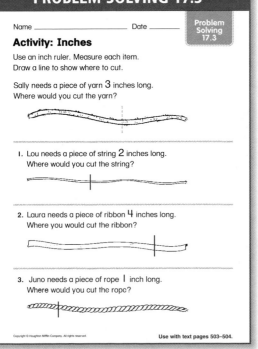

PROBLEM SOLVING 17.3

Name _____ Date _____ | Problem Solving 17.3

Activity: Inches

Use an inch ruler. Measure each item. Draw a line to show where to cut.

Sally needs a piece of yarn 3 inches long. Where would you cut the yarn?

1. Lou needs a piece of string 2 inches long. Where would you cut the string?

2. Laura needs a piece of ribbon 4 inches long. Where you would cut the ribbon?

3. Juno needs a piece of rope 1 inch long. Where would you cut the rope?

Copyright © Houghton Mifflin Company. All rights reserved. — Use with text pages 503–504.

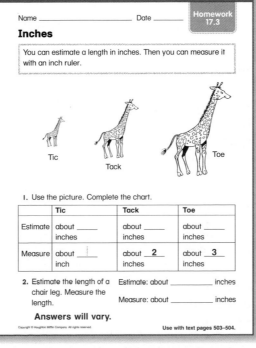

HOMEWORK 17.3

Name _____ Date _____ | Homework 17.3

Inches

You can estimate a length in inches. Then you can measure it with an inch ruler.

Tic   Tack   Toe

1. Use the picture. Complete the chart.

	Tic	Tack	Toe
Estimate	about _____ inches	about _____ inches	about _____ inches
Measure	about _____ inch	about 2 inches	about 3 inches

2. Estimate the length of a chair leg. Measure the length.
   Estimate: about _____ inches
   Measure: about _____ inches

Answers will vary.

Copyright © Houghton Mifflin Company. All rights reserved. — Use with text pages 503–504.

Homework Workbook Page 116

ENGLISH LEARNERS 17.3

Name _____ Date _____ | English Learners 17.3

Inches

Estimate the number of windows.
Estimate: 10

Count the number of windows.
Count: 8

Estimate and count.

1.   2.   3.

How many leaves?   How many flowers?   How many grapes?

Estimate: __15__   Estimate: __10__   Estimate: __20__

Count: __16__   Count: __9__   Count: __19__

To the Teacher: Use the example at the top of the page to contrast the concepts of estimating and counting. Then have children estimate and count the number of objects in each set.

Copyright © Houghton Mifflin Company. All rights reserved. — Use with text pages 503–504.

TEACHING LESSON 17.3

LESSON ORGANIZER

Objective Measure an object in inches using a ruler.

Resources Reteach, Practice, Enrichment, Problem Solving, Homework, English Learners, Transparencies, Math Center

Materials Cubes, ruler transparency, rulers (LT 37), blank transparency, 1-inch paper squares, 12-inch paper strips (use LT 28), paste

Activity

Warm-Up Activity
Modeling Same Size Units

iiii Small Group	⏱ 5–10 minutes	Visual, Tactile

Materials: *cubes*

1. Show children how to connect cubes to make a cube train for measuring. Explain that each cube train is the same length, so a cube train can be used as a unit for measuring.

2. Give each child in the group an object of the same length to measure. Have each child measure the length. **Why are all the measurements the same?** (The unit of measure is the same.)

3. Have children measure other like items. Emphasize that when they all use the same unit of measure, they all get the same measurement.

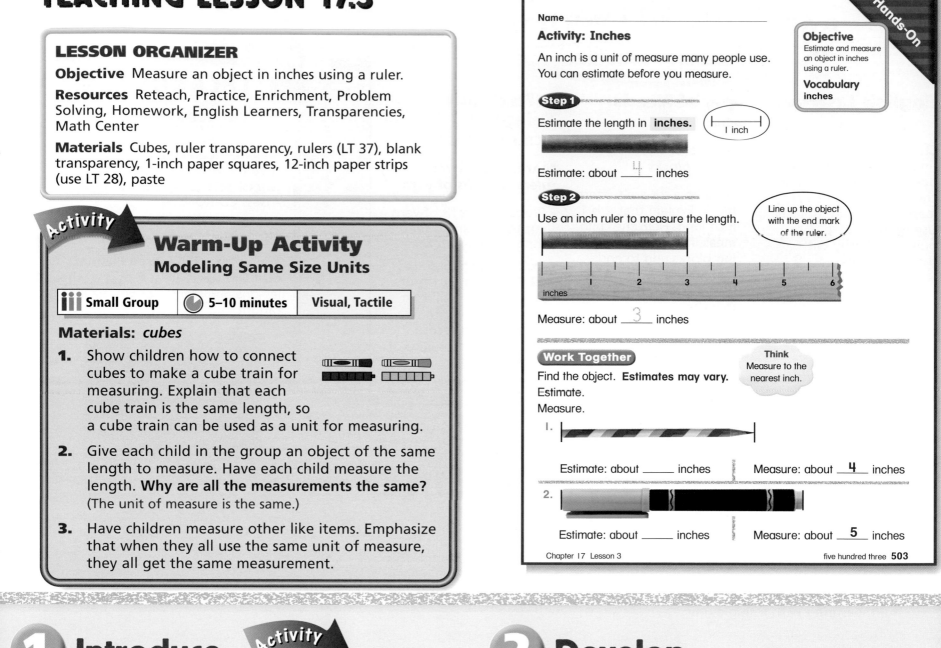

---

1 Introduce
Model Inches

iiii Whole Group	⏱ 10–15 minutes	Visual, Auditory

Materials: *ruler transparency, rulers (LT37), blank transparency*

1. Display the inch ruler on the overhead and point to the tick marks with numbers. Have children point to the marks on their rulers. Tell children that the space between each tick mark with a number is 1 inch. Frame an inch on the ruler with your thumb and forefinger and have children do the same. Emphasize that the projected image from the overhead is much larger than an inch.

2. Draw 2-inch, 4-inch, and 5-inch lines. Model measuring the 2-inch line with the ruler. **How do I know how many inches the line is?** (by reading the number on the ruler where the line ends) **Would my answer be correct if I placed the second tick mark of the ruler at the left end of the line?** (no) Measure the 4- and 5-inch lines.

3. Have children draw lines of other lengths.

2 Develop

Guided Learning

Teaching Example Read the objective and vocabulary with children. Guide them through the example. Emphasize how they can use the 1-inch line to help them estimate the length. Point out the importance of aligning the first tick mark of a ruler with the left end of the object when they measure.

Work Together

Remind children to use the 1-inch picture at the top of the page to make their estimates. Then have pairs complete **Exercises 1–2** as you observe. Discuss with students how they could order the objects on the page from shortest to longest. (chalk, pencil, marker)

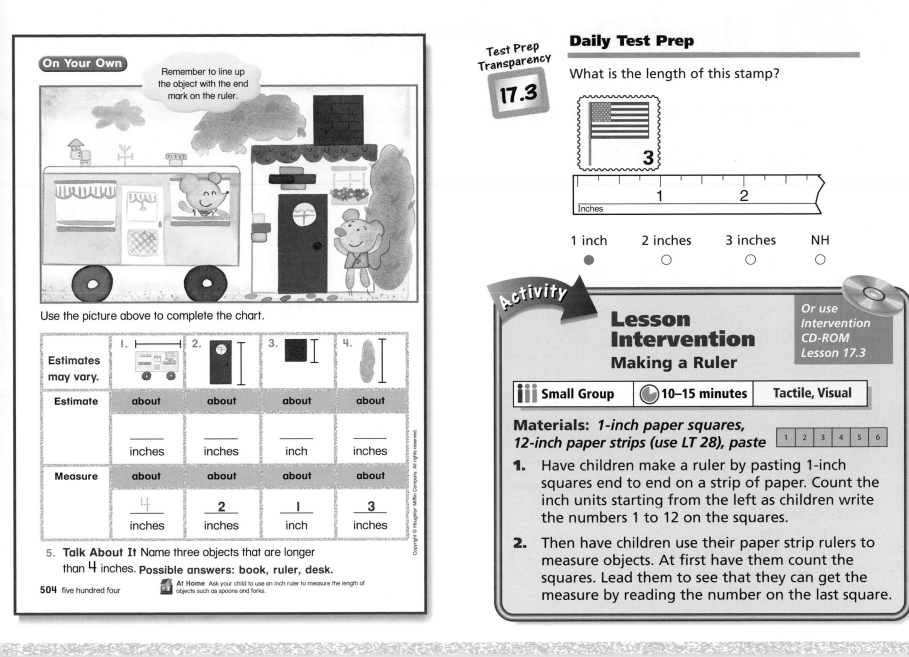

Remember to line up the object with the end mark on the ruler.

Use the picture above to complete the chart.

Estimates may vary.	1.	2.	3.	4.
Estimate	about ___ inches	about ___ inches	about ___ inch	about ___ inches
Measure	about 4 inches	about 2 inches	about 1 inch	about 3 inches

5. **Talk About It** Name three objects that are longer than 4 inches. **Possible answers: book, ruler, desk.**

At Home Ask your child to use an inch ruler to measure the length of objects such as spoons and forks.

Daily Test Prep

What is the length of this stamp?

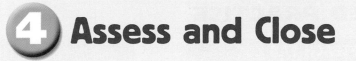

3

Inches | 1 | 2

- 1 inch ●
- 2 inches ○
- 3 inches ○
- NH ○

Activity

Lesson Intervention
Making a Ruler

Or use Intervention CD-ROM Lesson 17.3

iii Small Group	🕐 10–15 minutes	Tactile, Visual

Materials: *1-inch paper squares, 12-inch paper strips (use LT 28), paste*

| 1 | 2 | 3 | 4 | 5 | 6 |

1. Have children make a ruler by pasting 1-inch squares end to end on a strip of paper. Count the inch units starting from the left as children write the numbers 1 to 12 on the squares.

2. Then have children use their paper strip rulers to measure objects. At first have them count the squares. Lead them to see that they can get the measure by reading the number on the last square.

---

3 Practice

On Your Own

Discuss the picture and the objects to be measured. If children need help estimating, give them a model that is about 1 inch long (a connecting cube or a 1-inch square).

Children complete **Exercises 1–4** independently.

Have volunteers answer the **Talk About It** question in **Exercise 5**. Discuss their responses with the class. Check to see if children estimated or measured. Allow children to demonstrate their results.

Common Error

Not Aligning the Ruler Correctly
Demonstrate how misplacing the ruler gives the wrong measurement. Help children practice aligning objects with the end of the ruler and finding the length.

4 Assess and Close

- **Which is longer, a 6-inch line or a 7-inch line?** (7-inch line)
- **Draw a 3-inch line.**
- **Draw a 6-inch line.**

Keeping a Journal

Draw a 2-inch line. Draw an object that is the same length. Repeat with 4- and 6-inch lines.

Hands-On: Centimeters

PLANNING THE LESSON

Meeting North Carolina's Standards
Prepare for Grade 2 Standard 2.01 Estimate and measure using appropriate units.

MATHEMATICS OBJECTIVE
Measure an object in centimeters using a ruler.

Use Lesson Planner CD-ROM for Lesson 17.4.

Daily Routines

Calendar
Have children create patterns using the calendar. They should describe their rule and extend the pattern beyond the calendar numbers. Example: 2, 9, 16, 23, 30, 37, etc.

Vocabulary
To introduce **centimeter**, have children run their fingers along the length of a ones place-value block from left to right as they say: This block is one centimeter long.

Vocabulary Cards

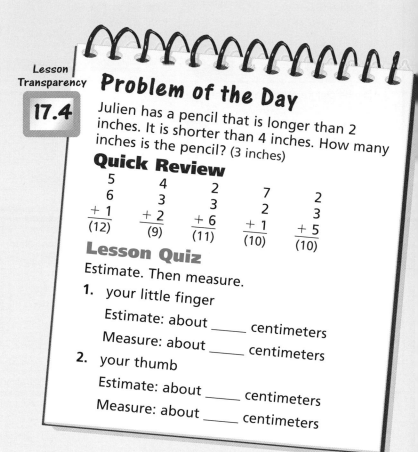

Lesson Transparency 17.4

Problem of the Day
Julien has a pencil that is longer than 2 inches. It is shorter than 4 inches. How many inches is the pencil? (3 inches)

Quick Review

$$\begin{array}{r}5\\6\\+1\\\hline(12)\end{array}\quad\begin{array}{r}4\\3\\+2\\\hline(9)\end{array}\quad\begin{array}{r}2\\3\\+6\\\hline(11)\end{array}\quad\begin{array}{r}7\\2\\+1\\\hline(10)\end{array}\quad\begin{array}{r}2\\3\\+5\\\hline(10)\end{array}$$

Lesson Quiz
Estimate. Then measure.
1. your little finger
   Estimate: about _____ centimeters
   Measure: about _____ centimeters
2. your thumb
   Estimate: about _____ centimeters
   Measure: about _____ centimeters

LEVELED PRACTICE

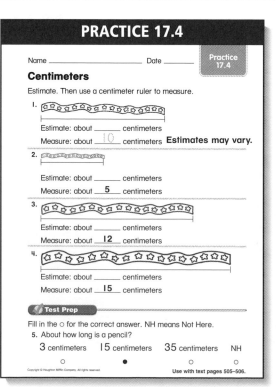

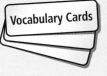

Practice Workbook Page 117

Reaching All Learners

Differentiated Instruction

English Learners

English-language learners may not have the language skills to explain the process behind their thinking. Use Worksheet 17.4 to provide children with sentence frames they can use to complete the Explain Your Thinking activity.

Special Needs
TACTILE, VISUAL

Materials: ones blocks

- Give the child a ones block. Explain that it is 1 centimeter long. Help the child measure the length of objects by placing blocks end to end along the object as the child counts to find the measure.

- Repeat with other objects.

Gifted and Talented
VISUAL, TACTILE

Materials: meterstick (teacher-made)

- Introduce the meterstick to children.

- Have children take turns. One child uses the meterstick to measure the floor length or a large object in the classroom. The partner records the measurement in both centimeters and meters.

TECHNOLOGY

Spiral Review

You can prepare students for standardized tests with **customized** spiral review on key skills using the *Ways to Assess* CD-ROM.

Education Place

You can visit **Education Place** at **eduplace.com/math/mw/** for teacher support materials.

Science Connection

Discuss the metric system with children. Tell them it is used in science so that scientists of different countries can share information. Show children a meterstick and have them measure the length of each other's feet.

MATH CENTER

Real-Life Activity

Help children understand the usefulness of mathematics. This activity makes math come alive by connecting the lesson skills to a real-life situation.

PROBLEM SOLVING 17.4

Name _____ Date _____

Problem Solving 17.4

Centimeters

Use a centimeter ruler. Measure each item.
Draw a line to show where to cut.

Julie wants a piece of carrot 10 centimeters long.
Where you would cut the carrot?

1. Paul wants a piece of bread stick 9 centimeters long.
Where would you cut the bread stick?

2. Dawn wants a piece of celery 6 centimeters long.
Where would you cut the celery?

3. Billy wants to share a pretzel with his friend.
Where would you cut the pretzel so that each boy gets half?

Use with text pages 505–506.

HOMEWORK 17.4

Name _____ Date _____

Homework 17.4

Centimeters

You can estimate a length in centimeters.
Then you can measure it with a centimeter ruler.

1. First estimate.
Then use a centimeter ruler to measure.

	Giggly	Squiggly	Wiggly
Estimate	about ___ centimeters	about ___ centimeters	about ___ centimeters
Measure	about 4 centimeters	about 8 centimeters	about 12 centimeters

2. Find an object in the kitchen. Estimate the length. Use a centimeter ruler to measure.

Estimate: about ___ centimeters

Measure: about ___ centimeters

Use with text pages 505–506.

ENGLISH LEARNERS 17.4

Name _____ Date _____

English Learners 17.4

Centimeters

An eraser is shorter than 10 centimeters.

Use a centimeter ruler. **Answers will vary**
Name three objects that are shorter than 10 centimeters.

1. I can measure a _____ with a centimeter ruler.
It is _____ centimeters long.
_____ is less than 10 centimeters.
A _____ is shorter than 10 centimeters.

2. I can measure a _____ with a centimeter ruler.
It is _____ centimeters long.
_____ is less than 10 centimeters.
A _____ is shorter than 10 centimeters.

3. I can measure a _____ with a centimeter ruler.
It is _____ centimeters long.
_____ is less than 10 centimeters.
A _____ is shorter than 10 centimeters.

To the Teacher: Use the example at the top of the page to demonstrate the length of 10 centimeters. Then have children choose classroom objects to measure. Have them complete the sentence frames that provide the language needed to solve the problem.

Use with text pages 509–510.

Homework Workbook Page 117

TEACHING LESSON 17.4

LESSON ORGANIZER

Objective Measure an object in centimeters using a ruler.

Resources Reteach, Practice, Enrichment, Problem Solving, Homework, English Learners, Transparencies, Math Center

Materials clips, pencils, ruler transparency, rulers (LT 37), overhead pattern blocks, blank transparency, centimeter grid paper (LT 30), self-stick note

Activity

Warm-Up Activity
Modeling the Need for a Standard Unit

| ⓘⓘ Pairs | 🕐 5–10 minutes | Tactile, Visual |

Materials: *large and small paper clips, unsharpened pencils*

1. Give one partner small clips and the other large clips. Have each partner use his or her clips to measure the length of a pencil.

2. Have partners compare results. **Were your measurements the same?** (no) **Why are your measurements different if you measured the same pencil?** (the paper clips are two different sizes) **How can you both get the same measurement when you measure an object?** (Possible answer: Measure with the same size unit.)

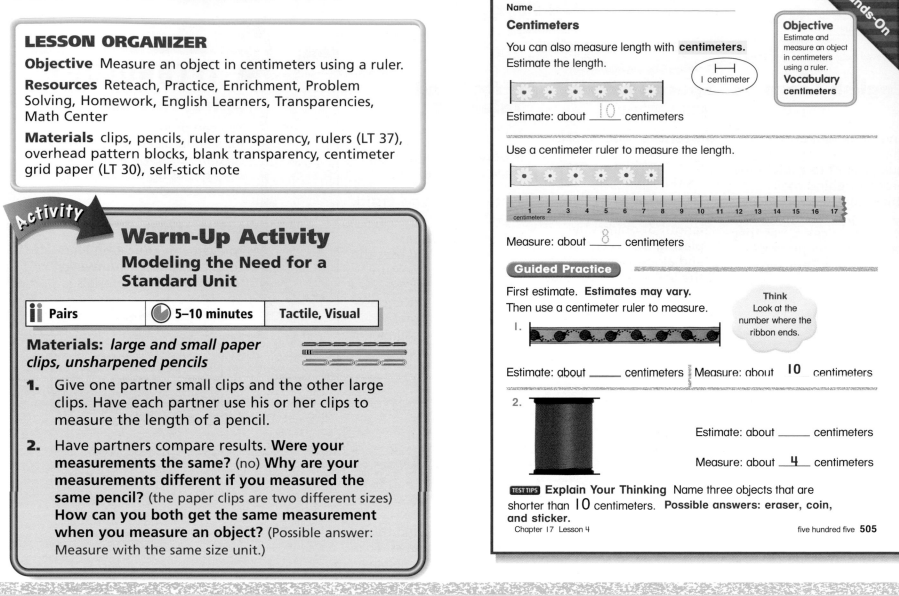

Hands-On

Name_____

Centimeters

You can also measure length with **centimeters**. Estimate the length.

| H⊣ 1 centimeter |

Estimate: about __10__ centimeters

Use a centimeter ruler to measure the length.

Measure: about __8__ centimeters

Objective
Estimate and measure an object in centimeters using a ruler.
Vocabulary
centimeters

Guided Practice

First estimate. **Estimates may vary.** Then use a centimeter ruler to measure.

Think
Look at the number where the ribbon ends.

1.
Estimate: about _____ centimeters   Measure: about __10__ centimeters

2.
Estimate: about _____ centimeters

Measure: about __4__ centimeters

TEST TIPS **Explain Your Thinking** Name three objects that are shorter than 10 centimeters. **Possible answers: eraser, coin, and sticker.**

Chapter 17 Lesson 4   five hundred five **505**

① Introduce
Activity
Model Centimeters

| ⓘⓘⓘⓘ Whole Group | 🕐 10–15 minutes | Visual, Auditory |

Materials: *ruler transparency, rulers (LT 37), overhead pattern blocks, blank transparency*

1. Place the centimeter ruler on the overhead. Point to the tick marks with numbers on the ruler. Have children point to the marks on their rulers. Tell children that the space between each tick mark with a number is 1 centimeter. Remind children that the projected image from the overhead is much larger than a centimeter.

2. Place a pattern block on the projector. Demonstrate how to use the ruler to measure the length of the sides in centimeters. **How do I know how many centimeters long this side is?** (by reading the number on the ruler nearest to where the side ends) Record the measurements.

3. Continue by inviting volunteers to measure different shape blocks. **Can you compare objects measured in centimeters?** (Yes, all centimeters are the same length.)

② Develop

Guided Learning

Teaching Example Read the objective and vocabulary with children. Guide them through the example emphasizing how they can use the picture of 1 centimeter to estimate the length. Then have them use a ruler on top of the pictured ruler to measure the ribbon. Observe children to ensure they align the ribbon and ruler correctly. Remind them how to read the number on the ruler to find the measure.

Guided Practice

Have children complete **Exercises 1–2** as you observe. Remind children to use the 1-centimeter picture at the top of the page to estimate. Be sure children understand they are to measure the height of the spool. Give children the opportunity to answer the Explain Your Thinking question. Then discuss their responses with the class. Ask them if they measured or estimated.

505   CHAPTER 17   Lesson 4

Practice

Remember to use the end marks to help you measure.

First estimate. **Estimates may vary.**
Then use a centimeter ruler to measure.

1.

Estimate: about _____ centimeters | Measure: about _17_ centimeters

2.

Estimate: about _____ centimeters | Measure: about _8_ centimeters

3.

Estimate: about _____ centimeters | Measure: about _13_ centimeters

4.

Estimate: about _____ centimeters

Measure: about _3_ centimeters

Reading Math ▶ Vocabulary

5. Color the shortest feather ▮▮▮▶ .

6. Color the longest feather ▮▮▮▶ .

blue

red

7. Circle the feather that is about 6 centimeters long.

At Home Ask your child to find objects at home that are longer than 10 centimeters. Then measure the objects.

Go on

Daily Test Prep

What is the length of this crayon?
○ about 3 centimeters
○ about 7 centimeters
● about 8 centimeters

Activity

Lesson Intervention

Using Centimeter Grid Paper

Or use Intervention CD-ROM Lesson 17.4

| ℹ Individual | 🕐 5 minutes | Visual, Tactile |

Materials: *centimeter grid paper (LT 30), rulers, self-stick notes*

1. Highlight a square on grid paper and tell children that each side is 1 centimeter long.

2. Place a self-stick note on the grid paper. Model measuring the length of the note by coloring 1 square on the grid paper for each centimeter. **About how many centimeters long is the note?** Record the measure.

3. Then have children check their measures with a ruler.

---

③ Practice

Independent Practice

Children complete **Exercises 1–4** independently. If children need help estimating give them a ones cube (each side is one centimeter).

Reading Math

After children complete **Exercises 5–7**, call on volunteers to share their answers.

Common Error

Not Holding the Ruler Straight

Demonstrate how not holding the ruler straight can give inaccurate measurements. Provide additional practice using the ruler on real objects and pictures.

④ Assess and Close

• Which is shorter, a 5-centimeter line or an 8-centimeter line? (5-centimeter line)

• Draw a line that is 4 centimeters long.

• Draw a line that is 11 centimeters long.

Keeping a Journal

Draw 3 objects. Use a centimeter ruler to measure each length. Record the measurements.

Lesson continues

Measure Up

Purpose: This game provides practice measuring in centimeters.

Materials: *For each pair of children: paper clip, pencil, centimeter ruler, cubes*

Before play begins, demonstrate how to use the paper clip as a pointer on the spinner by anchoring it with a pencil.

How to Play

• In turn, each child spins the spinner. Then the child finds a similar object in the classroom to the one shown on the spinner.

• Have the child use a centimeter ruler to measure the object to the nearest centimeter. Then the child takes cubes to match the number of centimeters measured. For example, if a piece of chalk measured 8 centimeters long, the child would take 8 cubes.

• Children continue playing until one player has 50 cubes. Have them group their cubes by 10s.

• Encourage partners to check each other's work.

Other Ways to Play

Children may continue to play during the same session, or this alternate version of the Practice Game could be used in the Math Center at a later date.

A. Have children use an inch ruler instead of a centimeter ruler and measure the objects in inches. Have them play until one player has 20 cubes.

B. Have pairs of children play. Each partner spins and measures. The partner with the longest object scores 1 point. The first player to score 5 points wins.

Name_____

Measure Up

2 to 4 Players
What You Need: cubes, centimeter ruler, pencil, paper clip, and items on the spinner

How to Play

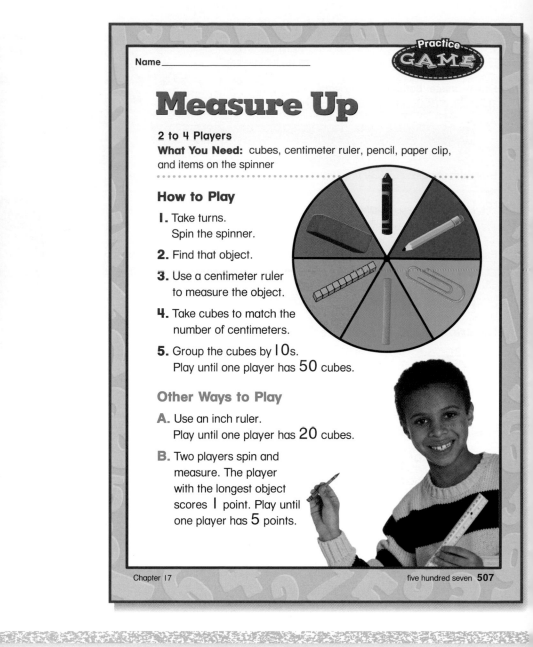

1. Take turns.
Spin the spinner.

2. Find that object.

3. Use a centimeter ruler to measure the object.

4. Take cubes to match the number of centimeters.

5. Group the cubes by 10s.
Play until one player has 50 cubes.

Other Ways to Play

A. Use an inch ruler.
Play until one player has 20 cubes.

B. Two players spin and measure. The player with the longest object scores 1 point. Play until one player has 5 points.

Literature Connection

Reread the unit poem *One Inch Tall* from **Where the Sidewalk Ends** by Shel Silverstein. Have children show an inch using their thumb and forefingers. Then, together brainstorm a list of things that are shorter than, about the same as, or just slightly longer than an inch. Then use the objects in sentences that tell how you would use each thing if you were only one inch tall.

Examples:

• If I were only 1 inch tall, I would use a stack of 3 pennies as a dinner table.

• If I were only 1 inch tall, I would use a mushroom as a beach umbrella.

• If I were only 1 inch tall, I would use a light switch as a lounge chair.

If time permits, create a class book with your sentences titled "If I Were Only 1 Inch Tall . . ."

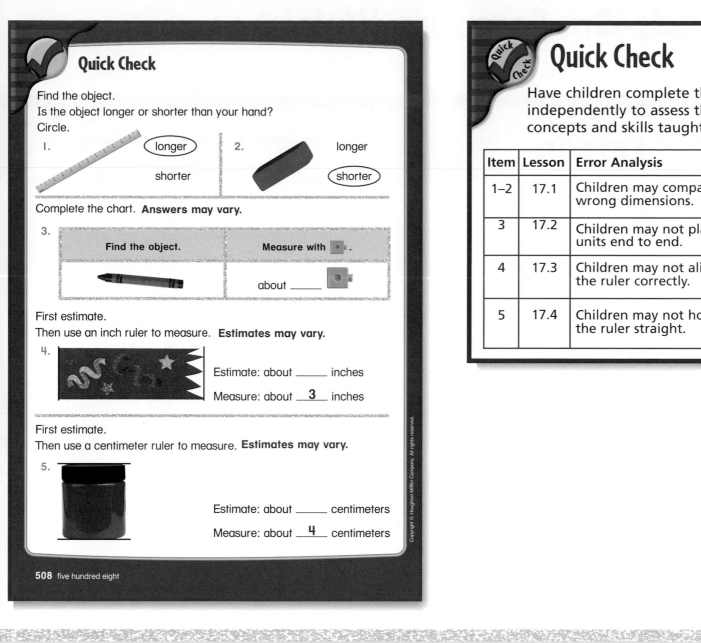

Quick Check

Find the object.
Is the object longer or shorter than your hand?
Circle.

1. (longer)   shorter

2. longer   (shorter)

Complete the chart. **Answers may vary.**

3.

Find the object.	Measure with .
	about _____

First estimate.
Then use an inch ruler to measure. **Estimates may vary.**

4.

Estimate: about _____ inches

Measure: about __3__ inches

First estimate.
Then use a centimeter ruler to measure. **Estimates may vary.**

5.

Estimate: about _____ centimeters

Measure: about __4__ centimeters

508 five hundred eight

Quick Check

Have children complete the Quick Check exercises independently to assess their understanding of concepts and skills taught in **Lessons 1–4**.

Item	Lesson	Error Analysis	Intervention
1–2	17.1	Children may compare wrong dimensions.	Reteach Resource 17.1 *Ways to Success* 17.1
3	17.2	Children may not place units end to end.	Reteach Resource 17.2 *Ways to Success* 17.2
4	17.3	Children may not align the ruler correctly.	Reteach Resource 17.3 *Ways to Success* 17.3
5	17.4	Children may not hold the ruler straight.	Reteach Resource 17.4 *Ways to Success* 17.4

Hands-On: Compare Weight

PLANNING THE LESSON

MATHEMATICS OBJECTIVE
Compare and order the weights of objects using nonstandard units and direct comparison.

Use Lesson Planner CD ROM for Lesson 17.5.

Daily Routines

Calendar
Point to today's date and ask children to count on 5 and say the date. Repeat with other dates.

Sunday	Monday	Tuesday	Wednesday	Thursday	Friday	Saturday
			1	2	3	4
5	6	7	8	9	10	11
12	13	14	15	16	17	18
19	20	21	22	23	24	25
26	27	28	29	30	31	

Vocabulary
Display a sheet of paper and a book. Ask children to hold up the Vocabulary Card for **heavier** when you pick up the heavier object (book), and the Vocabulary Card for **lighter** when you pick up the lighter object (paper). Pass the items around so students can compare how heavy and light the objects are.

Vocabulary Cards

Meeting North Carolina's Standards
2.01 For given objects:
- Select an attribute (length, capacity, mass) to measure (use non-standard units).
- Develop strategies to estimate size.
- Compare, using appropriate language, with respect to the attribute selected.

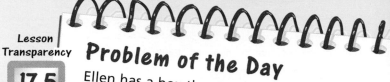

Lesson Transparency **17.5**

Problem of the Day
Ellen has a box that is 6 inches long. She has a blue book that is 8 inches long and a red book that is 5 inches long. Which book will fit in the box? (the red book)

Quick Review

$$\begin{array}{ccccc} 6 & 4 & 9 & 7 & 4 \\ +\,6 & +\,5 & +\,2 & +\,3 & +\,8 \\ \hline (12) & (9) & (11) & (10) & (12) \end{array}$$

Lesson Quiz
Number the objects in order from lightest to heaviest.

(2)   (1)   (3)

LEVELED PRACTICE

RETEACH 17.5

Name _____ Date _____   Reteach 17.5

Activity: Compare Weight

You can compare the weight of objects.
Use a balance scale to find which is heavier and which is lighter.

heavier   lighter

Find the objects. Estimate.
Which feels heavier? Which feels lighter?
Measure. Use a balance scale.   **Possible answers shown.**
Circle which is heavier.

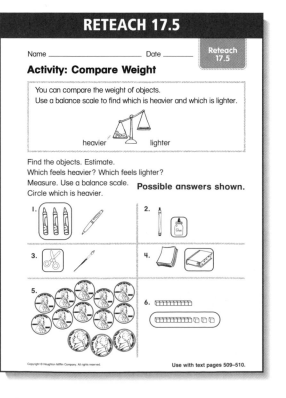

1. 2. 3. 4. 5. 6.

Use with text pages 509–510.

PRACTICE 17.5

Name _____ Date _____   Practice 17.5

Compare Weight

Choose a unit to measure the weight.
Write the measure. Circle the unit. **Answers may vary.**

Find the object.	Measure	Unit

1. [GLUE]   about _____   [clip] [box]

2. [calculator]   about _____   [clip] [box]

Number the objects in order from lightest to heaviest.

3. [book] [bus] [table]

    1   3   2

Test Prep

Fill in the ○ for the correct answer. NH means Not Here.

4. Kim has a book, a key, and a pencil in her backpack.
   Which is the heaviest?

   book ●   key ○   pencil ○   NH ○

Use with text pages 509–510.

ENRICHMENT 17.5

Name _____ Date _____   Enrichment 17.5

Heavier and Lighter

Read the question. Circle your answer.

1. Which is heavier than the pencil?

2. Which is lighter than the pencil?

3. Which is lighter than the math book?

4. Which is heavier than the stapler?

5. Which is heavier than the scissors?

6. Which is lighter than the pen?

Talk About It Of all the items shown, how could you prove the paper clip is the lightest?

I could compare the weight of the paper clip with other light items.

Use with text pages 509–510.

Practice Workbook Page 118

Reaching All Learners

Differentiated Instruction

English Learners

Children will need to understand the concepts of *heavier* and *lighter* as they compare and order the weight of objects. Use Worksheet 17.5 to help English-language learners develop understanding of these concepts.

Inclusion
KINESTHETIC, TACTILE

Materials: *balance scale, paper clip, stapler*

- Relate the balance scale to a seesaw.
- Give the child a paper clip and a stapler. Let the child hold each object and say which is heavier or lighter. Then place the objects on the balance scale to see which end goes down. Explain that this is the heavier object.

Early Finishers
TACTILE, VISUAL

Materials: *6 objects*

- Provide 6 objects of different weights.
- Have children make a display by arranging the 6 items by weight from lightest to heaviest.
- Encourage children to use their displays to help classmates see which objects are heavier and lighter.

TECHNOLOGY

Spiral Review

Create **customized** spiral review worksheets for individual students using the *Ways to Assess* CD-ROM.

Lesson Planner

You can customize your teaching plan or meet your curriculum requirements with the **Lesson Planner CD-ROM**.

Education Place

Recommends that parents visit **Education Place** at **eduplace.com/parents/mw/** for parent support activities.

Science Connection

Have children cut out pictures of animals that might be pets. Point out that different animals weigh different amounts. Help children arrange them from heaviest to lightest, using their own experience with pets as a guide.

MATH CENTER

Cross-Curricular Activity

As you use this activity to relate the mathematics of this lesson to another curriculum area, children will see how math can help them with other subjects.

PROBLEM SOLVING 17.5

Name _____ Date _____ | Problem Solving 17.5

Activity: Compare Weight

Read each problem.
Circle your answer.

Draw or write here.

The ⬛ is heavier than the ⧗.
The ⬛ is heavier than the ⬛.

Which object is the lightest?

I can find the objects.
I can hold each one.
I am sure the ⧗ is the lightest.

1. The ⬛ is lighter than the ⬛. The ß is lighter than the ⬛.

Which object is the heaviest?

Children might draw the objects in order of their weight.

2. The ⬛ is heavier than the ☾. The ⬛ is heavier than the ⬛.

Which object is the lightest?

Children might draw the objects in order of their weight.

Copyright © Houghton Mifflin Company. All rights reserved.

Use with text pages 509–510.

HOMEWORK 17.5

Name _____ Date _____ | Homework 17.5

Compare Weight

Objects may have different weights. A feather is lighter than a rock. A rock is heavier than a feather.

Find a tissue and a can of food. Circle the answer to the question.

1. Which feels heavier?   2. Which feels lighter?

Circle the heavier object.

3.   4.

Circle the lighter object.

5.   6.

7. Place three objects on a table. Order them from lightest to heaviest.

Write here.
1. _____
2. _____
3. _____

Answers will vary.

Copyright © Houghton Mifflin Company. All rights reserved.

Use with text pages 509–510.

ENGLISH LEARNERS 17.5

Name _____ Date _____ | English Learners 17.5

Compare Weight

heavier   lighter

heavier   lighter

Which word above best describes the weight of each item?

1.
_____ lighter   _____ heavier

2.
_____ lighter   _____ heavier

3.
_____ heavier   _____ lighter

To the Teacher: Use the example at the top of the page to help children understand the concepts of *heavier* and *lighter*. Then have children write *heavier* or *lighter* to describe the objects in each pair.

Copyright © Houghton Mifflin Company. All rights reserved.

Use with text pages 509–510.

Homework Workbook Page 118

TEACHING LESSON 17.5

LESSON ORGANIZER

Objective Compare and order the weights of objects using nonstandard units and direct comparison.

Resources Reteach, Practice, Enrichment, Problem Solving, Homework, English Learners, Transparencies, Math Center.

Materials Balance scale, cubes, paper clips, paper bags

Activity

Warm-Up Activity
Modeling Sorting by Weight

| **iii** Small Group | 🕐 5–10 minutes | Visual, Tactile |

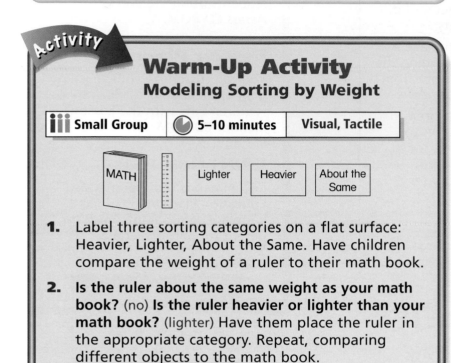

1. Label three sorting categories on a flat surface: Heavier, Lighter, About the Same. Have children compare the weight of a ruler to their math book.

2. **Is the ruler about the same weight as your math book?** (no) **Is the ruler heavier or lighter than your math book?** (lighter) Have them place the ruler in the appropriate category. Repeat, comparing different objects to the math book.

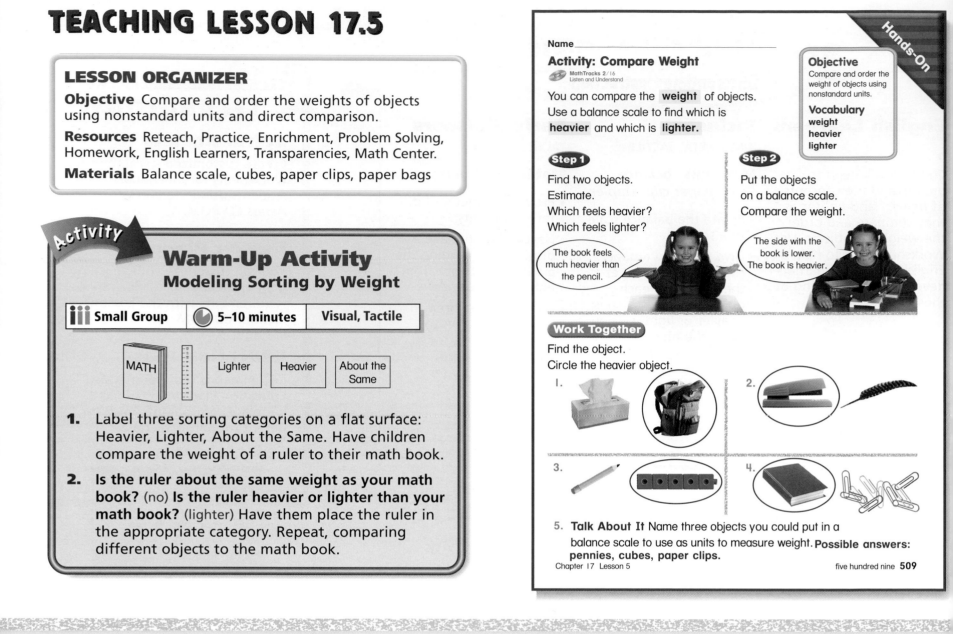

Name_____

Activity: Compare Weight
MathTracks 2/16
Listen and Understand

You can compare the **weight** of objects. Use a balance scale to find which is **heavier** and which is **lighter**.

Objective
Compare and order the weight of objects using nonstandard units.

Vocabulary
weight
heavier
lighter

Step 1
Find two objects. Estimate. Which feels heavier? Which feels lighter?

The book feels much heavier than the pencil.

Step 2
Put the objects on a balance scale. Compare the weight.

The side with the book is lower. The book is heavier.

Work Together
Find the object. Circle the heavier object.

1.
2.
3.
4.

5. **Talk About It** Name three objects you could put in a balance scale to use as units to measure weight. **Possible answers: pennies, cubes, paper clips.**

Chapter 17 Lesson 5   five hundred nine **509**

---

1 Introduce
Activity
Discuss Comparing Weight

| **iiii** Whole Group | 🕐 10–15 minutes | Visual, Auditory |

Materials: *balance scale, cubes, classroom objects*

1. Display the balance scale. Explain that you can use it to find how much an object weighs. You can also use a balance scale to compare the weight of objects.

2. Put a board eraser in one pan and a cube in the other pan of the balance. **Compare the weight. What happened to the balance?** (The eraser side went down.) **Which object is heavier?** (eraser) **Which is lighter?** (cube)

3. Now find out how much the eraser weighs in cubes. Have a volunteer add cubes until the pans are balanced. Have children count the cubes as they are added. **How many cubes does the eraser weigh?**

4. Repeat using various classroom objects.

2 Develop

Guided Learning

Teaching Example Read the objective and vocabulary with children. Point out to students that one way to estimate which object is heavier is to hold one in each hand. Remind them that on the balance scale, the heavier side is down or lower and the lighter side is up or higher.

Work Together

Have small groups of children follow the activity steps to complete **Exercises 1–4** as you observe. **Was your estimate always right?** Give children the opportunity to answer the **Talk About It** question in **Exercise 5**. Discuss their responses with the class.

Next, show each group how to use a balance to find weight. Place an object on one pan of a balance, then add units (cubes or clips) one at a time onto the other pan until they balance. Then have each group work together to complete **Exercises 6** and **7** on page 510 as you observe.

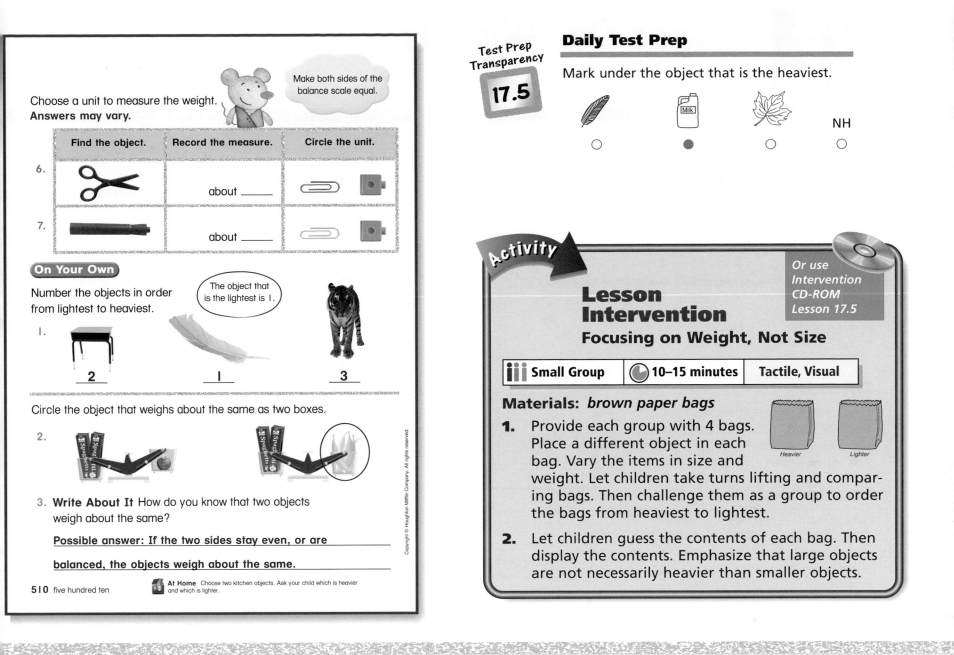

Choose a unit to measure the weight.
Answers may vary.

Make both sides of the balance scale equal.

Find the object.	Record the measure.	Circle the unit.
6. ✂	about _____	📎 🔲
7. ▬	about _____	📎 🔲

On Your Own

Number the objects in order from lightest to heaviest.

The object that is the lightest is 1.

1.

    2   1   3

Circle the object that weighs about the same as two boxes.

2.

3. **Write About It** How do you know that two objects weigh about the same?

Possible answer: If the two sides stay even, or are

balanced, the objects weigh about the same.

510 five hundred ten

At Home Choose two kitchen objects. Ask your child which is heavier and which is lighter.

Test Prep
Transparency

17.5

Daily Test Prep

Mark under the object that is the heaviest.

🪶   🥛 Milk   🍁   NH

○   ●   ○   ○

Activity

Or use Intervention CD-ROM Lesson 17.5

Lesson Intervention

Focusing on Weight, Not Size

👥 Small Group	🕐 10–15 minutes	Tactile, Visual

Materials: *brown paper bags*

Heavier   Lighter

1. Provide each group with 4 bags. Place a different object in each bag. Vary the items in size and weight. Let children take turns lifting and comparing bags. Then challenge them as a group to order the bags from heaviest to lightest.

2. Let children guess the contents of each bag. Then display the contents. Emphasize that large objects are not necessarily heavier than smaller objects.

---

③ Practice

On Your Own

Children complete **Exercises 1–3** independently. Invite volunteers to read their responses to the **Write About It** question and discuss the responses with the class. Be sure that students know how to order objects using 1, 2, 3 starting with the lightest object.

Common Error

Confusing the Position of Pans on a Balance
Have children act as a balance to feel the weight of 2 objects and then compare the objects on a balance.

④ Assess and Close

- **Which object is lighter on a balance scale, the lower object or the higher object?** (higher)
- **To weigh an object in cubes, you add cubes to one pan of the balance scale. When do you stop adding cubes?** (when both pans are equal or level)

✏ Keeping a Journal

Draw a line down the middle of your paper. Label one side *heavier* and the other side *lighter*.

Compare the weight of two objects.

Draw pictures to show your results.

Hands-On: Pounds

Lesson 17.6

PLANNING THE LESSON

MATHEMATICS OBJECTIVE
Compare and order the weight of an object to 1 pound by direct comparison.

Use Lesson Planner CD-ROM for Lesson 17.6.

Daily Routines

Calendar
Choose a date on the calendar and have children count back 2 from the number. Continue with other dates and numbers to count back.

Sunday	Monday	Tuesday	Wednesday	Thursday	Friday	Saturday
			1	2	3	4
5	6	7	8	9	10	11
12	13	14	15	16	17	18
19	20	21	22	23	24	25
26	27	28	29	30	31	

Vocabulary
Pass around a package of pasta and other familiar objects that weigh about 1 pound. Tell children that the objects weigh about 1 **pound**. As children hold the package, have them state that it weighs about 1 pound.

Vocabulary Cards

Meeting North Carolina's Standards
Prepare for Grade 3 Standard 2.02 Estimate and measure using appropriate units.

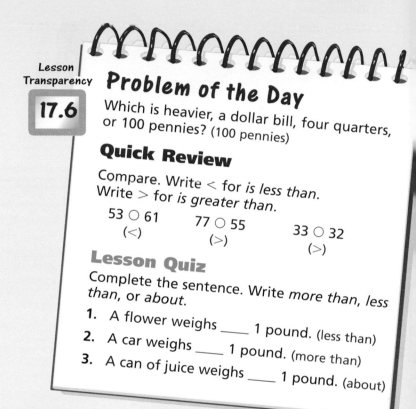

Lesson Transparency 17.6

Problem of the Day
Which is heavier, a dollar bill, four quarters, or 100 pennies? (100 pennies)

Quick Review
Compare. Write < for *is less than.* Write > for *is greater than.*

53 ○ 61   77 ○ 55   33 ○ 32
(<)   (>)   (>)

Lesson Quiz
Complete the sentence. Write *more than, less than,* or *about.*

1. A flower weighs ____ 1 pound. (less than)
2. A car weighs ____ 1 pound. (more than)
3. A can of juice weighs ____ 1 pound. (about)

LEVELED PRACTICE

RETEACH 17.6

Name _____ Date _____ **Reteach 17.6**

Pounds

You can measure weight in pounds.

less than 1 pound   about 1 pound   more than 1 pound

Find the object.
Put the object and a 1-pound measure on a balance scale.
Circle the weight.

Object			
1.	less than 1 pound	about 1 pound	more than 1 pound
2.	less than 1 pound	**about 1 pound**	more than 1 pound
3.	less than 1 pound	about 1 pound	more than 1 pound
4.	less than 1 pound	about 1 pound	**more than 1 pound**

Copyright © Houghton Mifflin Company. All rights reserved.   Use with text pages 511–512.

PRACTICE 17.6

Name _____ Date _____ **Practice 17.6**

Activity: Pounds
Circle.

Use ○ Red if the object weighs more than 1 pound.

Use ○ Blue if the object weighs less than 1 pound.

1.

red   blue   blue   red   blue   blue   red

Test Prep

Fill in the ○ for the correct answer. NH means Not Here.

2. Clare goes shopping.
Which item weighs about 1 pound?

DOG FOOD   NH

○   ○   ●   ○

Copyright © Houghton Mifflin Company. All rights reserved.   Use with text pages 511–512.

ENRICHMENT 17.6

Name _____ Date _____ **Enrichment 17.6**

All About Pounds

Estimate the weight of each object shown.
Circle your answer.

1.
less than a pound
about a pound
more than a pound

2.
less than a pound
about a pound
more than a pound

3.
less than a pound
about a pound
more than a pound

4.
less than a pound
about a pound
more than a pound

5.
less than a pound
about a pound
more than a pound

6.
less than a pound
about a pound
more than a pound

Talk About It What is your favorite food that weighs about a pound?
Answers will vary.

Copyright © Houghton Mifflin Company. All rights reserved.   Use with text pages 511–512.

Practice Workbook Page 119

Reaching All Learners
Differentiated Instruction

English Learners

Children will need to understand the terms *less than* and *more than* when they compare and order objects by weight. Use Worksheet 17.6 to develop English-language learners' ability to understand and use these terms.

Special Needs
VISUAL, TACTILE

Materials: *1-pound weight or object, balance scale*

- Tell the child that a pound is a unit used to measure weight.
- Let the child hold a 1-pound weight or object in one hand and an object in the other and estimate if the object is heavier or lighter than 1 pound. Place the object and weight on the balance to compare.

Early Finishers
TACTILE, VISUAL

Materials: *1-pound weights or objects, balance scale*

- Have children work in pairs.
- Guide children to use a balance scale and 1-pound weights or objects to determine the weight of objects to the nearest pound.

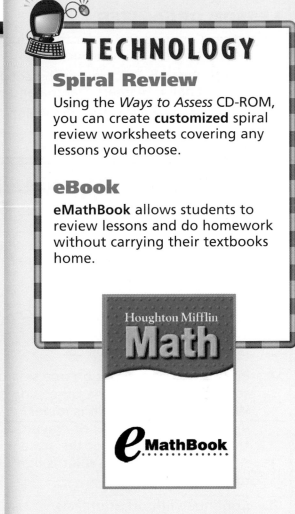

TECHNOLOGY

Spiral Review

Using the *Ways to Assess* CD-ROM, you can create **customized** spiral review worksheets covering any lessons you choose.

eBook

eMathBook allows students to review lessons and do homework without carrying their textbooks home.

Houghton Mifflin
Math

e **MathBook**

Music Connection

Discuss the size and weight of instruments found in bands. A tuba weighs about 15 pounds, a gong about 25 pounds, and a trumpet about 3 pounds. Arrange the instruments in order from lightest to heaviest.

MATH CENTER

Vocabulary Activity

This vocabulary-building activity helps children understand and remember new words. Encourage children to use the words in math discussion.

PROBLEM SOLVING 17.6

Name _____ Date _____ Problem Solving 17.6

Activity: Pounds

Read. Draw to solve.

Seth says he can think of 3 things that weigh less than 1 pound.

Draw here.

What are some things Seth might think of?

1. Mae says she can think of 3 things that weigh about 1 pound.

What are some things Mae might think of?

2. Ian says he can think of 3 things that weigh more than 1 pound.

What are some things Ian might think of?

Use with text pages 511–512.

HOMEWORK 17.6

Name _____ Date _____ Homework 17.6

Pounds

You can measure weight in pounds.

Circle the objects that weigh more than 1 pound.

1. 2.

Circle the objects that weigh less than 1 pound.

3. 4.

5. Look around your bedroom. Name an object less than 1 pound, an object about 1 pound, and an object more than 1 pound. Order the objects from lightest to heaviest.

Write here.

1. _____
2. _____
3. _____

Answers will vary.

Use with text pages 511–512.

Homework Workbook Page 119

ENGLISH LEARNERS 17.6

Name _____ Date _____ English Learners 17.6

Pounds

less than 5   5   more than 5

Circle the correct words.

1. less than 10 more than 10   2. less than 10 more than 10

3. less than 10 more than 10   4. less than 10 more than 10

To the Teacher: Use the examples at the top of the page to help children understand the terms *less than* and *more than*. Then read the labels with children and have them circle the label that describes each set of objects.

Use with text pages 511–512.

TEACHING LESSON 17.6

LESSON ORGANIZER

Objective Compare and order the weight of an object to 1 pound by direct comparison.

Resources Reteach, Practice, Enrichment, Problem Solving, Homework, English Learners, Transparencies, Math Center

Materials Balance scale, 1-pound weight or object

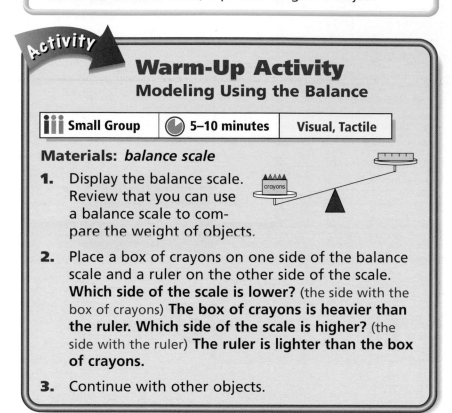

Warm-Up Activity
Modeling Using the Balance

iii Small Group	⏱ 5–10 minutes	Visual, Tactile

Materials: *balance scale*

1. Display the balance scale. Review that you can use a balance scale to compare the weight of objects.

2. Place a box of crayons on one side of the balance scale and a ruler on the other side of the scale. **Which side of the scale is lower?** (the side with the box of crayons) **The box of crayons is heavier than the ruler. Which side of the scale is higher?** (the side with the ruler) **The ruler is lighter than the box of crayons.**

3. Continue with other objects.

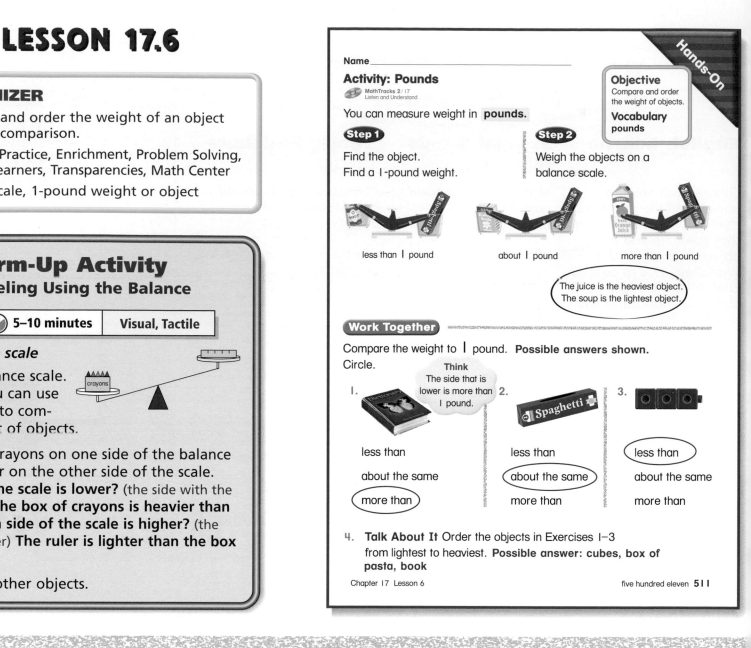

Name_____

Activity: Pounds

MathTracks 2/17
Listen and Understand

You can measure weight in **pounds.**

Objective
Compare and order the weight of objects.

Vocabulary
pounds

Step 1
Find the object.
Find a 1-pound weight.

Step 2
Weigh the objects on a balance scale.

less than 1 pound   about 1 pound   more than 1 pound

The juice is the heaviest object.
The soup is the lightest object.

Work Together

Compare the weight to 1 pound. **Possible answers shown.**
Circle.

Think The side that is lower is more than 1 pound.

1. less than / **about the same** / **more than**

2. less than / **about the same** / more than

3. less than / about the same / more than

4. **Talk About It** Order the objects in Exercises 1–3 from lightest to heaviest. **Possible answer: cubes, box of pasta, book**

Chapter 17 Lesson 6   five hundred eleven **511**

1 Introduce
Discuss Pounds

iiii Whole Group	⏱ 10–15 minutes	Visual, Auditory

Materials: *1-pound weight or object, balance scale*

1. Display a 1-pound weight or object. Tell children that it weighs 1 pound. Pass the weight around and let each child hold it. Then put the weight in one of the balance pans. **What happened when I put the weight in the pan?** (The pan lowered.) Tell children that you can put an object in the other pan to find out whether it weighs more than, less than, or about the same as the pound.

2. Have a volunteer place an object in the empty pan. **Does the object weigh more than, less than, or about 1 pound?**

3. Continue in the same manner with other objects.

2 Develop

Guided Learning

Teaching Example Read the objective and vocabulary with children. Point out that the box of spaghetti weighs about 1 pound and can be used to estimate weight. Guide them through each example, explaining how the position of the pans on the balance relates to the comparison of weight.

Work Together

Guide children through the activity steps as you complete **Exercise 1** together. Then have small groups of children follow the steps to complete **Exercises 2** and **3** as you observe. Give children the opportunity to answer the **Talk About It** question in **Exercise 4**. Then discuss their responses with the class. If all the objects are available children can hold the objects to estimate and compare their weights.

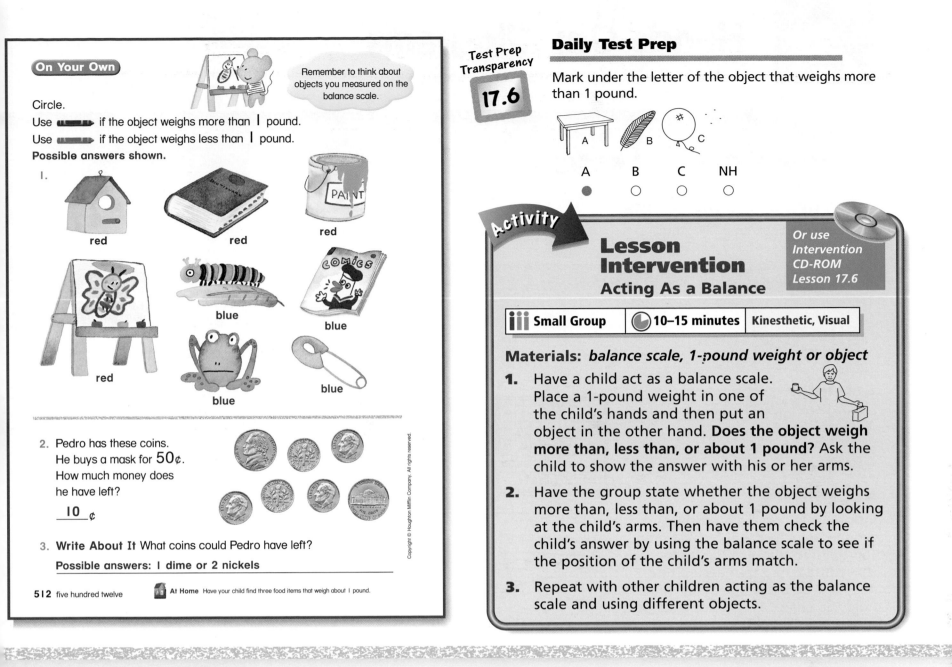

On Your Own

Circle.

Use ▬▬ if the object weighs more than 1 pound.
Use ▬▬ if the object weighs less than 1 pound.

Possible answers shown.

1.

red red red

red blue blue

blue blue

Remember to think about objects you measured on the balance scale.

2. Pedro has these coins.
He buys a mask for 50¢.
How much money does he have left?

___10___ ¢

3. **Write About It** What coins could Pedro have left?

Possible answers: 1 dime or 2 nickels

512 five hundred twelve

At Home Have your child find three food items that weigh about 1 pound.

Daily Test Prep

Mark under the letter of the object that weighs more than 1 pound.

A   B   C

A ●   B ○   C ○   NH ○

Activity

Lesson Intervention

Acting As a Balance

Or use Intervention CD-ROM Lesson 17.6

| 👥 Small Group | 🕐 10–15 minutes | Kinesthetic, Visual |

Materials: *balance scale, 1-pound weight or object*

1. Have a child act as a balance scale. Place a 1-pound weight in one of the child's hands and then put an object in the other hand. **Does the object weigh more than, less than, or about 1 pound?** Ask the child to show the answer with his or her arms.

2. Have the group state whether the object weighs more than, less than, or about 1 pound by looking at the child's arms. Then have them check the child's answer by using the balance scale to see if the position of the child's arms match.

3. Repeat with other children acting as the balance scale and using different objects.

3 Practice

On Your Own

Children complete **Exercise 1** independently. Have objects that weigh about 1 pound available for students to use.

After children complete **Exercise 2**, call on volunteers to share their solutions. Have children complete the **Write About It** question in **Exercise 3**. Ask volunteers to share their responses with the class. Discuss these responses.

Common Error

Relating Weight to an Object's Size

Demonstrate that size and weight are unrelated by having children hold a golf ball and a blown-up balloon.

4 Assess and Close

- **Name an object that weighs more than a pound.**
- **Name an object that weighs less than a pound.**
- **List the following objects in order from lightest to heaviest: a desk, a pencil, a 1-pound weight.** (a pencil, a 1-pound weight, a desk)

Keeping a Journal

Draw pictures or write the names of objects that weigh about 1 pound.

Hands-On: Kilograms

Lesson 17.7

PLANNING THE LESSON

MATHEMATICS OBJECTIVE
Compare objects to a kilogram.

Use Lesson Planner CD-ROM for Lesson 17.7.

Meeting North Carolina's Standards
Prepare for Grade 3 Standard 2.02 Estimate and measure using appropriate units.

Daily Routines

Calendar
Point to a 5 on the calendar. Ask children to count by 5s on the calendar. Then challenge them to count as high as they can by 5s.

Vocabulary
Introduce **kilogram** by passing around an object that is 1-kilogram. Tell children that a kilogram is a unit that can be used to measure how heavy an object is. Have the children hold the object as they say the name of the unit, kilogram.

Vocabulary Cards

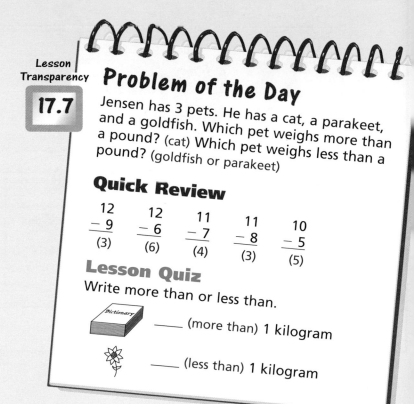

Lesson Transparency **17.7**

Problem of the Day
Jensen has 3 pets. He has a cat, a parakeet, and a goldfish. Which pet weighs more than a pound? (cat) Which pet weighs less than a pound? (goldfish or parakeet)

Quick Review
$$12 - 9 \quad (3)$$
$$12 - 6 \quad (6)$$
$$11 - 7 \quad (4)$$
$$11 - 8 \quad (3)$$
$$10 - 5 \quad (5)$$

Lesson Quiz
Write more than or less than.

_____ (more than) 1 kilogram

_____ (less than) 1 kilogram

LEVELED PRACTICE

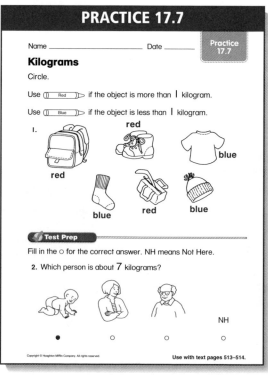

RETEACH 17.7

Name _____ Date _____
Reteach 17.7

Activity: Kilograms

You can measure how heavy an object is in kilograms.

less than 1 kilogram about 1 kilogram more than 1 kilogram

Find the object.
Put the object and a 1-kilogram measure on a balance scale.
Circle the weight. **Answers may vary.**

Object			
1.	less than 1 kilogram	about 1 kilogram	more than 1 kilogram
2.	less than 1 kilogram	about 1 kilogram	more than 1 kilogram
3.	less than 1 kilogram	about 1 kilogram	more than 1 kilogram
4.	less than 1 kilogram	about 1 kilogram	more than 1 kilogram

Copyright © Houghton Mifflin Company. All rights reserved.
Use with text pages 513–514.

PRACTICE 17.7

Name _____ Date _____
Practice 17.7

Kilograms

Circle.

Use ( ) Red if the object is more than 1 kilogram.

Use ( ) Blue if the object is less than 1 kilogram.

1.
red
blue
red
blue
blue

Test Prep

Fill in the ○ for the correct answer. NH means Not Here.

2. Which person is about 7 kilograms?

●   ○   ○   ○ NH

Copyright © Houghton Mifflin Company. All rights reserved.
Use with text pages 513–514.

ENRICHMENT 17.7

Name _____ Date _____
Enrichment 17.7

All About Kilograms

Estimate how heavy each object is.
Circle your answer.

1. less than a kilogram / about a kilogram / (more than a kilogram)
2. less than a kilogram / (about a kilogram) / more than a kilogram
3. (less than a kilogram) / about a kilogram / more than a kilogram
4. less than a kilogram / about a kilogram / (more than a kilogram)
5. less than a kilogram / (about a kilogram) / more than a kilogram
6. (less than a kilogram) / about a kilogram / more than a kilogram

Talk About It Would you use a kilogram to measure how heavy 20 paper clips are? Why? **No, because you use kilograms for heavy objects.**

Copyright © Houghton Mifflin Company. All rights reserved.
Use with text pages 513–514.

Practice Workbook Page 120

Reaching All Learners

Differentiated Instruction

English Learners

Worksheet 17.7 develops children's understanding of the word *under*. English-language learners will need to understand this term to follow directions as they solve problems.

Special Needs
VISUAL, TACTILE

Materials: *balance scale, 1-kilogram object*

- Review with the child that a kilogram is a unit used to measure how heavy an object is.

- Let the child hold a 1-kilogram object in one hand and an object in the other hand and estimate whether the object is heavier or lighter than 1 kilogram. Use a balance to compare.

Early Finishers
TACTILE, VISUAL

Materials: *balance scale, 1-kilogram objects*

- Have children work in pairs to use the balance scale to measure classroom objects in kilograms.

- Have one child place an object on one pan of the balance. Then have the child add 1-kilogram objects to the other side until the balance is level.

TECHNOLOGY

Spiral Review

To reinforce skills on lessons taught earlier, create **customized** spiral review worksheets using the *Ways to Assess* CD-ROM.

Lesson Planner

Use the **Lesson Planner CD-ROM** to see how objectives for this chapter are correlated to standards.

Education Place

Visit **Data Place** at **eduplace.com/dataplace/** to take a survey and see graphs of the results.

Literature Connection

Read *Just a Little Bit* by Ann Tompert. Discuss how the seesaw in the story is like a balance. In order to get the side with the heavier object (the elephant) to go up, you need to add more weight to the other side.

MATH CENTER

Vocabulary Activity

This vocabulary-building activity helps children understand and remember new words. Encourage children to use the words in math discussion.

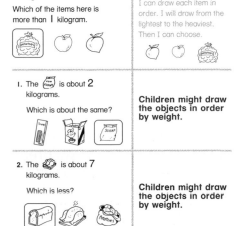

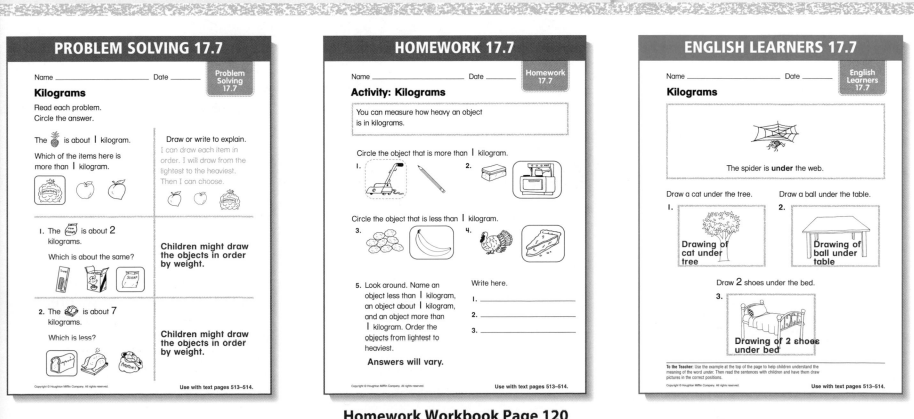

Homework Workbook Page 120

TEACHING LESSON 17.7

LESSON ORGANIZER

Objective Compare objects to a kilogram.

Resources Reteach, Practice, Enrichment, Problem Solving, Homework, English Learners, Transparencies, Math Center

Materials Cubes, paper bags, 1-kilogram object, balance scale, variety of objects

Activity

Warm-Up Activity
Modeling Heavier and Lighter

👥 Small Group	🕐 5–10 minutes	Visual, Tactile

Materials: *cubes, paper bags*

1. Prepare two bags with different numbers of cubes in each.

2. Then have a child close the bags and pass them around to the group. Have children lift the bags to estimate which bag is heavier and which bag is lighter.

3. Have the first child count the number of cubes in each bag and compare to the estimates. **Why is a bag with more cubes heavier than a bag with fewer cubes?** (Each cube weighs the same amount, so the more you have, the heavier the bag.)

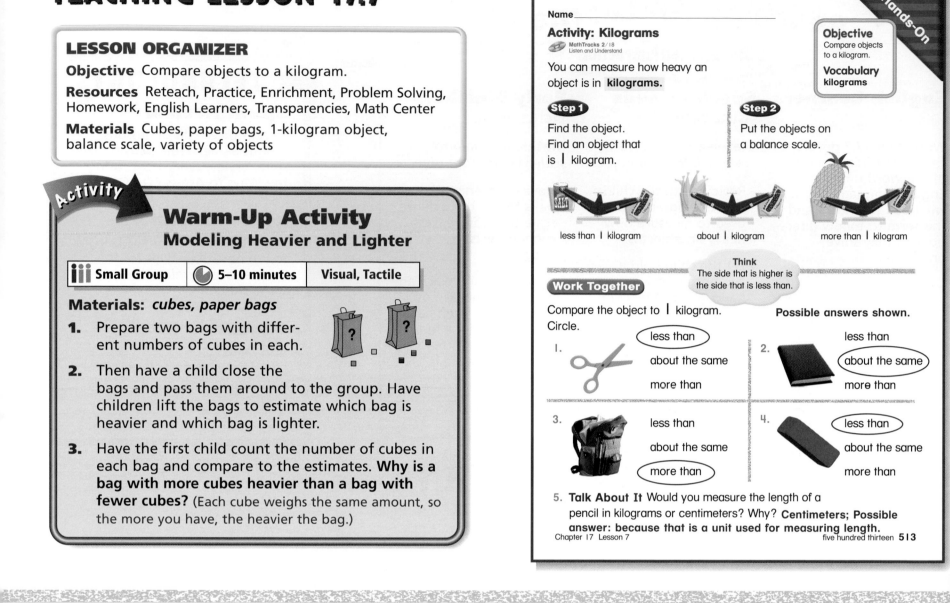

Name_____

Activity: Kilograms
MathTracks 2/18
Listen and Understand

You can measure how heavy an object is in **kilograms.**

Objective Compare objects to a kilogram.

Vocabulary kilograms

Step 1
Find the object. Find an object that is 1 kilogram.

Step 2
Put the objects on a balance scale.

less than 1 kilogram   about 1 kilogram   more than 1 kilogram

Think
The side that is higher is the side that is less than.

Work Together
Compare the object to 1 kilogram. Circle.

Possible answers shown.

1. (less than) / about the same / more than

2. less than / (about the same) / more than

3. less than / about the same / (more than)

4. (less than) / about the same / more than

5. **Talk About It** Would you measure the length of a pencil in kilograms or centimeters? Why? **Centimeters; Possible answer: because that is a unit used for measuring length.**

Chapter 17 Lesson 7   five hundred thirteen **513**

---

1 Introduce
Discuss Kilograms

👥 Whole Group	🕐 10–15 minutes	Visual, Auditory

Materials: *1-kilogram object, balance scale*

1. Display a 1-kilogram object that you will use as an estimate. Tell children you can measure how heavy an object is by using a kilogram as a unit. Pass the object around and let each child hold it. Then put it in the pan on one side of the balance. **What happened when I put the kilogram measure on the scale?** (The pan with the measure lowered.) Tell children that you can put an object in the pan on the other side to find out whether it is more than, less than, or about the same as 1 kilogram.

2. Continue with other objects.

2 Develop

Guided Learning

Teaching Example Read the objective and vocabulary with children. Guide them through each example, explaining how the position of the pans on the balance scale relates to the comparison. Point out that the bag of beans is about 1-kilogram and can be used to estimate.

You may want to avoid using *weight* when referring to measuring with kilograms, although children may use the term. The term *mass* will be introduced and used in grade 3.

Work Together

Guide children through the activity steps as you complete **Exercise 1** together. Then have small groups of children follow the steps to complete **Exercises 2–4** as you observe. Children may want to hold the objects to estimate. Give children the opportunity to answer the **Talk About It** question in **Exercise 5**. Then discuss their responses with the class.

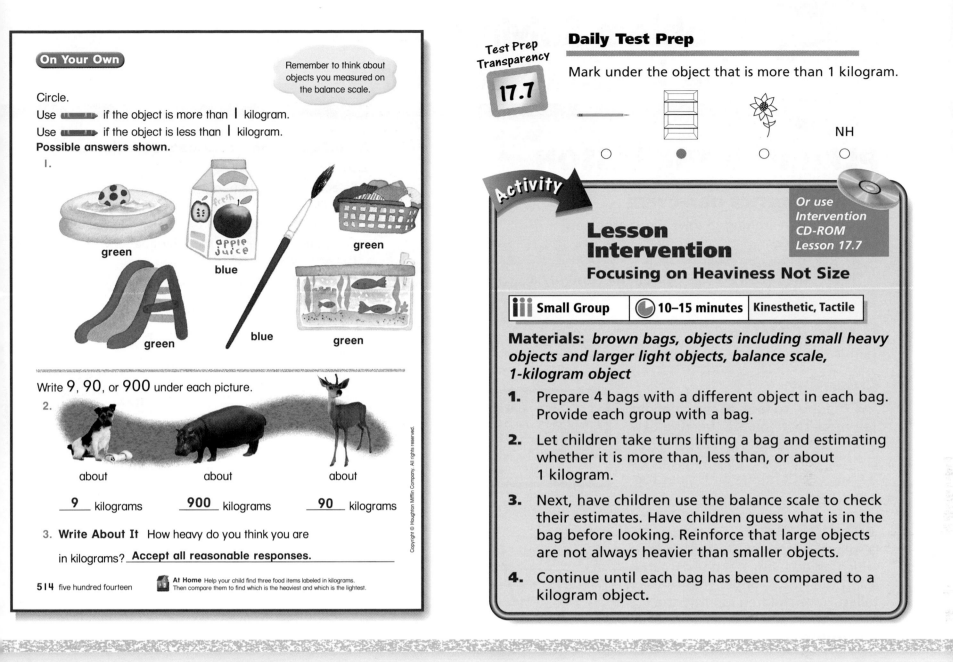

Daily Test Prep

Mark under the object that is more than 1 kilogram.

NH

○   ●   ○   ○

On Your Own

Remember to think about objects you measured on the balance scale.

Circle.

Use ▬▬▬ if the object is more than 1 kilogram.

Use ▬▬▬ if the object is less than 1 kilogram.

Possible answers shown.

1.

green   blue   green

green   blue   green

Write 9, 90, or 900 under each picture.

2.

about   about   about

<u>9</u> kilograms   <u>900</u> kilograms   <u>90</u> kilograms

3. **Write About It** How heavy do you think you are

in kilograms? **Accept all reasonable responses.**

514 five hundred fourteen

 **At Home** Help your child find three food items labeled in kilograms. Then compare them to find which is the heaviest and which is the lightest.

Activity

Lesson Intervention

Focusing on Heaviness Not Size

Or use Intervention CD-ROM Lesson 17.7

| Small Group | 10–15 minutes | Kinesthetic, Tactile |

Materials: *brown bags, objects including small heavy objects and larger light objects, balance scale, 1-kilogram object*

1. Prepare 4 bags with a different object in each bag. Provide each group with a bag.

2. Let children take turns lifting a bag and estimating whether it is more than, less than, or about 1 kilogram.

3. Next, have children use the balance scale to check their estimates. Have children guess what is in the bag before looking. Reinforce that large objects are not always heavier than smaller objects.

4. Continue until each bag has been compared to a kilogram object.

3 Practice

On Your Own

Children complete **Exercises 1–2** independently. Have objects that are about 1 kilogram available for students to use. When children are finished, invite volunteers to share their answers to the **Write About It** question in **Exercise 3**. Discuss the responses with the class.

Common Error

Thinking Objects Are Heavy Because They Are Large
Have children pick up a large empty cereal box and a full juice box. Have children tell you which is heavier.

4 Assess and Close

- If the sides of the balance are level, what does that mean? (One object is as heavy as the other.)
- Name an object that is more than 1 kilogram.
- Name an object that is less than 1 kilogram.

Keeping a Journal

Draw an object that is more than 1 kilogram. Draw an object that is less than 1 kilogram.

Problem Solving: Use Logical Reasoning

PLANNING THE LESSON

MATHEMATICS OBJECTIVE
Use logical reasoning to solve word problems.

Use Lesson Planner CD-ROM for Lesson 17.8.

Daily Routines

Calendar

Ask children to look at the calendar. Tell them that you are thinking of a day. It comes 2 days after Friday. It is 1 day before Monday. What day is it? (Sunday) Continue with clues for other days.

Sunday	Monday	Tuesday	Wednesday	Thursday	Friday	Saturday
			1	2	3	4
5	6	7	8	9	10	11
12	13	14	15	16	17	18
19	20	21	22	23	24	25
26	27	28	29	30	31	

Vocabulary

Display a picture or illustration in which objects in it can be compared using the words **longer**, **shorter**, and **taller**. Have children identify the *longer, shorter,* and *taller* objects in the picture.

Vocabulary Cards

Meeting North Carolina's Standards

2.01 For given objects:
- Select an attribute (length, capacity, mass) to measure (use non-standard units).
- Develop strategies to estimate size.
- Compare, using appropriate language, with respect to the attribute selected.

Lesson Transparency 17.8

Problem of the Day
There are 15 pears and apples on a plate. There is one more apple than pears. How many apples are on the plate? (8 apples)

Quick Review

$$\begin{array}{ccccc} 11 & 12 & 10 & 11 & 12 \\ -\ 9 & -\ 3 & -\ 7 & -\ 8 & -\ 8 \\ \hline (2) & (9) & (3) & (3) & (4) \end{array}$$

Lesson Quiz

1. It is longer than the black train. It is not the longest train. Which train matches the clues? (gray train)

2. It is shorter than the longest train. It is longer than the shortest train. Which train matches the clues? (gray train)

LEVELED PRACTICE

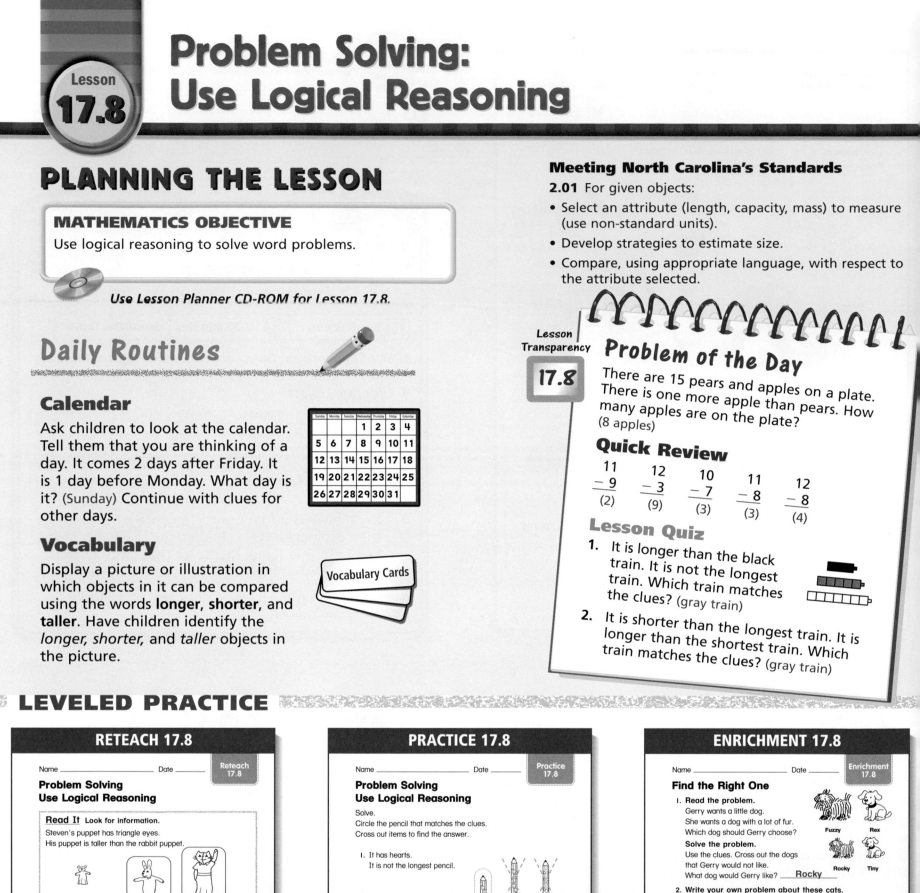

RETEACH 17.8

Name _____ Date _____ Reteach 17.8

Problem Solving
Use Logical Reasoning

Read It Look for information.
Steven's puppet has triangle eyes.
His puppet is taller than the rabbit puppet.

Picture It Here is a model of the problem.

Steven's Puppet	
First Clue	Triangle eyes
Second Clue	Taller than rabbit puppet

Solve It Use the model to solve the problem.

1. Read the first clue. Circle the puppets with triangle eyes.

2. Read the second clue. Underline the puppet that is taller than the rabbit puppet.

3. The puppet that is both circled and underlined is Steven's puppet. Steven has a ___cat___ puppet.

Use with text pages 515–516.

PRACTICE 17.8

Name _____ Date _____ Practice 17.8

Problem Solving
Use Logical Reasoning

Solve.
Circle the pencil that matches the clues.
Cross out items to find the answer.

1. It has hearts. It is not the longest pencil.

2. It is shorter than the dog pencil. It has birds.

3. It has stripes. It has an eraser.

Use with text pages 515–516.

ENRICHMENT 17.8

Name _____ Date _____ Enrichment 17.8

Find the Right One

1. Read the problem.
Gerry wants a little dog. She wants a dog with a lot of fur. Which dog should Gerry choose?

Fuzzy   Rex

Solve the problem.
Use the clues. Cross out the dogs that Gerry would not like.
What dog would Gerry like? ___Rocky___

Rocky   Tiny

2. Write your own problem about these cats.

Boots   Kitty   Lucky

_____

_____

Use clues in the problem to solve it. Write your answer.
Answers will vary.

3. Look back at the problem.
How can you check your answer?
Answers will vary.

Use with text pages 515–516.

Practice Workbook Page 121

Reaching All Learners
Differentiated Instruction

English Learners

In order to use logical reasoning to solve word problems, English-language learners will need to understand the meaning of the word *clue*. Use Worksheet 17.8 to develop an understanding of this word.

Inclusion
AUDITORY, TACTILE

- Use objects and present oral problems.
- For example, place a tissue box, a cube, and a milk carton on your desk. Give clues such as: *I am bigger than the cube and smaller than the tissue box. What am I?* (milk carton)
- Allow the child to remove the objects that do not match the clues. Have the child say the answer.

Gifted and Talented
AUDITORY, VISUAL

- Have children create word problems for pictures. For example: *It is shorter than the red one. It is not a pencil.*

- Children may solve each others problems.

TECHNOLOGY
Spiral Review

Help students remember skills they learned earlier by creating **customized** spiral review worksheets using the *Ways to Assess* CD-ROM.

Lesson Planner

You can use the **Lesson Planner CD-ROM** to create a report of the lessons and standards you have taught.

Intervention

Use the *Ways to Success* intervention software to support students who need more help in understanding the concepts and skills taught in this chapter.

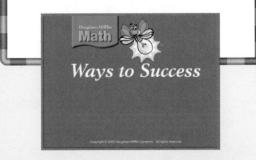

Social Studies Connection

Relate *fact* and *opinion* to newspaper reporting. Make statements about classroom objects. Have children decide whether it is a fact or an opinion. Examples: The desk has four legs. (fact) The reading corner rug is pretty. (opinion)

MATH CENTER

Number of the Week Activity

Display the Number of the Week to motivate children to use their problem-solving skills. The exercises cover topics across all math strands.

PROBLEM SOLVING 17.8

Name _____ Date _____ | Problem Solving 17.8

Use Logical Reasoning

Eddy can go swimming, to the zoo, or to the circus. It is too cold to swim. Eddy likes animals, but he is tired of going to the zoo. Where does Eddy go?

UNDERSTAND
| What do I know that can help me? | It is **too cold** to swim. Eddy is tired of the **zoo**. |

PLAN
| I could cross out the things Eddy won't do. Then I'll know where Eddy wants to go. | I **cross out swimming and the zoo** in the problem. |

SOLVE
| I know where Eddy goes. | **Eddy goes to the circus.** |

LOOK BACK
| How do I know my answer is correct? | I **can compare my answer with a classmate.** |

Use with text pages 515–516.

HOMEWORK 17.8

Name _____ Date _____ | Homework 17.8

Use Logical Reasoning

You can use clues to solve a problem.

Rick wants a new toy truck. It is smaller than the fire truck. It lifts dirt. Color the truck Rick wants.

Cross out the fire truck because Rick wants a smaller truck. Cross out the van because it does not lift dirt. Color the small truck that lifts dirt.

Solve. Color the object that matches the clues.

1. This truck has 4 wheels. It has a crane to pick up heavy boxes.

4 wheeled with crane

2. This truck is not the smallest truck. It has 8 wheels.

8 wheeled

Use with text pages 515–516.

ENGLISH LEARNERS 17.8

Name _____ Date _____ | English Learners 17.8

Use Logical Reasoning

| **Clues:** It has windows and doors. It is on a farm. Farm animals live in it. What is it? | |

Read the clues. Draw the answer.

1. **Clues:** It flies. It has wings. People can ride in it. What is it? | Drawing of an airplane

2. **Clues:** It has feathers. It swims. It says, "Quack." What is it? | Drawing of a duck

3. **Clues:** It has hands. It has numbers. It tells time. What is it? | Drawing of a clock

To the Teacher: Use the example at the top of the page to demonstrate the meaning of the word *clue*. Then read the clues with children and have them draw the answer to each riddle.

Use with text pages 515–516.

Homework Workbook Page 121

TEACHING LESSON 17.8

LESSON ORGANIZER

Objective Use logical reasoning to solve word problems.

Resources Reteach, Practice, Enrichment, Problem Solving, Homework, English Learners, Transparencies, Math Center

Materials Set of precut construction paper shapes (teacher-made), blank transparency

Activity
Warm-Up Activity
Modeling Visual Discrimination

| 👤👤👤 Small Group | 🕐 5 minutes | Auditory, Tactile |

Materials: *set of precut construction paper shapes (teacher-made)*

1. Prepare construction paper rectangles, triangles, squares, and circles in three colors (red, blue, yellow) and two sizes (large, small) for each child. Hold up the shapes one at a time. Have children hold up shapes exactly like yours. Have volunteers describe the shape, color, and size of the shape.

2. Then have children hold up shapes following directions such as: **Hold up a shape that is not round. Hold up a shape that is small. Hold up a shape that is red.**

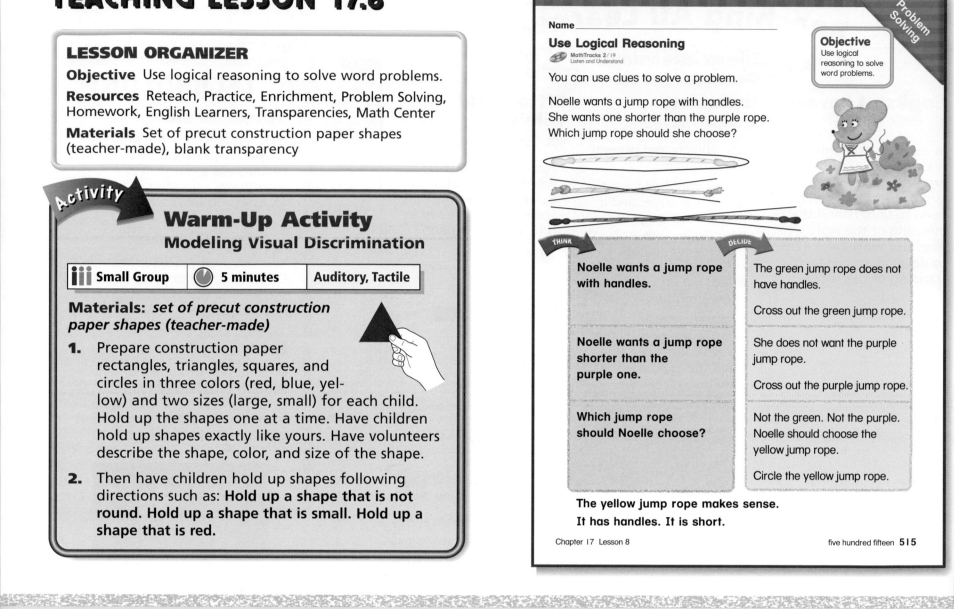

Name_____

Use Logical Reasoning
MathTracks 2/19
Listen and Understand

Objective
Use logical reasoning to solve word problems.

You can use clues to solve a problem.

Noelle wants a jump rope with handles.
She wants one shorter than the purple rope.
Which jump rope should she choose?

THINK / DECIDE

Noelle wants a jump rope with handles.	The green jump rope does not have handles. Cross out the green jump rope.
Noelle wants a jump rope shorter than the purple one.	She does not want the purple jump rope. Cross out the purple jump rope.
Which jump rope should Noelle choose?	Not the green. Not the purple. Noelle should choose the yellow jump rope. Circle the yellow jump rope.

The yellow jump rope makes sense.
It has handles. It is short.

Chapter 17 Lesson 8
five hundred fifteen **515**

---

1 Introduce
Activity
Discuss Logical Reasoning

| 👤👤👤👤 Whole Group | 🕐 10–15 minutes | Visual, Auditory |

Material: *blank transparency*

1. *Use reasoning to solve a problem.* Write 43, 33, 23, 11 on the transparency. Tell children to read the numbers.

2. Ask: **I am thinking of one of these numbers. Listen to the clues so you can decide which number.**
   - **It has the same digit in the ones places and the tens place.**
   - **It is 10 more than one of the other numbers. What is the number?** (33)

3. Guide children as they eliminate numbers based on each clue. Then compare the answer to the clues to determine if the answer is reasonable.

2 Develop

Guided Learning

Teaching Example Introduce the objective to the children. Then call on a volunteer to read the problem.

- Guide children through the decision-making process. Have children cross off each jump rope that does not match the clue given.

- **Does the jump rope that isn't crossed out match the clues?** (yes) Have children circle the jump rope that matches the clues.

- Have children look back at the original problem and compare their answer to the clues to determine if their answer is reasonable.

Guided Practice

Have children complete **Exercises 1** and **2** on page 516 as you observe.

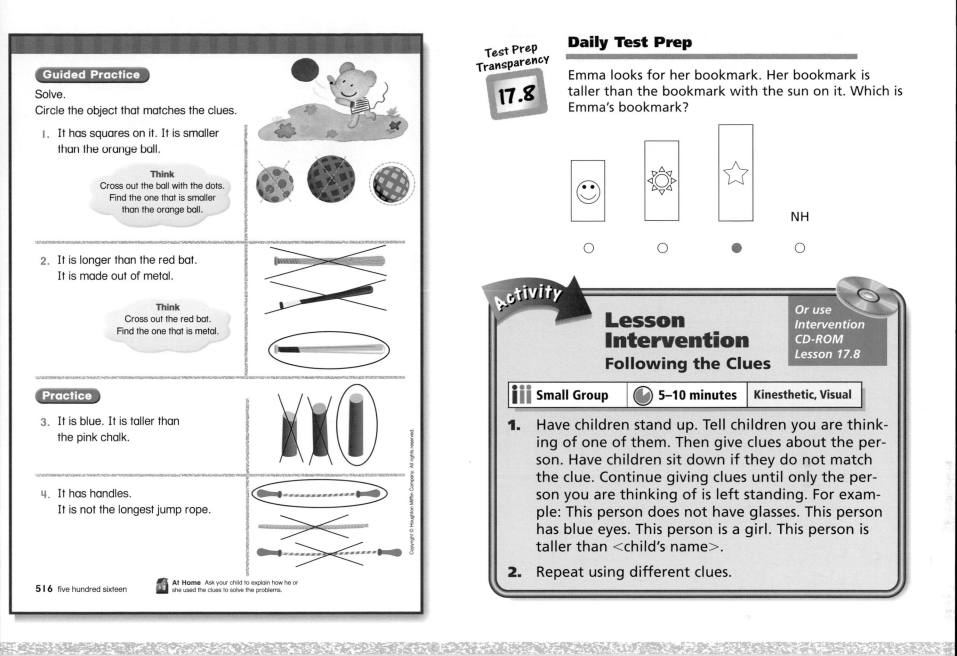

Guided Practice

Solve.
Circle the object that matches the clues.

1. It has squares on it. It is smaller than the orange ball.

   Think
   Cross out the ball with the dots.
   Find the one that is smaller than the orange ball.

2. It is longer than the red bat. It is made out of metal.

   Think
   Cross out the red bat.
   Find the one that is metal.

Practice

3. It is blue. It is taller than the pink chalk.

4. It has handles. It is not the longest jump rope.

516 five hundred sixteen

At Home Ask your child to explain how he or she used the clues to solve the problems.

Daily Test Prep

Emma looks for her bookmark. Her bookmark is taller than the bookmark with the sun on it. Which is Emma's bookmark?

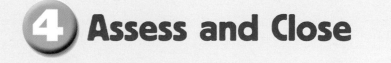

NH

○   ○   ●   ○

Activity

Lesson Intervention
Following the Clues

Or use Intervention CD-ROM Lesson 17.8

| iii Small Group | ⏱ 5–10 minutes | Kinesthetic, Visual |

1. Have children stand up. Tell children you are thinking of one of them. Then give clues about the person. Have children sit down if they do not match the clue. Continue giving clues until only the person you are thinking of is left standing. For example: This person does not have glasses. This person has blue eyes. This person is a girl. This person is taller than <child's name>.

2. Repeat using different clues.

---

③ Practice

Independent Practice

Children complete **Exercises 3–4** on page 516 independently. Remind students to cross out each object that does not match the given clues.

Common Error

Missing Clues
Remind children to look for describing words such as "shorter" or "longer" to help them identify clues.

④ Assess and Close

Display the following:
I am blue and small.
I have 4 sides.
I am not a square.
Who am I? (small blue rectangle)

Keeping a Journal

Draw a picture of your family. Write clues about yourself as you relate to the other family members. For example: I am taller than my sister, I am shorter than my brother. I am the only one with curly hair.

Quick Check

Have children complete the Quick Check exercises independently to assess their understanding of concepts and skills taught in **Lessons 5–8**.

Item	Lesson	Error Analysis	Intervention
1–2	17.5	Some children may confuse position of pans and weight.	Reteach Resource 17.5 *Ways to Success* 17.5
3	17.6	Children may relate weight to the size of the object.	Reteach Resource 17.6 *Ways to Success* 17.6
4	17.7	Some children may confuse the size of an object with the heaviness of the object.	Reteach Resource 17.7 *Ways to Success* 17.7
5	17.8	Some children may miss clues.	Reteach Resource 17.8 *Ways to Success* 17.8

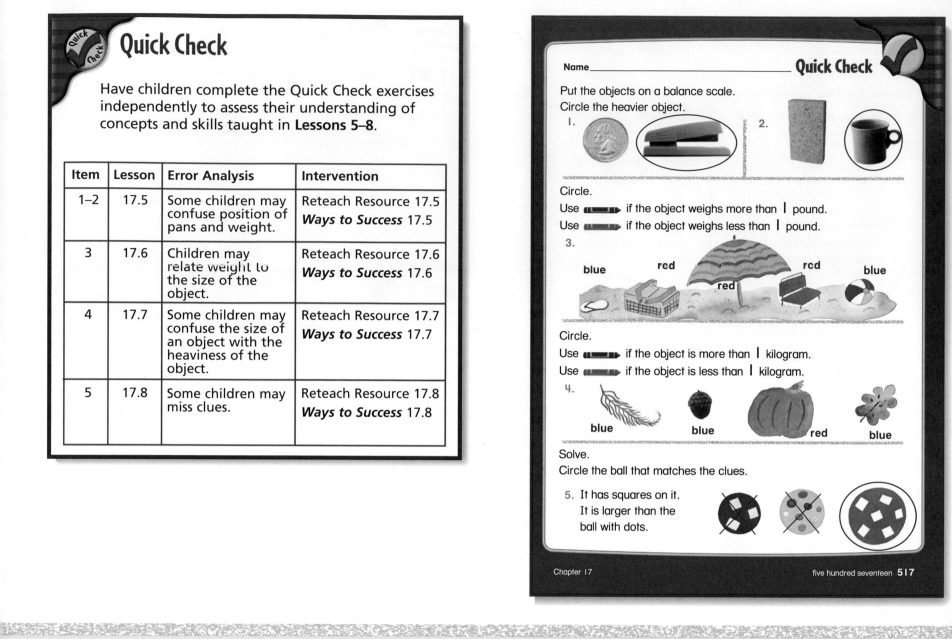

Name_____ **Quick Check**

Put the objects on a balance scale.
Circle the heavier object.

1.
2.

Circle.
Use ▬▬▶ if the object weighs more than 1 pound.
Use ▬▬▶ if the object weighs less than 1 pound.

3.

blue   red   red   blue
red

Circle.
Use ▬▬▶ if the object is more than 1 kilogram.
Use ▬▬▶ if the object is less than 1 kilogram.

4.

blue   blue   red   blue

Solve.
Circle the ball that matches the clues.

5. It has squares on it.
   It is larger than the ball with dots.

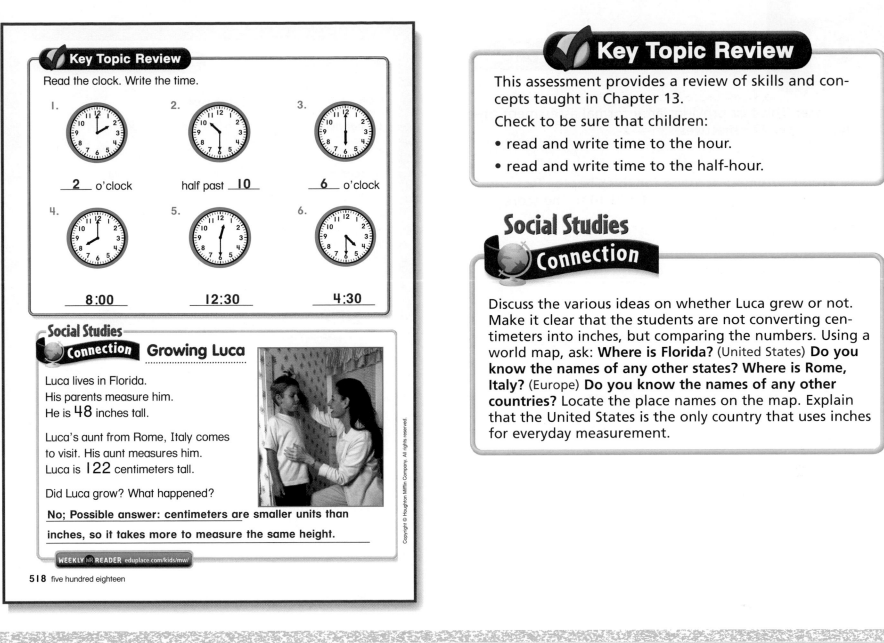

Key Topic Review

Read the clock. Write the time.

1. __2__ o'clock

2. half past __10__

3. __6__ o'clock

4. __8:00__

5. __12:30__

6. __4:30__

Social Studies Connection — Growing Luca

Luca lives in Florida.
His parents measure him.
He is 48 inches tall.

Luca's aunt from Rome, Italy comes
to visit. His aunt measures him.
Luca is 122 centimeters tall.

Did Luca grow? What happened?

**No; Possible answer: centimeters are smaller units than
inches, so it takes more to measure the same height.**

WEEKLY WR READER eduplace.com/kids/mw/

Key Topic Review

This assessment provides a review of skills and concepts taught in Chapter 13.

Check to be sure that children:

• read and write time to the hour.

• read and write time to the half-hour.

Social Studies Connection

Discuss the various ideas on whether Luca grew or not. Make it clear that the students are not converting centimeters into inches, but comparing the numbers. Using a world map, ask: **Where is Florida?** (United States) **Do you know the names of any other states? Where is Rome, Italy?** (Europe) **Do you know the names of any other countries?** Locate the place names on the map. Explain that the United States is the only country that uses inches for everyday measurement.

Chapter Review/Test

Purpose: This test provides an informal assessment of the Chapter 17 objectives.

Chapter Test Items 1–15

To assign a numerical grade for this Chapter Test, use 6 points for each test item and add 10 to the score.

Check Understanding

Use children's work on word problems to informally assess progress on chapter content.

Customizing Your Instruction

For children who have not yet mastered these objectives, you can use the reteaching resources listed in the chart below.

✓ Assessment Options

A summary test for this chapter is also provided in the Unit Resource Folder.

Name_____ ✓ **Chapter Review/Test**

Vocabulary ⓔ Glossary
Match the word to the correct statement.

1. **heavier** ———— a unit to measure length
2. **pound** ———— an object that weighs more
3. **centimeter** ———— a unit to measure weight
4. **height** ———————— a measurement of how tall something is

Concepts and Skills
Find the object.
Is the object longer or shorter than your hand?
Circle.

5. (longer) / shorter

6. longer / (shorter)

Choose a unit to measure the length. **Answers may vary.**

Find the object.	Record the measure.	Circle the unit.
7.	about _____	
8.	about _____	

First estimate.
Then use an inch ruler to measure.

9. Estimate: about _____ inches
   Measure: about __2__ inches

Chapter 17   five hundred nineteen **519**

Reteaching Support

Chapter Test Items	Summary Test Items	Chapter Objectives Tested	TE Pages	Use These Reteaching Resources
1–4	1–2	**17A** Develop and use math vocabulary relating to length and weight.	505A–506, 509A–512	Reteach Resources and *Ways to Success* CD: 17.4–17.6 Skillsheet 122
5–10	3–6	**17B** Estimate, compare, order, and measure lengths and heights of objects, using nonstandard units, inches, and centimeters.	499A–506	Reteach Resources and *Ways to Success* CD: 17.1–17.4 Skillsheets 123 and 124
11–14	7–8	**17C** Compare and order the weight of objects using nonstandard and standard units including comparing objects to pound and a kilogram.	509A–514	Reteach Resources and *Ways to Success* CD: 17.5–17.7 Skillsheet 125
15	9–10	**17D** Use logical reasoning to solve word problems.	515A–516	Reteach Resource and *Ways to Success* CD: 17.8, Skillsheet 126

CHAPTER SUMMARY TEST

Name_____ Date_____ Chapter 17 Test

Use the unit to measure the length.
Write the measure.

1. about __3__

2. WHITE about __2__

Circle the word.
Is the object longer or shorter than your hand?

3. longer (shorter)

4. (longer) shorter

Estimate. Then measure.

5. Use an inch ruler.
   Find the height.
   Estimates will vary.
   Estimate: about _____ inches
   Measure: about __4__ inches

6. Use a centimeter ruler.
   Find the length.
   Estimate: about _____ centimeters
   Measure: about __6__ centimeters

Go on

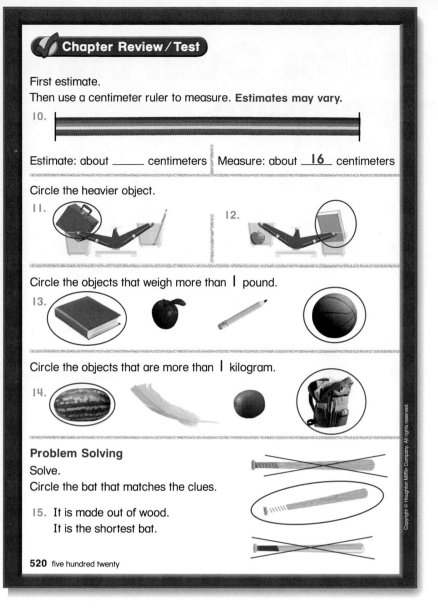

Chapter Review / Test

First estimate.
Then use a centimeter ruler to measure. **Estimates may vary.**

10.

Estimate: about _____ centimeters   Measure: about __16__ centimeters

Circle the heavier object.

11.

12.

Circle the objects that weigh more than 1 pound.

13.

Circle the objects that are more than 1 kilogram.

14.

Problem Solving
Solve.
Circle the bat that matches the clues.

15. It is made out of wood.
    It is the shortest bat.

520 five hundred twenty

Adequate Yearly Progress

Use the End of Grade Test Prep Assessment Guide to help familiarize your children with the format of standardized tests.

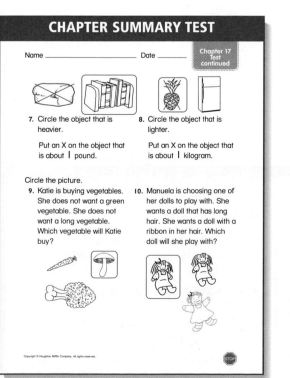

CHAPTER SUMMARY TEST

Name _____ Date _____

Chapter 17 Test continued

7. Circle the object that is heavier.

   Put an X on the object that is about 1 pound.

8. Circle the object that is lighter.

   Put an X on the object that is about 1 kilogram.

Circle the picture.

9. Katie is buying vegetables. She does not want a green vegetable. She does not want a long vegetable. Which vegetable will Katie buy?

10. Manuela is choosing one of her dolls to play with. She wants a doll that has long hair. She wants a doll with a ribbon in her hair. Which doll will she play with?

Lesson by Lesson Overview
Capacity and Temperature

Lesson 1

- This lesson introduces comparing and ordering by capacity.
- Children use real containers and determine which holds more or less than the other.
- Then children order pictured containers by numbering them.

Lesson 2

- Children are introduced to *cups, pints,* and *quarts.*
- They measure to find the relationship between the units.
- Then children compare measures.

Lesson 3

- The focus of this lesson is on measuring capacity to determine if a container holds more than, less than, or about 1 *liter.*
- First children work with real containers. Then they estimate capacity of pictured containers.
- Children also order pictured containers by numbering them.

Lesson 4

- This lesson introduces temperature and thermometers.
- Children look at thermometers with pictures and decide if the temperature is hot or cold.
- Problem solving has children order temperatures from coldest to hottest.

Lesson 5

- In problem solving, children choose the most reasonable measuring tool to solve problems.
- Children are guided through the process, which leads to appropriate decisions and correct answers.
- Problems involve choosing from rulers, thermometers, balances, and measuring cups.

SKILLS TRACE: CAPACITY AND TEMPERATURE

Grade K	Grade 1	Grade 2
• compare and order by capacity (ch. 12) • measure capacity in nonstandard units (ch. 12)	• compare and order by capacity • compare the capacity of cups, pints, and quarts • compare the capacity of containers to 1 liter • understand temperature; hot and cold	• estimate and measure capacity in cups, pints, quarts, and gallons (ch. 18) • estimate and measure capacity in liters (ch. 18) • understand temperature; read Fahrenheit and Celsius thermometers (ch. 18)

Chapter Planner

Lesson	Objective	Vocabulary	Materials	✔ NCTM Standards
18.1 **Compare and Order Capacity** (Hands-On) p. 523A	Compare and order the capacity/volume of containers.		containers, cubes, rice, plastic bowls, cups, sand	Recognize the attributes of length, volume, weight, area, and time; compare and order objects according to these attributes.
18.2 **Cups, Pints, and Quarts** (Hands-On) p. 525A	Compare the capacity of cups, pints, and quarts.	cups pints quarts	cup, pint, quart measures; sand, rice or water; various containers, 1/2 gallon pitcher	Recognize the attributes of length, volume, weight, area, and time; compare and order objects according to these attributes.
18.3 **Liters** (Hands-On) p. 527A	Compare the capacities of containers to a liter; order containers by capacity.	liters	1 liter measure, non-glass containers of various sizes; sand, rice, or water; old magazines, poster paper	Recognize the attributes of length, volume, weight, area, and time; compare and order objects according to these attributes.
18.4 **Temperature** p. 531A	Understand the difference between hot and cold.	hot cold temperature thermometer degrees	display thermometer (teacher-made), spinner labeled hot/cold (Learning Tool (LT) 38)	Develop common referents for measures to make comparisons and estimates.
18.5 **Problem Solving:** **Reasonable Answers** p. 533A	Determine the materials and strategies to be used to solve problems.		ruler, balance, liter measure, thermometer, quart measure, variety of measuring tools, classroom objects	Select an appropriate unit and tool for the attribute being measured.

Resources For Reaching All Learners

LESSON RESOURCES: Reteach, Practice, Enrichment, Problem Solving, Homework, English Learners, Daily Routines, Transparencies, Math Center.

ADDITIONAL RESOURCES FROM HOUGHTON MIFFLIN: Combination Classroom Planning Guide, Chapter Challenges, Every Day Counts, Math to Learn (Student Handbook)

Every Day Counts
The *Measurement* activities in Every Day Counts support the math in this chapter.

Assessing Prior Knowledge

Before beginning the chapter, you can assess student understandings in order to assist you in differentiating instruction.

Complete Chapter Pretest in Unit Resource Folder

Use this test to assess both prerequisite skills (**Are You Ready?** — one page) and chapter content (**Check What You Know** — two pages).

Chapter 18 Prerequisite Skills Pretest

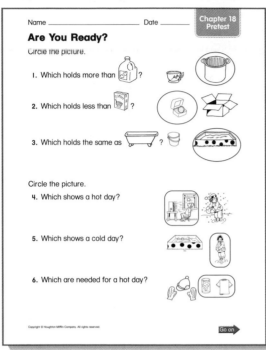

Chapter 18 New Content Pretest

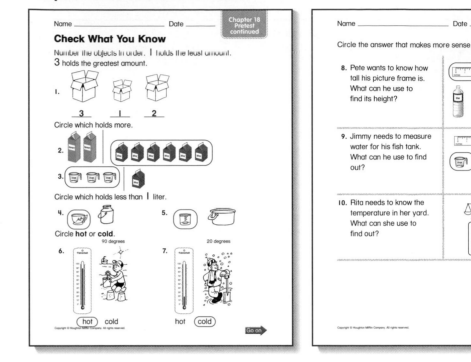

Customizing Instruction

For Students Having Difficulty

Items	Prerequisites	Ways to Success
1–3	Compare the capacity of containers.	CD: 18a Skillsheet 127
4–6	Understand reasonable temperature for occasions.	Skillsheet 128

Ways to Success: Intervention for every concept and skill (CD-ROM or Chapter Intervention Skillsheets).

For Students Having Success

Items	Objectives	Resources
6–7	18A Use vocabulary relating to capacity and temperature.	Enrichment 18.2–18.4
1–5	18B Compare and order the capacity of containers.	Enrichment 18.1–18.3
6–7	18C Understand hot and cold.	Enrichment 18.4
8–10	18D Choose the most reasonable measuring tool to solve problems.	Enrichment 18.5

Use **Chapter Challenges** with any students who have success with all new chapter content.

Other Pretest Options

Informal Pretest

The pretest assesses vocabulary and prerequisite skills needed for success in this chapter.

Ways to Success CD-ROM

The **Ways to Success** chapter pretest has automatic assignment of appropriate review lessons.

Chapter Resources

Assessing Prior Knowledge

Our Feet in Inches (measure in inches)

• Have children trace their feet and shoes on paper.
• Have them use a ruler to measure each of these.

Ongoing Skill Activity

Is It Hot or Cold Outside?   (understand the difference between hot and cold)

• Make a thermometer with colored construction paper. Mark it in °F.
• Slide the red paper to show that the temperature is 85°F. Have children draw pictures showing appropriate clothing and activities for 85°F. Display the pictures near the thermometer.
• Change the thermometer every few days to indicate various hot and cold temperatures.

Connecting to the Unit Project

• Tell children that they will be completing the bird feeders.
• Have children use cups to measure the birdseed and pour it into the feeders.
• Have children hang the feeders in various locations. At the end of the first week, ask **Do I need to add 1 or 2 cups of birdseed to refill the bird feeders?**
• Refill feeders as needed and keep track of cups of birdseed used.

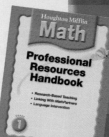

Professional Resources Handbook
Research, Mathematics Content, and Language Intervention

Research-Based Teaching

Piaget, Inhelder, & Szeminska (1948, 1960) demonstrated that children must use two kinds of reasoning to measure objects: transitive reasoning and unit iteration. Transitive reasoning involves comparing a whole quantity to another whole quantity. Unit iteration involves the ability to think about each whole object as consisting of many parts. See *Professional Resources Handbook, Grade 1,* Unit 7.

For more ideas relating to Unit 7, see the Teacher Support Handbook at the back of this Teacher's Edition.

Language Intervention

In East Asian countries, children learn that just as numbers can be composed and decomposed as sets and subsets, units of measurement can be composed and decomposed as well. For further explanation, see "Mathematical Language and Measurement" in the *Professional Resources Handbook Grade 1.*

Technology

Time-Saving Technology Support
Ways to Assess Customized Spiral Review
   Test Generator CD
Lesson Planner CD-ROM
Ways to Success Intervention CD-ROM
MathTracks CD-ROM
Education Place: www.eduplace.com/math/mw
Houghton Mifflin Math eBook CD-ROM
eManipulatives
eGames

Starting Chapter 18
Capacity and Temperature

CHAPTER OBJECTIVES

18A Develop and use math vocabulary relating to capacity and temperature.

18B Compare and order the capacity of containers using cups, pints, quarts, and liters.

18C Understand hot and cold.

18D Choose the most reasonable measuring tool to solve problems.

Math Background

Capacity and Temperature

Two concepts in measurement that are introduced at this level are capacity and temperature. Capacity is the volume of an object expressed in units of liquid measure. In the customary system, these units are fluid ounce, cup, pint, quart, and gallon. At this level children's learning focuses on cups, pints, and quarts. In the metric system, the most commonly used units of capacity are milliliter and liter. Liter is introduced to children at this level.

Temperature is a measure of the hotness or coldness of an object. A thermometer is used to measure temperature. It uses a vertical number line. In our customary measurement system, temperature is measured in degrees Fahrenheit. On this scale, water boils at 212°F and freezes at 32°F. Typical human body temperature is 98.6°F. Temperatures below zero are recorded as *integers*. The set of integers consists of the counting numbers 1, 2, 3 . . ., their opposites −1, −2, −3, . . ., and the number 0. Children will learn more about integers in future grades.

Capacity and Temperature

INVESTIGATION

Find the object that can hold the most water.

CHAPTER 18

LEMONADE 5¢

Chapter 18

five hundred twenty-one **521**

Using The Investigation

- Write vocabulary cards for the words *cup, pint, quart, liter, degrees,* and *thermometer.* Tell children that these words tell about how much something holds, or how hot or cold something is.

- Ask 6 volunteers to come forward. Tape one card to each child's shirt. Have the class help the children arrange themselves into two groups: one group for words related to capacity, and the other for temperature.

- Read the direction to children. **Look at the picture. Which object could hold the most water?** (fountain) **Find the object that can hold the least amount of water.** (drinking glass) **Order the objects from the least amount to the greatest amount they can hold.** (drinking glass, pitcher, watering can, bird bath, fountain)

For more information about projects and investigations, visit Education Place. eduplace.com/math/mw/

PEOPLE USING MATH

Ben Franklin

Ben Franklin playing his armonica.

Benjamin Franklin was an important person in our country in the 1700s. He was also a famous inventor who enjoyed music. Franklin once saw musical glasses filled with water. Different tunes were played on them. He invented an instrument called the armonica. Sounds are created on the instrument by rubbing water on different shaped glasses.

You Can Make Your Own Musical Glasses

The amount of water and thickness of the glasses can change the tune. Songs like "Twinkle, Twinkle, Little Star," "The Itsy, Bitsy Spider," or "I'm a Little Tea Pot" can be played on the glasses.

522 five hundred twenty-two

Meeting the Needs of Mathematically Promising Students

Chapter Challenges, an integral part of Houghton Mifflin Math, provides three worksheets for every chapter that will help mathematically promising students explore, extend, and connect the mathematics in the chapter. Designed to help you support independent student work, this resource provides Teacher Notes and a blackline master for each of the three chapter activities.

Explore: Measure Many Ways, page 103, after Lesson 1
Extend: Use Liters to Solve, page 105, after Lesson 3
Connect: Hot and Cold, page 107, after Lesson 5

Using This Page

- Read the paragraph about Benjamin Franklin to children.
- Tell children that the amount of water and the thickness of the glass will change the sound a glass makes when the rim is rubbed or the glass is tapped.
- Set up a row of 4 glasses of different sizes and thicknesses. Fill the glasses with various amounts of water. Invite volunteers to tap the glasses and rub the rims to create music.

NSF Children's Math Worlds

Using lessons from the *Children's Math Worlds* is a good way to ensure that your students will develop a deep understanding of capacity and temperature. The most effective approach is to use the *Children's Math Worlds* lessons along with the lessons in the chapter.

Capacity and Temperature   **522**

Hands On: Compare and Order Capacity

PLANNING THE LESSON

MATHEMATICS OBJECTIVE
Compare and order the capacity/volume of containers.

Use Lesson Planner CD ROM for Lesson 18.1.

Daily Routines

Calendar
Point to the week with the least number of days in the month. Have children find a week that has more days. Use the terms more, less, least, and greatest as you compare the number of days in the weeks.

Sunday	Monday	Tuesday	Wednesday	Thursday	Friday	Saturday
			1	2	3	4
5	6	7	8	9	10	11
12	13	14	15	16	17	18
19	20	21	22	23	24	25
26	27	28	29	30	31	

Vocabulary
Write the word **container** on the board and ask children for an example of a container in the classroom. Use containers to help children realize that containers can hold solids or liquids.

Vocabulary Cards

Meeting North Carolina's Standards
2.01 For given objects:
- Select an attribute (length, capacity, mass) to measure (use non-standard units).
- Develop strategies to estimate size.
- Compare, using appropriate language, with respect to the attribute selected.

Lesson Transparency 18.1

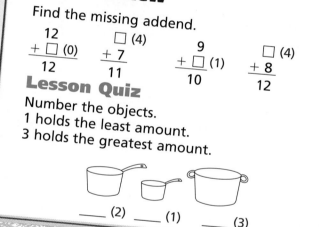

Problem of the Day
Julia counts to 100 by 5s. Elijah counts to 100 by 10s. Who counts only 10 numbers? (Elijah)

Quick Review
Find the missing addend.

$$\begin{array}{r} 12 \\ + \square \ (0) \\ \hline 12 \end{array} \qquad \begin{array}{r} \square \ (4) \\ + 7 \\ \hline 11 \end{array} \qquad \begin{array}{r} 9 \\ + \square \ (1) \\ \hline 10 \end{array} \qquad \begin{array}{r} \square \ (4) \\ + 8 \\ \hline 12 \end{array}$$

Lesson Quiz
Number the objects.
1 holds the least amount.
3 holds the greatest amount.

____ (2)   ____ (1)   ____ (3)

LEVELED PRACTICE

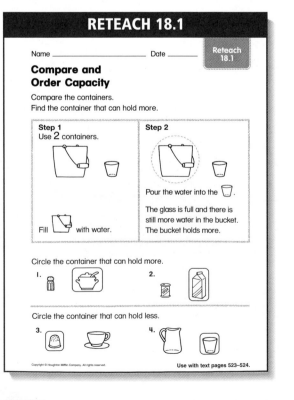

RETEACH 18.1
Name _____ Date _____   Reteach 18.1

Compare and Order Capacity
Compare the containers.
Find the container that can hold more.

Step 1
Use 2 containers.

Step 2
Pour the water into the ⊔.
The glass is full and there is still more water in the bucket. The bucket holds more.

Fill ⊔ with water.

Circle the container that can hold more.
1.   2.

Circle the container that can hold less.
3.   4.

Use with text pages 523–524.

PRACTICE 18.1
Name _____ Date _____   Practice 18.1

Compare and Order Capacity
Number the objects.
1 holds the least amount. 3 holds the greatest amount.

1.
3   2   1

2.
2   3   1

3.
1   2   3

▶ Test Prep
Fill in the ○ for the correct answer. NH means Not Here.
4. Which holds the most?

●   ○   ○   NH

Use with text pages 523–524.

ENRICHMENT 18.1

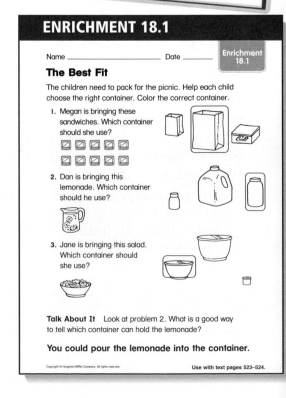

Name _____ Date _____   Enrichment 18.1

The Best Fit
The children need to pack for the picnic. Help each child choose the right container. Color the correct container.

1. Megan is bringing these sandwiches. Which container should she use?

2. Dan is bringing this lemonade. Which container should he use?

3. Jane is bringing this salad. Which container should she use?

Talk About It Look at problem 2. What is a good way to tell which container can hold the lemonade?

You could pour the lemonade into the container.

Use with text pages 523–524.

Practice Workbook Page 122

Reaching All Learners

Differentiated Instruction

English Learners

To compare and order the capacity of containers, English-language learners will need to understand the concepts of *full* and *not full*. Use Worksheet 18.1 to help develop an understanding of these concepts.

Inclusion
VISUAL, TACTILE

Materials: *containers, dry beans*

- Display 2 containers. Have the child predict which container holds more beans.
- Help the child fill the larger container with beans. Then pour them into the smaller container.
- The larger container holds more beans because beans are left over.

Gifted and Talented
VISUAL, TACTILE

Materials: *containers, rice*

- Challenge children to find 2 containers, of different heights and widths, that hold about the same amount of rice.
- Allow children to demonstrate their solutions.

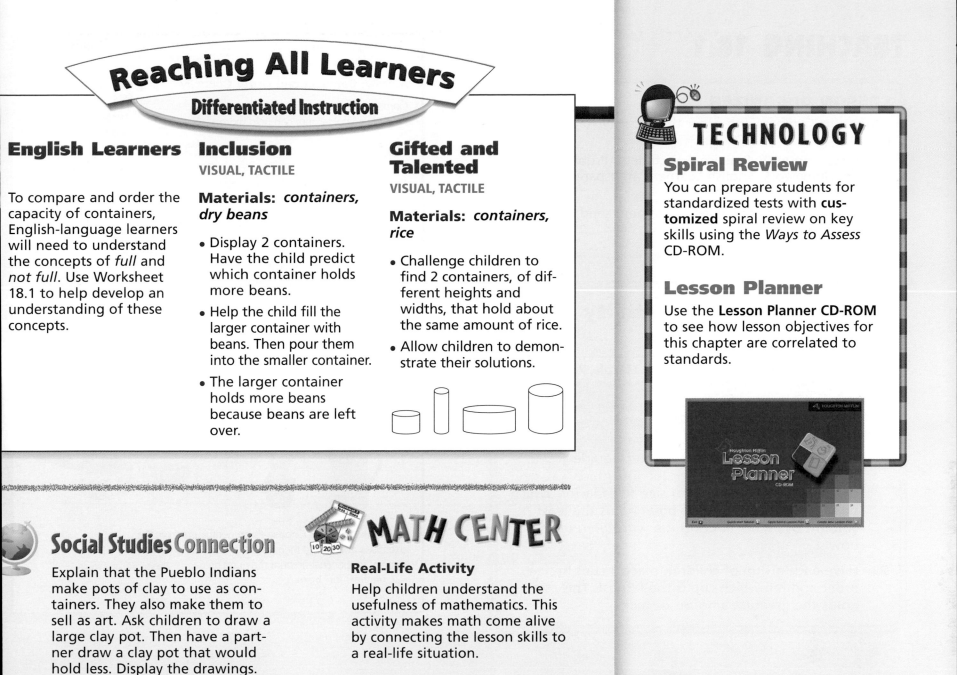

TECHNOLOGY

Spiral Review

You can prepare students for standardized tests with **customized** spiral review on key skills using the *Ways to Assess* CD-ROM.

Lesson Planner

Use the **Lesson Planner CD-ROM** to see how lesson objectives for this chapter are correlated to standards.

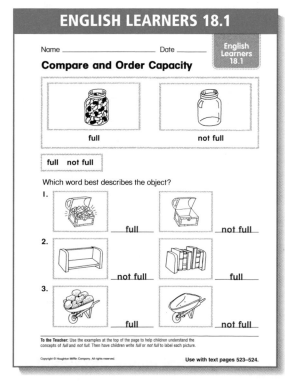

Social Studies Connection

Explain that the Pueblo Indians make pots of clay to use as containers. They also make them to sell as art. Ask children to draw a large clay pot. Then have a partner draw a clay pot that would hold less. Display the drawings.

MATH CENTER

Real-Life Activity

Help children understand the usefulness of mathematics. This activity makes math come alive by connecting the lesson skills to a real-life situation.

PROBLEM SOLVING 18.1

Name _____ Date _____ | Problem Solving 18.1

Activity: Compare and Order Capacity

Read to solve. | Draw or write to explain.

Beth wants to buy a container that will hold more water than this fish bowl.

Draw a container Beth should buy.

1. Kwan wants to buy a container that will hold less than the jar. Draw a container Kwan might buy.

Check children's drawings.

2. Ned wants a new bowl that will hold more than this bowl. Draw a bowl Ned might buy.

3. Iris needs a container that will hold more juice than this one. Draw a container that could hold more.

Copyright © Houghton Mifflin Company. All rights reserved. **Use with text pages 523–524.**

HOMEWORK 18.1

Name _____ Date _____ | Homework 18.1

Activity: Compare and Order Capacity

Find the container that holds more. | Fill the teacup. | Pour the teacup into the glass.

The glass is not full, so it holds more than the cup.

Number the objects in order. 1 holds the least amount. 3 holds the greatest amount. Try using real objects if you need help.

1.   1   3   2
2.   3   2   1
3.   2   3   1

4. Find containers with different shapes that hold about the same amount. Draw one pair. | Draw here.

Copyright © Houghton Mifflin Company. All rights reserved. **Use with text pages 523–524.**

ENGLISH LEARNERS 18.1

Name _____ Date _____ | English Learners 18.1

Compare and Order Capacity

full | not full

full   not full

Which word best describes the object?

1.   full   not full
2.   not full   full
3.   full   not full

To the Teacher: Use the examples at the top of the page to help children understand the concepts of *full* and *not full*. Then have children write *full* or *not full* to label each picture.

Copyright © Houghton Mifflin Company. All rights reserved. **Use with text pages 523–524.**

Homework Workbook Page 122

TEACHING 18.1

LESSON ORGANIZER

Objective Compare and order the capacity/volume of containers.

Resources Reteach, Practice, Enrichment, Problem Solving, Homework, English Learners, Transparencies, Math Center

Materials Plastic bowls, cups, containers, sand or rice, cubes

Activity

Warm-Up Activity
Compare Size

iii Small Group	◔ 5 minutes	Tactile, Visual

Materials: *3 bowls of different sizes, 3 paper cups of different sizes*

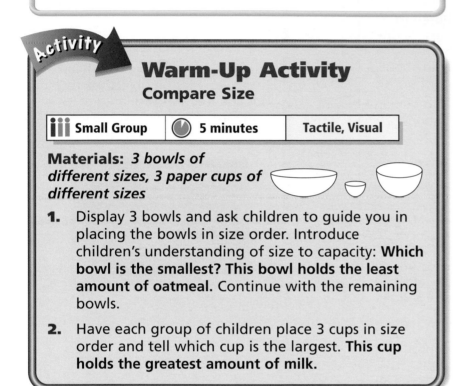

1. Display 3 bowls and ask children to guide you in placing the bowls in size order. Introduce children's understanding of size to capacity: **Which bowl is the smallest? This bowl holds the least amount of oatmeal.** Continue with the remaining bowls.

2. Have each group of children place 3 cups in size order and tell which cup is the largest. **This cup holds the greatest amount of milk.**

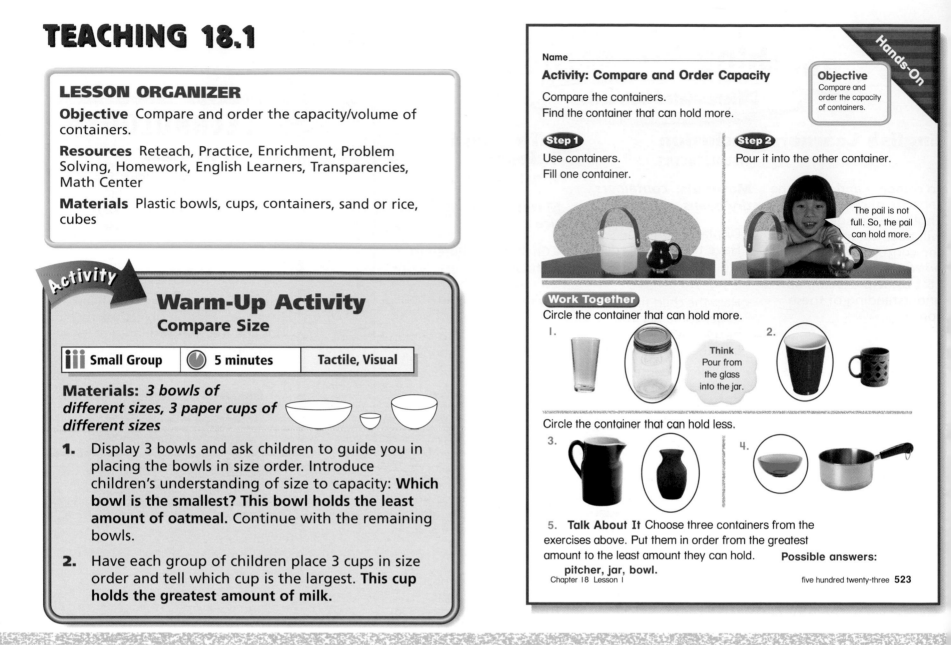

Name_____

Activity: Compare and Order Capacity

Compare the containers.
Find the container that can hold more.

Objective Compare and order the capacity of containers.

Step 1
Use containers.
Fill one container.

Step 2
Pour it into the other container.

The pail is not full. So, the pail can hold more.

Work Together
Circle the container that can hold more.

1.

Think Pour from the glass into the jar.

2.

Circle the container that can hold less.

3.

4.

5. **Talk About It** Choose three containers from the exercises above. Put them in order from the greatest amount to the least amount they can hold. **Possible answers: pitcher, jar, bowl.**

---

① Introduce
Activity
Discuss Capacity

iiii Whole Group	◔ 10–15 minutes	Visual, Tactile

Materials: *containers of different sizes, sand, cubes*

1. Discuss the idea that different-sized containers hold different amounts of water, milk, sand, and so on. Give a familiar example, such as small, medium, and large containers of cubes. Explain that we use the word *capacity* to tell how much something holds.

2. Display two containers of similar height but different width. Have children estimate capacity. **Both of these containers can hold sand. Which container do you think can hold more?** (Answers may vary.) **Why?** (Children's answers should connect the idea of size to capacity.) Ask a volunteer to pour sand to check. Help children generalize that larger containers hold more.

3. Repeat with three containers. Use the language of *least* and *greatest* amount as volunteers order the capacity.

② Develop

Read the objective with children. Guide them through the example as they use pails and plastic containers. Help children understand that the pail holds more because the contents of the smaller container does not fill the pail.

Work Together

Provide non-glass containers similar to those pictured. Emphasize that containers should be filled to the top when measuring. Observe as children use other containers to complete **Exercises 1–4.** Make sure children find the containers that hold *more* in **Exercises 1–2** and *less* in **Exercises 3–4.** As pairs of children finish, have them complete the **Talk About It** question in **Exercise 5.** Discuss children's answers and demonstrate the order they suggest.

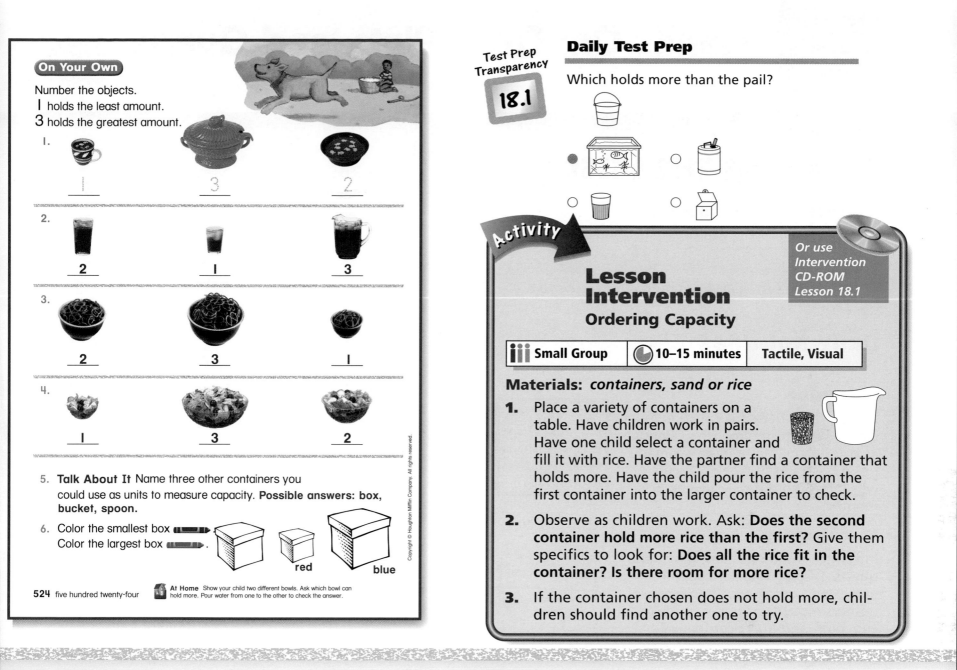

On Your Own

Number the objects.
1 holds the least amount.
3 holds the greatest amount.

1. 1   3   2

2. 2   1   3

3. 2   3   1

4. 1   3   2

5. **Talk About It** Name three other containers you could use as units to measure capacity. **Possible answers: box, bucket, spoon.**

6. Color the smallest box .
Color the largest box 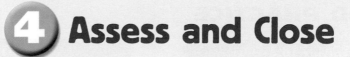.

red   blue

Copyright © Houghton Mifflin Company. All rights reserved.

524 five hundred twenty-four

At Home Show your child two different bowls. Ask which bowl can hold more. Pour water from one to the other to check the answer.

Daily Test Prep

Which holds more than the pail?

○ ● (fish tank)   ○ (can)

○ (wastebasket)   ○ (milk carton)

Activity

Or use Intervention CD-ROM Lesson 18.1

Lesson Intervention
Ordering Capacity

| 👥 Small Group | 🕐 10–15 minutes | Tactile, Visual |

Materials: *containers, sand or rice*

1. Place a variety of containers on a table. Have children work in pairs. Have one child select a container and fill it with rice. Have the partner find a container that holds more. Have the child pour the rice from the first container into the larger container to check.

2. Observe as children work. Ask: **Does the second container hold more rice than the first?** Give them specifics to look for: **Does all the rice fit in the container? Is there room for more rice?**

3. If the container chosen does not hold more, children should find another one to try.

---

3 Practice

On Your Own

Children complete **Exercises 1–4** independently. Use the **Talk About It** in **Exercise 5** to help children extend their thinking about other containers that can measure capacity.

After children complete **Exercise 6**, call on volunteers to share their solutions. Discuss the capacity of each box related to its size.

Common Error

Using Height to Determine Capacity
Some children may associate a taller container with holding more. Demonstrate that a tall thin container may hold less than a short wide one.

4 Assess and Close

Which container holds the least amount: a paper cup, a swimming pool, or a water bottle? (paper cup) **Which holds the greatest amount?** (pool)

Keeping a Journal

Draw a juice box. Draw a container that can hold more than a juice box. Label the container.

Hands-On: Cups, Pints, and Quarts

PLANNING THE LESSON

MATHEMATICS OBJECTIVE
Compare the capacity of cups, pints, and quarts.

Use Lesson Planner CD-ROM for Lesson 18.2.

Daily Routines

Calendar
Review that there are 7 days in 1 week. Refer to the month's calendar as you discuss that a month is made up of days and of weeks. Discuss which has more days—a week or a month.

Sunday	Monday	Tuesday	Wednesday	Thursday	Friday	Saturday
			1	2	3	4
5	6	7	8	9	10	11
12	13	14	15	16	17	18
19	20	21	22	23	24	25
26	27	28	29	30	31	

Vocabulary
Introduce the terms **cups, pints,** and **quarts.** Display familiar cup, pint, and quart containers. Then have volunteers match vocabulary cards to cup, pint, and quart containers.

Vocabulary Cards

Meeting North Carolina's Standards
Prepare for Grade 3 Standard 2.02 Estimate and measure using appropriate units.

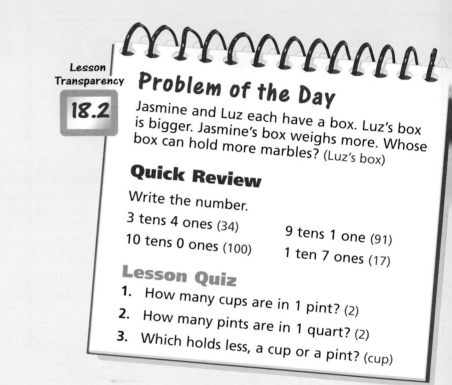

Lesson Transparency 18.2

Problem of the Day
Jasmine and Luz each have a box. Luz's box is bigger. Jasmine's box weighs more. Whose box can hold more marbles? (Luz's box)

Quick Review
Write the number.

3 tens 4 ones (34)   9 tens 1 one (91)

10 tens 0 ones (100)   1 ten 7 ones (17)

Lesson Quiz
1. How many cups are in 1 pint? (2)
2. How many pints are in 1 quart? (2)
3. Which holds less, a cup or a pint? (cup)

LEVELED PRACTICE

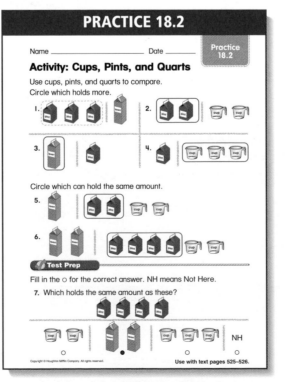

RETEACH 18.2

Name _____ Date _____
Reteach 18.2

Cups, Pints, and Quarts

You can use cups, pints, and quarts to tell how much a container holds.

2 cups = 1 pint   2 pints = 1 quart

Step 1
Fill the smaller container.
Pour it into the larger container.

Step 2
Continue until the large container is full.
Use cups, pints, and quarts.
Complete the table.

How many?	Number
1. cups in a quart	4 cups
2. cups in a pint	2 cups
3. pints in a quart	2 pints

Use with text pages 525–526.

PRACTICE 18.2

Name _____ Date _____
Practice 18.2

Activity: Cups, Pints, and Quarts

Use cups, pints, and quarts to compare.
Circle which holds more.

1.   2.

3.   4.

Circle which can hold the same amount.

5.

6.

Test Prep

Fill in the ○ for the correct answer. NH means Not Here.

7. Which holds the same amount as these?

○   ○   ●   ○   NH

Use with text pages 525–526.

ENRICHMENT 18.2

Name _____ Date _____
Enrichment 18.2

How Much in Here?

Read each problem.
Color the correct container.

1. Donny and Marie each have a cup of water. Together, how much will they drink?

2. Mark and Mindy have 2 cups of milk at breakfast and 2 cups at snack time. Together, how much milk will they drink?

3. Lee changes the water in the large goldfish bowl. About how much water does he use?

4. May fills a small glass with juice. About how much juice does she have?

Write About It If 4 friends each want a cup of juice, would 1 quart be enough? Why?

Yes, because there are 4 cups in a quart.

Use with text pages 525–526.

Practice Workbook Page 123

Reaching All Learners

Differentiated Instruction

English Learners

Children will need to understand the meaning of the words *smaller* and *larger* as they compare capacity. Use Worksheet 18.2 to help English-language learners develop understanding of these words.

Inclusion
VISUAL, TACTILE

Materials: *cup, pint, quart measures; sand*

- Have the child pour sand from a cup to a pint measure to find that 2 cups equal 1 pint. Then have the child determine how many pints equal 1 quart.

Help the child draw a picture to show equivalent measures.

Gifted and Talented
TACTILE, VISUAL

Materials: *cup, pint, and quart measures*

- Have children work in pairs. Demonstrate to children that 1 cup equals 8 ounces.

- Have children find how many ounces are in one pint, a half cup, and a quart.

TECHNOLOGY

Spiral Review
Create **customized** spiral review worksheets for individual students using the *Ways to Assess* CD-ROM.

eBook
An electronic version of this lesson can be found in **eMathBook**.

Education Place
Encourage students to visit **Education Place** at **eduplace.com/kids/mw/** for more student activities.

Literature Connection

Read aloud the story, *Lulu's Lemonade* by Barbara deRubertis. Draw the gallon container. Use it to demonstrate how all the measures total 1 gallon. Help children make their own recipe for 1 quart of lemonade.

MATH CENTER

Vocabulary Activity
This vocabulary-building activity helps children understand and remember new words. Encourage children to use the words in math discussion.

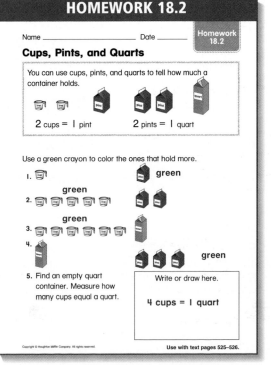

PROBLEM SOLVING 18.2

Name _____ Date _____

Activity: Cups, Pints, and Quarts

Read to solve.

Gene's container holds 2 cups of water. Larry's container holds 1 quart of water. Who has the container that holds more?

Draw or write to explain.

Gene / Larry

I know 1 quart equals 4 cups.

Larry

1. Mom needs 6 cups of milk for a recipe. How many quarts and pints of milk should she buy?

_1_ quart _1_ pint

2. Rick has 3 cups of juice in a container. Don has 5 cups of juice in a container. How many quarts of juice do they have?

_2_ quarts

3. Dad brings home 3 quarts of milk. How many cups is that?

_12_ cups

Use with text pages 525–526.

HOMEWORK 18.2

Name _____ Date _____

Cups, Pints, and Quarts

You can use cups, pints, and quarts to tell how much a container holds.

2 cups = 1 pint   2 pints = 1 quart

Use a green crayon to color the ones that hold more.

1. green
2. green
3. green
4. green

5. Find an empty quart container. Measure how many cups equal a quart.

Write or draw here.

4 cups = 1 quart

Use with text pages 525–526.

ENGLISH LEARNERS 18.2

Name _____ Date _____

Cups, Pints, and Quarts

smaller / larger

Circle the correct words.

1. The tack is (smaller) larger than the nail.
The nail is smaller (larger) than the tack.

2. The whale is smaller (larger) than the shark.
The shark is (smaller) larger than the whale.

3. The car is (smaller) larger than the bus.
The bus is smaller (larger) than the car.

To the Teacher: Use the examples at the top of the page to help children understand the words smaller and larger. Then read the sentences with children and have them circle the correct words.

Use with text pages 525–526.

TEACHING 18.2

LESSON ORGANIZER

Objective Compare the capacity of cups, pints, and quarts.

Resources Reteach, Practice, Enrichment, Problem Solving, Homework, English Learners, Transparencies, Math Center

Materials Containers; sand, rice, or water; cup, pint, quart measures, $\frac{1}{2}$ gallon pitcher

Activity

Warm-Up Activity
Modeling Capacity

iii Small Group	⏱ 5 minutes	Tactile, Visual

Materials: *various containers; sand, rice, or water*

1. Choose one small jar to use as a unit to measure capacity. Display it with a larger bowl. **How many jars will it take to fill the bowl?** Record estimates.

2. Pour 1 jar of sand into the bowl. Give children the opportunity to change their estimates. Record these changes.

3. Have a volunteer pour 2 more jars of sand into the bowl. Give children a chance to revise their estimates once more. Have another volunteer fill the bowl. Compare the actual measure to the estimates. **Did your estimate get closer as I poured more sand?** Discuss the estimates.

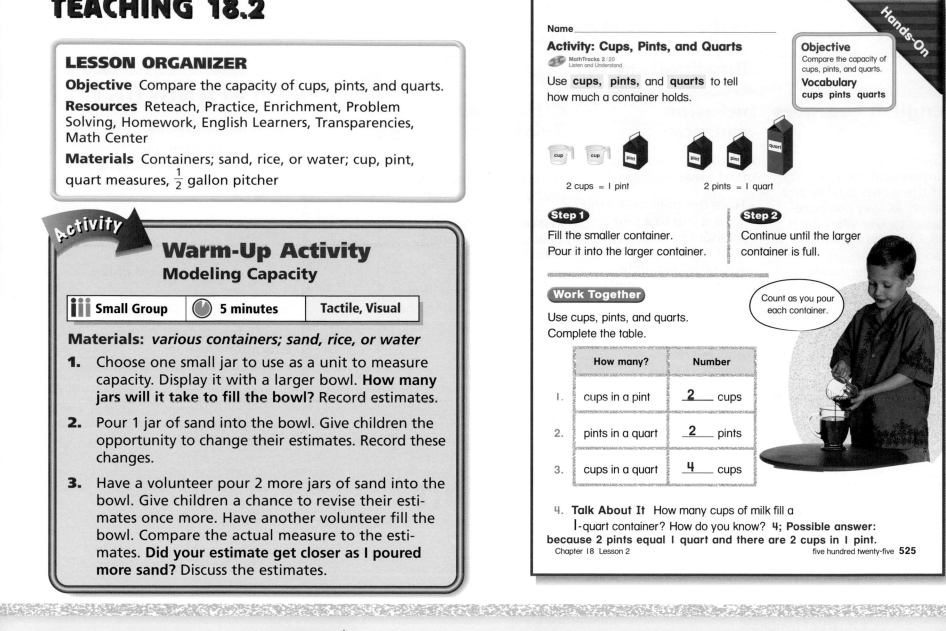

Name_____

Activity: Cups, Pints, and Quarts
MathTracks 2/20
Listen and Understand

Use **cups**, **pints**, and **quarts** to tell how much a container holds.

Objective
Compare the capacity of cups, pints, and quarts.
Vocabulary
cups pints quarts

2 cups = 1 pint   2 pints = 1 quart

Step 1
Fill the smaller container. Pour it into the larger container.

Step 2
Continue until the larger container is full.

Work Together
Use cups, pints, and quarts. Complete the table.

Count as you pour each container.

	How many?	Number
1.	cups in a pint	**2** cups
2.	pints in a quart	**2** pints
3.	cups in a quart	**4** cups

4. **Talk About It** How many cups of milk fill a 1-quart container? How do you know? **4; Possible answer: because 2 pints equal 1 quart and there are 2 cups in 1 pint.**

Chapter 18 Lesson 2   five hundred twenty-five **525**

1 Introduce
Discuss Cups, Pints, Quarts

iiii Whole Group	⏱ 5–10 minutes	Visual, Tactile

Materials: *cup, pint, quart measures; sand, rice, or water*

1. Display the 3 units of measure. Label and identify them as cup, pint, and quart measures. Hold up the pint and ask: **Which holds less than 1 pint?** (cup) **Which holds more than 1 pint?** (quart)

2. Order the containers by size. **Which holds the least amount?** (cup) **The greatest amount?** (quart)

3. Pour sand into the 1-cup measure. **We know 1 pint holds more than 1 cup. How many cups do you think will fill the pint?** (2) Pour 1 cup and ask children how many more are needed. Pour 1 more cup to show that 2 cups equal 1 pint.

2 Develop

Read the objective and vocabulary with children. Guide them through the example as they use the measures. Help children see the relationship between cups, pints, and quarts.

Work Together

Provide unbreakable containers similar to those pictured. Remind children to fill containers to measure. Observe as children use the measures to complete **Exercises 1–3**. As pairs of children finish, have them discuss the **Talk About It** question in **Exercise 4**.

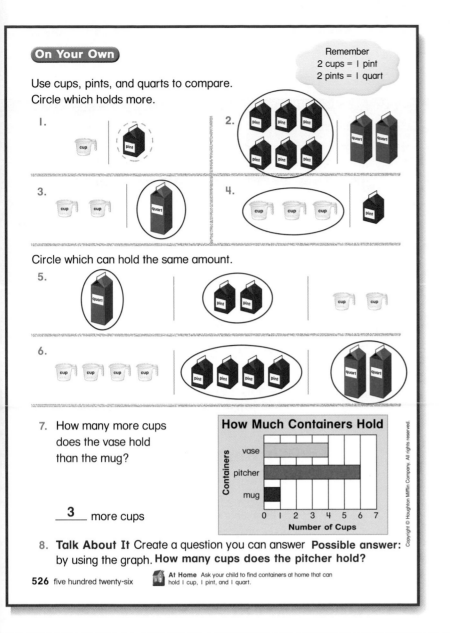

On Your Own

Use cups, pints, and quarts to compare.
Circle which holds more.

Remember
2 cups = 1 pint
2 pints = 1 quart

1.

2.

3.

4.

Circle which can hold the same amount.

5.

6.

7. How many more cups does the vase hold than the mug?

How Much Containers Hold

_____3_____ more cups

8. **Talk About It** Create a question you can answer **Possible answer:** by using the graph. **How many cups does the pitcher hold?**

526 five hundred twenty-six

At Home Ask your child to find containers at home that can hold 1 cup, 1 pint, and 1 quart.

Daily Test Prep

How many cups are in 1 pint?

1   2   3   4
○   ●   ○   ○

Activity

Or use Intervention CD-ROM Lesson 18.2

Lesson Intervention

How Many?

| iii Small Group | 🕐 10–15 minutes | Visual, Tactile |

Materials: $\frac{1}{2}$ gallon pitcher; cup, pint, quart measures; rice

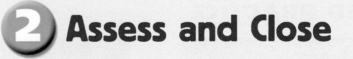

1. Have children work together to fill a pitcher with cups of rice. **How many cups did you use to fill the pitcher?** (8) Children empty the pitcher and repeat with the 1 pint measure. **How many pints did you need?** (4)

2. Explain that a cup holds less than a pint, so you need more cups to fill the pitcher. Have children predict whether it will take more or fewer quarts to fill the pitcher. (fewer) Ask a volunteer to demonstrate.

3. Invite children to find how many cups or pints they need to fill 1 quart. Discuss their findings.

---

1 Practice

On Your Own

Children complete **Exercises 1–6** independently. Be sure children find the containers that hold more in **Exercises 1–4** and find the containers that hold the same amount in **Exercises 5–6**. Guide children through **Exercise 7** as necessary. Call on volunteers to share the questions they wrote for the **Talk About It** question in **Exercise 8**.

Common Error

Confusing the Containers

Children may have difficulty remembering the relative sizes of cups, pints, and quarts. Point out that the names of the containers, when placed in alphabetical order, are in size order from smallest to largest.

2 Assess and Close

Which of the following have the same capacity: 4 cups, 4 pints, 1 quart? (4 cups and 1 quart)

If I have 2 pints of milk, how many cups do I have? (4 cups) How do you know? (There are 2 cups in 1 pint, so 2 + 2 = 4.)

Keeping a Journal

Draw a picture that shows 1 cup and 1 pint.

Hands-On: Liters

Lesson 18.3

PLANNING THE LESSON

MATHEMATICS OBJECTIVE
Compare the capacities of containers to a liter; order containers by compacity.

Use Lesson Planner CD-ROM for Lesson 18.3.

Meeting North Carolina's Standards
Prepare for Grade 3 Standard 2.02 Estimate and measure using appropriate units.

Daily Routines

Calendar
Use numbers to write today's date. For example, 04/10/05. Help children see that 04 represents April, the fourth month. Have a volunteer use numbers to write yesterday's date.

Sunday	Monday	Tuesday	Wednesday	Thursday	Friday	Saturday
				1	2	3	4
5	6	7	8	9	10	11
12	13	14	15	16	17	18
19	20	21	22	23	24	25
26	27	28	29	30	31	

Vocabulary
Introduce the term **liter** by showing children a *liter* container. Explain that *liter* is a *unit* of *measure* just like a *cup, pint,* and *quart.* Use *liter* in a sentence. Then have a volunteer do the same.

Vocabulary Cards

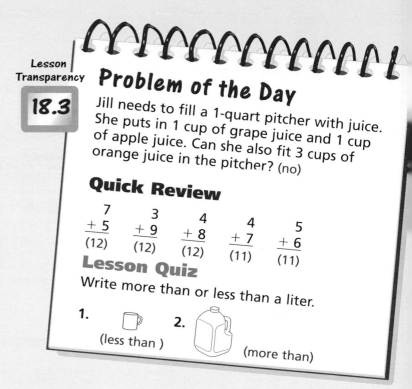

Lesson Transparency 18.3

Problem of the Day
Jill needs to fill a 1-quart pitcher with juice. She puts in 1 cup of grape juice and 1 cup of apple juice. Can she also fit 3 cups of orange juice in the pitcher? (no)

Quick Review

$$\begin{array}{r} 7 \\ + 5 \\ \hline (12) \end{array} \quad \begin{array}{r} 3 \\ + 9 \\ \hline (12) \end{array} \quad \begin{array}{r} 4 \\ + 8 \\ \hline (12) \end{array} \quad \begin{array}{r} 4 \\ + 7 \\ \hline (11) \end{array} \quad \begin{array}{r} 5 \\ + 6 \\ \hline (11) \end{array}$$

Lesson Quiz
Write more than or less than a liter.

1. (less than)   2. (more than)

LEVELED PRACTICE

RETEACH 18.3

Name _____ Date _____ **Reteach 18.3**

Liters

You can use liters to tell how much a container can hold.

less than | liter | liter   more than | liter

Step 1
Fill a liter bottle.

Step 2
Pour the liter into the object. Circle the capacity.
Answers may vary. Sample answers are shown.

Estimate.

	less than I liter	about the same	more than I liter
1.			**more than I liter**
2.		**about the same**	
3.		**about the same**	
4.	**less than I liter**		

Copyright © Houghton Mifflin Company. All rights reserved.   **Use with text pages 527–529.**

PRACTICE 18.3

Name _____ Date _____ **Practice 18.3**

Liters

Circle.
Use (Green) if the object can hold more than I liter.
Use (Yellow) if the object can hold less than I liter.

1. green crayon

green: fish tank, bucket, soup pot; yellow: milk carton, teacup, juice, ladle

Circle the containers that can hold more than I liter.

2.

Test Prep

Fill in the ○ for the correct answer. NH means Not Here.

3. Which holds less than I liter?

○   ○   ○   NH ○

Copyright © Houghton Mifflin Company. All rights reserved.   **Use with text pages 527–529.**

ENRICHMENT 18.3

Name _____ Date _____ **Enrichment 18.3**

A Little or a Lot About Liters

Look at each container.
Does the container hold more than, less than, or about the same as a liter?
Circle your answer.

1. more (less) about the same   2. (more) less about the same

3. more (less) about the same   4. more less (about the same)

5. more less (about the same)   6. (more) less about the same

Write About It If you get thirsty, would a liter of water be enough for you to drink? Why?

__A liter is about 4 cups, so it would be enough.__

Copyright © Houghton Mifflin Company. All rights reserved.   **Use with text pages 527–529.**

Practice Workbook Page 124

Reaching All Learners

Differentiated Instruction

English Learners

Worksheet 18.3 develops understanding of the term *about the same*. Children will need to understand this term in order to compare and order capacity.

Special Needs
TACTILE, VISUAL

Materials: *3 sorting rings, 1 liter measure, containers, sand*

- Display a 1 liter measure and containers of various sizes.
- Have the child compare each container to 1 liter and place the container in the sorting ring labeled less than, about the same, or more than. Allow the child to pour sand as needed to verify.

Early Finishers
VISUAL, TACTILE

Materials: *pictures of liters*

- Provide a picture of a liter container for each pair of children.
- Have children draw containers of various sizes and shapes that they believe hold more or less than 1 liter.
- Then have them work together to sort the pictures into 3 groups: less than 1 liter, about 1 liter, more than 1 liter.

TECHNOLOGY

Spiral Review

Using the *Ways to Assess* CD-ROM, you can create **customized** spiral review worksheets covering any lessons you choose.

Lesson Planner

You can use the **Lesson Planner CD-ROM** to create a report of the lessons and standards you have taught.

Games

Students can practice their math vocabulary using the Math Lingo game, available on the *Ways to Success* CD-ROM.

Social Studies Connection

Explain that in many countries, recipes use liters, which is a metric unit. Small amounts are measured in milliliters. 1,000 milliliters equal 1 liter. Let children make lemonade with 1 liter of water.

MATH CENTER

Vocabulary Activity

This vocabulary-building activity helps children understand and remember new words. Encourage children to use the words in math discussion.

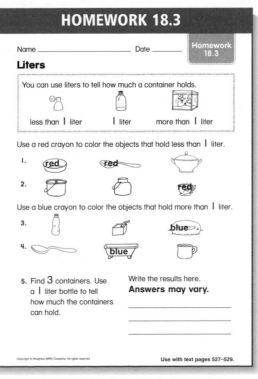

Homework Workbook Page 124

TEACHING 18.3

LESSON ORGANIZER

Objective Compare the capacities of containers to a liter; order containers by capacity.

Resources Reteach, Practice, Enrichment, Problem Solving, Homework, English Learners, Transparencies, Math Center

Materials Non-glass containers; sand, rice, or water, liter bottle, old magazines, poster paper

Activity

Warm-Up Activity
Comparing Capacity

Small Group	5 minutes	Tactile, Visual

Materials: *non-glass containers of various sizes; sand, rice, or water*

1. Give each group 2 containers. Have them estimate which one holds less. Ask a volunteer to fill the container with sand, and then pour the sand into the other container to check.

2. Discuss their results. **Which container holds more? How do you know?** (Children should realize they had to fill the smaller container more than once to fill the larger container.)

Name_____

Activity: Liters
MathTracks 2/21
Listen and Understand

You can also use **liters** to tell how much a container can hold.

Objective Compare and order the capacity of containers to a liter.
Vocabulary liters

Step 1 Fill a liter bottle. Find the container.

Step 2 Pour the liter bottle into the container.

The vase is not full. So, the vase can hold more than 1 liter.

less than 1 liter   1 liter   more than 1 liter

Work Together

Compare to 1 liter. Circle.

Think Does the liter bottle fill the vase?   **Possible answers shown.**

1. less than / about the same / (more than)

2. less than / (about the same) / more than

3. less than / (about the same) / more than

4. (less than) / about the same / more than

5. **Talk About It** Would you use a liter container to fill a swimming pool? Why? **No; Possible answer: It would take too long to fill the pool.**

---

1 Introduce
Activity
Model Comparing Containers to a Liter

Whole Group	5–10 minutes	Visual, Tactile

Materials: *non-glass containers of various sizes, liter bottle*

1. Put a 1-liter container on the table. Explain that a liter is a unit of measure that tells how much a container holds. Place a smaller container next to it. **Which container do you think holds more?** (the liter) **So the smaller container holds less than 1 liter.**

2. Remove the smaller container and put a larger container next to the liter. **Which container holds more?** (the larger container) **So the larger container holds more than 1 liter.**

3. Repeat as volunteers choose the containers and pour sand if needed to check. Have children discuss whether any containers hold about the same as 1 liter.

2 Develop

Read the objective and vocabulary with children. Guide them through the steps so they see the relative size of the containers. Explain that pouring one filled container into another is a way to estimate how much the second container holds (more than or less than).

Work Together

Provide non-glass containers similar to those pictured. Observe as children compare the containers to 1 liter as they complete **Exercises 1–4**. Be sure children try to fill each container being measured before they determine if it holds more, less, or about the same as the liter. Discuss children's responses to the **Talk About It** question in **Exercise 5**.

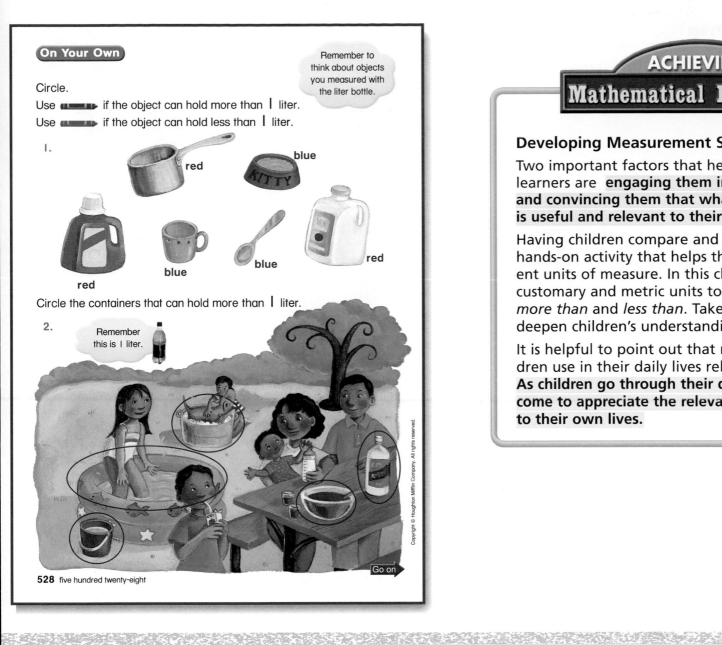

On Your Own

Remember to think about objects you measured with the liter bottle.

Circle.
Use ▬▬▶ if the object can hold more than 1 liter.
Use ▬▬▶ if the object can hold less than 1 liter.

1.

red

blue

red

blue

blue

red

Circle the containers that can hold more than 1 liter.

2.

Remember this is 1 liter.

Go on

528 five hundred twenty-eight

ACHIEVING
Mathematical Proficiency

Developing Measurement Sense

Two important factors that help children become learners are **engaging them in hands-on activities and convincing them that what they are learning is useful and relevant to their lives.**

Having children compare and order capacity is a hands-on activity that helps them understand different units of measure. In this chapter children use customary and metric units to learn the concepts of *more than* and *less than*. Taken together, these deepen children's understanding of measurement.

It is helpful to point out that nearly everything children use in their daily lives relates to measurement. **As children go through their daily activities they come to appreciate the relevance of measurement to their own lives.**

③ Practice

On Your Own

Children complete **Exercises 1–2** on page 528 independently. They may need to have a liter container available to use to estimate.

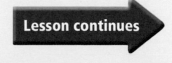
Lesson continues

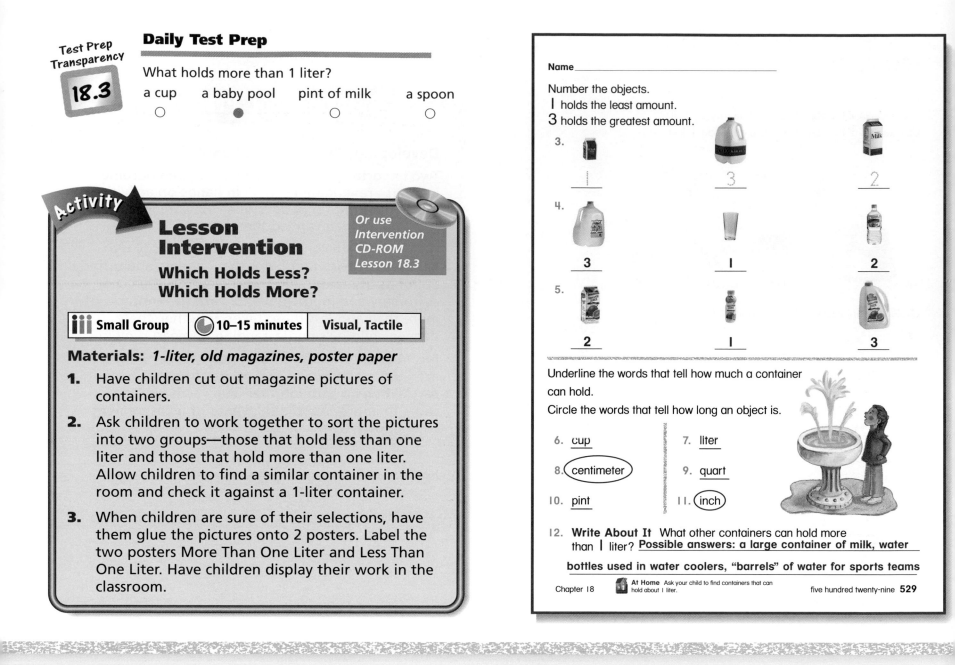

Daily Test Prep

What holds more than 1 liter?

a cup ○   a baby pool ●   pint of milk ○   a spoon ○

Activity

Or use Intervention CD-ROM Lesson 18.3

Lesson Intervention

Which Holds Less?
Which Holds More?

| 👥 Small Group | 🕐 10–15 minutes | Visual, Tactile |

Materials: *1-liter, old magazines, poster paper*

1. Have children cut out magazine pictures of containers.

2. Ask children to work together to sort the pictures into two groups—those that hold less than one liter and those that hold more than one liter. Allow children to find a similar container in the room and check it against a 1-liter container.

3. When children are sure of their selections, have them glue the pictures onto 2 posters. Label the two posters More Than One Liter and Less Than One Liter. Have children display their work in the classroom.

Name_____

Number the objects.
1 holds the least amount.
3 holds the greatest amount.

3.   1   3   2

4.   3   1   2

5.   2   1   3

Underline the words that tell how much a container can hold.

Circle the words that tell how long an object is.

6. cup   7. liter

8. (centimeter)   9. quart

10. pint   11. (inch)

12. **Write About It** What other containers can hold more than 1 liter? **Possible answers: a large container of milk, water bottles used in water coolers, "barrels" of water for sports teams**

Chapter 18   **At Home** Ask your child to find containers that can hold about 1 liter.   five hundred twenty-nine **529**

---

③ Practice

On Your Own

Read the directions on page 529 and work through **Exercise 3** with the class. Have children complete **Exercises 4–5** independently. Read the directions and have children complete **Exercises 6–11** independently. Use the **Write About It** in **Exercise 12** to extend children's thinking about estimating capacity.

Common Error

Confusing a Container's Shape with its Capacity
Remind children that having the same shape does not result in the same capacity. Check by pouring water from a liter into 2 containers of the same shape but different sizes.

④ Assess and Close

Does a mug hold more or less than a liter? (less) **How can you check?** (Fill a mug with water and pour it into a liter.)

Name a container that holds more than 1 liter. (Answers will vary.)

Keeping a Journal

Draw or write about what you can buy that comes in a liter container.

Quick Check

Number the objects.
1 holds the least amount.
3 holds the greatest amount.

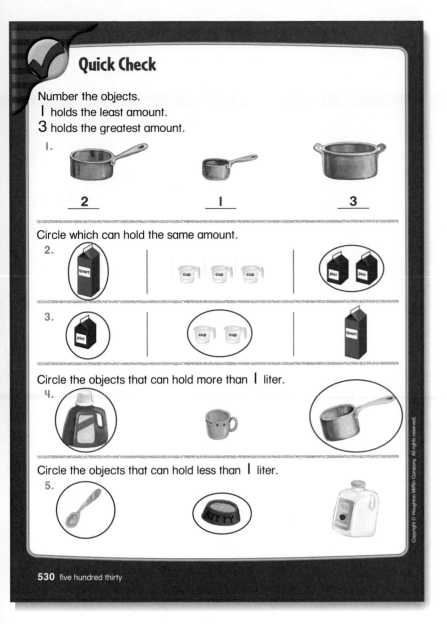

1.

    __2__   __1__   __3__

Circle which can hold the same amount.

2.

3.

Circle the objects that can hold more than 1 liter.

4.

Circle the objects that can hold less than 1 liter.

5.

Quick Check

Have children complete the Quick Check exercises independently to assess their understanding of concepts and skills taught in **Lessons 1–3**.

Item	Lesson	Error Analysis	Intervention
1	18.1	Children may assume a taller container holds more.	Reteach Resource 18.1 *Ways to Success* 18.1
2–3	18.2	Children may have difficulty remembering the relative size of a cup, pint, and quart.	Reteach Resource 18.2 *Ways to Success* 18.2
4–5	18.3	Children may try to determine capacity from the shape of a container and not consider the size.	Reteach Resource 18.3 *Ways to Success* 18.3

Temperature

PLANNING THE LESSON

MATHEMATICS OBJECTIVE
Understand the difference between hot and cold.

Use Lesson Planner CD-ROM for Lesson 18.4.

Daily Routines

Calendar
Have children look at the month on the calendar. Then ask children to name the season. Now have a volunteer describe today's weather. Discuss the kind of weather usually found during this season and whether today's weather is typical.

Sunday	Monday	Tuesday	Wednesday	Thursday	Friday	Saturday
			1	2	3	4
5	6	7	8	9	10	11
12	13	14	15	16	17	18
19	20	21	22	23	24	25
26	27	28	29	30	31	

Vocabulary
Explain that you can find the **temperature** by reading a **thermometer**. Temperature is measured in **degrees**. Ask children to say a temperature for a **hot** day and one for a **cold** day. Have children use one of the vocabulary terms to tell about today's weather.

Vocabulary Cards

Meeting North Carolina's Standards
Prepare for Grade 2 Standard 2.01 Estimate and measure using appropriate units.

Lesson Transparency
18.4

Problem of the Day
What unit should Trish use to measure her dog Spot?

How heavy Spot is (pounds or kilograms)

The length of Spot's tail (inches or centimeters)

Quick Review

2	3	7	8	6
3	2	0	0	3
+ 7	+3	+3	+3	+3
(12)	(8)	(10)	(11)	(12)

Lesson Quiz
Circle hot or cold.

1. 98 degrees (hot) cold
2. 31 degrees hot (cold)
3. 10 degrees hot (cold)

LEVELED PRACTICE

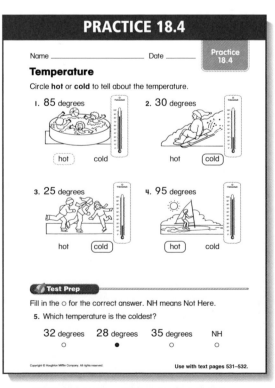

RETEACH 18.4

Name _____ Date _____ Reteach 18.4

Temperature
You can use the words **hot** and **cold** to describe the temperature.
Use a thermometer to measure temperature.

The temperature is 95 degrees.
95 degrees is hot.

The temperature is 30 degrees.
30 degrees is cold.

Circle **hot** or **cold** to tell about the temperature.

1. 25 degrees   hot (cold)
2. 100 degrees   (hot) cold

Copyright © Houghton Mifflin Company. All rights reserved.
Use with text pages 531–532.

PRACTICE 18.4

Name _____ Date _____ Practice 18.4

Temperature
Circle **hot** or **cold** to tell about the temperature.

1. 85 degrees   (hot) cold
2. 30 degrees   hot (cold)
3. 25 degrees   hot (cold)
4. 95 degrees   (hot) cold

Test Prep
Fill in the ○ for the correct answer. NH means Not Here.

5. Which temperature is the coldest?
32 degrees ○   28 degrees ●   35 degrees ○   NH ○

Copyright © Houghton Mifflin Company. All rights reserved.
Use with text pages 531–532.

ENRICHMENT 18.4

Name _____ Date _____ Enrichment 18.4

What to Wear
Read about the weather.
Decide what each child should wear.
Circle two things in each row.

1. It is very cold. The temperature is 30 degrees. What should Tim wear?

2. Megan is raking leaves. The temperature is 58 degrees. What should Megan wear?

3. It is a sunny day. The temperature is 80 degrees. What should John wear?

4. It is a very hot day. The temperature is 100 degrees. What should Lisa wear?

Talk About It How can knowing the temperature help you decide what to wear each day? **If I know the temperature, I know how hot or cold it is going to be.**

Copyright © Houghton Mifflin Company. All rights reserved.
Use with text pages 531–532.

Practice Workbook Page 125

Reaching All Learners

Differentiated Instruction

English Learners

Children will need to understand the words *hot* and *cold* in order to compare temperatures. Use Worksheet 18.4 to help English-language learners develop understanding of these words.

Inclusion
AUDITORY, TACTILE

Materials: *display thermometer (teacher-made)*

• Make a list of activities that take place in cold weather. Show appropriate cold temperatures on the thermometer, from 20 to 40 degrees.

• Then make a list of activities that take place in hot weather. Show hot temperatures from 90 to 110 degrees.

Early Finishers
VISUAL, AUDITORY

Materials: *cards with different temperature (teacher-made)*

• Have each child choose a card and draw a picture about what they might do, wear, or see on a day with this temperature.

• Have children create a hot-and-cold chart with pictures and temperatures. Display the chart for class discussion.

TECHNOLOGY

Spiral Review
To reinforce skills on lessons taught earlier, create **customized** spiral review worksheets using the *Ways to Assess* CD-ROM.

eBook
eMathBook allows students to review lessons and do homework without carrying their textbooks home.

Education Place
You can visit **Education Place** at **eduplace.com/math/mw/** for teacher support materials.

ScienceConnection

Introduce precipitation as water that falls to the Earth. 32°F is the freezing point of water. When the temperature is colder than 32°, it will fall as snow. When it is warmer than 32°, it will fall as rain. Ask children which weather they prefer—rain or snow.

MATH CENTER

Real-Life Activity

Help children understand the usefulness of mathematics. This activity makes math come alive by connecting the lesson skills to a real-life situation.

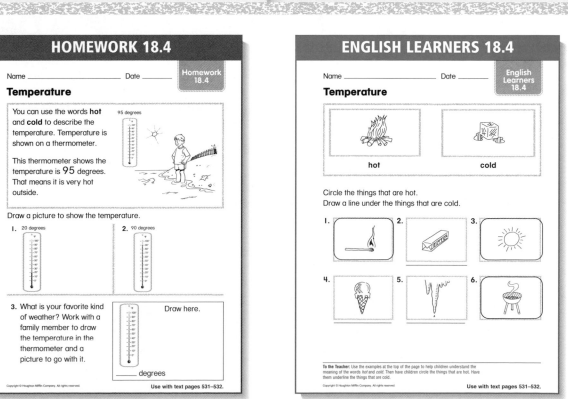

Homework Workbook Page 125

TEACHING LESSON 18.4

LESSON ORGANIZER

Objective Understand the difference between hot and cold.

Resources Reteach, Practice, Enrichment, Problem Solving, Homework, English Learners, Transparencies, Math Center

Materials Display thermometer (teacher-made), spinner (LT38)

Activity

Warm-Up Activity
Discussing Hot and Cold

| 👥 Small Group | 🕐 5–10 minutes | Auditory, Visual |

1. Have children discuss the weather in your area. Introduce weather that occurs in areas other than your own.

2. Have each group of children draw a story about what they do, see, and wear on a hot day in the summer.

3. Have children repeat using a cold day in the winter.

4. Have children exchange their stories. Discuss each picture with the class.

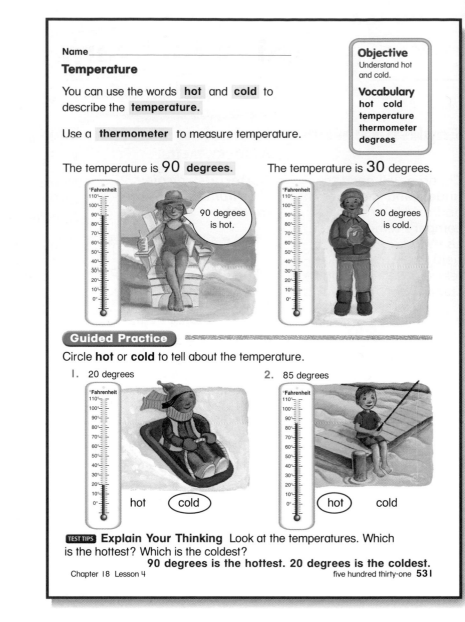

Name_____

Temperature

You can use the words **hot** and **cold** to describe the **temperature.**

Use a **thermometer** to measure temperature.

Objective
Understand hot and cold.

Vocabulary
hot cold
temperature
thermometer
degrees

The temperature is 90 **degrees.**   The temperature is 30 degrees.

90 degrees is hot.   30 degrees is cold.

Guided Practice

Circle **hot** or **cold** to tell about the temperature.

1. 20 degrees   2. 85 degrees

hot   (cold)   (hot)   cold

TEST TIPS **Explain Your Thinking** Look at the temperatures. Which is the hottest? Which is the coldest?

90 degrees is the hottest. 20 degrees is the coldest.

Chapter 18 Lesson 4   five hundred thirty-one **531**

---

1 Introduce
Activity
Discussing Temperture

| 👥 Whole Group | 🕐 10–15 minutes | Visual, Auditory |

Materials: *display thermometer (teacher-made)*

1. Discuss what children know about temperature and how a thermometer measures temperature. State the current temperature and show it on the thermometer.

2. **What might the thermometer look like on a hot day?** Show a thermometer reading 85 degrees. What do you wear when it is 85 degrees outside? (Answers may vary.)

3. Repeat for a cold day.

2 Develop

Guided Learning

Teaching Example Read the objective and vocabulary with children. Guide them through the example by reading the labels and referring to the picture and the thermometer. Emphasize that both can tell if the weather is hot or cold.

Guided Practice

Have children complete **Exercises 1–2** as you observe. Let children share their answers to the Explain Your Thinking question. You may want to write the four temperatures on the board as a reference.

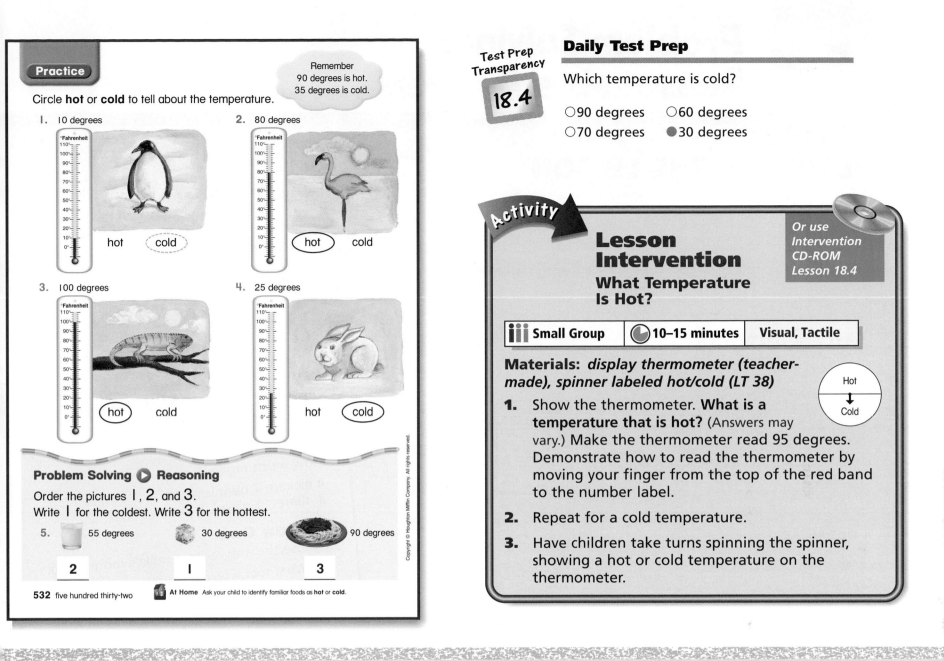

Practice

Circle **hot** or **cold** to tell about the temperature.

Remember
90 degrees is hot.
35 degrees is cold.

1. 10 degrees
hot ⟨cold⟩

2. 80 degrees
⟨hot⟩ cold

3. 100 degrees
⟨hot⟩ cold

4. 25 degrees
hot ⟨cold⟩

Problem Solving ▶ Reasoning

Order the pictures 1, 2, and 3.
Write 1 for the coldest. Write 3 for the hottest.

5. 55 degrees — **2**
30 degrees — **1**
90 degrees — **3**

532 five hundred thirty-two

At Home Ask your child to identify familiar foods as **hot** or **cold**.

Daily Test Prep

Which temperature is cold?

○ 90 degrees ○ 60 degrees
○ 70 degrees ● 30 degrees

Activity

Lesson Intervention

What Temperature Is Hot?

Or use Intervention CD-ROM Lesson 18.4

| 👤👤👤 Small Group | 🕙 10–15 minutes | Visual, Tactile |

Materials: *display thermometer (teacher-made), spinner labeled hot/cold (LT 38)*

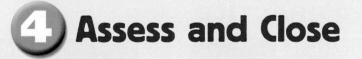

1. Show the thermometer. **What is a temperature that is hot?** (Answers may vary.) Make the thermometer read 95 degrees. Demonstrate how to read the thermometer by moving your finger from the top of the red band to the number label.

2. Repeat for a cold temperature.

3. Have children take turns spinning the spinner, showing a hot or cold temperature on the thermometer.

③ Practice

Independent Practice

Children complete **Exercises 1–4** independently.

Problem Solving

After children complete **Exercise 5,** call on volunteers to share their solutions. Record the temperatures from coldest to hottest on the board.

Common Error

Not Relating Hot and Cold to a Temperature

Some children may have difficulty relating the temperature to the concept of hot or cold. Help them make the relationship between the order of numbers and temperatures rising from cold to hot.

④ Assess and Close

What does a thermometer measure? (the temperature in degrees)

If the temperature is 85 degrees, is it hot or cold? (hot)
If the temperature is 35 degrees, is it hot or cold? (cold)

Keeping a Journal

Write about or draw a picture of yourself outside on a hot day.

Problem Solving: Reasonable Answers

PLANNING THE LESSON

MATHEMATICS OBJECTIVE
Determine the materials and strategies to be used to solve problems.

Use Lesson Planner CD-ROM for Lesson 18.5.

Daily Routines

Calendar
Ask children what tools they would use to find the hour of the day, the date, and the day of the week. Discuss the idea that different tools are useful for different jobs and the calendar is one of those tools.

Sunday	Monday	Tuesday	Wednesday	Thursday	Friday	Saturday
				1	2	3	4
5	6	7	8	9	10	11
12	13	14	15	16	17	18
19	20	21	22	23	24	25
26	27	28	29	30	31	

Vocabulary
Work with children to make a list of the words learned in the preceding measurement lessons—focus on tools and units. Have volunteers help you use the words in sentences.

Vocabulary Cards

Meeting North Carolina's Standards
2.01 For given objects:
- Select an attribute (length, capacity, mass) to measure (use non-standard units).

Lesson Transparency **18.5**

Problem of the Day
Rob and Luke each pick a pumpkin. Rob's pumpkin weighs 5 pounds. Together their pumpkins weigh 12 pounds. How many pounds is Luke's pumpkin? (7 pounds)

Quick Review
How much money?
4 nickels, 7 pennies (27¢)
3 dimes, 1 nickel, 8 pennies (43¢)

Lesson Quiz
Choose the answer that makes more sense.
1. What tool would you use to find which toy is heavier? ruler (balance)
2. What tool would you use to measure how long a car is? (ruler) balance

LEVELED PRACTICE

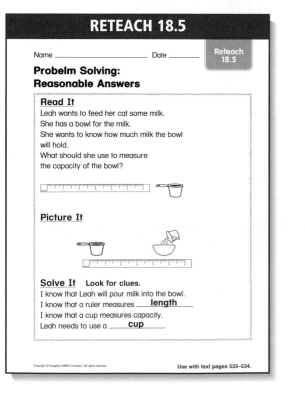

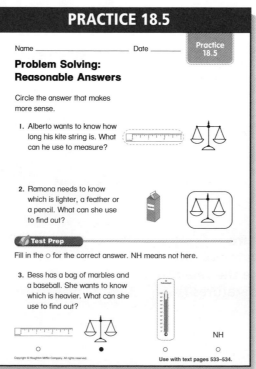

Practice Workbook Page 126

Reaching All Learners

Differentiated Instruction

English Learners

In order to generate reasonable answers to problems, children will need to understand the term *makes sense*. Use Worksheet 18.5 to develop English-language learners' ability to understand and use this term.

Inclusion
AUDITORY, TACTILE

Materials: *ruler, balance, liter measure, thermometer*

- Review the name of each tool and have the child tell you its use.
- Read a problem, such as, *I want to find out which rock is heavier. What tool should I use?* Have the child choose the tool. Repeat with different problems.

Early Finishers
AUDITORY

- Prepare problems that involve measuring tools.
- Have one child read the problem. For example, *Joni has a box that is 6 inches long. She has 3 books to put in the box. How can she measure the books to be sure they fit?* (with a ruler) Have the partner choose the correct measuring tool and explain why.

TECHNOLOGY

Spiral Review

Help students remember skills they learned earlier by creating **customized** spiral review worksheets using the *Ways to Assess* CD-ROM.

Lesson Planner

You can customize your teaching plan or meet your curriculum requirements with the **Lesson Planner CD-Rom.**

Intervention

Use the *Ways to Success* intervention software to support students who need more help in understanding the concepts and skills taught in this chapter.

Literature Connection

Share the book, *Numbers* (Math Counts) by Henry Pluckrose. Introduce the term 1 gallon as you discuss the photograph of the gasoline tank. Have children explore how much 1 gallon holds by pouring 4 quarts into an empty gallon container.

MATH CENTER

Number of the Week Activity

Display the Number of the Week to motivate children to use their problem-solving skills. The exercises cover topics across all math strands.

PROBLEM SOLVING 18.5

Name _____ Date _____

Problem Solving 18.5

Reasonable Answers

Paula needs 2 cups of milk to make hot chocolate. What tool should she use to measure the milk?

UNDERSTAND What do I need to find out?	I need to know what tool Paula will use to measure the milk.
PLAN What do I know about the tools in the pictures?	One measures height and length, one measures weight, and one measures capacity.
SOLVE Which tools do not measure milk?	ruler and scale
Which tool should Paula use?	cup
LOOK BACK How do I know my answer makes sense?	I can look carefully at a ruler and a scale in the classroom to see if they would work.

Copyright © Houghton Mifflin Company. All rights reserved.

Use with text pages 533–534.

HOMEWORK 18.5

Name _____ Date _____

Homework 18.5

Problem Solving Reasonable Answers

Terry wants to line up her teddy bears from the shortest to the tallest. Circle the tool she should use to measure the height of the bears.

Circle the answer that makes more sense.

1. Sadie is making cookies. She needs sugar. What can she use to measure it?

2. Pedro has 2 rocks. He wants to know which is heavier. What can he use to find out?

3. Rita needs to know the temperature in her greenhouse. What can she use to find out?

4. Work with a family member to make up problems about what tools to use.

Draw or write here.

Copyright © Houghton Mifflin Company. All rights reserved.

Use with text pages 533–534.

Homework Workbook Page 126

ENGLISH LEARNERS 18.5

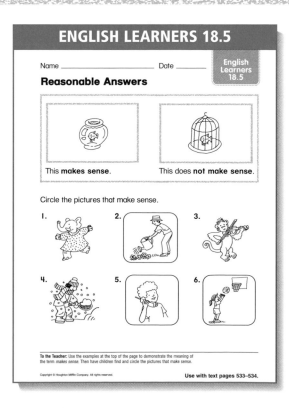

Name _____ Date _____

English Learners 18.5

Reasonable Answers

This **makes sense.**   This does **not make sense.**

Circle the pictures that make sense.

1.   2.   3.

4.   5.   6.

To the Teacher: Use the examples at the top of the page to demonstrate the meaning of the term *makes sense*. Then have children find and circle the pictures that make sense.

Copyright © Houghton Mifflin Company. All rights reserved.

Use with text pages 533–534.

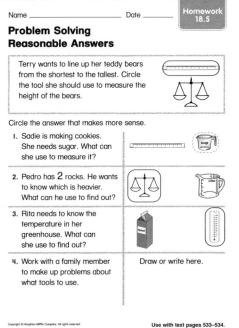

TEACHING 18.5

LESSON ORGANIZER

Objective Determine the materials and strategies to be used to solve problems.

Resources Reteach, Practice, Enrichment, Problem Solving, Homework, English Learners, Transparencies, Math Center

Materials Thermometer, ruler, balance, liter and quart measures, variety of measuring tools, classroom objects

Activity

Warm-Up Activity
Discuss Measuring Tools

| iii Small Group | 🕐 5 minutes | Auditory, Visual |

1. Review what children know about measuring tools. Make a chart with each tool.

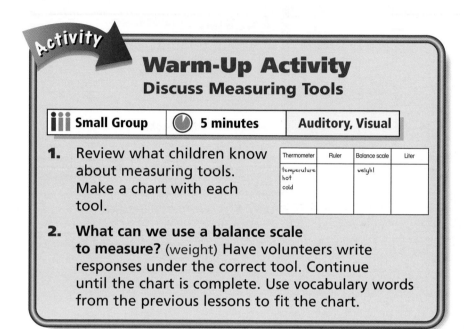

2. **What can we use a balance scale to measure?** (weight) Have volunteers write responses under the correct tool. Continue until the chart is complete. Use vocabulary words from the previous lessons to fit the chart.

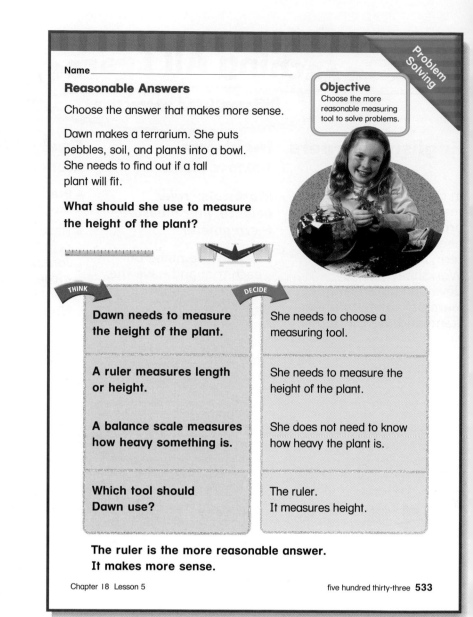

Name _____

Reasonable Answers

Choose the answer that makes more sense.

Dawn makes a terrarium. She puts pebbles, soil, and plants into a bowl. She needs to find out if a tall plant will fit.

What should she use to measure the height of the plant?

> **Objective**
> Choose the more reasonable measuring tool to solve problems.

THINK

Dawn needs to measure the height of the plant.	She needs to choose a measuring tool.
A ruler measures length or height.	She needs to measure the height of the plant.
A balance scale measures how heavy something is.	She does not need to know how heavy the plant is.
Which tool should Dawn use?	The ruler. It measures height.

DECIDE

The ruler is the more reasonable answer. It makes more sense.

---

1 Introduce
Model Reasonable Answers

| iiiii Whole Group | 🕐 10–15 minutes | Kinesthetic, Visual |

Materials: *thermometer, ruler, balance, liter and quart measures*

1. Display a hole puncher and scissors. Model how you would decide what tool to use for a job. **If you need to put holes in this paper, what's the best tool to use?** (the hole puncher) Reinforce it is the more reasonable of the two tools.

2. Display the measuring tools on a table. Pose problems that require measuring. For example: **I need to know the temperature of the hot water for our science experiment. What can I use to measure?** (the thermometer) Have volunteers come and identify the tool that makes the most sense for each job.

2 Develop

Guided Learning

Teaching Example Introduce the objective to the children. Guide them through the example problem. Encourage children to look for an answer that makes more sense. Emphasize that the answer is the name of a measuring tool and not a measurement.

Guided Practice

Have children complete **Exercises 1–2** on page 534 as you observe. Remind them to use the clues next to the problems.

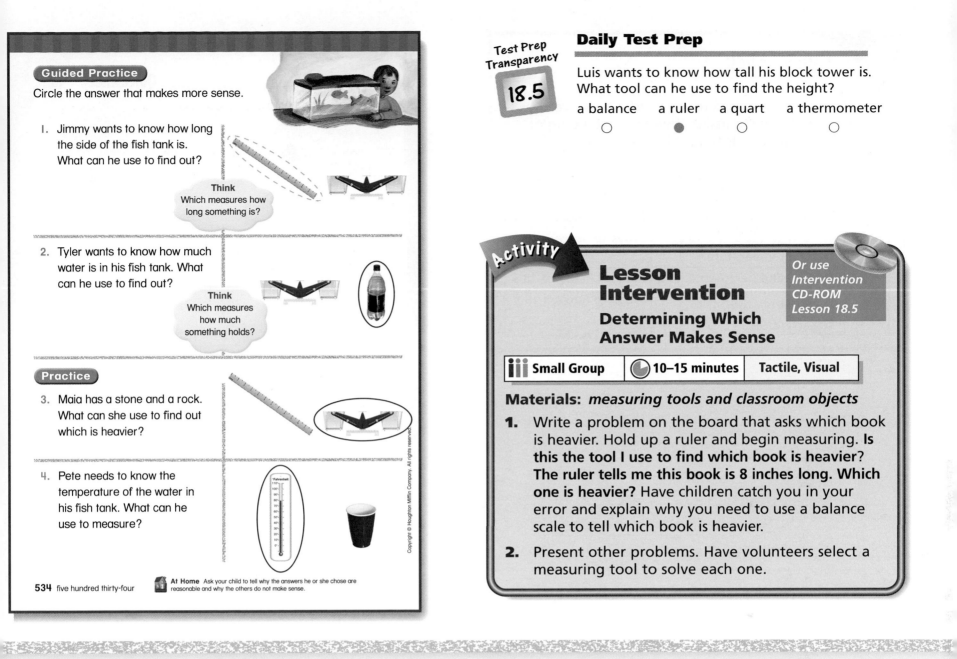

Daily Test Prep

Luis wants to know how tall his block tower is. What tool can he use to find the height?

a balance   a ruler   a quart   a thermometer
   ○   ●   ○   ○

Guided Practice

Circle the answer that makes more sense.

1. Jimmy wants to know how long the side of the fish tank is. What can he use to find out?

   Think Which measures how long something is?

2. Tyler wants to know how much water is in his fish tank. What can he use to find out?

   Think Which measures how much something holds?

Practice

3. Maia has a stone and a rock. What can she use to find out which is heavier?

4. Pete needs to know the temperature of the water in his fish tank. What can he use to measure?

534 five hundred thirty-four

 **At Home** Ask your child to tell why the answers he or she chose are reasonable and why the others do not make sense.

Activity

Lesson Intervention
Determining Which Answer Makes Sense

Or use Intervention CD-ROM Lesson 18.5

| 👥 Small Group | 🕐 10–15 minutes | Tactile, Visual |

Materials: *measuring tools and classroom objects*

1. Write a problem on the board that asks which book is heavier. Hold up a ruler and begin measuring. **Is this the tool I use to find which book is heavier? The ruler tells me this book is 8 inches long. Which one is heavier?** Have children catch you in your error and explain why you need to use a balance scale to tell which book is heavier.

2. Present other problems. Have volunteers select a measuring tool to solve each one.

③ Practice

Independent Practice

Children complete **Exercises 3–4** on page 534 independently.

Common Error

Confusing Tools and Their Use

Provide practice with discussing and selecting appropriate tools for different types of measures. Have children use the tools to make the measurements.

④ Assess and Close

You need to measure milk for a milkshake. Which measuring tool would you use? (Possible responses are a cup, pint, quart, or liter measure.)

What does a ruler measure? (length—how long something is, and height—how tall something is)

Keeping a Journal

Draw a picture or write the names of all the measuring tools you know.

Quick Check

Have children complete the Quick Check exercises independently to assess their understanding of concepts and skills taught in **Lessons 4–5**.

Item	Lesson	Error Analysis	Intervention
1–4	18.4	Children may not relate the concepts of hot and cold to temperature.	Reteach Resource 18.4 *Ways to Success* 18.4
5	18.5	Children may confuse tools and their use.	Reteach Resource 18.5 *Ways to Success* 18.5

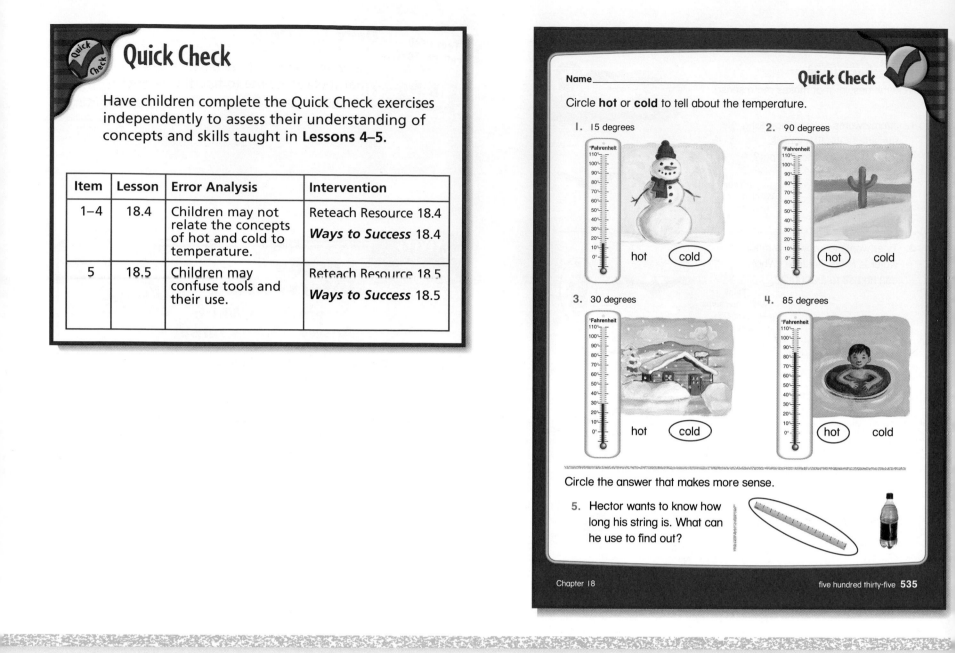

Name_____

Circle **hot** or **cold** to tell about the temperature.

1. 15 degrees

hot (cold)

2. 90 degrees

(hot) cold

3. 30 degrees

hot (cold)

4. 85 degrees

(hot) cold

Circle the answer that makes more sense.

5. Hector wants to know how long his string is. What can he use to find out?

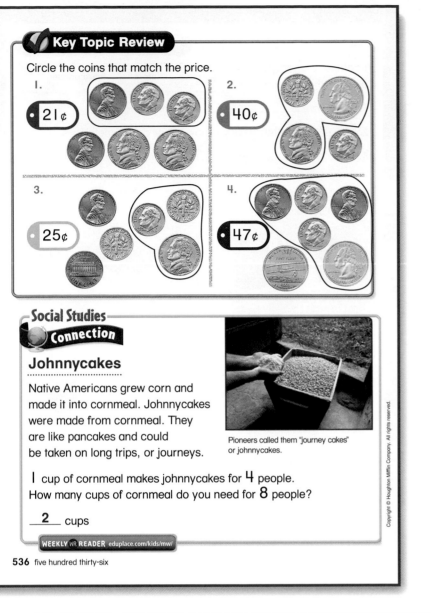

Circle the coins that match the price.

1. 21¢

2. 40¢

3. 25¢

4. 47¢

Social Studies Connection

Johnnycakes

Native Americans grew corn and made it into cornmeal. Johnnycakes were made from cornmeal. They are like pancakes and could be taken on long trips, or journeys.

Pioneers called them "journey cakes" or johnnycakes.

1 cup of cornmeal makes johnnycakes for 4 people. How many cups of cornmeal do you need for 8 people?

___2___ cups

WEEKLY WR READER eduplace.com/kids/mw/

Key Topic Review

This assessment provides a review of skills and concepts taught in Chapter 14.

Check to be sure that children:

• can find the value of a group of dimes, nickels and pennies

• can identify and count with quarters

Social Studies Connection

Johnnycakes

Corn has been grown in North America for over 7,000 years. The Native American name for corn was *maize*.

Pioneers used cornmeal to make Johnnycakes. The following recipe is more tasty than the original, which was made of cornmeal and water. A griddle is required, so all safety precautions must be taken. Have children help measure the ingredients.

1 cup cornmeal

1 egg

$1\frac{1}{2}$ cups milk

1 teaspoon sugar

1 teaspoon salt

Preheat a griddle to 375 degrees. Mix together milk and egg. Add remaining ingredients and mix into a thin batter. Put shortening in pan. Pour batter as you would for pancakes. Turn when bubbles appear and edges begin to dry. Cook other side. Serve alone or with syrup or jelly.

Chapter Review/Test

Purpose: This test provides an informal assessment of the Chapter 18 objectives.

Chapter Test Items 1–15

To assign a numerical grade for this Chapter Test, use 6 points for each test item and add 10 to the score.

Check Understanding

Use children's work on word problems to informally assess progress on chapter content.

Customizing Your Instruction

For children who have not yet mastered these objectives, you can use the reteaching resources listed in the chart below.

 Assessment Options

A summary test for this chapter is also provided in the Unit Resource Folder.

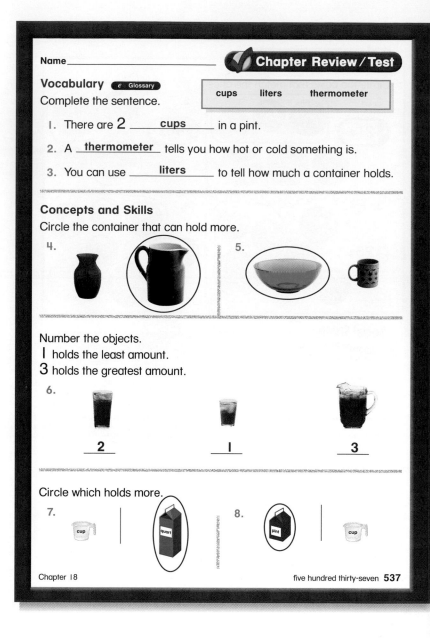

Reteaching Support

Chapter Test Items	Summary Test Items	Chapter Objectives Tested	TE Pages	Use These Reteaching Resources
1–3	6–7	**18A** Develop and use math vocabulary relating to capacity and temperature.	525A–529, 531A–532	Reteach Resources and *Ways to Success* CD: 18.2–18.4 Skillsheet 129
4–11	1–5	**18B** Compare and order the capacity of containers using cups, pints, quarts, and liters.	523A–529	Reteach Resources and *Ways to Success* CD: 18.1–18.3 Skillsheets 130 and 131
12–14	6–7	**18C** Understand hot and cold.	531A–532	Reteach Resource *Ways to Success* CD: 18.4 Skillsheet 132
15	8–10	**18D** Choose the most reasonable measuring tool to solve problems.	533A–534	Reteach Resource *Ways to Success* CD: 18.5 Skillsheet 133

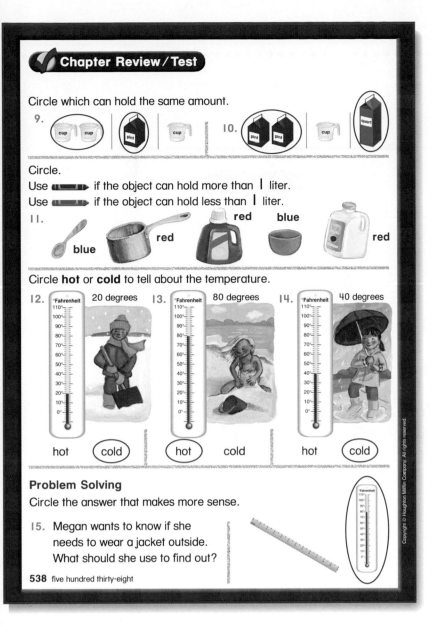

Chapter Review / Test

Circle which can hold the same amount.

9.

10.

Circle.
Use ▬▬▶ if the object can hold more than 1 liter.
Use ▬▬▶ if the object can hold less than 1 liter.

11.

blue   red   **red**   **blue**   red

Circle **hot** or **cold** to tell about the temperature.

12. 20 degrees   13. 80 degrees   14. 40 degrees

hot   (cold)   hot   cold   hot   (cold)

Problem Solving

Circle the answer that makes more sense.

15. Megan wants to know if she needs to wear a jacket outside. What should she use to find out?

Adequate Yearly Progress

Use the End of Grade Test Prep Assessment Guide to help familiarize your children with the format of standardized tests.

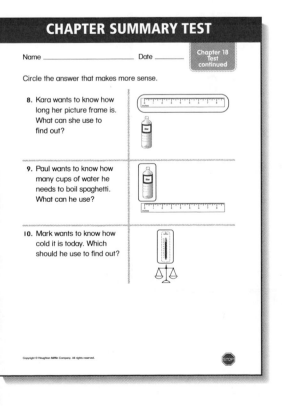

CHAPTER SUMMARY TEST

Name _____ Date _____

Chapter 18
Test
continued

Circle the answer that makes more sense.

8. Kara wants to know how long her picture frame is. What can she use to find out?

9. Paul wants to know how many cups of water he needs to boil spaghetti. What can he use?

10. Mark wants to know how cold it is today. Which should he use to find out?

Facts Practice ....

Name_____

Add.
Write the sum.

1.
$\begin{array}{r} 5 \\ +7 \\ \hline 12 \end{array}$
$\begin{array}{r} 2 \\ +9 \\ \hline 11 \end{array}$
$\begin{array}{r} 5 \\ +5 \\ \hline 10 \end{array}$
$\begin{array}{r} 8 \\ +1 \\ \hline 9 \end{array}$
$\begin{array}{r} 1 \\ +3 \\ \hline 4 \end{array}$
$\begin{array}{r} 5 \\ +3 \\ \hline 8 \end{array}$
$\begin{array}{r} 3 \\ +6 \\ \hline 9 \end{array}$

2.
$\begin{array}{r} 5 \\ +2 \\ \hline 7 \end{array}$
$\begin{array}{r} 7 \\ +1 \\ \hline 8 \end{array}$
$\begin{array}{r} 9 \\ +0 \\ \hline 9 \end{array}$
$\begin{array}{r} 6 \\ +4 \\ \hline 10 \end{array}$
$\begin{array}{r} 3 \\ +3 \\ \hline 6 \end{array}$
$\begin{array}{r} 1 \\ +4 \\ \hline 5 \end{array}$
$\begin{array}{r} 7 \\ +4 \\ \hline 11 \end{array}$

3.
$\begin{array}{r} 2 \\ +6 \\ \hline 8 \end{array}$
$\begin{array}{r} 7 \\ +3 \\ \hline 10 \end{array}$
$\begin{array}{r} 4 \\ +2 \\ \hline 6 \end{array}$
$\begin{array}{r} 3 \\ +4 \\ \hline 7 \end{array}$
$\begin{array}{r} 7 \\ +2 \\ \hline 9 \end{array}$
$\begin{array}{r} 6 \\ +6 \\ \hline 12 \end{array}$
$\begin{array}{r} 3 \\ +7 \\ \hline 10 \end{array}$

4.
$\begin{array}{r} 6 \\ +4 \\ \hline 10 \end{array}$
$\begin{array}{r} 3 \\ +5 \\ \hline 8 \end{array}$
$\begin{array}{r} 8 \\ +0 \\ \hline 8 \end{array}$
$\begin{array}{r} 0 \\ +0 \\ \hline 0 \end{array}$
$\begin{array}{r} 1 \\ +5 \\ \hline 6 \end{array}$
$\begin{array}{r} 9 \\ +2 \\ \hline 11 \end{array}$
$\begin{array}{r} 3 \\ +5 \\ \hline 8 \end{array}$

5.
$\begin{array}{r} 3 \\ +9 \\ \hline 12 \end{array}$
$\begin{array}{r} 6 \\ +5 \\ \hline 11 \end{array}$
$\begin{array}{r} 2 \\ +7 \\ \hline 9 \end{array}$
$\begin{array}{r} 9 \\ +1 \\ \hline 10 \end{array}$
$\begin{array}{r} 0 \\ +6 \\ \hline 6 \end{array}$
$\begin{array}{r} 3 \\ +8 \\ \hline 11 \end{array}$
$\begin{array}{r} 1 \\ +1 \\ \hline 2 \end{array}$

6.
$\begin{array}{r} 4 \\ +8 \\ \hline 12 \end{array}$
$\begin{array}{r} 2 \\ +5 \\ \hline 7 \end{array}$
$\begin{array}{r} 0 \\ +1 \\ \hline 1 \end{array}$
$\begin{array}{r} 2 \\ +3 \\ \hline 5 \end{array}$
$\begin{array}{r} 9 \\ +3 \\ \hline 12 \end{array}$
$\begin{array}{r} 3 \\ +2 \\ \hline 5 \end{array}$
$\begin{array}{r} 2 \\ +2 \\ \hline 4 \end{array}$

7.
$\begin{array}{r} 2 \\ +4 \\ \hline 6 \end{array}$
$\begin{array}{r} 4 \\ +0 \\ \hline 4 \end{array}$
$\begin{array}{r} 8 \\ +3 \\ \hline 11 \end{array}$
$\begin{array}{r} 6 \\ +2 \\ \hline 8 \end{array}$
$\begin{array}{r} 4 \\ +7 \\ \hline 11 \end{array}$
$\begin{array}{r} 4 \\ +5 \\ \hline 9 \end{array}$
$\begin{array}{r} 8 \\ +4 \\ \hline 12 \end{array}$

Chapter 18   five hundred thirty-nine **539**

Facts Practice

Subtract.
Write the difference.

1.
$$\begin{array}{r} 12 \\ -\ 5 \\ \hline 7 \end{array} \quad \begin{array}{r} 10 \\ -\ 2 \\ \hline 8 \end{array} \quad \begin{array}{r} 7 \\ -1 \\ \hline 6 \end{array} \quad \begin{array}{r} 10 \\ -\ 7 \\ \hline 3 \end{array} \quad \begin{array}{r} 9 \\ -4 \\ \hline 5 \end{array} \quad \begin{array}{r} 7 \\ -5 \\ \hline 2 \end{array} \quad \begin{array}{r} 11 \\ -\ 4 \\ \hline 7 \end{array}$$

2.
$$\begin{array}{r} 9 \\ -9 \\ \hline 0 \end{array} \quad \begin{array}{r} 11 \\ -\ 2 \\ \hline 9 \end{array} \quad \begin{array}{r} 10 \\ -\ 5 \\ \hline 5 \end{array} \quad \begin{array}{r} 5 \\ -4 \\ \hline 1 \end{array} \quad \begin{array}{r} 12 \\ -\ 4 \\ \hline 8 \end{array} \quad \begin{array}{r} 10 \\ -\ 8 \\ \hline 2 \end{array} \quad \begin{array}{r} 9 \\ -3 \\ \hline 6 \end{array}$$

3.
$$\begin{array}{r} 11 \\ -\ 7 \\ \hline 4 \end{array} \quad \begin{array}{r} 12 \\ -\ 3 \\ \hline 9 \end{array} \quad \begin{array}{r} 10 \\ -\ 9 \\ \hline 1 \end{array} \quad \begin{array}{r} 6 \\ -2 \\ \hline 4 \end{array} \quad \begin{array}{r} 4 \\ -4 \\ \hline 0 \end{array} \quad \begin{array}{r} 10 \\ -\ 3 \\ \hline 7 \end{array} \quad \begin{array}{r} 9 \\ -2 \\ \hline 7 \end{array}$$

4.
$$\begin{array}{r} 12 \\ -\ 8 \\ \hline 4 \end{array} \quad \begin{array}{r} 7 \\ -6 \\ \hline 1 \end{array} \quad \begin{array}{r} 8 \\ -3 \\ \hline 5 \end{array} \quad \begin{array}{r} 12 \\ -\ 7 \\ \hline 5 \end{array} \quad \begin{array}{r} 9 \\ -6 \\ \hline 3 \end{array} \quad \begin{array}{r} 6 \\ -4 \\ \hline 2 \end{array} \quad \begin{array}{r} 11 \\ -\ 5 \\ \hline 6 \end{array}$$

5.
$$\begin{array}{r} 11 \\ -\ 6 \\ \hline 5 \end{array} \quad \begin{array}{r} 2 \\ -0 \\ \hline 2 \end{array} \quad \begin{array}{r} 12 \\ -\ 6 \\ \hline 6 \end{array} \quad \begin{array}{r} 7 \\ -2 \\ \hline 5 \end{array} \quad \begin{array}{r} 8 \\ -1 \\ \hline 7 \end{array} \quad \begin{array}{r} 10 \\ -\ 4 \\ \hline 6 \end{array} \quad \begin{array}{r} 12 \\ -\ 8 \\ \hline 4 \end{array}$$

6.
$$\begin{array}{r} 12 \\ -\ 4 \\ \hline 8 \end{array} \quad \begin{array}{r} 9 \\ -5 \\ \hline 4 \end{array} \quad \begin{array}{r} 11 \\ -\ 9 \\ \hline 2 \end{array} \quad \begin{array}{r} 5 \\ -3 \\ \hline 2 \end{array} \quad \begin{array}{r} 7 \\ -4 \\ \hline 3 \end{array} \quad \begin{array}{r} 8 \\ -2 \\ \hline 6 \end{array} \quad \begin{array}{r} 6 \\ -5 \\ \hline 1 \end{array}$$

7.
$$\begin{array}{r} 12 \\ -\ 3 \\ \hline 9 \end{array} \quad \begin{array}{r} 4 \\ -3 \\ \hline 1 \end{array} \quad \begin{array}{r} 7 \\ -3 \\ \hline 4 \end{array} \quad \begin{array}{r} 11 \\ -\ 5 \\ \hline 6 \end{array} \quad \begin{array}{r} 8 \\ -4 \\ \hline 4 \end{array} \quad \begin{array}{r} 6 \\ -3 \\ \hline 3 \end{array} \quad \begin{array}{r} 12 \\ -\ 7 \\ \hline 5 \end{array}$$

Science Connection

PURPOSE

To use an inch ruler and compare and order length and capacity.

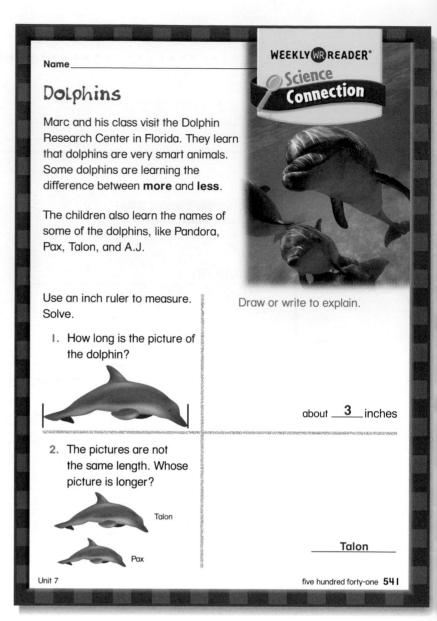

Name_____

Dolphins

Marc and his class visit the Dolphin Research Center in Florida. They learn that dolphins are very smart animals. Some dolphins are learning the difference between **more** and **less**.

The children also learn the names of some of the dolphins, like Pandora, Pax, Talon, and A.J.

Use an inch ruler to measure. Solve.

Draw or write to explain.

1. How long is the picture of the dolphin?

   about ___3___ inches

2. The pictures are not the same length. Whose picture is longer?

   Talon

   Pax

   ___Talon___

Unit 7   five hundred forty-one 541

Using These Pages

Discussion Topics

- Read the paragraphs on dolphins and have the children solve problems one and two.

- Tell children that a dolphin's snout, or nose, is called a *rostrum*. The rostrum is usually about 3 inches long. **Is this length longer or shorter than your hand?** Measure to check.

- Read and discuss the chart on the amount of food the dolphins eat.

- Refer children to the chart. **Which dolphin eats the fewest fish?** (Pandora)

- **Which fish bucket would be heavier, A.J.'s or Pax's?** (A.J.'s)

Dolphin	Pounds of Fish
Pandora	9
A.J.	12
Pax	11
Talon	20

Dolphins eat fish every day. This is how much fish each dolphin eats in one day.

Solve.

Draw or write to explain.

1. A.J. and Pandora are eating together. How many more pounds of fish does A.J. eat than Pandora?

   ___**3**___ more pounds of fish

2. Which dolphin eats the most pounds of fish?

   Talon

Circle.

3. In the morning Pax eats fewer pounds of fish than Talon. Which bucket holds fewer pounds of fish?

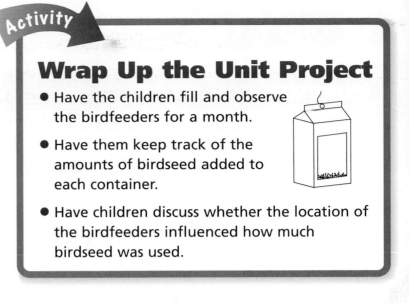

Technology
Visit *Education Place* at **eduplace.com/kids/mw/** to learn more about this topic.

Activity

Wrap Up the Unit Project

- Have the children fill and observe the birdfeeders for a month.

- Have them keep track of the amounts of birdseed added to each container.

- Have children discuss whether the location of the birdfeeders influenced how much birdseed was used.

PURPOSE

This test provides an informal assessment of the Unit 7 objectives.

Unit Test Items 1-15

To assign a numerical grade for this Unit Test, use 6 points for each test item and add 10 to the score.

Customizing Your Instruction

For children who have not yet mastered these objectives, you can use the **Reteaching Resources** listed in the chart below. **Ways to Success** is Houghton Mifflin's Intervention program available in CD-ROM and blackline master formats.

Name_____ **Unit 7 Test**

Vocabulary *e Glossary*

Match the word to the correct statement.

1. inch — a measure of how heavy an object is
2. weight — a unit to measure temperature
3. degree — a unit to measure length
4. pound — a unit to measure weight

Concepts and Skills

First estimate.
Then use an inch ruler to measure. **Estimates may vary.**

5.

Estimate: about _____ inches | Measure: about __3__ inches

First estimate.
Then use a centimeter ruler to measure. **Estimates may vary.**

6.

Estimate: about _____ centimeters | Measure: about __6__ centimeters

Circle the heavier object.

7. 8.

Circle the objects that weigh more than 1 pound.

9.

Unit 7 five hundred forty-three **543**

Reteaching Support

Unit Test Item			Unit Objectives Tested		TE Pages	Use These Reteaching Resources
P. 543–544 1, 5–6	Tests A & B 1–6	7A	Estimate and measure length using nonstandard units, inches, and centimeters.		501A–506	Reteach Resources and *Ways to Success*, 17.2–7.4
2, 4, 7–10	7–11	7B	Compare and order objects using nonstandard weights, pounds, and kilograms.		509A–514	Reteach Resources and *Ways to Success*, 17.5–7.7
11–12	2–17, 20	7C	Compare and order capacity of containers.		525A–526	Reteach Resource and *Ways to Success*, 18.2
3, 13–14	18–19	7D	Understand hot and cold using a F° thermometer.		531A–532	Reteach Resource *and Ways to Success*, 18.4
15	21–23	7E	Choose an appropriate measuring tool.		533A–534	Reteach Resource and *Ways to Success*, 18.5
15	24–25	7F	Apply skills and strategies to solve problems.		533A–534	Reteach Resource and *Ways to Success*, 18.5

Unit 7 Test

Circle the objects that are more than 1 kilogram.

10.

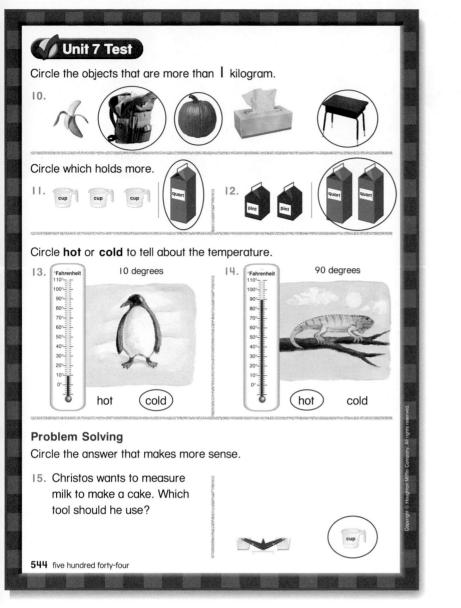

Circle which holds more.

11.

12.

Circle **hot** or **cold** to tell about the temperature.

13. 10 degrees

hot (cold)

14. 90 degrees

(hot) cold

Problem Solving

Circle the answer that makes more sense.

15. Christos wants to measure milk to make a cake. Which tool should he use?

544 five hundred forty-four

Assessment Options

Formal Tests for this unit are also provided in the Unit Resource Folder.

- **Unit 7 Test A (Open Response)**
- **Unit 7 Test B (Multiple Choice)**

Performance Assessment

You may want to use the Performance Assessment instead of, or in addition to, the Unit Test. Three Performance Assessment tasks can be found on Student Book pages 545–546.

Adequate Yearly Progress

Use the *End of Grade Test Prep Assessment Guide* to help familiarize your children with the format of standardized tests.

UNIT TEST A

Name _____ Date _____ Unit 7 Test A

Circle the item that is about as long as the paper clips.

1.

2.

Circle the item that is about as long as the number of inches shown.

3. 3 inches

4. 2 inches

Copyright © Houghton Mifflin Company. All rights reserved.

Go on

Unit 7 Tests

See pages 545A–545B for answers.

UNIT TEST B

Name _____ Date _____ Unit 7 Test B

Fill in the ○ for the correct answers.

Find the picture that is about as long as the measure shown.

1.

2.

3. 5 inches

4. 2 inches

Copyright © Houghton Mifflin Company. All rights reserved.

Go on

Unit Test Answers: Form A

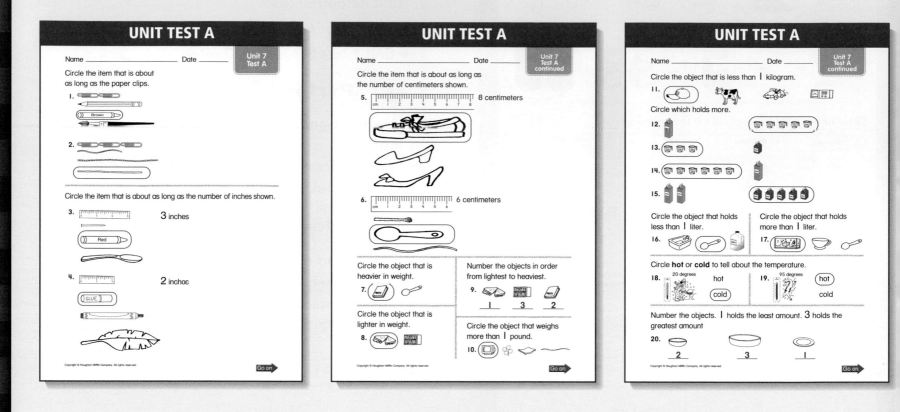

Unit Test Answers: Form B

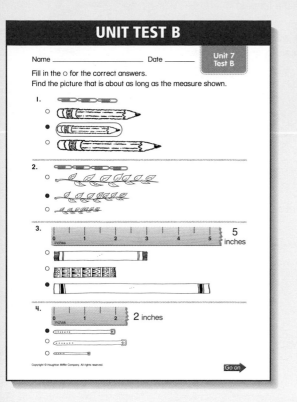

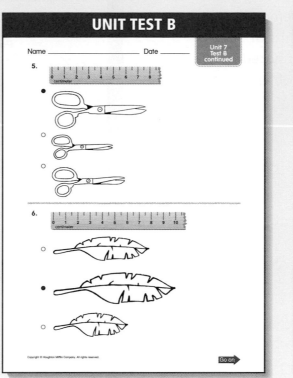

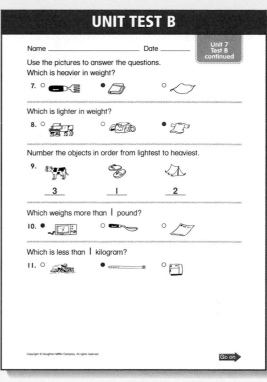

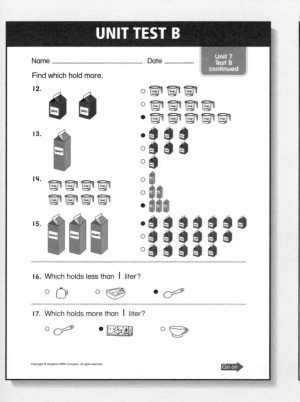

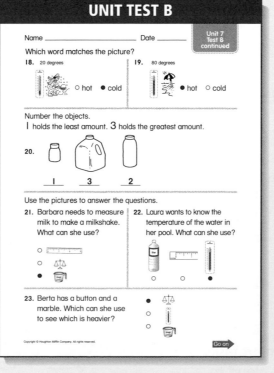

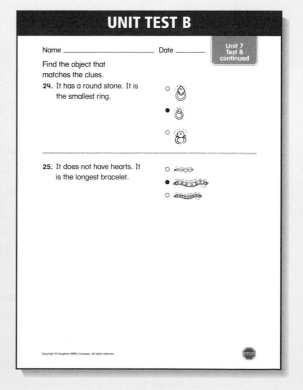

Performance Assessment

PURPOSE

This assessment focuses on concepts of length and weight. Children should be able to demonstrate an understanding of the tools and units of measure in the customary and metric systems, and apply skills and strategies to solve problems.

1. Draw a fish that is about **2** inches long.
   Draw a turtle that is about **15** centimeters long.
   Draw a worm that is shorter than the fish.

   Which animal is the longest?

   Show your work using pictures, numbers, or words.
   Possible answer shown.

   turtle

2. Draw a picture of something that weighs less than **1** pound.

   Show your work using pictures, numbers, or words.

   Answers may vary.

Using These Pages

- Draw a line 1 inch long on the board. **What can you find in the classroom that is about one inch long?** Allow children to bring objects to the board to measure against the line. Help them classify the objects as: about one inch long; shorter than one inch; and longer than one inch.

- Draw a line 5 centimeters long on the board. **What can you find in the classroom that is about 5 centimeters long?** Continue the activity as you did for 1 inch long objects.

- Direct children's attention to assessment tasks. You may wish to read the directions aloud to the children.

- Observe children as they work to complete the tasks.

Exercise One

In Exercise 1, children should be able to compare and draw approximations of given lengths.

Exercise Two

In Exercise 2, children should be able to identify and draw an object that weighs less than a pound.

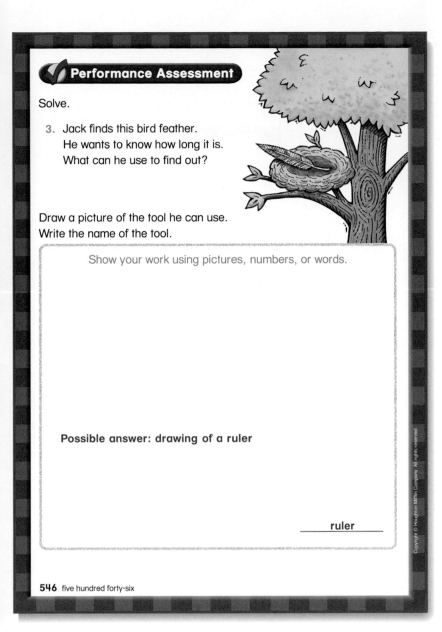

Performance Assessment

Solve.

3. Jack finds this bird feather. He wants to know how long it is. What can he use to find out?

Draw a picture of the tool he can use. Write the name of the tool.

Show your work using pictures, numbers, or words.

Possible answer: drawing of a ruler

_____ruler_____

546 five hundred forty-six

Exercise Three

In Exercise 3 children should be able to choose the appropriate measuring tool needed to solve the problem. (ruler)

Assessing Student Work

Use the **Scoring Rubric** to evaluate children's performance on these tasks.

Scoring Rubric

4 EXEMPLARY

Estimates, compares, and draws figures to given lengths and weight correctly, and chooses the appropriate tool to solve problems.

3 PROFICIENT

Estimates, compares, and draws figures to given lengths and weight correctly. Solution to problems demonstrates mathematical reasoning, although the reasoning is faulty.

2 ACCEPTABLE

Estimates, compares, and draws figures to given lengths and weight correctly. Solution to problems is incorrect or incomplete.

1 LIMITED

Estimates, compares, or draws figures to given lengths or weight incorrectly. Solution to problems shows no mathematical reasoning.

UNIT 7

Enrichment

▶ Using a Ruler

PURPOSE

This page provides an opportunity for children to apply their understanding of measurement by having them identify and measure inches and centimeters.

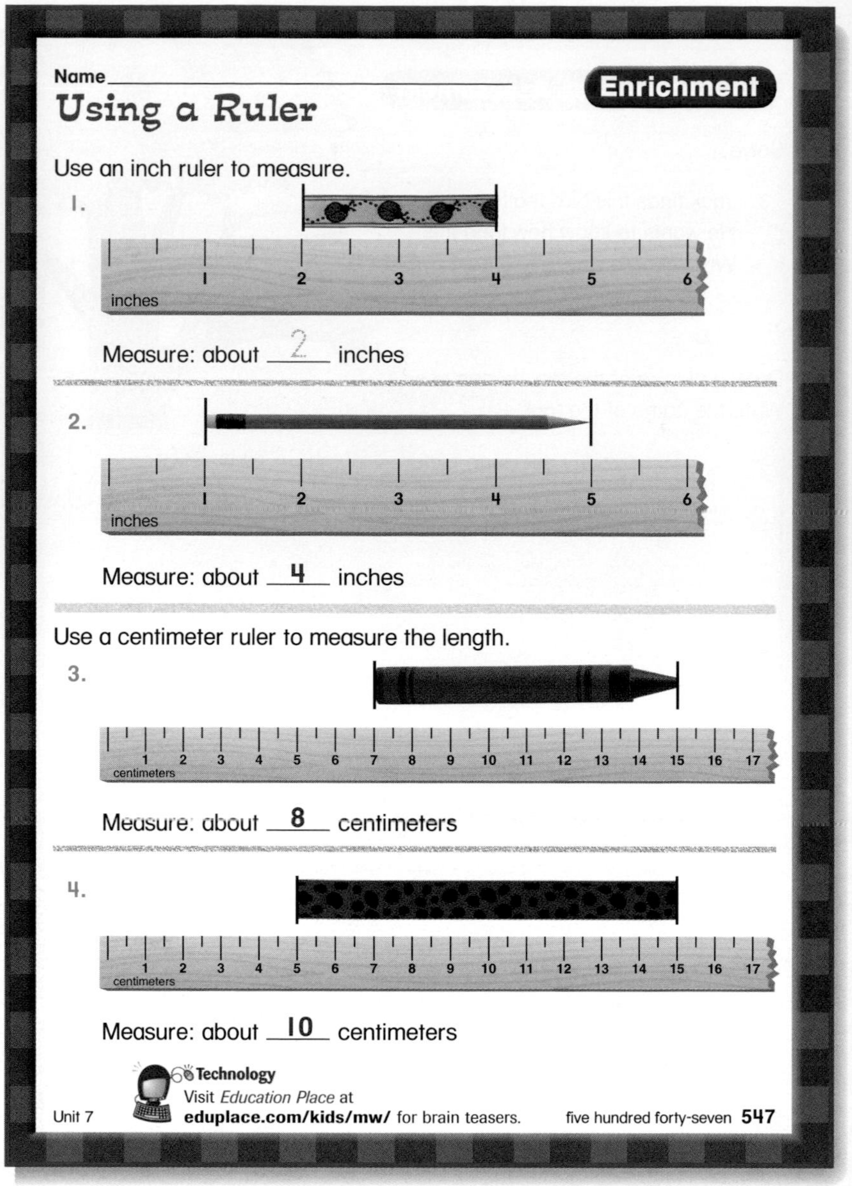

Name_____

Using a Ruler

Enrichment

Use an inch ruler to measure.

1.

Measure: about __2__ inches

2.

Measure: about __4__ inches

Use a centimeter ruler to measure the length.

3.

Measure: about __8__ centimeters

4.

Measure: about __10__ centimeters

Technology
Visit *Education Place* at
eduplace.com/kids/mw/ for brain teasers.

Unit 7

five hundred forty-seven **547**

Using This Page

Discussion Topics

- This page extends Chapter 17, Lessons 3 and 4, by having children identify and measure inches and centimeters.

- You may want to begin by reviewing how rulers are used to measure. Stress that when measuring, the end of the ruler can match up with the end of the object being measured or lined up with any inch or centimeter mark on the ruler. Measurement doesn't begin at the number 1 on the ruler. Be sure students count the spaces between the inch or centimeter marks from the beginning to the end of the object to get the correct measurement.

- Explain that length can be measured with inch rulers and centimeter rulers. Have the children find the two kinds of rulers shown on p. 547. Emphasize that Exercises 1–2 use inch rulers while Exercises 3–4 use centimeter rulers.

- Have children work individually or in pairs to complete the page. Children can take turns solving the exercises and then checking each other's work.

Technology Time

Calculator
Fill It Up!

There are 2 pints in 1 quart.
How many pints are in 5 quarts?

Use a 🖩 .

Find the number of pints in 5 quarts.

Press: 2 + 2 = ▢4

> Each time you press = ,
> 2 more will be added.

Press: = = = ▢10   ___10___ pints

Use a 🖩 .
Complete the table.

1.

Pints	1 pint	2 pints	3 pints	4 pints
Cups	2 cups	4 cups	6 cups	8 cups

2.

Quarts	1 quart	2 quarts	3 quarts	4 quarts
Pints	2 pints	4 pints	6 pints	8 pints

3.

Quarts	1 quart	2 quarts	3 quarts	4 quarts
Cups	4 cups	8 cups	12 cups	16 cups

Explain Your Thinking Which is greater, 6 cups or
4 pints? Why?   **4 pints is greater. There are 8 cups in 4
pints. 8 cups is greater than 6 cups.**

548 five hundred forty-eight

Technology Time

FILL IT UP!

PURPOSE

To provide an opportunity for children to use a
calculator when working with measurement.

Using This Page

Discussion Topics

- This is another way for the children to work with
  cups, pints, and quarts.

- You may want to review using the equal sign on a
  calculator when adding the same number several
  times.

- Work through the example with the children. Ask:
  How many cups are in a pint? (2) **How many pints
  are in a quart?** (2) **How many pints are in 3 quarts?**
  (6)

- Read the remaining questions and allow time for
  the children to complete. When the page is
  completed, have children share answers with a
  partner. Discuss Explain Your Thinking with the class.

Cumulative Test Prep

▶ Practice Test

PURPOSE

This page will familiarize children with the multiple-choice and open-response formats of many standardized state tests. Children can mark their responses directly on these pages. You may wish to read each multiple choice test item and the answer choices aloud to the children.

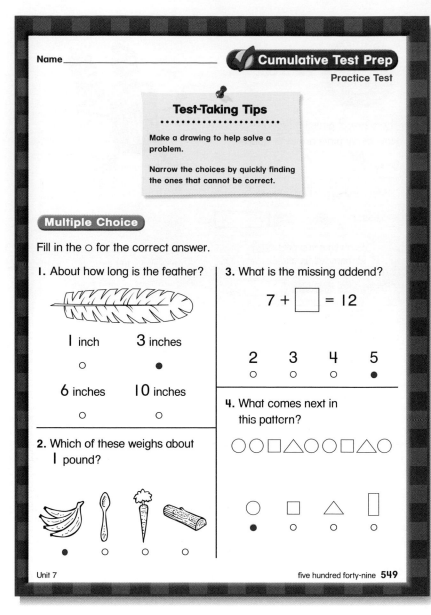

Name_____

✓ Cumulative Test Prep
Practice Test

Test-Taking Tips
....

Make a drawing to help solve a problem.

Narrow the choices by quickly finding the ones that cannot be correct.

Multiple Choice

Fill in the ○ for the correct answer.

1. About how long is the feather?

1 inch   3 inches
○   ●

6 inches   10 inches
○   ○

2. Which of these weighs about 1 pound?

●   ○   ○   ○

3. What is the missing addend?

7 + ☐ = 12

2   3   4   5
○   ○   ○   ●

4. What comes next in this pattern?

○○□△○○□△○

○   □   △   ▯
●   ○   ○   ○

Unit 7   five hundred forty-nine **549**

Test-Taking TIPS

Review the test-taking tips with children before they begin the test. Remind children to narrow their choices by ruling out obviously incorrect answers.

- Remind children to be sure their answer fits what the question asked.
- Encourage children to look for important word clues like *next, after, before, between*.

- Remind children to go back and check their work.
- Remind children that NH means Not Here. Tell them that this means that the correct answer is not shown.

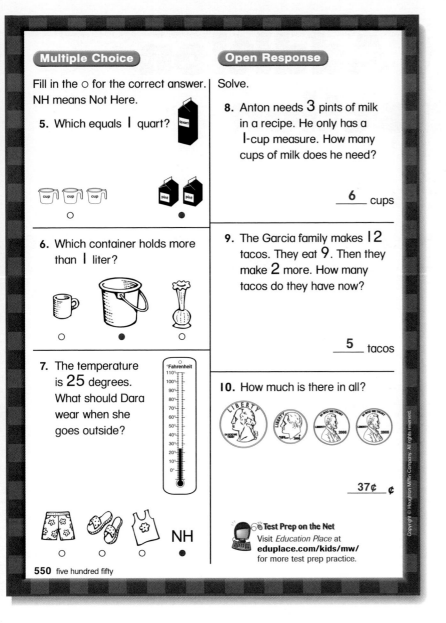

Multiple Choice

Fill in the ○ for the correct answer.
NH means Not Here.

5. Which equals 1 quart?

○   ●

6. Which container holds more than 1 liter?

○   ●   ○

7. The temperature is 25 degrees. What should Dara wear when she goes outside?

°Fahrenheit

○   ○   ○   ● NH

Open Response

Solve.

8. Anton needs 3 pints of milk in a recipe. He only has a 1-cup measure. How many cups of milk does he need?

_____6_____ cups

9. The Garcia family makes 12 tacos. They eat 9. Then they make 2 more. How many tacos do they have now?

_____5_____ tacos

10. How much is there in all?

_____37¢_____ ¢

Test Prep on the Net
Visit *Education Place* at
eduplace.com/kids/mw/
for more test prep practice.

Test-Taking Vocabulary

- Have a volunteer measure the *length* of two objects. Have another volunteer name tools and units for measuring length.

- Review weight and capacity terms with children. Say words like *pound, kilogram, liter, cup, pint, quart,* aloud. Have children tell you whether they belong in a column labeled *Weight* or *Capacity*. Write the words in the appropriate column on the board.

- Ask a volunteer to give an example of when to use a *thermometer*. Discuss temperature during different seasons.

National and state tests may use these words with measurement problems:

- *height*
- *length*

Two-Digit Addition and Subtraction

Unit at a Glance

Assessment System

Assessing Prior Knowledge

Check whether children understand the prerequisite concepts and skills.

- **CHAPTER PRETEST** (Unit Resource Folder or Ways to Success Intervention CD-ROM)
- **WARM-UP ACTIVITY:** Every TE Lesson
- **UNIT LITERATURE ACTIVITY:** PE p. 552

Ongoing Assessment

Monitor whether children are acquiring new concepts and skills.

- **PROBLEM OF THE DAY:** First page of every TE lesson
- **QUICK REVIEW:** First page of every TE lesson
- **LESSON QUIZ:** First page of every TE lesson
- **COMMON ERROR:** Every TE Lesson
- **QUICK CHECK:** PE pp. 564, 575, 588, 597, 610, 619, 634, 643
- **KEY TOPIC REVIEW:** PE pp. 576, 598, 620, 644

Test Prep and Practice

Help children prepare for state and standardized tests.

- **DAILY TEST PREP:** Every TE Lesson
- **CUMULATIVE TEST PREP:** PE pp. 655–656
- **PROBLEM SOLVING FOR TESTS:** PE pp. 574, 618
- **TEST PREP ON THE NET:** eduplace.com/kids/mw
- **TEST-TAKING STRATEGIES:** eduplace.com/math/mw

Summary Assessment

Assess children's mastery of new concepts and skills.

- **CHAPTER TEST:**
    - ✔ PE pp. 577–578, 599–600, 621–622, 645–646
    - ✔ Unit Resource Folder
- **UNIT TEST:**
    - ✔ PE pp. 649–650
    - ✔ Test A, Unit Resource Folder
    - ✔ Test B, Unit Resource Folder

TEST TIPS Student Self-Assessment

Allow children to evaluate their own understanding.

- **EXPLAIN YOUR THINKING:** PE pp. 557, 559, 561, 565, 567, 569, 581, 583, 585, 589, 591, 593, 603, 605, 607, 611, 613, 625, 627, 629, 631, 635, 637

Performance Assessment

Evaluate children's ability to use mathematics in real-world situations.

PERFORMANCE ASSESSMENT: PE pp. 651–652
WRITE ABOUT IT OR TALK ABOUT IT: in Hands-On lessons
WRITING MATH: CREATE AND SOLVE: PE p. 587

Technology Options

Use computer-based assessment to make testing and reporting easier.

- **WAYS TO ASSESS** (CD-ROM, LAN, or Web spiral review and test creation, administration, scoring, and report generation)
- **LEARNER PROFILE** (observations, evaluations, and reports from your handheld or desktop computer)

Reaching All Learners

Resources	On Level Students	Extra Support Students	English Learners	Inclusion/ Special Needs	Advanced Learners	Mathematically Promising
Student Editions						
Building Vocabulary	●	●	●	●	●	●
Guided Practice ✱	●	●	●	●	●	●
MathTracks MP3 Audio CD	●	●	○	○		
Teacher's Editions						
Building Vocabulary Strategies	●	●	●	○		
Teacher Support	●	○	●		○	○
Intervention Activities	○	●	●	●		
Other Resources						
Chapter Challenges	○				●	●
Combination Classroom Guide	●	●	●	●	●	●
English Learners Handbook	○	○	●	○		
Ways to Success CD-ROM	○	●	●	●		

KEY   ● **Highly Appropriate**   ○ **Appropriate**   ✱ **Scaffolded Instruction**

Documenting Adequate Yearly Progress
National Test Correlations

UNIT 8 Objectives		ITBS	Terra Nova (CTBS)	CAT	SAT	MAT
8A	Use addition concepts and strategies to find the sum of two and three addends to 20.	●	●	●	●	●
8B	Subtract from 20 using subtraction concepts and strategies.	●	●	●	●	●
8C	Add 2-digit numbers, including money amounts, without regrouping.	●	●	●	●	●
8D	Subtract 2-digit numbers, including money amounts, without regrouping.	●	●	●	●	●
8E	Apply skills and strategies to solve problems.	●	●	●	●	●

Activities for Reaching All Learners

Home-School Activity

Totally Tens

Materials: number cards 3–7 (3 sets), 4-part spinner labeled: add 10, subtract 10, add 20, subtract 20

Shuffle number cards and place facedown. One player chooses 2 cards and makes a two-digit number. Player spins the spinner and follows the directions. Next player repeats. After each round players compare their sums and differences, the greatest number scores 1 point. Play 5 rounds.

Unit Vocabulary Activity

Double Points

Materials: vocabulary cards: make a ten, doubles, doubles plus one; addition/subtraction cards (with doubles, doubles plus one, and make a ten exercises)

Place vocabulary cards face up. Place addition/subtraction cards facedown. Each child takes a card, solves it, and places it below the strategy they used. Score 1 point for each correct answer. Play 5 rounds.

Remediation

MathTracks Lessons 19.3, 19.5, 19.6, 20.5, 20.6, 20.7, 21.2, 21.3, 21.6, 22.2, 22.3, 22.6

Use the MathTracks CD-ROM to help children who need a quick review or extra support for the lesson, to provide children who were absent with complete lesson presentation, or to assist children with reading difficulties.

Intervention

Ways to Success CD-ROM

Use the Ways to Success CD-ROM to help children who need extra help with lessons. This software is designed to reteach the lesson objective, provide extra guided and independent practice, and if needed, reteach a key prerequisite skill.

Unit Project

Books, Books, Books!

Math Topics:

- use parts and wholes in addition
- relate addition to subtraction
- add two-digit numbers
- subtract two-digit numbers

To Begin

- Set up a book area for 20–30 books. Have children sort the books. For example: animal stories, picture books and holiday books.
- Explain to children that in this Unit Project, they will select, read, and keep track of the number of books read.

Ongoing

- Have children write 2-digit addition and subtraction stories about characters in the books. Then children trade stories and use place value blocks to solve
- For Connecting to the Unit Project see page 555D for Chapter 19, page 579D for Chapter 20, page 601D for Chapter 21, and page 623D for Chapter 22.

To Finish

- Create "Bella the Bookworm" to show the total number of books read each week. Make a head from construction paper. Give children colored circles to add for each book read. Change the color for each 10 books read.
- When the project is finished, have children count to find the total number of books read by the class.
- See page 648 to Wrap Up the Unit Project.

Starting Unit 8
Accessing Prior Knowledge

UNIT 8

Two-Digit Addition and Subtraction

From the Read-Aloud Anthology
one watermelon seed
story by Celia Barker Lottridge • pictures by Karen Patkau

Access Prior Knowledge
This story will help you review
· Counting by tens
· Tens and ones

551a

Max and Josephine planted a garden.

The rain fell and the sun shone. The seeds and the leaves, the stalks and the vines grew and grew and grew.

Max and Josephine weeded and watered and waited. One day they looked at their garden and saw there was plenty to pick. So . . .

551b from *one watermelon seed*

Accessing Prior Knowledge

In Unit 4, children:

• count and regroup tens and ones

• read and write numbers through 100

• choose the appropriate operation

This selection from the Unit Opener gives you the opportunity to review some of these prerequisite skills.

• You may wish to review counting by tens by having children count by tens from 10 to 100. Have a different child say each number.

• You may also wish to review tens and ones by writing 57 on the board and asking a volunteer to tell how many tens and how many ones.

Story Summary

Today you will be reading a story about plants in a garden. The title of the story is *One Watermelon Seed*. The author is Celia Barker Lottridge.

Reading the Story

You can find the entire text of the book at the end of the Teacher's Edition on page T57.

Read the selection aloud to children. Then read it again, having children write the number words they hear.

This story is available in the Read-Aloud Anthology, Volume 4

Max picked thirty eggplants, dark and purple,
and forty peppers, shiny yellow.

551c

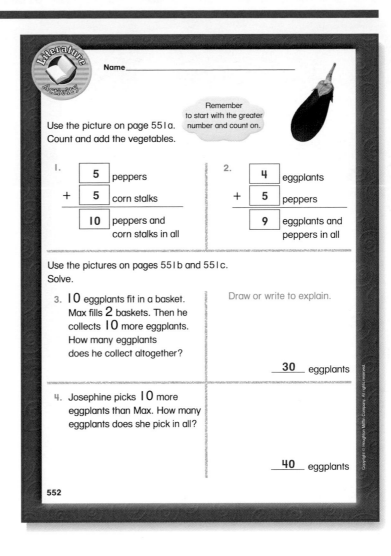

Name _____

Use the picture on page 551a.
Count and add the vegetables.

Remember to start with the greater number and count on.

1.
| 5 | peppers |
+ | 5 | corn stalks |
| 10 | peppers and corn stalks in all |

2.
| 4 | eggplants |
+ | 5 | peppers |
| 9 | eggplants and peppers in all |

Use the pictures on pages 551b and 551c.
Solve.

3. 10 eggplants fit in a basket. Max fills 2 baskets. Then he collects 10 more eggplants. How many eggplants does he collect altogether?

Draw or write to explain.

___30___ eggplants

4. Josephine picks 10 more eggplants than Max. How many eggplants does she pick in all?

___40___ eggplants

552

Unit Bibliography

A Collection for Kate
by Barbara deRubertis

Counting Cranes
by Mary Beth Owens

Dinner at the Panda Palace
by Stephanie Calmenson

Lights Out!
by Lucille Recht Penner

One Watermelon Seed
by Celia Barker Lottridge

See also the **Math and Literature Bibliography** in the Teacher Support Handbook at the back of this Teacher's Edition.

Literature Activity

Purpose: This activity provides an opportunity to informally assess children's understanding of adding tens and counting on to add.

Using This Page

- Begin by discussing which types of vegetables are shown on page 551a. Note that some may be partially hidden behind leaves or other vegetables. Then point out the peppers and eggplants on pages 551b and 551c again noting that some may be partially covered by others.

- Observe children as they work to complete Exercises 1–2. **When we add, do we count on or back?** (count on)

- As children complete Exercises 3–4, be sure they line up tens and ones correctly. Ask a volunteer to share his or her work for Exercise 3.
(10 + 10 + 10 = 30)

UNIT 8   Two-Digit Addition and Subtraction
Math At Home

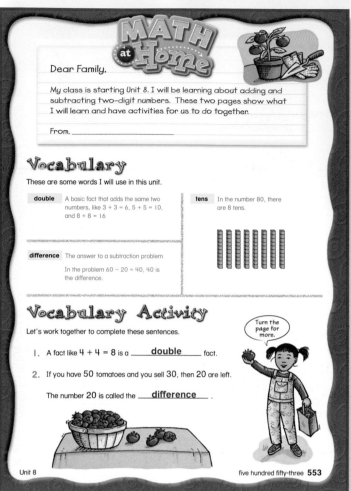

Dear Family,

My class is starting *Unit 8.* I will be learning about adding and subtracting two-digit numbers. These two pages show what I will learn and have activities for us to do together.

From, _____

Vocabulary

These are some words I will use in this unit.

| **double** | A basic fact that adds the same two numbers, like 3 + 3 = 6, 5 + 5 = 10, and 8 + 8 = 16 |
| **tens** | In the number 80, there are 8 tens. |

| **difference** | The answer to a subtraction problem. In the problem 60 − 20 = 40, 40 is the difference. |

Vocabulary Activity

Let's work together to complete these sentences.

1. A fact like 4 + 4 = 8 is a ___**double**___ fact.

2. If you have 50 tomatoes and you sell 30, then 20 are left. The number 20 is called the ___**difference**___ .

Turn the page for more.

Unit 8   five hundred fifty-three **553**

How To subtract two-digit numbers

This two-digit subtraction problem is an example of what I will be learning. Sometimes I will use tens and ones blocks to help me find the answer.

Find 38 − 15.

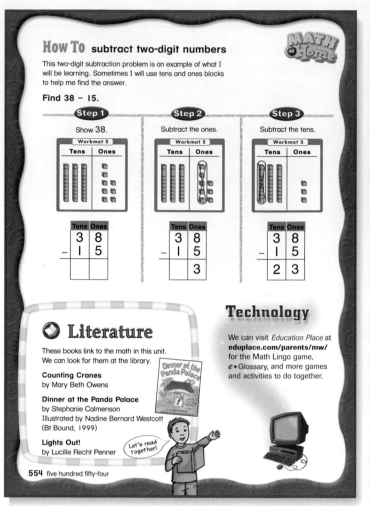

Step 1	Step 2	Step 3
Show 38.	Subtract the ones.	Subtract the tens.

Literature

These books link to the math in this unit. We can look for them at the library.

Counting Cranes
by Mary Beth Owens

Dinner at the Panda Palace
by Stephanie Calmenson
Illustrated by Nadine Bernard Westcott
(Bt Bound, 1999)

Lights Out!
by Lucille Recht Penner

Let's read together!

Technology

We can visit *Education Place* at **eduplace.com/parents/mw/** for the Math Lingo game, *e•*Glossary, and more games and activities to do together.

554 five hundred fifty-four

Math at Home

Discuss the letter to the family with children. You may want to use this letter as an introduction to the unit. Highlight for children what they will be learning in the unit. Tell children that as they go through the unit they will be able to answer the questions on these pages.

Math at Home is available in Spanish and other languages on Education Place.
www.eduplace.com/math/mw/

Literature

Encourage parents to find the suggested books and read them with their children.

Technology

Education Place is an award-winning website with engaging activities for students and helpful information for parents. Look for the eGlossary, the Math Lingo Game, and more.

Building Vocabulary

Strategies for Building Vocabulary

Using Doubles

Make a **doubles, doubles plus 1,** and **doubles plus 2** sequence train on the board. Remind children that **doubles** problems use the same addend twice. Ask a volunteer for an example of a doubles number sentence. Have him or her write the number sentence on the chalkboard in the first car of a new train. Ask another volunteer to continue the train with the matching **doubles plus 1** fact. Have a third volunteer complete the train for **doubles plus 2**.

Ask volunteers if they notice any patterns in the train. Make another train beginning with a new doubles fact.

Graphic Organizer: Sequence Train

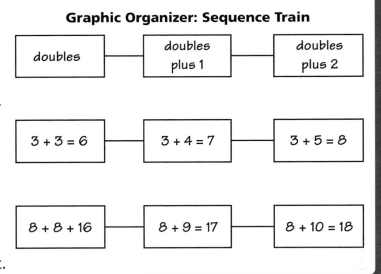

doubles		doubles plus 1		doubles plus 2
$3 + 3 = 6$		$3 + 4 = 7$		$3 + 5 = 8$
$8 + 8 + 16$		$8 + 9 = 17$		$8 + 10 = 18$

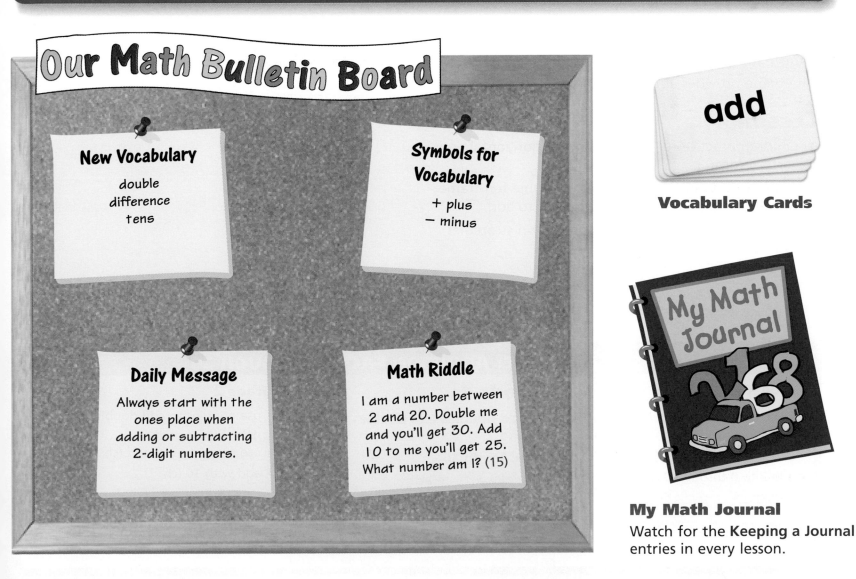

Our Math Bulletin Board

New Vocabulary
double
difference
tens

Symbols for Vocabulary
+ plus
− minus

Daily Message
Always start with the ones place when adding or subtracting 2-digit numbers.

Math Riddle
I am a number between 2 and 20. Double me and you'll get 30. Add 10 to me you'll get 25. What number am I? (15)

add

Vocabulary Cards

My Math Journal

My Math Journal
Watch for the **Keeping a Journal** entries in every lesson.

Lesson by Lesson Overview
Addition Facts Through 20

Lesson 1

- This lesson focuses on doubles and doubles plus one.
- Children find the sum of the double and then use that fact to find the double plus one. $6 + 6$ $6 + 7$ $7 + 6$

Lesson 2

- In this lesson, children explore adding with 10.
- They use counters on a double ten-frame workmat to show 10 and add from 1 to 10 more. Then they write the addition sentence. This skill is used in the next lesson.
- Practice is also provided in vertical form.

Lesson 3

- Ten frames are also used in this lesson as children make a 10 to add facts such as $8 + 4$.
- Children show both addends. Then they move counters to make a 10 and find the sum of 10 plus the new addend. $8 + 4$ has the same sum as $10 + 2$.
- A game provides addition practice.

Lesson 4

- Children practice sums through 20 in horizontal and vertical form.
- A part-part-whole workmat and a double ten-frame workmat are used to model two ways to add.
- Children use these methods or their own strategies to find sums.

Lesson 5

- Part-part-whole is used as children find all the facts for a given sum.
- Algebra readiness has children find the missing part, given the whole and one part.

Lesson 6

- This lesson teaches children to use addition strategies to add 3 numbers.
- Adding in any order is a practical strategy. Children use doubles or make a 10. They also look for facts they know.

Lesson 7

- Children are taught to write a number sentence to solve a problem.
- A part-part-whole model is used to help children organize the information in the problem.
- Children choose a strategy to practice previously learned problem-solving strategies.

SKILLS TRACE: ADDITION FACTS THROUGH 20

Grade K	Grade 1	Grade 2
• model addition (ch. 13)	• add doubles and doubles plus one	• use doubles to add doubles plus one (ch. 2)
• complete addition sentences (ch. 13)	• add with 10	• use properties to add (ch. 2)
• add 1 to 0 through 9 (ch. 13)	• make a 10 to add	• add with 10 (ch. 2)
• add 2 to 0 through 8 (ch. 13)	• practice addition	• make a 10 to add 7, 8, or 9 (ch. 2)
	• find facts for a given sum	• find the sum of three 1-digit numbers (ch. 2)
	• find the sum of three numbers	

Chapter Planner

Lesson	Objective	Vocabulary	Materials	✔ NCTM Standards
19.1 **Doubles Plus One** p. 557A	Find doubles and doubles plus one to sums of 20.	double	two-color counters, overhead counters, blank transparency, cubes	Develop fluency with basic number combinations for addition and subtraction.
19.2 **Add with Ten** **(Hands-On)** p. 559A	Add numbers 1 through 10 to the number 10.		cubes, Workmat 2, place-value blocks, two-color counters, overhead two color counters, ten frame transparency	Develop fluency with basic number combinations for addition and subtraction.
19.3 **Make a Ten to Add** **(Hands-On)** p. 561A	Make a 10 as a strategy to learn addition facts.		two-color counters, ten frames transparency, overhead two-color counters, cubes, Workmat 2, ten frame transparency	Compute fluently and make reasonable estimates.
19.4 **Addition Practice** **(Hands-On)** p. 565A	Use strategies to practice addition.		two-color counters, Part-Part-Whole Mat transparency, Workmat 3, overhead two-color counters, Workmat 2, ten frames transparency	Compute fluently and make reasonable estimates.
19.5 **Names for Numbers** **(Hands-On)** p. 567A	Find different names for the same number.		two-color counters, Part-Part-Whole Mat transparency, cubes, Workmat 3, overhead two-color counters	Understand numbers, ways of representing numbers, relationships among numbers, and number systems.
19.6 **Add Three Numbers** p. 569A	Find the sum of three numbers.		cubes, number cards (Learning Tools (LT) 14 and 15), 2 sets of number cards 1–12, two-color counters	Understand meanings of operations and how they relate to one another.
19.7 **Problem Solving: Write a Number Sentence** p. 571A	Write a number sentence to solve a problem.		Workmat 3, Part-Part-Whole Mat transparency, two-color counters, overhead two-color counters	Solve problems that arise in mathematics and in other contexts.

Resources For Reaching All Learners

LESSON RESOURCES: Reteach, Practice, Enrichment, Problem Solving, Homework, English Learners, Daily Routines, Transparencies, Math Center.

ADDITIONAL RESOURCES FROM HOUGHTON MIFFLIN: Chapter Challenges, Combination Classroom Planning Guide, Every Day Counts, Math to Learn (Student Handbook)

Every Day Counts
The *Counting Tape* activities in **Every Day Counts** support the math in this chapter.

Assessing Prior Knowledge

Before beginning the chapter, you can assess student understandings in order to assist you in differentiating instruction.

Complete Chapter Pretest in Unit Resource Folder

Use this test to assess both prerequisite skills (**Are You Ready?** — one page) and chapter content (**Check What You Know** — two pages).

Chapter 19 Prerequisite Skills Pretest

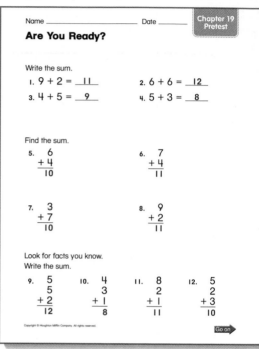

Chapter 19 New Content Pretest

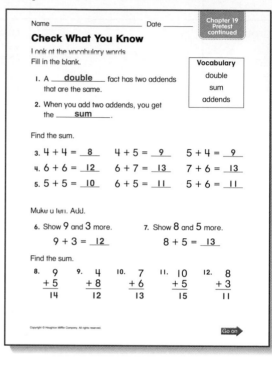

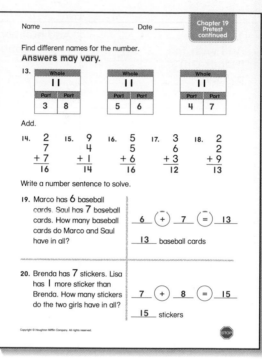

Customizing Instruction

For Students Having Difficulty

Items	Prerequisites	Ways to Success
1–4	Complete horizontal addition with sums through 12.	CD:19b Skillsheet 134
5–8	Complete vertical addition with sums through 12.	CD:5a Skillsheet 135
9–12	Add 3 digits with sums through 12.	CD:19d Skillsheet 136

Ways to Success: Intervention for every concept and skill (CD-ROM or Chapter Intervention Skillsheets).

For Students Having Success

Items	Objectives	Resources
1–2	19A Use vocabulary relating to addition facts through 20.	Enrichment 19.1, 19.2
3–12	19B Use strategies to find sums to 20.	Enrichment 19.1–19.4
13–18	19C Add three numbers and use parts and wholes to find different names for numbers.	Enrichment 19.5–19.6
19–20	19D Write a number sentence to solve a problem.	Enrichment 19.7

Use **Chapter Challenges** with any students who have success with all new chapter content.

Other Pretest Options

Informal Pretest

The pretest assesses vocabulary and prerequisite skills needed for success in this chapter.

Ways to Success **CD-ROM**

The *Ways to Success* chapter pretest has automatic assignment of appropriate review lessons.

Chapter Resources

Assessing Prior Knowledge

Names for 8 (use addition facts to name numbers)

- Display a number, such as 8, in the math center.
- Have children use addition facts to write as many ways as they can to make 8. (4 + 4, 5 + 3, 6 + 2, 7 + 1, 8 + 0) Have them compare their responses.
- Repeat the activity for the numbers 9–12.

Ongoing Skill Activity

Addition Stories (find sums to 20)

- Have children work with partners for this activity. Give each pair two number cubes 4–9.
- Have one child roll the cubes and make up an addition story for the numbers. The partner writes an addition sentence for the story and solves. The first child checks the addition.
- Children take turns making up addition stories and solving.

Connecting to the Unit Project

- Tell children the following problem: **Carlos sorts 18 books in two equal piles. How many books are in each pile?**
- Tell children to record the number of 18 as the whole, and then determine the two parts. Have them record the numbers.
- Ask volunteers to tell how many books are in each pile. (9 books)

Professional Resources Handbook

Research, Mathematics Content, and Language Intervention

Research-Based Teaching

Research has shown that primary-grade children tend to use direct modeling, counting, and derived-fact strategies (Bergeron & Herscovics, 1990). Usually, direct modeling is the first strategy to appear for any given type of problem. Then children replace direct modeling by mental counting strategies such as "using doubles" or "making 10s." See *Professional Resources Handbook, Grade 1*, Unit 8.

For more ideas relating to Unit 8, see the Teacher Support Handbook at the back of this Teacher's Edition.

Language Intervention

In China, the basic addition facts are taught using an approach that reinforces the importance of 10 as a special organizer of our number system. When sums from 11 to 18 are introduced, children use the make-a-ten strategy. For further explanation, see "Mathematical Language and Addition Facts" in the *Professional Resources Handbook Grade 1*.

Technology

Time-Saving Technology Support
Ways to Assess Customized Spiral Review
   Test Generator CD
Lesson Planner CD-ROM
Ways to Success Intervention CD-ROM
MathTracks CD-ROM
Education Place: www.eduplace.com/math/mw
Houghton Mifflin Math eBook CD-ROM
eManipulatives
eGames

Starting Chapter 19
Addition Facts Through 20

CHAPTER OBJECTIVES

19A Develop and use math vocabulary relating to addition facts through 20.

19B Use strategies such as doubles, doubles plus one, and make ten to find sums through 20.

19C Add three numbers and use parts and wholes to practice addition and to find different names for the same number.

19D Write a number sentence to solve a problem.

Math Background

Addition Facts Through 20

Using addition strategies is an important part in children's learning addition facts through 20. One strategy children use is counting on by 1, 2, or 3. Children are familiar with using doubles to add. The doubles are $1 + 1$, $2 + 2$, and so on, up to $9 + 9$. Doubles plus one is another strategy that children can use to learn addition facts. The answer to the addition fact $8 + 9$ can be easily found by thinking of it as a double plus one: $8 + 8 + 1 = 17$.

Children may also use the combinations to 10 strategy. Using this strategy enables children to recognize numbers whose sums are 10, for example, $6 + 4$ or $1 + 9$. Learning to make a ten is a key skill as children progress to finding the sum of three numbers. Once children learn the addition facts through 20, they are introduced to different ways to make the same sum. For example, $8 + 6 = 14$ and $9 + 5 = 14$.

Using The Investigation

- Write the doubles fact $5 + 5 = 10$ on the board. Remind children that a *double fact* adds the same number twice. Ask another volunteer to tell the matching *doubles plus one fact*. ($5 + 6 = 11$) Write it below the double fact. Repeat with other double facts and doubles plus one facts. Tell children that *doubles* and *doubles plus* one are more strategies to help them add.

- Read the directions to children. **Look at the picture. Count how many plants there are in all.** (13) **Write a number sentence to show how you found your answer.** ($10 + 3 = 13$)

- Have children look around the classroom for examples of objects that are displayed as *doubles* or *doubles plus one*. Then say the number sentence.

 For more information about projects and investigations, visit Education Place. eduplace.com/math/mw/

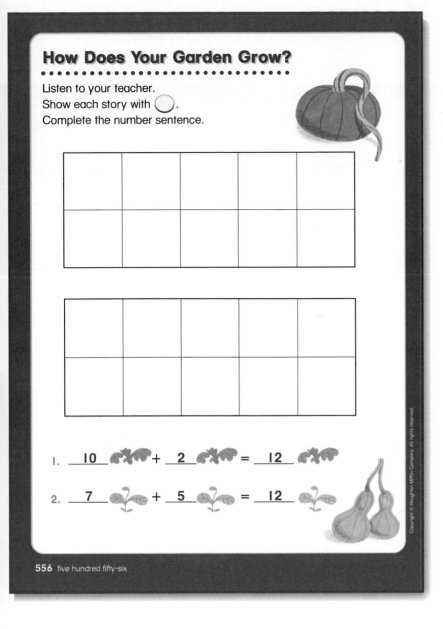

How Does Your Garden Grow?

Listen to your teacher.
Show each story with ◯.
Complete the number sentence.

1. __10__ 🌿 + __2__ 🌿 = __12__ 🌿

2. __7__ 🌱 + __5__ 🌱 = __12__ 🌱

For Mathematically Promising Students

The *Chapter Challenges* resource book provides blackline masters for activities that explore, extend, and connect the mathematics in every chapter. To support this independent work, see the Teacher Notes for each activity.

Explore: Cubby Code, page 109, after Lesson 1
Extend: Pennies make a Ten, page 111, after Lesson 3
Connect: Pocket Change, page 113, after Lesson 5

Using This Page

- Give each child a set of two-color counters.
- Tell children to listen carefully to the following stories. **Use your counters in the ten frames to act out each story. Use the numbers you hear to complete the number sentences.**
- For Exercise 1, read the following addition story to children:

Sara bought 10 tomato plants and 2 sweet pea plants at the garden store. How many plants did she buy in all? (12)

- Ask a volunteer to share his or her answer and tell what strategy was used to add.
- For Exercise 2, read the following addition story to children:

Leon planted 7 ferns and 5 rose bushes in the garden. How many plants did he plant in all? (12)

- Ask a volunteer to share his or her answer and tell what strategy was used to add.

NSF · Children's Math Worlds

Build stronger conceptual understanding of addition facts through 20 with *Children's Math Worlds* lessons. The most effective approach is to use the *Children's Math Worlds* lessons along with the lessons in the chapter.

Addition Facts Through 20   **556**

Doubles Plus 1

Lesson 19.1

PLANNING THE LESSON

MATHEMATICS OBJECTIVE
Find doubles and doubles plus one to sums of 20.

Use Lesson Planner CD-ROM for Lesson 19.1.

Meeting North Carolina's Standards

1.03 Develop fluency with single-digit addition and corresponding differences using strategies such as modeling, composing and decomposing quantities, using doubles, and making tens.

Also 1.04

Daily Routines

Calendar
Have children find the date for the first Friday in the month and double it. Have them point to the new date and name the date with a number that is one more.

Sunday	Monday	Tuesday	Wednesday	Thursday	Friday	Saturday
			1	2	3	4
5	6	7	8	9	10	11
12	13	14	15	16	17	18
19	20	21	22	23	24	25
26	27	28	29	30	31	

Vocabulary
Write the word **double** on the board. Ask for examples of the word. Remind children that a double fact has two addends that are the same.

Vocabulary Cards

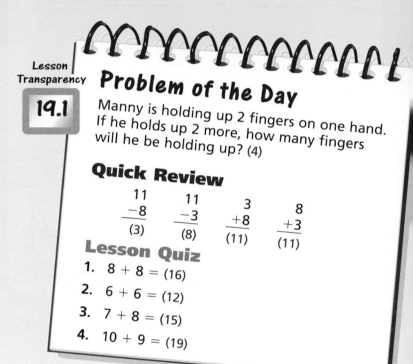

Lesson Transparency **19.1**

Problem of the Day
Manny is holding up 2 fingers on one hand. If he holds up 2 more, how many fingers will he be holding up? (4)

Quick Review

$$\begin{array}{cccc} 11 & 11 & 3 & 8 \\ -8 & -3 & +8 & +3 \\ \hline (3) & (8) & (11) & (11) \end{array}$$

Lesson Quiz
1. $8 + 8 =$ (16)
2. $6 + 6 =$ (12)
3. $7 + 8 =$ (15)
4. $10 + 9 =$ (19)

LEVELED PRACTICE

RETEACH 19.1

Name _____ Date _____ Reteach 19.1

Doubles Plus One

Double facts have two addends that are the same.
Add 1 to a double fact to help you find another sum.

Double Fact	Double Plus 1
●●●●● ○○○○○	●●●●● ○○○○○ ✽
	5 + 5 and 1 more
5 + 5 = _10_	5 + 6 = _11_

Use the double fact.
Draw 1 more.
Find the sum.

1. 6 + 6 = _12_

●●●●●● ○○○○○○   ●●●●●●● ○○○○○○○

6 + 7 = _13_   7 + 6 = _13_

2. 4 + 4 = _8_

●●●● ○○○○   ●●●●● ○○○○○

4 + 5 = _9_   5 + 4 = _9_

Use with text pages 557–558.

PRACTICE 19.1

Name _____ Date _____ Practice 19.1

Doubles Plus One

Find the sum.

Think Use a double fact. Add 1 more.

1. ●●●●●
○○○○○ ✽

5 + 5 = _10_ | 5 + 6 = _11_

2.	3.	4.	5.	6.	7.
5 +5 10	1 +1 2	1 +2 3	5 +6 11	4 +4 8	5 +4 9

8.	9.	10.	11.	12.	13.
7 +7 14	7 +8 15	3 +3 6	4 +3 7	3 +4 7	10 +9 19

14.	15.	16.	17.	18.	19.
9 +9 18	8 +9 17	9 +8 17	4 +5 9	6 +5 11	8 +7 15

Test Prep

20. There are 9 robins in a tree. There are 8 robins on a fence. How many robins are there in all?

_17_ robins

Draw or write to explain.

Use with text pages 557–558.

ENRICHMENT 19.1

Name _____ Date _____ Enrichment 19.1

Near Doubles

Complete the sentence.
Write the matching doubles plus 1 fact.
Order of addends may vary.

1. 17 is double _8_ and 1 more.

_8_ + _9_ = _17_

2. Double _9_ add 1 is 19.

_9_ + _10_ = _19_

3. 1 more than double _7_ is 15.

_7_ + _8_ = _15_

4. 13 is double _6_ add 1.

_6_ + _7_ = _13_

5. 9 is double _4_ and 1 more.

_4_ + _5_ = _9_

Write About It Are the sums of doubles plus 1 facts odd or even? _Odd._

Why? _Possible Response: With doubles when you add 1 to an even number, you make it an odd number._

Use with text pages 557–558.

Practice Workbook Page 127

Reaching All Learners

Differentiated Instruction

English Learners

English-language learners may not have the language skills to explain the process behind their thinking. Use Worksheet 19.1 to provide children with sentence frames they can use to complete the Explain Your Thinking activity.

Inclusion
VISUAL, TACTILE

Materials: *two-color counters*

- Draw a 2-part mat.
- Model 2 + 2 with red counters. Guide the child to write 2 + 2 = 4.
- Have the child add a yellow counter and write 2 + 3 = 5.

Early Finishers
TACTILE, VISUAL

Materials: *20 two-color counters, paper bag*

- In turn, each child takes a handful of counters from the bag and models a double or double plus one fact.
- The partner writes the addition sentence.

 3 + 4 = 7

TECHNOLOGY

Spiral Review
Using the *Ways to Assess* CD-ROM, you can create **customized** spiral review worksheets covering any lessons you choose.

eBook
An electronic version of this lesson can be found in **eMathBook**.

Lesson Planner
Use the **Lesson Planner CD-ROM** to see how lesson objectives for this chapter are correlated to standards.

Art Connection

Refer to the unit story, *One Watermelon Seed* by Celia Barker Lottridge. Tell children that one day Max picked 3 pumpkins and Josephine picked 4 pumpkins. Have them write a number sentence to find how many pumpkins they picked in all.

MATH CENTER

Basic Skills Activity

Motivate children to build basic skills. Use this activity to address multiple learning styles using hands-on activities related to the skills of this lesson.

PROBLEM SOLVING 19.1

Name _____ Date _____ | Problem Solving 19.1

Doubles Plus One

Read the story problem and solve.

1. Susan puts 8 red apples and 7 green apples in the bowl. How many apples are there in all?

   Draw or write to explain

   __15__ apples

2. Ben draws 6 ducks swimming in a pond. He draws 7 ducks in the grass. How many ducks does he draw in all?

   __13__ ducks

3. Tami eats 5 red grapes and 6 green grapes. How many grapes does Tami eat altogether?

   __11__ grapes

4. Lamar sees 9 ants on the tree branch. He sees the same number of ants on the tree trunk. How many ants does Lamar see in all?

   __18__ ants

Copyright © Houghton Mifflin Company. All rights reserved.

Use with text pages 557–558.

HOMEWORK 19.1

Name _____ Date _____ | Homework 19.1

Doubles Plus One

Use a double fact and add 1 more.

$7 + 7 = \underline{14}$

$7 + 8 = \underline{15}$ $8 + 7 = \underline{15}$

Find the sum.

1. $9 + 9 = \underline{18}$ 2. $10 + 9 = \underline{19}$

3.	4.	5.	6.	7.
6	6	8	9	7
+ 6	+ 7	+ 8	+ 8	+ 7
12	13	16	17	14

8.	9.	10.	11.	12.
8	7	7	5	5
+ 7	+ 8	+ 6	+ 5	+ 6
15	15	13	10	11

13. Juan has 4 marbles. Mario has 1 more marble than Juan. How many marbles do they have together?

    Draw or write to explain

    __9__ marbles

Copyright © Houghton Mifflin Company. All rights reserved.

Use with text pages 557–558.

ENGLISH LEARNERS 19.1

Name _____ Date _____ | English Learners 19.1

Doubles Plus One

3 + 3 = 6

How can you use a double fact to find the sum of 5 + 6?

I can use a double fact to help me find the sum.

I know that $5 + 5 = \underline{10}$.

If I add one more, I get __11__.

$5 + 6 = \underline{11}$

To the Teacher: Use the example at the top of the page to demonstrate how to add doubles. Then have children complete the sentences that provide the language needed to solve the problem.

Copyright © Houghton Mifflin Company. All rights reserved.

Use with text pages 557–558.

Homework Workbook Page 127

TEACHING LESSON 19.1

LESSON ORGANIZER

Objective Find doubles and doubles plus one to sums of 20.

Resources Reteach, Practice, Enrichment, Problem Solving, Homework, English Learners, Transparencies, Math Center

Materials Overhead counters, blank transparency, cubes, two-color counters

Activity

Warm-Up Activity
Modeling Doubles

| 👥 Whole Group | ⏱ 5 minutes | Auditory, Tactile |

Materials: *overhead counters, blank transparency*

1. Review double facts by writing $5 + 5 = 10$ on the blank transparency. Use counters to model the fact.

   $5 + 5 = 10$
   ●●●●●
   ○○○○○

2. Ask: **How many counters are in each part?** (5) **How many counters in all?** (10) Repeat with other double facts.

3. Lead children in reciting the double facts in order from $1 + 1 = 2$ through $6 + 6 = 12$.

Name_____

Doubles Plus One

Objective
Find doubles and doubles plus one for sums through 20.
Vocabulary
double

A **double** fact has two addends that are the same.

$6 + 6 = \underline{12}$ ●●●●●●
                          ○○○○○○

Use the double fact to help you find other sums.

$6 + 7$	$7 + 6$
Draw 1 more.	Draw 1 more.
●●●●●●	●●●●●●
○○○○○○◌	○○○○○○
Find the sum.	Find the sum.
$6 + 7 = \underline{13}$	$7 + 6 = \underline{13}$

Guided Practice

Use the double fact.
Draw 1 more. Find the sum.

Think
I know the sum of $8 + 8$.
I draw 1 more to find
$8 + 9$ and $9 + 8$.

1. $8 + 8 = \underline{16}$
   ●●●●●●●●   ●●●●●●●●
   ○○○○○○○●   ○○○○○○○○

   $8 + 9 = \underline{17}$ $9 + 8 = \underline{17}$

2. $7 + 7 = \underline{14}$
   ●●●●●●●   ●●●●●●●
   ○○○○○○○●   ○○○○○○○

   $7 + 8 = \underline{15}$ $8 + 7 = \underline{15}$

TEST TIPS **Explain Your Thinking** How can you use a double fact to find the sum of $5 + 6$? **Use the double 5 + 5 and add 1 more to it.**

Chapter 19 Lesson 1   five hundred fifty-seven **557**

---

① Introduce
Activity
Modeling the Doubles Plus One

| 👥 Whole Group | ⏱ 10–15 minutes | Auditory, Tactile |

Materials: *overhead counters, blank transparency, two-color counters*

1. Give each child 10 counters. Model how to use a double fact to find the sum of a double plus one fact. Begin by writing $4 + 4 = 8$ on the blank transparency. Use counters to model the fact. Then have children show the double fact with counters.

2. Place an additional counter in the second group of 4. **How many counters are in each part?** (4 in the first part and 5 in the other part) **How many counters in all?** (9) Write the addition fact $4 + 5 = 9$ on the transparency. Show $5 + 4 = 9$ the same way.

3. Summarize by telling children that they can use a double fact to solve addition problems when one addend is one more than the other addend. They add the double and then add 1 more.

② Develop

Guided Learning

Teaching Example Introduce the objective and vocabulary to the children. Guide them through the examples. Have the children draw 1 more counter to show the double plus one $6 + 7$ and then $7 + 6$.

Guided Practice

Have children complete **Exercises 1–2** as you observe. Give children the opportunity to answer the Explain Your Thinking question. Then discuss their responses with the class.

Use a double fact and add 1 more.

Find the sum.

1. ●●●●● ○○○○○   ●●●●●● ○○○○○   ●●●●● ○○○○○○

$5 + 5 = \underline{10}$ $6 + 5 = \underline{11}$ $5 + 6 = \underline{11}$

2. $6 + 6 = \underline{12}$ $7 + 6 = \underline{13}$ $6 + 7 = \underline{13}$

3. $8 + 8 = \underline{16}$ $9 + 8 = \underline{17}$ $8 + 9 = \underline{17}$

4. $\begin{array}{r} 4 \\ +5 \\ \hline 9 \end{array}$
5. $\begin{array}{r} 3 \\ +3 \\ \hline 6 \end{array}$
6. $\begin{array}{r} 4 \\ +3 \\ \hline 7 \end{array}$
7. $\begin{array}{r} 5 \\ +5 \\ \hline 10 \end{array}$
8. $\begin{array}{r} 6 \\ +5 \\ \hline 11 \end{array}$
9. $\begin{array}{r} 6 \\ +6 \\ \hline 12 \end{array}$

10. $\begin{array}{r} 4 \\ +4 \\ \hline 8 \end{array}$
11. $\begin{array}{r} 5 \\ +4 \\ \hline 9 \end{array}$
12. $\begin{array}{r} 3 \\ +4 \\ \hline 7 \end{array}$
13. $\begin{array}{r} 7 \\ +6 \\ \hline 13 \end{array}$
14. $\begin{array}{r} 8 \\ +7 \\ \hline 15 \end{array}$
15. $\begin{array}{r} 9 \\ +10 \\ \hline 19 \end{array}$

16. $\begin{array}{r} 7 \\ +7 \\ \hline 14 \end{array}$
17. $\begin{array}{r} 9 \\ +9 \\ \hline 18 \end{array}$
18. $\begin{array}{r} 7 \\ +8 \\ \hline 15 \end{array}$
19. $\begin{array}{r} 6 \\ +7 \\ \hline 13 \end{array}$
20. $\begin{array}{r} 9 \\ +8 \\ \hline 17 \end{array}$
21. $\begin{array}{r} 10 \\ +9 \\ \hline 19 \end{array}$

Problem Solving ▶ Reasoning

22. Kate wants to put the coins into equal groups. Circle groups of coins to show one way she can do this.

Possible answers: circle 2 groups of 6, 3 groups of 4, 6 groups of 2, or 4 groups of 3

558 five hundred fifty-eight

At Home Have your child tell you the sum for 6 + 5 and 5 + 6. Ask what double fact helps to find the sums.

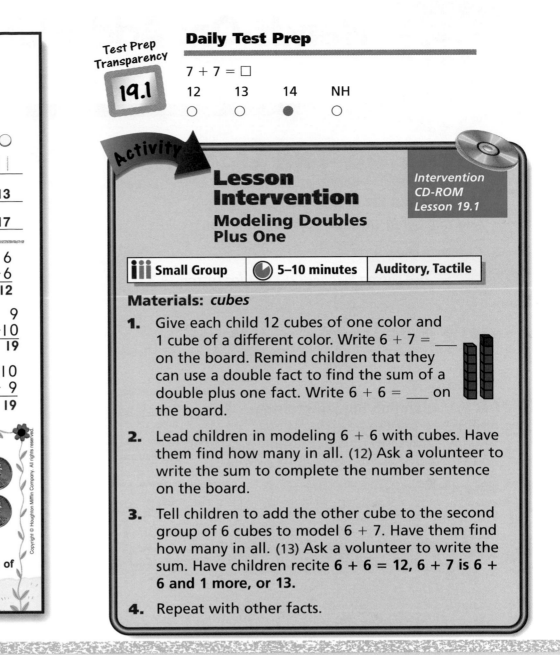

Test Prep Transparency 19.1

Daily Test Prep

$7 + 7 = \square$

12 ○   13 ○   14 ●   NH ○

Activity

Lesson Intervention

Intervention CD-ROM Lesson 19.1

Modeling Doubles Plus One

| 👥 Small Group | ⏱ 5–10 minutes | Auditory, Tactile |

Materials: *cubes*

1. Give each child 12 cubes of one color and 1 cube of a different color. Write $6 + 7 = \underline{\quad}$ on the board. Remind children that they can use a double fact to find the sum of a double plus one fact. Write $6 + 6 = \underline{\quad}$ on the board.

2. Lead children in modeling $6 + 6$ with cubes. Have them find how many in all. (12) Ask a volunteer to write the sum to complete the number sentence on the board.

3. Tell children to add the other cube to the second group of 6 cubes to model $6 + 7$. Have them find how many in all. (13) Ask a volunteer to write the sum. Have children recite $6 + 6 = 12$, $6 + 7$ is $6 + 6$ and 1 more, or 13.

4. Repeat with other facts.

---

③ Practice

Independent Practice

Children complete **Exercises 1–21** independently. Students may use counters to solve the problems.

Problem Solving

After children complete **Exercise 22,** ask children to share several different solutions. Provide coins to those who may need to use them.

Common Error

Forgetting to Add One to the Double Fact

Children may forget to add 1 to the sum of the double fact to show the double plus one fact. Provide practice with pairs of exercises that include a double and a related double plus one fact.

④ Assess and Close

Explain how to use a double fact to find the sum of 6 + 7.
(Begin with 6 + 6 = 12. Add one to the sum to get 13.)

What double fact helps you find the sum of 8 + 9?
(8 + 9 = 16)

Keeping a Journal

Draw counters to show a doubles plus one fact. Write the number sentence that the counters show.

Hands-On: Add with Ten

PLANNING THE LESSON

MATHEMATICS OBJECTIVE
Add numbers 1 through 10 to the number 10.

Use Lesson Planner CD-ROM for Lesson 19.2.

Daily Routines

Calendar
Have children find the tenth of the month and say the day. Then find the day 3 days after, 5 days after, and so on.

Sunday	Monday	Tuesday	Wednesday	Thursday	Friday	Saturday
				1	2	3	4
5	6	7	8	9	10	11
12	13	14	15	16	17	18
19	20	21	22	23	24	25
26	27	28	29	30	31	

Vocabulary
Write several addition facts on the board. Have volunteers circle the **equal sign** in each fact to review the word **equals**.

Vocabulary Cards

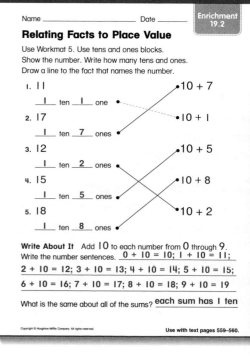

Meeting North Carolina's Standards
1.03 Develop fluency with single-digit addition and corresponding differences using strategies such as modeling, composing and decomposing quantities, using doubles, and making tens.

Also 1.04

Lesson Transparency 19.2

Problem of the Day
Mark bought two boxes of markers. Each box has 6 markers. How many markers did Mark buy? (12) How many markers does Mark have if he has 1 marker at home? (13)

Quick Review
Write the number.
1 ten 7 ones (17)
1 ten 1 one (11)
1 ten 5 ones (15)

Lesson Quiz
Find the sum.

1. $10 + 3$ (13) 2. $4 + 10$ (14) 3. $10 + 6$ (16) 4. $9 + 10$ (19)

LEVELED PRACTICE

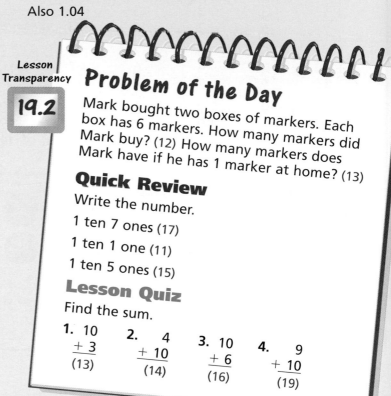

Practice Workbook Page 128

Reaching All Learners
Differentiated Instruction

English Learners

English-language learners may not have the language skills to explain the process behind their thinking. Use Worksheet 19.2 to provide children with sentence frames they can use to complete the Explain Your Thinking activity.

Inclusion
AUDITORY, TACTILE

Materials: *cubes*

- Help the child make a 10-cube train.
- Have the child attach 1 cube of a different color and write the addition fact $10 + 1 = 11$.
- Continue to add 1 cube at a time and write the number sentences.

Gifted and Talented
AUDITORY, VISUAL

- Have children write five missing addend sentences for adding a number to 10.
- Have children exchange papers with a partner and challenge the partners to find the missing addends.

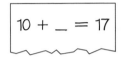

$$10 + \_ = 17$$

TECHNOLOGY

Spiral Review

To reinforce skills on lessons taught earlier, create **customized** spiral review worksheets using the *Ways to Assess* CD-ROM.

Education Place

Encourage students to visit **Education Place** at eduplace.com/kids/mw/ for more student activities.

Manipulatives

Interactive **Counters** with several workmats are available on the *Ways to Success* CD-ROM.

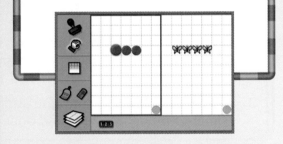

Music Connection

Have children use percussion instruments to "play" adding with 10. Write number sentences such as $10 + 3$ on the board. Ask one volunteer to strike a drum for 10. Have another clap cymbals for ones.

MATH CENTER

Cross-Curricular Activity

As you use this activity to relate the mathematics of this lesson to another curriculum area, children will see how math can help them with other subjects.

PROBLEM SOLVING 19.2

Name _____ Date _____ Problem Solving 19.2

Add With Ten

You can draw a picture to help you solve problems about adding with ten.

1. Dennis plants 10 flowers in a large pot. He plants 4 flowers in a small pot. How many flowers does he plant in all?

   Draw a picture to show the flowers.

   Check children's drawings

   __14__ flowers in all

2. Ms. Chan takes 10 books from a box. She takes 7 books from the table. How many books does Ms. Chan take altogether?

   Draw a picture to show the books.

   __17__ books in all

3. There are 10 lemons in the bag. There are 5 lemons in the bowl. How many lemons are there in all?

   Draw a picture to show the lemons.

   __15__ lemons in all

Use with text pages 559–560.

HOMEWORK 19.2

Name _____ Date _____ Homework 19.2

Add with Ten

Use ten frames to add a number to 10.
Find $10 + 6$.

Show 10.   Show 6 more.

$10 + 6 = \underline{16}$

Find the sum.

1. $\begin{array}{r} 10 \\ + 5 \\ \hline 15 \end{array}$
2. $\begin{array}{r} 10 \\ + 7 \\ \hline 17 \end{array}$
3. $\begin{array}{r} 10 \\ + 3 \\ \hline 13 \end{array}$
4. $\begin{array}{r} 2 \\ +10 \\ \hline 12 \end{array}$
5. $\begin{array}{r} 8 \\ + 2 \\ \hline 10 \end{array}$

6. $\begin{array}{r} 10 \\ + 6 \\ \hline 16 \end{array}$
7. $\begin{array}{r} 10 \\ + 8 \\ \hline 18 \end{array}$
8. $\begin{array}{r} 10 \\ + 2 \\ \hline 12 \end{array}$
9. $\begin{array}{r} 10 \\ +10 \\ \hline 20 \end{array}$
10. $\begin{array}{r} 3 \\ +10 \\ \hline 13 \end{array}$

11. Sandi walks up 10 steps. Then she walks up 4 more. How many steps does she walk up in all?
    __14__

    Draw or write to explain.

Use with text pages 559–560.

Homework Workbook Page 128

ENGLISH LEARNERS 19.2

Name _____ Date _____ English Learners 19.2

Add With Ten

10 ones
1 ten

How is adding $10 + 5$ like showing 15 with 1 ten and 5 ones?

I know that $10 + 5 = 15$.

I know that you can show 10 in two ways. You can show it with __10__ ones. You can also show it with __1__ ten.

I know you can show 5 with __5__ ones.

That's how I know that you can show 15 with 1 ten and 5 ones.

1 ten and 5 ones = 15

To the Teacher: Use the example at the top of the page to demonstrate that ten can be represented in different ways. Then have children complete the sentence frames that provide the language needed to answer the question.

Use with text pages 559–560.

TEACHING LESSON 19.2

LESSON ORGANIZER

Objective Add numbers 1 through 10 to the number 10.

Resources Reteach, Practice, Enrichment, Problem Solving, Homework, English Learners, Transparencies, Math Center

Materials Place-value blocks, ten frame transparency, overhead two-color counters, Workmat 2, two-color counters, cubes

Activity

Warm-Up Activity
Discuss Regrouping 10 Ones as 1 Ten

iiii Whole Group	⏱ 5 minutes	Auditory, Tactile

Materials: *place-value blocks*

1. Review regrouping 10 ones as 1 ten. Have children show 10 ones blocks.

2. **Can you trade the 10 ones?** (yes, for 1 ten) Have children trade 10 ones for 1 ten. Next have children show 1 more one and say the number. (11) Remind children that 1 ten and 1 one equals 11.

3. Invite volunteers to continue adding, 1 one at a time, to model the tens and ones for 12 through 19.

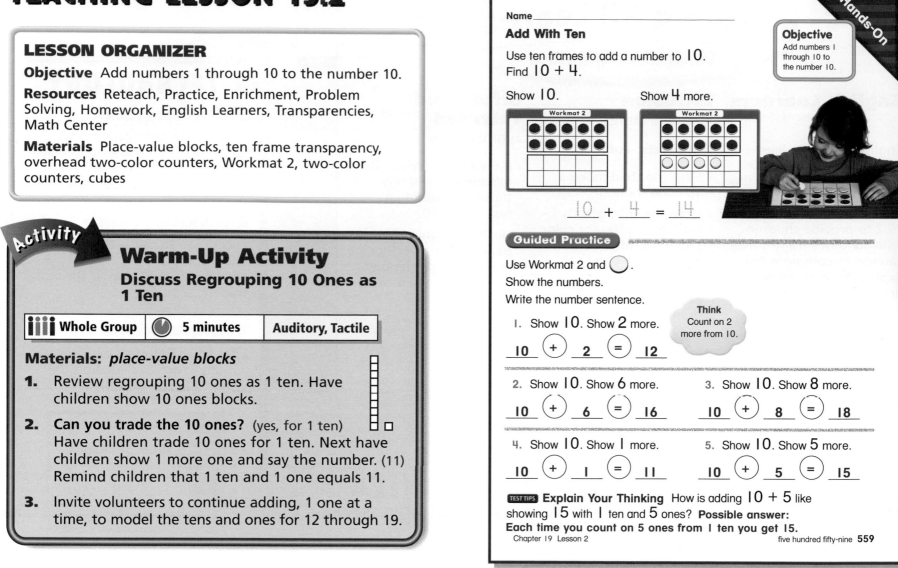

Name_____

Add With Ten

Use ten frames to add a number to 10.
Find $10 + 4$.

Objective
Add numbers 1 through 10 to the number 10.

Show 10.   Show 4 more.

$$\underline{10} + \underline{4} = \underline{14}$$

Guided Practice

Use Workmat 2 and ◯.
Show the numbers.
Write the number sentence.

Think
Count on 2 more from 10.

1. Show 10. Show 2 more.

$$\underline{10} \; (+) \; \underline{2} \; (=) \; \underline{12}$$

2. Show 10. Show 6 more.

$$\underline{10} \; (+) \; \underline{6} \; (=) \; \underline{16}$$

3. Show 10. Show 8 more.

$$\underline{10} \; (+) \; \underline{8} \; (=) \; \underline{18}$$

4. Show 10. Show 1 more.

$$\underline{10} \; (+) \; \underline{1} \; (=) \; \underline{11}$$

5. Show 10. Show 5 more.

$$\underline{10} \; (+) \; \underline{5} \; (=) \; \underline{15}$$

TEST TIPS Explain Your Thinking How is adding $10 + 5$ like showing 15 with 1 ten and 5 ones? **Possible answer: Each time you count on 5 ones from 1 ten you get 15.**

Chapter 19 Lesson 2   five hundred fifty-nine **559**

---

① Introduce
Model Adding with Ten

iiii Whole Group	⏱ 10–15 minutes	Tactile, Auditory

Materials: *ten frame transparency, overhead two-color counters, Workmat 2, two-color counters*

1. Give each child counters and Workmat 2. Write ___ + ___ = ___ on the board. Show 10 red counters in the top ten frame. Have children do the same.

2. Write 10 as the first addend on the board. Explain to children that it stands for the 10 counters.

3. Show 2 yellow counters in the second ten frame. Write 2 as the second addend on the board. Explain to children that it stands for the 2 yellow counters.

4. **How do we know how many in all?** (Begin with 10 and add the 2 ones. There are 12 in all.) Write the sum, 12. Repeat with $10 + 3$.

② Develop

Guided Learning

Teaching Example Introduce the objective to children. Guide them through the example to model how to add a number to 10. Emphasize that starting with 10 and then counting on makes it easy to add with 10.

Guided Practice

Have children complete **Exercises 1–5** as you observe. Give children the opportunity to answer the Explain Your Thinking question. Then discuss their responses with the class.

Remember to fill one ten frame first.

Use Workmat 2 and ◯.
Show the numbers.
Write the number sentence.

1. Show 10. Show 7 more.
   10 ⊕ 7 ⊜ 17

2. Show 10. Show 3 more.
   10 ⊕ 3 ⊜ 13

3. Show 10. Show 9 more.
   10 ⊕ 9 ⊜ 19

4. Show 10. Show 10 more.
   10 ⊕ 10 ⊜ 20

Find the sum.

5. $\begin{array}{r} 10 \\ +\ 3 \\ \hline 13 \end{array}$
6. $\begin{array}{r} 3 \\ +10 \\ \hline 13 \end{array}$
7. $\begin{array}{r} 10 \\ +\ 4 \\ \hline 14 \end{array}$
8. $\begin{array}{r} 9 \\ +10 \\ \hline 19 \end{array}$
9. $\begin{array}{r} 10 \\ +\ 7 \\ \hline 17 \end{array}$

10. $\begin{array}{r} 8 \\ +2 \\ \hline 10 \end{array}$
11. $\begin{array}{r} 2 \\ +10 \\ \hline 12 \end{array}$
12. $\begin{array}{r} 10 \\ +\ 5 \\ \hline 15 \end{array}$
13. $\begin{array}{r} 10 \\ +\ 8 \\ \hline 18 \end{array}$
14. $\begin{array}{r} 10 \\ +\ 9 \\ \hline 19 \end{array}$

15. $\begin{array}{r} 1 \\ +9 \\ \hline 10 \end{array}$
16. $\begin{array}{r} 10 \\ +\ 6 \\ \hline 16 \end{array}$
17. $\begin{array}{r} 10 \\ +10 \\ \hline 20 \end{array}$
18. $\begin{array}{r} 10 \\ +\ 2 \\ \hline 12 \end{array}$
19. $\begin{array}{r} 4 \\ +10 \\ \hline 14 \end{array}$

Algebra Readiness ▶ Number Sentences

Write a related subtraction fact for the addition fact.

20. 5 + 6 = 11

    11 − 6 = 5 or 11 − 5 = 6

21. 7 + 5 = 12

    12 − 5 = 7 or 12 − 7 = 5

At Home Say a number between 1 and 10. Ask your child to add it to 10 to find the sum. Repeat with other numbers.

560 five hundred sixty

Daily Test Prep

Test Prep Transparency

19.2

7 + 8 = □

14   ● 15   ○ 16   ○ NH
○

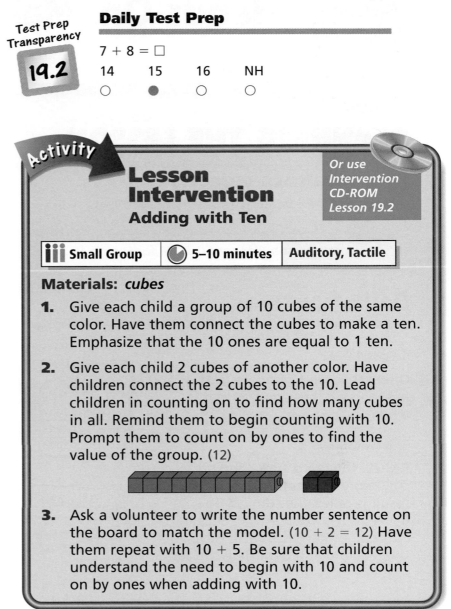

Activity

Lesson Intervention
Adding with Ten

Or use Intervention CD-ROM Lesson 19.2

| 👥 Small Group | 🕐 5–10 minutes | Auditory, Tactile |

Materials: *cubes*

1. Give each child a group of 10 cubes of the same color. Have them connect the cubes to make a ten. Emphasize that the 10 ones are equal to 1 ten.

2. Give each child 2 cubes of another color. Have children connect the 2 cubes to the 10. Lead children in counting on to find how many cubes in all. Remind them to begin counting with 10. Prompt them to count on by ones to find the value of the group. (12)

3. Ask a volunteer to write the number sentence on the board to match the model. (10 + 2 = 12) Have them repeat with 10 + 5. Be sure that children understand the need to begin with 10 and count on by ones when adding with 10.

---

③ Practice

Independent Practice

Children complete **Exercises 1–19** independently.

Algebra Readiness

After children complete **Exercises 20** and **21,** call on volunteers to share their solutions.

Common Error

Transposing Digits

Children may transpose the tens and ones digits when adding with 10. Remind them that in each case they have only 1 ten. Have children check to make sure they put the 1 in the tens place in the sum.

④ Assess and Close

Explain how you would add 10 + 5.

(Start with 10 and count on 5 ones to 15.)

Why do you begin counting with 10 when you add 10 + 4?

(Because it is easier to add if you start with the greater number and count on.)

✏️ Keeping a Journal

Draw a group of counters or cubes to show 10 + 6. Find the sum.

Hands-On: Make a Ten to Add

PLANNING THE LESSON

MATHEMATICS OBJECTIVE
Make a 10 as a strategy to learn addition facts.

Use Lesson Planner CD-ROM for Lesson 19.3.

Daily Routines

Calendar
Direct children to find pairs of numbers on the calendar that when added have a sum of 10.

Sunday	Monday	Tuesday	Wednesday	Thursday	Friday	Saturday
			1	2	3	4
5	6	7	8	9	10	11
12	13	14	15	16	17	18
19	20	21	22	23	24	25
26	27	28	29	30	31	

Vocabulary
Review the word **sum.** Remind children that when they add, the result is called the sum. Write 6 + 4 = ___, 3 + 7 = ___, and 8 + 2 = ___ on the board. Have volunteers find and underline the sums.

Vocabulary Cards

Meeting North Carolina's Standards

1.03 Develop fluency with single-digit addition and corresponding differences using strategies such as modeling, composing and decomposing quantities, using doubles, and making tens.

Also 1.04

Lesson Transparency **19.3**

Problem of the Day
Cindy plants 9 little trees in a row. Then she plants a row of 5 little trees. What addition sentence shows how many trees she planted? (9 + 5 = 14)

Quick Review
2 + 8 = (10)
7 + 3 = (10)
1 + 9 = (10)

Lesson Quiz
Find the sum.

1. $\begin{array}{r} 9 \\ + 4 \\ \hline (13) \end{array}$
2. $\begin{array}{r} 9 \\ + 6 \\ \hline (15) \end{array}$
3. $\begin{array}{r} 8 \\ + 4 \\ \hline (12) \end{array}$

LEVELED PRACTICE

RETEACH 19.3

Name _____ Date _____   Reteach 19.3

Make a Ten to Add
To help you add 7, 8, or 9, make a 10.

Find 8 + 5.	
Show 8 cubes.	Move 2 cubes to make a ten train.
Show 5 more cubes.	8 + 5 has the same sum as 10 + 3.
8 + 5 = 13	10 + 3 = 13

Use cubes to make a ten train.
Find the sum.

1. Show 8 and 4 more.	2. Show 7 and 5 more.
8 + 4 = 12	7 + 5 = 12
3. Show 9 and 4 more.	4. Show 8 and 6 more.
9 + 4 = 13	8 + 6 = 14
5. Show 7 and 4 more.	6. Show 9 and 5 more.
7 + 4 = 11	9 + 5 = 14

Copyright © Houghton Mifflin Company. All rights reserved.   Use with text pages 561–562.

PRACTICE 19.3

Name _____ Date _____   Practice 19.3

Make a Ten to Add
Use Workmat 2 and ○.
Make a ten.
Find the sum.

1. Show 8 and 7 more.	2. Show 6 and 8 more.
8 + 7 = 15	6 + 8 = 14
3. Show 9 and 3 more.	4. Show 7 and 9 more.
9 + 3 = 12	7 + 9 = 16

Add.

5. $\begin{array}{r} 8 \\ +8 \\ \hline 16 \end{array}$
6. $\begin{array}{r} 6 \\ +8 \\ \hline 14 \end{array}$
7. $\begin{array}{r} 9 \\ +3 \\ \hline 12 \end{array}$
8. $\begin{array}{r} 7 \\ +9 \\ \hline 16 \end{array}$
9. $\begin{array}{r} 9 \\ +7 \\ \hline 16 \end{array}$
10. $\begin{array}{r} 4 \\ +9 \\ \hline 13 \end{array}$

11. $\begin{array}{r} 7 \\ +6 \\ \hline 13 \end{array}$
12. $\begin{array}{r} 7 \\ +8 \\ \hline 15 \end{array}$
13. $\begin{array}{r} 3 \\ +8 \\ \hline 11 \end{array}$
14. $\begin{array}{r} 5 \\ +9 \\ \hline 14 \end{array}$
15. $\begin{array}{r} 9 \\ +2 \\ \hline 11 \end{array}$
16. $\begin{array}{r} 7 \\ +7 \\ \hline 14 \end{array}$

Test Prep

17. Paul has 8 pennies. Dena has 5 pennies. Make a ten and show how many pennies they have in all.
___13___ pennies

Draw or write to explain.
Check children's work. Children's drawings should show 10 pennies in one group and 3 pennies in another group.

Copyright © Houghton Mifflin Company. All rights reserved.   Use with text pages 561–562.

ENRICHMENT 19.3

Name _____ Date _____   Enrichment 19.3

Make a 10 with Coins
Use Workmat 2 and pennies.
Show each addend with pennies.
Make a 10 to add. Trade 10 pennies for 1 dime.
Draw the coins that show the total amount.

1. 8¢ + 3¢ = 11 ¢	2. 9¢ + 4¢ = 13 ¢
1 dime and 1 penny drawn here	1 dime and 3 pennies drawn here
3. 8¢ + 6¢ = 14 ¢	4. 8¢ + 5¢ = 13 ¢
1 dime and 4 pennies drawn here	1 dime and 3 pennies drawn here
5. 7¢ + 5¢ = 12 ¢	6. 9¢ + 5¢ = 14 ¢
1 dime and 2 pennies drawn here	1 dime and 4 pennies drawn here

Write About It You want to buy a sticker for 5¢ and a pencil for 8¢. What is the fewest number of coins you could use to pay for both? Explain.
4 coins. The total cost is 13¢.
You could pay with 1 dime and 3 pennies, which is 4 coins.

Copyright © Houghton Mifflin Company. All rights reserved.   Use with text pages 561–562.

Practice Workbook Page 129

Reaching All Learners

Differentiated Instruction

English Learners

Worksheet 19.3 develops understanding of the word *move*. Children will need to understand this word as they learn to make a ten as a strategy to add.

Special Needs
AUDITORY, TACTILE

Materials: *two-color counters, number strip 1–10 (teacher-made)*

- Write $7 + 4 =$ ___. Help the child put 7 red counters on the number strip and continue with 4 yellow counters. Compare the sum of $10 + 1$ to $7 + 4$.
- Repeat with other examples.

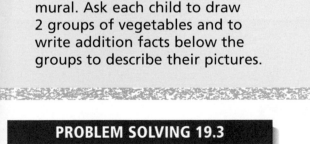

Gifted and Talented
VISUAL, TACTILE

Materials: *paper triangles (teacher-made)*

- Have each child write the numbers for a fact family in the points of a triangle and the related addition facts on the reverse.
- Have pairs use the cards for fact review.

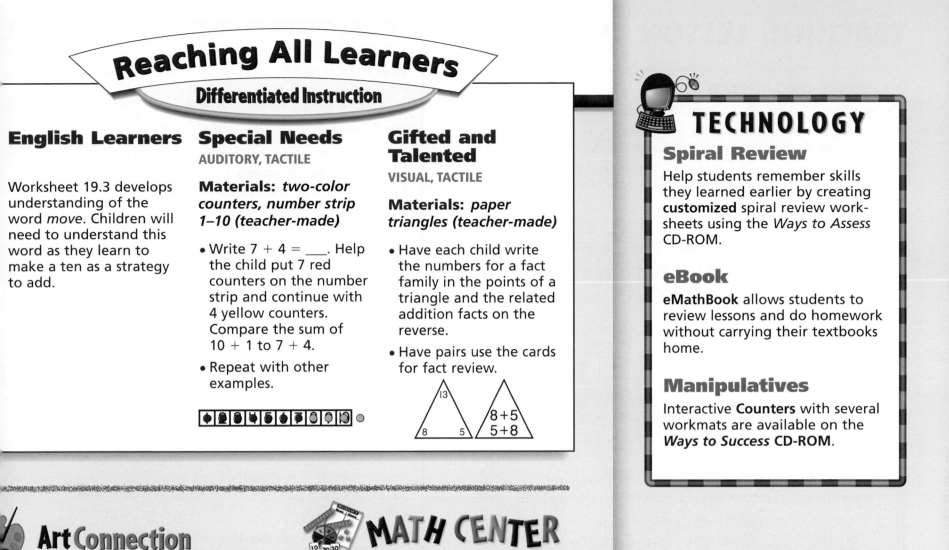

TECHNOLOGY

Spiral Review

Help students remember skills they learned earlier by creating **customized** spiral review worksheets using the *Ways to Assess* CD-ROM.

eBook

eMathBook allows students to review lessons and do homework without carrying their textbooks home.

Manipulatives

Interactive **Counters** with several workmats are available on the *Ways to Success* CD-ROM.

Art Connection

Have children create an addition mural. Ask each child to draw 2 groups of vegetables and to write addition facts below the groups to describe their pictures.

MATH CENTER

Basic Skills Activity

Motivate children to build basic skills. Use this activity to address multiple learning styles using hands-on activities related to the skills of this lesson.

PROBLEM SOLVING 19.3

Name _____ Date _____   Problem Solving 19.3

Make a Ten to Add

Make a ten to help you solve addition problems.

1. Lim Sing draws 8 big cards. Then she draws 6 more cards.
How many cards does she draw in all?

   Draw or write to explain.
   Check children's drawings

   __14__ cards in all

2. Paul brings 9 bags of popcorn. Greg brings 6 bags of popcorn.
How many bags of popcorn do the boys bring altogether?

   __15__ bags altogether

3. The clown has 7 flowers in a hat. She has 8 flowers in a pocket.
How many flowers does the clown have in all?

   __15__ flowers in all

Use with text pages 561–562.

HOMEWORK 19.3

Name _____ Date _____   Homework 19.3

Make a Ten to Add

Make a 10 to help you add 7, 8, or 9.
Find $7 + 4$.

Show $7 + 4$.   Make a 10.

$7 + 4 = 11$

Add. Make a 10 first.

1. $8 + 4 = 12$ 2. $9 + 3 = 12$

3. $\begin{array}{r} 9 \\ +5 \\ \hline 14 \end{array}$ 4. $\begin{array}{r} 9 \\ +4 \\ \hline 13 \end{array}$ 5. $\begin{array}{r} 9 \\ +3 \\ \hline 12 \end{array}$ 6. $\begin{array}{r} 9 \\ +6 \\ \hline 15 \end{array}$ 7. $\begin{array}{r} 9 \\ +8 \\ \hline 17 \end{array}$ 8. $\begin{array}{r} 9 \\ +9 \\ \hline 18 \end{array}$

9. $\begin{array}{r} 8 \\ +4 \\ \hline 12 \end{array}$ 10. $\begin{array}{r} 8 \\ +5 \\ \hline 13 \end{array}$ 11. $\begin{array}{r} 8 \\ +6 \\ \hline 14 \end{array}$ 12. $\begin{array}{r} 8 \\ +7 \\ \hline 15 \end{array}$ 13. $\begin{array}{r} 7 \\ +4 \\ \hline 11 \end{array}$ 14. $\begin{array}{r} 7 \\ +6 \\ \hline 13 \end{array}$

15. Ben has 8 books. He gets 5 more books. How many books does he have now?

   __13__ books

   Draw or write to explain

Use with text pages 561–562.

ENGLISH LEARNERS 19.3

Name _____ Date _____   English Learners 19.3

Make a Ten to Add

The cat can **move**.

Circle the correct words.

1. See the boy sit (**move**).

2. See the dog **move** (sleep).

3. See the girl (**move**) eat.

4. See the horse (stand) move.

To the Teacher: Use the illustration and sentence at the top of the page to help children understand the meaning of the word *move*. Then read the sentences with children and have them circle the word to complete each one.

Use with text pages 561–564.

TEACHING LESSON 19.3

LESSON ORGANIZER

Objective Make a 10 as a strategy to learn addition facts.

Resources Reteach, Practice, Enrichment, Problem Solving, Homework, English Learners, Transparencies, Math Center

Materials ten frame transparency, ten frames transparency, overhead two-color counters, two-color counters, Workmat 2, cubes

Activity

Warm-Up Activity
Model Facts for Ten

iiii Whole Group	⏱ 5 minutes	Auditory, Visual

Materials: *ten frame transparency, overhead two-color counters*

1. Model how to use a ten frame to show sums of 10. Write 6 + 4 = ___ on the transparency. Show 6 red counters in the ten frame. Relate the 6 counters to the addend 6.

2. Show 4 yellow counters in the ten frame and relate them to the second addend on the board.

3. Ask: **How do we find how many counters in all?** Children may say count on from 6, but remind them that they have filled a ten frame so the sum must be 10. Count to show children this is true.

4. Repeat with 8 + 2 and 5 + 5.

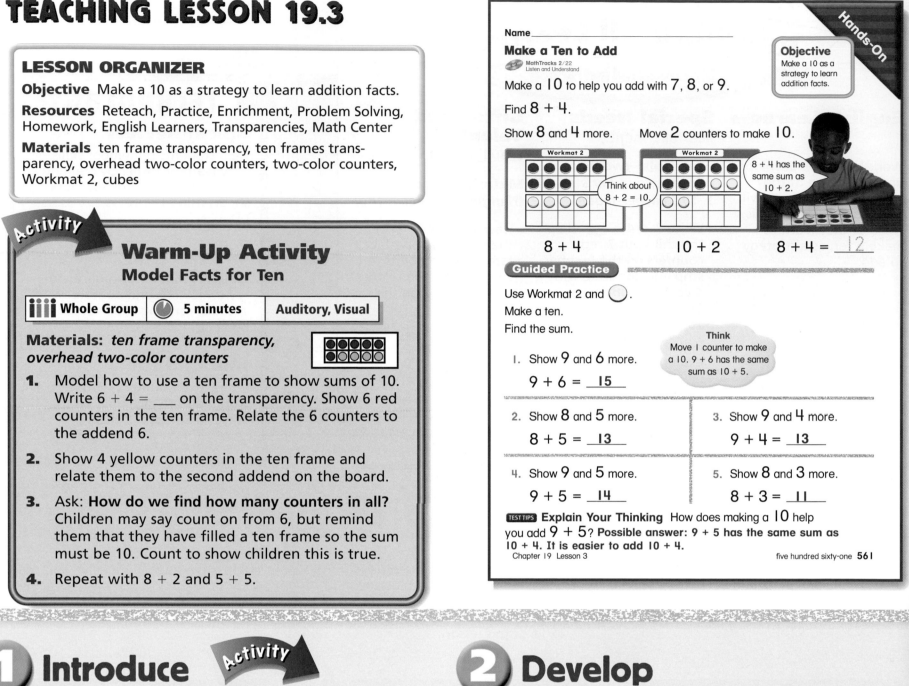

1 Introduce
Make a Ten to Add

iiii Whole Group	⏱ 10–15 minutes	Tactile, Auditory

Materials: *ten frames transparency, overhead two-color counters, two-color counters, Workmat 2*

1. Write 7 + 4 = ___ on the transparency. Show 7 red counters in one ten frame and 4 yellow in the other. Ask children to do the same. Emphasize that the 7 red counters and the 4 yellow counters represent the addends.

2. Tell children that it is easy to add 7 + 4 if you make a ten and then add. Model how to move 3 yellow counters from the bottom ten frame to the top to make a ten.

3. **How many counters are in the top 10 frame?** (10) **How many are in the bottom ten frame?** (1) **What is the sum of 10 + 1?** (11) **What is the sum of 7 + 4?** (11)

2 Develop

Guided Learning

Teaching Example Introduce the objective to the children. Guide them through the example to model how to make a ten to add 8 + 4. Direct children's attention to the step in which 2 counters are moved to make 10. Emphasize how adding 10 + 2 has the same sum as 8 + 4.

Guided Practice

Have children complete **Exercises 1–5** as you observe. Give children the opportunity to answer the Explain Your Thinking question. Then discuss their responses with the class.

Practice

Use Workmat 2 and ◯.
Make a ten. Find the sum.

Remember to make a 10 first.

1. Show 8 and 6 more.

$8 + 6 = \underline{14}$

2. Show 7 and 5 more.

$7 + 5 = \underline{12}$

3. Show 9 and 7 more.

$9 + 7 = \underline{16}$

4. Show 8 and 7 more.

$8 + 7 = \underline{15}$

Add.

5. $\begin{array}{r} 7 \\ +4 \\ \hline 11 \end{array}$	6. $\begin{array}{r} 7 \\ +5 \\ \hline 12 \end{array}$	7. $\begin{array}{r} 7 \\ +6 \\ \hline 13 \end{array}$	8. $\begin{array}{r} 7 \\ +7 \\ \hline 14 \end{array}$	9. $\begin{array}{r} 7 \\ +8 \\ \hline 15 \end{array}$	10. $\begin{array}{r} 7 \\ +9 \\ \hline 16 \end{array}$
11. $\begin{array}{r} 8 \\ +4 \\ \hline 12 \end{array}$	12. $\begin{array}{r} 8 \\ +5 \\ \hline 13 \end{array}$	13. $\begin{array}{r} 8 \\ +6 \\ \hline 14 \end{array}$	14. $\begin{array}{r} 8 \\ +7 \\ \hline 15 \end{array}$	15. $\begin{array}{r} 8 \\ +8 \\ \hline 16 \end{array}$	16. $\begin{array}{r} 8 \\ +9 \\ \hline 17 \end{array}$
17. $\begin{array}{r} 9 \\ +4 \\ \hline 13 \end{array}$	18. $\begin{array}{r} 9 \\ +5 \\ \hline 14 \end{array}$	19. $\begin{array}{r} 9 \\ +6 \\ \hline 15 \end{array}$	20. $\begin{array}{r} 9 \\ +7 \\ \hline 16 \end{array}$	21. $\begin{array}{r} 9 \\ +8 \\ \hline 17 \end{array}$	22. $\begin{array}{r} 9 \\ +9 \\ \hline 18 \end{array}$

Problem Solving ▶ Reasoning

23. Raja scores 9 points. Then he scores 8 more. How many points does he have now?

Draw or write to explain.

$\underline{17}$ points

562 five hundred sixty-two

 **At Home** Ask your child how he or she could make a 10 to help add 7 + 6.

Go on

Daily Test Prep

Test Prep Transparency **19.3**

$10 + 5 = \square$

13 ○   14 ○   15 ●   NH ○

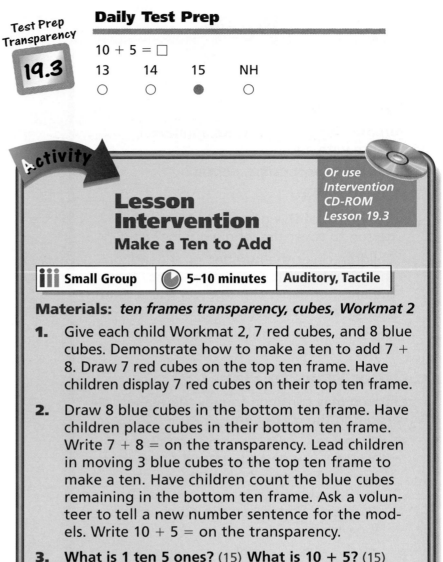

Activity

Lesson Intervention
Make a Ten to Add

Or use Intervention CD-ROM Lesson 19.3

👤👤👤 Small Group	🕐 5–10 minutes	Auditory, Tactile

Materials: *ten frames transparency, cubes, Workmat 2*

1. Give each child Workmat 2, 7 red cubes, and 8 blue cubes. Demonstrate how to make a ten to add 7 + 8. Draw 7 red cubes on the top ten frame. Have children display 7 red cubes on their top ten frame.

2. Draw 8 blue cubes in the bottom ten frame. Have children place cubes in their bottom ten frame. Write 7 + 8 = on the transparency. Lead children in moving 3 blue cubes to the top ten frame to make a ten. Have children count the blue cubes remaining in the bottom ten frame. Ask a volunteer to tell a new number sentence for the models. Write 10 + 5 = on the transparency.

3. **What is 1 ten 5 ones?** (15) **What is 10 + 5?** (15) **What is 7 + 8?** (15)

---

③ Practice

Independent Practice

Children complete **Exercises 1–22** independently. Ask children what pattern they see in each row of exercises. (One addend is the same and the other is one more each time. The sum increases by one.)

Problem Solving

After children complete **Exercise 23,** call on volunteers to share their solutions. Then ask **If Raja scores 8 points first then scores 9 points, will Raja still have 17 points in all?** (Yes, because changing the order of the addends does not change the sum.)

Common Error

Adding the Original Addend to 10
Children may make a ten and then add the original number instead of the reduced number. Have children rewrite the addition to reflect the models.

④ Assess and Close

Explain how to make a ten to help you add 8 + 6. (Show 8 and 6 and then move 2 counters to make 10. 1 ten 4 ones is 14.)

What is the sum of 9 + 5? (14) **Explain how you found the sum.** (Take 1 counter from 5 to make a 10; 1 ten 4 ones is 14.)

✏️ Keeping a Journal

Write an addition sentence using 6, 7, or 8 as one addend. Make a ten to find the sum. Use words and pictures to explain your work.

 **Lesson continues**

Totally Twelve

Purpose This game provides additional practice with addition.

Materials: *paper clips, pencils*

How to Play

• The object of this game is to be the first person to cover the whole number strip.

• Children cover the number, or addend, on their number strip with a paper clip. They use another paper clip to cover the second addend that will result in a sum of 12.

• Game continues until one player covers the whole number strip.

Other Ways to Play

Children may continue to play these alternate versions in the Math Center.

A. Players take turns with one number strip. Player 1 says an addend and covers it on the number strip. Player 2 covers the second addend to make a sum of 12. The game ends when the number strip is covered.

B. Players take turns. Player 1 covers 2 addends on the number strip. Player 2 says the sum. Play continues in this way until the number strip is covered.

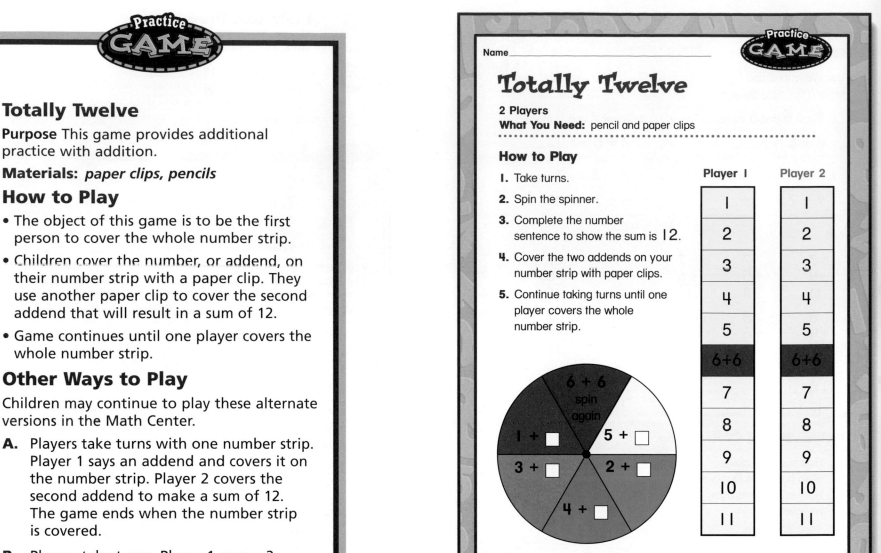

Name_____

Totally Twelve

2 Players
What You Need: pencil and paper clips

How to Play

1. Take turns.

2. Spin the spinner.

3. Complete the number sentence to show the sum is 12.

4. Cover the two addends on your number strip with paper clips.

5. Continue taking turns until one player covers the whole number strip.

Chapter 19   five hundred sixty-three **563**

Connection

Refer back to the unit story, *One Watermelon Seed* by Celia Barker Lottridge. Have children solve some of the following problems based on the passage that appears in the student book.

Count by tens. Solve.

• **How many eggplants did Max pick?** (30)

• **How many peppers?** (40)

• **How many eggplants and peppers did Max pick altogether?** (70)

Count on from 10. Solve.

Josephine picked ten peppers one day. She picked 6 more the next day.

How many peppers did she pick altogether? (16)

Quick Check

Find the sum.

1. $6 + 6 = \underline{12}$ $6 + 7 = \underline{13}$ $7 + 6 = \underline{13}$

2. $8 + 8 = \underline{16}$ $8 + 9 = \underline{17}$ $9 + 8 = \underline{17}$

3. $\begin{array}{r} 10 \\ +\ 5 \\ \hline 15 \end{array}$
4. $\begin{array}{r} 10 \\ +\ 4 \\ \hline 14 \end{array}$
5. $\begin{array}{r} 4 \\ +10 \\ \hline 14 \end{array}$
6. $\begin{array}{r} 10 \\ +\ 9 \\ \hline 19 \end{array}$

Use Workmat 2 and ⬭.
Make a ten. Find the sum.

7. Show 9 and 5 more.

$9 + 5 = \underline{14}$

8. Show 7 and 6 more.

$7 + 6 = \underline{13}$

Math Challenge

Number Neighbors

Look for two numbers next to each other that have a sum of 13.

Find as many as you can. Circle the numbers you find.

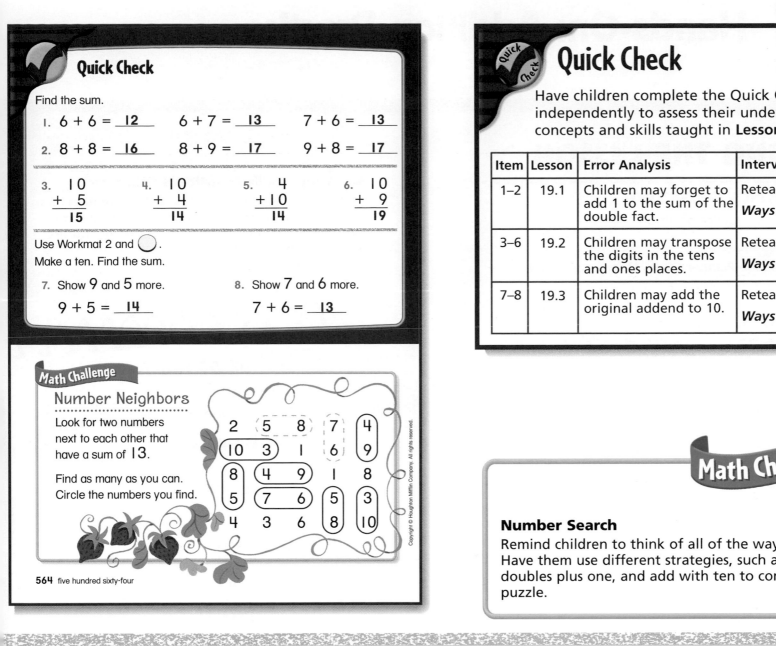

564 five hundred sixty-four

Quick Check

Have children complete the Quick Check exercises independently to assess their understanding of concepts and skills taught in **Lessons 1–3**.

Item	Lesson	Error Analysis	Intervention
1–2	19.1	Children may forget to add 1 to the sum of the double fact.	Reteach Resource 19.1 *Ways to Success* 19.1
3–6	19.2	Children may transpose the digits in the tens and ones places.	Reteach Resource 19.2 *Ways to Success* 19.2
7–8	19.3	Children may add the original addend to 10.	Reteach Resource 19.3 *Ways to Success* 19.3

Math Challenge

Number Search

Remind children to think of all of the ways to name 13. Have them use different strategies, such as doubles, doubles plus one, and add with ten to complete the puzzle.

Hands-On: Addition Practice

PLANNING THE LESSON

MATHEMATICS OBJECTIVE
Use strategies to practice addition.

Use Lesson Planner CD-ROM for Lesson 19.4.

Meeting North Carolina's Standards
1.03 Develop fluency with single-digit addition and corresponding differences using strategies such as modeling, composing and decomposing quantities, using doubles, and making tens.

Daily Routines

Calendar
Have children find 2 dates on the calendar whose sum is 15. Have a volunteer write a number sentence to show the addition.

Sunday	Monday	Tuesday	Wednesday	Thursday	Friday	Saturday
			1	2	3	4
5	6	7	8	9	10	11
12	13	14	15	16	17	18
19	20	21	22	23	24	25
26	27	28	29	30	31	

Vocabulary
Write 7 + 7 = 14 on the board. Remind children that the **addends** 7 and 7 are **parts** and the **sum** 14 is the **whole**. Further remind children that 7 + 7 is a **double fact**.

Vocabulary Cards

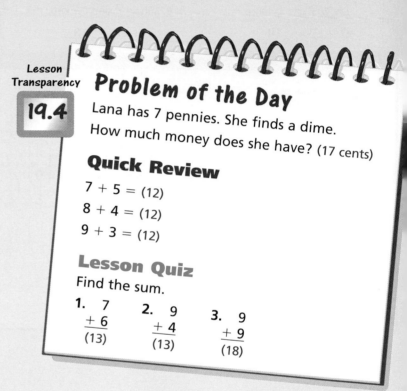

Lesson Transparency 19.4

Problem of the Day
Lana has 7 pennies. She finds a dime. How much money does she have? (17 cents)

Quick Review
7 + 5 = (12)
8 + 4 = (12)
9 + 3 = (12)

Lesson Quiz
Find the sum.

1. 7 + 6 (13) **2.** 9 + 4 (13) **3.** 9 + 9 (18)

LEVELED PRACTICE

RETEACH 19.4

Name _____ Date _____ Reteach 19.4

Addition Practice

Add 8 + 5.
You can use counters to show the parts.
Add to find the whole.

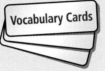

Whole

Part | Part

Think Add the parts 8 and 5 to find the whole, 13.

$\underline{8} + \underline{5} = \underline{13}$

Use counters. Show the parts.
Add.

1. 7 + 4 = 11   2. 9 + 7 = 16   3. 5 + 8 = 13

4. 8 + 7 = 15   5. 6 + 5 = 11   6. 7 + 7 = 14

7. 6 + 9 = 15   8. 8 + 4 = 12   9. 6 + 8 = 14

Copyright © Houghton Mifflin Company. All rights reserved.   Use with text pages 565–566.

PRACTICE 19.4

Name _____ Date _____ Practice 19.4

Addition Practice

Choose a way to add.
Find the sum.

Use parts and wholes. Make a ten. Use a double fact.

1. 6 + 4 = 10   2. 9 + 7 = 16   3. 5 + 5 = 10

4. 6 + 6 = 12   5. 1 + 8 = 9   6. 10 + 2 = 12   7. 4 + 9 = 13   8. 8 + 6 = 14   9. 3 + 2 = 5

10. 9 + 9 = 18   11. 4 + 7 = 11   12. 2 + 8 = 10   13. 10 + 9 = 19   14. 5 + 8 = 13   15. 5 + 9 = 14

16. 7 + 6 = 13   17. 5 + 6 = 11   18. 7 + 5 = 12   19. 8 + 8 = 16   20. 7 + 7 = 14   21. 8 + 7 = 15

Test Prep

Fill in the ○ for the correct answer.
NH means Not Here.

22. Ben has 9 pieces of a puzzle. Dee has the other 6 puzzle pieces. How many pieces are in the whole puzzle?

○ 3 pieces   ● 15 pieces   ○ 16 pieces   ○ NH

Copyright © Houghton Mifflin Company. All rights reserved.   Use with text pages 565–566.

ENRICHMENT 19.4

Name _____ Date _____ Enrichment 19.4

Greater or Less?

Add. Compare the sums.
Write >, <, or =.

1. 8 + 6 = 14   (=)   9 + 5 = 14
2. 9 + 8 = 17   (<)   9 + 9 = 18
3. 8 + 7 = 15   (>)   9 + 4 = 13
4. 8 + 8 = 16   (>)   6 + 7 = 13
5. 6 + 6 = 12   (>)   2 + 8 = 10
6. 6 + 5 = 11   (<)   9 + 3 = 12
7. 2 + 8 = 10   (=)   5 + 5 = 10
8. 5 + 7 = 12   (<)   7 + 9 = 16

Write About It List all the facts with sums greater than 10 but less than 12.

0 + 11; 1 + 10; 2 + 9; 3 + 8; 4 + 7; 5 + 6; 6 + 5; 7 + 4; 8 + 3; 9 + 2; 10 + 1; 11 + 0

Copyright © Houghton Mifflin Company. All rights reserved.   Use with text pages 565–566.

Practice Workbook Page 130

Reaching All Learners

Differentiated Instruction

English Learners

English-language learners will need to understand the term *a way* as they choose different ways to practice addition. Use Worksheet 19.4 to develop children's understanding of this term.

Inclusion
AUDITORY, TACTILE

Materials: *cubes, Workmat 3*

- Help the child model $6 + 5$ with cubes on the workmat.

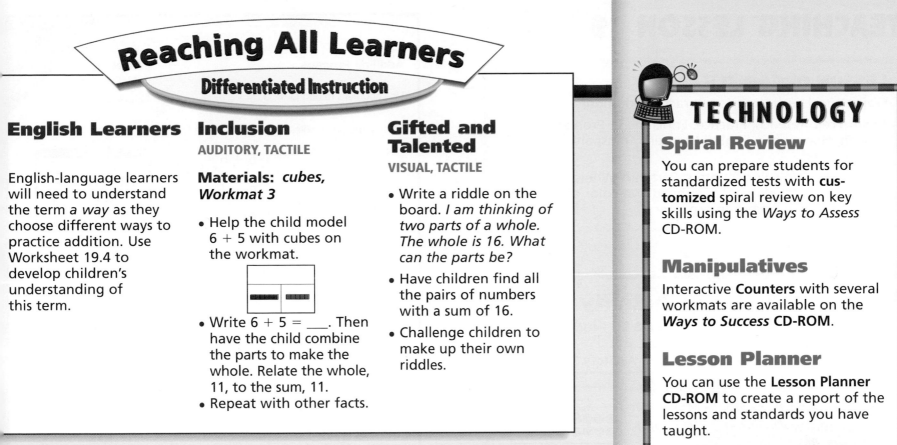

- Write $6 + 5 =$ ___. Then have the child combine the parts to make the whole. Relate the whole, 11, to the sum, 11.
- Repeat with other facts.

Gifted and Talented
VISUAL, TACTILE

- Write a riddle on the board. *I am thinking of two parts of a whole. The whole is 16. What can the parts be?*
- Have children find all the pairs of numbers with a sum of 16.
- Challenge children to make up their own riddles.

TECHNOLOGY

Spiral Review

You can prepare students for standardized tests with **customized** spiral review on key skills using the *Ways to Assess* CD-ROM.

Manipulatives

Interactive **Counters** with several workmats are available on the *Ways to Success* CD-ROM.

Lesson Planner

You can use the **Lesson Planner** CD-ROM to create a report of the lessons and standards you have taught.

Social Studies Connection

Ask children to tell about times when they add in daily life. Give children this problem to solve. *Anna bought 1 pencil for 10¢ and an eraser for 5¢. Write a number sentence to find how much money she spent.* $(10¢ + 5¢ = 15¢)$

MATH CENTER

Basic Skills Activity

Motivate children to build basic skills. Use this activity to address multiple learning styles using hands-on activities related to the skills of this lesson.

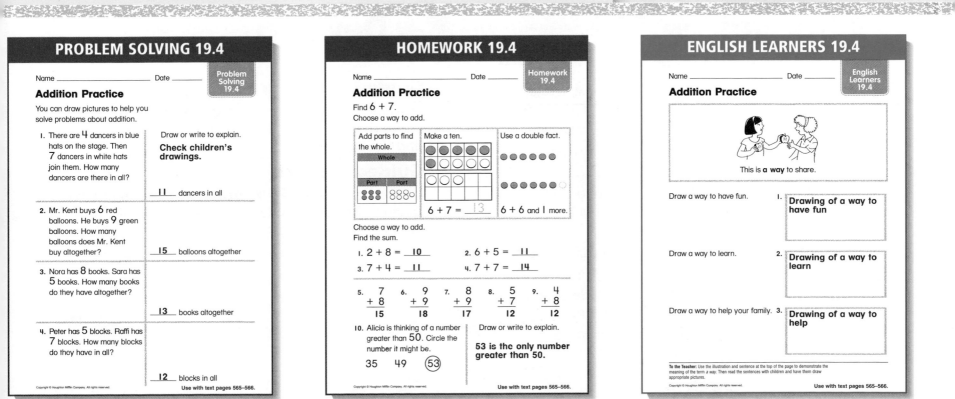

Homework Workbook Page 130

TEACHING LESSON 19.4

LESSON ORGANIZER

Objective Use strategies to practice addition.

Resources Reteach, Practice, Enrichment, Problem Solving, Homework, English Learners, Transparencies, Math Center

Materials Two-color counters, Part-Part-Whole Mat transparency, Workmat 3, overhead two-color counters, Workmat 2, ten frames transparency

Activity

Warm-Up Activity
Model Adding Parts to Find a Whole

| iiii Whole Group | ⏱ 5 minutes | Auditory, Tactile |

Materials: *overhead two-color counters, Part-Part-Whole Mat transparency, Workmat 3, two-color counters*

1. Write 8 + 4 = ___ on the board. Model 8 + 4 on the part-part-whole mat transparency. Guide children to do the same.

2. **How many counters are in the first part?** (8) **How many are in the second part?** (4) **If you add the parts together, what is the whole?** (12) Repeat with other examples.

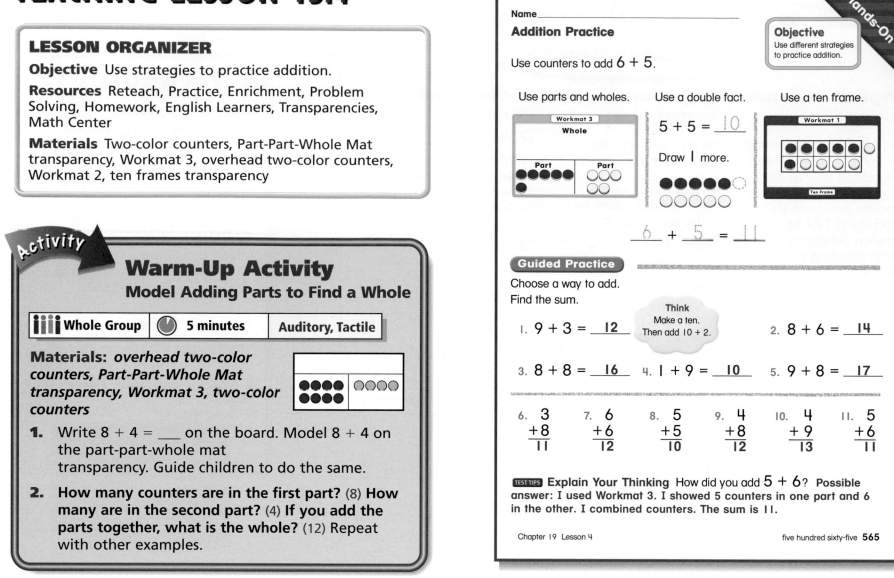

Name_____

Addition Practice

Objective Use different strategies to practice addition.

Use counters to add 6 + 5.

Use parts and wholes. Use a double fact. Use a ten frame.

5 + 5 = 10

Draw 1 more.

___6__ + __5__ = _11_

Guided Practice

Choose a way to add. Find the sum.

Think: Make a ten. Then add 10 + 2.

1. 9 + 3 = _12_   2. 8 + 6 = _14_

3. 8 + 8 = _16_   4. 1 + 9 = _10_   5. 9 + 8 = _17_

6. 3	7. 6	8. 5	9. 4	10. 4	11. 5
+8	+6	+5	+8	+9	+6
11	12	10	12	13	11

TEST TIPS Explain Your Thinking How did you add 5 + 6? **Possible answer: I used Workmat 3. I showed 5 counters in one part and 6 in the other. I combined counters. The sum is 11.**

Chapter 19 Lesson 4   five hundred sixty-five **565**

1 Introduce *Activity*
Model Using Strategies to Find a Sum

| iiii Whole Group | ⏱ 10–15 minutes | Visual, Tactile |

Materials: *two-color counters, Workmat 2, Workmat 3*

1. Have children model how to use various strategies to find a sum.

2. Guide children as they add 8 + 5 using two-color counters on a part-part-whole mat. Discuss the parts and how to find the whole, or sum.

3. Write 8 + 9 on the board and ask: **How can we use a double fact to find the sum?** (Add 8 + 8 and 1 more is 17.)

4. Focus attention on the ten frame and guide children as they find the sum of 9 + 4 by making a ten.

2 Develop

Guided Learning

Teaching Example Introduce the objective to children. Guide them through the examples to model three ways to find the sum for 6 + 5.

Guided Practice

Have children complete **Exercises 1–11** as you observe. Give children the opportunity to answer the Explain Your Thinking question. Then discuss their responses with the class.

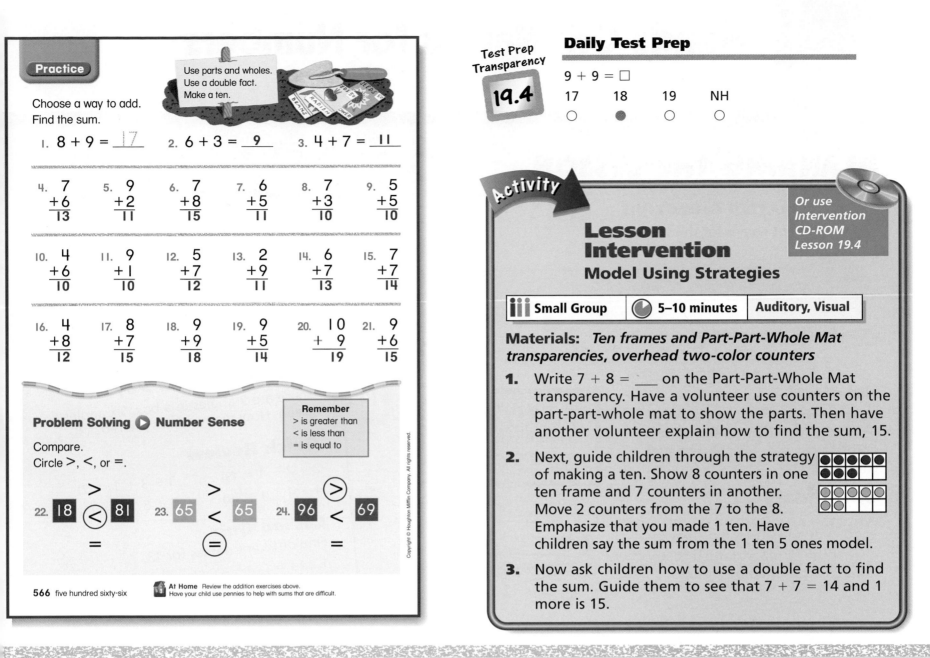

Practice

Use parts and wholes.
Use a double fact.
Make a ten.

Choose a way to add.
Find the sum.

1. 8 + 9 = __17__   2. 6 + 3 = __9__   3. 4 + 7 = __11__

4. 7   5. 9   6. 7   7. 6   8. 7   9. 5
   +6   +2   +8   +5   +3   +5
   ‾13   ‾11   ‾15   ‾11   ‾10   ‾10

10. 4   11. 9   12. 5   13. 2   14. 6   15. 7
    +6   +1   +7   +9   +7   +7
    ‾10   ‾10   ‾12   ‾11   ‾13   ‾14

16. 4   17. 8   18. 9   19. 9   20. 10   21. 9
    +8   +7   +9   +5   + 9   +6
    ‾12   ‾15   ‾18   ‾14   ‾19   ‾15

Problem Solving ▶ Number Sense

Remember
> is greater than
< is less than
= is equal to

Compare.
Circle >, <, or =.

22. 18 ⊙< 81   23. 65 <○ 65   24. 96 ⓥ> 69
    >   >   >
    =   ⊜=   =

566 five hundred sixty-six

At Home Review the addition exercises above.
Have your child use pennies to help with sums that are difficult.

Daily Test Prep

9 + 9 = ☐
17   ●18   19   NH
○   ●   ○   ○

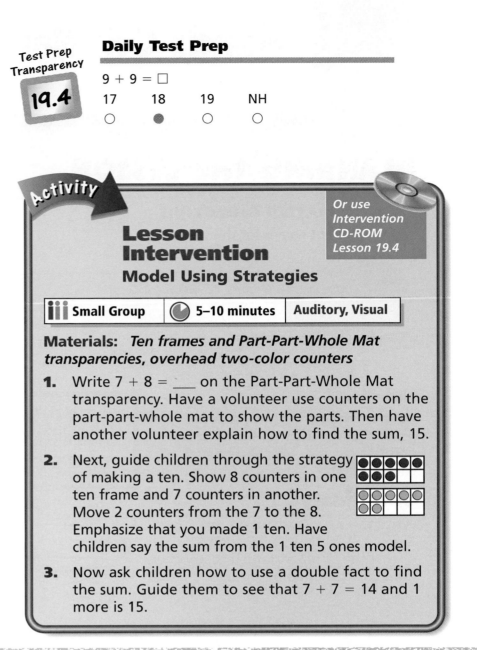

Activity

Or use Intervention CD-ROM Lesson 19.4

Lesson Intervention
Model Using Strategies

| 👤👤👤 Small Group | ⏱ 5–10 minutes | Auditory, Visual |

Materials: *Ten frames and Part-Part-Whole Mat transparencies, overhead two-color counters*

1. Write 7 + 8 = ___ on the Part-Part-Whole Mat transparency. Have a volunteer use counters on the part-part-whole mat to show the parts. Then have another volunteer explain how to find the sum, 15.

2. Next, guide children through the strategy of making a ten. Show 8 counters in one ten frame and 7 counters in another. Move 2 counters from the 7 to the 8. Emphasize that you made 1 ten. Have children say the sum from the 1 ten 5 ones model.

3. Now ask children how to use a double fact to find the sum. Guide them to see that 7 + 7 = 14 and 1 more is 15.

③ Practice

Independent Practice

Children complete **Exercises 1–21** independently.

Problem Solving

After children complete **Exercises 22–24**, call on volunteers to share their solutions.

Common Error

Confusing Strategies

Some children may mix elements of different strategies and come up with incorrect sums. Encourage children to use the strategy that works best for them.

④ Assess and Close

Explain how to use parts to find a whole to add 3 + 8.
(Show 8 yellow counters and 3 red counters. That makes 11.)

How can you use a double fact to find 6 + 7? (Add 6 + 6 to get 12 and 1 more is 13.)

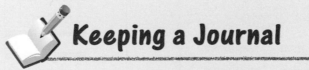 **Keeping a Journal**

Draw to show three ways to find the sum of 8 + 6.

Hands-On: Names for Numbers

PLANNING THE LESSON

MATHEMATICS OBJECTIVE
Find different names for the same number.

Use Lesson Planner CD-ROM for Lesson 19.5.

Meeting North Carolina's Standards
1.03 Develop fluency with single-digit addition and corresponding differences using strategies such as modeling, composing and decomposing quantities, using doubles, and making tens.

Daily Routines

Calendar
Have children skip count in unison using the calendar. Have a volunteer point to the date on the calendar as children count.

Sunday	Monday	Tuesday	Wednesday	Thursday	Friday	Saturday
			1	2	3	4
5	6	7	8	9	10	11
12	13	14	15	16	17	18
19	20	21	22	23	24	25
26	27	28	29	30	31	

Vocabulary
Write the word **addend** on the board. Remind children that an addend is one of the numbers added to another number when finding a **sum**.

Vocabulary Cards

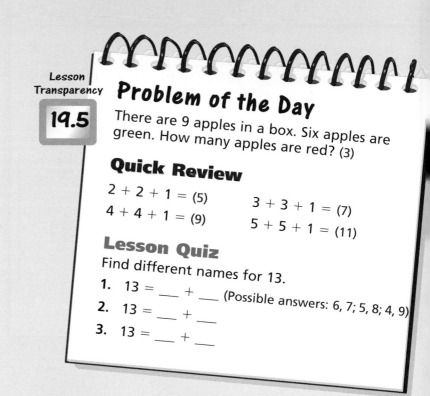

Problem of the Day
There are 9 apples in a box. Six apples are green. How many apples are red? (3)

Quick Review
$2 + 2 + 1 = (5)$ $\qquad$ $3 + 3 + 1 = (7)$
$4 + 4 + 1 = (9)$ $\qquad$ $5 + 5 + 1 = (11)$

Lesson Quiz
Find different names for 13.
1. $13 = \underline{} + \underline{}$ (Possible answers: 6, 7; 5, 8; 4, 9)
2. $13 = \underline{} + \underline{}$
3. $13 = \underline{} + \underline{}$

LEVELED PRACTICE

RETEACH 19.5

Name _____ Date _____ Reteach 19.5

Names for Numbers

You can use different parts to make a whole.
The different parts are names for the same number.
Use counters to find different parts for 16.

Whole
16

Part	Part
○○○○○	○○○○○

Think of all the different ways you can make 16.

Whole		Whole		Whole	
16		16		16	
Part	Part	Part	Part	Part	Part
8	8	9	7	7	9

Use Workmat 3 and ○.
Find different names for the number. **Answers may vary.**

1.
Whole		Whole		Whole		Whole	
12		12		12		12	
Part	Part	Part	Part	Part	Part	Part	Part
9	3	8	4	7	5	6	6

2.
Whole		Whole		Whole		Whole	
11		11		11		11	
Part	Part	Part	Part	Part	Part	Part	Part
9	2	8	3	7	4	6	5

Use with text pages 567–568.

PRACTICE 19.5

Name _____ Date _____ Practice 19.5

Names for Numbers

Use Workmat 3 and ○.
Find different names for the number. **Possible answers are given.**

1.
Whole		Whole		Whole		Whole	
12		12		12		12	
Part	Part	Part	Part	Part	Part	Part	Part
5	7	3	9	8	4	5	7

2.
Whole		Whole	
15		15	
Part	Part	Part	Part
9	6	7	8

3.
Whole		Whole	
14		14	
Part	Part	Part	Part
6	8	7	7

4.
Whole		Whole	
13		13	
Part	Part	Part	Part
4	9	8	5

5.
Whole		Whole	
16		16	
Part	Part	Part	Part
8	8	9	7

Test Prep

Fill in the ○ for the correct answer.
NH means Not Here.

6. Which of these ways will make the sum?

Whole
18
Part	Part
?	?

$1 + 8$ $\quad$ $8 + 9$ $\quad$ $9 + 9$ ● $\quad$ NH

Use with text pages 567–568.

ENRICHMENT 19.5

Name _____ Date _____ Enrichment 19.5

Patterns in Names

Complete the names for the number.
Write how many names in all.

1. Names for 12	2. Names for 11	3. Names for 10
$0 + 12$	$0 + 11$	$0 + 10$
$1 + 11$	$1 + 10$	$1 + 9$
$2 + 10$	$2 + 9$	$2 + 8$
$3 + 9$	$3 + 8$	$3 + 7$
$4 + 8$	$4 + 7$	$4 + 6$
$5 + 7$	$5 + 6$	$5 + 5$
$6 + 6$	$6 + 5$	$6 + 4$
$7 + 5$	$7 + 4$	$7 + 3$
$8 + 4$	$8 + 3$	$8 + 2$
$9 + 3$	$9 + 2$	$9 + 1$
$10 + 2$	$10 + 1$	$10 + 0$
$11 + 1$	$11 + 0$	
$12 + 0$		
13 names	**12** names	**11** names

Write About It What patterns do you see?

Possible response: The first addend increases by 1, the second addend decreases by 1.

Use with text pages 567–568.

Practice Workbook Page 131

Reaching All Learners

Differentiated Instruction

English Learners

English-language learners may not have the language skills to explain the process behind their thinking. Use Worksheet 19.5 to provide children with sentence frames they can use to complete the Explain Your Thinking activity.

Special Needs

Materials: *12 two-color counters, paper cup*

- Have the child shake and gently spill the counters from the cup.
- Have the child count the red and then the yellow counters. Guide her or him to write the addition sentence.
- Repeat until at least 4 different names for 12 have been shown.

Gifted and Talented

VISUAL, SPATIAL

Materials: *grid paper (LT 29)*

- Have children color rows on the grid paper to show the names for 12.

Science Connection

Display pairs of simple flower pictures. Have children count the petals on each flower and write a number sentence to find the total.

MATH CENTER

Vocabulary Activity

This vocabulary-building activity helps children understand and remember new words. Encourage children to use the words in math discussion.

PROBLEM SOLVING 19.5

Name _____ Date _____ Problem Solving 19.5

Names for Numbers

You can draw a picture to solve problems about different names for numbers.

1. Mel picks 14 tomatoes in all. He puts some tomatoes in a red basket and some in a yellow basket. What are three different ways Mel could put tomatoes in the baskets?

   Draw or write to explain.

   Check children's drawings.

   Answers may vary. Possible answers are shown.

   __5__ tomatoes and
   __9__ tomatoes

   __6__ tomatoes and
   __8__ tomatoes

   __7__ tomatoes and
   __7__ tomatoes

2. Amy finds 15 shells in all. She puts some in a bag and some in a pail. What are two different ways Amy could put the shells in the bag and pail?

   __6__ shells in a pail
   __9__ shells in a bag

   __7__ shells in a pail
   __8__ shells in a bag

Use with text pages 567–568.

HOMEWORK 19.5

Name _____ Date _____ Homework 19.5

Names for Numbers

Use different ways to make the same sum.

Names for 16

Whole	Whole
16	16
Part Part	Part Part
9 7	8 8

Find names for the number.

Answers may vary. Possible answers given.

1.
Whole	Whole	Whole	Whole
12	12	12	12
Part Part	Part Part	Part Part	Part Part
9 3	8 4	7 5	6 6

2.
Whole	Whole
15	15
Part Part	Part Part
9 6	8 7

3.
Whole	Whole
14	14
Part Part	Part Part
9 5	8 6

Find the missing part.

4.
Whole
11
Part Part
3 8

5.
Whole
13
Part Part
6 7

6.
Whole
18
Part Part
9 9

Use with text pages 567–568.

ENGLISH LEARNERS 19.5

Name _____ Date _____ English Learners 19.5

Names for Numbers

6 + 7 = 13
6 + 7 equals 13.
6 + 7 is a name for 13.

Tell why 9 + 3 is not a name for 14.

9 + 3 = __12__

9 + 3 does not equal __14__.

9 + 3 is not a name for 14.

It does not equal 14.

To the Teacher: Use the example at the top of the page to demonstrate how to find names for a number. Then have children complete the sentence frames that provide the language needed to explain why 9 + 3 is not a name for 14.

Use with text pages 567–568.

Homework Workbook Page 131

TEACHING LESSON 19.5

LESSON ORGANIZER

Objective Find different names for the same number.

Resources Reteach, Practice, Enrichment, Problem Solving, Homework, English Learners, Transparencies, Math Center

Materials Part-Part-Whole Mat transparency, Workmat 3, overhead 2-color counters, cubes, two-color counters

Activity

Warm-Up Activity
Modeling Addition

iiii Whole Group	⏱ 5 minutes	Visual, Auditory

1. Have children fold a sheet of paper into four sections.

2. Have them write an addition sentence in each section such as 4 + 2 = ___ or 5 + 4 = ___.

3. Have children exchange their papers with a classmate and make up a story for each sentence. Then have them draw the parts and find the sum. Allow children to share their stories with the class.

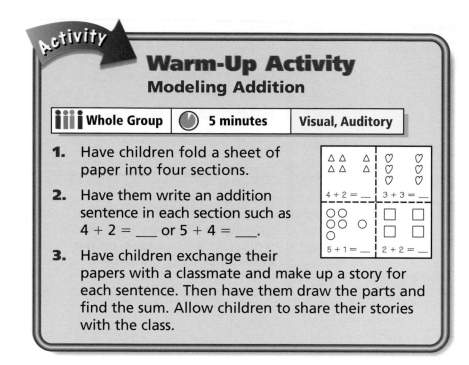

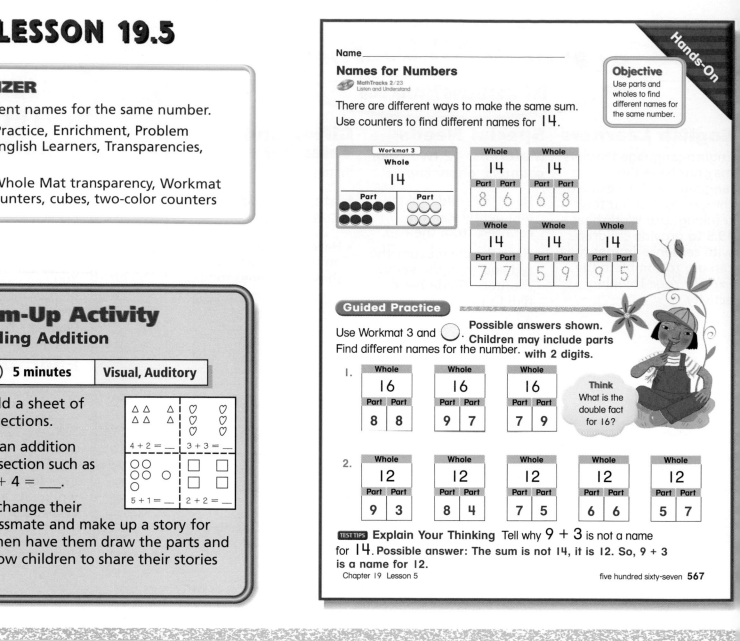

Name_____

Names for Numbers

MathTracks 2/23
Listen and Understand

Objective
Use parts and wholes to find different names for the same number.

There are different ways to make the same sum. Use counters to find different names for 14.

Workmat 3

Whole
14

Part	Part
●●●●● ●●●	○○○ ○○○

Whole		Whole	
14		14	
Part	**Part**	**Part**	**Part**
8	6	6	8

Whole		Whole		Whole	
14		14		14	
Part	**Part**	**Part**	**Part**	**Part**	**Part**
7	7	5	9	9	5

Guided Practice

Use Workmat 3 and ⬤. **Possible answers shown. Children may include parts** Find different names for the number. **with 2 digits.**

1.

Whole		Whole		Whole	
16		16		16	
Part	**Part**	**Part**	**Part**	**Part**	**Part**
8	8	9	7	7	9

Think What is the double fact for 16?

2.

Whole		Whole		Whole		Whole		Whole	
12		12		12		12		12	
Part	**Part**	**Part**	**Part**	**Part**	**Part**	**Part**	**Part**	**Part**	**Part**
9	3	8	4	7	5	6	6	5	7

TEST TIPS **Explain Your Thinking** Tell why 9 + 3 is not a name for 14. Possible answer: The sum is not 14, it is 12. So, 9 + 3 is a name for 12.

Chapter 19 Lesson 5

five hundred sixty-seven **567**

---

① Introduce

Activity

Model Names for Numbers

iiii Whole Group	⏱ 10–15 minutes	Visual, Tactile

Materials: *Part-Part-Whole Mat transparency, Workmat 3, overhead 2-color counters*

1. Place 15 counters in the whole part of the workmat transparency as children do the same at their desks.

2. Ask a volunteer to tell you one way that you can arrange the counters into two parts that make a whole of 15. Have the child arrange the counters into two parts on the mat. Have children find other names for 15 and continue having the parts modeled on the overhead.

② Develop

Guided Learning

Teaching Example Introduce the objective to the children. Guide them through the example to show how they can use counters to model names for numbers.

Guided Practice

Have children complete **Exercises 1–2** as you observe. Discuss children's responses to the Explain Your Thinking question.

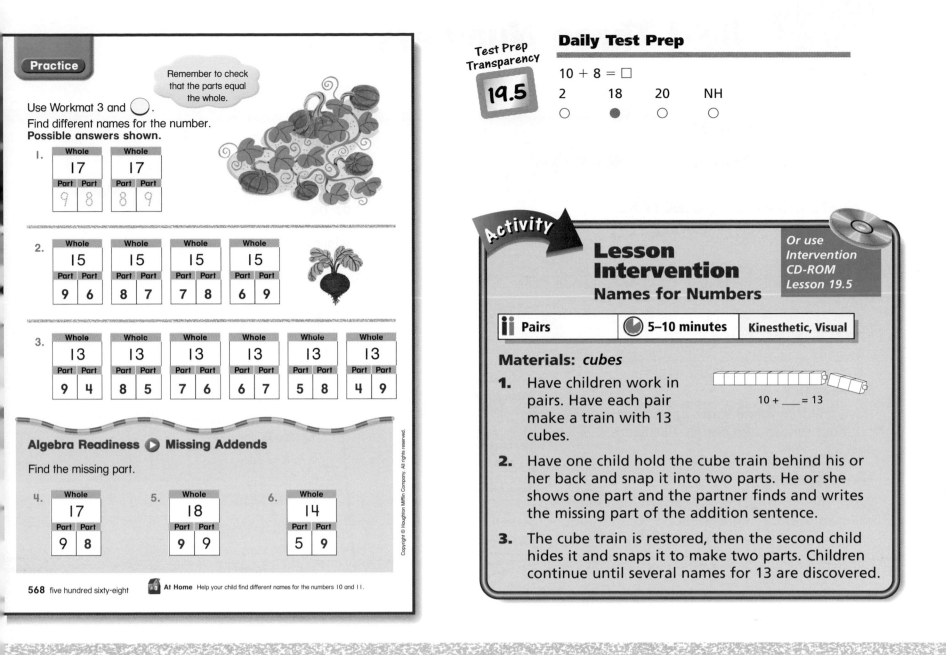

Remember to check that the parts equal the whole.

Use Workmat 3 and ◯.
Find different names for the number.
Possible answers shown.

1.

Whole		Whole	
17		17	
Part	Part	Part	Part
9	8	8	9

2.

Whole		Whole		Whole		Whole	
15		15		15		15	
Part	Part	Part	Part	Part	Part	Part	Part
9	6	8	7	7	8	6	9

3.

Whole		Whole		Whole		Whole		Whole		Whole	
13		13		13		13		13		13	
Part	Part	Part	Part	Part	Part	Part	Part	Part	Part	Part	Part
9	4	8	5	7	6	6	7	5	8	4	9

Algebra Readiness ▶ Missing Addends

Find the missing part.

4.

Whole	
17	
Part	Part
9	8

5.

Whole	
18	
Part	Part
9	9

6.

Whole	
14	
Part	Part
5	9

At Home Help your child find different names for the numbers 10 and 11.

Daily Test Prep

Test Prep Transparency **19.5**

$10 + 8 = \Box$

2	18	20	NH
○	●	○	○

Activity

Lesson Intervention
Names for Numbers

Or use Intervention CD-ROM Lesson 19.5

👥 Pairs	🕐 5–10 minutes	Kinesthetic, Visual

Materials: *cubes*

1. Have children work in pairs. Have each pair make a train with 13 cubes.

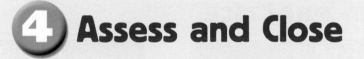
$10 + \underline{\quad} = 13$

2. Have one child hold the cube train behind his or her back and snap it into two parts. He or she shows one part and the partner finds and writes the missing part of the addition sentence.

3. The cube train is restored, then the second child hides it and snaps it to make two parts. Children continue until several names for 13 are discovered.

3 Practice

Independent Practice

Children complete **Exercises 1–3** independently.

Algebra Readiness

After children complete **Exercises 4–6**, call on volunteers to share their solutions. Encourage them to explain how they arrived at their answers.

Common Error

Counting Incorrectly

Some children may count an item more than once and get an incorrect answer. Have children arrange the counters in a line and then touch each counter as they say each number.

4 Assess and Close

How can you use counters to show names for 16? (Possible answer: Show 16 counters and then make two parts and write the numbers. Then make two different parts and write the numbers.)

What are three names for 6? (Possible answers: 1 + 5; 2 + 4; 3 + 3.)

✏️ Keeping a Journal

Draw pictures to show all the names for 13.

Add Three Numbers

PLANNING THE LESSON

MATHEMATICS OBJECTIVE
Find the sum of three numbers.

Use Lesson Planner CD-ROM for Lesson 19.6.

Meeting North Carolina's Standards
1.03 Develop fluency with single-digit addition and corresponding differences using strategies such as modeling, composing and decomposing quantities, using doubles, and making tens.

Also 1.04

Daily Routines

Calendar
Have children name three dates on the calendar whose sum equals 10 such as 1, 3, and 6.

Vocabulary
Write the word *fact* on the board. Remind children that an addition fact is an addition sentence that shows the sum of two 1-digit numbers.

Vocabulary Cards

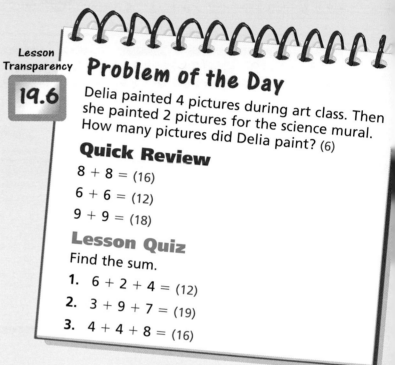

Lesson Transparency 19.6

Problem of the Day
Delia painted 4 pictures during art class. Then she painted 2 pictures for the science mural. How many pictures did Delia paint? (6)

Quick Review
$8 + 8 =$ (16)
$6 + 6 =$ (12)
$9 + 9 =$ (18)

Lesson Quiz
Find the sum.
1. $6 + 2 + 4 =$ (12)
2. $3 + 9 + 7 =$ (19)
3. $4 + 4 + 8 =$ (16)

LEVELED PRACTICE

RETEACH 19.6

Name _____ Date _____ Reteach 19.6

Add Three Numbers
There are different ways that you can add three numbers.

Look for a double fact.	Make a 10.	Add in any order.
$\begin{matrix}4\\2\\+6\\\hline12\end{matrix}$ 6, $6+6$	$\begin{matrix}4\\2\\+6\\\hline12\end{matrix}$ 10, $+2$	$\begin{matrix}4\\2\\+6\\\hline12\end{matrix}$ 8, $+4$
I know that $4+2=6$. $6+6$ is a double fact for 12.	I know that $2+6=8$. Then I add 2 more.	I know that $2+6=8$. Then $8+4=12$.

Look for a fact you know. Add.

Answers in boxes may vary. Possible answers are shown.

1. $\begin{matrix}4\\6\\+1\\\hline11\end{matrix}$ [10] [1] 11
2. $\begin{matrix}4\\8\\+4\\\hline16\end{matrix}$ [8] [8] 16
3. $\begin{matrix}2\\3\\+6\\\hline11\end{matrix}$ [5] [6] 11
4. $\begin{matrix}9\\5\\+1\\\hline15\end{matrix}$ [10] [5] 15
5. $\begin{matrix}3\\7\\+3\\\hline13\end{matrix}$ [6] [7] 13
6. $\begin{matrix}3\\2\\+5\\\hline10\end{matrix}$ [5] [5] 10

Use with text pages 569–570.

PRACTICE 19.6

Name _____ Date _____ Practice 19.6

Add Three Numbers
Find the sum.

Think Can I use a double? Can I make a ten?

1. $\begin{matrix}8\\8\\+1\\\hline17\end{matrix}$
2. $\begin{matrix}6\\3\\+3\\\hline12\end{matrix}$
3. $\begin{matrix}9\\1\\+3\\\hline13\end{matrix}$
4. $\begin{matrix}4\\9\\+4\\\hline17\end{matrix}$
5. $\begin{matrix}8\\3\\+7\\\hline18\end{matrix}$

6. $\begin{matrix}2\\2\\+7\\\hline11\end{matrix}$
7. $\begin{matrix}6\\4\\+5\\\hline15\end{matrix}$
8. $\begin{matrix}2\\5\\+5\\\hline12\end{matrix}$
9. $\begin{matrix}7\\7\\+2\\\hline16\end{matrix}$
10. $\begin{matrix}1\\1\\+8\\\hline10\end{matrix}$

11. $1 + 9 + 1 = \underline{11}$
12. $2 + 2 + 2 = \underline{6}$
13. $6 + 6 + 4 = \underline{16}$
14. $8 + 5 + 4 = \underline{17}$

Test Prep

Fill in the ○ for the correct answer. NH means Not Here.

15. Which double fact can you use to find the sum?
$\begin{matrix}4\\6\\+2\end{matrix}$

$2+2=4$ ○ $4+4=8$ ○ $6+6=12$ ● NH ○

Use with text pages 569–570.

ENRICHMENT 19.6

Name _____ Date _____ Enrichment 19.6

Use Strategies with Three Addends
During 3 nights, 4 friends counted falling stars. Find the total number of stars for each friend.

Anka counted 6, 9, and 3 stars.	Joseph counted 4, 7, and 5 stars.	Lin counted 8, 1, and 8 stars.	Gabe counted 9, 4, and 6 stars.
$\begin{matrix}6\\9\\+3\\\hline18\end{matrix}$	$\begin{matrix}4\\7\\+5\\\hline16\end{matrix}$	$\begin{matrix}8\\1\\+8\\\hline17\end{matrix}$	$\begin{matrix}9\\4\\+6\\\hline19\end{matrix}$

1. For which friend can you find a double among the 3 numbers? __Lin__

2. Add the total number of stars counted on night 1, night 2, and night 3.

Night 1 __27__ stars Night 2 __21__ stars Night 3 __22__ stars
Total stars __70__

Write About It Explain how you found the answers in Exercise 2. **Possible response: For Night 1, I added the numbers in the top row 6, 4, 8, and 9. For Night 2, I added the numbers in the second row. Then I added the totals for the 3 nights together.**

Use with text pages 569–570.

Practice Workbook Page 132

Reaching All Learners

Differentiated Instruction

English Learners

English-language learners may not be familiar with the concept of contractions. Use Worksheet 19.6 to develop children's knowledge of the contraction *I'll*.

Inclusion

VISUAL, TACTILE

Materials: *8-section spinner numbered 1–6 (LT 38); red, blue, and green cubes*

- Have the child spin 3 times and model each number with a different color cube.
- The child writes the addition sentence and finds the sum.

Early Finishers

VISUAL, SPATIAL

Materials: *number cards (LT 14 and 15)*

- Give each child three number cards.
- Have children use their 3 numbers to write a story problem.
- Combine the story problems into a class math book.

TECHNOLOGY

Spiral Review

Using the *Ways to Assess* CD-ROM, you can create **customized** spiral review worksheets covering any lessons you choose.

Education Place

Recommend that parents visit **Education Place** at **eduplace.com/parents/mw/** for parent support activities.

Games

Students can practice their computational skills using the **Find a Friend** game on the *Ways to Success* CD-ROM.

Science Connection

Line the bottom of a shoebox with yellow, blue, and red paper. Spill collected berries, acorns, etc. into the box. Have children write addition sentences about the number of items on each color of paper.

MATH CENTER

Real-Life Activity

Help children understand the usefulness of mathematics. This activity makes math come alive by connecting the lesson skills to a real-life situation.

PROBLEM SOLVING 19.6

Name _____ Date _____ Problem Solving 19.6

Add Three Numbers

The table shows the birds Wendy saw for three days. Use the table for problems 1–6.

Birds Wendy Saw

	Friday	Saturday	Sunday
Robins	3	5	7
Blue Jays	4	6	2
Pigeons	5	5	8

Solve.

1. How many robins did Wendy see in all?
   $3 + 5 + 7 = 15$
   15 robins

2. How many blue jays did Wendy see in all?
   $4 + 6 + 2 = 12$
   12 blue jays

3. How many pigeons did Wendy see in all?
   $5 + 5 + 8 = 18$
   18 pigeons

4. How many birds did Wendy see on Friday altogether?
   $3 + 4 + 5 = 12$
   12 birds

5. How many birds did Wendy see on Saturday altogether?
   $5 + 6 + 5 = 16$
   16 birds

6. How many birds did Wendy see on Sunday altogether?
   $7 + 2 + 8 = 17$
   17 birds

Use with text pages 569–570.

HOMEWORK 19.6

Name _____ Date _____ Homework 19.6

Add Three Numbers

Look for facts you know to help you add three numbers.

Make a 10. $7 + 3$

$$\begin{array}{r} 7 \\ 3 \\ +7 \\ \hline 17 \end{array}$$

Find a double. $7 + 7$

Add.

1. $\begin{array}{r} 5 \\ 2 \\ +5 \\ \hline 12 \end{array}$
2. $\begin{array}{r} 8 \\ 2 \\ +6 \\ \hline 16 \end{array}$
3. $\begin{array}{r} 6 \\ 6 \\ +3 \\ \hline 15 \end{array}$
4. $\begin{array}{r} 1 \\ 9 \\ +7 \\ \hline 17 \end{array}$
5. $\begin{array}{r} 9 \\ 7 \\ +2 \\ \hline 18 \end{array}$

6. $6 + 4 + 3 = 13$ 7. $4 + 3 + 7 = 14$

8. $2 + 9 + 2 = 13$ 9. $3 + 1 + 7 = 11$

Solve.

10. Lisa scored 3 points in Game 3. How many points did she score in all?

Lisa	Points
Game 1	5
Game 2	5
Game 3	

$5 + 5 + 3 = 13$

Use with text pages 569–570.

Homework Workbook Page 132

ENGLISH LEARNERS 19.6

Name _____ Date _____ English Learners 19.6

Add Three Numbers

I'll fly a kite.
I will fly a kite.

Write a word to take the place of **I will**.

1.
I will read.
_____**I'll**_____ read.

2.
I will jump.
_____**I'll**_____ jump.

3.
I will cook.
_____**I'll**_____ cook.

4.
I will rake.
_____**I'll**_____ rake.

To the Teacher: Use the example at the top of the page to help children understand the contraction *I'll*. Then read the sentences with children and have them write the contractions.

Use with text pages 569–570.

TEACHING LESSON 19.6

LESSON ORGANIZER

Objective Find the sum of three numbers.

Resources Reteach, Practice, Enrichment, Problem Solving, Homework, English Learners, Transparencies, Math Center

Materials Cubes, number cards (LT 14 and 15), two-color counters

Warm-Up Activity
Discuss Addition Strategies

𝗂𝗂𝗂𝗂 Whole Group	🕐 5 minutes	Visual, Auditory

Materials: *cubes*

1. Review with children addition strategies previously learned such as *counting on*, *doubles plus one*, or *make a ten*.

2. Write 9 + 4 = ___ on the board and ask a volunteer to choose a strategy to find the sum. Work through the strategy with the children. For example: Make a 10 and add 10 + 3.

3. **How would you use the strategy *count on* to add 8 + 2?** (Count on from 8: 9, 10.)

4. Repeat with other strategies.

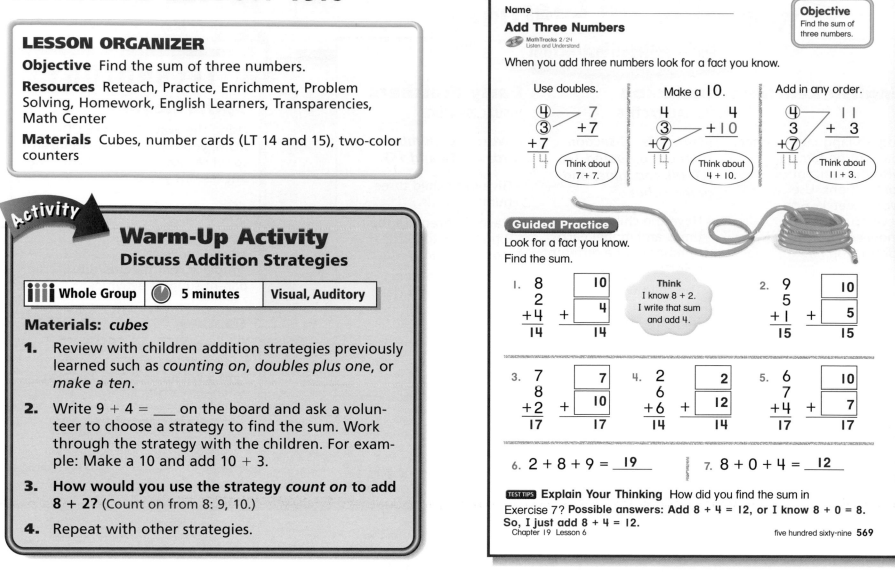

Name_____

Add Three Numbers

MathTracks 2/24
Listen and Understand

Objective
Find the sum of three numbers.

When you add three numbers look for a fact you know.

Use doubles.

Make a 10.

Add in any order.

Guided Practice

Look for a fact you know.
Find the sum.

Think
I know 8 + 2.
I write that sum and add 4.

6. 2 + 8 + 9 = __19__   7. 8 + 0 + 4 = __12__

TEST TIPS **Explain Your Thinking** How did you find the sum in Exercise 7? **Possible answers: Add 8 + 4 = 12, or I know 8 + 0 = 8. So, I just add 8 + 4 = 12.**

Chapter 19 Lesson 6   five hundred sixty-nine **569**

---

① Introduce
Model Adding Three Numbers

𝗂𝗂𝗂𝗂 Whole Group	🕐 10–15 minutes	Visual, Auditory

1. Write 2 + 8 + 2 in vertical form on the board. Remind children that when they add three addends they first have to add two of the addends. Then they add the third addend.

2. Demonstrate making a ten by adding 2 + 8. Then add 10 + 2 to get 12.

3. Remind children that they can add in any order. Then demonstrate adding the double 2 + 2 to get 4, and add 8 + 4 to get 12.

4. Repeat with 4 + 3 + 6 and have children choose a strategy to demonstrate.

② Develop

Guided Learning

Teaching Example Introduce the objective to the children. Guide them through the example to show how they can add three numbers in different ways. Check that children understand and see each strategy as presented.

Guided Practice

Have children complete **Exercises 1–7** as you observe. Have children share their responses to the Explain Your Thinking question.

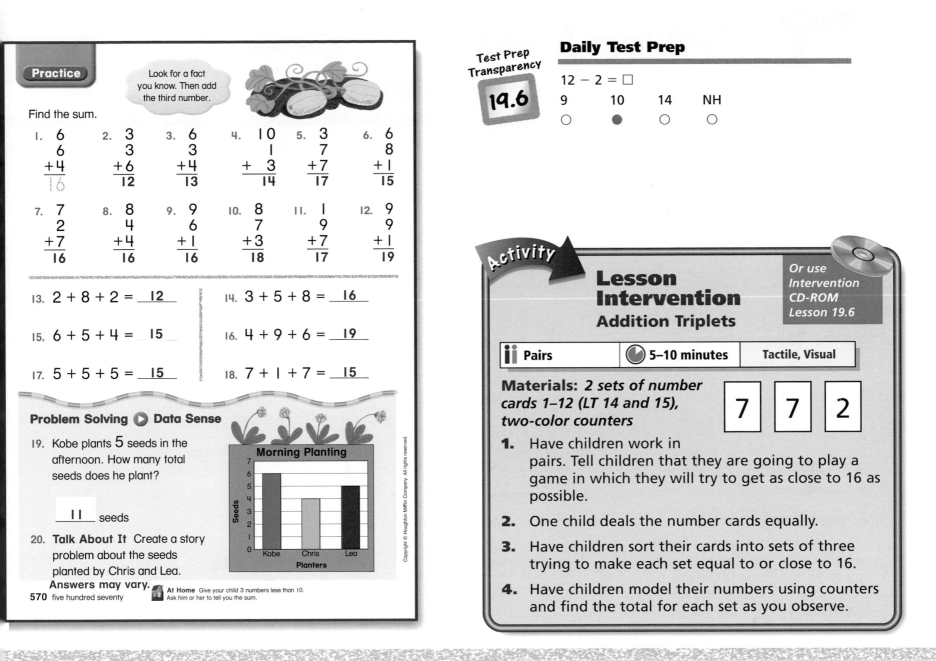

Practice

Look for a fact you know. Then add the third number.

Find the sum.

1. 6 6 +4 16	2. 3 3 +6 12	3. 6 3 +4 13	4. 10 1 + 3 14	5. 3 7 +7 17	6. 6 8 +1 15
7. 7 2 +7 16	8. 8 4 +4 16	9. 9 6 +1 16	10. 8 7 +3 18	11. 1 9 +7 17	12. 9 9 +1 19

13. 2 + 8 + 2 = __12__

14. 3 + 5 + 8 = __16__

15. 6 + 5 + 4 = __15__

16. 4 + 9 + 6 = __19__

17. 5 + 5 + 5 = __15__

18. 7 + 1 + 7 = __15__

Problem Solving ▶ Data Sense

19. Kobe plants 5 seeds in the afternoon. How many total seeds does he plant?

    __11__ seeds

Morning Planting

20. **Talk About It** Create a story problem about the seeds planted by Chris and Lea.
    Answers may vary.

570 five hundred seventy

 **At Home** Give your child 3 numbers less than 10. Ask him or her to tell you the sum.

Daily Test Prep

12 − 2 = ☐

9   10   14   NH

○   ●   ○   ○

Activity

Lesson Intervention
Addition Triplets

Or use Intervention CD-ROM Lesson 19.6

👥 Pairs	🕐 5–10 minutes	Tactile, Visual

Materials: *2 sets of number cards 1–12 (LT 14 and 15), two-color counters*

7	7	2

1. Have children work in pairs. Tell children that they are going to play a game in which they will try to get as close to 16 as possible.

2. One child deals the number cards equally.

3. Have children sort their cards into sets of three trying to make each set equal to or close to 16.

4. Have children model their numbers using counters and find the total for each set as you observe.

---

3 Practice

Independent Practice

Children complete **Exercises 1–18** independently.

Problem Solving

After children complete **Exercise 19**, call on volunteers to share their solutions. Encourage them to explain how they arrived at their answers. Use the **Talk About It** in **Exercise 20** to let children share story problems for the class to solve.

Common Error

Adding Incorrectly

Some children may forget to add all three numbers. Have children use counters to model each number and then count the counters to find the sum.

4 Assess and Close

Which strategy can you use to add 6 + 4 + 6? (Possible answers: make a ten; doubles; add in any order.)

📝 Keeping a Journal

Explain what strategy you will use to add 2 + 3 + 8.

Problem Solving: Write a Number Sentence

PLANNING THE LESSON

MATHEMATICS OBJECTIVE
Write a number sentence to solve a problem.

Use Lesson Planner CD-ROM for Lesson 19.7.

Daily Routines

Calendar
Point to the date on the calendar. Ask children if they were to have a test next week on the day before Wednesday, on what date would the test take place?

Sunday	Monday	Tuesday	Wednesday	Thursday	Friday	Saturday
			1	2	3	4
5	6	7	8	9	10	11
12	13	14	15	16	17	18
19	20	21	22	23	24	25
26	27	28	29	30	31	

Vocabulary
Review the words **parts** and **whole**. Write an addition sentence on the board. Relate the addends to parts and the sum to the whole. If you have parts of 4 and 5, what is the whole? (9)

Vocabulary Cards

Meeting North Carolina's Standards
1.04 Create, model, and solve problems that use addition, subtraction, and fair shares (between two or three).

Also 1.03

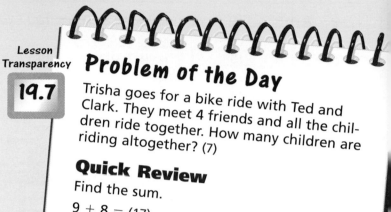

Lesson Transparency 19.7

Problem of the Day
Trisha goes for a bike ride with Ted and Clark. They meet 4 friends and all the children ride together. How many children are riding altogether? (7)

Quick Review
Find the sum.
$9 + 8 = (17)$
$7 + 6 = (13)$
$8 + 7 = (15)$

Lesson Quiz
Write a number sentence to solve.
Scott picks 8 peppers. Carol picks 7 peppers. How many peppers do they pick altogether? $(8 + 7 = 15;$ 15 peppers)

LEVELED PRACTICE

RETEACH 19.7

Name _____ Date _____

Reteach 19.7

Problem Solving
Write a Number Sentence

Read It Look for information.
Tim has 5 baseballs. Elena has 9 baseballs. How many baseballs do Tim and Elena have altogether?

Picture It Here is a model of the problem.

How many baseballs altogether?	
Tim's baseballs	Elena's baseballs

Solve It Use the model to solve the problem.

14 baseballs altogether	
Tim: 5 baseballs	Elena: 9 baseballs

1. Circle the sign you would use.
   (+) −

   Think Do I add or subtract to find how many altogether?

2. Write a number sentence.
   5 (+) $9 = 14$

3. How many baseballs do Tim and Elena have altogether?
   14 baseballs

Copyright © Houghton Mifflin Company. All rights reserved.

Use with text pages 571–572.

PRACTICE 19.7

Name _____ Date _____

Practice 19.7

Problem Solving
Write a Number Sentence

Write a number sentence to solve.

1. There are 10 carrot plants in the first row. In the next row there are 9 carrot plants. How many carrot plants are there in all?

   10 (+) $9 = 19$

   Draw or write to explain.

   Check children's drawings.

   19 plants in all

2. Cindy picks 3 baskets of apples the first day. She picks 4 baskets the next day. She picks 1 basket the third day. How many baskets of apples does she pick?

   3 (+) 4 (+) $1 = 8$

   8 baskets in all

Test Prep

Fill in the ○ for the correct answer.
NH means Not Here.

3. Meg has 2 bags of plums. Each bag has 7 plums. Which number sentence tells how to find the total number of plums Meg has?

   ○ $2 + 7 = 9$
   ○ $7 − 2 = 5$
   ● $7 + 7 = 14$
   ○ NH

Copyright © Houghton Mifflin Company. All rights reserved.

Use with text pages 571–572.

ENRICHMENT 19.7

Name _____ Date _____

Enrichment 19.7

Baseball Story Problems

Read the story problem.
Put numbers in the problem.
Write a number sentence to solve.

Answers will vary. Possible answers shown.

1. Mary gets 3 base hits.
   Ed gets 2 base hits.
   Ruth gets 5 base hits.
   How many base hits do they get in all?
   Write a number sentence to solve.

   3 (+) 2 (+) 5 (=) 10

   10 base hits

2. There are 9 players on the field.
   There are 3 players on the bench.
   There are 2 players on bases.
   How many players are there in all?

   9 (+) 3 (+) 2 (=) 14

   14 players

Write About It Write a story problem that matches the number sentence.
Solve. $3 + 2 + 8 = 13$

Answers may vary. Sample Response: The blue team scores 3 runs. The red team scores 2 runs. The green team scores 8 runs. How many runs do the teams score altogether? 13 runs.

Copyright © Houghton Mifflin Company. All rights reserved.

Use with text pages 571–574.

Practice Workbook Page 133

Reaching All Learners

Differentiated Instruction

English Learners

Children will need to understand the word *altogether* in order to solve some word problems that involve addition. Use Worksheet 19.7 to develop children's ability to understand and use this word.

Inclusion
AUDITORY, TACTILE

Materials: *cubes, Workmat 3*

- Guide the child through the following problem.
- *Billy has 4 red toy cars. He also has 3 blue cars. How many cars does Billy have altogether?*
- Have the child use cubes on the workmat.

4 + 3 = ___

Gifted and Talented
TACTILE, AUDITORY

- Explain that children are to write a story problem that can be solved by finding the whole from the parts. For example, *Casey put 7 seeds in 1 pot. She put 8 seeds in another pot. How many seeds did Casey plant in all?* (15)
- Children may exchange story problems and solve.

TECHNOLOGY

Spiral Review
To reinforce skills on lessons taught earlier, create **customized** spiral review worksheets using the *Ways to Assess* CD-ROM.

Education Place
Visit **Data Place** at **eduplace.com/dataplace/** to take a survey and see graphs of the results.

Intervention
Use the *Ways to Success* intervention software to support students who need more help in understanding the concepts and skills taught in this chapter.

Literature Connection

Read *Dinner at the Panda Palace* by Stephanie Calmenson. Ask questions such as: **How many monkeys and penguins were at the Panda Palace?** Have children write the number sentence. (8 + 5 = 13)

MATH CENTER

Number of the Week Activity

Display the Number of the Week to motivate children to use their problem-solving skills. The exercises cover topics across all math strands.

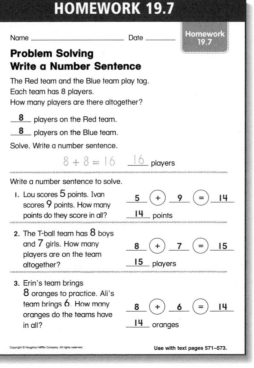

TEACHING LESSON 19.7

LESSON ORGANIZER

Objective Write a number sentence to solve a problem.

Resources Reteach, Practice, Enrichment, Problem Solving, Homework, English Learners, Transparencies, Math Center

Materials Part-Part-Whole Mat transparency, overhead two-color counters, Workmat 3, two-color counters

Activity

Warm-Up Activity
Model Writing a Number Sentence

▮▮▮▮ Whole Group	⏱ 10 minutes	Visual, Auditory

Materials: *Part-Part-Whole Mat transparency, overhead two-color counters*

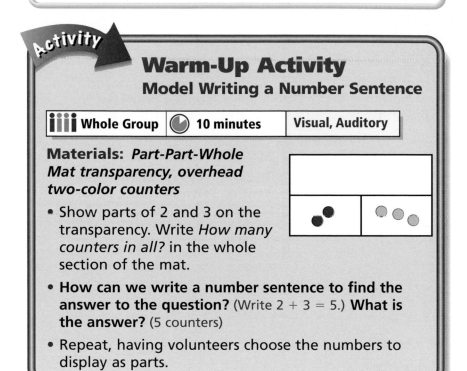

- Show parts of 2 and 3 on the transparency. Write *How many counters in all?* in the whole section of the mat.

- **How can we write a number sentence to find the answer to the question?** (Write 2 + 3 = 5.) **What is the answer?** (5 counters)

- Repeat, having volunteers choose the numbers to display as parts.

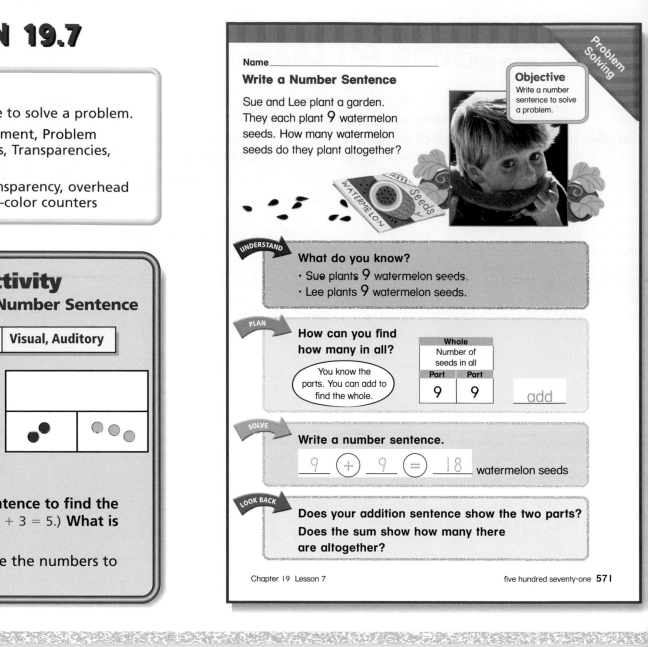

Name

Write a Number Sentence

Sue and Lee plant a garden. They each plant 9 watermelon seeds. How many watermelon seeds do they plant altogether?

UNDERSTAND

What do you know?
- Sue plants 9 watermelon seeds.
- Lee plants 9 watermelon seeds.

PLAN

How can you find how many in all?

You know the parts. You can add to find the whole.

Whole		
Number of seeds in all		
Part	**Part**	
9	9	add

SOLVE

Write a number sentence.

9 (+) 9 (equals) 18 watermelon seeds

LOOK BACK

Does your addition sentence show the two parts? Does the sum show how many there are altogether?

---

1 Introduce
Modeling Writing a Number Sentence to Solve a Problem

▮▮▮▮ Whole Group	⏱ 10–15 minutes	Visual, Auditory

Materials: *Part-Part-Whole Mat transparency*

1. Write this problem on the board. **The Johnsons sell 4 pumpkins. The Greens sell 7 pumpkins. How many pumpkins were sold altogether?** Read the problem to the children. Then write the numbers as parts on the transparency.

2. **How can you find how many altogether?** (Write the parts as a number sentence and add to find the whole.)

3. Ask a volunteer to write the addition sentence on the transparency. **How many pumpkins were sold?** (11)

2 Develop

Guided Learning

Teaching Example Introduce the objective to the children. Then read the problem to them.

UNDERSTAND What do you know? (Sue plants 9 watermelon seeds and Lee plants 9 watermelon seeds.)

PLAN How can you find the number of seeds in all? (add)

SOLVE Have children trace the addition sentence. **What is the answer to the question?** (18 watermelon seeds) **Trace the answer.**

LOOK BACK Does 9 + 9 match the two parts in the mat? (yes) **Does 18 show the whole?** (yes)

Guided Practice

Have children complete **Exercises 1–2** on page 572 as you observe. Encourage children to explain how they found their answers.

Guided Practice

Write a number sentence to solve.

1. The Greens bring 8 ears of corn to the picnic. The Riveras bring 7. How many ears of corn do they bring in all?

   Think
   I add to find how many ears of corn in all.

   $\underline{8}$ (+) $\underline{7}$ (=) $\underline{15}$

   $\underline{15}$ ears of corn

2. The Clarks sell 5 melons. The Hales sell 4 melons. How many melons do they sell altogether?

   Think
   I add to find how many melons altogether.

   $\underline{5}$ (+) $\underline{4}$ (=) $\underline{9}$

   $\underline{9}$ melons

Practice

3. Luke picks 6 peppers. Donna picks 8 peppers. How many peppers do they pick in all?

   $\underline{6}$ (+) $\underline{8}$ (=) $\underline{14}$

   $\underline{14}$ peppers

4. **Multistep** Kasey plants 1 row of pumpkin seeds. Then she plants 1 row of squash seeds. Each row has 10 seeds. How many seeds does she plant?

   $\underline{10}$ (+) $\underline{10}$ (=) $\underline{20}$

   $\underline{20}$ seeds

Go on ►

572 five hundred seventy-two

KEEPING SKILLS SHARP

Play Sum It Up
Materials: *4 × 6 index cards*

Divide class into teams of three. Give each child a 4 × 6 index card. Each child begins a number sentence at the top of the card. Instruct children not to write the sum.

- Children pass the card to the team member on the right. This child draws a picture to illustrate the number sentence.

- Cards are then passed to the team member on the right again. This child finds the sum and writes it on the back of the card.

- Teams check the sums. Each correct number sentence gains 1 point. Continue with another round of play.

ACHIEVING
Mathematical Proficiency

Learning Basic Facts

While some children proceed naturally through the sequence of solution methods when learning addition facts, instruction of these methods speeds up the process for all students. Research indicates that children learn doubles facts earlier than other number combinations. When they are able to recompose numbers—that is, think of 7 as 6 + 1—they are ready to use doubles facts to find the sum of 6 + 7. They do so by reasoning that if 6 + 6 = 12, then 6 + 7 must be 1 more than 12.

Drawings can be used to model how the method works. Drawings can give children a visual model of the double plus one strategy. Gradually, children are able to visualize the models and incorporate using doubles as a strategy to use in learning addition facts.

---

3 Practice

Independent Practice

Children complete **Exercises 3–4** on page 572 independently.

Lesson continues

Daily Test Prep

$17 - 8 = \square$

7   8   9   10
○   ○   ●   ○

Activity

Lesson Intervention

Writing a Number Sentence

Or use Intervention CD-ROM Lesson 19.7

| iii Small Group | ⏱ 5–10 minutes | Auditory, Tactile |

Materials: *two-color counters, Workmat 3*

1. Give each group a workmat and counters. Have one child from each group place red counters in one part of the mat. Have another child place yellow counters in the other part.

$4 + 5 = \_\_$

2. Have one child write a number sentence to describe the counters. Have all children add to find the sum. Check to see that the number sentence is correct.

3. Continue until every child has had a turn modeling parts, writing number sentences, and adding to find the sum.

Name_____

Strategies
Write a Number Sentence
Draw a Picture

Choose a Strategy

Solve.

Draw or write to explain.
Allow children to use any method or strategy to solve.

1. The garden store owner has 10 rakes. He sells 3 rakes. How many rakes does he have now?

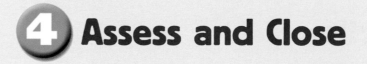

___7___ rakes

2. Ella fills 5 watering cans with water. Kyle fills 9 cans. How many watering cans do they fill?

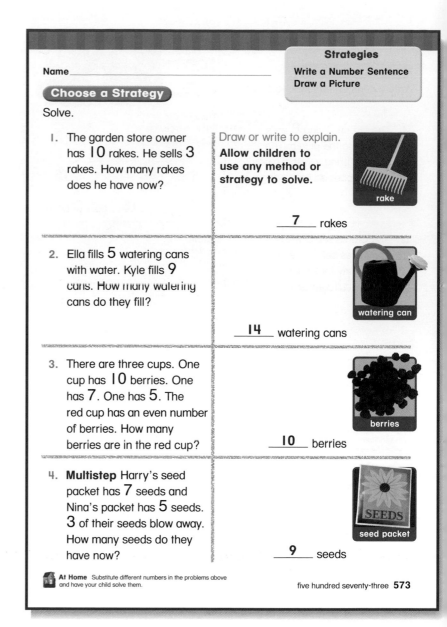

___14___ watering cans

3. There are three cups. One cup has 10 berries. One has 7. One has 5. The red cup has an even number of berries. How many berries are in the red cup?

___10___ berries

4. **Multistep** Harry's seed packet has 7 seeds and Nina's packet has 5 seeds. 3 of their seeds blow away. How many seeds do they have now?

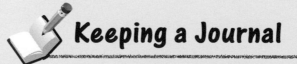

___9___ seeds

At Home Substitute different numbers in the problems above and have your child solve them.

five hundred seventy-three **573**

---

③ Practice

Mixed Strategy Practice

Read the problem-solving strategies with the children. Make sure children can read and comprehend the problems in **Exercises 1–4** on page 573. If necessary, pair more proficient readers with less proficient readers. Encourage them to discuss the problems before solving.

Common Error

Children May Write the Wrong Addends.

Some children may have difficulty copying numbers into the sentence frames. Provide extra practice with writing addition sentences for models, then have children model problems before writing.

④ Assess and Close

How do you know what number sentence to write to solve a problem? (Write the numbers in the problem.) **How can you use a number sentence to help you solve a problem?** (Possible answer: a number sentence can help you write the parts. You can add them to find the whole and solve the problem.)

Keeping a Journal

Write a story problem. Write a number sentence to solve it.

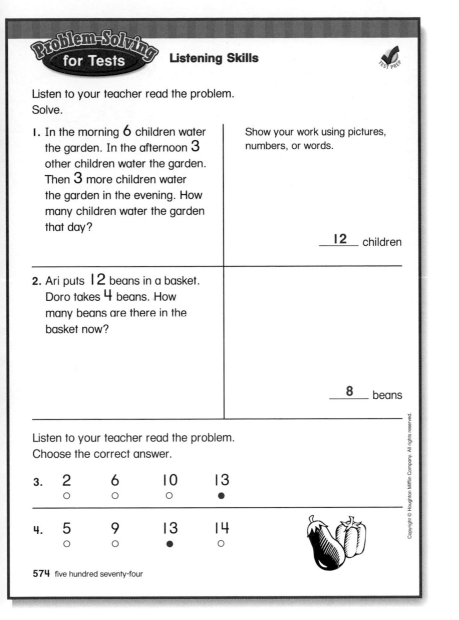

Listen to your teacher read the problem. Solve.

1. In the morning 6 children water the garden. In the afternoon 3 other children water the garden. Then 3 more children water the garden in the evening. How many children water the garden that day?

Show your work using pictures, numbers, or words.

_12_ children

2. Ari puts 12 beans in a basket. Doro takes 4 beans. How many beans are there in the basket now?

_8_ beans

Listen to your teacher read the problem. Choose the correct answer.

3. 2   6   10   13
    ○   ○   ○   ●

4. 5   9   13   14
    ○   ○   ●   ○

574 five hundred seventy-four

Problem-Solving for Tests

Listening Skills

This page provides children practice with the oral problem-solving format used in some standardized test items.

You may want to read each item only once to mimic the style of oral tests.

Use with Items 1 and 2

Listening Strategy: Read the problem silently while the teacher reads it aloud.

- *This problem is on the page. Read it to yourself while I read it aloud.*
- *Listen to the whole problem. Wait until I finish reading to start writing.*

Use with Item 3

Listening Strategy: Listen to the problem and write the numbers you need.

Alexi's pumpkin patch has 2 rows. One row has 6 pumpkins. The other row has 7 pumpkins. How many pumpkins does Alexi have to pick?

- *Use the numbers to solve the problem. Then mark your answer.*

Use with Item 4

Listening Strategy: Listen for important words and numbers in the problem.

The farmer sells her vegetables at a farm stand. She sells 4 peppers and 9 eggplants. How many vegetables does she sell in all?

- *Use the numbers to solve the problem. Then mark your answer.*

Quick Check

Have children complete the Quick Check exercises independently to assess their understanding of concepts and skills taught in **Lessons 4–7.**

Item	Lesson	Error Analysis	Intervention
1–3	19.4	Children may use elements of different strategies.	Reteach Resource 19.4 **Ways to Success** 19.4
4–5	19.5	Children may count incorrectly when using models.	Reteach Resource 19.5 **Ways to Success** 19.5
6–12	19.6	Children may forget to add the third number.	Reteach Resource 19.6 **Ways to Success** 19.6
13	19.7	Children may identify the parts incorrectly and write the wrong addends.	Reteach Resource 19.7 **Ways to Success** 19.7

Name_____ **Quick Check**

Find the sum.

1. 8 + 3 = __11__   2. 2 + 9 = __11__   3. 7 + 8 = __15__

Use Workmat 3 and ◯.

Find different names for the number.   **Possible answers shown.**

4.

Whole	Whole	Whole
16	16	16
Part Part	**Part Part**	**Part Part**
9 7	8 8	7 9

5.

Whole	Whole
17	17
Part Part	**Part Part**
9 8	8 9

Find the sum.

6. 2
    8
  +4
  ‾‾
   14

7. 1
    5
  +5
  ‾‾
   11

8. 4
    4
  +8
  ‾‾
   16

9. 7
    3
  +5
  ‾‾
   15

10. 9
     3
   +1
   ‾‾
    13

11. 3 + 7 + 7 = __17__   12. 8 + 0 + 8 = __16__

Write a number sentence to solve.

13. Ami waters 8 plants in the morning. She waters 9 plants in the afternoon. How many plants does she water that day?

__8__ (+) __9__ (=) __17__

__17__ plants

 five hundred seventy-five **575**

575   **CHAPTER 19   Lesson 7**

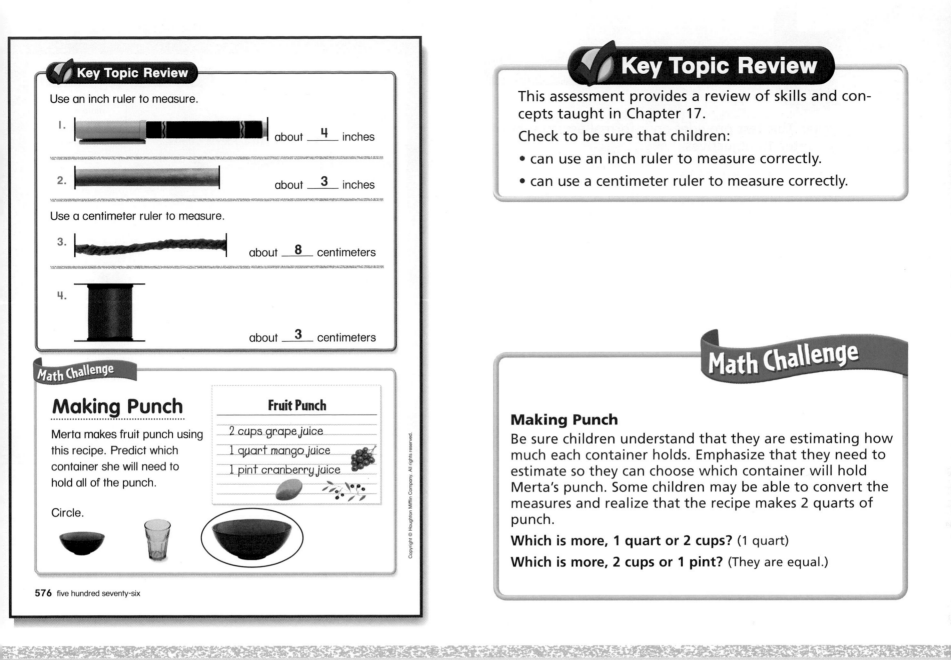

Key Topic Review

Use an inch ruler to measure.

1. about __4__ inches

2. about __3__ inches

Use a centimeter ruler to measure.

3. about __8__ centimeters

4. about __3__ centimeters

Math Challenge

Making Punch

Merta makes fruit punch using this recipe. Predict which container she will need to hold all of the punch.

Circle.

Fruit Punch

2 cups grape juice

1 quart mango juice

1 pint cranberry juice

Copyright © Houghton Mifflin Company. All rights reserved.

576 five hundred seventy-six

Key Topic Review

This assessment provides a review of skills and concepts taught in Chapter 17.

Check to be sure that children:

• can use an inch ruler to measure correctly.

• can use a centimeter ruler to measure correctly.

Math Challenge

Making Punch

Be sure children understand that they are estimating how much each container holds. Emphasize that they need to estimate so they can choose which container will hold Merta's punch. Some children may be able to convert the measures and realize that the recipe makes 2 quarts of punch.

Which is more, 1 quart or 2 cups? (1 quart)

Which is more, 2 cups or 1 pint? (They are equal.)

Chapter Review/Test

Purpose: This test provides an informal assessment of the Chapter 19 objectives.

Chapter Test Items 1–30

To assign a numerical grade for this Chapter Test, use 3 points for each test item and add 10 to the score.

Check Understanding

Use children's work on word problems to informally assess progress on chapter content.

Customizing Your Instruction

For children who have not yet mastered these objectives, you can use the reteaching resources listed in the chart below.

✔ **Assessment Options**

A summary test for this chapter is also provided in the Unit Resource Folder.

Name_____ ✔ Chapter Review/Test

Vocabulary *e* Glossary

| double |
| related facts |

Complete the sentence.

1. $6 + 7$ and $7 + 6$ are ___related facts___ .

2. $8 + 8$ is a ___double___ fact.

Concepts and Skills

Find the sum.

3. $6 + 6 =$ __12__ $6 + 7 =$ __13__ $7 + 6 =$ __13__

4. $8 + 8 =$ __16__ $8 + 9 =$ __17__ $9 + 8 =$ __17__

Use Workmat 2 and ◯.
Show the numbers.
Write the number sentence.

5. Show 10. Show 5 more.

__10__ ⊕ __5__ ⊜ __15__

6. Show 10. Show 2 more.

__10__ ⊕ __2__ ⊜ __12__

Add.

7. $\begin{array}{r} 9 \\ +7 \\ \hline 16 \end{array}$ 8. $\begin{array}{r} 9 \\ +5 \\ \hline 14 \end{array}$ 9. $\begin{array}{r} 8 \\ +4 \\ \hline 12 \end{array}$ 10. $\begin{array}{r} 8 \\ +5 \\ \hline 13 \end{array}$ 11. $\begin{array}{r} 7 \\ +4 \\ \hline 11 \end{array}$

12. $\begin{array}{r} 10 \\ + 5 \\ \hline 15 \end{array}$ 13. $\begin{array}{r} 6 \\ +7 \\ \hline 13 \end{array}$ 14. $\begin{array}{r} 2 \\ +9 \\ \hline 11 \end{array}$ 15. $\begin{array}{r} 9 \\ +9 \\ \hline 18 \end{array}$ 16. $\begin{array}{r} 7 \\ +7 \\ \hline 14 \end{array}$

Chapter 19   five hundred seventy-seven **577**

Reteaching Support

Chapter Test Items	Summary Test Items	Chapter Objectives Tested	TE Pages	Use These Reteaching Resources
1–2	1–2	**19A** Develop and use math vocabulary relating to addition facts through 20.	557A–560	Reteach Resources and *Ways to Success* CD: 19.1, 19.2 Skillsheet 137
3–16	3–12	**19B** Use strategies such as doubles, doubles plus one, and make a ten to find sums through 20.	557A–562, 565A–566	Reteach Resources and *Ways to Success* CD: 19.1–19.4 Skillsheet 138 and 139
17–29	13–18	**19C** Add three numbers and use parts and wholes to practice addition and to find different names for the same number.	567A–570	Reteach Resources and *Ways to Success* CD: 19.5–19.6 Skillsheet 140 and 141
30	19–20	**19D** Write a number sentence to solve a problem.	571A–574	Reteach Resource and *Ways to Success* CD: 19.7 Skillsheet 142

CHAPTER SUMMARY TEST

Name _____ Date _____ Chapter 19 Test

Look at the vocabulary words.
Fill in the blank.

| Vocabulary |
| sum |
| double |
| addends |

1. When you add two numbers that are the same, it is ___double___ fact.

2. $8 + 3 = 11$. 11 is the ___sum___ .

Find the sum.

3. $5 + 5 =$ __10__ $6 + 5 =$ __11__ $5 + 6 =$ __11__

4. $8 + 8 =$ __16__ $8 + 9 =$ __17__ $9 + 8 =$ __17__

5. $7 + 7 =$ __14__ $8 + 7 =$ __15__ $7 + 8 =$ __15__

Make a ten. Add.

6. Show 9 and 7 more.

$9 + 7 =$ __16__

7. Show 8 and 4 more.

$8 + 4 =$ __12__

Find the sum.

8. $\begin{array}{r} 5 \\ +7 \\ \hline 12 \end{array}$ 9. $\begin{array}{r} 3 \\ +9 \\ \hline 12 \end{array}$ 10. $\begin{array}{r} 6 \\ +8 \\ \hline 14 \end{array}$ 11. $\begin{array}{r} 9 \\ +8 \\ \hline 17 \end{array}$ 12. $\begin{array}{r} 6 \\ +9 \\ \hline 15 \end{array}$

Go on ▶

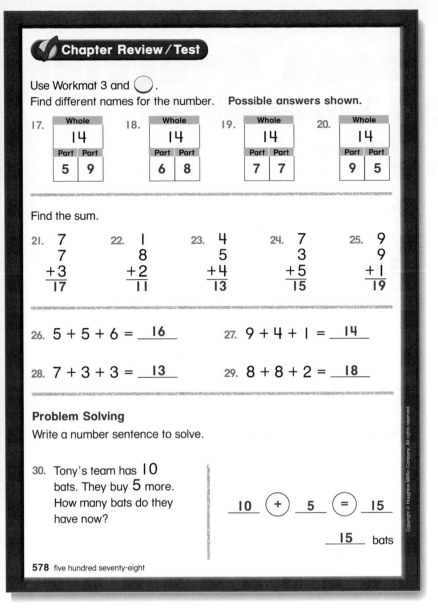

Chapter Review/Test

Use Workmat 3 and ◯.
Find different names for the number. **Possible answers shown.**

17.	Whole		18.	Whole		19.	Whole		20.	Whole	
	14			14			14			14	
	Part	Part		Part	Part		Part	Part		Part	Part
	5	9		6	8		7	7		9	5

Find the sum.

21.
$$\begin{array}{r} 7 \\ 7 \\ +3 \\ \hline 17 \end{array}$$

22.
$$\begin{array}{r} 1 \\ 8 \\ +2 \\ \hline 11 \end{array}$$

23.
$$\begin{array}{r} 4 \\ 5 \\ +4 \\ \hline 13 \end{array}$$

24.
$$\begin{array}{r} 7 \\ 3 \\ +5 \\ \hline 15 \end{array}$$

25.
$$\begin{array}{r} 9 \\ 9 \\ +1 \\ \hline 19 \end{array}$$

26. $5 + 5 + 6 = \underline{16}$ 27. $9 + 4 + 1 = \underline{14}$

28. $7 + 3 + 3 = \underline{13}$ 29. $8 + 8 + 2 = \underline{18}$

Problem Solving

Write a number sentence to solve.

30. Tony's team has 10 bats. They buy 5 more. How many bats do they have now?

$\underline{10} \; \oplus \; \underline{5} \; \ominus \; \underline{15}$

$\underline{15}$ bats

578 five hundred seventy-eight

Adequate Yearly Progress

Use the End of Grade Test Prep Assessment Guide to help familiarize your children with the format of standardized tests.

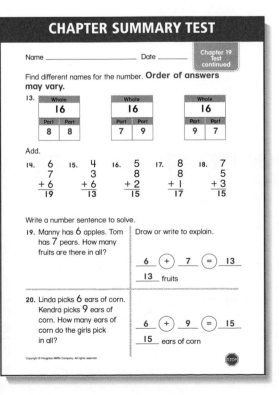

CHAPTER SUMMARY TEST

Name _____ Date _____

Chapter 19 Test continued

Find different names for the number. **Order of answers may vary.**

13.

Whole			Whole			Whole		
16			16			16		
Part	Part		Part	Part		Part	Part	
8	8		7	9		9	7	

Add.

14.
$$\begin{array}{r} 6 \\ 7 \\ +6 \\ \hline 19 \end{array}$$

15.
$$\begin{array}{r} 4 \\ 3 \\ +6 \\ \hline 13 \end{array}$$

16.
$$\begin{array}{r} 5 \\ 8 \\ +2 \\ \hline 15 \end{array}$$

17.
$$\begin{array}{r} 8 \\ 8 \\ +1 \\ \hline 17 \end{array}$$

18.
$$\begin{array}{r} 7 \\ 5 \\ +3 \\ \hline 15 \end{array}$$

Write a number sentence to solve.

19. Manny has 6 apples. Tom has 7 pears. How many fruits are there in all?

Draw or write to explain.

$\underline{6} \; \oplus \; \underline{7} \; \ominus \; \underline{13}$

$\underline{13}$ fruits

20. Linda picks 6 ears of corn. Kendra picks 9 ears of corn. How many ears of corn do the girls pick in all?

$\underline{6} \; \oplus \; \underline{9} \; \ominus \; \underline{15}$

$\underline{15}$ ears of corn

Addition Facts Through 20   578

Lesson by Lesson Overview
Subtraction Facts Through 20

Lesson 1

- This lesson focuses on using addition doubles facts to subtract.
- Children recall that addition and subtraction are related. Therefore, if they know an addition fact, they know the related subtraction fact.

  $7 + 7 = 14$ So, $14 - 7 = 7$

Lesson 2

- In this lesson, children subtract from 13 and 14 using a part-part-whole model.
- They add to find the whole. Then they subtract to find each part for the related subtraction facts.

Lesson 3

- Children continue to learn new facts as they subtract from 15 and 16.
- Again, part-part-whole is used and children add as well as subtract.
- A problem directs children to draw objects and then write 2 addition and 2 subtraction sentences for the picture.

Lesson 4

- Children subtract from 17 through 20 in horizontal and vertical form.
- Part-part-whole continues as the model as children practice these and previously learned facts.
- Algebra readiness has children find missing numbers in subtraction sentences.

Lesson 5

- This lesson moves to the next step as children use addition facts to help them subtract.
- Here the related addition is presented as a missing addend sentence.

Lesson 6

- Thus far, children have completed fact families to sum 12. This lesson extends the concept to greater sums.
- Children are given the parts and the whole and they complete the set of facts.

Lesson 7

- Identifying extra information in a problem is an important skill.
- Children are taught basic steps through questions they ask themselves that lead them to decide which information they need to use to solve the problems.

SKILLS TRACE: SUBTRACTION FACTS THROUGH 20

Grade K	Grade 1	Grade 2
• model subtraction (ch. 14) • complete subtraction sentences (ch. 14) • subtract 1 from 1 through 10 (ch. 14) • subtract 2 from 2 through 10 (ch. 14)	• use doubles facts to subtract • subtract from 13 and 14 • subtract from 15 and 16 • subtract from 17 through 20 • use related addition facts to subtract • complete fact families	• use related addition facts to subtract (ch 3) • identify and write fact families (ch. 3) • find the missing number in addition and subtraction sentences (ch. 3)

Chapter Planner

Lesson	Objective	Vocabulary	Materials	✔ NCTM Standards
20.1 **Use Doubles to Subtract** p. 581A	Subtract by using a doubles fact.		two-color counters, index cards, number cubes 1–6, number cube labeled 4–9, Workmat 2, Workmat 3	Understand various meanings of addition and subtraction of whole numbers and the relationship between the two operations.
20.2 **Subtract From 13 and 14** p. 583A	Subtract from 13 and 14 by using related addition facts.	difference	two-color counters, Part-Part-Whole Mat transparency, number cube labeled 4–9, Workmat 3, overhead counters	Understand various meanings of addition and subtraction of whole numbers and the relationship between the two operations.
20.3 **Subtract From 15 and 16** p. 585A	Use addition facts to aid in subtraction.		two-color counters, Part-Part-Whole Mat transparency, number cards 15 and 16 (Learning Tool (LT) 15), Workmat 3	Develop and use strategies for whole-number computations, with a focus on addition and subtraction.
20.4 **Subtract From 17 Through 20** p. 589A	Subtract from 17 through 20 by relating addition to subtraction.		counters, addition and subtraction cards (teacher made), Workmat 3	Develop and use strategies for whole-number computations, with a focus on addition and subtraction.
20.5 **Relate Addition and Subtraction** p. 591A	Find missing addends by relating addition and subtraction.		cubes, number line 0–12 (LT 8), dot cards 4–9 (LT 17)	Understand various meanings of addition and subtraction of whole numbers and the relationship between the two operations.
20.6 **Fact Families** p. 593A	Use the inverse relationship between addition and subtraction to make a fact family.		cubes, two-color counters, Workmat 3, paper cup	Understand various meanings of addition and subtraction of whole numbers and the relationship between the two operations.
20.7 **Problem Solving:** **Too Much Information** p. 595A Solve problems with too much information.		cubes in 3 colors, large cup		Monitor an reflect on the process of mathematical problem solving.

Resources For Reaching All Learners

LESSON RESOURCES: Reteach, Practice, Enrichment, Problem Solving, Homework, English Learners, Daily Routines, Transparencies, Math Center.

ADDITIONAL RESOURCES FROM HOUGHTON MIFFLIN: Chapter Challenges, Combination Classroom Planning Guide, Every Day Counts, Math to Learn (Student Handbook)

Every Day Counts
The *Counting Tape* activities in Every Day Counts support the math in this chapter.

Assessing Prior Knowledge

Before beginning the chapter, you can assess student understandings in order to assist you in differentiating instruction.

Complete Chapter Pretest in Unit Resource Folder

Use this test to assess both prerequisite skills (**Are You Ready?** — one page) and chapter content (**Check What You Know** — two pages).

Chapter 20 Prerequisite Skills Pretest

Chapter 20 New Content Pretest

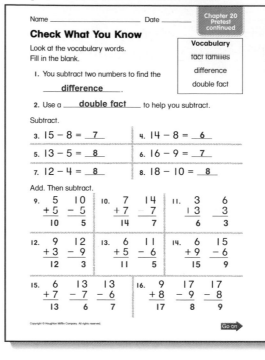

Customizing Instruction

For Students Having Difficulty

Items	Prerequisites	Ways to Success
1–6	Complete subtraction sentences with differences through 12.	CD: 16.2, 16.3 Skillsheet 143
7–8	Use addition to solve subtraction.	CD: 16.4 Skillsheet 144
9–10	Complete basic fact families.	CD: 16.5, 16.6 Skillsheet 145

Ways to Success: Intervention for every concept and skill (CD-ROM or Chapter Intervention Skillsheets).

For Students Having Success

Items	Objectives	Resources
1–2	20A Use vocabulary relating to subtraction facts through 20.	Enrichment 20.2, 20.6
3–16	20B Subtract from 20 and use related addition to subtract.	Enrichment 20.1–20.5
17–18	20C Use addition and subtraction to make fact families.	Enrichment 20.6
19–20	20D Solve problems with too much information.	Enrichment 20.7

Other Pretest Options

Informal Pretest

The pretest assesses vocabulary and prerequisite skills needed for success in this chapter.

Ways to Success CD-ROM

The *Ways to Success* chapter pretest has automatic assignment of appropriate review lessons.

Use **Chapter Challenges** with any students who have success with all new chapter content.

Chapter Resources

Activity

Assessing Prior Knowledge

Calendar Subtraction (subtract from 17 to 20)

- Use calendar time as an opportunity to practice subtraction.
- Point to the date and say, **The date for today is 17. What was the date 3 days ago? What was the date 5 days ago? What was the date 2 days ago?**
- Repeat the activity for dates up to 19.

Activity

Ongoing Skill Activity

Subtraction Pattern (subtraction facts)

- Display a number in the math center, such as 15.
- Tell children that they will write subtraction sentences for the number 15. Tell them to start with 15 − 9, and continue until they write 15 − 1.
- When children finish, invite volunteers to describe the pattern the answers create.

Activity

Connecting to the Unit Project

- Read this problem aloud to children: **Olivia buys a book about apples. There were 25 apples on the tree. 13 apples fell off the tree. How many apples are still on the tree?**
- Discuss the problem and elicit that Olivia used subtraction. Have children tell the subtraction they use to solve the problem. (25 − 13 = 12, 12 apples)
- Explain that children can use related addition facts to check subtraction.
- Ask a volunteer to write the related addition fact he or she used. (12 + 13 = 25)

Teacher Support

Professional Resources Handbook

Research, Mathematics Content, and Language Intervention

Research-Based Teaching

The basic premise of many current reforms in primary-grade mathematics is that teachers need to recognize and build on the informal but rich mathematical knowledge that children bring to school (Baroody, 1992; Fuson, 1988; Isaacs & Carroll, 1999). During the early years in school, teachers present basic arithmetical facts that should help children develop and strengthen their sense of number. See *Professional Resources Handbook, Grade 1,* Unit 8.

For more ideas relating to Unit 8, see the Teacher Support Handbook at the back of this Teacher's Edition.

Language Intervention

In China, the basic subtraction facts are also taught using an approach that reinforces the importance of 10 as a special organizer of our number system. For basic facts greater than 10, thinking about the numbers 11 through 18 as "ten" and "some more" is the first step. For further explanation, see "Mathematical Language and Subtraction Facts" in the *Professional Resources Handbook Grade 1.*

Technology

Time-Saving Technology Support
Ways to Assess Customized Spiral Review
   Test Generator CD
Lesson Planner CD-ROM
Ways to Success Intervention CD-ROM
MathTracks CD-ROM
Education Place: www.eduplace.com/math/mw
Houghton Mifflin Math eBook CD-ROM
eManipulatives
eGames

Starting Chapter 20
Subtraction Facts Through 20

CHAPTER OBJECTIVES

20A Develop and use math vocabulary relating to subtraction facts through 20.

20B Subtract from 20 and solve related addition and subtraction problems.

20C Use addition and subtraction to make fact families.

20D Solve problems with too much information.

Math Background

Subtraction Facts Through 20

Subtraction is one of the four basic operations that form the foundation of arithmetic and is an essential part of the computation work of the elementary school grades.

Subtraction facts are taught by relating each fact to the related addition fact. Children are also encouraged to use manipulatives, pictures, or counting back to solve subtraction problems. Because addition and subtraction are related, children can use doubles to subtract, just as they use doubles to add. For example, $12 - 6$ can be easily found using the double fact $6 + 6$: $6 + 6 = 12$, so $12 - 6 = 6$. The addition and subtraction are related because both have the same parts and the same whole.

Using related addition facts to subtract from 13 through 20 reinforces the connection between addition and subtraction. Using related addition facts is a powerful strategy because it is based on the inverse relationship between addition and subtraction. The use of fact families and related facts, first written vertically and then written horizontally, provides practice as well as introduces the algebraic concept of equations.

Subtraction Facts Through 20

INVESTIGATION

Mr. Rabbit needs to use 4 carrots in his soup. How many will he have left?

Chapter 20
five hundred seventy-nine **579**

Using The Investigation

- Ask a volunteer to define the word *related*. Have the child name people related to him or her. Tell children that when facts are part of the same fact family, they are called *related facts*. Write the subtraction sentence $17 - 9 = 8$ on the board. Have volunteers name the related facts in the fact family. ($17 - 8 = 9$; $9 + 8 = 17$; $8 + 9 = 17$)

- Read the question to children. **Look at the picture. Tell how many carrots are left after Mr. Rabbit finishes cooking.** (8 carrots) **How many carrots does he use in his soup?** (4 carrots) **How many carrots does he have in all?** (12 carrots)

- Have volunteers share their number sentences with the class.

- Then have children write or make-up more stories about Mr. Rabbit and illustrate them.

 For more information about projects and investigations, visit Education Place. **eduplace.com/math/mw/**

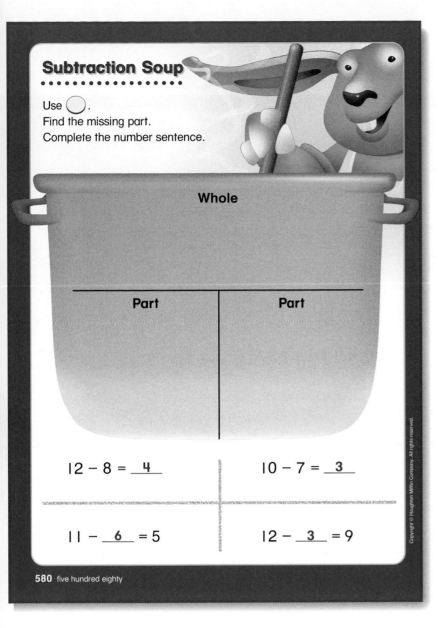

Subtraction Soup

Use ◯.
Find the missing part.
Complete the number sentence.

Whole

Part	Part

$12 - 8 = \underline{4}$ $10 - 7 = \underline{3}$

$11 - \underline{6} = 5$ $12 - \underline{3} = 9$

580 five hundred eighty

CHAPTER CHALLENGES

For Mathematically Promising Students

The *Chapter Challenges* resource book provides blackline masters for activities that explore, extend, and connect the mathematics in every chapter. To support this independent work, see the Teacher Notes for each activity.

Explore: Doubles Flip, page 115, after Lesson 1
Extend: Use a Calculator, page 117, after Lesson 3
Connect: Find the Fact, page 119, after Lesson 5

Using This Page

- Give each child a set of two-color counters.
- Direct children to the workmat on page 580. **Look at the number sentences. There is a number missing on each one.**
- **Use your counters and the workmat to help you model the numbers and find the missing part. Then use your work to complete the number sentences.**

NSF Children's Math Worlds

Children's Math Worlds focuses on the use of models to represent mathematical situations. Thus, using a *Children's Math Worlds* lesson helps students develop a general facility with drawing models to support their thinking that will transfer to all their mathematical work.

Subtraction Facts Through 20   **580**

Use Doubles to Subtract

PLANNING THE LESSON

MATHEMATICS OBJECTIVE
Subtract by using a doubles fact.

Use Lesson Planner CD-ROM for Lesson 20.1.

Meeting North Carolina's Standards

1.03 Develop fluency with single-digit addition and corresponding differences using strategies such as modeling, composing and decomposing quantities, using doubles, and making tens.

Also 1.04

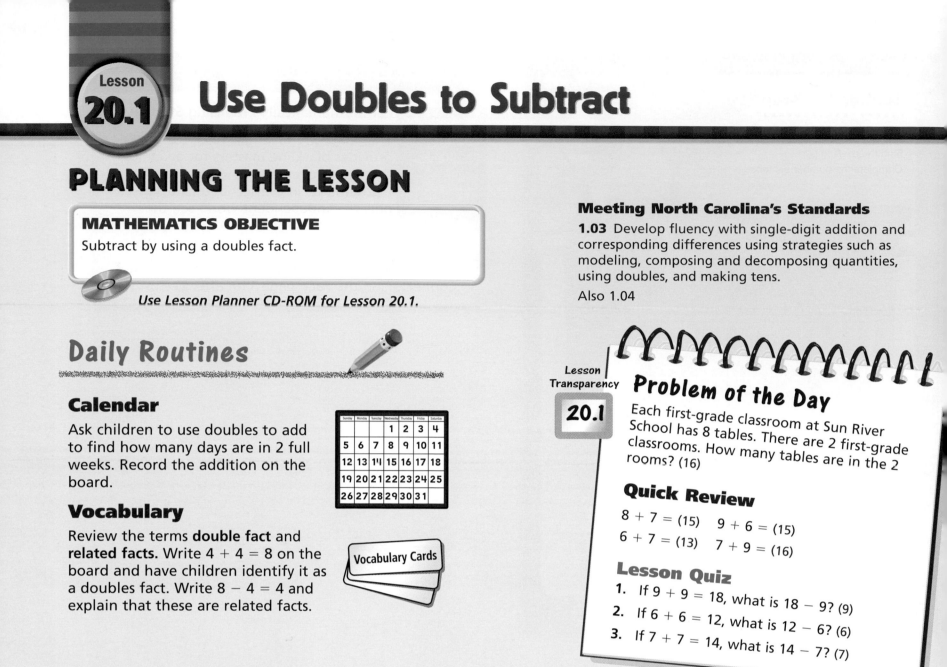

Daily Routines

Calendar
Ask children to use doubles to add to find how many days are in 2 full weeks. Record the addition on the board.

Sunday	Monday	Tuesday	Wednesday	Thursday	Friday	Saturday
			1	2	3	4
5	6	7	8	9	10	11
12	13	14	15	16	17	18
19	20	21	22	23	24	25
26	27	28	29	30	31	

Vocabulary
Review the terms **double fact** and **related facts**. Write $4 + 4 = 8$ on the board and have children identify it as a doubles fact. Write $8 - 4 = 4$ and explain that these are related facts.

Vocabulary Cards

Lesson Transparency
20.1

Problem of the Day
Each first-grade classroom at Sun River School has 8 tables. There are 2 first-grade classrooms. How many tables are in the 2 rooms? (16)

Quick Review
$8 + 7 = $ (15) $9 + 6 = $ (15)
$6 + 7 = $ (13) $7 + 9 = $ (16)

Lesson Quiz
1. If $9 + 9 = 18$, what is $18 - 9$? (9)
2. If $6 + 6 = 12$, what is $12 - 6$? (6)
3. If $7 + 7 = 14$, what is $14 - 7$? (7)

LEVELED PRACTICE

RETEACH 20.1

Name _____ Date _____   Reteach 20.1

Use Doubles to Subtract

Think about adding doubles to help you subtract.

Find $12 - 6$.

Double Fact

You know $6 + 6 = 12$ So, $12 - 6 = $ ___6___

Add.
Then subtract.

1.
$5\ 15 = $ ___10___
$10 - 5 = $ ___5___

2.
$7 + 7 = $ ___14___
$14 - 7 = $ ___7___

| 3. | 9
+ 9
18 | 18
- 9
9 | 4. | 8
+ 8
16 | 16
- 8
8 | 5. | 10
+ 10
20 | 20
- 10
10 |

Copyright © Houghton Mifflin Company. All rights reserved.   Use with text pages 581–582.

PRACTICE 20.1

Name _____ Date _____   Practice 20.1

Use Doubles to Subtract

Add. Then subtract.

1. $1 + 1 = $ ___2___
   $2 - 1 = $ ___1___
2. $2 + 2 = $ ___4___
   $4 - 2 = $ ___2___
3. $3 + 3 = $ ___6___
   $6 - 3 = $ ___3___

4. $4 + 4 = $ ___8___
   $8 - 4 = $ ___4___
5. $6 + 6 = $ ___12___
   $12 - 6 = $ ___6___
6. $9 + 9 = $ ___18___
   $18 - 9 = $ ___9___

7. $8 + 8 = $ ___16___
   $16 - 8 = $ ___8___
8. $5 + 5 = $ ___10___
   $10 - 5 = $ ___5___
9. $7 + 7 = $ ___14___
   $14 - 7 = $ ___7___

| 10. | 1
+ 1
2 | 2
- 1
1 | 11. | 2
+ 2
4 | 4
- 2
2 | 12. | 4
+ 4
8 | 8
- 4
4 |
| 13. | 5
+ 5
10 | 10
- 5
5 | 14. | 7
+ 7
14 | 14
- 7
7 | 15. | 10
+ 10
20 | 20
- 10
10 |

Test Prep

Solve.
16. Ellen has 16 balloons. She gives 8 balloons to Sam. How many balloons does Ellen have now?
___8___ balloons

Draw or write to explain.
Check children's drawing.

Copyright © Houghton Mifflin Company. All rights reserved.   Use with text pages 581–582.

ENRICHMENT 20.1

Name _____ Date _____   Enrichment 20.1

Doubles for Symmetry

Subtract.

Draw that number of dots on the other side of the line to show symmetry.

1. $10 - 5 = $ ___5___

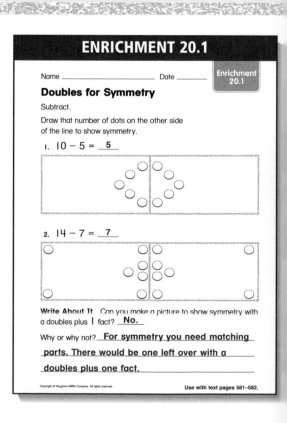

2. $14 - 7 = $ ___7___

Write About It Can you make a picture to show symmetry with a doubles plus 1 fact? __No.__

Why or why not? __For symmetry you need matching parts. There would be one left over with a doubles plus one fact.__

Copyright © Houghton Mifflin Company. All rights reserved.   Use with text pages 581–582.

Practice Workbook Page 134

Reaching All Learners

Differentiated Instruction

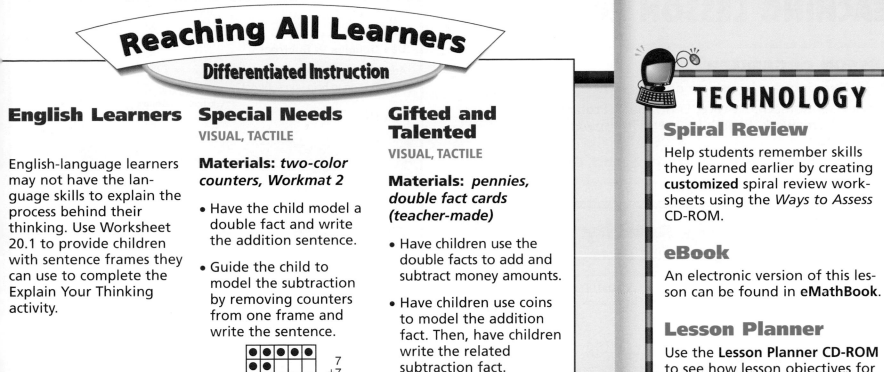

English Learners

English-language learners may not have the language skills to explain the process behind their thinking. Use Worksheet 20.1 to provide children with sentence frames they can use to complete the Explain Your Thinking activity.

Special Needs
VISUAL, TACTILE

Materials: *two-color counters, Workmat 2*

- Have the child model a double fact and write the addition sentence.

- Guide the child to model the subtraction by removing counters from one frame and write the sentence.

Gifted and Talented
VISUAL, TACTILE

Materials: *pennies, double fact cards (teacher-made)*

- Have children use the double facts to add and subtract money amounts.

- Have children use coins to model the addition fact. Then, have children write the related subtraction fact.

TECHNOLOGY

Spiral Review

Help students remember skills they learned earlier by creating **customized** spiral review worksheets using the *Ways to Assess* CD-ROM.

eBook

An electronic version of this lesson can be found in **eMathBook**.

Lesson Planner

Use the **Lesson Planner CD-ROM** to see how lesson objectives for this chapter are correlated to standards.

Social Studies Connection

Introduce dominoes as a game that originated in China. It is played using rectangular tiles called "bones." Each bone has 2 sets of dots. Draw one domino and add the 2 sets of dots. Then have children double the sum and write the doubles fact.

MATH CENTER

Basic Skills Activity

Motivate children to build basic skills. Use this activity to address multiple learning styles using hands-on activities related to the skills of this lesson.

PROBLEM SOLVING 20.1

Name _____ Date _____ Problem Solving 20.1

Use Doubles to Subtract

Add. Then subtract to solve.

Draw or write to explain.

1. There are 4 birds in a tree. Then 4 more birds join them. How many birds are in the tree?

$\underline{4} + \underline{4} = \underline{8}$

___8___ birds

Now 4 birds fly away. How many birds are left in the tree?

$\underline{8} - \underline{4} = \underline{4}$

___4___ birds

2. There are 7 children in the park. 7 more children come to the park. How many children are in the park in all?

$\underline{7} + \underline{7} = \underline{14}$

___14___ children

Then 7 children go home. How many children are in the park now?

$\underline{14} - \underline{7} = \underline{7}$

___7___ children

Copyright © Houghton Mifflin Company. All rights reserved.

Use with text pages 581–582.

HOMEWORK 20.1

Name _____ Date _____ Homework 20.1

Use Doubles to Subtract

Find $16 - 8$.
Use a double fact to help you subtract.

$8 + 8 = \underline{16}$

So, $16 - 8 = \underline{8}$

Add. Then subtract.

1. $5 + 5 = \underline{10}$
   $10 - 5 = \underline{5}$

2. $6 + 6 = \underline{12}$
   $12 - 6 = \underline{6}$

3. $10 + 10 = \underline{20}$
   $20 - 10 = \underline{10}$

4. $9 + 9 = \underline{18}$
   $18 - 9 = \underline{9}$

5. $\begin{array}{r} 3 \\ +3 \\ \hline 6 \end{array}$ $\begin{array}{r} 6 \\ -3 \\ \hline 3 \end{array}$

6. $\begin{array}{r} 4 \\ +4 \\ \hline 8 \end{array}$ $\begin{array}{r} 8 \\ -4 \\ \hline 4 \end{array}$

7. $\begin{array}{r} 8 \\ +8 \\ \hline 16 \end{array}$ $\begin{array}{r} 16 \\ -8 \\ \hline 8 \end{array}$

8. $\begin{array}{r} 7 \\ +7 \\ \hline 14 \end{array}$ $\begin{array}{r} 14 \\ -7 \\ \hline 7 \end{array}$

Solve.

9. Tom is 5 years old. In how many years will he be 10?

___5___ years

Draw or write to explain.
Check children's drawings.
$10 - 5 = 5$

Copyright © Houghton Mifflin Company. All rights reserved.

Use with text pages 581–582.

ENGLISH LEARNERS 20.1

Name _____ Date _____ English Learners 20.1

Use Doubles to Subtract

$6 + 4 = 10$ $10 - 6 = 4$
Parts: 6, 4   Parts: 6, 4
Whole: 10   Whole: 10

Why are $5 + 5 = 10$ and $10 - 5 = 5$ related facts?

$5 + 5 = 10$
The parts are ___5___ and ___5___.

The whole is ___10___.

$10 - 5 = 5$
The parts are ___5___ and ___5___.

The whole is ___10___.

The parts and whole in both facts are the same. That means that they are related.

To the Teacher: Use the examples at the top of the page to demonstrate how to determine the parts and whole of addition and subtraction facts. Then have children complete the sentence frames that provide the language needed to explain how to answer the question.

Copyright © Houghton Mifflin Company. All rights reserved.

Use with text pages 581–582.

Homework Workbook Page 134

TEACHING LESSON 20.1

LESSON ORGANIZER

Objective Subtract by using a doubles fact.

Resources Reteach, Practice, Enrichment, Problem Solving, Homework, English Learners, Transparencies, Math Center

Materials Number cubes, Workmats 2 and 3, counters

Activity
Warm-Up Activity
Modeling Doubles Facts

iii Small Group	5 minutes	Visual, Tactile

Materials: *number cubes 1–6, Workmat 3, counters*

5 + 5 = 10

1. Have children work in pairs. Distribute a part-part-whole mat and number cube to each pair. Have one child roll the cube and show the number with counters on one part of the mat. Have the partner place the same number of counters in the other part. For example: **How many counters are in one part?** (5) **In the other part?** (5) **How many in all?** (10) **What is 5 + 5?** (10)

2. Remind children that this is a doubles fact. **Why is a fact such as 5 + 5 called a double?** (The addends are the same number.)

3. Continue with 2 or 3 more rolls.

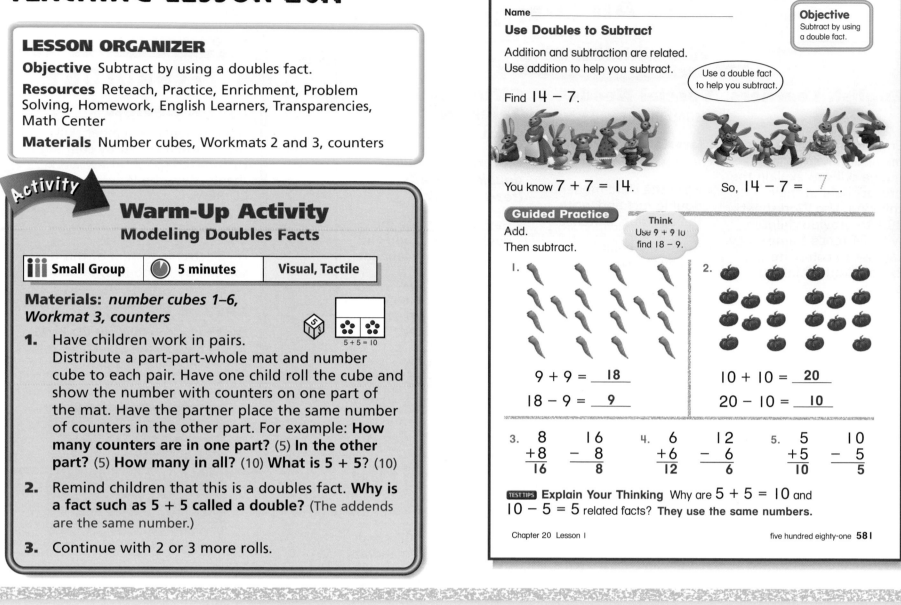

---

1 Introduce
Activity
Model Subtracting Doubles Facts

iiii Whole Group	5–10 minutes	Kinesthetic, Visual

1. Ask 6 children to come to the front of the class. Have them form 2 groups of 3 children each. Point to one group. **How many children are in this group?** (3) Point to the second group. **How many children are in this group?** (3) **How many children in all?** (6) **How can we write this number sentence?** (3 + 3 = 6) Point out that this is a doubles fact.

2. Ask the second group to sit down. **How many children did we start with?** (6) **How many children sat down?** (3) **How many children are still standing?** (3) **How can we write this subtraction sentence?** (6 − 3 = 3)

3. Point to the two number sentences and discuss how they are related. **What are the parts in both sentences?** (3 and 3) **What is the whole?** (6)

2 Develop

Guided Learning

Teaching Example

Read the objective with children. Guide them through the example by helping them interpret the picture. Have children count the rabbits in both parts of the picture to find 14. Ask how many rabbits are going away. (7) Ask how many rabbits are left. (7)

Guided Practice

Have children complete **Exercises 1–5** as you observe. Give children the opportunity to answer the Explain Your Thinking question. Then discuss why each pair of facts on the page are related facts.

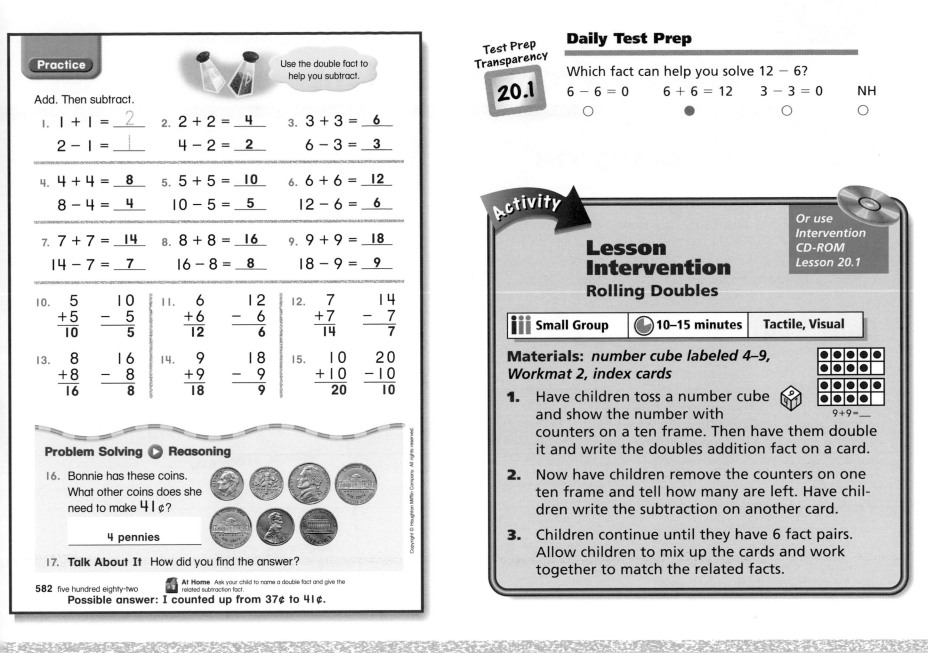

Practice

Use the double fact to help you subtract.

Add. Then subtract.

1. $1 + 1 = \underline{2}$
   $2 - 1 = \underline{1}$

2. $2 + 2 = \underline{4}$
   $4 - 2 = \underline{2}$

3. $3 + 3 = \underline{6}$
   $6 - 3 = \underline{3}$

4. $4 + 4 = \underline{8}$
   $8 - 4 = \underline{4}$

5. $5 + 5 = \underline{10}$
   $10 - 5 = \underline{5}$

6. $6 + 6 = \underline{12}$
   $12 - 6 = \underline{6}$

7. $7 + 7 = \underline{14}$
   $14 - 7 = \underline{7}$

8. $8 + 8 = \underline{16}$
   $16 - 8 = \underline{8}$

9. $9 + 9 = \underline{18}$
   $18 - 9 = \underline{9}$

10. $\begin{array}{r} 5 \\ +5 \\ \hline 10 \end{array}$ $\begin{array}{r} 10 \\ -5 \\ \hline 5 \end{array}$

11. $\begin{array}{r} 6 \\ +6 \\ \hline 12 \end{array}$ $\begin{array}{r} 12 \\ -6 \\ \hline 6 \end{array}$

12. $\begin{array}{r} 7 \\ +7 \\ \hline 14 \end{array}$ $\begin{array}{r} 14 \\ -7 \\ \hline 7 \end{array}$

13. $\begin{array}{r} 8 \\ +8 \\ \hline 16 \end{array}$ $\begin{array}{r} 16 \\ -8 \\ \hline 8 \end{array}$

14. $\begin{array}{r} 9 \\ +9 \\ \hline 18 \end{array}$ $\begin{array}{r} 18 \\ -9 \\ \hline 9 \end{array}$

15. $\begin{array}{r} 10 \\ +10 \\ \hline 20 \end{array}$ $\begin{array}{r} 20 \\ -10 \\ \hline 10 \end{array}$

Problem Solving ▶ Reasoning

16. Bonnie has these coins. What other coins does she need to make 41¢?

    4 pennies

17. **Talk About It** How did you find the answer?

582 five hundred eighty-two

At Home Ask your child to name a double fact and give the related subtraction fact.

Possible answer: I counted up from 37¢ to 41¢.

Daily Test Prep

20.1

Which fact can help you solve $12 - 6$?

$6 - 6 = 0$ ○ $6 + 6 = 12$ ● $3 - 3 = 0$ ○   NH ○

Activity

Lesson Intervention
Rolling Doubles

Or use Intervention CD-ROM Lesson 20.1

| iii Small Group | ⏱ 10–15 minutes | Tactile, Visual |

Materials: *number cube labeled 4–9, Workmat 2, index cards*

$9 + 9 = \underline{}$

1. Have children toss a number cube and show the number with counters on a ten frame. Then have them double it and write the doubles addition fact on a card.

2. Now have children remove the counters on one ten frame and tell how many are left. Have children write the subtraction on another card.

3. Children continue until they have 6 fact pairs. Allow children to mix up the cards and work together to match the related facts.

---

③ Practice

Independent Practice

Children complete **Exercises 1–15** independently.

Problem Solving

After children complete **Exercise 16,** call on volunteers to share their solutions. Use the **Talk About It** question in Exercise 17 to discuss different strategies.

Common Error

Adding Both Facts

Some children may mistakenly add to solve both related facts. Have children circle the operation sign to focus them on the operation to use.

④ Assess and Close

What doubles fact can help you solve $18 - 9$? ($9 + 9 = 18$)

Explain how you know that $7 + 7 = 14$ and $14 - 7 = 7$ are related facts. (They have the same parts and whole numbers.)

✎ Keeping a Journal

Draw a picture to show $6 + 6 = 12$ and $12 - 6 = 6$.

Subtract From 13 and 14

PLANNING THE LESSON

MATHEMATICS OBJECTIVE
Subtract from 13 and 14 by using related addition facts.

Use Lesson Planner CD-ROM for Lesson 20.2.

Meeting North Carolina's Standards
1.03 Develop fluency with single-digit addition and corresponding differences using strategies such as modeling, composing and decomposing quantities, using doubles, and making tens.

Also 1.04

Daily Routines

Calendar
Circle the 13th of the current month. Have children count back to find the date that is 3 days before. Repeat by having children count back 2, and then 1, from the 13th.

Sunday	Monday	Tuesday	Wednesday	Thursday	Friday	Saturday
				1	2	3	4
5	6	7	8	9	10	11
12	13	14	15	16	17	18
19	20	21	22	23	24	25
26	27	28	29	30	31	

Vocabulary
Review the term **difference** as the result of subtraction. Use the vocabulary cards to have children practice differentiating between difference and sum.

Vocabulary Cards

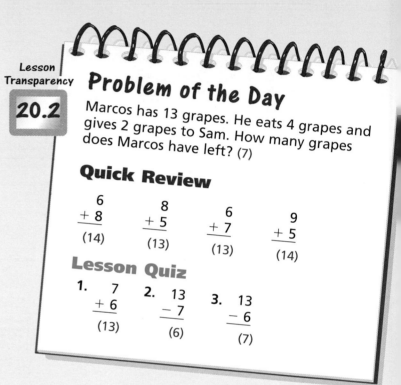

Lesson Transparency 20.2

Problem of the Day
Marcos has 13 grapes. He eats 4 grapes and gives 2 grapes to Sam. How many grapes does Marcos have left? (7)

Quick Review

$$\begin{array}{r} 6 \\ + 8 \\ \hline (14) \end{array} \qquad \begin{array}{r} 8 \\ + 5 \\ \hline (13) \end{array} \qquad \begin{array}{r} 6 \\ + 7 \\ \hline (13) \end{array} \qquad \begin{array}{r} 9 \\ + 5 \\ \hline (14) \end{array}$$

Lesson Quiz

$$\textbf{1.} \begin{array}{r} 7 \\ + 6 \\ \hline (13) \end{array} \qquad \textbf{2.} \begin{array}{r} 13 \\ - 7 \\ \hline (6) \end{array} \qquad \textbf{3.} \begin{array}{r} 13 \\ - 6 \\ \hline (7) \end{array}$$

LEVELED PRACTICE

RETEACH 20.2

Name _____ Date _____   Reteach 20.2

Subtract from 13 and 14

These are related facts.
They have the same parts and wholes.

$$\begin{array}{r} 9 \\ + 4 \\ \hline 13 \end{array}$$

Whole	
13	
Part	Part

$$\begin{array}{r} 13 \\ - 9 \\ \hline 4 \end{array} \qquad \begin{array}{r} 13 \\ - 4 \\ \hline 9 \end{array}$$

A related fact can help you find the difference.

You can use 9 + 4 to find 13 – 9 and 13 – 4.

Add.
Then find the differences.

1. $\begin{array}{r} 5 \\ + 8 \\ \hline 13 \end{array}$ Whole 13, Part Part $\begin{array}{r} 13 \\ - 5 \\ \hline 8 \end{array} \quad \begin{array}{r} 13 \\ - 8 \\ \hline 5 \end{array}$

2. $\begin{array}{r} 5 \\ + 9 \\ \hline 14 \end{array}$ Whole 14, Part Part $\begin{array}{r} 14 \\ - 5 \\ \hline 9 \end{array} \quad \begin{array}{r} 14 \\ - 9 \\ \hline 5 \end{array}$

3. $\begin{array}{r} 6 \\ + 8 \\ \hline 14 \end{array} \quad \begin{array}{r} 14 \\ - 6 \\ \hline 8 \end{array} \quad \begin{array}{r} 14 \\ - 8 \\ \hline 6 \end{array}$

4. $\begin{array}{r} 7 \\ + 6 \\ \hline 13 \end{array} \quad \begin{array}{r} 13 \\ - 7 \\ \hline 6 \end{array} \quad \begin{array}{r} 13 \\ - 6 \\ \hline 7 \end{array}$

Use with text pages 583–584.

PRACTICE 20.2

Name _____ Date _____   Practice 20.2

Subtract From 13 and 14

Add. Then find the difference.

1. $\begin{array}{r} 9 \\ + 4 \\ \hline 13 \end{array} \quad \begin{array}{r} 13 \\ - 9 \\ \hline 4 \end{array} \quad \begin{array}{r} 13 \\ - 4 \\ \hline 9 \end{array}$ **2.** $\begin{array}{r} 6 \\ + 8 \\ \hline 14 \end{array} \quad \begin{array}{r} 14 \\ - 6 \\ \hline 8 \end{array} \quad \begin{array}{r} 14 \\ - 8 \\ \hline 6 \end{array}$

3. $\begin{array}{r} 7 \\ + 5 \\ \hline 12 \end{array} \quad \begin{array}{r} 12 \\ - 7 \\ \hline 5 \end{array} \quad \begin{array}{r} 12 \\ - 5 \\ \hline 7 \end{array}$ **4.** $\begin{array}{r} 5 \\ + 8 \\ \hline 13 \end{array} \quad \begin{array}{r} 13 \\ - 5 \\ \hline 8 \end{array} \quad \begin{array}{r} 13 \\ - 8 \\ \hline 5 \end{array}$

5. $\begin{array}{r} 6 \\ + 7 \\ \hline 13 \end{array} \quad \begin{array}{r} 13 \\ - 6 \\ \hline 7 \end{array} \quad \begin{array}{r} 13 \\ - 7 \\ \hline 6 \end{array}$ **6.** $\begin{array}{r} 9 \\ + 3 \\ \hline 12 \end{array} \quad \begin{array}{r} 12 \\ - 9 \\ \hline 3 \end{array} \quad \begin{array}{r} 12 \\ - 3 \\ \hline 9 \end{array}$

Test Prep

Fill in the ○ for the correct answer.
NH means Not Here.

7. Look at the addition sentence.   7 + 6 = 13

Choose a related subtraction fact.

13 – 7 = 6 ●   13 – 5 = 8 ○   13 – 4 = 9 ○   NH ○

Use with text pages 583–584.

ENRICHMENT 20.2

Name _____ Date _____   Enrichment 20.2

Related Facts for Missing Addends

Subtract.
Then find the missing addend.

Think
The difference is the missing part.

Whole	
14	
Part	Part

14 – 8 = 6
8 + 6 = 14

Whole	
13	
Part	Part

13 – 6 = 7
6 + 7 = 13

Whole	
14	
Part	Part

14 – 5 = 9
5 + 9 = 14

Write About It What subtraction fact can help you find the missing addend in ___ + 9 = 12?   12 – 9 = 3

Use with text pages 583–584.

Practice Workbook Page 135

Reaching All Learners

Differentiated Instruction

English Learners

Children will need to understand the word *match* in order to solve some word problems. Use Worksheet 20.2 to develop understanding of this word.

Inclusion
VISUAL, TACTILE

Materials: *two-color counters, Workmat 3*

- Guide the child to model 8 + 6 with counters. Have him or her count to find the whole, 14.
- Write the addition in vertical form and have the child write the sum.
- Guide the child through the two related subtraction facts.

$$\begin{array}{r} 8 \\ +6 \\ \hline 14 \end{array} \quad \begin{array}{r} 14 \\ -6 \\ \hline 8 \end{array} \quad \begin{array}{r} 14 \\ -8 \\ \hline 6 \end{array}$$

Gifted and Talented
VISUAL, TACTILE

Materials: *index cards*

- Have each child write related addition and subtraction facts on index cards. Tell children not to include the plus, minus, or equal sign.
- When children have completed 5 cards, have them exchange cards and solve. Partners can check each other's work.

TECHNOLOGY

Spiral Review

You can prepare students for standardized tests with **customized** spiral review on key skills using the *Ways to Assess* CD-ROM.

Lesson Planner

You can use the **Lesson Planner CD-ROM** to create a report of the lessons and standards you have taught.

Education Place

Encourage students to visit **Education Place** at **eduplace.com/kids/mw/** for more student activities.

Social Studies Connection

Point out that some things are sold in groups of 12, or one dozen. Then introduce a baker's dozen as a dozen plus one. Explain that some bakers give people one extra when they buy a dozen rolls or bagels. Have children draw a baker's dozen of their favorite dessert.

MATH CENTER

Basic Skills Activity

Motivate children to build basic skills. Use this activity to address multiple learning styles using hands-on activities related to the skills of this lesson.

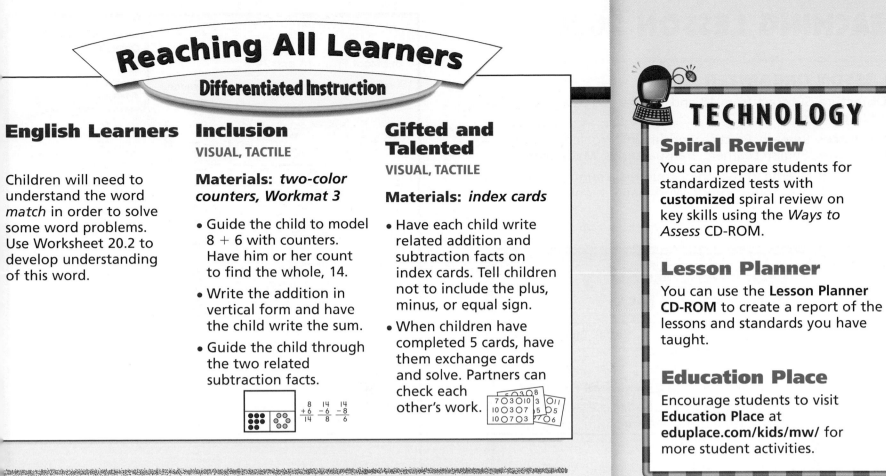

PROBLEM SOLVING 20.2

Name _____ Date _____
Problem Solving 20.2

Subtract From 13 and 14

Add. Then subtract to solve.

Draw or write to explain.

1. There are 8 round buttons and 5 square buttons in the box. How many buttons are there in all?

   __13__ buttons

   8 + 5 = 13

   If Ms. Tran uses 8 of the buttons, how many buttons are left?

   __5__ buttons

   13 – 8 = 5

2. Stan puts 9 plums on a plate. Then he puts 4 more plums on the plate. How many plums are on the plate?

   __13__ plums

   9 + 4 = 13

   Jared takes away 4 of the plums. How many plums are left on the plate?

   __9__ plums

   13 – 4 = 9

Use with text pages 583–584.

HOMEWORK 20.2

Name _____ Date _____
Homework 20.2

Subtract From 13 and 14

A related fact can help you find the difference.

Add. Then find the difference.

1. 9 + 4 = 13   13 – 9 = 4   13 – 4 = 9
2. 6 + 8 = 14   14 – 6 = 8   14 – 8 = 6
3. 8 + 4 = 12   12 – 8 = 4   12 – 4 = 8
4. 8 + 5 = 13   13 – 5 = 8   13 – 8 = 5
5. 5 + 9 = 14   14 – 5 = 9   14 – 9 = 5
6. 5 + 7 = 12   12 – 5 = 7   12 – 7 = 5

Use the numbers to write an addition fact. Then write the related subtraction facts.

7. 5 + 8 = 13
8. 13 – 5 = 8
9. 13 – 8 = 5

Use with text pages 583–584.

ENGLISH LEARNERS 20.2

Name _____ Date _____
English Learners 20.2

Subtract From 13 and 14

These shoes **match**.   These shoes **do not match**.

Circle the correct word or words.

1. These mittens (match) do not match.
2. These socks (match) do not match.
3. These gloves match (do not match).
4. These boots (match) do not match.

To the Teacher: Use the illustrations and sentences at the top of the page to help children understand the meaning of the word match. Then read the sentences with children and have them circle the correct word or words.

Use with text pages 583–584.

TEACHING LESSON 20.2

LESSON ORGANIZER

Objective Subtract from 13 and 14 by using related addition facts.

Resources Reteach, Practice, Enrichment, Problem Solving, Homework, English Learners, Transparencies, Math Center

Materials Overhead two-color counters, counters, Part-Part-Whole Mat transparency, Workmat 3, number cube labeled 4–9

Activity

Warm-Up Activity
Discuss Related Facts

Small Group	5 minutes	Visual, Tactile

Materials: *counters*

1. **What doubles fact can help you subtract 12 − 6?** (6 + 6 = 12) Remind children that these 2 facts are related because they use the same numbers—they have the same parts and the same whole.
2. Give each group an addition fact to 12. Make counters available. Have children work together to find a related subtraction fact. Have children write the subtraction fact.
3. Have each group share their related facts.

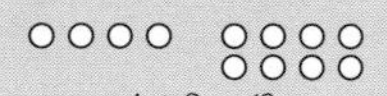

4 + 8 = 12
12 − 8 = 4

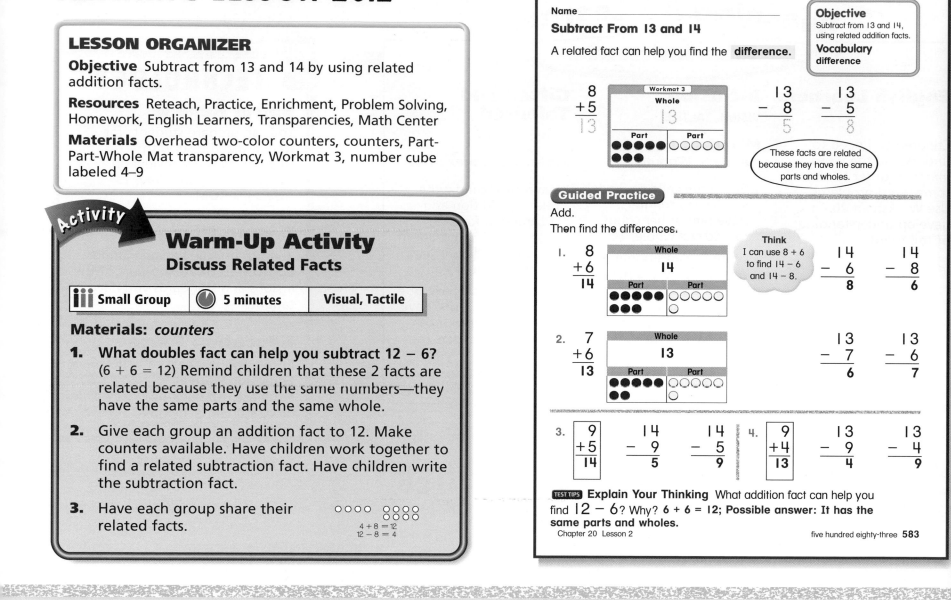

Name ______________________

Subtract From 13 and 14

A related fact can help you find the **difference.**

Objective
Subtract from 13 and 14, using related addition facts.
Vocabulary
difference

$\begin{array}{r} 8 \\ +5 \\ \hline 13 \end{array}$

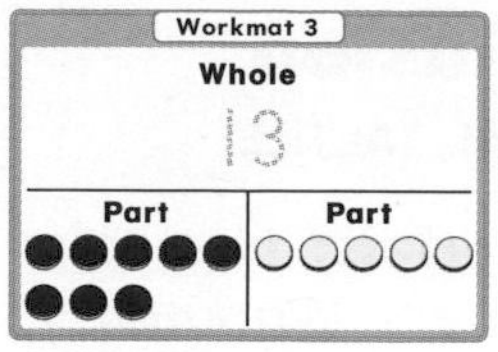

$\begin{array}{r} 13 \\ -8 \\ \hline 5 \end{array}$ $\begin{array}{r} 13 \\ -5 \\ \hline 8 \end{array}$

These facts are related because they have the same parts and wholes.

Guided Practice

Add.
Then find the differences.

1. $\begin{array}{r} 8 \\ +6 \\ \hline 14 \end{array}$

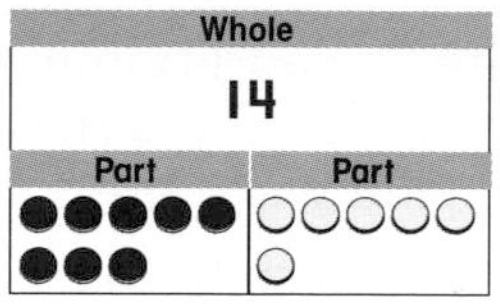

Think I can use 8 + 6 to find 14 − 6 and 14 − 8.

$\begin{array}{r} 14 \\ -6 \\ \hline 8 \end{array}$ $\begin{array}{r} 14 \\ -8 \\ \hline 6 \end{array}$

2. $\begin{array}{r} 7 \\ +6 \\ \hline 13 \end{array}$

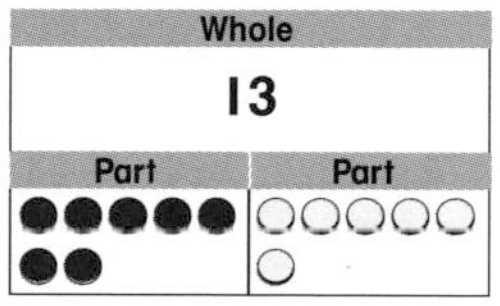

$\begin{array}{r} 13 \\ -7 \\ \hline 6 \end{array}$ $\begin{array}{r} 13 \\ -6 \\ \hline 7 \end{array}$

3. $\begin{array}{r} 9 \\ +5 \\ \hline 14 \end{array}$ $\begin{array}{r} 14 \\ -9 \\ \hline 5 \end{array}$ $\begin{array}{r} 14 \\ -5 \\ \hline 9 \end{array}$

4. $\begin{array}{r} 9 \\ +4 \\ \hline 13 \end{array}$ $\begin{array}{r} 13 \\ -9 \\ \hline 4 \end{array}$ $\begin{array}{r} 13 \\ -4 \\ \hline 9 \end{array}$

TEST TIPS **Explain Your Thinking** What addition fact can help you find 12 − 6? Why? **6 + 6 = 12; Possible answer: It has the same parts and wholes.**

Chapter 20 Lesson 2 five hundred eighty-three **583**

1 Introduce

Activity

Model Subtraction From 13 and 14

Whole Group	10–15 minutes	Visual, Tactile

Materials: ***overhead two-color counters, Part-Part-Whole Mat transparency, counters, Workmat 3***

1. Put the part-part-whole transparency on the overhead and model 6 + 7 with counters. Have children model the addition at the same time on Workmat 3. **What is the whole?** (13) Write the addition fact vertically on the transparency. Cover the 7. **The whole is 13 and one part is 6. What is the missing part?** (7) Record the subtraction fact. Lift your hand and this time cover 6. **The whole is 13 and one part is 7. What is the missing part?** (6) **What is the difference for 13 − 6? (7) 13 − 7?** (6) Look at the 3 facts and point out that they are related because they have the same parts and whole.
2. Repeat with 9 + 5 = 14 as children follow along. Have volunteers record the 3 related facts.

2 Develop

Guided Learning

Teaching Example

Read the objective and vocabulary with children. Guide them through the example as they use counters on Workmat 3.

Guided Practice

Have children complete **Exercises 1–4** as you observe. Give children the opportunity to answer the Explain Your Thinking question. Then discuss why all the facts in each exercise are related facts.

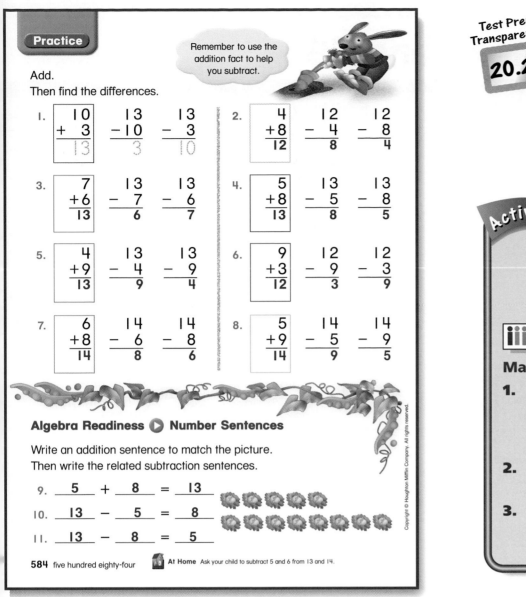

Practice

Remember to use the addition fact to help you subtract.

Add.
Then find the differences.

1.
10	13	13
+ 3	−10	− 3
13	3	10

2.
4	12	12
+8	− 4	− 8
12	8	4

3.
7	13	13
+6	− 7	− 6
13	6	7

4.
5	13	13
+8	− 5	− 8
13	8	5

5.
4	13	13
+9	− 4	− 9
13	9	4

6.
9	12	12
+3	− 9	− 3
12	3	9

7.
6	14	14
+8	− 6	− 8
14	8	6

8.
5	14	14
+9	− 5	− 9
14	9	5

Algebra Readiness ▶ Number Sentences

Write an addition sentence to match the picture.
Then write the related subtraction sentences.

9. __5__ + __8__ = __13__

10. __13__ − __5__ = __8__

11. __13__ − __8__ = __5__

584 five hundred eighty-four

At Home Ask your child to subtract 5 and 6 from 13 and 14.

Daily Test Prep

What subtraction fact is related to 9 + 6 = 15?

9	6	15	6
− 6	− 6	− 9	+ 9
3	0	6	15

○ ○ ● ○

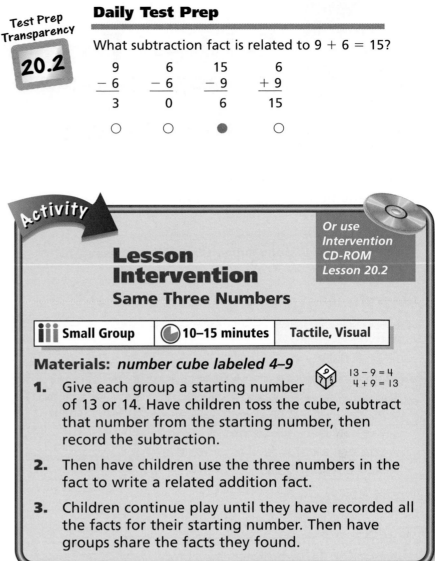

Activity

Lesson Intervention
Same Three Numbers

Or use Intervention CD-ROM Lesson 20.2

👥 Small Group	🕐 10–15 minutes	Tactile, Visual

Materials: *number cube labeled 4–9*

13 − 9 = 4
4 + 9 = 13

1. Give each group a starting number of 13 or 14. Have children toss the cube, subtract that number from the starting number, then record the subtraction.

2. Then have children use the three numbers in the fact to write a related addition fact.

3. Children continue play until they have recorded all the facts for their starting number. Then have groups share the facts they found.

3 Practice

Independent Practice
Children complete **Exercises 1–8** independently.

Algebra Readiness
After children complete **Exercises 9–11,** call on volunteers to share their solutions. Record each number sentence on the board.

Common Error

Subtracting Incorrectly
Remind children to check their subtraction against the addition, because all the facts in each set of exercises use the same numbers.

4 Assess and Close

Since 8 + 6 = 14, what is 14 − 6? (8)

How can a related addition fact help you subtract? (Since related facts use the same numbers, the difference is the same as one of the addends in the addition.)

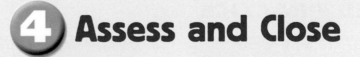

Keeping a Journal

Draw and write to show how you subtract 13 − 5.

Subtract From 15 and 16

PLANNING THE LESSON

MATHEMATICS OBJECTIVE
Use addition facts to aid in subtraction.

Use Lesson Planner CD-ROM for Lesson 20.3.

Meeting North Carolina's Standards
1.03 Develop fluency with single-digit addition and corresponding differences using strategies such as modeling, composing and decomposing quantities, using doubles, and making tens.

Daily Routines

Calendar
Remind children that a calendar includes one page for each of the 12 months of the year. Subtract the number of the current month from 12 and ask a volunteer to write the related addition facts.

Sunday	Monday	Tuesday	Wednesday	Thursday	Friday	Saturday
				1	2	3	4
5	6	7	8	9	10	11
12	13	14	15	16	17	18
19	20	21	22	23	24	25
26	27	28	29	30	31	

Vocabulary
Review the terms **sum** and **difference**. Name an addition or subtraction fact and have the class identify the sum or the difference. Then have volunteers name facts.

Vocabulary Cards

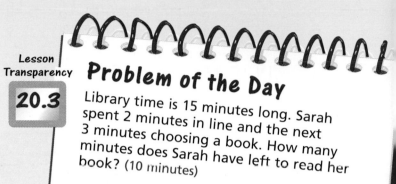

Lesson Transparency 20.3

Problem of the Day
Library time is 15 minutes long. Sarah spent 2 minutes in line and the next 3 minutes choosing a book. How many minutes does Sarah have left to read her book? (10 minutes)

Quick Review

$$\begin{array}{r} 6 \\ + 9 \\ \hline (15) \end{array} \quad \begin{array}{r} 7 \\ + 8 \\ \hline (15) \end{array} \quad \begin{array}{r} 9 \\ + 7 \\ \hline (16) \end{array} \quad \begin{array}{r} 8 \\ + 8 \\ \hline (16) \end{array} \quad \begin{array}{r} 9 \\ + 6 \\ \hline (15) \end{array}$$

Lesson Quiz

$$\textbf{1.} \begin{array}{r} 5 \\ + 10 \\ \hline (15) \end{array} \qquad \textbf{2.} \begin{array}{r} 15 \\ - 5 \\ \hline (10) \end{array} \qquad \textbf{3.} \begin{array}{r} 15 \\ - 10 \\ \hline (5) \end{array}$$

LEVELED PRACTICE

RETEACH 20.3

Name _____ Date _____ **Reteach 20.3**

Subtract from 15 and 16

Use a related addition fact to help you subtract.

$$\begin{array}{r} 9 \\ + 6 \\ \hline 15 \end{array} \qquad \begin{array}{r} 15 \\ - 9 \\ \hline 6 \end{array} \quad \begin{array}{r} 15 \\ - 6 \\ \hline 9 \end{array}$$

Whole 15 — Part / Part

Remember, related facts have the same parts and wholes.

You can use 9 + 6 to find 15 − 9 and 15 − 6.

Add.
Then find the difference.

1.
$$\begin{array}{r} 10 \\ + 5 \\ \hline 15 \end{array} \qquad \begin{array}{r} 15 \\ - 10 \\ \hline 5 \end{array} \quad \begin{array}{r} 15 \\ - 5 \\ \hline 10 \end{array}$$
Whole 15 — Part / Part

2.
$$\begin{array}{r} 10 \\ + 6 \\ \hline 16 \end{array} \qquad \begin{array}{r} 16 \\ - 10 \\ \hline 6 \end{array} \quad \begin{array}{r} 16 \\ - 6 \\ \hline 10 \end{array}$$
Whole 16 — Part / Part

3.
$$\begin{array}{r} 7 \\ + 8 \\ \hline 15 \end{array} \quad \begin{array}{r} 15 \\ - 7 \\ \hline 8 \end{array} \quad \begin{array}{r} 15 \\ - 8 \\ \hline 7 \end{array}$$

4.
$$\begin{array}{r} 7 \\ + 9 \\ \hline 16 \end{array} \quad \begin{array}{r} 16 \\ - 7 \\ \hline 9 \end{array} \quad \begin{array}{r} 16 \\ - 9 \\ \hline 7 \end{array}$$

Copyright © Houghton Mifflin Company. All rights reserved. Use with text pages 585–586.

PRACTICE 20.3

Name _____ Date _____ **Practice 20.3**

Subtract From 15 and 16

Add.
Then find the difference.

Remember to use the addition fact to help you subtract.

1.
$$\begin{array}{r} 8 \\ + 6 \\ \hline 14 \end{array} \quad \begin{array}{r} 14 \\ - 8 \\ \hline 6 \end{array} \quad \begin{array}{r} 14 \\ - 6 \\ \hline 8 \end{array}$$

2.
$$\begin{array}{r} 9 \\ + 6 \\ \hline 15 \end{array} \quad \begin{array}{r} 15 \\ - 9 \\ \hline 6 \end{array} \quad \begin{array}{r} 15 \\ - 6 \\ \hline 9 \end{array}$$

3.
$$\begin{array}{r} 7 \\ + 6 \\ \hline 13 \end{array} \quad \begin{array}{r} 13 \\ - 7 \\ \hline 6 \end{array} \quad \begin{array}{r} 13 \\ - 6 \\ \hline 7 \end{array}$$

4.
$$\begin{array}{r} 8 \\ + 7 \\ \hline 15 \end{array} \quad \begin{array}{r} 15 \\ - 7 \\ \hline 8 \end{array} \quad \begin{array}{r} 15 \\ - 8 \\ \hline 7 \end{array}$$

5.
$$\begin{array}{r} 6 \\ + 10 \\ \hline 16 \end{array} \quad \begin{array}{r} 16 \\ - 6 \\ \hline 10 \end{array} \quad \begin{array}{r} 16 \\ - 10 \\ \hline 6 \end{array}$$

6.
$$\begin{array}{r} 7 \\ + 9 \\ \hline 16 \end{array} \quad \begin{array}{r} 16 \\ - 7 \\ \hline 9 \end{array} \quad \begin{array}{r} 16 \\ - 9 \\ \hline 7 \end{array}$$

Test Prep

Fill in the ○ for the correct answer.
NH means Not Here.

7. Kim has 16 pears.
She keeps 7 pears and gives away the rest.
Which tells how many pears Kim gives away?

○ 9 − 7   ○ 9 + 7   ● 16 − 7   ○ NH

Copyright © Houghton Mifflin Company. All rights reserved. Use with text pages 585–586.

ENRICHMENT 20.3

Name _____ Date _____ **Enrichment 20.3**

Patterns in Related Facts

Complete the names for 15.
Complete each related subtraction fact.

1. 0 + 15	15 − 0 = 15	15 − 15 = 0
2. 1 + 14	15 − 1 = 14	15 − 14 = 1
3. 2 + 13	15 − 2 = 13	15 − 13 = 2
4. 3 + 12	15 − 3 = 12	15 − 12 = 3
5. 4 + 11	15 − 4 = 11	15 − 11 = 4
6. 5 + 10	15 − 5 = 10	15 − 10 = 5
7. 6 + 9	15 − 6 = 9	15 − 9 = 6
8. 7 + 8	15 − 7 = 8	15 − 8 = 7
9. 8 + 7	15 − 8 = 7	15 − 7 = 8
10. 9 + 6	15 − 9 = 6	15 − 6 = 9
11. 10 + 5	15 − 10 = 5	15 − 5 = 10
12. 11 + 4	15 − 11 = 4	15 − 4 = 11
13. 12 + 3	15 − 12 = 3	15 − 3 = 12
14. 13 + 2	15 − 13 = 2	15 − 2 = 13
15. 14 + 1	15 − 14 = 1	15 − 1 = 14
16. 15 + 0	15 − 15 = 0	15 − 0 = 15

Write About It What patterns do you see? **Possible answer: The differences in related facts match addends in the number names. In the middle column differences decrease by 1, in the last column differences increase by 1.**

Copyright © Houghton Mifflin Company. All rights reserved. Use with text pages 585–586.

Practice Workbook Page 136

Reaching All Learners

Differentiated Instruction

English Learners

English-language learners may not have the language skills to explain the process behind their thinking. Use Worksheet 20.3 to provide children with sentence frames they can use to complete the Explain Your Thinking activity.

Inclusion
VISUAL, TACTILE

Materials: *two-color counters, Workmat 3*

Have the child model 9 + 6 and count to find the whole, 15. Write the addition in vertical form and have the child write the sum. Guide the child to model the related subtraction facts. Repeat for 8 + 7

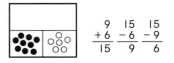

$$\begin{array}{r} 9 \\ +6 \\ \hline 15 \end{array} \quad \begin{array}{r} 15 \\ -6 \\ \hline 9 \end{array} \quad \begin{array}{r} 15 \\ -9 \\ \hline 6 \end{array}$$

Early Finishers
VISUAL, TACTILE

Materials: *two sets of number cards for 1–15 (LT 14 and 15)*

- Have the child choose a card from one set and find the card from the second set that will equal 16. Encourage them to arrange their pairs of cards in a pattern.

- Then have children write the two related subtraction facts for each addition fact.

Literature Connection

Read *Lights Out!* by Lucille Recht Penner. Point out that the girl is subtracting to keep track of the number of lights that are still lit. Have children identify subtraction facts they know: 15 − 8 = 7, 7 − 1 = 6, and so on.

MATH CENTER

Basic Skills Activity

Motivate children to build basic skills. Use this activity to address multiple learning styles using hands-on activities related to the skills of this lesson.

TECHNOLOGY

Spiral Review

Create **customized** spiral review worksheets for individual students using the *Ways to Assess* CD-ROM.

Lesson Planner

You can customize your teaching plan or meet your curriculum requirements with the **Lesson Planner CD-ROM.**

eBook

eMathBook allows students to review lessons and do homework without carrying their textbooks home.

Education Place

You can visit **Education Place** at **eduplace.com/math/mw/** for teacher support materials.

PROBLEM SOLVING 20.3

Name _____ Date _____

Problem Solving 20.3

Subtract From 15 and 16

Add. Then subtract to solve.

Draw or write to explain.

1. Juan has 6 yellow balloons and 10 red balloons. How many balloons does he have altogether?

    $\underline{6} + \underline{10} = \underline{16}$

    __16__ balloons

    Juan gives 6 balloons away. How many balloons does he have left?

    $\underline{16} - \underline{6} = \underline{10}$

    __10__ balloons

2. There are 7 ducks in the pond. 8 ducks join them. How many ducks are in the pond in all?

    $\underline{7} + \underline{8} = \underline{15}$

    __15__ ducks

    Now 7 of the ducks fly away. How many ducks are in the pond now?

    $\underline{15} - \underline{7} = \underline{8}$

    __8__ ducks

Use with text pages 585–588.

HOMEWORK 20.3

Name _____ Date _____

Homework 20.3

Subtract From 15 and 16

| Workmat 3 |
| Whole 16 |
| Part / Part |

$$\begin{array}{r} 9 \\ +7 \\ \hline 16 \end{array} \quad \begin{array}{r} 16 \\ -9 \\ \hline 7 \end{array} \quad \begin{array}{r} 16 \\ -7 \\ \hline 9 \end{array}$$

Add.
Then find the difference.

1. $\begin{array}{r} 7 \\ +8 \\ \hline 15 \end{array} \quad \begin{array}{r} 15 \\ -7 \\ \hline 8 \end{array} \quad \begin{array}{r} 15 \\ -8 \\ \hline 7 \end{array}$ 2. $\begin{array}{r} 10 \\ +5 \\ \hline 15 \end{array} \quad \begin{array}{r} 15 \\ -10 \\ \hline 5 \end{array} \quad \begin{array}{r} 15 \\ -5 \\ \hline 10 \end{array}$

3. $\begin{array}{r} 6 \\ +9 \\ \hline 15 \end{array} \quad \begin{array}{r} 15 \\ -6 \\ \hline 9 \end{array} \quad \begin{array}{r} 15 \\ -9 \\ \hline 6 \end{array}$ 4. $\begin{array}{r} 10 \\ +6 \\ \hline 16 \end{array} \quad \begin{array}{r} 16 \\ -10 \\ \hline 6 \end{array} \quad \begin{array}{r} 16 \\ -6 \\ \hline 10 \end{array}$

5. $\begin{array}{r} 9 \\ +5 \\ \hline 14 \end{array} \quad \begin{array}{r} 14 \\ -9 \\ \hline 5 \end{array} \quad \begin{array}{r} 14 \\ -5 \\ \hline 9 \end{array}$ 6. $\begin{array}{r} 8 \\ +5 \\ \hline 13 \end{array} \quad \begin{array}{r} 13 \\ -8 \\ \hline 5 \end{array} \quad \begin{array}{r} 13 \\ -5 \\ \hline 8 \end{array}$

Solve.

7. Sixteen minus seven equals __nine or 9__.

8. Fifteen minus five equals __ten or 10__.

Use with text pages 585–586.

ENGLISH LEARNERS 20.3

Name _____ Date _____

English Learners 20.3

Subtract From 15 and 16

$$12 + 2 = 14$$

| Whole |
| 14 |
| Part / Part |
| 12 / 2 |

If you know 10 + 6 = 16, what two related subtraction facts do you know?

10 + 6 = 16

The parts are __10__ and __6__.

The whole is __16__.

Related facts have the same whole and parts.
I can use the same whole and parts to make two subtraction facts.

16 − 10 = __6__ is one fact.

16 − 6 = __10__ is the other fact.

To the Teacher: Use the example at the top of the page to demonstrate how to determine the whole and parts of an addition fact. Then have children complete the sentence frames that provide the language needed to explain how to answer the question.

Use with text pages 585–588.

Homework Workbook Page 136

TEACHING LESSON 20.3

LESSON ORGANIZER

Objective Use addition facts to aid in subtraction.

Resources Reteach, Practice, Enrichment, Problem Solving, Homework, English Learners, Transparencies, Math Center

Materials Counters, part-part-whole transparency, Workmat 3, number cards 15 and 16 (LT 15)

Warm-Up Activity
Modeling Related Facts

⚏ Small Group	⏱ 5 minutes	Tactile, Visual

Materials: *counters*

1. Have children show a row of 6 counters above a row of 7 counters. **What addition fact did you model?** (6 + 7 = 13) Have a volunteer write the addition fact vertically. **What related subtraction facts can we make from this addition fact?** (13 − 7 = 6; 13 − 6 = 7) Prompt children to cover one row at a time. Then record both subtraction facts.

2. Have groups work independently to find other related addition and subtraction facts for 13.

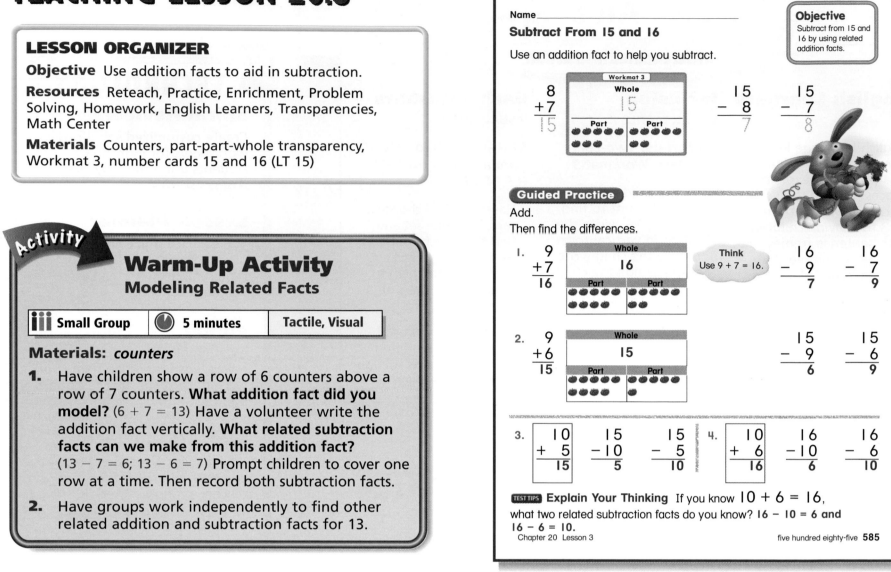

Name _____

Subtract From 15 and 16

Objective Subtract from 15 and 16 by using related addition facts.

Use an addition fact to help you subtract.

Guided Practice

Add.
Then find the differences.

TEST TIPS Explain Your Thinking If you know $10 + 6 = 16$, what two related subtraction facts do you know? $16 − 10 = 6$ and $16 − 6 = 10$.

Chapter 20 Lesson 3

five hundred eighty-five **585**

---

1. Introduce
Model Using Addition to Subtract

⚏ Whole Group	⏱ 10–15 minutes	Tactile, Visual

Materials: *counters, part-part-whole transparency, Workmat 3*

1. **I can use the addition fact 9 + 7 = 16 to help me subtract 16 − 7.** Use the part-part-whole mat on the overhead to model 9 + 7. Ask a volunteer to write the completed addition fact. **I have 16. One part is 7. What is the other part?** (9) Ask a volunteer to record the subtraction fact. Repeat for 16 − 9, then point out that the facts have the same parts and whole.

2. Repeat with 9 + 6 as children follow along with counters on Workmat 3. Record the 3 related facts.

2. Develop

Guided Learning

Teaching Example

Read the objective with children. Guide them through the example as they use counters on Workmat 3.

Guided Practice

Have children complete **Exercises 1–4** as you observe. Give children the opportunity to answer the Explain Your Thinking question. Then remind children that all the facts in each exercise are related.

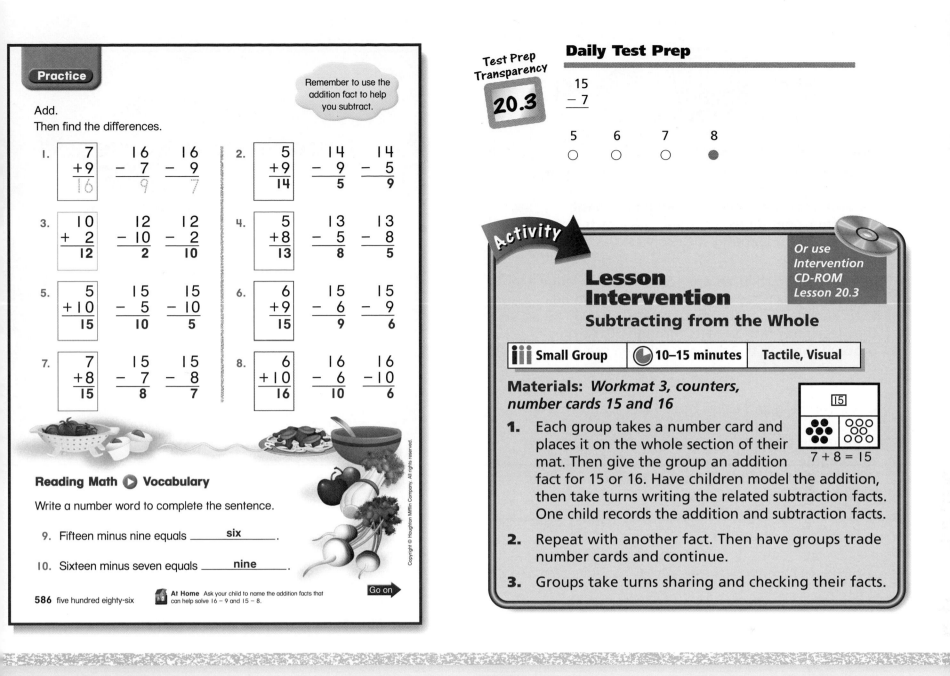

Practice

Add.
Then find the differences.

Remember to use the addition fact to help you subtract.

1.
$$\begin{array}{r} 7 \\ +9 \\ \hline 16 \end{array}$$
$$\begin{array}{r} 16 \\ -\ 7 \\ \hline 9 \end{array}$$
$$\begin{array}{r} 16 \\ -\ 9 \\ \hline 7 \end{array}$$

2.
$$\begin{array}{r} 5 \\ +9 \\ \hline 14 \end{array}$$
$$\begin{array}{r} 14 \\ -\ 9 \\ \hline 5 \end{array}$$
$$\begin{array}{r} 14 \\ -\ 5 \\ \hline 9 \end{array}$$

3.
$$\begin{array}{r} 10 \\ +\ 2 \\ \hline 12 \end{array}$$
$$\begin{array}{r} 12 \\ -10 \\ \hline 2 \end{array}$$
$$\begin{array}{r} 12 \\ -\ 2 \\ \hline 10 \end{array}$$

4.
$$\begin{array}{r} 5 \\ +8 \\ \hline 13 \end{array}$$
$$\begin{array}{r} 13 \\ -\ 5 \\ \hline 8 \end{array}$$
$$\begin{array}{r} 13 \\ -\ 8 \\ \hline 5 \end{array}$$

5.
$$\begin{array}{r} 5 \\ +10 \\ \hline 15 \end{array}$$
$$\begin{array}{r} 15 \\ -\ 5 \\ \hline 10 \end{array}$$
$$\begin{array}{r} 15 \\ -10 \\ \hline 5 \end{array}$$

6.
$$\begin{array}{r} 6 \\ +9 \\ \hline 15 \end{array}$$
$$\begin{array}{r} 15 \\ -\ 6 \\ \hline 9 \end{array}$$
$$\begin{array}{r} 15 \\ -\ 9 \\ \hline 6 \end{array}$$

7.
$$\begin{array}{r} 7 \\ +8 \\ \hline 15 \end{array}$$
$$\begin{array}{r} 15 \\ -\ 7 \\ \hline 8 \end{array}$$
$$\begin{array}{r} 15 \\ -\ 8 \\ \hline 7 \end{array}$$

8.
$$\begin{array}{r} 6 \\ +10 \\ \hline 16 \end{array}$$
$$\begin{array}{r} 16 \\ -\ 6 \\ \hline 10 \end{array}$$
$$\begin{array}{r} 16 \\ -10 \\ \hline 6 \end{array}$$

Reading Math ▶ Vocabulary

Write a number word to complete the sentence.

9. Fifteen minus nine equals ____six____.

10. Sixteen minus seven equals ____nine____.

586 five hundred eighty-six

At Home Ask your child to name the addition facts that can help solve 16 − 9 and 15 − 8.

Go on ▶

Daily Test Prep

$$\begin{array}{r} 15 \\ -\ 7 \\ \hline \end{array}$$

5 ○   6 ○   7 ○   8 ●

Activity

Lesson Intervention

Or use Intervention CD-ROM Lesson 20.3

Subtracting from the Whole

👥 Small Group	🕐 10–15 minutes	Tactile, Visual

Materials: *Workmat 3, counters, number cards 15 and 16*

15

7 + 8 = 15

1. Each group takes a number card and places it on the whole section of their mat. Then give the group an addition fact for 15 or 16. Have children model the addition, then take turns writing the related subtraction facts. One child records the addition and subtraction facts.

2. Repeat with another fact. Then have groups trade number cards and continue.

3. Groups take turns sharing and checking their facts.

---

3 Practice

Independent Practice

Children complete **Exercises 1–8** independently.

Reading Math

After children complete **Exercises 9–10,** call on volunteers to share their answers. Record each number word on the board so children can check their work.

Common Error

Adding Rather than Subtracting

Children may try to add the numbers in the subtraction exercises. Make a card for the child to refer to: + add; − subtract.

4 Assess and Close

Subtract 9 from 15. What is the difference? (6)

If you know that 8 + 7 = 15, does that help you subtract 15 − 8 or 15 − 9? (15 − 8) **How?** (The subtraction fact has the same parts as the addition fact.)

Keeping a Journal

Draw a picture to show 15 − 10 and the related addition fact.

Lesson continues

Learning Algorithms for Operations

An algorithm is a systematic method for carrying out a computation. Algorithms are important because they help **children understand basic arithmetic operations**. Learning basic facts is the foundation for learning such concepts as place algorithms.

In this chapter, children are acquiring knowledge about basic facts for subtraction. They build on their knowledge of subtraction facts through 12 as they learn subtraction facts through 20. As they proceed through the chapter, children use doubles to subtract and find differences using part-part-whole mats.

Understanding and using basic facts is an important prerequisite skill for understanding and using subtraction algorithms. Children will be unable to compute symbolically—the goal of algorithm development—until they have mastered basic facts for subtraction.

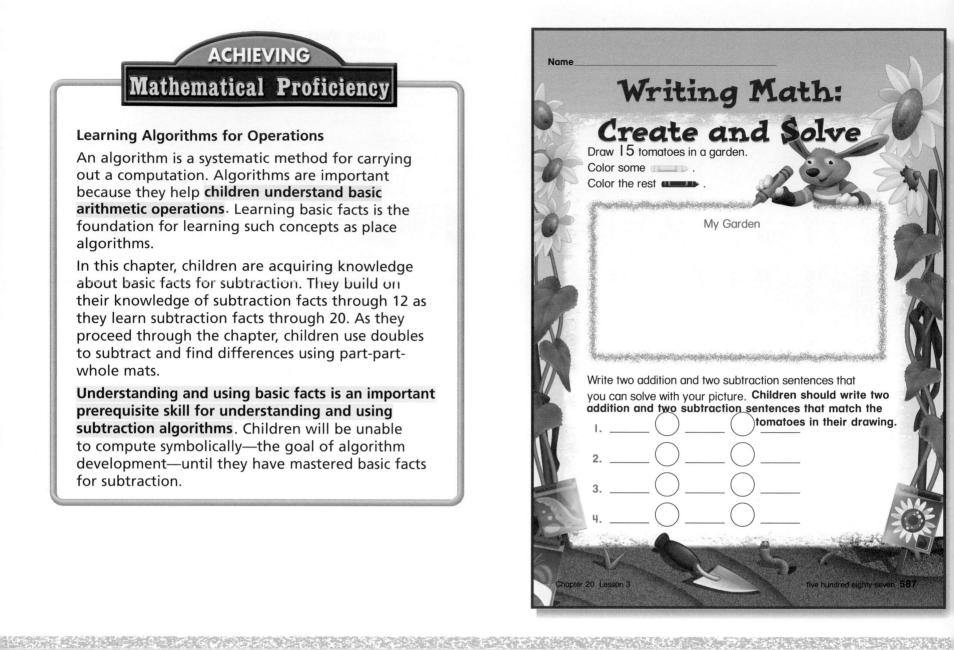

Writing Math: Create and Solve

Point to the drawing box. Be sure children understand that they should draw a picture of 15 tomatoes in the box. Remind children that the drawing can be simple. Call on volunteers to suggest shapes that could represent tomatoes. Instruct children to color some of the tomatoes yellow and the others red.

After children complete their picture, have them write the 4 addition and subtraction sentences that can be solved with the picture. The four number sentences should be the related facts that reflect the number of red and yellow tomatoes in the picture.

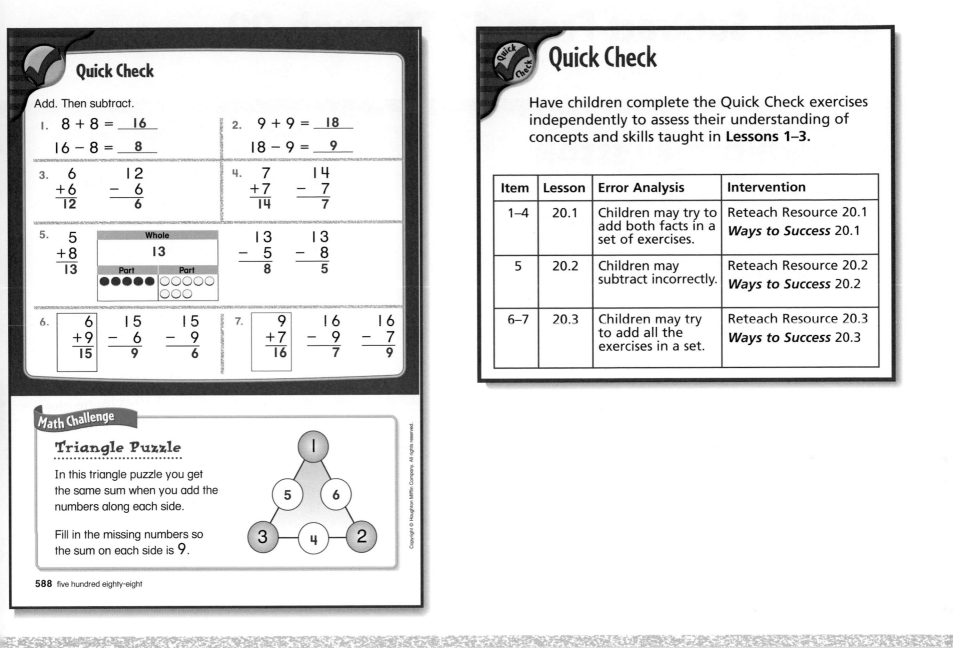

Quick Check

Add. Then subtract.

1. $8 + 8 = \underline{16}$
    $16 - 8 = \underline{8}$

2. $9 + 9 = \underline{18}$
    $18 - 9 = \underline{9}$

3. $\begin{array}{r} 6 \\ +6 \\ \hline 12 \end{array}$ $\begin{array}{r} 12 \\ -\ 6 \\ \hline 6 \end{array}$

4. $\begin{array}{r} 7 \\ +7 \\ \hline 14 \end{array}$ $\begin{array}{r} 14 \\ -\ 7 \\ \hline 7 \end{array}$

5. $\begin{array}{r} 5 \\ +8 \\ \hline 13 \end{array}$

Whole	
13	
Part	Part
●●●●	○○○○○ ○○○

    $\begin{array}{r} 13 \\ -\ 5 \\ \hline 8 \end{array}$ $\begin{array}{r} 13 \\ -\ 8 \\ \hline 5 \end{array}$

6. $\begin{array}{r} 6 \\ +9 \\ \hline 15 \end{array}$ $\begin{array}{r} 15 \\ -\ 6 \\ \hline 9 \end{array}$ $\begin{array}{r} 15 \\ -\ 9 \\ \hline 6 \end{array}$

7. $\begin{array}{r} 9 \\ +7 \\ \hline 16 \end{array}$ $\begin{array}{r} 16 \\ -\ 9 \\ \hline 7 \end{array}$ $\begin{array}{r} 16 \\ -\ 7 \\ \hline 9 \end{array}$

Math Challenge

Triangle Puzzle

In this triangle puzzle you get the same sum when you add the numbers along each side.

Fill in the missing numbers so the sum on each side is 9.

Quick Check

Have children complete the Quick Check exercises independently to assess their understanding of concepts and skills taught in **Lessons 1–3**.

Item	Lesson	Error Analysis	Intervention
1–4	20.1	Children may try to add both facts in a set of exercises.	Reteach Resource 20.1 *Ways to Success* 20.1
5	20.2	Children may subtract incorrectly.	Reteach Resource 20.2 *Ways to Success* 20.2
6–7	20.3	Children may try to add all the exercises in a set.	Reteach Resource 20.3 *Ways to Success* 20.3

Math Challenge

Triangle Puzzle

Suggest that children try different numbers before writing them in the circles. You may want to help children who are having difficulty by giving them one of the numbers, or allowing them to use counters. Be sure children know that the sum of each side needs to equal 9.

Children who are successful may want to make up their own triangle puzzles for other sums.

Subtract From 17 Through 20

PLANNING THE LESSON

MATHEMATICS OBJECTIVE

Subtract from 17 through 20 by relating addition to subtraction.

Use Lesson Planner CD-ROM for Lesson 20.4.

Meeting North Carolina's Standards

1.03 Develop fluency with single-digit addition and corresponding differences using strategies such as modeling, composing and decomposing quantities, using doubles, and making tens.

Daily Routines

Calendar

Ask children to pretend it is the tenth of the month and you want to find the number of days until the twentieth. Have volunteers share their methods for solving.

Sunday	Monday	Tuesday	Wednesday	Thursday	Friday	Saturday
				1	2	3	4
5	6	7	8	9	10	11
12	13	14	15	16	17	18
19	20	21	22	23	24	25
26	27	28	29	30	31	

Vocabulary

Review the number words for **one** through **ten** by writing an addition number sentence with words. Have children solve. Let children use the vocabulary cards to review the words.

Vocabulary Cards

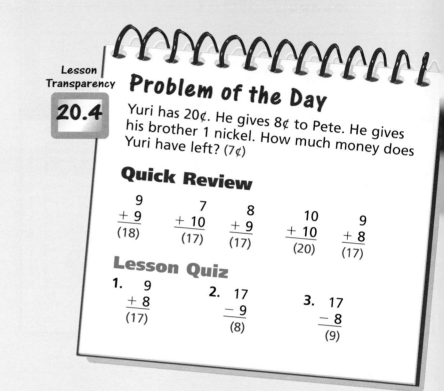

Lesson Transparency 20.4

Problem of the Day

Yuri has 20¢. He gives 8¢ to Pete. He gives his brother 1 nickel. How much money does Yuri have left? (7¢)

Quick Review

$$\begin{array}{r} 9 \\ +\ 9 \\ \hline (18) \end{array} \qquad \begin{array}{r} 7 \\ +\ 10 \\ \hline (17) \end{array} \qquad \begin{array}{r} 8 \\ +\ 9 \\ \hline (17) \end{array} \qquad \begin{array}{r} 10 \\ +\ 10 \\ \hline (20) \end{array} \qquad \begin{array}{r} 9 \\ +\ 8 \\ \hline (17) \end{array}$$

Lesson Quiz

$$\textbf{1.} \begin{array}{r} 9 \\ +\ 8 \\ \hline (17) \end{array} \qquad \textbf{2.} \begin{array}{r} 17 \\ -\ 9 \\ \hline (8) \end{array} \qquad \textbf{3.} \begin{array}{r} 17 \\ -\ 8 \\ \hline (9) \end{array}$$

LEVELED PRACTICE

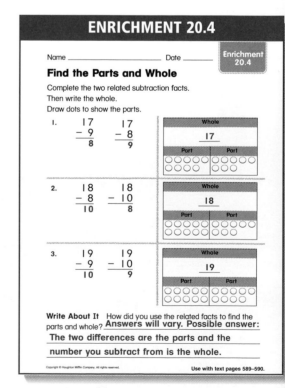

RETEACH 20.4

Name _____ Date _____

Reteach 20.4

Subtract from 17 Through 20

You can use a related addition fact to subtract.

$$\begin{array}{r} 10 \\ +\ 8 \\ \hline 18 \end{array}$$

Whole	
18	
Part	**Part**

$$\begin{array}{r} 18 \\ -\ 8 \\ \hline 10 \end{array} \qquad \begin{array}{r} 18 \\ -\ 10 \\ \hline 8 \end{array}$$

You can use 8 + 10 to find
18 − 8 and 18 − 10.

Add.
Then find the differences.

1.
$$\begin{array}{r} 8 \\ +\ 9 \\ \hline 17 \end{array}$$

Whole	
17	
Part	**Part**

$$\begin{array}{r} 17 \\ -\ 8 \\ \hline 9 \end{array} \qquad \begin{array}{r} 17 \\ -\ 9 \\ \hline 8 \end{array}$$

2.
$$\begin{array}{r} 10 \\ +\ 9 \\ \hline 19 \end{array}$$

Whole	
19	
Part	**Part**

$$\begin{array}{r} 19 \\ -\ 10 \\ \hline 9 \end{array} \qquad \begin{array}{r} 19 \\ -\ 9 \\ \hline 10 \end{array}$$

3. $\begin{array}{r} 17 \\ -\ 8 \\ \hline 9 \end{array}$ 4. $\begin{array}{r} 18 \\ -\ 9 \\ \hline 9 \end{array}$ 5. $\begin{array}{r} 20 \\ -\ 10 \\ \hline 10 \end{array}$ 6. $\begin{array}{r} 17 \\ -\ 10 \\ \hline 7 \end{array}$ 7. $\begin{array}{r} 19 \\ -\ 9 \\ \hline 10 \end{array}$

Use with text pages 589–590.

PRACTICE 20.4

Name _____ Date _____

Practice 20.4

Subtract From 17 Through 20

Subtract.

1. $\begin{array}{r} 17 \\ -\ 8 \\ \hline 9 \end{array}$ 2. $\begin{array}{r} 18 \\ -10 \\ \hline 8 \end{array}$ 3. $\begin{array}{r} 20 \\ -10 \\ \hline 10 \end{array}$ 4. $\begin{array}{r} 16 \\ -\ 7 \\ \hline 9 \end{array}$ 5. $\begin{array}{r} 15 \\ -\ 6 \\ \hline 9 \end{array}$

6. $\begin{array}{r} 17 \\ -\ 9 \\ \hline 8 \end{array}$ 7. $\begin{array}{r} 16 \\ -\ 9 \\ \hline 7 \end{array}$ 8. $\begin{array}{r} 16 \\ -\ 8 \\ \hline 8 \end{array}$ 9. $\begin{array}{r} 14 \\ -\ 6 \\ \hline 8 \end{array}$ 10. $\begin{array}{r} 15 \\ -\ 5 \\ \hline 10 \end{array}$

11. $\begin{array}{r} 15 \\ -\ 8 \\ \hline 7 \end{array}$ 12. $\begin{array}{r} 16 \\ -\ 6 \\ \hline 10 \end{array}$ 13. $\begin{array}{r} 13 \\ -\ 9 \\ \hline 4 \end{array}$ 14. $\begin{array}{r} 14 \\ -\ 9 \\ \hline 5 \end{array}$ 15. $\begin{array}{r} 17 \\ -\ 8 \\ \hline 9 \end{array}$

Test Prep

Fill in the ○ for the correct answer.
NH means Not Here.

16. Peter has 19 marbles.
He gives 9 marbles to Sarah.
Which sentence tells how many marbles Peter has now?

19 − 10 = 9   19 − 9 = 10   10 + 9 = 19   NH
○   ●   ○   ○

Use with text pages 589–590.

ENRICHMENT 20.4

Name _____ Date _____

Enrichment 20.4

Find the Parts and Whole

Complete the two related subtraction facts.
Then write the whole.
Draw dots to show the parts.

1. $\begin{array}{r} 17 \\ -\ 9 \\ \hline 8 \end{array} \quad \begin{array}{r} 17 \\ -\ 8 \\ \hline 9 \end{array}$

Whole	
17	
Part	**Part**

2. $\begin{array}{r} 18 \\ -\ 8 \\ \hline 10 \end{array} \quad \begin{array}{r} 18 \\ -10 \\ \hline 8 \end{array}$

Whole	
18	
Part	**Part**

3. $\begin{array}{r} 19 \\ -\ 9 \\ \hline 10 \end{array} \quad \begin{array}{r} 19 \\ -10 \\ \hline 9 \end{array}$

Whole	
19	
Part	**Part**

Write About It How did you use the related facts to find the parts and whole? Answers will vary. Possible answer: The two differences are the parts and the number you subtract from is the whole.

Use with text pages 589–590.

Practice Workbook Page 137

Reaching All Learners

Differentiated Instruction

English Learners

Worksheet 20.4 develops the concepts of *easy* and *hard*. Children will need to understand these concepts to understand the Explain Your Thinking question.

Special Needs
VISUAL, TACTILE

Materials: *counters*

- Help the child model $9 + 8$ with counters. Have the child add as you write the number sentence.
- Have the child take away 8 counters to model $17 - 8$ and find the difference.
- Continue modeling related addition and subtraction exercises.

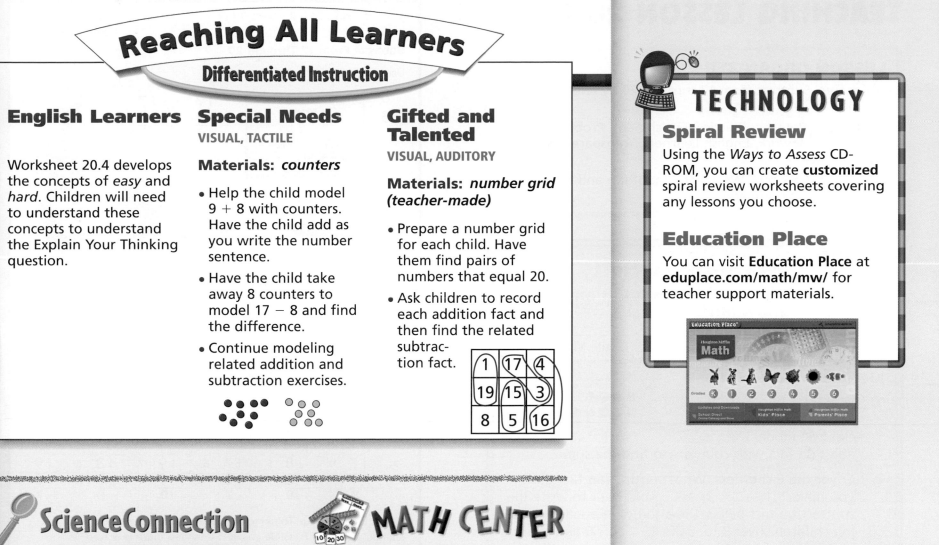

Gifted and Talented
VISUAL, AUDITORY

Materials: *number grid (teacher-made)*

- Prepare a number grid for each child. Have them find pairs of numbers that equal 20.
- Ask children to record each addition fact and then find the related subtraction fact.

TECHNOLOGY

Spiral Review

Using the *Ways to Assess* CD-ROM, you can create **customized** spiral review worksheets covering any lessons you choose.

Education Place

You can visit **Education Place** at **eduplace.com/math/mw/** for teacher support materials.

Science Connection

Explain that people have 20 baby teeth in all. Ask children how many baby teeth they have lost. Record the data in a chart. Have children write the subtraction to show the number of baby teeth they have left.

MATH CENTER

Basic Skills Activity

Motivate children to build basic skills. Use this activity to address multiple learning styles using hands-on activities related to the skills of this lesson.

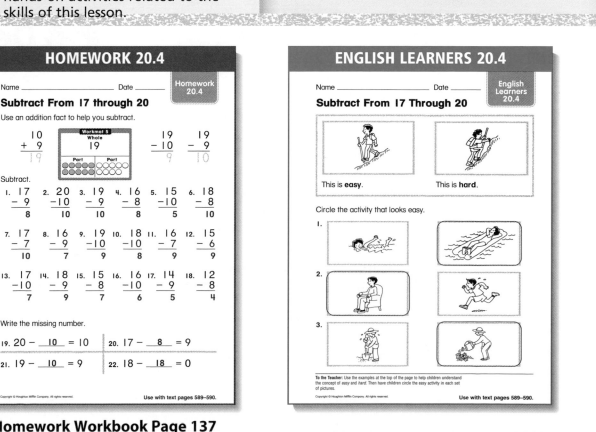

Homework Workbook Page 137

TEACHING LESSON 20.4

LESSON ORGANIZER

Objective Subtract from 17 through 20 by relating addition to subtraction.

Resources Reteach, Practice, Enrichment, Problem Solving, Homework, English Learners, Transparencies, Math Center

Materials Counters, Workmat 3, addition and subtraction cards (teacher-made)

Activity

Warm-Up Activity
Discuss Relating Addition and Subtraction

iii Small Group	⏱ 5 minutes	Tactile, Visual

Materials: *counters*

1. Write 9 + 6 in vertical form on the board. Have children model the addition fact with counters to find the sum.

$$\begin{array}{r} 9 \\ +6 \\ \hline 15 \end{array}$$

2. **Cover the 6 counters. What subtraction fact did you make?** (15 − 6 = 9) Ask a volunteer to write the subtraction fact below the addition. Repeat by having children cover 9 to make 15 − 9 = 6 and record.

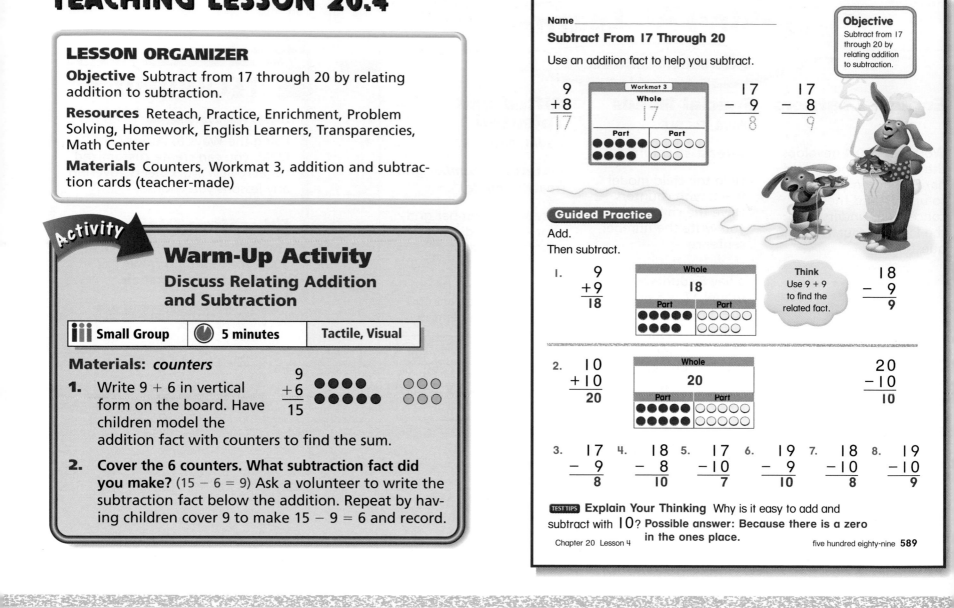

Name_____

Subtract From 17 Through 20

Use an addition fact to help you subtract.

$$\begin{array}{r} 9 \\ +8 \\ \hline 17 \end{array}$$

Workmat 3
Whole
17
| Part | Part |

$$\begin{array}{r} 17 \\ -\ 9 \\ \hline 8 \end{array} \qquad \begin{array}{r} 17 \\ -\ 8 \\ \hline 9 \end{array}$$

Guided Practice

Add.
Then subtract.

1.
$$\begin{array}{r} 9 \\ +9 \\ \hline 18 \end{array}$$

Whole
18
| Part | Part |

Think
Use 9 + 9 to find the related fact.

$$\begin{array}{r} 18 \\ -\ 9 \\ \hline 9 \end{array}$$

2.
$$\begin{array}{r} 10 \\ +10 \\ \hline 20 \end{array}$$

Whole
20
| Part | Part |

$$\begin{array}{r} 20 \\ -10 \\ \hline 10 \end{array}$$

3. $\begin{array}{r} 17 \\ -\ 9 \\ \hline 8 \end{array}$ 4. $\begin{array}{r} 18 \\ -\ 8 \\ \hline 10 \end{array}$ 5. $\begin{array}{r} 17 \\ -10 \\ \hline 7 \end{array}$ 6. $\begin{array}{r} 19 \\ -\ 9 \\ \hline 10 \end{array}$ 7. $\begin{array}{r} 18 \\ -10 \\ \hline 8 \end{array}$ 8. $\begin{array}{r} 19 \\ -10 \\ \hline 9 \end{array}$

TEST TIPS **Explain Your Thinking** Why is it easy to add and subtract with 10? **Possible answer: Because there is a zero in the ones place.**

Chapter 20 Lesson 4   five hundred eighty-nine **589**

---

1 Introduce   *Activity*

Model Subtraction by Relating It to Addition

iiii Whole Group	⏱ 10–15 minutes	Tactile, Visual

Materials: *counters, Workmat 3*

1. **I want to subtract 20 − 10. I know 10 + 10 = 20, so I can use this to subtract 20 − 10.** Show 10 + 10 on the part-part-whole mat. Write the addition on the board. **I have 20 and I need to subtract 10. What is the difference?** (10) Record the subtraction.

2. **Repeat with 18 − 9 and 17 − 7.** Have children follow along at their desks with counters on Workmat 3.

2 Develop

Guided Learning

Teaching Example

Read the objective with children. Guide them through the example as they use counters on Workmat 3.

Guided Practice

Have children complete **Exercises 1–8** as you observe. Give children the opportunity to share their answers to the Explain Your Thinking question.

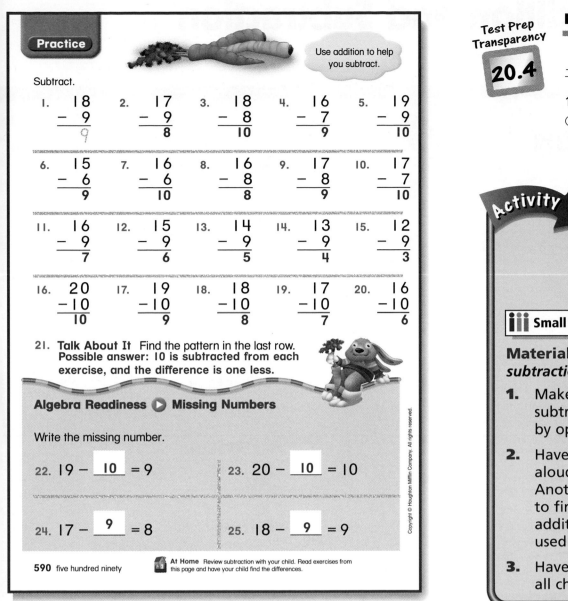

Use addition to help you subtract.

Subtract.

1.	2.	3.	4.	5.
18 − 9 9	17 − 9 8	18 − 8 10	16 − 7 9	19 − 9 10

6.	7.	8.	9.	10.
15 − 6 9	16 − 6 10	16 − 8 8	17 − 8 9	17 − 7 10

11.	12.	13.	14.	15.
16 − 9 7	15 − 9 6	14 − 9 5	13 − 9 4	12 − 9 3

16.	17.	18.	19.	20.
20 −10 10	19 −10 9	18 −10 8	17 −10 7	16 −10 6

21. **Talk About It** Find the pattern in the last row. Possible answer: 10 is subtracted from each exercise, and the difference is one less.

Algebra Readiness ▶ Missing Numbers

Write the missing number.

22. 19 − 10 = 9

23. 20 − 10 = 10

24. 17 − 9 = 8

25. 18 − 9 = 9

590 five hundred ninety

At Home Review subtraction with your child. Read exercises from this page and have your child find the differences.

Daily Test Prep

18
− 9

1   9   11   27
○   ●   ○   ○

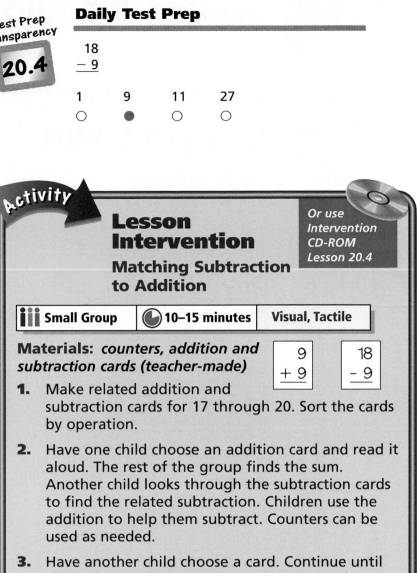

Activity

Lesson Intervention

Matching Subtraction to Addition

Or use Intervention CD-ROM Lesson 20.4

👥 Small Group	⏱ 10–15 minutes	Visual, Tactile

Materials: *counters, addition and subtraction cards (teacher-made)*

9
+ 9

18
− 9

1. Make related addition and subtraction cards for 17 through 20. Sort the cards by operation.

2. Have one child choose an addition card and read it aloud. The rest of the group finds the sum. Another child looks through the subtraction cards to find the related subtraction. Children use the addition to help them subtract. Counters can be used as needed.

3. Have another child choose a card. Continue until all children in the group have chosen a card.

---

❸ Practice

Independent Practice

Children complete **Exercises 1–20** independently. Use the **Talk About It** in **Exercise 21** to discuss the subtraction patterns in the row of exercises.

Algebra Readiness

After children complete **Exercises 22–25,** call on volunteers to share their answers. Record each number sentence on the board so children can check their work.

Common Error

Making a Subtraction Error

Children may make errors in subtracting. Remind them to use part-part-whole and the related addition to check their subtraction.

❹ Assess and Close

Subtract 9 from 17. What is the difference? (8)

What addition fact can help you subtract 18 − 9? (9 + 9 =18) **What is the difference?** (9)

✎ Keeping a Journal

Draw a picture to show 20 − 10. Write a related addition fact.

Relate Addition and Subtraction

PLANNING THE LESSON

MATHEMATICS OBJECTIVE
Find missing addends by relating addition and subtraction.

Use Lesson Planner CD-ROM for Lesson 20.5.

Meeting North Carolina's Standards

1.03 Develop fluency with single-digit addition and corresponding differences using strategies such as modeling, composing and decomposing quantities, using doubles, and making tens.

Also 1.04

Daily Routines

Calendar

Lead children in reciting the 12 months of the year in order. Show that September is the ninth month. Then use the calendar to find the number of months between September and the end of the year.

Sunday	Monday	Tuesday	Wednesday	Thursday	Friday	Saturday
			1	2	3	4
5	6	7	8	9	10	11
12	13	14	15	16	17	18
19	20	21	22	23	24	25
26	27	28	29	30	31	

Vocabulary

Review **addend** by writing addition facts on the board and having children idenify the addends in each. Write 7 + ___ = 10 and review missing addends.

Vocabulary Cards

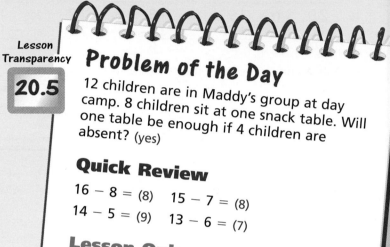

Lesson Transparency **20.5**

Problem of the Day
12 children are in Maddy's group at day camp. 8 children sit at one snack table. Will one table be enough if 4 children are absent? (yes)

Quick Review
$16 - 8 =$ (8) $15 - 7 =$ (8)
$14 - 5 =$ (9) $13 - 6 =$ (7)

Lesson Quiz
Find the missing number.
1. $12 - 8 = 4$, $8 + $ ___ $= 12$ (4)
2. $15 - 9 = 6$, $9 + $ ___ $= 15$ (6)
3. $18 - 9 = 9$, $9 + $ ___ $= 18$ (9)

LEVELED PRACTICE

RETEACH 20.5

Name _____ Date _____ Reteach 20.5

Relate Addition and Subtraction

Use related addition facts to help you subtract.

Find $13 - 5$.

Think 5 plus what number equals 13?

$5 + \underline{8} = 13$

So, $13 - 5 = \underline{8}$

Remember: Related facts all have the same parts and wholes. Think about the parts that equal 13.

Whole
13
Part | Part

Write the missing numbers.

1. $14 - 7 = \underline{7}$
   $7 + \underline{7} = 14$
2. $13 - 8 = \underline{5}$
   $8 + \underline{5} = 13$
3. $12 - 4 = \underline{8}$
   $4 + \underline{8} = 12$
4. $17 - 9 = \underline{8}$
   $9 + \underline{8} = 17$
5. $15 - 6 = \underline{9}$
   $6 + \underline{9} = 15$
6. $16 - 9 = \underline{7}$
   $9 + \underline{7} = 16$

Use with text pages 591–592.

PRACTICE 20.5

Name _____ Date _____ Practice 20.5

Relate Addition and Subtraction

Write the missing numbers.

1. $13 - 8 = \underline{5}$
   $8 + \underline{5} = 13$
2. $12 - 7 = \underline{5}$
   $7 + \underline{5} = 12$
3. $20 - 10 = \underline{10}$
   $10 + \underline{10} = 20$
4. $16 - 8 = \underline{8}$
   $8 + \underline{8} = 16$
5. $14 - 8 = \underline{6}$
   $8 + \underline{6} = 14$
6. $17 - 8 = \underline{9}$
   $8 + \underline{9} = 17$
7. $18 - 9 = \underline{9}$
   $9 + \underline{9} = 18$
8. $13 - 6 = \underline{7}$
   $6 + \underline{7} = 13$

Test Prep

Fill in the ○ for the correct answer.
NH means Not Here.

13. What number do you need to complete the addition and the subtraction sentences?

$8 + $ ___ $= 14$ $14 - 8 = $ ___

6   8   14   NH
○   ●   ○   ○

Use with text pages 591–592.

ENRICHMENT 20.5

Name _____ Date _____ Enrichment 20.5

How Many More?

Draw as many more as needed, or draw a line through those that are not needed. Then write the related fact.

1. Steven wants 16 ☆.
   He needs $\underline{7}$ more.
   $9 \; (+) \; 7 \; = \; 16$

2. Maria wants 16 🌙.
   She needs $\underline{8}$ more.
   $8 \; (+) \; 8 \; = \; 16$

3. Rod has 17 🌐.
   He gives away 9.
   $17 \; (-) \; 9 \; = \; 8$

Write About It Write a subtraction story to match $20 - 10$. Solve. Write the related addition fact.
Stories will vary. Example: There are 20 children. 10 like grilled cheese. How many do not? 10 children do not. $10 + 10 = 20$.

Use with text pages 591–592.

Practice Workbook Page 138

Reaching All Learners
Differentiated Instruction

English Learners

Children will need to understand the words *outside* and *inside* in order to solve some word problems. Use Worksheet 20.5 to help children develop understanding of these words.

Inclusion
TACTILE, VISUAL

Materials: *cubes*

- Have the child make a 13-cube train. Snap off 9 cubes. Have the child count how many are left and record the subtraction. $(13 - 9 = 4)$
- Write $9 + \_\_\_ = 13$. Guide the child to see that he or she can use the subtraction fact to find the missing addend. $(9 + 4 = 13)$
- Repeat with similar pairs of exercises.

Gifted and Talented
VISUAL, AUDITORY

Materials: *index cards*

- Have children work in pairs. Have each child write a different subtraction fact, without the difference, on 5 cards.
- Have children exchange cards and write a related missing addend fact on the card.
- Children exchange cards again and solve.

TECHNOLOGY

Spiral Review

To reinforce skills on lessons taught earlier, create **customized** spiral review worksheets using the *Ways to Assess* CD-ROM.

Lesson Planner

Use the **Lesson Planner CD-ROM** to see how lesson objectives for this chapter are correlated to standards.

eBook

An electronic version of this lesson can be found in **eMathBook**.

Music Connection

Play a song tape as children dance. Explain that when the music stops, children need to freeze. Each time count how many children did not stop. Write a subtraction sentence to show the number of children left.

MATH CENTER

Real Life Activity

Help children understand the usefulness of mathematics. This activity makes math come alive by connecting the lesson skills to a real-life situation.

PROBLEM SOLVING 20.5

Name _____ Date _____   Problem Solving 20.5

Relate Addition and Subtraction

Write the missing numbers.

1. Riley has 12 eggs. He uses 9 eggs to make custard. How many eggs does he have left?

   ___3___ eggs

   Draw or write to explain.

   $12 - 9 = \underline{3}$
   $9 + \underline{3} = 12$

2. Katie has 15 roses. She put 8 roses in a vase. How many roses are not in the vase?

   ___7___ roses

   $15 - 8 = 7$
   $8 + \underline{7} = 15$

3. Art writes 13 stories. He draws pictures for 4 stories. How many stories do not have pictures?

   ___9___ stories

   $13 - 4 = 9$
   $\underline{9} + 4 = 13$

Copyright © Houghton Mifflin Company. All rights reserved.

Use with text pages 591–592.

HOMEWORK 20.5

Name _____ Date _____   Homework 20.5

Relate Addition and Subtraction

Find $15 - 9$.

Think What number can I add to 9 to get 15?

$9 + \underline{6} = 15$

So, $15 - 9 = \underline{6}$

Write the missing numbers.

1. $13 - 4 = \underline{9}$
   $4 + \underline{9} = 13$

2. $16 - 7 = \underline{9}$
   $7 + \underline{9} = 16$

3. $15 - 8 = \underline{7}$
   $8 + \underline{7} = 15$

4. $14 - 8 = \underline{6}$
   $8 + \underline{6} = 14$

5. $16 - 8 = \underline{8}$
   $8 + \underline{8} = 16$

6. $17 - 8 = \underline{9}$
   $8 + \underline{9} = 17$

7. $16 - 9 = \underline{7}$
   $9 + \underline{7} = 16$

8. $17 - 9 = \underline{8}$
   $9 + \underline{8} = 17$

9. $18 - 9 = \underline{9}$
   $9 + \underline{9} = 18$

Solve.

10. Lin needs to find $13 - 8$. What addition fact can help him?

    Draw or write to explain.
    Check children's drawings.

    $\underline{8} + \underline{5} = 13$

Copyright © Houghton Mifflin Company. All rights reserved.

Use with text pages 591–592.

ENGLISH LEARNERS 20.5

Name _____ Date _____   English Learners 20.5

Relate Addition and Subtraction

outside   inside

Circle the correct words.

1. The hamster is **outside** (**inside**) the cage.

2. The bike is (**outside**) **inside** the shed.

3. The toy is (**outside**) **inside** the box.

4. The dog is **outside** (**inside**) the doghouse.

To the Teacher: Use the examples at the top of the page to demonstrate the meaning of the words *outside* and *inside*. Then read the sentences with children and have them circle the correct words.

Copyright © Houghton Mifflin Company. All rights reserved.

Use with text pages 591–592.

Homework Workbook Page 138

CHAPTER 20   Lesson 5   **591B**

TEACHING LESSON 20.5

LESSON ORGANIZER

Objective Find missing addends by relating addition and subtraction.

Resources Reteach, Practice, Enrichment, Problem Solving, Homework, English Learners, Transparencies, Math Center

Materials Number line 0–12 (LT 8), cubes, dot cards (LT 17)

Activity

Warm-Up Activity
Finding Missing Addends

👥 Small Group	⏱ 5 minutes	Visual, Auditory

Materials: *number line 0–12*

1. Display the number line. **Look at the number line. Count on from 9 to see how many you need to count on to get to 12. Say 9. Count: 10, 11, 12. How many did you count?** (3) Complete the addition. **Does 9 + 3 = 12?** (yes)
   Write 9 + ___ = 12 on the board.

2. Repeat with other missing addends for sums 10 to 12. Have children use the number line to count on and solve.

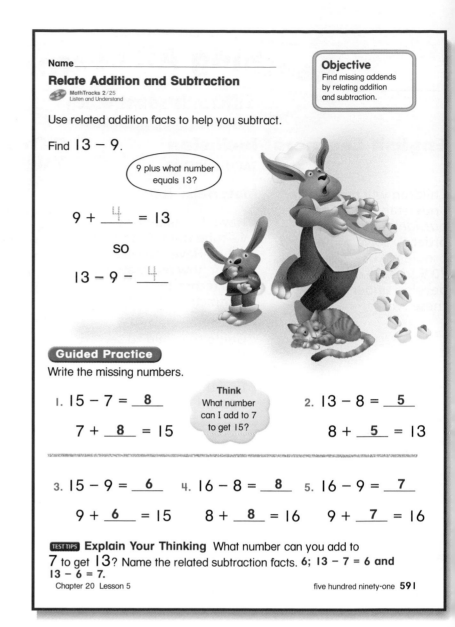

Name_____

Relate Addition and Subtraction

🔵 MathTracks 2/25
Listen and Understand

Objective
Find missing addends by relating addition and subtraction.

Use related addition facts to help you subtract.

Find 13 − 9.

9 plus what number equals 13?

$$9 + \underline{4} = 13$$

SO

$$13 - 9 - \underline{4}$$

Guided Practice

Write the missing numbers.

1. $15 - 7 = \underline{8}$
   $7 + \underline{8} = 15$

   Think What number can I add to 7 to get 15?

2. $13 - 8 = \underline{5}$
   $8 + \underline{5} = 13$

3. $15 - 9 = \underline{6}$
   $9 + \underline{6} = 15$

4. $16 - 8 = \underline{8}$
   $8 + \underline{8} = 16$

5. $16 - 9 = \underline{7}$
   $9 + \underline{7} = 16$

TEST TIPS **Explain Your Thinking** What number can you add to 7 to get 13? Name the related subtraction facts. **6; 13 − 7 = 6 and 13 − 6 = 7.**

Chapter 20 Lesson 5   five hundred ninety-one **591**

---

1 Introduce

Model Relating Addition and Subtraction

👥 Whole Group	⏱ 10–15 minutes	Tactile, Visual

Materials: *cubes*

1. Write 6 + ___ = 14 on the board. **You can use subtraction to find the missing addend.** Write 14 − 6 = ___ on the board.

2. Display a 14-cube train. Snap off 6 cubes. **How many cubes are left?** (8) Write the difference. **Look at the addition. If 14 − 6 = 8, what is the missing addend?** (8)

3. Repeat with cube trains for sums 13 to 18. Have children follow along at their seats. Ask volunteers to record the addition and subtraction.

2 Develop

Guided Learning

Teaching Example

Read the objective with children. Guide them through the example, emphasizing the use of related facts to help them find the difference and the missing addend.

Guided Practice

Have children complete **Exercises 1–5** as you observe. Give children the opportunity to share their answers to the Explain Your Thinking question. Record the number sentences on the board.

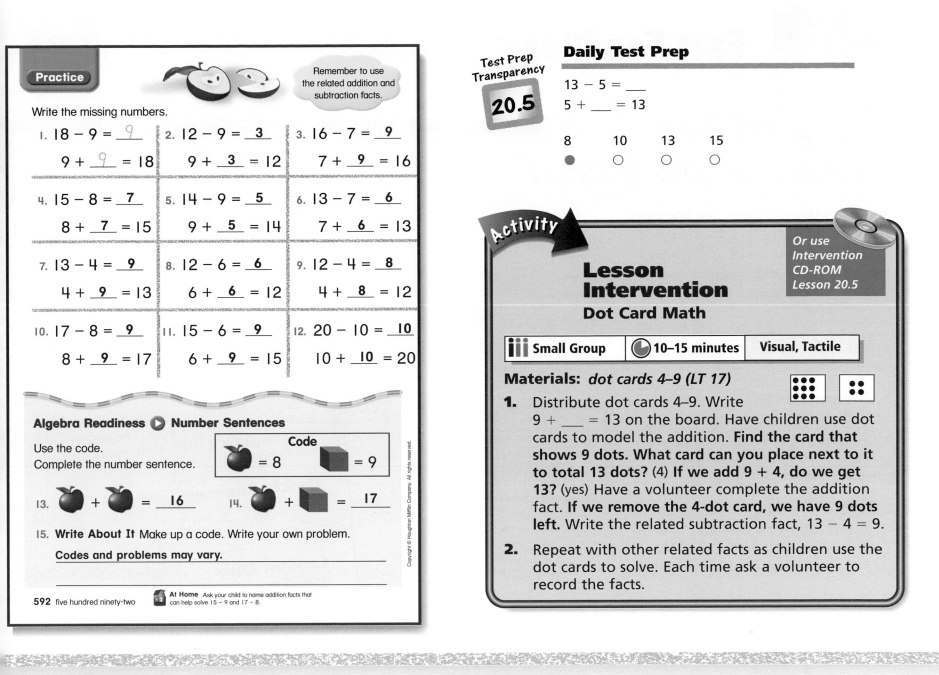

Practice

Remember to use the related addition and subtraction facts.

Write the missing numbers.

1. $18 - 9 = \underline{9}$
   $9 + \underline{9} = 18$

2. $12 - 9 = \underline{3}$
   $9 + \underline{3} = 12$

3. $16 - 7 = \underline{9}$
   $7 + \underline{9} = 16$

4. $15 - 8 = \underline{7}$
   $8 + \underline{7} = 15$

5. $14 - 9 = \underline{5}$
   $9 + \underline{5} = 14$

6. $13 - 7 = \underline{6}$
   $7 + \underline{6} = 13$

7. $13 - 4 = \underline{9}$
   $4 + \underline{9} = 13$

8. $12 - 6 = \underline{6}$
   $6 + \underline{6} = 12$

9. $12 - 4 = \underline{8}$
   $4 + \underline{8} = 12$

10. $17 - 8 = \underline{9}$
    $8 + \underline{9} = 17$

11. $15 - 6 = \underline{9}$
    $6 + \underline{9} = 15$

12. $20 - 10 = \underline{10}$
    $10 + \underline{10} = 20$

Algebra Readiness ▶ Number Sentences

Use the code.
Complete the number sentence.

Code
🍎 = 8   ◼ = 9

13. 🍎 + 🍎 = $\underline{16}$

14. 🍎 + ◼ = $\underline{17}$

15. **Write About It** Make up a code. Write your own problem.

Codes and problems may vary.

At Home Ask your child to name addition facts that can help solve $15 - 9$ and $17 - 8$.

Daily Test Prep

Test Prep Transparency

20.5

$13 - 5 = \underline{}$
$5 + \underline{} = 13$

8 ●   10 ○   13 ○   15 ○

Activity

Lesson Intervention
Dot Card Math

Or use Intervention CD-ROM Lesson 20.5

👥 Small Group	⏱ 10–15 minutes	Visual, Tactile

Materials: *dot cards 4–9 (LT 17)*

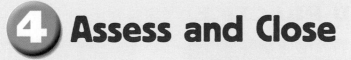

1. Distribute dot cards 4–9. Write $9 + \underline{} = 13$ on the board. Have children use dot cards to model the addition. **Find the card that shows 9 dots. What card can you place next to it to total 13 dots?** (4) **If we add 9 + 4, do we get 13?** (yes) Have a volunteer complete the addition fact. **If we remove the 4-dot card, we have 9 dots left.** Write the related subtraction fact, $13 - 4 = 9$.

2. Repeat with other related facts as children use the dot cards to solve. Each time ask a volunteer to record the facts.

---

③ Practice

Independent Practice

Children complete **Exercises 1–12** independently.

Algebra Readiness

After children complete **Exercises 13–14,** call on volunteers to share their answers. Allow children to discuss their responses to the **Write About It** question in **Exercise 15.**

Common Error

Using Incorrect Numbers
Remind children that the three numbers in each pair of related facts must be the same.

④ Assess and Close

What is 13 − 7? (6) **How can knowing this help you find the missing addend in 7 + ___ = 13?** (The facts have the same whole and one part, so the missing number is the same as the difference.)

How do you know if an addition and subtraction fact are related? (They have the same parts and the same whole; they have the same three numbers.)

✏ Keeping a Journal

Write a pair of related addition and subtraction facts.

Fact Families

PLANNING THE LESSON

MATHEMATICS OBJECTIVE
Use the inverse relationship between addition and subtraction to make a fact family.

Use Lesson Planner CD-ROM for Lesson 20.6.

Daily Routines

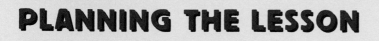

Calendar
Discuss today's date with the children. Ask what date is one week from today's date. Ask what date was one week ago.

Sunday	Monday	Tuesday	Wednesday	Thursday	Friday	Saturday
			1	2	3	4
5	6	7	8	9	10	11
12	13	14	15	16	17	18
19	20	21	22	23	24	25
26	27	28	29	30	31	

Vocabulary
Review the terms **addition fact** and **subtraction fact**. Also review the terms **related facts** and **fact family**.

Vocabulary Cards

Meeting North Carolina's Standards
1.03 Develop fluency with single-digit addition and corresponding differences using strategies such as modeling, composing and decomposing quantities, using doubles, and making tens.

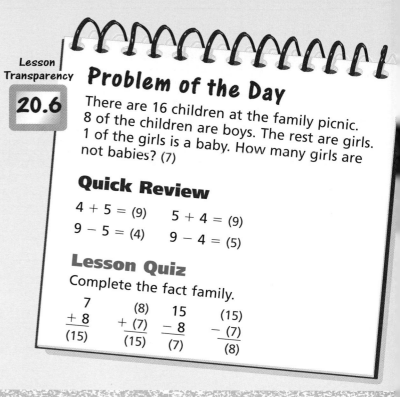

Lesson Transparency
20.6

Problem of the Day
There are 16 children at the family picnic. 8 of the children are boys. The rest are girls. 1 of the girls is a baby. How many girls are not babies? (7)

Quick Review
$4 + 5 = (9)$ $5 + 4 = (9)$
$9 - 5 = (4)$ $9 - 4 = (5)$

Lesson Quiz
Complete the fact family.

$$\begin{array}{cccc} 7 & (8) & 15 & (15) \\ + 8 & + (7) & - 8 & - (7) \\ \hline (15) & (15) & (7) & (8) \end{array}$$

LEVELED PRACTICE

RETEACH 20.6

Name _____ Date _____   Reteach 20.6

Fact Families

You use related facts to make a fact family. The facts in a fact family all have the same parts and wholes.

These four related facts make a fact family.

14		8	6	14	14
8	6	+ 6	+ 8	− 8	− 6
		14	14	6	8

Complete the fact family.

1.
16		7	9	16	16
7	9	+ 9	+ 7	− 7	− 9
		16	16	9	7

2.
13		5	8	13	13
5	8	+ 8	+ 5	− 5	− 8
		13	13	8	5

Copyright © Houghton Mifflin Company. All rights reserved.   Use with text pages 593–594.

PRACTICE 20.6

Name _____ Date _____   Practice 20.6

Fact Families

Complete the fact family.

1.
15		8	7	15	15
8	7	+ 7	+ 8	− 7	− 8
		15	15	8	7

2.
12		7	5	12	12
7	5	+ 5	+ 7	− 7	− 5
		12	12	5	7

Test Prep

Fill in the ○ for the correct answer.
NH means Not Here.
3. Which number sentence completes the fact family?

$8 + 7 = 15$ $15 - 7 = 8$ $15 - 8 = 7$
$7 + 6 = 14$ $6 + 9 = 15$ $9 + 6 = 15$ NH
   ○   ○   ○   ●

Copyright © Houghton Mifflin Company. All rights reserved.   Use with text pages 593–594.

ENRICHMENT 20.6

Name _____ Date _____   Enrichment 20.6

Fact Family Patterns

Complete the fact family.
Then use only the shapes not the numbers, to complete the fact family.

1.
Whole 12	
Part 7	Part 5

7	5	12	12
+ 5	+ 7	− 5	− 7
12	12	7	5

2.
(shapes: ○ □ △)

Write About It What pattern do you see? <u>Answers will vary. Possible answer: The same numbers or shapes are used in each exercise in a fact family.</u>

Copyright © Houghton Mifflin Company. All rights reserved.   Use with text pages 593–594.

Practice Workbook Page 139

Reaching All Learners

Differentiated Instruction

English Learners

Children will need to understand the concept of a *code* in order to solve some word problems. Use Worksheet 20.6 to build familiarity with this concept.

Special Needs
VISUAL, TACTILE

Materials: *cubes*

- Write 4 facts in a fact family. Have the child use a two-color cube train to model the facts.
- Now write 2 facts in a fact family. Have the child complete the fact family by finding the remaining 2 related facts with cubes.

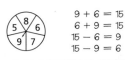

7 + 6 = 13

6 + 7 = 13

Early Finishers
VISUAL, AUDITORY

Materials: *spinner 5-9 (LT 38)*

- Have children work in pairs taking turns.
- Have one child spin the spinner two times. He or she uses the numbers to write two addition facts. Then have the partner write the related subtraction facts.

9 + 6 = 15
6 + 9 = 15
15 − 6 = 9
15 − 9 = 6

TECHNOLOGY

Spiral Review

Help students remember skills they learned earlier by creating **customized** spiral review worksheets using the *Ways to Assess* CD-ROM.

Education Place

Recommend that parents visit **Education Place** at **eduplace.com/parents/mw/** for parent support activities

Games

Students can practice their computational skills using the **Find a Friend** game on the *Ways to Success* CD-ROM.

Art Connection

Prepare fact family cards. Each child in a group of 4 chooses 1 of the 4 facts to illustrate on a card. Mix the completed cards and redistribute. Children find the other members of their fact family. Reshuffle cards and repeat.

MATH CENTER

Basic Skills Activity

Motivate children to build basic skills. Use this activity to address multiple learning styles using hands-on activities related to the skills of this lesson.

PROBLEM SOLVING 20.6

Name _____ Date _____ Problem Solving 20.6

Fact Families

Write fact families to solve. Draw or write to explain.

1. Lia sees 14 ladybugs. She sees 8 ladybugs in the trees. She sees 6 ladybugs in fallen logs.

   8 + 6 = __14__

   __6__ + __8__ = __14__

   Complete the fact family for the number of ladybugs Lia sees.

   14 − 8 = __6__

   __14__ − __6__ = __8__

2. Charles has 16 sports cards. He has 9 baseball cards and 7 football cards.

   9 + 7 = __16__

   __7__ + __9__ = __16__

   Complete the fact family for the number of sports cards Charles has.

   16 − 9 = __7__

   __16__ − __7__ = __9__

Copyright © Houghton Mifflin Company. All rights reserved. **Use with text pages 593–594.**

HOMEWORK 20.6

Name _____ Date _____ Homework 20.6

Fact Families

The 4 related facts make a fact family.

16
9 7

9 + 7 = 16
7 + 9 = 16
16 − 9 = 7
16 − 7 = 9

Complete the fact family.

1.
13
8 5

8 + 5 = 13
5 + 8 = 13
13 − 8 = 5
13 − 5 = 8

2.
15
9 6

9 + 6 = 15
6 + 9 = 15
15 − 9 = 6
15 − 6 = 9

3. Color the △ green. △△△△△
   Color the ○ red. ○○○○○
   Write a fact family to tell about the shapes.

   __6__ + __5__ = __11__   __11__ − __6__ = __5__

   __5__ + __6__ = __11__   __11__ − __5__ = __6__

Copyright © Houghton Mifflin Company. All rights reserved. **Use with text pages 593–594.**

Homework Workbook Page 139

ENGLISH LEARNERS 20.6

Name _____ Date _____ English Learners 20.6

Fact Families

■ =

This is a **code**.
The ■ stands for a horse.

■ = horse   ◆ = cow   ▲ = goat   ● = pig

Use the code to figure out the missing words.

1. The ◆ is in the barn.

   The __cow__ is in the barn.

2. The ▲ rests in the shade.

   The __goat__ rests in the shade.

3. The ● rolls in the mud.

   The __pig__ rolls in the mud.

4. The ■ drinks water.

   The __horse__ drinks water.

To the Teacher: Use the example at the top of the page to demonstrate the concept of a code. Then read the sentences with children and have them use the code to find and write the missing words.

Copyright © Houghton Mifflin Company. All rights reserved. **Use with text pages 593–594.**

TEACHING LESSON 20.6

LESSON ORGANIZER

Objective Use the inverse relationship between addition and subtraction to make a fact family.

Resources Reteach, Practice, Enrichment, Problem Solving, Homework, English Learners, Transparencies, Math Center

Materials Workmat 3, two-color counters, cubes, paper cup

Activity

Warm-Up Activity
Modeling Related Addition Facts

iiii Small Group	⏱ 5 minutes	Visual, Auditory

Materials: *Workmat 3, two-color counters*

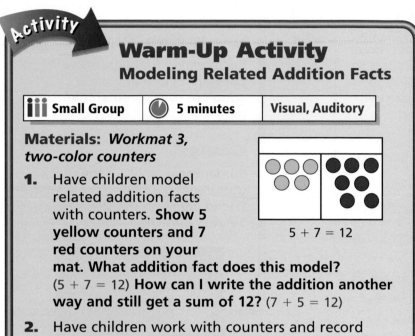

$5 + 7 = 12$

1. Have children model related addition facts with counters. **Show 5 yellow counters and 7 red counters on your mat. What addition fact does this model?** ($5 + 7 = 12$) **How can I write the addition another way and still get a sum of 12?** ($7 + 5 = 12$)

2. Have children work with counters and record other related addition facts.

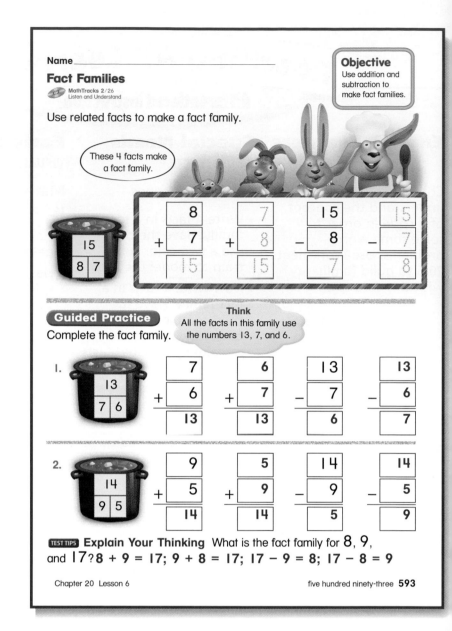

Fact Families

MathTracks 2/26
Listen and Understand

Objective Use addition and subtraction to make fact families.

Use related facts to make a fact family.

These 4 facts make a fact family.

8	7	15	15
$+ 7$	$+ 8$	$- 8$	$- 7$
15	15	7	8

Guided Practice
Complete the fact family.

Think All the facts in this family use the numbers 13, 7, and 6.

1.
7	6	13	13
$+ 6$	$+ 7$	$- 7$	$- 6$
13	13	6	7

2.
9	5	14	14
$+ 5$	$+ 9$	$- 9$	$- 5$
14	14	5	9

TEST TIPS **Explain Your Thinking** What is the fact family for 8, 9, and 17? $8 + 9 = 17$; $9 + 8 = 17$; $17 - 9 = 8$; $17 - 8 = 9$

Chapter 20 Lesson 6   five hundred ninety-three **593**

---

1 Introduce
Model Fact Families

iiii Whole Group	⏱ 10–15 minutes	Tactile, Visual

Materials: *cubes*

1. Combine a red 8-cube train with a blue 5-cube train. **Add 8 and 5. How many in all?** (13) Write the addition fact $8 + 5 = 13$. **If I turn the train to show 5 blues and 8 reds, how can we write this addition fact?** ($5 + 8 = 13$)

2. **Now I take the 13 and snap off 5 blue cubes. How many are left?** (8 red cubes) Write the subtraction, then rejoin the 5-cube train. **If I snap off the 8 red cubes, how many are left?** (5 blue cubes) Write the subtraction.

3. Show how the 4 facts are related by identifying the parts and whole in each. Explain that these 4 facts are a fact family.

4. Repeat with the fact family for 4 and 9.

2 Develop

Guided Learning

Teaching Example

Read the objective with the children. Guide them through the example by having them trace the numbers to complete the fact family.

Guided Practice

Have children complete **Exercises 1–2** as you observe.

Record children's responses to the Explain Your Thinking question. Let volunteers explain how they know it is a fact family.

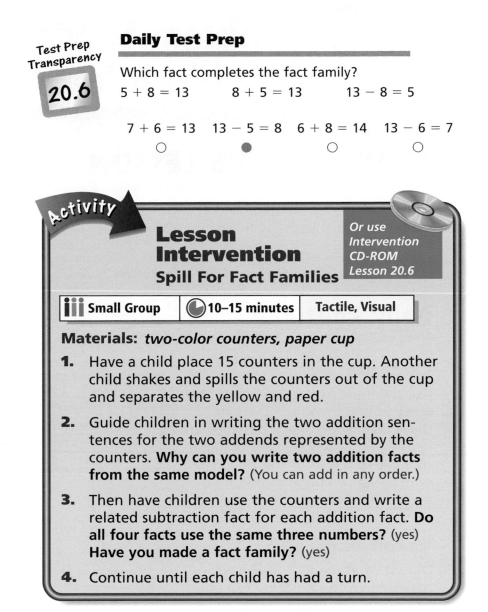

Practice

Remember that each fact family has the same numbers.

Complete the fact family.

1.
17
9 8

9	8	17	17
+ 8	+ 9	− 9	− 8
17	17	8	9

2.
13
8 5

8	5	13	13
+ 5	+ 8	− 8	− 5
13	13	5	8

3.
14
8 6

8	6	14	14
+ 6	+ 8	− 8	− 6
14	14	6	8

Problem Solving ▶ Visual Thinking

4. Find the numbers that are outside the circle but inside the square. Use them to write a fact family.

9 10 8
5   3   9
14 7 17

$8 + 9 = 17$

$9 + 8 = 17$

$17 − 9 = 8$

$17 − 8 = 9$

594 five hundred ninety-four

At Home Ask your child to write a fact family using the numbers 13, 9, and 4.

Daily Test Prep

Test Prep Transparency

20.6

Which fact completes the fact family?

$5 + 8 = 13$ $8 + 5 = 13$ $13 − 8 = 5$

$7 + 6 = 13$	$13 − 5 = 8$	$6 + 8 = 14$	$13 − 6 = 7$
○	●	○	○

Activity

Lesson Intervention

Or use Intervention CD-ROM Lesson 20.6

Spill For Fact Families

👤👤👤 Small Group	🕐 10–15 minutes	Tactile, Visual

Materials: *two-color counters, paper cup*

1. Have a child place 15 counters in the cup. Another child shakes and spills the counters out of the cup and separates the yellow and red.

2. Guide children in writing the two addition sentences for the two addends represented by the counters. **Why can you write two addition facts from the same model?** (You can add in any order.)

3. Then have children use the counters and write a related subtraction fact for each addition fact. **Do all four facts use the same three numbers?** (yes) **Have you made a fact family?** (yes)

4. Continue until each child has had a turn.

---

3 Practice

Independent Practice

Children complete **Exercises 1–3** independently.

Problem Solving

After children complete **Exercise 4,** write the fact family for 8, 9, 17 on the board so children can check their work.

Common Error

Writing Unrelated Addition or Subtraction Facts

Children may not write the related addition or subtraction fact for the one given. Remind children that the addition or subtraction fact they create should use the same numbers as those in the given fact.

4 Assess and Close

How many facts are in most fact families? (4) **How many are addition facts?** (2) **If you know that 9 + 8 = 17 is one fact in a family, what is the other addition fact?** (8 + 9 = 17)

Why are there only 2 facts in the fact family that include 7 + 7 = 14? (Because it is a doubles fact. There is only 1 addition and 1 subtraction fact.)

Keeping a Journal

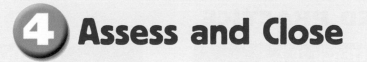

Write a fact family for the numbers 12, 3, and 9.

Problem Solving: Too Much Information

PLANNING THE LESSON

MATHEMATICS OBJECTIVE
Solve problems with too much information.

Use Lesson Planner CD-ROM for Lesson 20.7.

Daily Routines

Calendar
Ask children to guess the day of the week of which you are thinking. Give three clues, only 2 of which are helpful. For example, I am thinking of a day that is after the 29th. The date is an even number and is not my birthday. Discuss which clue was extra information.

Sunday	Monday	Tuesday	Wednesday	Thursday	Friday	Saturday
			1	2	3	4
5	6	7	8	9	10	11
12	13	14	15	16	17	18
19	20	21	22	23	24	25
26	27	28	29	30	31	

Vocabulary
Discuss what the word **subtract** means. Be sure to include examples of everyday situations when you subtract to compare. Ask volunteers to tell about times when they subtract.

Vocabulary Cards

Meeting North Carolina's Standards
1.04 Create, model, and solve problems that use addition, subtraction, and fair shares (between two or three).
Also 1.03

Lesson Transparency **20.7**

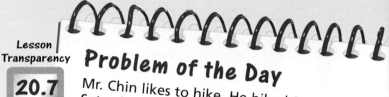

Problem of the Day
Mr. Chin likes to hike. He hiked 9 miles on Saturday and 15 miles on Sunday. How many more miles did Mr. Chin hike on Sunday than Saturday? (6 miles)

Quick Review

$7 + 6 =$ ___ (13) $6 + 7 =$ ___ (13)

$13 - 6 =$ ___ (7) $13 - 7 =$ ___ (6)

Lesson Quiz
Cross out information you do not need.

16 ants are on the wall. ~~There are 2 kinds of ants.~~ 8 ants crawl away. How many ants are on the wall now? (8 ants)

LEVELED PRACTICE

RETEACH 20.7

Name _____ Date _____

Reteach 20.7

Too Much Information

Read It Look for information.

Megan has 8 postcards.
4 of the postcards have pictures of animals.
She gets 6 more postcards.
How many postcards does she have now?

Organize It Decide what information you need.

Read the question again.
Then circle the information you need in the problem.

Which numbers should you use?

__8__ and __6__

Solve It Use the information to solve the problem.

__14__ postcards now	
8 postcards	6 more postcards

Think
Do I add or subtract?

1. Use the numbers to write a number sentence.

$8 (+) 6 = 14$

2. How many postcards does Megan have now?

__14__ postcards

Copyright © Houghton Mifflin Company. All rights reserved.   Use with text pages 595–596.

PRACTICE 20.7

Name _____ Date _____

Practice 20.7

Problem Solving
Too Much Information

Cross out the information you do not need. Solve.

Draw or write to explain.
Check children's drawings.

1. Ted sees 17 goats in a barn. ~~There are 8 black and 9 brown goats.~~ 10 goats leave the barn. How many goats are in the barn now?

__7__ goats

2. Reva finds 12 big stones. Evan finds 8 small stones. ~~Reva says 5 of her stones are red.~~ How many more stones did Reva find than Evan?

__4__ stones

Test Prep

Fill in the ○ for the correct answer.
NH means Not Here.

3. Bob bought 19 goldfish. 10 are orange. The rest are black. 15 are male. How many goldfish are black?

Which information is not needed?

○ 10 goldfish are orange.   ● 15 goldfish are male.

○ Bob bought 19 goldfish.   ○ NH

Copyright © Houghton Mifflin Company. All rights reserved.   Use with text pages 595–596.

ENRICHMENT 20.7

Name _____ Date _____

Enrichment 20.7

Create Stories

Read the story problem. Use the picture. Put the correct numbers in the problem. Cross out the information you do not need. Subtract to solve.

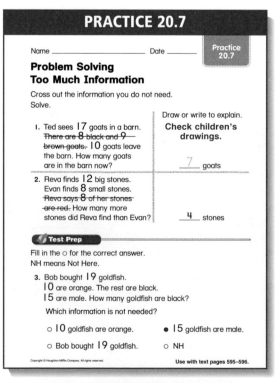

1. There are __20__ fish in the tank.

__10__ fish have stripes.

~~__4__ fish are on the bottom.~~

How many fish do not have stripes?

$20 - 10 = 10$ __10__ fish without stripes

2. __10__ fish have stripes.

__6__ fish have spots.

~~__4__ fish look like cats.~~

How many more fish have stripes than spots?

$10 - 6 = 4$ __4__ more fish with stripes

Write About It Write your own subtraction story problem about the fish in the tank. Solve. **Stories will vary. Example: There are 20 fish in the tank. 6 fish have spots. How many fish do not have spots? Answer: 14 fish.**

Copyright © Houghton Mifflin Company. All rights reserved.   Use with text pages 595–596.

Practice Workbook Page 140

Reaching All Learners

Differentiated Instruction

English Learners

In order to solve problems with too much information, children will need to understand the word *extra*. Use Worksheet 20.7 to help develop understanding of this word.

Inclusion

VISUAL, AUDITORY

- Prepare problems using rebus art for the objects.
- Read a problem together. Have the child focus on the question asked at the end of the problem.
- Help the child sort through the information and cross out what is not needed to help solve the problem.

> There are 10 ⊘ in a box.
> There is 1 ◡ in the box.
> Amy took 2 ⊘ out.
> How many ⊘ are left?

Gifted and Talented

TACTILE, VISUAL

- Have children work in pairs to create problems with extra information.
- Have one child write the first part. For example: *I have 12 bears.* Have the partner write a piece of extra information. *6 bears are yellow.* The first child finishes the problem. *I take 6 bears to bed. How many bears are left?*
- Pairs solve each other's problems.

TECHNOLOGY

Spiral Review

You can prepare students for standardized tests with **customized** spiral review on key skills using the *Ways to Assess* CD-ROM.

Lesson Planner

You can use the **Lesson Planner CD-ROM** to create a report of the lessons and standards you have taught.

Intervention

Use the *Ways to Success* intervention software to support students who need more help in understanding the concepts and skills taught in this chapter.

Ways to Success

Literature Connection

Reread the first page of *Lights Out!* by Lucille Recht Penner. Ask children questions such as, *How many hours later does the brother go to bed than the girl in the story?*

MATH CENTER

Number of the Week Activity

Display the Number of the Week to motivate children to use their problem-solving skills. The exercises cover topics across all math strands.

PROBLEM SOLVING 20.7

Name _____ Date _____

Problem Solving Too Much Information

There are 13 dogs and cats in the store.
8 of the pets are dogs.
3 of the cats are white.
How many cats are there?

> Cross out extra information in the problem.

UNDERSTAND
What do I need to find out? **How many cats are in the pet store.**

PLAN
Do I need to know there are 13 dogs and cats? **Yes.**

Do I need to know there are 8 dogs? **Yes.**

Do I need to know that 3 cats are white? **No.**

SOLVE
Subtract to compare. 13 – 8 = 5
There are **5** cats.

LOOK BACK
How did you decide what to do?
Draw or write to explain. **Answers will vary. Possible answer: Cross out the extra information in the problem.**

Use with text pages 595–596.

HOMEWORK 20.7

Name _____ Date _____

Problem Solving Too Much Information

Choose the information that you need.
Cross out information that you do not need.

José finds 18 sand dollars.
~~Then he finds 3 starfish.~~
Later he finds 9 clam shells.
How many more sand dollars than clam shells did José find?

18 – 9 = 9

9 more sand dollars

Cross out the information you do not need.
Solve.   Draw or write to explain.

1. There are 15 boats in the harbor. ~~It is 7 o'clock in the morning.~~ Now 6 boats sail away. How many boats are still in the harbor?

15 – 6 = 9

2. ~~Zoe's class has 2 teachers.~~ The class of 17 children play on the beach. 9 children go for snacks. How many children are still playing?

17 – 9 = 8

Use with text pages 595–596.

ENGLISH LEARNERS 20.7

Name _____ Date _____

Too Much Information

The pumpkin has an **extra** stem.

Circle each picture that has an extra part.

1.

2.

To the Teacher: Use the example at the top of the page to help children understand the meaning of the word *extra*. Then have them circle each picture with an extra part.

Use with text pages 595–598.

TEACHING LESSON 20.7

LESSON ORGANIZER

Objective Solve problems with too much information.

Resources Reteach, Practice, Enrichment, Problem Solving, Homework, English Learners, Transparencies, Math Center

Materials Cubes, large cup

Activity
Warm-Up Activity
Subtract to Compare

iii Small Group	⏱ 5 minutes	Visual, Auditory

1. Present a classroom situation that requires children to subtract to compare. **We have 15 boys and 8 girls. How many more boys than girls are there?**

   $15 - 8 = 7$

   7 more boys

2. **What do we need to find out?** (how many more boys than girls) **How can we solve this problem?** (Subtract 15 − 8.) Have a volunteer record the subtraction to solve. (15 − 8 = 7)

Name_____

Too Much Information

MathTracks 2/27
Listen and Understand

Objective
Solve problems with too much information.

Some problems have more information than you need.

17 eels are in the lagoon.
9 catfish are in the lagoon.
8 eels are black.

How many more eels than catfish are there?

Decide what information you need.

THINK

DECIDE

Do I need to know that there are **17** eels?	Yes. I need to compare the number of eels to the number of catfish.
Do I need to know that there are **9** catfish?	Yes. I need to know the number of catfish.
Do I need to know that **8** of the eels are black?	No. I need to know the number of eels, not the color.

17 eels are in the lagoon.
9 catfish are in the lagoon.
~~8 eels are black.~~   Cross out the extra information.
How many more eels than catfish are there?

Subtract to compare the numbers.

$\underline{17} - \underline{9} = \underline{8}$ 8 more eels

Chapter 20 Lesson 7   five hundred ninety-five **595**

---

1 Introduce Activity

Model How to Solve Problems With Too Much Information

iiii Whole Group	⏱ 10–15 minutes	Tactile, Visual

Materials: *cubes in 3 colors, large cup*

1. Take a cupful of cubes from a container. **I have 6 red, 2 green, and 3 blue cubes. How many more reds than greens do I have?** (4 more reds) Write the subtraction sentence on the board. **Why didn't we subtract the 3 blues to solve?** (The problem asked you to only compare the reds and greens, not the blues.) Point out that the information about the 3 blue cubes was not needed to solve the problem.

2. Repeat. Count the 3 color cubes and pose a similar problem. Have children discuss before solving: **What information do we need to solve the problem?**

3. Continue by having volunteers scoop up cubes and count each color. Help the child present a problem with too much information. Have a volunteer solve the problem.

2 Develop

Guided Learning

Teaching Example

Introduce the objective to children. Guide them through the steps of the example problem. Emphasize that they use only the information needed to solve.

Guided Practice

Have children complete **Exercises 1–2** on page 596 as you observe. Remind them to use the hints. Encourage children to show their work. Point out that some exercises (Exercises 2 and 4) do not have any extra information. Children will need all the information in those problems to solve.

Guided Practice

Cross out information you do not need.
Solve.

Draw or write to explain.

1. 16 trout are near the shore. ~~There are 10 kinds of fish in the lake.~~ 8 trout swim away. How many trout are near the shore now?

Think
What information do I need to solve the problem?

_8_ trout

2. 18 codfish swim by the dock. 9 codfish swim away. How many codfish are by the dock now?

Think
Do I need to know how many codfish swim away?

_9_ codfish

Practice

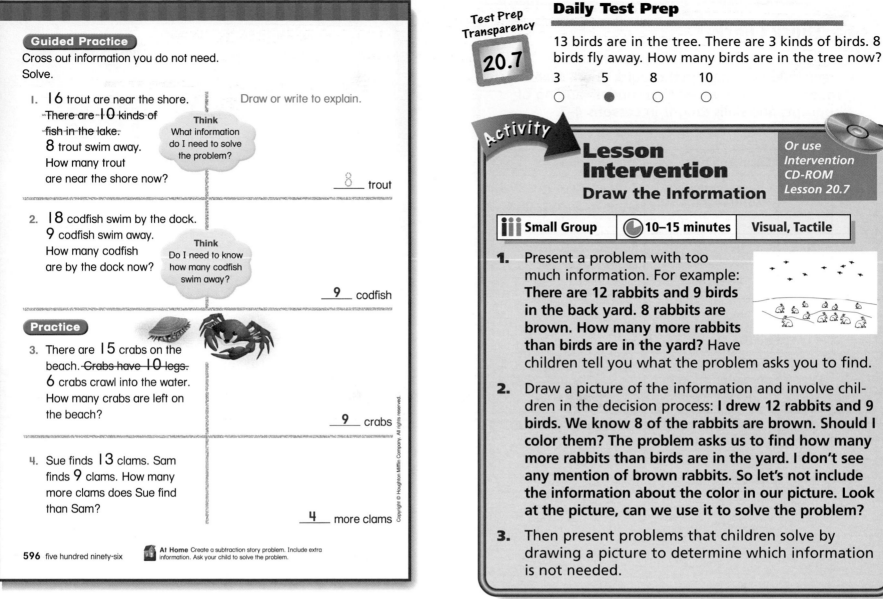

3. There are 15 crabs on the beach. ~~Crabs have 10 legs.~~ 6 crabs crawl into the water. How many crabs are left on the beach?

_9_ crabs

4. Sue finds 13 clams. Sam finds 9 clams. How many more clams does Sue find than Sam?

_4_ more clams

At Home Create a subtraction story problem. Include extra information. Ask your child to solve the problem.

Daily Test Prep

13 birds are in the tree. There are 3 kinds of birds. 8 birds fly away. How many birds are in the tree now?

3   ● 5   ○ 8   ○ 10

Activity

Lesson Intervention
Draw the Information

Or use Intervention CD-ROM Lesson 20.7

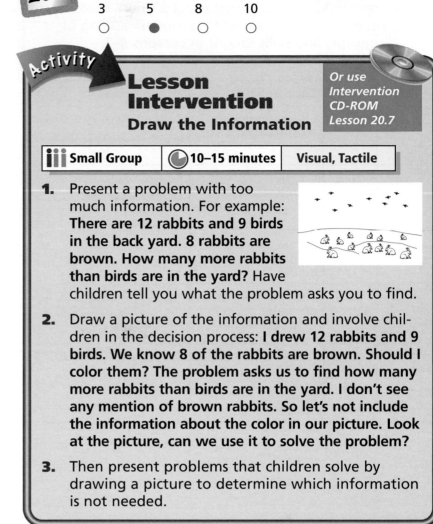

| Small Group | 10–15 minutes | Visual, Tactile |

1. Present a problem with too much information. For example: **There are 12 rabbits and 9 birds in the back yard. 8 rabbits are brown. How many more rabbits than birds are in the yard?** Have children tell you what the problem asks you to find.

2. Draw a picture of the information and involve children in the decision process: **I drew 12 rabbits and 9 birds. We know 8 of the rabbits are brown. Should I color them? The problem asks us to find how many more rabbits than birds are in the yard. I don't see any mention of brown rabbits. So let's not include the information about the color in our picture. Look at the picture, can we use it to solve the problem?**

3. Then present problems that children solve by drawing a picture to determine which information is not needed.

 **Practice**

Independent Practice

Children complete **Exercises 3–4** on page 596 independently.

Common Error

Children may select the wrong numbers to use to solve the problem. As you read the problem, have children cross out the extra information and then make sure that the remaining information makes sense.

4 Assess and Close

If you need to know how many more dimes than nickels you have, would you count the pennies you have? (no) **Why not?** (The number of pennies is extra information.)

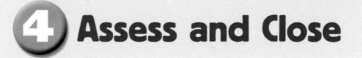 **Keeping a Journal**

Make up a problem with extra information. Draw a picture and solve the problem.

Quick Check

Have children complete the Quick Check exercises independently to assess their understanding of concepts and skills taught in **Lessons 4–7.**

Item	Lesson	Error Analysis	Intervention
1–2	20.4	Children may make a subtraction error.	Reteach Resource 20.4 *Ways to Success* 20.4
3–4	20.5	Children may not write the correct number because they do not remember that the numbers in the related facts must be the same.	Reteach Resource 20.5 *Ways to Success* 20.5
5	20.6	Children may write unrelated facts for those given.	Reteach Resource 20.6 *Ways to Success* 20.6
6	20.7	Children may select the wrong numbers to solve the problem.	Reteach Resource 20.7 *Ways to Success* 20.7

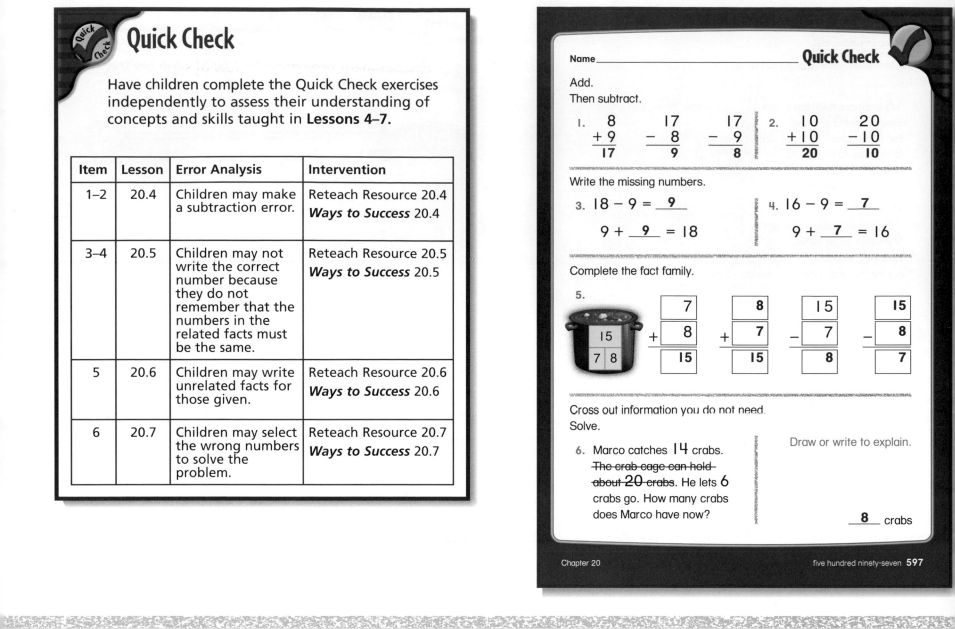

Name_____ **Quick Check**

Add.
Then subtract.

1.
$$8 + 9 = 17 \qquad 17 - 8 = 9 \qquad 17 - 9 = 8$$

2.
$$10 + 10 = 20 \qquad 20 - 10 = 10$$

Write the missing numbers.

3. $18 - 9 = \underline{9}$

   $9 + \underline{9} = 18$

4. $16 - 9 = \underline{7}$

   $9 + \underline{7} = 16$

Complete the fact family.

5.
$$\begin{array}{c} 15 \\ 7 \quad 8 \end{array}$$

$$7 + 8 = 15 \qquad 8 + 7 = 15 \qquad 15 - 7 = 8 \qquad 15 - 8 = 7$$

Cross out information you do not need.
Solve.

6. Marco catches 14 crabs. ~~The crab cage can hold about 20 crabs.~~ He lets 6 crabs go. How many crabs does Marco have now?

Draw or write to explain.

_____8____ crabs

Write the number in different ways.

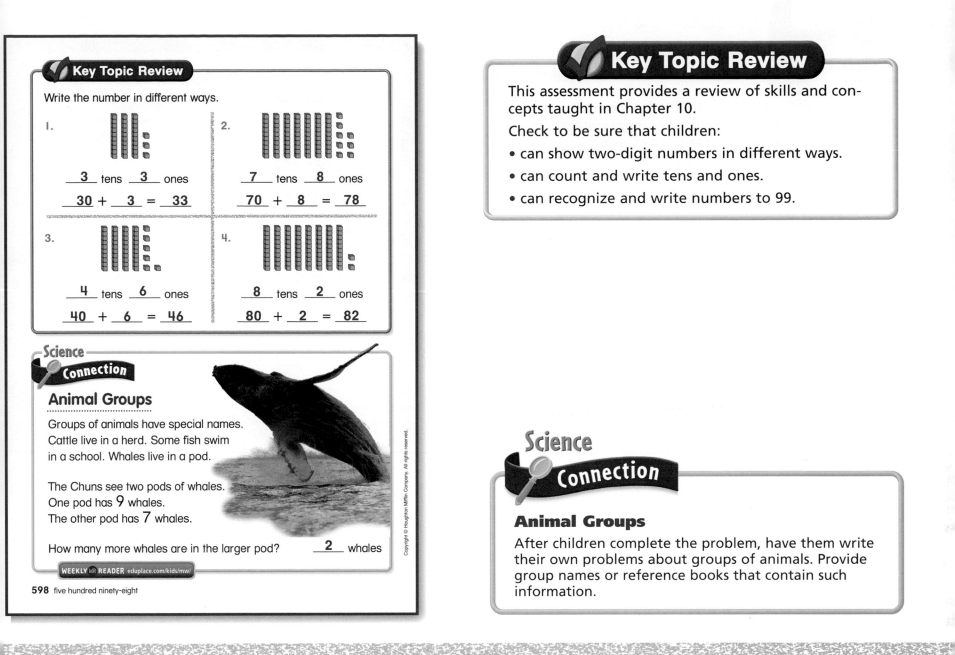

1.

___3___ tens ___3___ ones

___30___ + ___3___ = ___33___

2.

___7___ tens ___8___ ones

___70___ + ___8___ = ___78___

3.

___4___ tens ___6___ ones

___40___ + ___6___ = ___46___

4.

___8___ tens ___2___ ones

___80___ + ___2___ = ___82___

Science Connection

Animal Groups

Groups of animals have special names.
Cattle live in a herd. Some fish swim
in a school. Whales live in a pod.

The Chuns see two pods of whales.
One pod has 9 whales.
The other pod has 7 whales.

How many more whales are in the larger pod? ___2___ whales

WEEKLY WR READER eduplace.com/kids/mw/

Key Topic Review

This assessment provides a review of skills and concepts taught in Chapter 10.

Check to be sure that children:

• can show two-digit numbers in different ways.

• can count and write tens and ones.

• can recognize and write numbers to 99.

Science Connection

Animal Groups

After children complete the problem, have them write their own problems about groups of animals. Provide group names or reference books that contain such information.

Chapter Review/Test

Purpose: This test provides an informal assessment of the Chapter 20 objectives.

Chapter Test Items 1–25

To assign a numerical grade for this Chapter Test, use 4 points for each test item.

Check Understanding

Use children's work on word problems to informally assess progress on chapter content.

Customizing Your Instruction

For children who have not yet mastered these objectives, you can use the reteaching resources listed in the chart below.

Assessment Options

A summary test for this chapter is also provided in the Unit Resource Folder.

Name_____ **Chapter Review/Test**

Vocabulary *Glossary*

Complete the sentence.

| difference | fact family |

1. A ___fact family___ has related addition and subtraction facts.

2. Subtract to find the ___difference___.

Concepts and Skills

Add.
Then subtract.

3. $5 + 5 = \underline{10}$ 4. $4 + 4 = \underline{8}$ 5. $8 + 8 = \underline{16}$

$10 - 5 = \underline{5}$ $8 - 4 = \underline{4}$ $16 - 8 = \underline{8}$

6.
$$\begin{array}{r} 7 \\ +7 \\ \hline 14 \end{array} \quad \begin{array}{r} 14 \\ -7 \\ \hline 7 \end{array}$$

7.
$$\begin{array}{r} 3 \\ +3 \\ \hline 6 \end{array} \quad \begin{array}{r} 6 \\ -3 \\ \hline 3 \end{array}$$

8.
$$\begin{array}{r} 9 \\ +9 \\ \hline 18 \end{array} \quad \begin{array}{r} 18 \\ -9 \\ \hline 9 \end{array}$$

Add.
Then find the differences.

9.
$$\begin{array}{r} 5 \\ +7 \\ \hline 12 \end{array} \quad \begin{array}{r} 12 \\ -5 \\ \hline 7 \end{array} \quad \begin{array}{r} 12 \\ -7 \\ \hline 5 \end{array}$$

10.
$$\begin{array}{r} 4 \\ +9 \\ \hline 13 \end{array} \quad \begin{array}{r} 13 \\ -4 \\ \hline 9 \end{array} \quad \begin{array}{r} 13 \\ -9 \\ \hline 4 \end{array}$$

11.
$$\begin{array}{r} 6 \\ +10 \\ \hline 16 \end{array} \quad \begin{array}{r} 16 \\ -6 \\ \hline 10 \end{array} \quad \begin{array}{r} 16 \\ -10 \\ \hline 6 \end{array}$$

12.
$$\begin{array}{r} 7 \\ +8 \\ \hline 15 \end{array} \quad \begin{array}{r} 15 \\ -7 \\ \hline 8 \end{array} \quad \begin{array}{r} 15 \\ -8 \\ \hline 7 \end{array}$$

Chapter 20   five hundred ninety-nine **599**

Reteaching Support

Chapter Test Items	Summary Test Items	Chapter Objectives Tested	TE Pages	Use These Reteaching Resources
1–2	1–2	**20A** Develop and use math vocabulary relating to subtraction facts through 20.	583A–584, 593A–594	Reteach Resources and *Ways to Success* CD: 20.2, 20.6 Skillsheet 146
3–23	3–16	**20B** Subtract from 20 and solve related addition and subtraction problems.	581A–586, 589A–592	Reteach Resources and *Ways to Success* CD: 20.1–20.5 Skillsheets 147 and 148
24	17–18	**20C** Use addition and subtraction to make fact families.	593A–594	Reteach Resource and *Ways to Success* CD: 20.6 Skillsheet 149
25	19–20	**20D** Solve problems with too much information.	595A–596	Reteach Resource and *Ways to Success* CD: 20.7 Skillsheet 150

CHAPTER SUMMARY TEST

Name _____ Date _____

Chapter 20 Test

Look at the vocabulary words.
Fill in the blank.

Vocabulary
subtraction sentence
fact family
minus sign

1. The symbol for subtraction is the ___minus sign___.

2. A ___subtraction sentence___ is $12 - 8 = 4$.

Subtract.

3. $13 - 8 = \underline{5}$ 4. $16 - 7 = \underline{9}$

5. $18 - 9 = \underline{9}$ 6. $14 - 7 = \underline{7}$

7. $15 - 6 = \underline{9}$ 8. $17 - 9 = \underline{8}$

Add. Then subtract.

9.
$$\begin{array}{r} 8 \\ +8 \\ \hline 16 \end{array} \quad \begin{array}{r} 16 \\ -8 \\ \hline 8 \end{array}$$

10.
$$\begin{array}{r} 9 \\ +9 \\ \hline 18 \end{array} \quad \begin{array}{r} 18 \\ -9 \\ \hline 9 \end{array}$$

11.
$$\begin{array}{r} 3 \\ +3 \\ \hline 6 \end{array} \quad \begin{array}{r} 6 \\ -3 \\ \hline 3 \end{array}$$

12.
$$\begin{array}{r} 8 \\ +9 \\ \hline 17 \end{array} \quad \begin{array}{r} 17 \\ -8 \\ \hline 9 \end{array} \quad \begin{array}{r} 17 \\ -9 \\ \hline 8 \end{array}$$

13.
$$\begin{array}{r} 7 \\ +5 \\ \hline 12 \end{array} \quad \begin{array}{r} 12 \\ -7 \\ \hline 5 \end{array} \quad \begin{array}{r} 12 \\ -5 \\ \hline 7 \end{array}$$

Write the missing numbers.

14. $14 - 8 = \underline{6}$ 15. $15 - 7 = \underline{8}$ 16. $12 - 9 = \underline{3}$

$8 + \underline{6} = 14$ $7 + \underline{8} = 15$ $9 + \underline{3} = 12$

Go on ▶

Subtract.

13. 17   14. 18   15. 14   16. 16   17. 20
    − 8   − 9   − 6   − 7   −10
    ───   ───   ───   ───   ───
      9   9   8   9   10

Write the missing numbers.

18. $12 − 6 = \underline{6}$ 19. $17 − 8 = \underline{9}$ 20. $16 − 9 = \underline{7}$

$6 + \underline{6} = 12$ $8 + \underline{9} = 17$ $9 + \underline{7} = 16$

21. $13 − 8 = \underline{5}$ 22. $15 − 9 = \underline{6}$ 23. $13 − 4 = \underline{9}$

$8 + \underline{5} = 13$ $9 + \underline{6} = 15$ $4 + \underline{9} = 13$

Complete the fact family.

24.

15
7 8

| 7 | | 8 | | 15 | | 15 |
| 8 | + | 7 | + | 7 | − | 8 | −
| 15 | | 15 | | 8 | | 7 |

Problem Solving

Cross out information you do not need.
Solve.

Draw or write to explain.

25. Ryan finds 8 shells.
Kaylee finds 9 shells.
~~Oscar has 2 stones.~~
How many shells do
they find?

$\underline{17}$ shells

600 six hundred

Adequate Yearly Progress

Use the End of Grade Test Prep Assessment Guide
to help familiarize your children with the format
of standardized tests.

CHAPTER SUMMARY TEST

Name _____ Date _____

Chapter 20
Test
continued

Complete the fact family.

17.

13
7 6

| 7 | | 6 | | 13 | | 13 |
| 6 | + | 7 | + | 7 | − | 6 | −
| 13 | | 13 | | 6 | | 7 |

18.

14
9 5

| 9 | | 5 | | 14 | | 14 |
| 5 | + | 9 | + | 9 | − | 5 | −
| 14 | | 14 | | 5 | | 9 |

Cross out the information you do not need.
Solve.

Draw or write to explain.

19. Sarah has 16 pennies.
Tom has 9 pennies. ~~Tom's pennies are shiny.~~ How many
more pennies does Sarah
have than Tom?

$\underline{7}$ pennies

20. There are 18 snails on the
rock. ~~Some of the snails have stripes.~~ 9 snails crawl
off the rock. How many
snails are still on the rock?

$\underline{9}$ snails

STOP

CHAPTER 21 Lesson by Lesson Overview
Adding Two-Digit Numbers

Lesson 1

- Introduces two digit addition using place-value blocks as the model.
- The use of basic facts and mental math to add tens is emphasized.
  $3 + 5 = 8$
  3 tens + 5 tens = 8 tens
  $30 + 50 = 80$

Lesson 2

- This lesson introduces the algorithm for adding 1-digit to 2-digit numbers, without regrouping.
- Children use place-value blocks on a workmat to model each exercise.
- Children understand the connection made between the modeling and what is recorded.

Lesson 3

- Children continue to use place-value blocks as they add two 2-digit numbers.
- Children are reminded to start adding with the ones. This is preparation for second-grade addition, which includes regrouping.
- Problem solving has children use what they have learned to determine which of three addition problems has the greatest sum.

- The lesson is extended to include adding money amounts for sums of 99¢ or less.

Lesson 4

- In this lesson, children review and practice different ways to add.
- They choose from *mental math, paper and pencil,* and *tens and ones blocks.* The choice depends on the problem and the child's abilities.

Lesson 5

- Children practice addition of 2-digit numbers.
- The practice has children add, compare, and color according to a key. Then they decipher a coded message.

Lesson 6

- Children are taught to use the guess and check strategy to solve problems.
- Information needed is contained in pictures. Children guess and then check to find which of two numbers equal a target number.
- Children choose a strategy to practice previously learned problem solving strategies.

SKILLS TRACE: ADDING TWO-DIGIT NUMBERS

Grade K	Grade 1	Grade 2
• model addition (ch. 13)	• use mental math and basic facts to add tens	• use mental math and basic facts to add tens (ch. 10)
• complete addition sentences (ch. 13)	• add 1-digit to 2-digit numbers, no regrouping	• count on by tens to add (ch. 10)
• add 1 to 0 through 9 (ch. 13)	• add two 2-digit numbers, no regrouping	• regroup ones as tens (ch. 10)
• add 2 to 0 through 8 (ch. 13)	• use different ways to add	• use models to add 1-digit to 2-digit numbers, with and without regrouping (ch. 10)
		• add 1-digit to 2-digit numbers; add two 2-digit numbers (ch. 10)
		• estimate the sum of 2-digit numbers (ch. 11)
		• choose a computation method (ch. 11)

Chapter Planner

Lesson	Objective	Vocabulary	Materials	✔ NCTM Standards
21.1 Mental Math: Add Tens p. 603A	Use basic facts to add tens.	tens	place-value blocks, blank transparency, Workmat 5	Develop and use strategies for whole-number computations, with a focus on addition and subtraction.
21.2 Add With Two-Digit Numbers (Hands-On) p. 605A	Add a one-digit number to a two-digit number without regrouping.		place-value blocks, Workmat 5, 2-digit addition charts (teacher-made), spinner (Learning Tool (LT) 38), tens and ones chart transparency	Use a variety of methods and tools to compute, including objects, mental computation, estimation, paper and pencil, and calculators.
21.3 Add Two-Digit Numbers (Hands-On) p. 607A	Add two-digit numbers without regrouping.		place-value blocks, tens and ones chart transparency, dimes, pennies, Workmat 5	Use a variety of methods and tools to compute, including objects, mental computation, estimation, paper and pencil, and calculators.
21.4 Different Ways to Add p. 611A	Use different ways to add.		place-value blocks, Workmat 5	Use a variety of methods and tools to compute, including objects, mental computation, estimation, paper and pencil, and calculators.
21.5 Two-Digit Addition Practice p. 613A	Practice adding two-digit numbers.		index cards with addition exercises (teacher-made), number cards 0–20 (LT 14 and 15) and tens 10–90 (LT 16), Workmat 5, place-value blocks	Use a variety of methods and tools to compute, including objects, mental computation, estimation, paper and pencil, and calculators.
21.6 Problem Solving: Guess and Check p. 615A	Use guess and check to solve problems.		clear plastic bags	Solve problems that arise in mathematics and other contexts.

Resources For Reaching All Learners

LESSON RESOURCES: Reteach, Practice, Enrichment, Problem Solving, Homework, English Learners, Daily Routines, Transparencies, Math Center.

ADDITIONAL RESOURCES FROM HOUGHTON MIFFLIN: Chapter Challenges, Combination Classroom Planning Guide, Every Day Counts, Math to Learn (Student Handbook)

Every Day Counts
The *Totally Ten Count* and *Daily Depositor* activities in Every Day Counts support the math in this chapter.

Assessing Prior Knowledge

Before beginning the chapter, you can assess student understandings in order to assist you in differentiating instruction.

Complete Chapter Pretest in Unit Resource Folder

Use this test to assess both prerequisite skills (**Are You Ready?** — one page) and chapter content (**Check What You Know** — two pages).

Chapter 21 Prerequisite Skills Pretest

Chapter 21 New Content Pretest

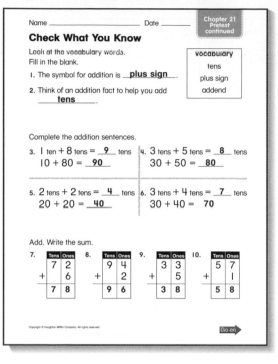

Customizing Instruction

For Students Having Difficulty

Items	Prerequisites	Ways to Success
1–6	Addition facts with facts through 10.	CD: 5.4 Skillsheet 151
7–18	Vertical addition with facts through 10	CD: 5a Skillsheet 152

Ways to Success Intervention for every concept and skill (CD-ROM or Chapter Intervention Skillsheets).

For Students Having Success

Items	Objectives	Resources
1–2	21A Use vocabulary for adding 2-digit numbers.	Enrichment 21.1, 21.2
3–14	21B Use basic facts to add 10s. Add 2-digit numbers, including money amounts, without regrouping.	Enrichment 21.1, 21.3
15–18	21C Use different ways to add.	Enrichment 21.4, 21.5
19–20	21D Use guess and check to solve problems.	Enrichment 21.6

Use **Chapter Challenges** with any students who have success with all new chapter content.

Other Pretest Options

Informal Pretest

The pretest assesses vocabulary and prerequisite skills needed for success in this chapter.

Ways to Success CD-ROM

The ***Ways to Success*** chapter pretest has automatic assignment of appropriate review lessons.

Chapter Resources

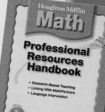

Activity

Assessing Prior Knowledge

Adding Tens (count on tens)

- Have children work in pairs.
- In the math center place a number cube 4–9. Have one child roll the cube and record the number.
- The partner makes that many groups of ten items. (Children can make groups of counters, cubes, or other manipulatives.) Then he or she counts by tens. Have the child write this next to the number rolled.
- Partners switch roles and continue.

Activity

Ongoing Skill Activity

Fish for Addition Problems (add 2-digit numbers)

- In advance, cut out paper fish shapes and write a 2-digit addition example (not requiring regrouping) on each. Place the fish shapes into a clear bowl or container.
- Invite children to reach in and "catch" a fish. Ask them to copy the addition example onto a sheet of paper. Then have them find the sum.
- Children return the fish to the bowl and "catch" another fish.

Activity

Connecting to the Unit Project

- Write 2-digit addition word problems about book characters on index cards. Place the pile facedown on the table.
- Invite children to choose a card and solve the problem.
- Encourage interested children to write their own problems about characters in a book they are reading. Include these problems in the pile.

Teacher Support

Professional Resources Handbook

Research, Mathematics Content, and Language Intervention

Research-Based Teaching

Research has shown that children's facility with basic arithmetical facts is enhanced by their first developing effective thinking strategies (Cobb & Merket, 1989; Thornton, 1990). For example, as children begin to understand the meaning of place notation in arithmetic—so that the child feels comfortable when encountering two-digit numbers—it becomes much easier to extend some problem-solving strategy from single-digit numbers to two-digit numbers. See *Professional Resources Handbook, Grade 1,* Unit 8.

For more ideas relating to Unit 8, see the Teacher Support Handbook at the back of this Teacher's Edition.

Language Intervention

When students are asked to explain their thinking, have students share their responses. This will help students to improve their communication skills and their mathematics vocabulary.

 Technology

Time-Saving Technology Support
Ways to Assess Customized Spiral Review
  Test Generator CD
Lesson Planner CD-ROM
Ways to Success Intervention CD-ROM
MathTracks CD-ROM
Education Place: www.eduplace.com/math/mw
Houghton Mifflin Math eBook CD-ROM
eManipulatives
eGames

Starting Chapter 21
Adding Two-Digit Numbers

CHAPTER OBJECTIVES

21A Develop and use math vocabulary relating to adding two-digit numbers.

21B Use basic facts to add tens. Add two-digit numbers, including money amounts, without regrouping.

21C Use different ways to add.

21D Use guess and check to solve problems.

Math Background

Adding Two-Digit Numbers

Addition of two-digit numbers is developed sequentially, beginning by finding the sums of numbers that are multiples of 10. Next in the sequential development is the addition of two-digit numbers limited to addends that would give sums no greater than two-digit numbers. This means the sum of the tens must be less than 10 tens. This avoids the skill of regrouping, that is exchanging, for example, 15 tens for 1 hundred 5 tens.

The addition algorithm is based on our base-ten positional numeration system and when adding two-digit numbers, place value must be considered. By focusing on the positional value of the digits, children will develop a strong conceptual foundation that will prepare them for the concept of regrouping when it is formally introduced.

It is worth noting that many children, when first confronted with the problem of adding two-digit numbers, will devise a variety of their own methods for finding the sum. However, it is important to move children in the direction of standard algorithms due to their efficiency and standard of use.

For more information about projects and investigations, visit Education Place. **eduplace.com/math/mw/**

Adding Two-Digit Numbers — CHAPTER 21

INVESTIGATION

Add to find how many blue and red fish there are in all.

Chapter 21   six hundred one **601**

Using The Investigation

- Review the words *tens* and *ones* with children. Make a tens and ones chart on the board. Show children a bundle of 10 pencils. Then separate the pencils and have a volunteer count them. Ask the child to tell how the loose pencils and the bundle of pencils are same. Write *1* in the tens column and *0* in the ones column. Repeat with multiples of ten up to 50.

- Read the statement to children. **Look at the photograph. Add to find how many blue and red fish are there in all.** (12 + 8 = 20) **Add to find how many green and yellow fish there are in all.** (7 + 5 = 12) **Which color fish has the least amount?** (yellow) **Which color fish has the greatest amount?** (blue)

- Discuss or find what other animals "travel" together.

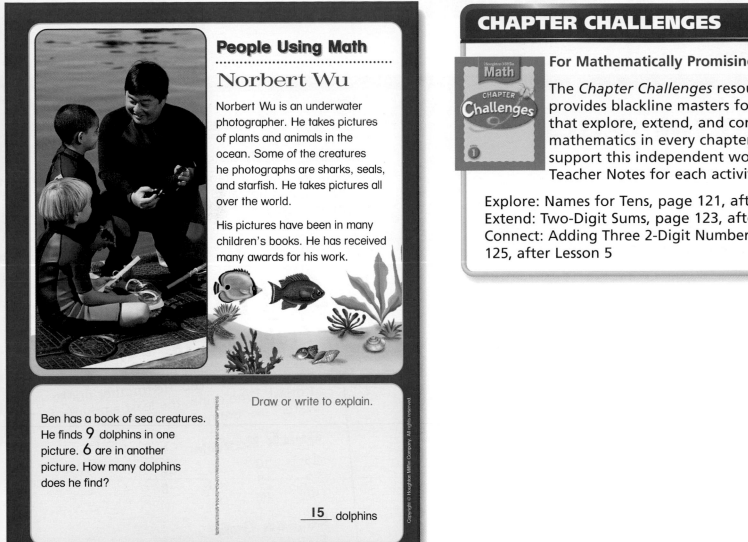

People Using Math

Norbert Wu

Norbert Wu is an underwater photographer. He takes pictures of plants and animals in the ocean. Some of the creatures he photographs are sharks, seals, and starfish. He takes pictures all over the world.

His pictures have been in many children's books. He has received many awards for his work.

Ben has a book of sea creatures. He finds **9** dolphins in one picture. **6** are in another picture. How many dolphins does he find?

Draw or write to explain.

15 dolphins

CHAPTER CHALLENGES

For Mathematically Promising Students

The *Chapter Challenges* resource book provides blackline masters for activities that explore, extend, and connect the mathematics in every chapter. To support this independent work, see the Teacher Notes for each activity.

Explore: Names for Tens, page 121, after Lesson 1
Extend: Two-Digit Sums, page 123, after Lesson 3
Connect: Adding Three 2-Digit Numbers, page 125, after Lesson 5

Using This Page

- Read children the paragraphs about underwater photographer, Norbert Wu.
- Ask volunteers to tell about the fish and sea creatures they have seen. Make a list. Use the numbers of creatures to make addition and subtraction sentences.

NSF Children's Math Worlds

Build stronger conceptual understanding of adding two-digit numbers with *Children's Math Worlds* lessons. The most effective approach is to use the *Children's Math Worlds* lessons with the lessons in the chapter.

Mental Math: Add Tens

PLANNING THE LESSON

MATHEMATICS OBJECTIVE
Use basic facts to add tens.

Use Lesson Planner CD-ROM for Lesson 21.1.

Meeting North Carolina's Standards
Prepare for Grade 2 Standard 1.04 Develop fluency with multi-digit addition and subtraction through 999 using multiple strategies.

Daily Routines

Calendar
Display a 12-month calendar. Have children use the calendar to find how many days in all are in April and June. (60) Then have them find the total number of days in September and November. (60)

Sunday	Monday	Tuesday	Wednesday	Thursday	Friday	Saturday
			1	2	3	4
5	6	7	8	9	10	11
12	13	14	15	16	17	18
19	20	21	22	23	24	25
26	27	28	29	30	31	

Vocabulary
Review the fact that 10 ones equal **1 ten**. Display place-value blocks and have children tell how many **tens** and the number. For example, 2 tens is 20.

Vocabulary Cards

Lesson Transparency 21.1

Problem of the Day
Sophie drinks 1 pint of water a day. Her brother drinks 1 cup. Her mother drinks 1 quart. Who drinks the least amount of water? (her brother)

Quick Review

$5 + 5 = (10)$ $10 - 5 = (5)$ $8 + 8 = (16)$ $16 - 8 = (8)$

Lesson Quiz
1. What is 2 tens + 4 tens? (6 tens or 60)
2. What is 3 tens + 6 tens? (9 tens or 90)
3. What is 7 tens + 1 ten? (8 tens or 80)

LEVELED PRACTICE

RETEACH 21.1

Name _____ Date _____   Reteach 21.1

Mental Math: Add Tens

Think of an addition fact when you add tens.

You know that 2 + 4 = 6.

$2 + 4 = 6$
2 tens + 4 tens = 6 tens
$20 + 40 = 60$

So, 2 tens + 4 tens = 6 tens.
$20 + 40 = 60$

Complete the addition sentences.

1.
$3 + 2 = 5$
3 tens + 2 tens = 5 tens
$30 + 20 = 50$

2.
$4 + 3 = 7$
4 tens + 3 tens = 7 tens
$40 + 30 = 70$

3.
$3 + 3 = 6$
3 tens + 3 tens = 6 tens
$30 + 30 = 60$

4.
$2 + 7 = 9$
2 tens + 7 tens = 9 tens
$20 + 70 = 90$

Copyright © Houghton Mifflin Company. All rights reserved.   Use with text pages 603–604.

PRACTICE 21.1

Name _____ Date _____   Practice 21.1

Mental Math: Add Tens

Complete the addition sentences.

1.
$3 + 4 = 7$
3 tens + 4 tens = 7 tens
$30 + 40 = 70$

2. 1 ten + 4 tens = 5 tens
$10 + 40 = 50$

3. 5 tens + 3 tens = 8 tens
$50 + 30 = 80$

4. 2 tens + 7 tens = 9 tens
$20 + 70 = 90$

5. 4 tens + 5 tens = 9 tens
$40 + 50 = 90$

Test Prep

Fill in the ○ for the correct answer.
NH means Not Here.

6. Anya has 4 groups of 10 pennies. How many pennies does she have?

○ 4 pennies   ○ 10 pennies   ● 40 pennies   ○ NH

Copyright © Houghton Mifflin Company. All rights reserved.   Use with text pages 603–604.

ENRICHMENT 21.1

Name _____ Date _____   Enrichment 21.1

Add Tens to Solve

Read the story problem.
Complete the addition sentence.
Write the answer.

1. Tom has 20 baseball cards. Bill has 20 more than Tom. How many cards do they have together?
$20 + 40 = 60$
60 cards

2. There are 40 boys on the playground. There are 10 more girls than boys. How many children are there in all?
$40 + 50 = 90$
90 children

3. Jenny jumps rope 30 times. Ed jumps rope 10 times more than Jenny. How many times do they jump rope altogether?
$30 + 40 = 70$
70 times

Write About It How did you solve Exercise 1?
Answers may vary. Possible answer: Tom has 20 cards. Bill has 20 more. 20 + 20 = 40. So Bill has 40. I added Tom's cards to Bill's cards, 20 + 40 = 60.

Copyright © Houghton Mifflin Company. All rights reserved.   Use with text pages 603–604.

Practice Workbook Page 141

Reaching All Learners
Differentiated Instruction

English Learners

English-language learners may not have the language skills to explain the process behind their thinking. Use Worksheet 21.1 to provide children with sentence frames they can use to complete the Explain Your Thinking activity.

Special Needs
TACTILE, VISUAL

Materials: *place-value blocks*

- Write 2 tens + 5 tens. Have the child model the addition to get 7 tens. Write the addition as 20 + 50 = 70. Relate it to the addition fact 2 + 5 = 7.
- Continue with similar exercises.

Gifted and Talented
VISUAL, AUDITORY

- Have children work in pairs. One child writes an addition sentence using tens.
- Then the partner writes the addition with numerals. He or she writes another addition sentence using tens.

3 tens + 4 tens
30 + 40 = 70
2 tens + 3 tens

TECHNOLOGY

Spiral Review

Using the *Ways to Assess* CD-ROM, you can create **customized** spiral review worksheets covering any lessons you choose.

Lesson Planner

Use the **Lesson Planner CD-ROM** to see how lesson objectives for this chapter are correlated to standards.

eBook

An electronic version of this lesson can be found in **eMathBook.**

Houghton Mifflin
Math

e MathBook

Social Studies Connection

Discuss the numbers on speed limit signs. Explain that a speed limit is how fast a car should drive. A speed limit sign says *50 mph. If a car is moving at 10 mph over the speed limit, what is its speed?* (60 mph)

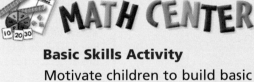

MATH CENTER

Basic Skills Activity

Motivate children to build basic skills. Use this activity to address multiple learning styles using hands-on activities related to the skills of this lesson.

PROBLEM SOLVING 21.1

Name _____ Date _____
Problem Solving 21.1

Mental Math: Add Tens

The table shows postcard collections.

Use the table to solve problems 1–4.

Postcard Collections

Child	Number of Postcards
Ashley	30
Leon	40
Marta	50
Phil	20
Chan	40

Check children's drawings

1. Which two children have the same number of postcards? How many postcards do they have altogether?

   Draw or write to explain.

   Leon and **Chan**
   80 postcards

2. How many postcards do Ashley and Marta have in all?

   80 postcards

3. Marta gets 10 more postcards. How many does she have now?

   60 postcards

4. Phil gets 20 more postcards from his grandparents. How many postcards does Phil have now?

   40 postcards

Use with text pages 603–604.

HOMEWORK 21.1

Name _____ Date _____
Homework 21.1

Mental Math: Add Tens

An addition fact can help you add tens.

$1 + 2 = \underline{3}$
1 ten $+ 2$ tens $= \underline{3}$ tens
$\underline{10} + \underline{20} = \underline{30}$

Complete the addition sentences.

1. $1 + 4 = \underline{5}$
   1 ten $+ 4$ tens $= \underline{5}$ tens
   $\underline{10} + \underline{40} = \underline{50}$

2. $3 + 2 = \underline{5}$
   3 tens $+ 2$ tens $= \underline{5}$ tens
   $\underline{30} + \underline{20} = \underline{50}$

3. 2 tens $+ 7$ tens $= \underline{9}$ tens
   $\underline{20} + \underline{70} = \underline{90}$

4. 6 tens $+ 3$ tens $= \underline{9}$ tens
   $\underline{60} + \underline{30} = \underline{90}$

5. Jack puts 40 marbles in a box. Then he puts in more. Now there are 70 marbles in the box. How many more marbles did he put in?

   check children's drawings

   Draw or write to explain.

   __30__ marbles

Use with text pages 603–604.

Homework Workbook Page 141

ENGLISH LEARNERS 21.1

Name _____ Date _____
English Learners 21.1

Mental Math: Add Tens

3 tens $+ 2$ tens $= 5$ tens
$30 + 20 = 50$

How does knowing $2 + 5 = 7$ help you solve $20 + 50 = 70$?

I know that $2 + 5 = 7$.

That helps me know that __2__ tens + __5__ tens = 7 tens

2 tens = __20__
5 tens = __50__
7 tens = __70__

Now I know that $20 + 50 = 70$.

To the Teacher: Use the example at the top of the page to model how to add tens. Then have children complete the sentence frames that provide the language needed to explain how to solve the problem.

Use with text pages 603–604.

TEACHING LESSON 21.1

LESSON ORGANIZER

Objective Use basic facts to add tens.

Resources Reteach, Practice, Enrichment, Problem Solving, Homework, English Learners, Transparencies, Math Center

Materials Place-value blocks, Workmat 5, blank transparency

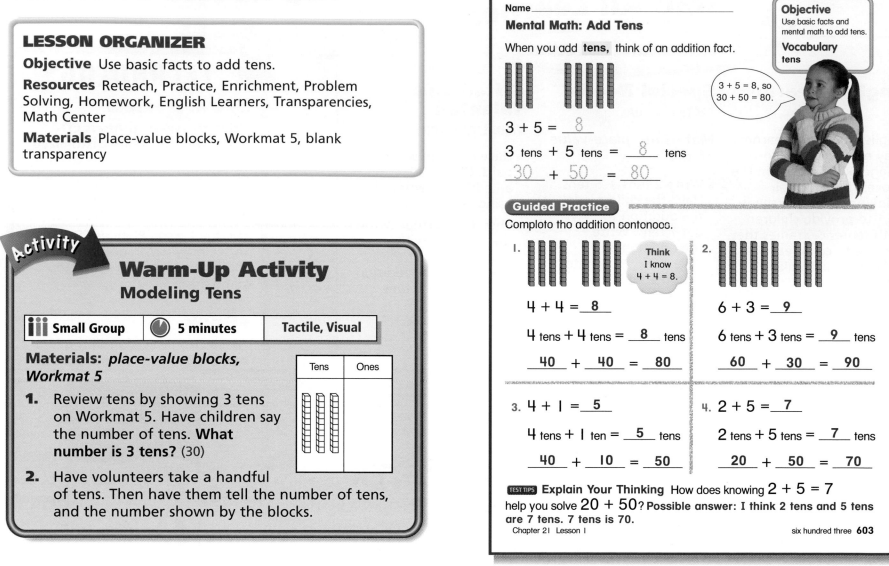

Name_____

Mental Math: Add Tens

When you add **tens**, think of an addition fact.

3 + 5 = __8__

3 tens + 5 tens = __8__ tens

__30__ + __50__ = __80__

3 + 5 = 8, so 30 + 50 = 80.

Objective Use basic facts and mental math to add tens.

Vocabulary tens

Guided Practice

Complete the addition sentences.

1.
4 + 4 = __8__
Think I know 4 + 4 = 8.
4 tens + 4 tens = __8__ tens
__40__ + __40__ = __80__

2.
6 + 3 = __9__
6 tens + 3 tens = __9__ tens
__60__ + __30__ = __90__

3. 4 + 1 = __5__
4 tens + 1 ten = __5__ tens
__40__ + __10__ = __50__

4. 2 + 5 = __7__
2 tens + 5 tens = __7__ tens
__20__ + __50__ = __70__

TEST TIPS **Explain Your Thinking** How does knowing 2 + 5 = 7 help you solve 20 + 50? **Possible answer: I think 2 tens and 5 tens are 7 tens. 7 tens is 70.**

Chapter 21 Lesson 1

six hundred three **603**

Warm-Up Activity
Modeling Tens

👤👤👤 Small Group	⏱ 5 minutes	Tactile, Visual

Materials: *place-value blocks, Workmat 5*

Tens	Ones

1. Review tens by showing 3 tens on Workmat 5. Have children say the number of tens. **What number is 3 tens?** (30)

2. Have volunteers take a handful of tens. Then have them tell the number of tens, and the number shown by the blocks.

---

1 Introduce
Model Using Facts to Add Tens

👤👤👤👤 Whole Group	⏱ 10–15 minutes	Visual, Auditory

Materials: *blank transparency, place-value blocks*

1. Show 4 ones and 2 ones and write the addition below as 4 + 2 = ___. **What is the sum?** (6) **What if I show 4 tens and 2 tens?** Show the models. **4 tens is 40, 2 tens is 20.** Write 40 + 20 below the models. **What is the sum of 4 + 2?** (6) **What is the sum of 4 tens + 2 tens?** (6 tens) **What is 6 tens?** (60) **If you know that 4 + 2 = 6, then you know that 40 + 20 = 60.**

2. Continue with other examples and have children try to find the sum without models. Record the basic fact and the tens addition at each step and guide children to find the sum.

2 Develop

Guided Learning

Teaching Example Read the objective and vocabulary with children. Guide children through each step of the example. Explain that the models are there to show the tens. Encourage children to try to find the sums using the basic fact and mental math.

Guided Practice

Have children complete **Exercises 1–4** as you observe. Give children the opportunity to answer the Explain Your Thinking question. Discuss how using a fact they know to add tens is a mental-math strategy.

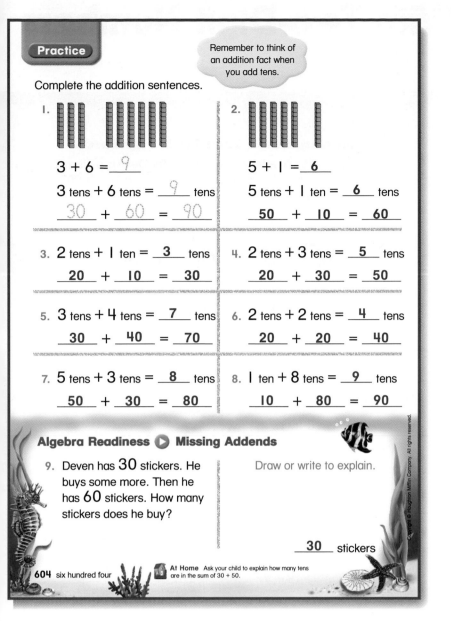

Practice

Remember to think of an addition fact when you add tens.

Complete the addition sentences.

1.

$3 + 6 = \underline{9}$

$3 \text{ tens} + 6 \text{ tens} = \underline{9} \text{ tens}$

$\underline{30} + \underline{60} = \underline{90}$

2.

$5 + 1 = \underline{6}$

$5 \text{ tens} + 1 \text{ ten} = \underline{6} \text{ tens}$

$\underline{50} + \underline{10} = \underline{60}$

3. $2 \text{ tens} + 1 \text{ ten} = \underline{3} \text{ tens}$

$\underline{20} + \underline{10} = \underline{30}$

4. $2 \text{ tens} + 3 \text{ tens} = \underline{5} \text{ tens}$

$\underline{20} + \underline{30} = \underline{50}$

5. $3 \text{ tens} + 4 \text{ tens} = \underline{7} \text{ tens}$

$\underline{30} + \underline{40} = \underline{70}$

6. $2 \text{ tens} + 2 \text{ tens} = \underline{4} \text{ tens}$

$\underline{20} + \underline{20} = \underline{40}$

7. $5 \text{ tens} + 3 \text{ tens} = \underline{8} \text{ tens}$

$\underline{50} + \underline{30} = \underline{80}$

8. $1 \text{ ten} + 8 \text{ tens} = \underline{9} \text{ tens}$

$\underline{10} + \underline{80} = \underline{90}$

Algebra Readiness ▶ Missing Addends

9. Deven has 30 stickers. He buys some more. Then he has 60 stickers. How many stickers does he buy?

Draw or write to explain.

$\underline{30}$ stickers

At Home Ask your child to explain how many tens are in the sum of 30 + 50.

604 six hundred four

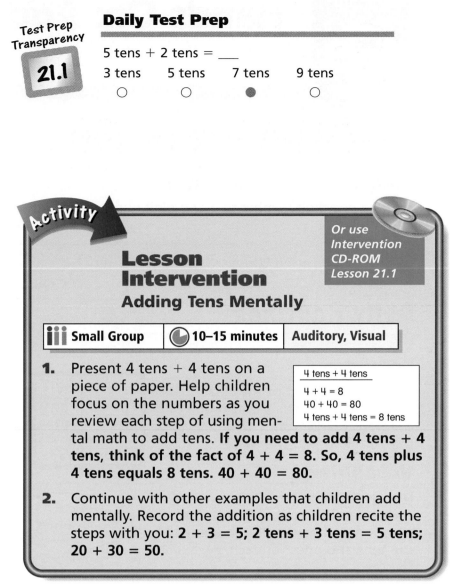

Daily Test Prep

$5 \text{ tens} + 2 \text{ tens} = \underline{}$

3 tens	5 tens	7 tens	9 tens
○	○	●	○

Activity

Or use Intervention CD-ROM Lesson 21.1

Lesson Intervention

Adding Tens Mentally

👥 Small Group	⏱ 10–15 minutes	Auditory, Visual

1. Present 4 tens + 4 tens on a piece of paper. Help children focus on the numbers as you review each step of using mental math to add tens. **If you need to add 4 tens + 4 tens, think of the fact of 4 + 4 = 8. So, 4 tens plus 4 tens equals 8 tens. 40 + 40 = 80.**

   > 4 tens + 4 tens
   > 4 + 4 = 8
   > 40 + 40 = 80
   > 4 tens + 4 tens = 8 tens

2. Continue with other examples that children add mentally. Record the addition as children recite the steps with you: **2 + 3 = 5; 2 tens + 3 tens = 5 tens; 20 + 30 = 50.**

③ Practice

Independent Practice

Children complete **Exercises 1–8** independently.

Algebra Readiness

After children complete **Exercise 9,** call on volunteers to share their solution.

Common Error

Leaving Out the Zero

Some children may forget to write a zero when they add tens. Point out that 3 tens is written as 30: 3 tens 0 ones. Compare 3 to 30 with models to emphasize the difference.

④ Assess and Close

What is 3 + 2? (5)

What is 3 tens + 2 tens? (5 tens)

What is 30 + 20? (50)

 **Keeping a Journal**

Draw and write to show how to use facts and mental math to add 50 + 10.

Hands-On: Add With Two-Digit Numbers

PLANNING THE LESSON

MATHEMATICS OBJECTIVE
Add a one-digit number to a two-digit number without regrouping.

Use Lesson Planner CD-ROM for Lesson 21.2.

Daily Routines

Calendar
Highlight the 20th of the current month. Ask questions that require children to add from 1 to 9 days to the 20th and find that date.

Sunday	Monday	Tuesday	Wednesday	Thursday	Friday	Saturday
				1	2	3 4
5	6	7	8	9	10	11
12	13	14	15	16	17	18
19	20	21	22	23	24	25
26	27	28	29	30	31	

Vocabulary
Discuss the term *two-digit* number. Give several examples of two-digit numbers and have children identify the tens and ones for each.

Vocabulary Cards

Meeting North Carolina's Standards
Prepare for Grade 2 Standard 1.04 Develop fluency with multi-digit addition and subtraction through 999 using multiple strategies.

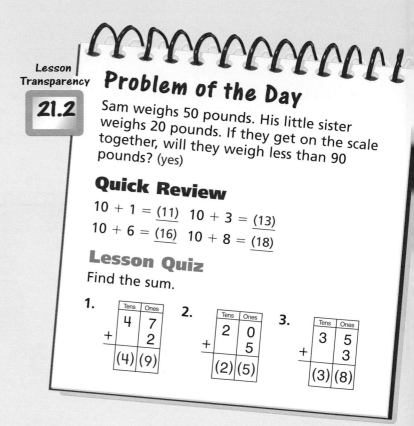

Lesson Transparency 21.2

Problem of the Day
Sam weighs 50 pounds. His little sister weighs 20 pounds. If they get on the scale together, will they weigh less than 90 pounds? (yes)

Quick Review
$10 + 1 = \underline{(11)}$ $10 + 3 = \underline{(13)}$
$10 + 6 = \underline{(16)}$ $10 + 8 = \underline{(18)}$

Lesson Quiz
Find the sum.

1.
Tens	Ones
4	7
+	2
(4)	(9)

2.
Tens	Ones
2	0
+	5
(2)	(5)

3.
Tens	Ones
3	5
+	3
(3)	(8)

LEVELED PRACTICE

RETEACH 21.2

Name _____ Date _____   **Reteach 21.2**

Add With Two-Digit Numbers
When you add a one-digit number to a two-digit number, add the ones first.

Find $32 + 5$.

Step 1 Show each number.

Workmat 5
Tens	Ones
3	2
+	5

Step 2 Add the ones.

Workmat 5
Tens	Ones
3	2
+	5
	7

Step 3 Add the tens.

Workmat 5
Tens	Ones
3	2
+	5
3	7

Use Workmat 5 and ▭▭▭▭ and ○.
Add. Write the sum.

1.
Tens	Ones
2	4
+	3
2	7

2.
Tens	Ones
4	2
+	5
4	7

3.
Tens	Ones
6	3
+	2
6	5

Use with text pages 605–606.

PRACTICE 21.2

Name _____ Date _____   **Practice 21.2**

Add With 2-Digit Numbers
Use Workmat 5 and ▭▭▭▭ and ○.
Add. Write the sum.

1.
Tens	Ones
3	2
+	5
3	7

2.
Tens	Ones
8	2
+	7
8	9

3.
Tens	Ones
6	6
+	3
6	9

4.
Tens	Ones
2	4
+	4
2	8

5.
Tens	Ones
5	1
+	7
5	8

6.
Tens	Ones
7	7
+	2
7	9

7.
Tens	Ones
6	2
+	3
6	5

8.
Tens	Ones
4	5
+	4
4	9

Test Prep

Fill in the ○ for the correct answer.
NH means Not Here.

9. Which exercise is shown by these models?

Tens	Ones
5	4
+	2

Tens	Ones
5	0
+	6

Tens	Ones
5	0
+	2

NH
○

Use with text pages 605–606.

ENRICHMENT 21.2

Name _____ Date _____   **Enrichment 21.2**

Find the Missing Number
Use Workmat 5 with ▭▭▭▭ and ○.
How many more do you need to show the sum? Write the missing number.

1.
Tens	Ones
3	2
+	7
3	9

2.
Tens	Ones
8	2
+	7
8	9

3.
Tens	Ones
6	5
+	2
6	7

4.
Tens	Ones
7	3
+	6
7	9

5.
Tens	Ones
3	5
+	1
3	6

6.
Tens	Ones
4	6
+	3
4	9

7.
Tens	Ones
5	3
+	5
5	8

8.
Tens	Ones
2	2
+	4
2	6

9.
Tens	Ones
3	1
+	7
3	8

Write About It Write a story problem. Use one of the exercises above. Solve.
Answers will vary. Example: Neil has 53 ants in his ant farm. He finds 5 more ants for the farm. How many ants are in his farm now? 58 ants

Use with text pages 605–606.

Practice Workbook Page 142

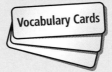

Reaching All Learners

Differentiated Instruction

English Learners

Children will have to understand the meaning of the word *first* in order to understand the steps involved when adding a one-digit number to a two-digit number without regrouping. Use Worksheet 21.2 to teach children the meaning of the word.

Special Needs
VISUAL, AUDITORY

Materials: *place-value blocks, Workmat 5, 2-digit addition charts (teacher-made)*

Place the workmat and the addition chart side by side. Have the child use place-value blocks to model the exercise as he or she adds.

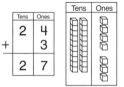

Gifted and Talented
VISUAL, TACTILE

Materials: *2 spinners (LT 38)*

- Have one child spin both spinners. He or she records the addition. The partner finds the sum.
- Partners switch roles and continue until all the possible combinations are found.

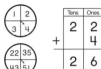

TECHNOLOGY

Spiral Review
To reinforce skills on lessons taught earlier, create **customized** spiral review worksheets using the *Ways to Assess* CD-ROM.

Education Place
Encourage students to visit **Education Place** at **eduplace.com/kids/mw/** for more student activities.

Manipulatives
Interactive **Base Ten Blocks** with several workmats are available on the *Ways to Success* CD-ROM.

Science Connection

Discuss tree rings with children. Explain that every year a tree lives, its trunk grows another ring of sapwood. Present problems for children to solve: *The tree in my backyard is 32 years old. How many rings will it have in 5 years?*

MATH CENTER

Real-Life Activity

Help children understand the usefulness of mathematics. This activity makes math come alive by connecting the lesson skills to a real-life situation.

PROBLEM SOLVING 21.2

Name _____ Date _____

Problem Solving 21.2

Add With Two-Digit Numbers

You can draw a picture or use models to help you add two-digit numbers. Solve.

1. Bonnie has 73 coins. Her father gives her 5 more. How many coins does Bonnie have now?

   Draw or write to explain. **Check children's work.**

   __78__ coins

2. There are 21 fish in Bobby's tank. He puts 3 new fish in the tank. How many fish are in the tank now?

   __24__ fish

3. There are 32 children in the park. Then 4 more children join them. How many children are in the park altogether?

   __36__ children

Copyright © Houghton Mifflin Company. All rights reserved.
Use with text pages 605–606.

HOMEWORK 21.2

Name _____ Date _____

Homework 21.2

Add With Two-Digit Numbers

Find $52 + 6$.

Add the ones.

Tens	Ones
5	2
+	6
	8

Think $2 + 6 = 8$

Add the tens.

Tens	Ones
5	2
+	6
5	8

So, $52 + 6 = 58$.

Add. Write the sum.

1.
Tens	Ones
3	4
+	2
3	6

2.
Tens	Ones
4	1
+	5
4	6

3.
Tens	Ones
6	3
+	4
6	7

4.
Tens	Ones
2	5
+	3
2	8

5.
Tens	Ones
8	7
+	2
8	9

6.
Tens	Ones
7	6
+	1
7	7

7.
Tens	Ones
9	4
+	3
9	7

8.
Tens	Ones
5	5
+	4
5	9

For each exercise, circle the addition problem with the least sum.

9. $90 + 5$
   $(90 + 3)$
   $90 + 7$

10. $64 + 4$
    $64 + 5$
    $(64 + 2)$

11. $(31 + 3)$
    $31 + 8$
    $31 + 6$

Copyright © Houghton Mifflin Company. All rights reserved.
Use with text pages 605–606.

ENGLISH LEARNERS 21.2

Name _____ Date _____

English Learners 21.2

Add With Two-Digit Numbers

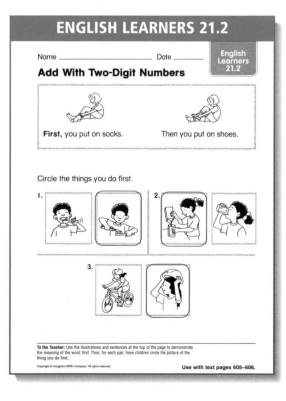

First, you put on socks. Then you put on shoes.

Circle the things you do first.

1.

2.

3.

To the Teacher: Use the illustrations and sentences at the top of the page to demonstrate the meaning of the word first. Then, for each pair, have children circle the picture of the thing you do first.

Copyright © Houghton Mifflin Company. All rights reserved.
Use with text pages 605–606.

Homework Workbook Page 142

TEACHING LESSON 21.2

LESSON ORGANIZER

Objective Add a one-digit number to a two-digit number without regrouping.

Resources Reteach, Practice, Enrichment, Problem Solving, Homework, English Learners, Transparencies, Math Center

Materials Place-value blocks, Workmat 5, tens and ones chart transparency, spinner (LT 38), two-digit addition chart (teacher-made)

Activity

Warm-Up Activity
Modeling Tens and Ones

Small Group	5 minutes	Tactile, Visual

Materials: *place-value blocks, Workmat 5*

1. Review one- and two-digit numbers. Have children use place-value blocks to model each number on Workmat 5.

2. Have a volunteer say a number and write it on the board. Ask another volunteer to tell the number of tens and ones blocks used to model the number.

3. Continue by asking volunteers to present both one- and two-digit numbers to model.

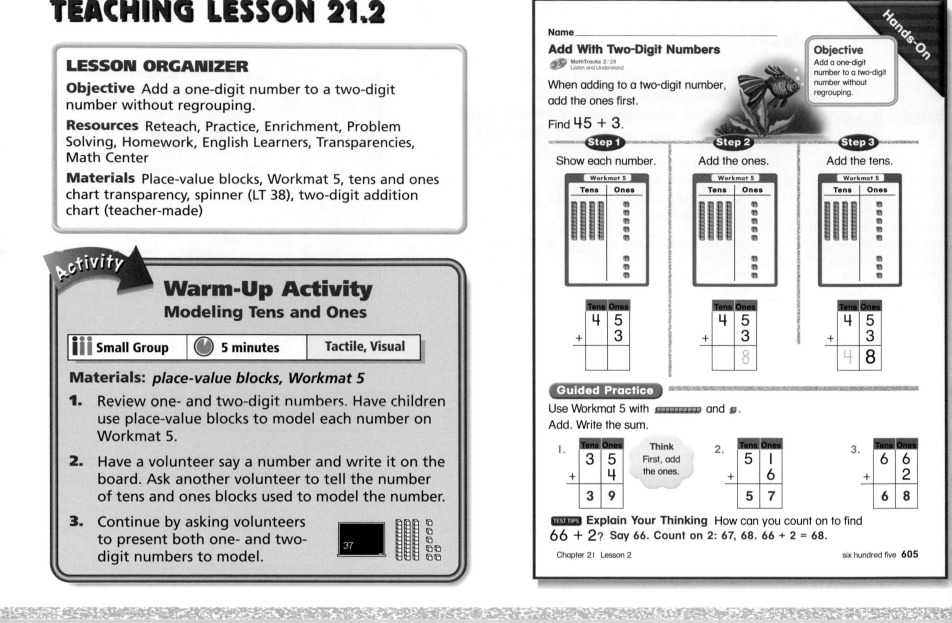

Add With Two-Digit Numbers

MathTracks 2/28
Listen and Understand

Objective Add a one-digit number to a two-digit number without regrouping.

When adding to a two-digit number, add the ones first.

Find 45 + 3.

Step 1 Show each number.

Step 2 Add the ones.

Step 3 Add the tens.

Guided Practice

Use Workmat 5 with ▭▭▭ and ▪.
Add. Write the sum.

1.
Tens	Ones
3	5
+	4
3	9

Think First, add the ones.

2.
Tens	Ones
5	1
+	6
5	7

3.
Tens	Ones
6	6
+	2
6	8

TEST TIPS **Explain Your Thinking** How can you count on to find 66 + 2? Say 66. Count on 2: 67, 68. 66 + 2 = 68.

Chapter 21 Lesson 2

six hundred five **605**

---

1 Introduce Activity

Model Adding One-Digit to Two-Digit Numbers

Whole Group	10–15 minutes	Tactile, Visual

Materials: *place-value blocks, Workmat 5, tens and ones chart transparency*

1. Model the number 54 with blocks. Review its value of 5 tens 4 ones. Point out that 54 is a two-digit number because it has both tens and ones. **I want to add 3 to this number. How do I show 3?** (3 ones) Position the ones blocks on the chart and emphasize their placement below 4 in the ones column. Identify 3 as a one-digit number.

2. Explain that when you add to a two-digit number, you begin by adding the ones. **What is 4 ones + 3 ones?** (7 ones) **Now we go to the tens. Are we adding anything to the 5 tens?** (no) **So we have 5 tens. The sum of is 54 + 3 is 57.**

3. Repeat with another example. Have children model the addition at their seats as you work on the overhead.

2 Develop

Guided Learning

Teaching Example Read the objective with children. Guide children through each step of the example as they model it with place-value blocks on Workmat 5.

Guided Practice

Have children complete **Exercises 1–3** as you observe. Give children the opportunity to answer the Explain Your Thinking question. Then discuss that there are many strategies and methods for adding. Help children understand why counting on is quicker than using models to add 66 + 2.

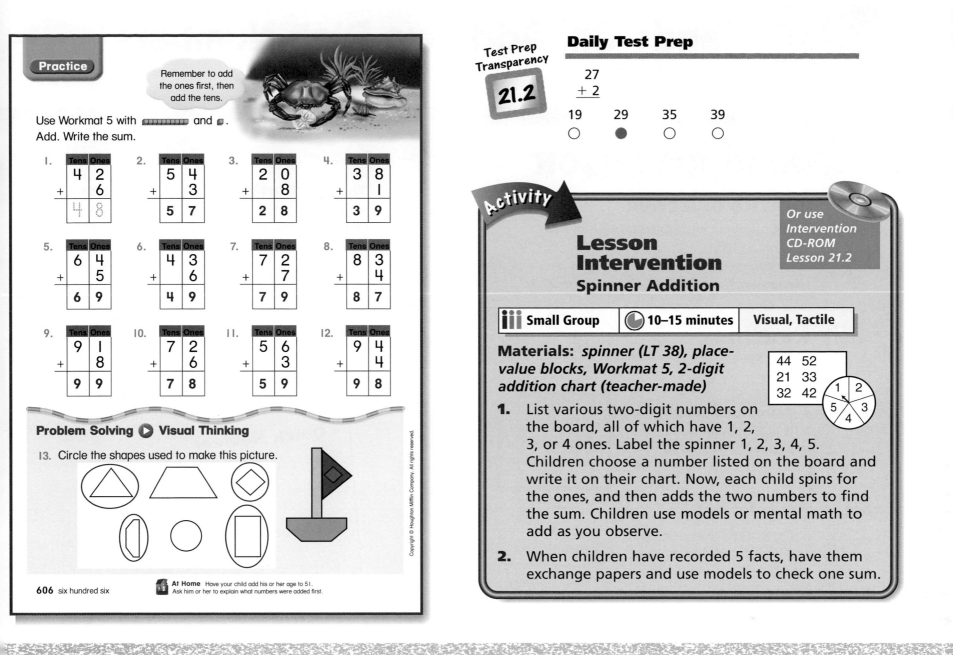

Remember to add the ones first, then add the tens.

Use Workmat 5 with ▭▭▭ and ▪. Add. Write the sum.

	Tens	Ones			Tens	Ones			Tens	Ones			Tens	Ones
1.	4	2		2.	5	4		3.	2	0		4.	3	8
+		6		+		3		+		8		+		1
	4	**8**			5	7			2	8			3	9

	Tens	Ones			Tens	Ones			Tens	Ones			Tens	Ones
5.	6	4		6.	4	3		7.	7	2		8.	8	3
+		5		+		6		+		7		+		4
	6	9			4	9			7	9			8	7

	Tens	Ones			Tens	Ones			Tens	Ones			Tens	Ones
9.	9	1		10.	7	2		11.	5	6		12.	9	4
+		8		+		6		+		3		+		4
	9	9			7	8			5	9			9	8

Problem Solving ▶ Visual Thinking

13. Circle the shapes used to make this picture.

606 six hundred six

At Home Have your child add his or her age to 51. Ask him or her to explain what numbers were added first.

Daily Test Prep

$$\begin{array}{r} 27 \\ +\ 2 \\ \hline \end{array}$$

19 ○   29 ●   35 ○   39 ○

Activity

Lesson Intervention

Spinner Addition

Or use Intervention CD-ROM Lesson 21.2

👤👤👤 Small Group	🕐 10–15 minutes	Visual, Tactile

Materials: *spinner (LT 38), place-value blocks, Workmat 5, 2-digit addition chart (teacher-made)*

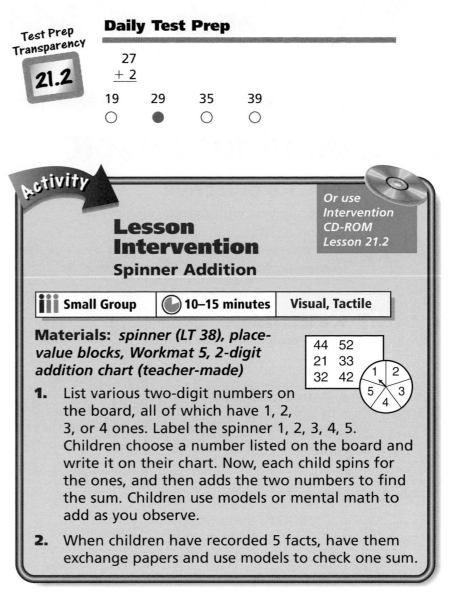

44 52
21 33
32 42

1. List various two-digit numbers on the board, all of which have 1, 2, 3, or 4 ones. Label the spinner 1, 2, 3, 4, 5. Children choose a number listed on the board and write it on their chart. Now, each child spins for the ones, and then adds the two numbers to find the sum. Children use models or mental math to add as you observe.

2. When children have recorded 5 facts, have them exchange papers and use models to check one sum.

---

❸ Practice

Independent Practice

Children complete **Exercises 1–12** independently.

Problem Solving

After children complete **Exercise 13,** call on volunteers to share their solutions. Use the shapes chosen to draw the boat and check the solution.

Common Error

Adding Ones to the Tens

Some children may mistakenly add the one-digit number to the tens. Point to the tens and ones headings on the Workmat as you reinforce that the one-digit number only has ones and is added to the ones above it.

❹ Assess and Close

If you need to add 35 + 4, what numbers do you add first? (5 ones and 4 ones)

What is 5 ones + 4 ones? (9 ones)

Then what do you add? (3 tens)

What is the sum of 35 + 4? (39)

✏️ Keeping a Journal

Draw and write to show how you add 33 + 6.

PLANNING THE LESSON

MATHEMATICS OBJECTIVE
Add two-digit numbers without regrouping.

Use Lesson Planner CD-ROM for Lesson 21.3.

Daily Routines

Calendar
Point to the 14th of the month. Have children use the calendar to find the date that is 2 weeks later. Then show how the sum of 14 + 14 is also 28.

Sunday	Monday	Tuesday	Wednesday	Thursday	Friday	Saturday
			1	2	3	4
5	6	7	8	9	10	11
12	13	14	15	16	17	18
19	20	21	22	23	24	25
26	27	28	29	30	31	

Vocabulary
Review the words **tens** and **ones** by highlighting the tens and ones in a two-digit number. Then say a number and have a volunteer tell how many tens and ones.

Vocabulary Cards

Meeting North Carolina's Standards
Prepare for Grade 2 Standard 1.04 Develop fluency with multi-digit addition and subtraction through 999 using multiple strategies.

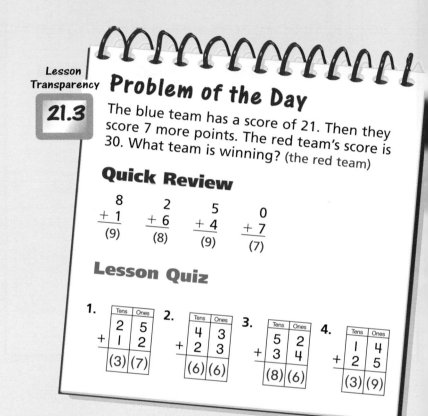

Lesson Transparency **21.3**

Problem of the Day
The blue team has a score of 21. Then they score 7 more points. The red team's score is 30. What team is winning? (the red team)

Quick Review

$$\begin{array}{r} 8 \\ + 1 \\ \hline (9) \end{array} \qquad \begin{array}{r} 2 \\ + 6 \\ \hline (8) \end{array} \qquad \begin{array}{r} 5 \\ + 4 \\ \hline (9) \end{array} \qquad \begin{array}{r} 0 \\ + 7 \\ \hline (7) \end{array}$$

Lesson Quiz

	Tens	Ones
	2	5
+	1	2
	(3)	(7)

1.

	Tens	Ones
	4	3
+	2	3
	(6)	(6)

2.

	Tens	Ones
	5	2
+	3	4
	(8)	(6)

3.

	Tens	Ones
	1	4
+	2	5
	(3)	(9)

4.

LEVELED PRACTICE

RETEACH 21.3

Name _____ Date _____ Reteach 21.3

Add Two-Digit Numbers
Find 24 + 15.

Step 1 Show each number.
Workmat 5 — Tens | Ones

Step 2 Add the ones.
Workmat 5 — Tens | Ones

Step 3 Add the tens.
Workmat 5 — Tens | Ones

	Tens	Ones
	2	4
+	1	5

	Tens	Ones
	2	4
+	1	5
		9

	Tens	Ones
	2	4
+	1	5
	3	9

Use Workmat 5 and ▭▭▭ and □.
Add. Write the sum.

1.
	Tens	Ones
	1	7
+	3	2
	4	9

2.
	Tens	Ones
	5	2
+	2	6
	7	8

3.
	Tens	Ones
	4	3
+	4	5
	8	8

4.
	Tens	Ones
	3	6
+	4	2
	7	8

Use with text pages 607–608.

PRACTICE 21.3

Name _____ Date _____ Practice 21.3

Add Two-Digit Numbers
Use Workmat 5 and ▭▭▭▭ and □.
Add. Write the sum.

1.
	Tens	Ones
	3	1
+	1	4
	4	5

2.
	Tens	Ones
	4	5
+	2	2
	6	7

3.
	Tens	Ones
	1	8
+	4	1
	5	9

4.
	Tens	Ones
	6	3
+	2	5
	8	8

5.
	Tens	Ones
	1	7
+	6	2
	7	9

6.
	Tens	Ones
	2	4
+	3	3
	5	7

7.
	Tens	Ones
	6	0
+	1	9
	7	9

8.
	Tens	Ones
	4	6
+	4	3
	8	9

9.
	Tens	Ones
	1	2
+	7	6
	8	8

10.
	Tens	Ones
	7	0
+	2	7
	9	7

11.
	Tens	Ones
	5	2
+	3	1
	8	3

12.
	Tens	Ones
	5	7
+	1	1
	6	8

Test Prep

Solve.
13. Molly plays catch for 23 minutes. Later she plays catch for 16 minutes. How many minutes does Molly play catch in all ?

Draw or write to explain.

_39_ minutes

Use with text pages 607–608.

ENRICHMENT 21.3

Name _____ Date _____ Enrichment 21.3

Two-Digit Number Addition Patterns

Continue the pattern.

1.
	Tens	Ones
	4	3
+	1	5
	5	8

2.
	Tens	Ones
	4	2
+	1	6
	5	8

3.
	Tens	Ones
	4	1
+	1	7
	5	8

4.
	Tens	Ones
	4	0
+	1	8
	5	8

5.
	Tens	Ones
	8	0
+	1	2
	9	2

6.
	Tens	Ones
	8	0
+	1	4
	9	4

7.
	Tens	Ones
	8	0
+	1	6
	9	6

8.
	Tens	Ones
	8	0
+	1	8
	9	8

Write About It Write your own addition pattern. Explain the pattern.
Answers will vary. Possible response:

$$\begin{array}{r} 1\ 7 \\ + 1\ 0 \\ \hline 2\ 7 \end{array} \qquad \begin{array}{r} 1\ 8 \\ + 1\ 0 \\ \hline 2\ 8 \end{array} \qquad \begin{array}{r} 1\ 9 \\ + 1\ 0 \\ \hline 2\ 9 \end{array} \qquad \begin{array}{r} 2\ 0 \\ + 1\ 0 \\ \hline 3\ 0 \end{array}$$

The first addend increases by 1, the second addend stays the same, so the sum increases by 1.

Use with text pages 607–608.

Practice Workbook Page 143

Reaching All Learners

Differentiated Instruction

English Learners

English-language learners will need to understand the meaning of the word *amount* in order to understand word problems that require adding money. Use Worksheet 21.3 to help children develop understanding of this word.

Inclusion
VISUAL, AUDITORY

Materials: *place-value blocks, Workmat 5*

- Have the child model an exercise with blocks on the workmat.
- Emphasize the steps of adding the ones and then the tens.
- Repeat with other exercises.

Gifted and Talented
VISUAL, TACTILE

- Have children work in pairs. One child writes a two-digit number. The partner writes two numbers whose sum totals that number.
- Children switch roles and repeat.

$$24 \quad \begin{array}{r} 12 \\ +12 \\ \hline 24 \end{array}$$

Literature Connection

Share the book, *A Collection for Kate* by Barbara deRubertis. Pause after reading page 10 and have children add to find how many magnets Emma has. Use the context of collections to present other addition problems.

MATH CENTER

Cross-Curricular Activity

As you use this activity to relate the mathematics of this lesson to another curriculum area, children will see how math can help them with other subjects.

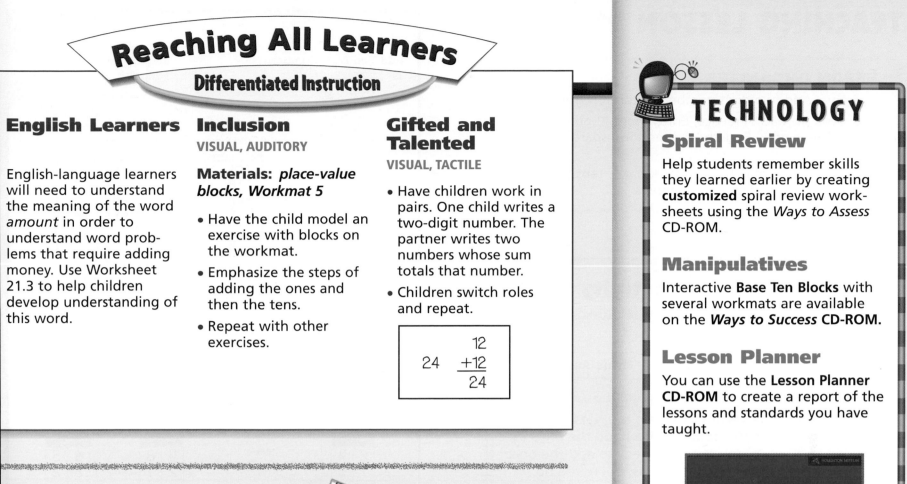

PROBLEM SOLVING 21.3

Name _____ Date _____ Problem Solving 21.3

Add Two-Digit Numbers

You can draw a picture or use models to solve.

1. Daria collects 24 shells. Then she collects 31 rocks. How many shells and rocks does she collect in all?

   Draw or show each number.

   Check children's work.

   __55__ shells and rocks

2. There are 64 apple trees on the farm. There are 32 pear trees on the farm. How many fruit trees are on the farm altogether?

   Draw or show each number.
   Check children's work.

   __96__ fruit trees

3. Ryan buys a comic book for 75¢. He buys a pencil for 12¢. How much money does he spend in all?

   Draw or show each amount.
   Check children's work.

   __87__ ¢

Copyright © Houghton Mifflin Company. All rights reserved.

Use with text pages 607–608.

HOMEWORK 21.3

Name _____ Date _____ Homework 21.3

Add Two-Digit Numbers

Find 43 + 25.

Tens	Ones
4	3
+ 2	5
6	8

Think Add the ones. Then add 4 tens + 2 tens.

Add. Write the sum.

1. Tens Ones: 22 + 14 = 36
2. Tens Ones: 56 + 32 = 88
3. Tens Ones: 38 + 20 = 58
4. Tens Ones: 75 + 23 = 98
5. Tens Ones: 17 + 42 = 59
6. Tens Ones: 63 + 23 = 86
7. Tens Ones: 50 + 29 = 79
8. Tens Ones: 33 + 54 = 87
9. Tens Ones: 61 + 24 = 85
10. Tens Ones: 45 + 30 = 75
11. Tens Ones: 84 + 13 = 97
12. Tens Ones: 65 + 24 = 89

13. Sara has 25 baseball cards. Joe has 10 baseball cards. How many baseball cards do they have in all?

   __35__ baseball cards

   Draw or write to explain.

Copyright © Houghton Mifflin Company. All rights reserved.

Use with text pages 607–608.

ENGLISH LEARNERS 21.3

Name _____ Date _____ English Learners 21.3

Add Two-Digit Numbers

Amount means *how much.*
This **amount** is 26¢.

Write the amount.

1. This amount is __15¢__ ¢.
2. This amount is __30¢__ ¢.
3. This amount is __6¢__ ¢.
4. This amount is __11¢__ ¢.

To the Teacher: Use the example and sentences at the top of the page to teach children the meaning of the word amount. Then have children write the amount of each group of coins.

Copyright © Houghton Mifflin Company. All rights reserved.

Use with text pages 607–610.

Homework Workbook Page 143

TEACHING LESSON 21.3

LESSON ORGANIZER

Objective Add two-digit numbers without regrouping.

Resources Reteach, Practice, Enrichment, Problem Solving, Homework, English Learners, Transparencies, Math Center

Materials Place-value blocks, Workmat 5, tens and ones chart transparency, dimes and pennies

Activity

Warm-Up Activity

Adding A One-Digit Number to a Two-Digit Number

iiii Small Group	🕐 5 minutes	Tactile, Auditory

Materials: *place-value blocks, Workmat 5*

1. Write 24 + 5 in vertical form on the board. Have children model the addition. **Do I add the ones or tens first?** (ones) Invite a volunteer to add the ones on the board. **Now add the tens.** There are no tens to add, so we can just bring down the 2 tens. Have a volunteer complete the addition.

2. Have volunteers share how they first add the ones, then the tens.

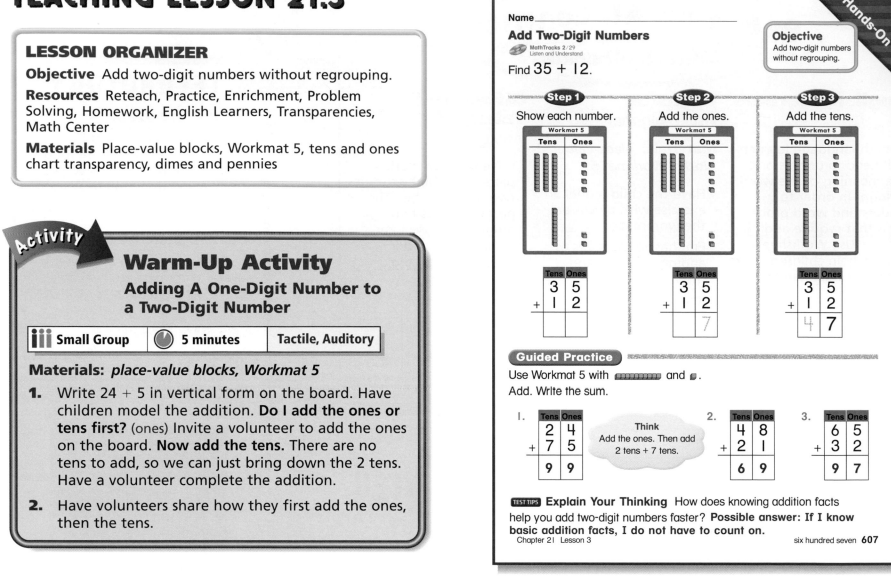

Name _____

Add Two-Digit Numbers
MathTracks 2/29
Listen and Understand

Find 35 + 12.

Hands-On

Objective
Add two-digit numbers without regrouping.

Step 1 Show each number.

Step 2 Add the ones.

Step 3 Add the tens.

Guided Practice

Use Workmat 5 with ▭▭▭ and ▫.
Add. Write the sum.

Think
Add the ones. Then add
2 tens + 7 tens.

TEST TIPS Explain Your Thinking How does knowing addition facts help you add two-digit numbers faster? **Possible answer: If I know basic addition facts, I do not have to count on.**

Chapter 21 Lesson 3   six hundred seven **607**

---

① Introduce **Activity**

Model Adding Two-Digit Numbers

iiii Whole Group	🕐 10–15 minutes	Tactile, Visual

Materials: *place-value blocks, Workmat 5, tens and ones chart transparency*

1. Write 46 + 32. Model the number 46 with blocks on the transparency. **We show 46 as 4 tens 6 ones. I need to add 32 to this number. How can I show 32?** (3 tens, 2 ones) Point out that both 46 and 32 are two-digit numbers because they have tens and ones.

2. Remind children that you begin by adding the ones. **How much is 6 ones + 2 ones?** (8 ones) **Now we add the tens. 4 tens + 3 tens = 7 tens. The sum is 7 tens 8 ones, or 78.**

3. Repeat with another example. Have children model the addition at their seats and share their work as you show the addition on the overhead.

② Develop

Guided Learning

Teaching Example Read the objective with children. Guide children through each step of the example as they model the addition with place-value models on Workmat 5.

Guided Practice

Have children complete **Exercises 1–3** as you observe. Give children the opportunity to answer the Explain Your Thinking question.

First add the ones.
Then add the tens.

Use Workmat 5 with ▭▭▭ and ▫.
Add. Write the sum.

	Tens	Ones			Tens	Ones			Tens	Ones			Tens	Ones
1.	2	1	2.		1	8	3.		3	2	4.		2	3
+	2	4	+		2	1	+		1	3	+		4	2
	4	5			3	9			4	5			6	5

	Tens	Ones			Tens	Ones			Tens	Ones			Tens	Ones
5.	4	2	6.		7	5	7.		3	4	8.		4	2
+	3	7	+		1	0	+		4	5	+		1	6
	7	9			8	5			7	9			5	8

	Tens	Ones			Tens	Ones			Tens	Ones			Tens	Ones
9.	5	5	10.		6	4	11.		6	1	12.		7	2
+	3	3	+		3	1	+		2	6	+		1	4
	8	8			9	5			8	7			8	6

Problem Solving ▷ Number Sense

Can you tell which addition problem has the greatest sum without adding?
Circle the problem.

13.	32 + 25	14.	44 + 11	15.	53 + 14
	32 + 15		(44 + 31)		(53 + 44)
	(32 + 45)		44 + 21		53 + 34

16. **Talk About It** How did you find your answer? **Possible answer:
All the first addends are the same, so the greatest sum
would be the one with the greatest second addend.**

608 six hundred eight

At Home Ask your child to add 73 + 22 and explain how he or she found the sum.

Go on

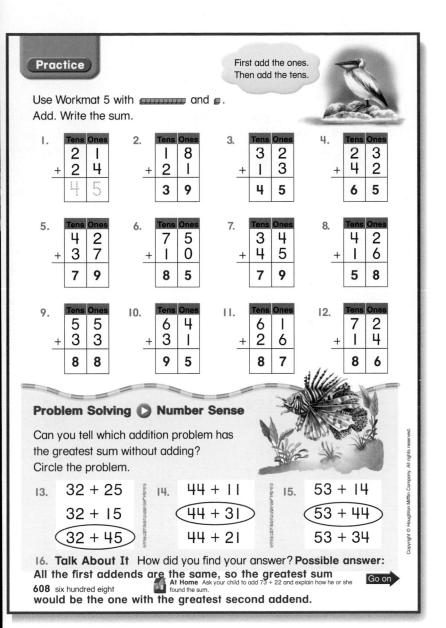

Learning To Do Mental Arithmetic

There should be a continuing emphasis in the contemporary American classroom on encouraging the use of mental math. This is because research suggests that mental arithmetic leads to deeper understanding of the number system. **Mental arithmetic activities can provide opportunities for practicing and using numbers and operations in ways that make sense to children.**

In this chapter, children are encouraged to use basic facts and mental math to add tens. **They explain how knowing 2 + 5 = 7 helps them solve 20 + 50.** This helps them to relate a basic fact using the mental math strategy.

Using mental arithmetic encourages children to reason about a problem situation and the numbers used in it. It also encourages them to choose methods to simplify a computation and find the answer.

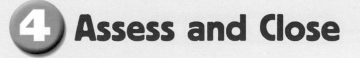

3 Practice

Independent Practice

Children complete **Exercises 1–12** independently.

Problem Solving

After children complete **Exercises 13–15,** call on volunteers to share their answers. Use the **Talk About It** question in **Exercise 16** to share methods used by children in solving the problems.

Common Error

Forgetting to Add Tens

Some children may add only the ones and omit the tens. Have children check each column from top to bottom to look for numbers to add.

4 Assess and Close

If you need to add 25 + 14, what numbers do you add first? (5 ones and 4 ones)

What do you add after you add the ones? (add the tens; 2 tens plus 1 ten)

What is the sum of 25 + 14? (39)

Keeping a Journal

Draw and write to show how you add 12 + 15.

Lesson continues

Daily Test Prep

$$41$$
$$+ 15$$

34   46   56   96
○   ○   ●   ○

Activity

Or use Intervention CD-ROM Lesson 21.3

Lesson Intervention
Addition with Zeros

| 👥 Small Group | 🕐 10–15 minutes | Auditory, Visual |

Materials: *tens and ones chart transparency, place-value blocks, Workmat 5*

1. Write 35 + 20 in a tens and ones chart on the transparency. **How do you add a number that has 0 ones?** (5 ones + 0 ones is 5 ones.) Have children model the steps of the addition as you record.

2. Have children complete similar addition exercises. Allow children to use place-value blocks to model the addition. Invite volunteers to show their results.

Name_____

Now Try This Add Money Amounts

Add money the same way you add numbers. Think of dimes and pennies as tens and ones.

Add.

Tens	Ones
4	1 ¢
+ 5	4 ¢
9	5 ¢

Read 41¢ as 41 cents.

Add.

1. $\begin{array}{r} 32¢ \\ +57¢ \\ \hline 89¢ \end{array}$

2. $\begin{array}{r} 70¢ \\ +10¢ \\ \hline 80¢ \end{array}$

3. $\begin{array}{r} 52¢ \\ +15¢ \\ \hline 67¢ \end{array}$

4. $\begin{array}{r} 32¢ \\ + 6¢ \\ \hline 38¢ \end{array}$

5. $\begin{array}{r} 25¢ \\ + 4¢ \\ \hline 29¢ \end{array}$

6. $\begin{array}{r} 75¢ \\ +20¢ \\ \hline 95¢ \end{array}$

7. $\begin{array}{r} 55¢ \\ +34¢ \\ \hline 89¢ \end{array}$

8. $\begin{array}{r} 43¢ \\ + 6¢ \\ \hline 49¢ \end{array}$

9. $\begin{array}{r} 35¢ \\ +12¢ \\ \hline 47¢ \end{array}$

10. $\begin{array}{r} 34¢ \\ +45¢ \\ \hline 79¢ \end{array}$

11. $\begin{array}{r} 78¢ \\ +21¢ \\ \hline 99¢ \end{array}$

12. $\begin{array}{r} 44¢ \\ +32¢ \\ \hline 76¢ \end{array}$

Chapter 21   six hundred nine **609**

Now Try This

Add Money Amounts

Materials: *dimes, pennies*

Introduce Review the value of 1 dime as 10 cents and 1 penny as 1 cent. Connect this to tens and ones.

Develop Have children look at the example and count aloud the number of dimes and pennies that equal 41¢. Repeat for 54¢. Explain that you can add 41¢ + 54¢ the same way you add tens and ones. Review the example shown.

Practice Have children complete **Exercises 1–12** as you observe. Let children use dimes and pennies to model the addition as needed.

Quick Check

Complete the addition sentences.

1. 5 tens + 3 tens = __8__ tens
   $$\underline{50} + \underline{30} = \underline{80}$$

2. 1 ten + 6 tens = __7__ tens
   $$\underline{10} + \underline{60} = \underline{70}$$

Use Workmat 5 with ▭▭▭ and ▪.
Add. Write the sum.

3.
Tens	Ones
3	8
+	1
3	9

4.
Tens	Ones
7	3
+	5
7	8

5.
Tens	Ones
6	5
+ 2	4
8	9

6.
Tens	Ones
4	6
+ 2	1
6	7

Science Connection

Icebergs

Icebergs float in the ocean. In one area, there are **26** large icebergs and **32** small icebergs.

Write a number sentence that shows how many icebergs there are in that one area.

$$\underline{26} \; (+) \; \underline{32} \; (=) \; \underline{58}$$

WEEKLY WR READER eduplace.com/kids/mw/

610 six hundred ten

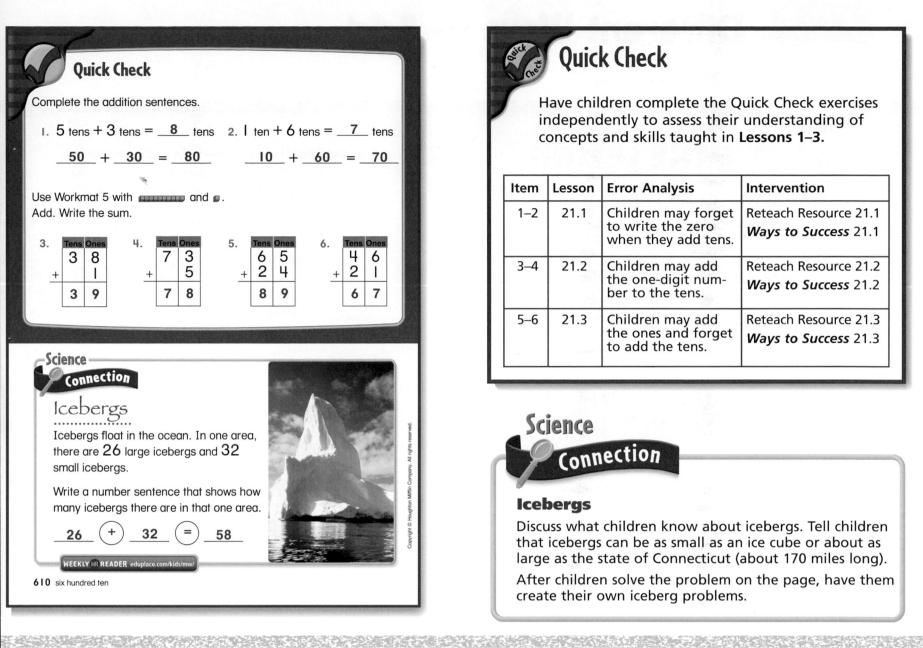

Quick Check

Have children complete the Quick Check exercises independently to assess their understanding of concepts and skills taught in **Lessons 1–3.**

Item	Lesson	Error Analysis	Intervention
1–2	21.1	Children may forget to write the zero when they add tens.	Reteach Resource 21.1 *Ways to Success* 21.1
3–4	21.2	Children may add the one-digit number to the tens.	Reteach Resource 21.2 *Ways to Success* 21.2
5–6	21.3	Children may add the ones and forget to add the tens.	Reteach Resource 21.3 *Ways to Success* 21.3

Science Connection

Icebergs

Discuss what children know about icebergs. Tell children that icebergs can be as small as an ice cube or about as large as the state of Connecticut (about 170 miles long).

After children solve the problem on the page, have them create their own iceberg problems.

Different Ways to Add

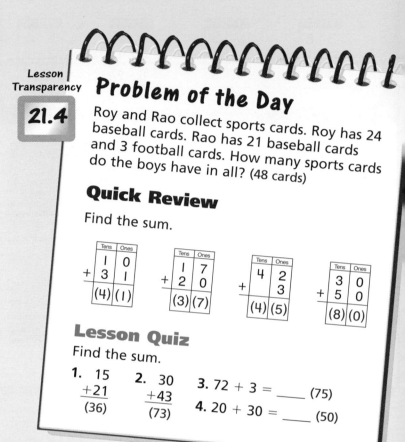

PLANNING THE LESSON

MATHEMATICS OBJECTIVE
Use different ways to add.

Use Lesson Planner CD-ROM for Lesson 21.4.

Daily Routines

Calendar
Use the calendar to record how many days are in the current month and in the next month. Have children add to find how many days in all are in both months.

Sunday	Monday	Tuesday	Wednesday	Thursday	Friday	Saturday
			1	2	3	4
5	6	7	8	9	10	11
12	13	14	15	16	17	18
19	20	21	22	23	24	25
26	27	28	29	30	31	

Vocabulary
Discuss the meaning of the term *mental math* by giving examples of mental math strategies such as counting on and making a ten. Ask volunteers to tell when they use mental math.

Vocabulary Cards

Meeting North Carolina's Standards
Prepare for Grade 2 Standard 1.04 Develop fluency with multi-digit addition and subtraction through 999 using multiple strategies.

Lesson Transparency
21.4

Problem of the Day
Roy and Rao collect sports cards. Roy has 24 baseball cards. Rao has 21 baseball cards and 3 football cards. How many sports cards do the boys have in all? (48 cards)

Quick Review
Find the sum.

Tens	Ones
1	0
+3	1
(4)	(1)

Tens	Ones
1	7
+2	0
(3)	(7)

Tens	Ones
4	2
+	3
(4)	(5)

Tens	Ones
3	0
+5	0
(8)	(0)

Lesson Quiz
Find the sum.

1. 15
   +21
   (36)

2. 30
   +43
   (73)

3. 72 + 3 = _____ (75)

4. 20 + 30 = _____ (50)

LEVELED PRACTICE

RETEACH 21.4

Name _____ Date _____ | Reteach 21.4

Different Ways to Add
You can use different ways to add.

Use mental math. Think of an addition fact.	Use pencil and paper. Add the ones first. Then add the tens.	Use tens and ones blocks. Show the numbers.
Think 3 + 4 = 7		
30 +40 70	43 +15 58	30 +16 46

Choose a way to add. Write the sum.

1.
Tens	Ones
2	0
+4	0
6	0

2.
Tens	Ones
1	4
+2	3
3	7

3.
Tens	Ones
5	2
+3	0
8	2

4.
Tens	Ones
4	2
+	7
4	9

5. 50   6. 53   7. 82   8. 48   9. 12
   +15   + 4   +13   +20   +65
    65   57   95   68   77

Copyright © Houghton Mifflin Company. All rights reserved.

Use with text pages 611–612.

PRACTICE 21.4

Name _____ Date _____ | Practice 21.4

Different Ways to Add
Choose a way to add. Write the sum.

Think
You can use mental math.
You can use paper and pencil.
You can use tens and ones blocks.

1. 76   2. 38   3. 74   4. 63
   +13   +10   +12   +25
    89   48   86   88

5. 20   6. 16   7. 40   8. 13
   + 8   + 3   +29   +55
    28   19   69   68

9. 25 + 4 = __29__   10. 30 + 10 = __40__

11. 10 + 25 = __35__   12. 73 + 5 = __78__

13. 85 + 4 = __89__   14. 15 + 60 = __75__

Test Prep

Fill in the ○ for the correct answer.
NH means Not Here.

15. Roland keeps 32 toy cars in a box. The box holds 35 toy cars. How many more toy cars can Roland put into the box before it is full?

67   35   3   NH
○   ○   ●   ○

Copyright © Houghton Mifflin Company. All rights reserved.

Use with text pages 611–612.

ENRICHMENT 21.4

Name _____ Date _____ | Enrichment 21.4

Adding and Finding the Greatest Sum

Choose a way to add. Write the sums.
Circle the greatest sum in each row.

1. 43   62   51   59
   +33   +16   +26   +20
    76   78   77   (79)

2. 60   31   55   13
   +12   +24   +10   +34
    (72)   55   65   47

3. 46   63   37   31
   +22   +15   +10   +11
    68   (78)   47   42

Write About It Write the sums in Exercise I in order from greatest to least.

__79__ __78__ __77__ __76__

What pattern do you see?
Answers will vary. Possible answer:

__Sums decrease by 1.__

Copyright © Houghton Mifflin Company. All rights reserved.

Use with text pages 611–612.

Reaching All Learners

Differentiated Instruction

English Learners

Some English-language learners may not be familiar with speech balloons. Use Worksheet 21.4 to help children understand that speech balloons represent dialogue.

Special Needs

TACTILE, VISUAL

Materials: *place-value blocks, Workmat 5, number line 20–50 (LT 8)*

• Display the number line and blocks. Write 24 + 3 and 24 + 55 in vertical form. Discuss why the number line works for one exercise and not the other. Also discuss why the blocks work for both exercises, but the number line is faster and easier.

Early Finishers

TACTILE, VISUAL

• Have children each choose an exercise from page 611 and use the numbers to write a story problem.

• Display the problems for children to solve.

> I have 33 red buttons and 46 white buttons. How many buttons do I have?

TECHNOLOGY

Spiral Review

You can prepare students for standardized tests with **customized** spiral review on key skills using the *Ways to Assess* CD-ROM.

eBook

eMathBook allows students to review lessons and do homework without carrying their textbooks home.

Games

Students can practice their computational skills using the **Rock Hopper** math game, available on the *Ways to Success* CD-ROM.

Literature Connection

Read the book, *A Collection for Kate* by Barbara deRubertis. Stop at page 20 and have children discuss what method they would use to find the total number of postcards. After they add, turn the page and point out that Kate uses paper and pencil.

MATH CENTER

Real-Life Activity

Help children understand the usefulness of mathematics. This activity makes math come alive by connecting the lesson skills to a real-life situation.

PROBLEM SOLVING 21.4

Name _____ Date _____

Problem Solving 21.4

Different Ways to Add

Use mental math, pencil and paper, or tens and ones blocks to solve.

	Draw or write to explain.
1. There are 58 cows in the field. There are 21 cows in the barn. How many cows are there in all? ___79___ cows	
2. Mel played piano for 20 minutes on Saturday. He played for 25 minutes on Sunday. How long did Mel play during the weekend? ___45___ minutes	
3. Ana Maria waters 26 tomato plants. She waters 10 bean plants. How many plants does Ana Maria water altogether? ___36___ plants	
4. Rory walks her dog 15 minutes one day. She walks her dog 30 minutes the next day. How long does Rory walk her dog both days? ___45___ minutes	

Copyright © Houghton Mifflin Company. All rights reserved.

Use with text pages 611–612.

HOMEWORK 21.4

Name _____ Date _____

Homework 21.4

Different Ways to Add

Use mental math.

Tens	Ones
3	0
+ 2	0
5	0

Use paper and pencil.

Tens	Ones
4	7
+ 1	2
5	9

Choose a way to add. Write the sum.

1.
Tens	Ones
4	5
+	1
4	6

2.
Tens	Ones
5	3
+ 2	5
7	8

3.
Tens	Ones
1	6
+ 2	3
3	9

4.
$$20 + 3 = 23$$

5.
$$44 + 11 = 55$$

6.
$$62 + 10 = 72$$

7.
$$24 + 34 = 58$$

8.
$$60 + 5 = 65$$

9.
$$33 + 20 = 53$$

10.
$$21 + 48 = 69$$

11.
$$76 + 10 = 86$$

12. $30 + 10 = $ ___40___

13. $55 + 1 = $ ___56___

14. Ray picks 13 red apples. Then he picks 12 yellow apples. How many apples does he pick?

Draw or write to explain.

___25___ apples

Copyright © Houghton Mifflin Company. All rights reserved.

Use with text pages 611–612.

ENGLISH LEARNERS 21.4

Name _____ Date _____

English Learners 21.4

Different Ways to Add

> My name is Juan

The boy is saying, "My name is Juan."

Draw a picture of yourself. Then fill in the speech balloon with something you want to say.

> Words the child is saying

Drawing of a child

To the Teacher: Use the example at the top of the page to teach children about speech balloons. Then have children draw a picture of themselves. Have them write something in the speech balloon that they would like to say.

Copyright © Houghton Mifflin Company. All rights reserved.

Use with text pages 611–612.

TEACHING LESSON 21.4

LESSON ORGANIZER

Objective Use different ways to add.

Resources Reteach, Practice, Enrichment, Problem Solving, Homework, English Learners, Transparencies, Math Center

Materials Place-value blocks, Workmat 5

Activity

Warm-Up Activity
Model Mental Math Strategies

👥 Small Group	⏱ 5 minutes	Auditory, Visual

1. Ask children to add 60 + 3 without using paper and pencil. Have volunteers share the different ways they found the sum. Some children may count on in their heads or use a number line.

2. Repeat with 12 + 6. Some children may add the ones first (2 + 6) and then add 1 ten to get 18.

3. Continue with other problems children may solve using mental math.

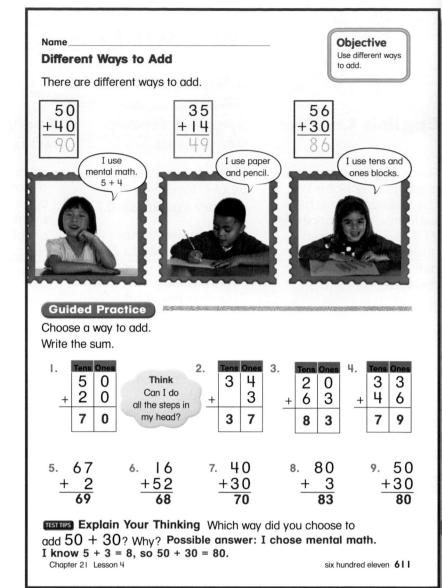

1 Introduce
Discuss Different Ways to Add

👥 Whole Group	⏱ 10–15 minutes	Tactile, Visual

Materials: *place-value blocks, Workmat 5*

1. Write 30 + 20. **What ways could you use to add these numbers?** (mental math using the fact 3 + 2; tens blocks; paper and pencil) Have a volunteer demonstrate how to solve with each method as you discuss. Point out that for this exercise, using the basic fact 3 + 2 was a fast way to add.

2. Present 31 + 45. **What method would you use to solve this addition?** (Answers will vary.) Suggest children try pencil and paper or place-value blocks, then discuss the methods used. If a child can find the sum using mental math, have him or her explain.

2 Develop

Guided Learning

Teaching Example Read the objective with children. Guide children through the three example problems using each method indicated. Encourage children to share other methods for a given exercise. Be sure children understand that they should use the strategy that works best for them on any problem.

Guided Practice

Have children complete **Exercises 1–9** as you observe. Give children the opportunity to answer the Explain Your Thinking question. Continue discussion until you have reviewed all the different methods used to solve.

Choose a way to add.
Write the sum.

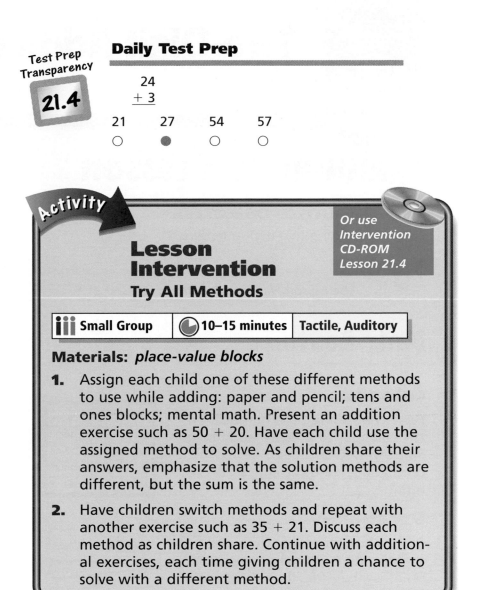

Ways to Add
Use mental math.
Use paper and pencil.
Use tens and ones blocks.

1.
Tens	Ones
1	8
+ 4	1
5	9

2.
Tens	Ones
5	3
+ 4	4
9	7

3. 58
   +10
    68

4. 14
   +83
    97

5. 72
   + 7
    79

6. 36
   + 0
    36

7. 45
   + 2
    47

8. 10
   +50
    60

9. 43
   +35
    78

10. 40
    +46
     86

11. 24
    +55
     79

12. 85
    + 4
     89

13. 85 + 3 = __88__   14. 66 + 2 = __68__   15. 40 + 50 = __90__

16. 58 + 1 = __59__   17. 10 + 40 = __50__   18. 20 + 30 = __50__

Problem Solving ▶ Reasoning

19. Maria has 35 fish cards in one book. She has 54 cards in another book. How many cards does she have in all?

Draw or write to explain.

__89__ cards

612 six hundred twelve

At Home Have your child use dimes and pennies to show the last row of exercises and find the sums.

Daily Test Prep

  24
 + 3

21   27   54   57
○   ●   ○   ○

Activity

Or use
Intervention
CD-ROM
Lesson 21.4

Lesson Intervention
Try All Methods

| iii Small Group | ⏱ 10–15 minutes | Tactile, Auditory |

Materials: *place-value blocks*

1. Assign each child one of these different methods to use while adding: paper and pencil; tens and ones blocks; mental math. Present an addition exercise such as 50 + 20. Have each child use the assigned method to solve. As children share their answers, emphasize that the solution methods are different, but the sum is the same.

2. Have children switch methods and repeat with another exercise such as 35 + 21. Discuss each method as children share. Continue with additional exercises, each time giving children a chance to solve with a different method.

---

3 Practice

Independent Practice

Children complete **Exercises 1–18** independently.

Problem Solving

After children complete **Exercise 19,** call on volunteers to share their answers.

Common Error

Adding Ones to Tens in Horizontal Form

Some children may have difficulty adding in horizontal form. Help children rewrite horizontal exercises in tens and ones charts to line up the digits.

4 Assess and Close

How could you use mental math to add 32 + 1? (Answers may vary. Possible response: Count on 1 from 32: 33.)

Which method would you use to add 43 + 35? (Answers may vary.) **What is the sum?** (78)

✎ Keeping a Journal

Show an addition problem you can solve with mental math. Show another exercise in which you would use paper and pencil to solve.

Two-Digit Addition Practice

PLANNING THE LESSON

MATHEMATICS OBJECTIVE
Practice adding two-digit numbers.

Use Lesson Planner CD-ROM for Lesson 21.5.

Daily Routines

Calendar

Have children use the numbers on the calendar to practice addition. Point to two dates and have children add to find the sum of the numbers.

Sunday	Monday	Tuesday	Wednesday	Thursday	Friday	Saturday
			1	2	3	4
5	6	7	8	9	10	11
12	13	14	15	16	17	18
19	20	21	22	23	24	25
26	27	28	29	30	31	

Vocabulary

Review the terms **less than** and **greater than**. Choose a benchmark on a number line, then have volunteers use one of these terms to describe whether a number is less than or is greater than the benchmark number.

Vocabulary Cards

Meeting North Carolina's Standards
Prepare for Grade 2 Standard 1.04 Develop fluency with multi-digit addition and subtraction through 999 using multiple strategies.

Lesson Transparency 21.5

Problem of the Day

Alex has 50¢. He wants to buy milk for 25¢ and a snack for 30¢. Does he have enough money? (no)

Quick Review

Write the sum.

```
    4        3        0        5
  + 5      + 6      + 7      + 4
  ---      ---      ---      ---
  (9)      (9)      (7)      (9)
```

Lesson Quiz

Write the sum.

```
1.  62      2.  50      3. 62 + 3 = ____ (65)
  + 15        + 38
  ----        ----      4. 10 + 60 = ____ (70)
  (77)        (88)
```

LEVELED PRACTICE

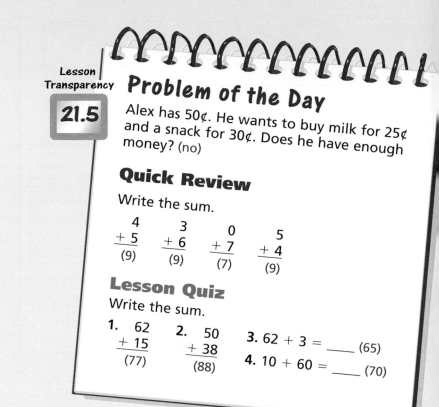

RETEACH 21.5

Name _____ Date _____ Reteach 21.5

Two-Digit Addition Practice

Find 27 + 41.

Step 1 Add the ones.	Step 2 Add the tens.
27 +41 = 8	27 +41 = 68
Think 7 + 1 = 8	Think 2 tens + 4 tens = 6 tens

Write the sum.

```
1.  23    2.  47    3.  25    4.  62    5.  43
  + 16      + 31      + 54      +  5      + 30
  ----      ----      ----      ----      ----
   39        78        79        67        73

6.  40    7.  32    8.  12    9.  53   10.  40
  +  9      + 41      + 70      +  3      + 20
  ----      ----      ----      ----      ----
   49        73        82        56        60
```

11. 10 + 40 = __50__   12. 21 + 6 = __27__

13. 31 + 5 = __36__   14. 60 + 8 = __68__

15. 36 + 2 = __38__   16. 50 + 30 = __80__

Copyright © Houghton Mifflin Company. All rights reserved. Use with text pages 613–614.

PRACTICE 21.5

Name _____ Date _____ Practice 21.5

Two-Digit Addition Practice

Write the sum.

```
1.  14    2.  50    3.  60    4.  46
  + 11      + 23      +  9      + 13
  ----      ----      ----      ----
   25        73        69        59

5.  76    6.  54    7.  20    8.  44
  + 22      + 32      + 53      + 43
  ----      ----      ----      ----
   98        86        73        87

9.  18   10.  21   11.  80   12.  62
  + 50      + 58      + 14      + 23
  ----      ----      ----      ----
   68        79        94        85

13.  25  14.  36   15.  51   16.  46
   + 40     + 21      + 15      + 11
   ----     ----      ----      ----
    65       57        66        57
```

Test Prep

Solve.   Draw or write to explain.

17. The children collected 34 box tops in April. They collected 42 box tops in May. The children need 70 box tops in all. Do they have enough?

Yes, they have 76.

Use with text pages 613–614.

ENRICHMENT 21.5

Name _____ Date _____ Enrichment 21.5

Number Names

Use mental math, paper and pencil, or draw a picture.

Look at the number in the box.

Find 2 different addends to name each number.

Answers will vary. Possible answers shown.

```
1.  19      10        12
          +  9      +  7
          ----      ----
           19        19

2.  39      19        35
          + 20   +   +  4
          ----      ----
           39        39

3.  56      16        24
          + 40   +   + 32
          ----      ----
           56        56
```

Write About It Explain how you found the different names for each number.

Answers will vary. Possible answer: I picked a number that was less than or equal to the sum. Then I found the number I needed to add to get the sum.

Use with text pages 613–614.

Practice Workbook Page 145

Reaching All Learners
Differentiated Instruction

English Learners

In order to learn the two-step process required when adding two-digit numbers, children will have to understand the meaning of the word *start*. Worksheet 21.5 will help them to understand this word.

Inclusion
VISUAL, AUDITORY

• Write these exercises.

Tens	Ones
2	4
+	3
(2)	(7)

Tens	Ones
3	0
+ 2	0
(5)	(0)

Tens	Ones
5	2
+ 2	6
(7)	(8)

• Guide the child through each exercise, discussing the possible strategies for each. Encourage the child to use whatever works best for him or her.

Gifted and Talented
VISUAL, AUDITORY

• Assign each pair of children a 2-digit number, such as 38.

• Then have children find pairs of numbers that equal their given number.

```
  (38)      24
          + 14

            31
          +  7
```

TECHNOLOGY
Spiral Review

Create **customized** spiral review worksheets for individual students using the *Ways to Assess* CD-ROM.

Lesson Planner

You can customize your teaching plan or to meet your curriculum requirements with the **Lesson Planner CD-ROM**.

eBook

An electronic version of this lesson can be found in **eMathBook**.

Education Place

You can visit **Education Place** at **eduplace.com/math/mw/** for teacher support materials.

Art Connection

Share pictures from *Numbers at Play* by Charles Sullivan or find copies of *I Saw the Figure 5* by Charles Demuth and *Numbers in Color* by Jasper Johns. Challenge children to find an artistic way to communicate that 20 + 20 = 40.

MATH CENTER
Cross-Curricular Activity

As you use this activity to relate the mathematics of this lesson to another curriculum area, children will see how math can help them with other subjects.

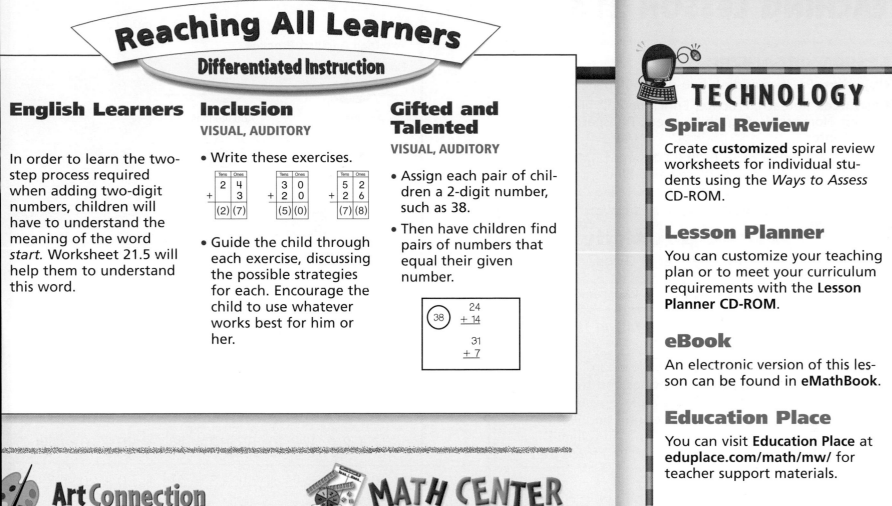

Homework Workbook Page 145

TEACHING LESSON 21.5

LESSON ORGANIZER

Objective Practice adding two-digit numbers.

Resources Reteach, Practice, Enrichment, Problem Solving, Homework, English Learners, Transparencies, Math Center

Materials Number cards 0–20 (LT 14 and 15) and tens 10–90 (LT 16), Workmat 5, place-value blocks, index cards

Activity

Warm-Up Activity
Aligning Tens and Ones

iii Small Group	⏱ 5 minutes	Visual, Auditory

Materials: *number cards 0–20 (LT 14 and 15) and tens 10–90 (LT 16), Workmat 5*

1. Write a two-digit number on the board. Have children identify the number of ones and the number of tens in the number. Draw a place-value grid around the number. **Which column do I label ones?** (the right column) **tens?** (the left column) Repeat with a one-digit number. Reinforce that one-digit numbers do not have tens.

2. Give each group 8 cards, with both one- and two-digit numbers. Each child takes a pair of cards and positions them vertically on the Workmat. Have children identify the tens and ones in each number. Have children find the sum.

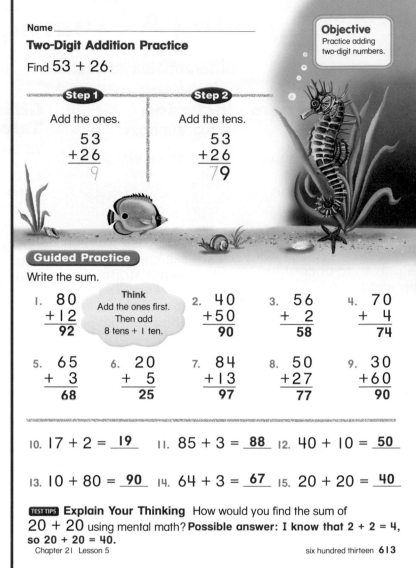

Name_____

Two-Digit Addition Practice

Find 53 + 26.

Objective
Practice adding two-digit numbers.

Step 1	Step 2
Add the ones.	Add the tens.
53 +26 9	53 +26 79

Guided Practice

Write the sum.

1. 80 +12 **92**	**Think** Add the ones first. Then add 8 tens + 1 ten.	2. 40 +50 **90**	3. 56 + 2 **58**	4. 70 + 4 **74**
5. 65 + 3 **68**	6. 20 + 5 **25**	7. 84 +13 **97**	8. 50 +27 **77**	9. 30 +60 **90**

10. 17 + 2 = __19__   11. 85 + 3 = __88__   12. 40 + 10 = __50__

13. 10 + 80 = __90__   14. 64 + 3 = __67__   15. 20 + 20 = __40__

TEST TIPS **Explain Your Thinking** How would you find the sum of 20 + 20 using mental math? **Possible answer: I know that 2 + 2 = 4, so 20 + 20 = 40.**

Chapter 21 Lesson 5   six hundred thirteen **613**

---

1 Introduce
Discuss Adding Tens and Ones

iiii Whole Group	⏱ 10–15 minutes	Visual, Auditory

1. Write 62 + 27 on the board vertically. **How do we use paper and pencil to add?** Children should direct you to first add the ones, then the tens. Ask a volunteer to record the addition.

2. Repeat with 65 + 2. **How would you find the sum?** (Answers may vary.) **What is the value of 2?** (2 ones) Be sure children realize that you are adding 2 ones to 5 ones, 0 tens to 6 tens.

3. Now, write 20 + 50 = ____ on the board. **How would you add these two numbers?** (Use a basic fact, 2 + 5 = 7 to find 20 + 50 = 70.) Maintain place value in children's minds by emphasizing 20 + 50 is 2 tens + 5 tens. Ask a volunteer to complete the sentence on the board.

2 Develop

Guided Learning

Teaching Example Read the objective with children. Guide children through each step of the example.

Guided Practice

Have children complete **Exercises 1–15** as you observe. Give children the opportunity to answer the Explain Your Thinking question.

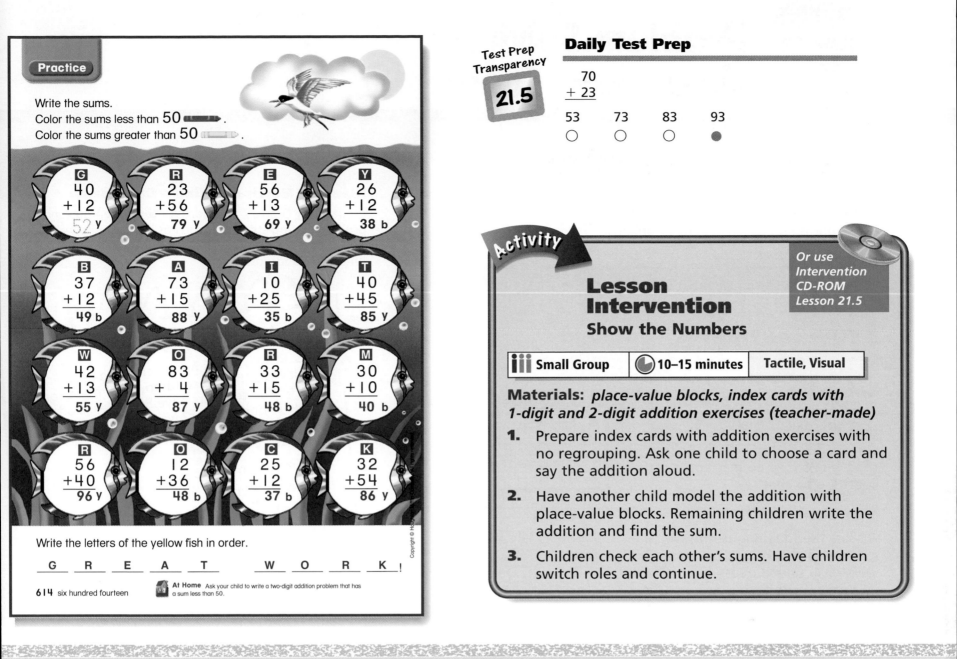

Practice

Write the sums.
Color the sums less than 50 .
Color the sums greater than 50 .

G	R	E	Y
40 +12 = 52 y	23 +56 = 79 y	56 +13 = 69 y	26 +12 = 38 b

B	A	I	T
37 +12 = 49 b	73 +15 = 88 y	10 +25 = 35 b	40 +45 = 85 y

W	O	R	M
42 +13 = 55 y	83 + 4 = 87 y	33 +15 = 48 b	30 +10 = 40 b

R	O	C	K
56 +40 = 96 y	12 +36 = 48 b	25 +12 = 37 b	32 +54 = 86 y

Write the letters of the yellow fish in order.

G R E A T   W O R K !

614 six hundred fourteen

At Home Ask your child to write a two-digit addition problem that has a sum less than 50.

Daily Test Prep

Test Prep Transparency **21.5**

$$\begin{array}{r} 70 \\ +\ 23 \\ \hline \end{array}$$

53   73   83   93
○   ○   ○   ●

Activity

Lesson Intervention

Show the Numbers

Or use Intervention CD-ROM Lesson 21.5

iii Small Group	⏱ 10–15 minutes	Tactile, Visual

Materials: *place-value blocks, index cards with 1-digit and 2-digit addition exercises (teacher-made)*

1. Prepare index cards with addition exercises with no regrouping. Ask one child to choose a card and say the addition aloud.

2. Have another child model the addition with place-value blocks. Remaining children write the addition and find the sum.

3. Children check each other's sums. Have children switch roles and continue.

3 Practice

Independent Practice

Children complete the exercises independently. Be sure they understand how they are to color. If necessary, help children write the letters on the yellow fish in order to find the message.

Common Error

Making Fact Errors
Some children may be distracted by choosing a strategy and may make careless errors. Other children may not recall some facts or the strategies for finding a sum. Observe and question children as they work to determine the problem.

4 Assess and Close

How do you add 20 + 70? (Possible answers: use the fact 2 + 7; 2 tens + 7 tens = 9 tens.)

How do you add the tens in 34 + 2? (3 tens plus 0 tens equals 3 tens.)

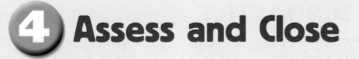 **Keeping a Journal**

Draw and write to show how you add 31 + 16.

CHAPTER 21   Lesson 5   **614**

Problem Solving: Guess and Check

PLANNING THE LESSON

MATHEMATICS OBJECTIVE
Use guess and check to solve problems.

Use Lesson Planner CD-ROM for Lesson 21.6.

Daily Routines

Calendar
Ask children to guess how many days there are from today until a certain day of the month. Record their guesses, then lead them in counting to check.

Sunday	Monday	Tuesday	Wednesday	Thursday	Friday	Saturday
				1	2	3	4
5	6	7	8	9	10	11
12	13	14	15	16	17	18
19	20	21	22	23	24	25
26	27	28	29	30	31	

Vocabulary
Discuss the meaning of the words **guess** and **check**. Give an example of when you take a guess and tell how you would check your answer. Have volunteers give situations of their own.

Vocabulary Cards

Meeting North Carolina's Standards
Prepare for Grade 2 Standard **1.05** Create and solve problems using strategies such as modeling, composing and decomposing quantities, using doubles, and making tens and hundreds.

Lesson Transparency
21.6

Problem of the Day
Ms. Brown's class has 23 children and Mr. Hall's class has 25 children. They meet for a party. The teachers have 50 plates. Do they have enough plates? (yes)

Quick Review
Use mental math to solve.
2 tens + 2 tens = ____ (4) tens
50 + 20 = ____ (70)
3 tens + 6 tens = ____ (9) tens
2 tens + 6 tens = ____ (8) tens

Lesson Quiz
Beads come in bags of 15, 30, and 50. Kyla only needs 65 beads. Which two bags should she buy? (50 and 15)

LEVELED PRACTICE

RETEACH 21.6

Name _____ Date _____
Reteach 21.6

Problem Solving Guess and Check

Read It Look for information.
Rita buys 2 jars of beads.
She buys 38 beads in all.
Which 2 jars does she buy?

red 15   yellow 23   blue 12

Picture It Here is a model of the problem.

38 beads in all	
first color: _____	second color: _____

Solve It Use the model to solve the problem.
Numbers chosen will vary.

1. Choose 2 colors. Add to find a total.

$$15 + 12 = 27$$

2. Try again.

$$23 + 15 = 38$$

Is the sum 38?
If not, try 2 other colors.

Is the sum 38?
If not, try 2 other colors.

3. Which 2 jars does Rita buy?
red and **yellow**

Copyright © Houghton Mifflin Company. All rights reserved.
Use with text pages 615–618.

PRACTICE 21.6

Name _____ Date _____
Practice 21.6

Problem Solving: Guess and Check
Use Guess and Check to solve.

Crayon Boxes			
A	B	C	D
12	24	45	62

Draw or write to explain.

1. Sophie takes 2 boxes with 57 crayons to her friends. Which 2 boxes does she take?

box **A** and box **C**

2. Leando gives away 74 crayons. Which 2 boxes does he give away?

box **A** and box **D**

Test Prep

Fill in the ○ for the correct answer.
NH means Not Here.

3. José and Fredrico want 86 crayons. Which boxes do they want? Use the chart above to solve.

A and B   B and D   C and A   NH
   ○   ●   ○   ○

Copyright © Houghton Mifflin Company. All rights reserved.
Use with text pages 615–616.

ENRICHMENT 21.6

Name _____ Date _____
Enrichment 21.6

How Many Cups and Plates?

The first graders are having a class picnic.
Add to find which bags each child should bring.
Use guess and check to solve.

Plates   Cups

Bag A   Bag B   Bag C   Bag D   Bag E   Bag F   Bag G   Bag H
17   12   41   32   35   42   14   24
plates plates plates plates   cups   cups   cups   cups

1. Emily needs to bring 53 plates. Which two bags should she bring?
Bag **B** and Bag **C**

2. There are 49 children at the picnic. Ray needs to bring 1 cup for each child. Which two bags should he bring?
Bag **E** and bag **G**

Write About It Write and solve a story problem using the plates or cups. Explain your work.
Answers will vary. Possible answer: Seth needs to bring 73 plates to the picnic. Which two bags should he bring? He should bring Bags C and D because 41 + 32 = 73.

Copyright © Houghton Mifflin Company. All rights reserved.
Use with text pages 615–618.

Reaching All Learners
Differentiated Instruction

English Learners

In order to solve some problems, children will need to guess and check. Use Worksheet 21.6 to help them understand the meaning of the word *guess*.

Inclusion
TACTILE, VISUAL

Materials: *plastic bags, blocks*

• Make bags of blocks.

• Present a problem. *I need 19 blocks. Which two bags should I use?* Guide the child through the guess and check strategy to find that 12 and 7 are needed. Repeat to find 47. (12 and 35)

Gifted and Talented
TACTILE, VISUAL

Materials: *coin set, clear plastic bags*

• Have children bag groups of coins and label each bag with the amount inside. Have children create money problems that can be solved by guess and check.

• Children exchange problems and corresponding bags and solve.

Science Connection

The tallest bird in North America is the whooping crane. At one time there were fewer than 20 of them in the world. Have children write addition problems about cranes.

MATH CENTER

Number of the Week Activity

Display the Number of the Week to motivate children to use their problem-solving skills. The exercises cover topics across all math strands.

TECHNOLOGY

Spiral Review

Using the *Ways to Assess* CD-ROM, you can create **customized** spiral review worksheets covering any lessons you choose.

Education Place

Recommend that parents visit **Education Place** at **eduplace.com/parents/mw/** for parent support activities.

Intervention

Use the *Ways to Success* intervention software to support students who need more help in understanding the concepts and skills taught in this chapter.

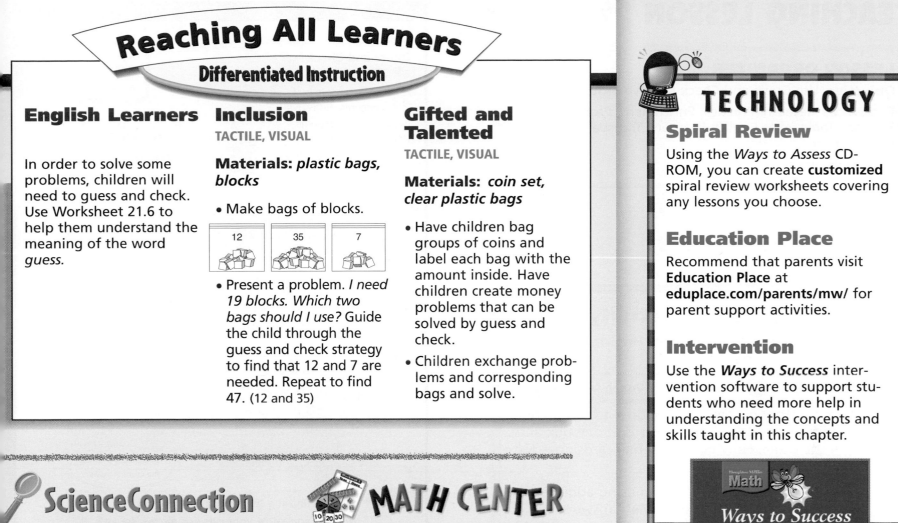

TEACHING LESSON 21.6

LESSON ORGANIZER

Objective Use Guess and Check to solve problems.

Resources Reteach, Practice, Enrichment, Problem Solving, Homework, English Learners, Transparencies, Math Center

Materials Bags

Warm-Up Activity

Modeling Solving Problems with Addition

👥 Small Group	🕐 5 minutes	Visual, Auditory

1. Present a story problem for children to solve. For example, Joe has 23 baseball cards in one box and 12 in the other. How many baseball cards does Joe have? (35)

2. Have children solve the problem using addition. Allow children time to discuss their answers.

3. Continue with a problem to add.

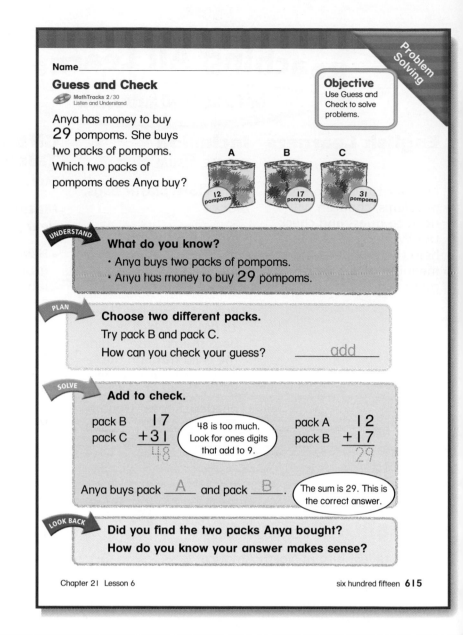

1 Introduce

Model Guess and Check to Solve Problems

👥 Whole Group	🕐 10–15 minutes	Visual, Auditory

Materials: *bags*

1. Model how to approach a problem that you need to first guess and then add to solve. Display 3 bags labeled with the numbers: 11, 14, 20. Explain that each bag contains counters for a game. **Maya needs exactly 25 counters for her game. Which two bags should she use?**

2. Have children guess which two numbers will total 25. Record their guesses. **We can check our guess by adding the numbers to see if the total is 25.** Have a volunteer add. If the numbers do not total 25, have children choose a different combination. Prompt children to think about whether they need a greater number or a lesser number. Continue until the bags for 11 and 14 are selected.

2 Develop

Guided Learning

Teaching Example Read the objective with children. Guide them through each step of the example.

Understand **What do you know?** (Anya buys two packs of pompoms. She has money to buy 29 pompoms.)

Plan **You can use guess and check, because there is no other way to begin to solve.**

Solve **You could guess 17 and 31. Add to check. 48 is too many. You need smaller numbers. Try the smaller numbers and add. Which two packs should Anya buy?** (A and B)

Check **Did you answer the question?** (yes) Point out the answer is not a number, but two letters.

Guided Practice

Have children complete **Exercises 1–2** on page 616 as you observe.

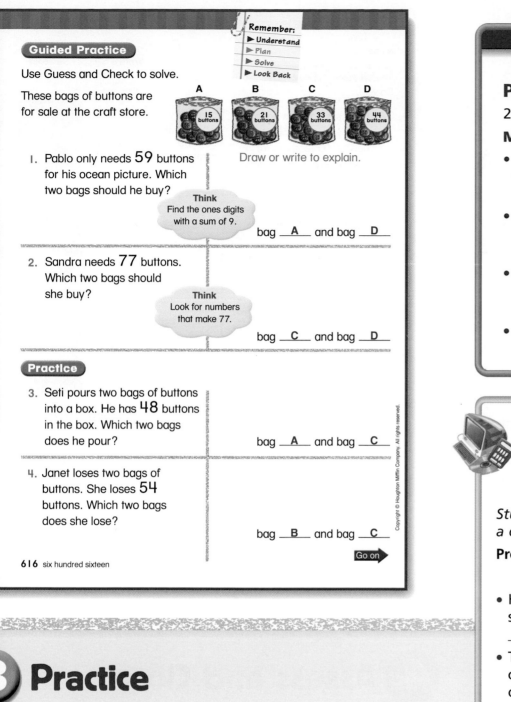

Guided Practice

Use Guess and Check to solve.

These bags of buttons are for sale at the craft store.

A   B   C   D

15 buttons   21 buttons   33 buttons   44 buttons

Draw or write to explain.

1. Pablo only needs 59 buttons for his ocean picture. Which two bags should he buy?

Think
Find the ones digits with a sum of 9.

bag __A__ and bag __D__

2. Sandra needs 77 buttons. Which two bags should she buy?

Think
Look for numbers that make 77.

bag __C__ and bag __D__

Practice

3. Seti pours two bags of buttons into a box. He has 48 buttons in the box. Which two bags does he pour?

bag __A__ and bag __C__

4. Janet loses two bags of buttons. She loses 54 buttons. Which two bags does she lose?

bag __B__ and bag __C__

616 six hundred sixteen

Go on

Practice

Independent Practice

Children complete **Exercises 3–4** on page 616 independently.

KEEPING SKILLS SHARP

Play "Football Addition"

2 players

Materials: *spinner (LT 38), blank scoreboard*

- Label each section of a 4-part spinner: 1, 2, 3, 6. Give each child a "scoreboard" and group children in pairs to play this addition practice game.

- Each child takes a turn being the team with the ball by spinning for a score. The child records his or her score.

- Play continues as children take turns spinning. Each new score is added to the previous sum to find their current score.

- The game is over when one of the players reaches a score of 50.

Technology Connection
Use Calculators with Estimation

Students will estimate sums of given addends and use a calculator to check.

Provide students with the list of addends below.

11, 14, 15, 20, 23, 27, 32

- Have students copy the following addition sentences:

___ + ___ = 26   ___ + ___ = 47   ___ + ___ = 55

- Tell students to predict which addends correctly complete each sentence. Each addend may be used only once with one left over. Have students explain their predictions.

- Have students use calculators to check their predictions. Allow them to revise incorrect predictions.

- Have students find 3 new sums using these addends. Have them swap sums with a partner and do the activity again.

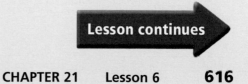
Lesson continues

Stamps come in packs of 5, 10, and 20. Greg needs 25 stamps. Which two packs should he buy?

5, 10   10, 20   5, 20   NH
○   ○   ●   ○

Activity

Lesson Intervention

Or use Intervention CD-ROM Lesson 21.6

Using Strategies to Make a Guess

| 👤👤👤 Small Group | 🕐 10–15 minutes | Visual, Tactile |

1. Write a guess and check story problem on the board. For example: Craft sticks are sold in bags of 10, 25, and 28. Kendra can buy 35 sticks to build a box. Which two bags will she buy?

2. **What does the problem tell us?** (Kendra can buy 35 sticks.) **We need to find out which of the 2 bags shown she should buy.** Write the 3 numbers. **Look at the 3 numbers. Can you guess which 2 equal 35?** (Record children's guesses.)

3. Give children a strategy to use: **Look at the ones in each number. Which 2 numbers have ones that total 5?** (10, 25) **How do you know?** (0 + 5 = 5) Have a volunteer write the addition sentence on the board to check.

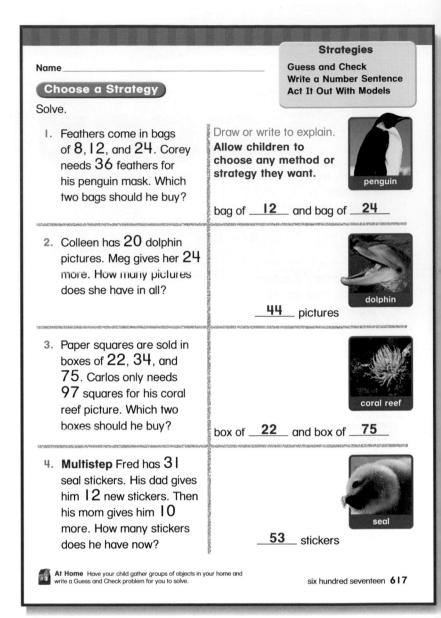

Name_____

Strategies
Guess and Check
Write a Number Sentence
Act It Out With Models

Choose a Strategy

Solve.

1. Feathers come in bags of 8, 12, and 24. Corey needs 36 feathers for his penguin mask. Which two bags should he buy?

   Draw or write to explain.
   Allow children to choose any method or strategy they want.

   penguin

   bag of __12__ and bag of __24__

2. Colleen has 20 dolphin pictures. Meg gives her 24 more. How many pictures does she have in all?

   dolphin

   __44__ pictures

3. Paper squares are sold in boxes of 22, 34, and 75. Carlos only needs 97 squares for his coral reef picture. Which two boxes should he buy?

   coral reef

   box of __22__ and box of __75__

4. **Multistep** Fred has 31 seal stickers. His dad gives him 12 new stickers. Then his mom gives him 10 more. How many stickers does he have now?

   seal

   __53__ stickers

At Home Have your child gather groups of objects in your home and write a Guess and Check problem for you to solve.

six hundred seventeen **617**

3 Practice

Mixed Strategy Practice

Read the problem-solving strategies in **Exercises 1–4** with children. Make sure children can read and comprehend each problem on page 617. You might pair more proficient readers with less proficient readers.

Common Error

Recording the Wrong Information

Children may do the addition to check, but then record the wrong information. Have children show the addition and use it to check that the correct information is written in the answer lines.

4 Assess and Close

If you want 25 collectible cards, and they come in packs of 10, 15, and 20, which 2 should you buy? (10 and 15)

How can you add to check your answer? (10 + 15 = 25)

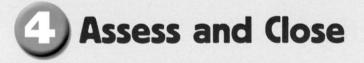

Keeping a Journal

Show how you would add to check that a bag of 16 marbles and a bag of 11 marbles will give you 27 marbles.

Listen to your teacher read the problem.
Solve.

	Show your work using pictures, numbers, or words.
1. Mr. Akers brings his class of 26 children to the seal show. Ms. Char brings her class of 23 children. How many children do Mr. Akers and Ms. Char bring to the seal show?	___49___ children
2. Andrea has 18 tubes of paint. Lee has 31 tubes of paint. How many tubes of paint do Andrea and Lee have in all?	___49___ tubes of paint

Listen to your teacher read the problem.
Choose the correct answer.

3.   38 sticks   35 sticks   25 sticks   22 sticks
        ○   ●   ○   ○

4.   36 feathers   27 feathers   26 feathers   16 feathers
        ○   ○   ●   ○

Problem-Solving for Tests

Listening Skills

This page provides children practice with the oral problem-solving format used in some standardized test items.

You may want to read each item only once to mimic the style of oral tests.

Use with Items 1 and 2

Listening Strategy: Read the problem silently as the teacher reads it aloud.

- *When a problem is on the page, look at the problem as I am reading it.*
- *Do not start writing until I finish reading.*

Use with Item 3

Listening Strategy: Listen for important facts and details.

- *Listen to the question so you will know how to use the numbers.*

  Hannah is making a toy chair out of craft sticks. She has 23 sticks. She needs 12 more sticks. How many sticks will she use for the chair?

- *Use the numbers to find the answer to your question. Mark your answer.*

Use with Item 4

Listening Strategy: Listen to the problem and then look at the picture.

- *Look at me when I read a problem that is not on the page.*

  Eric has 14 feathers for his bird picture. He needs 12 more feathers to finish the picture. How many feathers will be on the picture when it is finished?

- *Use the numbers to find the answer. Mark your answer.*

Quick Check

Have children complete the Quick Check exercises independently to assess their understanding of concepts and skills taught in **Lessons 4–6.**

Item	Lesson	Error Analysis	Intervention
1–4	21.4	Children may add the ones to the tens.	Reteach Resource 21.4 *Ways to Success* 21.4
5–12	21.5	Children may make fact errors when faced with choosing strategies.	Reteach Resource 21.5 *Ways to Success* 21.5
13–14	21.6	Children may add correctly, but then not record the correct information.	Reteach Resource 21.6 *Ways to Success* 21.6

Name_____ **Quick Check**

Choose a way to add.
Write the sum.

1.
$$\begin{array}{r} 40 \\ +50 \\ \hline 90 \end{array}$$

2.
$$\begin{array}{r} 63 \\ +5 \\ \hline 68 \end{array}$$

3.
$$\begin{array}{r} 36 \\ +3 \\ \hline 39 \end{array}$$

4.
$$\begin{array}{r} 14 \\ +85 \\ \hline 99 \end{array}$$

5.
$$\begin{array}{r} 55 \\ +12 \\ \hline 67 \end{array}$$

6.
$$\begin{array}{r} 72 \\ +7 \\ \hline 79 \end{array}$$

7.
$$\begin{array}{r} 30 \\ +40 \\ \hline 70 \end{array}$$

8.
$$\begin{array}{r} 70 \\ +13 \\ \hline 83 \end{array}$$

9. $16 + 2 = \underline{18}$

10. $43 + 1 = \underline{44}$

11. $85 + 3 = \underline{88}$

12. $60 + 10 = \underline{70}$

Use Guess and Check to solve.

13. Fish stickers are sold in packs of 10, 20, and 40. Joshua needs 60 fish to finish his ocean picture. Which two packs should he buy?

Draw or write to explain.

pack of __20__ and pack of __40__

14. Sam has 18 buttons. Kim has 10. How many more buttons does Sam have than Kim?

__8__ buttons

Write the sum.

1. 4
   +5
   ───
    9

2. 8
   +4
   ───
   12

3. 5
   +6
   ───
   11

4. 3
   +7
   ───
   10

5. 6
   +6
   ───
   12

6. 9 + 2 = __11__   7. 2 + 8 = __10__   8. 7 + 5 = __12__

Write the difference.

9. 11
   − 4
   ───
    7

10. 12
   − 5
   ───
    7

11. 10
   − 6
   ───
    4

12. 11
   − 8
   ───
    3

13. 11
   − 5
   ───
    6

14. 12 − 3 = __9__   15. 9 − 6 = __3__   16. 12 − 8 = __4__

Art Connection

Murals

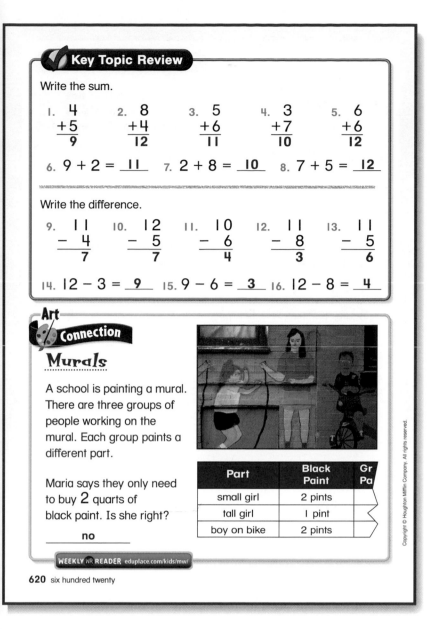

A school is painting a mural. There are three groups of people working on the mural. Each group paints a different part.

Maria says they only need to buy 2 quarts of black paint. Is she right?

__no__

Part	Black Paint	Gr Pa
small girl	2 pints	
tall girl	1 pint	
boy on bike	2 pints	

WEEKLY WR READER eduplace.com/kids/mw/

620 six hundred twenty

Key Topic Review

This assessment provides a review of skills and concepts taught in **Chapters 15 and 16**.

Check to be sure that children:

- can use addition strategies to find sums to 12.
- can find sums to 12 by counting on 1, 2, or 3.
- can find differences for subtraction facts.

Art Connection

Murals

Explain what a mural is to children. Discuss what steps might be involved in painting a large mural on a wall. Then introduce the problem and read the tasks in the chart. Have children work independently to solve. Then ask volunteers to share the methods they used to solve the problem.

Chapter Review/Test

Purpose: This test provides an informal assessment of the Chapter 21 objectives.

Chapter Test Items 1–25

To assign a numerical grade for this Chapter Test, use 4 points for each test item.

Check Understanding

Use children's work on word problems to informally assess progress on chapter content.

Customizing Your Instruction

For children who have not yet mastered these objectives, you can use the reteaching resources listed in the chart below.

✓ Assessment Options

A summary test for this chapter is also provided in the Unit Resource Folder.

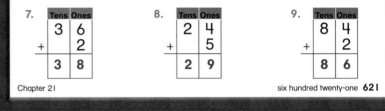

Name_____ **Chapter Review/Test**

Vocabulary *e Glossary*
Complete the sentence.

| tens |
| ones |

1. There are 6 ___ones___ in the number 76.

2. There are 8 ___tens___ in the number 86.

Concepts and Skills
Complete the addition sentences.

3. $3 + 2 =$ __5__
   3 tens + 2 tens = __5__ tens
   __30__ + __20__ = __50__

4. $4 + 4 =$ __8__
   4 tens + 4 tens = __8__ tens
   __40__ + __40__ = __80__

5. $1 + 5 =$ __6__
   1 ten + 5 tens = __6__ tens
   __10__ + __50__ = __60__

6. $6 + 3 =$ __9__
   6 tens + 3 tens = __9__ tens
   __60__ + __30__ = __90__

Use Workmat 5 with ▭▭▭ and ▫.
Add. Write the sum.

7.
Tens	Ones
3	6
+	2
3	8

8.
Tens	Ones
2	4
+	5
2	9

9.
Tens	Ones
8	4
+	2
8	6

Chapter 21   six hundred twenty-one **621**

Reteaching Support

Chapter Test Items	Summary Test Items	Chapter Objectives Tested	TE Pages	Use These Reteaching Resources
1–2	1–2	**21A** Develop and use math vocabulary relating to adding two-digit numbers.	603A–606	Reteach Resources and *Ways to Success* CD: 21.1, 21.2 Skillsheet 153
3–17	3–14	**21B** Use basic facts to add tens. Add two-digit numbers, including money amounts, without regrouping.	603A–608	Reteach Resources and *Ways to Success* CD: 21.1, 21.3 Skillsheets 154–155
18–24	15–18	**21C** Use different ways to add.	611A–614	Reteach Resources and *Ways to Success* CD: 21.4, 21.5 Skillsheet 156
25	19–20	**21D** Use guess and check to solve problems.	615A–618	Reteach Resource and *Ways to Success* CD: 21.6 Skillsheet 157

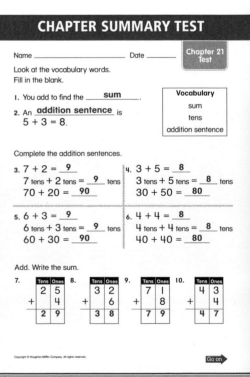

CHAPTER SUMMARY TEST

Name _____ Date _____ Chapter 21 Test

Look at the vocabulary words.
Fill in the blank.

1. You add to find the ___sum___.

2. An **addition sentence** is $5 + 3 = 8$.

| Vocabulary |
| sum |
| tens |
| addition sentence |

Complete the addition sentences.

3. $7 + 2 =$ __9__
   7 tens + 2 tens = __9__ tens
   70 + 20 = __90__

4. $3 + 5 =$ __8__
   3 tens + 5 tens = __8__ tens
   30 + 50 = __80__

5. $6 + 3 =$ __9__
   6 tens + 3 tens = __9__ tens
   60 + 30 = __90__

6. $4 + 4 =$ __8__
   4 tens + 4 tens = __8__ tens
   40 + 40 = __80__

Add. Write the sum.

7.
Tens	Ones
2	5
+	4
2	9

8.
Tens	Ones
3	2
+	6
3	8

9.
Tens	Ones
7	1
+	8
7	9

10.
Tens	Ones
4	3
+	4
4	7

Copyright © Houghton Mifflin Company. All rights reserved.

Go on ▶

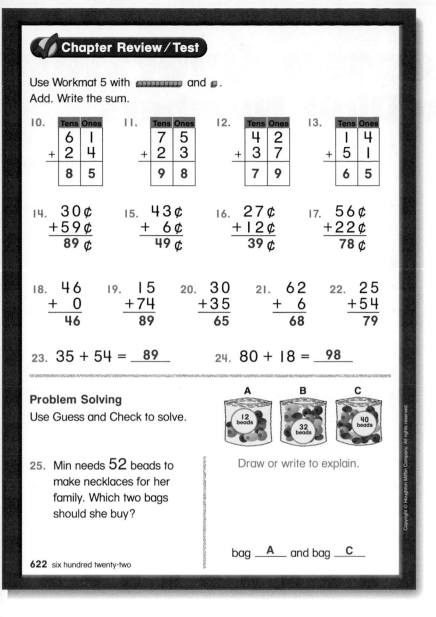

Chapter Review/Test

Use Workmat 5 with ▬▬▬▬ and ◨.
Add. Write the sum.

10.

Tens	Ones
6	1
+ 2	4
8	5

11.

Tens	Ones
7	5
+ 2	3
9	8

12.

Tens	Ones
4	2
+ 3	7
7	9

13.

Tens	Ones
1	4
+ 5	1
6	5

14. 30¢
   +59¢
    89¢

15. 43¢
   + 6¢
    49¢

16. 27¢
   +12¢
    39¢

17. 56¢
   +22¢
    78¢

18. 46
   + 0
    46

19. 15
   +74
    89

20. 30
   +35
    65

21. 62
   + 6
    68

22. 25
   +54
    79

23. 35 + 54 = __89__   24. 80 + 18 = __98__

Problem Solving

Use Guess and Check to solve.

25. Min needs 52 beads to make necklaces for her family. Which two bags should she buy?

A — 12 beads
B — 32 beads
C — 40 beads

Draw or write to explain.

bag __A__ and bag __C__

CHAPTER SUMMARY TEST

Name _____ Date _____

Chapter 21 Test continued

Add. Write the sum.

11. 67
   +32
    99

12. 25
   +40
    65

13. 17¢
   +12¢
    29¢

14. 54¢
   +44¢
    98¢

15. 60
   +30
    90

16. 47
   + 2
    49

17. 30
   +54
    84

18. 55
   +33
    88

Use Guess and Check to solve.

19. Today 96 children are having a picnic. Paper plates come in bags of 33, 44, and 63. Which two bags of plates should Mr. Edgar buy?

bag of __33__ paper plates and bag of __63__ paper plates

20. Kayla and her mother bake 28 muffins. They need 48 muffins. Do they need to bake 20 more muffins or 40 more muffins?

__20__ more muffins

STOP

Adequate Yearly Progress

Use the End of Grade Test Prep Assessment Guide to help familiarize your children with the format of standardized tests.

Lesson by Lesson Overview
Subtracting Two-Digit Numbers

Lesson 1

- This introduction to two-digit subtraction shows place-value blocks as the model.

- The use of basic facts and mental math to subtract tens is emphasized.

Lesson 2

- This lesson introduces the algorithm for subtracting 1-digit from 2-digit numbers, without regrouping.

- Children use place-value blocks on a workmat to model each exercise.

- It is important that the connection is made between the modeling and what is recorded.

Lesson 3

- Children continue to use place-value blocks as they subtract 2-digit numbers.

- Children are reminded that they should start subtracting with the ones. This is in preparation for second-grade subtracting, which includes regrouping.

Lesson 4

- Children review and practice different ways to subtract.

- They choose from *mental math, paper and pencil,* and *tens and ones blocks.* The choice depends on the problem and the child's abilities or comfort level.

- The lesson is extended to include subtracting money amounts from 99¢ or less.

Lesson 5

- Children practice subtraction of 2-digit numbers.

- The second page of practice is in a game-like format.

Lesson 6

- Children use addition to check subtraction.

- Boxes are provided to help children write the addition and connect it to the subtraction.

Lesson 7

- Children choose the operation to solve problems which are analyzed with a part-part-whole model.

- Problems require children to add to find the whole or subtract to find the missing part.

- Children also choose a strategy to practice previously learned problem solving strategies.

SKILLS TRACE: SUBTRACTING TWO-DIGIT NUMBERS

Grade K	Grade 1	Grade 2
• model subtraction (ch. 14)	• **use mental math and basic facts to subtract tens**	• use mental math, count back, and basic facts to subtract tens (ch. 12)
• complete subtraction sentences (ch. 14)	• **subtract 1-digit from 2-digit numbers, no regrouping**	• regroup tens as ones (ch. 12)
• subtract 1 from 1 through 10 (ch. 14)	• **subtract 2-digit numbers, no regrouping**	• use models and algorithims to subtract 1-digit from 2-digit numbers, with and without regrouping (ch. 12)
• subtract 2 from 2 through 10 (ch. 14)	• **use different ways to subtract**	• subtract 2-digit numbers (ch. 12)
	• **use addition to check subtraction**	• estimate the difference of 2-digit numbers (ch. 13)
		• choose an appropriate computation method (ch. 13)
		• use addition to check subtraction (ch. 13)

Chapter Planner

Lesson	Objective	Vocabulary	Materials	✔ NCTM Standards
22.1 **Mental Math:** **Subtract Tens** p. 625A	Use basic facts and mental math to subtract tens.		place-value blocks, blank transparencies, pennies	Develop and use strategies for whole-number computations, with a focus on addition and subtraction.
22.2 **Subtract With** **Two-Digit Numbers** **(Hands-On)** p. 627A	Subtract one-digit numbers from two-digit numbers.	difference	place-value blocks, Workmat 5, tens and ones chart transparency	Develop and use strategies for whole-number computations, with a focus on addition and subtraction.
22.3 **Subtract Two-Digit** **Numbers** **(Hands-On)** p. 629A	Subtract two-digit numbers.		place-value blocks, Workmat 5, tens and ones chart transparency, one-inch graph paper (Learning Tool (LT) 28)	Use a variety of methods and tools to compute, including objects, mental computation, estimation, paper and pencil, and calculators.
22.4 **Different Ways to** **Subtract** p. 631A	Use different ways to subtract.		place-value blocks	Use a variety of methods and tools to compute, including objects, mental computation, estimation, paper and pencil, and calculators.
22.5 **Two-Digit** **Subtraction Practice** p. 635A	Practice two-digit subtraction.		index cards, number cubes, blank transparency, dimes, pennies	Use a variety of methods and tools to compute, including objects, mental computation, estimation, paper and pencil, and calculators.
22.6 **Check Subtraction** **(Algebra Readiness)** p. 637A	Use addition to check two-digit subtraction.		place-value blocks, blank transparency	Understand various meanings of addition and subtraction of whole numbers and the relationship between the two operations.
22.7 **Problem Solving:** **Choose the Operation** p. 639A	Choose the operation to solve word problems.		index cards, dimes, pennies, Part-Part-Whole Mat transparency, game board labeled START and FINISH, game pieces	Build new mathematical knowledge through problem solving.

Resources For Reaching All Learners

LESSON RESOURCES: Reteach, Practice, Enrichment, Problem Solving, Homework, English Learners, Daily Routines, Transparencies, Math Center.

ADDITIONAL RESOURCES FROM HOUGHTON MIFFLIN: Chapter Challenges, Combination Classroom Planning Guide, Every Day Counts, Math to Learn (Student Handbook)

Every Day Counts
The *Totally Ten Count* and *Daily Depositor* activities in **Every Day Counts** support the math in this chapter.

Assessing Prior Knowledge

Before beginning the chapter, you can assess student understandings in order to assist you in differentiating instruction.

Complete Chapter Pretest in Unit Resource Folder

Use this test to assess both prerequisite skills (**Are You Ready?** — one page) and chapter content (**Check What You Know** — two pages).

Chapter 22 Prerequisite Skills Pretest

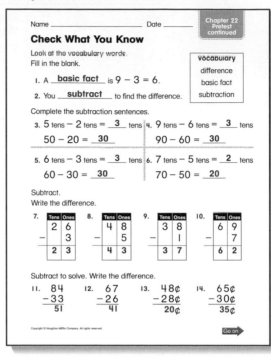

Chapter 22 New Content Pretest

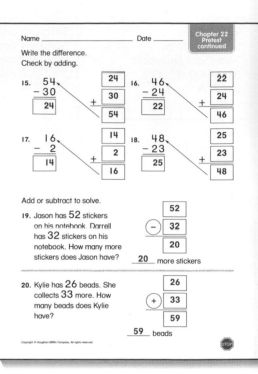

Customizing Instruction

For Students Having Difficulty

Items	Prerequisites	Ways to Success
1–6	Subtraction facts through 10.	CD: 6.1 Skillsheet 158
7–18	Vertical subtraction facts through 10.	CD: 6.6 Skillsheet 159

Ways to Success: Intervention for every concept and skill (CD-ROM or Chapter Intervention Skillsheets).

For Students Having Success

Items	Objectives	Resources
1–2	22A Use vocabulary relating to subtracting 2-digit numbers.	Enrichment 22.1, 22.2
3–14	22B Subtract 2-digit numbers without regrouping.	Enrichment 22.1–22.3
15–18	22C Use addition to check 2-digit subtraction.	Enrichment 22.4–22.6
19–20	22D Choose the operation to solve problems.	Enrichment 22.7

Use **Chapter Challenges** with any students who have success with all new chapter content.

Other Pretest Options

Informal Pretest

The pretest assesses vocabulary and prerequisite skills needed for success in this chapter.

Ways to Success CD-ROM

The **Ways to Success** chapter pretest has automatic assignment of appropriate review lessons.

Chapter Resources

Professional Resources Handbook

Research, Mathematics, Content, and Language Intervention

Assessing Prior Knowledge

Subtraction Review (subtraction facts)

- Write math examples involving 1-digit subtraction and 1-digit numbers to 19 on sheets of paper.
- Display the examples in a "path." Have children walk along the path and read the math examples aloud.
- Invite children to make up examples for a subtraction path. Display the new examples and allow children to review.

Research-Based Teaching

Research shows that some strategies for basic facts can be extended to two-digit numbers and, ultimately, to arbitrarily large numbers. Some strategies do need to be adapted. For instance, using counters might become using base-ten blocks. Further, in *Principles and Standards* (2000) it is pointed out that children also need to realize there are different methods of completing computations. See *Professional Resources Handbook, Grade 1*, Unit 8.

For more ideas relating to Unit 8, see the Teacher Support Handbook at the back of this Teacher's Edition.

Ongoing Skill Activity

Subtraction Stories (subtraction facts)

- Write subtraction stories on index cards and place them into a box in the math center.
- Children select a card from the box, read the story problem, and solve it. Encourage children to use models if they need them.
- You might want to include children's work in a book of subtraction solutions.

Language Intervention

When students are working together on hands-on activities, encourage them to verbalize what they are doing and why. This will help them build their own understanding and math vocabulary. It will also benefit the other students in the group.

Technology

Time-Saving Technology Support

Ways to Assess Customized Spiral Review
  Test Generator CD
Lesson Planner CD-ROM
Ways to Success Intervention CD-ROM
MathTracks CD-ROM
Education Place: www.eduplace.com/math/mw
Houghton Mifflin Math eBook CD-ROM
eManipulatives
eGames

Connecting to the Unit Project

- Write problems requiring children to subtract on index cards.
- Have children work with partners to act out the events in the problems.
- Encourage children to use addition to check their subtraction.

Starting Chapter 22
Subtracting Two-Digit

CHAPTER OBJECTIVES

22A Develop and use math vocabulary relating to subtracting two-digit numbers.

22B Subtract two-digit numbers, including money amounts, without regrouping.

22C Use different ways to subtract and use addition to check two-digit subtraction.

22D Choose the correct operation to solve word problems.

Chapter 22   six hundred twenty-three **623**

Math Background

Subtracting Two-Digit Numbers

Subtraction of two-digit numbers without regrouping follows a sequence similar to that followed for addition. First, children find the differences of numbers that are multiples of 10, then they move to subtraction of one-digit numbers from two-digit numbers using a place-value chart and finally, they use the subtraction algorithm. Consider the example of $56 - 32$.

$$
\begin{array}{rr}
56 & 50 + 6 \\
- 32 & - (30 + 2) \\
\hline
24 & 20 + 4 = 24
\end{array}
$$

The expanded form illustrates why the standard algorithm of subtracting the ones and then subtracting the tens works. Parentheses are used to make the expression mathematically correct, that is, to illustrate that what is being subtracted is 3 tens and 2 ones. Additionally, children are shown how to use addition to check subtraction. If a, b, and c are whole numbers and $c - a = b$, then $b + a = c$.

The focus when teaching both addition and subtraction should be not only carrying out the algorithms correctly to find sums and differences, but also understanding why the algorithms work.

Using The Investigation

- Write the number 22 on the board. **How many tens?** (2 tens) **How many ones?** (2 ones)

- Write $22 + 5$ in vertical format on the board. Emphasize to children that it is important to keep the ones and tens lined up when they add. Ask a volunteer to find the sum.

- Read the question to children. **Look at the picture. How many more pins than patches are there?** (8) **Add to find how many pins and patches there are altogether.** Direct students to find the patches on the front pocket of the backpack. ($14 + 6 = 20$) Ask other questions using 14 pins, 6 patches, and 5 key chains.

For more information about projects and investigations, visit Education Place. eduplace.com/math/mw/

Collect and Connect

Connect the dots.
Start at 50.
Finish at 100.

Meeting the Needs of Mathematically Promising Students

The Chapter Challenges resource book provides blackline masters for activities that explore, extend, and connect the mathematics in every chapter. To support this independent work, see the Teacher Notes for each activity.

Explore: Mystery Difference, page 127, after Lesson 1

Extend: Magic Square, page 129, after Lesson 3

Connect: Lunch Money, page 131, after Lesson 5

Using This Page

- Tell children that when they connect the dots on page 624, they will make a picture.
- **Put your pencil on dot 50. Then draw a line to dot 51. Keep connecting the dots in order until you reach dot 100.**
- Ask a volunteer to tell about the picture the connected dots make.
- Have children create their own connect-the-dot pictures using numbers 50 to 100. Have them trade papers with a partner and connect the dots.

Children's Math Worlds

Using the *Children's Math Worlds* helps develop student communication skills because of the daily work with Math Talk, a teaching practice that can be used with all lessons. The emphasis on building a helping community will also enhance student participation in all classroom discussion.

Mental Math: Subtract Tens

PLANNING THE LESSON

MATHEMATICS OBJECTIVE
Use basic facts and mental math to subtract tens.

Use Lesson Planner CD-ROM for Lesson 22.1.

Meeting North Carolina's Standards
Prepare for Grade 2 Standard 1.04 Develop fluency with multi-digit addition and subtraction through 999 using multiple strategies.

Daily Routines

Calendar

Point to 30 on the calendar. Have children count back 10, say the number, and then count back another 10 and say the number.

Vocabulary

Review the term *basic fact* with children. Remind children that they can use a basic fact when adding tens. Have them use a basic fact to solve 50 − 20.

Vocabulary Cards

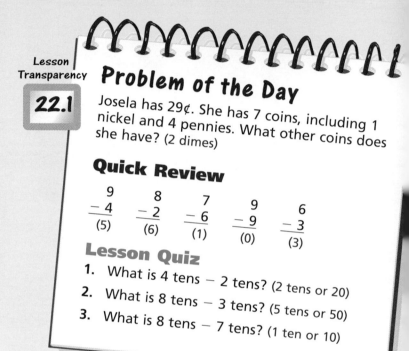
Lesson Transparency **22.1**

Problem of the Day
Josela has 29¢. She has 7 coins, including 1 nickel and 4 pennies. What other coins does she have? (2 dimes)

Quick Review

$$
\begin{array}{ccccc}
9 & 8 & 7 & 9 & 6 \\
-4 & -2 & -6 & -9 & -3 \\
\hline
(5) & (6) & (1) & (0) & (3)
\end{array}
$$

Lesson Quiz
1. What is 4 tens − 2 tens? (2 tens or 20)
2. What is 8 tens − 3 tens? (5 tens or 50)
3. What is 8 tens − 7 tens? (1 ten or 10)

LEVELED PRACTICE

RETEACH 22.1

Name _____ Date _____
Reteach 22.1
Mental Math: Subtract Tens

Think of a subtraction fact when you subtract tens.

You know that 7 − 4 = 3.
So, 7 tens − 4 tens = 3 tens.
70 − 40 = 30

7 − 4 = __3__
7 tens − 4 tens = __3__ tens
__70__ − __40__ = __30__

Complete the subtraction sentences.

1. 8 − 4 = __4__
   8 tens − 4 tens = __4__ tens
   __80__ − __40__ = __40__

2. 9 − 7 = __2__
   9 tens − 7 tens = __2__ tens
   __90__ − __70__ = __20__

3. 6 − 2 = __4__
   6 tens − 2 tens = __4__ tens
   __60__ − __20__ = __40__

Use with text pages 625–626.

PRACTICE 22.1

Name _____ Date _____
Practice 22.1
Subtract Tens

Complete the subtraction sentences.

1. 7 tens − 2 tens = __5__ tens
   __70__ − __20__ = __50__

2. 9 tens − 6 tens = __3__ tens
   90 − 60 = __30__

3. 8 tens − 4 tens = __4__ tens
   80 − 40 = __40__

4. 3 tens − 2 tens = __1__ ten
   30 − 20 = __10__

Test Prep

5. There are 50 children in a drawing class. There are 30 children in a pottery class. How many more children are in the drawing class?

   Draw or write to explain
   50 − 30 = 20

   __20__ more children

Use with text pages 625–626.

ENRICHMENT 22.1

Name _____ Date _____
Enrichment 22.1
Subtract Tens to Solve

Read the story problem. Complete the subtraction sentence. Write the answer.

1. John has 90 marbles. He gives 30 marbles to Jim. How many marbles does John have now?
   __9__ tens − __3__ tens = __6__ tens
   __60__ marbles

2. Maria has 50 pebbles in a box. She counts 20 white pebbles. How many pebbles are not white?
   __5__ tens − __5__ tens = __3__ tens
   __30__ not white

3. Michael has 80 cards. He gives Amy 40 cards. How many cards does Michael have left?
   __8__ tens − __4__ tens = __4__ tens
   __40__ cards

Write About It Write a story problem where you subtract tens. Write a matching subtraction sentence.
Answers will vary. Possible answer: Lulu has 40 cans. Trent has 30 cans. How many more cans does Lulu have? 4 tens − 3 tens = 1 ten, so 40 − 30 = 10.

Use with text pages 625–626.

Practice Workbook Page 147

Reaching All Learners
Differentiated Instruction

English Learners

In order to answer questions about bar graphs, children will have to understand and use the phrase *more ____ than ____*. Use Worksheet 22.1 to help English-language learners become familiar with this phrase.

Special Needs
TACTILE, VISUAL

Materials: *place-value blocks*

- Write $5 - 2 =$ ____. Have the child show 5 ones blocks, take away 2 ones and write the difference.
- Ask the child to show 5 tens and then take away 2 tens and tell the difference. Write the sentence $50 - 20 = 30$.
- Relate the two subtraction sentences.

Early Finishers
TACTILE, VISUAL

Materials: *measuring tape*

- Have one child write a subtraction sentence with a missing number.
- Have the partner use a tape measure as a number line to find the missing number.

$$50 - \boxed{} = 30$$

TECHNOLOGY

Spiral Review
To reinforce skills on lessons taught earlier, create **customized** spiral review worksheets using the *Ways to Assess* CD-ROM.

eBook
An electronic version of this lesson can be found in **eMathBook.**

Lesson Planner
Use the **Lesson Planner CD-ROM** to see how lesson objectives for this chapter are correlated to standards.

Social Studies Connection

Explain that in ancient Egypt this symbol stood for 10: ∩. Have children draw subtraction sentences using this symbol.

$$\underset{50}{\cap\cap\cap\cap\cap} - \underset{30}{\cap\cap\cap} = \underset{20}{\cap\cap}$$

MATH CENTER

Basic Skills Activity
Motivate children to build basic skills. Use this activity to address multiple learning styles using hands-on activities related to the skills of this lesson.

PROBLEM SOLVING 22.1

Name _____ Date _____

Problem Solving 22.1

Mental Math: Subtract Tens

The table shows the number of children in an after-school program.

Use the table for 1–3.

After-School Program	
Class	Number of Children
Art	50
Piano	20
Gym	70
Band	90
Soccer	60

1. How many more children are in the art class than in the piano class?

   Draw or write to explain.

   __30__ children

2. Are more children in piano class or in soccer?

   How many more?

   __soccer__

   __40__ more children

3. Are more children in the band class or in the art class?

   How many more?

   __band__

   __40__ more children

Use with text pages 625–626.

HOMEWORK 22.1

Name _____ Date _____

Homework 22.1

Mental Math: Subtract Tens

A subtraction fact can help you subtract tens.

$8 - 5 = \underline{3}$
8 tens $- 5$ tens $= \underline{3}$ tens
$\underline{80} - \underline{50} = \underline{30}$

Complete the subtraction sentences.

1. $6 - 1 = \underline{5}$
   6 tens $- 1$ ten $= \underline{5}$ tens
   $\underline{60} - \underline{10} = \underline{50}$

2. $4 - 3 = \underline{1}$
   4 tens $- 3$ tens $= \underline{1}$ ten
   $\underline{40} - \underline{30} = \underline{10}$

3. 9 tens $- 6$ tens $= \underline{3}$ tens
   $\underline{90} - \underline{60} = \underline{30}$

4. 7 tens $- 3$ tens $= \underline{4}$ tens
   $\underline{70} - \underline{30} = \underline{40}$

5. 5 tens $- 2$ tens $= \underline{3}$ tens
   $\underline{50} - \underline{20} = \underline{30}$

6. 8 tens $- 4$ tens $= \underline{4}$ tens
   $\underline{80} - \underline{40} = \underline{40}$

7. The art class has 30 children. The music class has 20 children. How many more children are in the art class?

   Draw or write to explain.

   __10__ more children

Use with text pages 625–626.

ENGLISH LEARNERS 22.1

Name _____ Date _____

English Learners 22.1

Subtract Tens

There are **more** boots **than** sneakers.

Draw more crayons than pencils.

1. | Drawing of more than 3 crayons |

Draw more oranges than bananas.

2. | Drawing of more than 2 oranges |

Draw more triangles than squares.

3. | Drawing of more than 4 triangles |

To the Teacher: Use the pictures and sentence at the top of the page to demonstrate the meaning of the comparative phrase *more ___ than ___*. Then have children draw pictures to show more.

Use with text pages 625–626.

Homework Workbook Page 147

TEACHING LESSON 22.1

LESSON ORGANIZER

Objective Use basic facts and mental math to subtract tens.

Resources Reteach, Practice, Enrichment, Problem Solving, Homework, English Learners, Transparencies, Math Center

Materials Blank transparencies, place-value blocks, pennies

Activity

Warm-Up Activity
Modeling Adding Tens

iiii Whole Group	⏱ 5 minutes	Auditory, Visual

Materials: *blank transparency, place-value blocks*

1. Review adding tens. Write 3 tens + 4 tens = ____ tens. Show a group of 3 tens blocks and a group of 4 tens blocks. **What addition fact can we use to help us add 3 tens and 4 tens?** (3 + 4 = 7)

2. Combine the groups of tens. **What is the sum of 3 tens plus 4 tens?** (7 tens)

3. **What is another way to write 3 tens plus 4 tens?** (30 + 40 = 70)

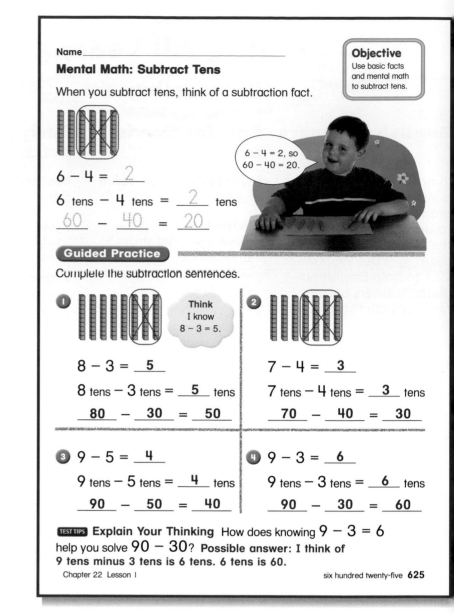

Name_____

Mental Math: Subtract Tens

Objective Use basic facts and mental math to subtract tens.

When you subtract tens, think of a subtraction fact.

$6 - 4 = \underline{2}$

6 tens − 4 tens = $\underline{2}$ tens

$\underline{60} - \underline{40} = \underline{20}$

6 − 4 = 2, so 60 − 40 = 20.

Guided Practice

Complete the subtraction sentences.

① Think I know 8 − 3 = 5.

$8 - 3 = \underline{5}$

8 tens − 3 tens = $\underline{5}$ tens

$\underline{80} - \underline{30} = \underline{50}$

②

$7 - 4 = \underline{3}$

7 tens − 4 tens = $\underline{3}$ tens

$\underline{70} - \underline{40} = \underline{30}$

③ $9 - 5 = \underline{4}$

9 tens − 5 tens = $\underline{4}$ tens

$\underline{90} - \underline{50} = \underline{40}$

④ $9 - 3 = \underline{6}$

9 tens − 3 tens = $\underline{6}$ tens

$\underline{90} - \underline{30} = \underline{60}$

TEST TIPS **Explain Your Thinking** How does knowing $9 - 3 = 6$ help you solve $90 - 30$? **Possible answer: I think of 9 tens minus 3 tens is 6 tens. 6 tens is 60.**

Chapter 22 Lesson 1   six hundred twenty-five **625**

---

① Introduce
Activity

Discuss Subtracting Tens

iiii Whole Group	⏱ 10–15 minutes	Visual, Auditory

Materials: *blank transparencies, place-value blocks*

1. Show 5 tens blocks on a transparency. **How many tens are there?** (5) Place another transparency over the blocks.

2. Circle and cross out 2 tens. **How many tens did I cross out?** (2) **How many tens are left?** (3) Write 5 tens − 2 tens = 3 tens. Have students draw the tens and cross out two to model the subtraction.

3. When you subtract tens you can use basic facts. Circle the 5 and the 2. **What is 5 − 2?** (3) **If you know that 5 − 2 = 3, then you also know 5 tens − 2 tens = 3 tens.**

4. **What is another way to write 5 tens?** (50) **What is another way to write 2 tens?** (20) **What is another way to write 3 tens?** (30) **What is 50 − 20?** (30)

② Develop

Guided Learning

Teaching Example Introduce the objective to children. Guide them through the example to show how 6 − 4 can be used to find the difference of 60 − 40 using mental math. Explain that the tens blocks are shown to help children see the tens.

Guided Practice

Have children complete **Exercises 1–4** as you observe. Give children the opportunity to answer the Explain Your Thinking question. Then discuss their responses with the class.

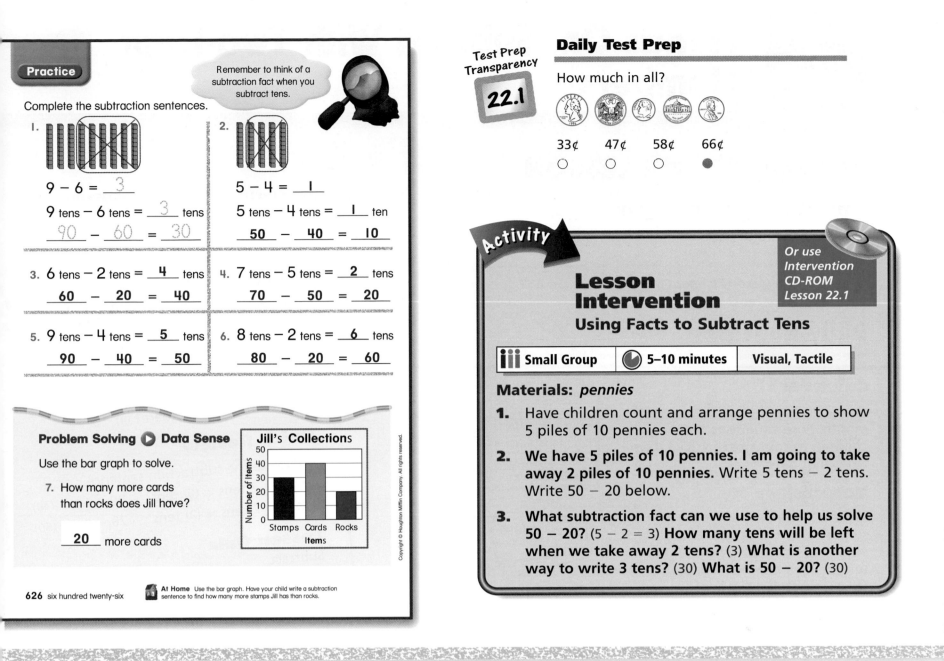

Practice

Remember to think of a subtraction fact when you subtract tens.

Complete the subtraction sentences.

1.

$9 - 6 = \underline{3}$

$9 \text{ tens} - 6 \text{ tens} = \underline{3} \text{ tens}$

$\underline{90} - \underline{60} = \underline{30}$

2.

$5 - 4 = \underline{1}$

$5 \text{ tens} - 4 \text{ tens} = \underline{1} \text{ ten}$

$\underline{50} - \underline{40} = \underline{10}$

3. $6 \text{ tens} - 2 \text{ tens} = \underline{4} \text{ tens}$

$\underline{60} - \underline{20} = \underline{40}$

4. $7 \text{ tens} - 5 \text{ tens} = \underline{2} \text{ tens}$

$\underline{70} - \underline{50} = \underline{20}$

5. $9 \text{ tens} - 4 \text{ tens} = \underline{5} \text{ tens}$

$\underline{90} - \underline{40} = \underline{50}$

6. $8 \text{ tens} - 2 \text{ tens} = \underline{6} \text{ tens}$

$\underline{80} - \underline{20} = \underline{60}$

Problem Solving ▶ Data Sense

Use the bar graph to solve.

7. How many more cards than rocks does Jill have?

$\underline{20}$ more cards

Jill's Collections

Number of Items: 50, 40, 30, 20, 10, 0
Items: Stamps, Cards, Rocks

626 six hundred twenty-six

At Home Use the bar graph. Have your child write a subtraction sentence to find how many more stamps Jill has than rocks.

Daily Test Prep

How much in all?

33¢   47¢   58¢   66¢
○   ○   ○   ●

Activity

Or use Intervention CD-ROM Lesson 22.1

Lesson Intervention

Using Facts to Subtract Tens

| 👥 Small Group | 🕐 5–10 minutes | Visual, Tactile |

Materials: *pennies*

1. Have children count and arrange pennies to show 5 piles of 10 pennies each.

2. We have 5 piles of 10 pennies. I am going to take away 2 piles of 10 pennies. Write 5 tens − 2 tens. Write 50 − 20 below.

3. What subtraction fact can we use to help us solve 50 − 20? (5 − 2 = 3) How many tens will be left when we take away 2 tens? (3) What is another way to write 3 tens? (30) What is 50 − 20? (30)

Practice

Independent Practice

Children complete **Exercises 1–6** independently.

Problem Solving

After children complete **Exercise 7**, call on volunteers to share their solutions. Discuss reading the graph and writing a subtraction sentence to solve.

Common Error

Omitting Zeros

Children may omit zeros when they record numbers. Remind them that when there are no ones, a zero must be written in the ones place. Compare 3 and 30 using models to emphasize the place value.

4 Assess and Close

40 people want to ride the train. There is room for only 30 people. How many people cannot ride the train? (10)

Will made 70 tacos for a party. 50 tacos were eaten. How many tacos are left? (20)

Keeping a Journal

Write and solve a story problem about 80 − 20. What subtraction fact helps you find the difference?

Hands-On: Subtract With Two-Digit Numbers

PLANNING THE LESSON

MATHEMATICS OBJECTIVE
Subtract one-digit numbers from two-digit numbers.

Use Lesson Planner CD-ROM for Lesson 22.2.

Daily Routines

Calendar
Highlight the 29th of the current month. Pose situations that require children to count back 1 to 3 days from that date.

Sunday	Monday	Tuesday	Wednesday	Thursday	Friday	Saturday
			1	2	3	4
5	6	7	8	9	10	11
12	13	14	15	16	17	18
19	20	21	22	23	24	25
26	27	28	29	30	31	

Vocabulary
Write a *two-digit* subtraction sentence on the board. Call on volunteers to identify the ones and tens in each number. Ask a volunteer to identify the **difference**.

Vocabulary Cards

Meeting North Carolina's Standards
Prepare for Grade 2 Standard 1.04 Develop fluency with multi-digit addition and subtraction through 999 using multiple strategies.

Lesson Transparency 22.2

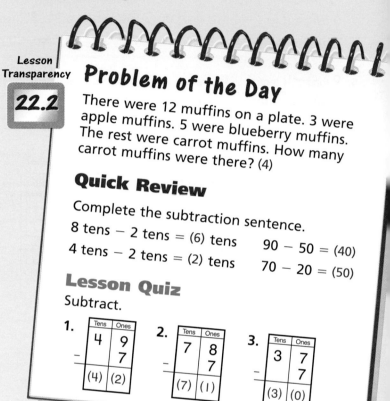

Problem of the Day
There were 12 muffins on a plate. 3 were apple muffins. 5 were blueberry muffins. The rest were carrot muffins. How many carrot muffins were there? (4)

Quick Review
Complete the subtraction sentence.

8 tens − 2 tens = (6) tens   90 − 50 = (40)

4 tens − 2 tens = (2) tens   70 − 20 = (50)

Lesson Quiz
Subtract.

1.
Tens	Ones
4	9
−	7
(4)	(2)

2.
Tens	Ones
7	8
−	7
(7)	(1)

3.
Tens	Ones
3	7
−	7
(3)	(0)

LEVELED PRACTICE

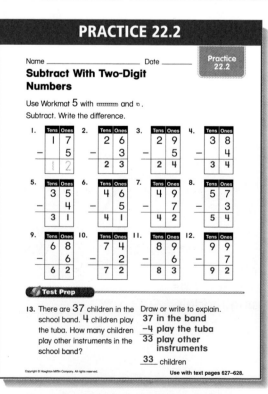

RETEACH 22.2

Name _____ Date _____   Reteach 22.2

Subtract With Two-Digit Numbers

Find 36 − 4.

Step 1 Show 36.   **Step 2** Subtract the ones.   **Step 3** Subtract the tens.

There are 0 tens to subtract.

Tens	Ones
3	6
−	4
3	2

Use Workmat 5 with ▭ and ▫.
Subtract. Write the difference.

1.
Tens	Ones
5	9
−	8
5	1

2.
Tens	Ones
4	9
−	6
4	3

3.
Tens	Ones
7	8
−	4
7	4

Copyright © Houghton Mifflin Company. All rights reserved.   Use with text pages 627–628.

PRACTICE 22.2

Name _____ Date _____   Practice 22.2

Subtract With Two-Digit Numbers

Use Workmat 5 with ▭ and ▫.
Subtract. Write the difference.

1.
Tens	Ones
1	7
−	5
1	2

2.
Tens	Ones
2	6
−	3
2	3

3.
Tens	Ones
2	9
−	5
2	4

4.
Tens	Ones
3	8
−	4
3	4

5.
Tens	Ones
3	5
−	4
3	1

6.
Tens	Ones
4	6
−	5
4	1

7.
Tens	Ones
4	9
−	7
4	2

8.
Tens	Ones
5	7
−	3
5	4

9.
Tens	Ones
6	8
−	6
6	2

10.
Tens	Ones
7	4
−	2
7	2

11.
Tens	Ones
8	9
−	6
8	3

12.
Tens	Ones
9	9
−	7
9	2

Test Prep

13. There are 37 children in the school band. 4 children play the tuba. How many children play other instruments in the school band?

Draw or write to explain.

37 in the band
−4 play the tuba
33 play other instruments

33 children

Copyright © Houghton Mifflin Company. All rights reserved.   Use with text pages 627–628.

ENRICHMENT 22.2

Name _____ Date _____   Enrichment 22.2

Find the Missing Number

Use Workmat 5 with ▭ and ▫.
How many ones do you need to take away to show the difference?
Write the missing number.

1.
Tens	Ones
2	6
−	4
2	2

2.
Tens	Ones
2	9
−	5
2	4

3.
Tens	Ones
3	7
−	5
3	2

4.
Tens	Ones
3	8
−	7
3	1

5.
Tens	Ones
4	6
−	4
4	2

6.
Tens	Ones
5	9
−	1
5	8

7.
Tens	Ones
5	6
−	6
5	0

8.
Tens	Ones
6	9
−	2
6	7

9.
Tens	Ones
7	6
−	5
7	1

10.
Tens	Ones
7	8
−	2
7	6

11.
Tens	Ones
8	8
−	3
8	5

12.
Tens	Ones
9	7
−	3
9	4

Write About It Write a story problem. Use one of the completed exercises above. Solve.

Answers will vary. Possible answer: There are 56 children at the school picnic. 6 children go home. How many children stay at the picnic? 50 children.

Copyright © Houghton Mifflin Company. All rights reserved.   Use with text pages 627–628.

Practice Workbook Page 148

Reaching All Learners
Differentiated Instruction

English Learners

In order to understand the process for subtracting two-digit numbers, children will have to understand the terms *Step 1*, *Step 2*, and *Step 3*. Use Worksheet 22.2 to develop children's understanding of these terms.

Special Needs
VISUAL, TACTILE

Materials: *cubes*
- Give the child 49 cubes. Have the child connect cubes to make tens. **How many cubes do you have?** (49; 4 tens 9 ones)
- Write 49 − 2 in vertical form. **How will you subtract 2?** (Take away 2 cubes.) **How many ones are left?** (7) Write the difference, emphasizing that there are no tens to subtract.
- Repeat with other numbers.

Early Finishers
TACTILE, KINESTHETIC

Materials: *index cards, number cube 1–6*
- Write numbers with 6–9 in the ones place on cards.
- Have children draw a card and roll the cube. Use the numbers to write a subtraction exercise, then solve.

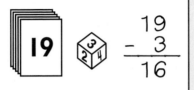

$$\begin{array}{r} 19 \\ -3 \\ \hline 16 \end{array}$$

TECHNOLOGY

Spiral Review
Help students remember skills they learned earlier by creating **customized** spiral review worksheets using the *Ways to Assess* CD-ROM.

Education Place
Encourage students to visit **Education Place** at **eduplace.com/kids/mw/** for more student activities.

Manipulatives
Base Ten Blocks with several workmats are available on the *Ways to Success* CD-ROM.

Art Connection
Refer to the unit story, *Lights Out!* by Lucille Recht Penner. Invite children to draw window scenes. Make a building with 28 windows. Cover from 1 to 8 windows and have children write the subtraction.

MATH CENTER
Basic Skills Activity
Motivate children to build basic skills. Use this activity to address multiple learning styles using hands-on activities related to the skills of this lesson.

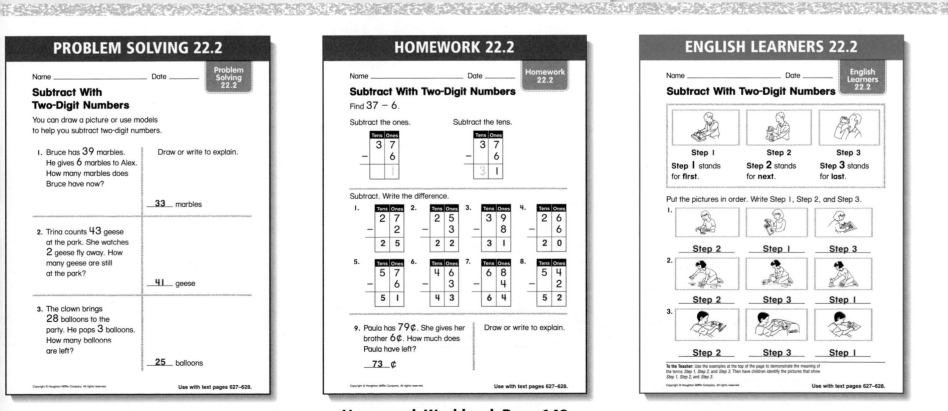

Homework Workbook Page 148

CHAPTER 22   Lesson 2   **627B**

TEACHING LESSON 22.2

LESSON ORGANIZER

Objective Subtract one-digit numbers from two-digit numbers.

Resources Reteach, Practice, Enrichment, Problem Solving, Homework, English Learners, Transparencies, Math Center

Materials Place-value blocks, tens and ones chart transparency, Workmat 5

Activity

Warm-Up Activity
Model Counting Back to Subtract

iiii Whole Group	🕐 5 minutes	Auditory, Visual

1. Draw a number line from 0 to 20 on the board. Write 8 − 3 = _____. Remind children that they can use a number line to count on or count back.

2. **If we want to subtract 3 from 8, do we count on or count back?** (count back) **What number do we start with?** (8) **How many numbers will we count back?** (3) Have children count back aloud. **What is 8 − 3?** (5)

3. Complete the fact and repeat with other numbers.

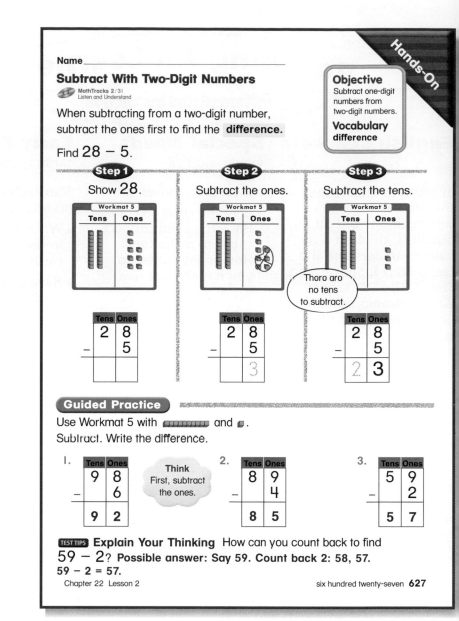

Name _____

Subtract With Two-Digit Numbers

When subtracting from a two-digit number, subtract the ones first to find the **difference**.

Objective Subtract one-digit numbers from two-digit numbers.

Vocabulary difference

Find 28 − 5.

Step 1 Show 28.

Step 2 Subtract the ones.

Step 3 Subtract the tens.

There are no tens to subtract.

Guided Practice

Use Workmat 5 with ▭▭▭▭ and ▫. Subtract. Write the difference.

1.
Tens	Ones
9	8
−	6
9	2

Think First, subtract the ones.

2.
Tens	Ones
8	9
−	4
8	5

3.
Tens	Ones
5	9
−	2
5	7

TEST TIPS **Explain Your Thinking** How can you count back to find 59 − 2? **Possible answer: Say 59. Count back 2: 58, 57. 59 − 2 = 57.**

Chapter 22 Lesson 2   six hundred twenty-seven **627**

---

① Introduce

Activity

Discuss Subtracting with Two-Digit Numbers

iiii Whole Group	🕐 10–15 minutes	Visual, Auditory

Materials: *place-value blocks, tens and ones chart transparency, Workmat 5*

1. Give each student place-value blocks and Workmat 5. Write 57 − 4 on the transparency. Use place-value blocks to show 57.

2. Explain that you start subtracting with the ones. Point to the 7 and the 4. Remove 4 blocks. Have students do the same. **What is 7 − 4?** (3) Write 3 in the ones place of the difference.

3. **Is there a number to subtract from 5 in the tens place?** (no) Explain that you still have 5 tens, so you write a 5 in the tens place of the difference.

4. **What is the difference?** (53) Relate the models to the exercise. Repeat with other numbers.

② Develop

Guided Learning

Teaching Example Introduce the objective to the children. Guide them through the three steps as they model 28 with place-value blocks, then subtract the ones and the tens to find the difference.

Guided Practice

Have children complete **Exercises 1–3** as you observe. Give children the opportunity to answer the Explain Your Thinking question. Then discuss their responses with the class.

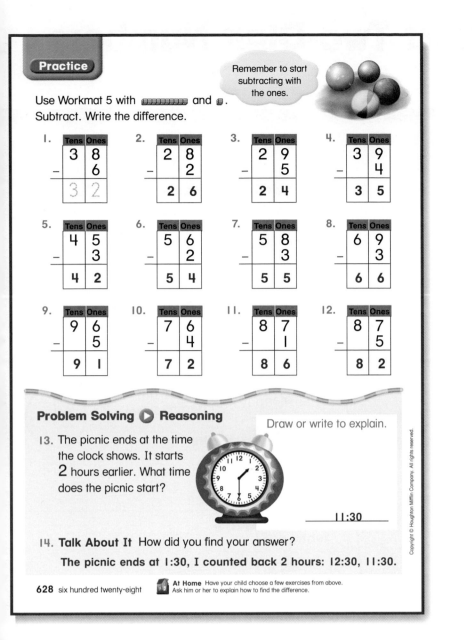

Remember to start subtracting with the ones.

Use Workmat 5 with ▭▭▭ and ▪.
Subtract. Write the difference.

1.	Tens	Ones
	3	8
−		6
	3	2

2.	Tens	Ones
	2	8
−		2
	2	6

3.	Tens	Ones
	2	9
−		5
	2	4

4.	Tens	Ones
	3	9
−		4
	3	5

5.	Tens	Ones
	4	5
−		3
	4	2

6.	Tens	Ones
	5	6
−		2
	5	4

7.	Tens	Ones
	5	8
−		3
	5	5

8.	Tens	Ones
	6	9
−		3
	6	6

9.	Tens	Ones
	9	6
−		5
	9	1

10.	Tens	Ones
	7	6
−		4
	7	2

11.	Tens	Ones
	8	7
−		1
	8	6

12.	Tens	Ones
	8	7
−		5
	8	2

Problem Solving ▶ Reasoning

13. The picnic ends at the time the clock shows. It starts 2 hours earlier. What time does the picnic start?

Draw or write to explain.

_____ 11:30

14. **Talk About It** How did you find your answer?

The picnic ends at 1:30, I counted back 2 hours: 12:30, 11:30.

At Home Have your child choose a few exercises from above. Ask him or her to explain how to find the difference.

Daily Test Prep

$$\begin{array}{r} 56 \\ + 33 \\ \hline \end{array}$$

23   59   89   93
○   ○   ●   ○

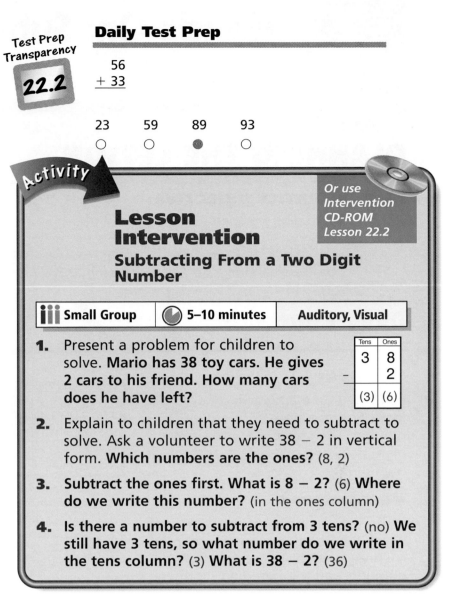

Activity

Or use Intervention CD-ROM Lesson 22.2

Lesson Intervention

Subtracting From a Two Digit Number

👥 Small Group	🕐 5–10 minutes	Auditory, Visual

1. Present a problem for children to solve. **Mario has 38 toy cars. He gives 2 cars to his friend. How many cars does he have left?**

	Tens	Ones
	3	8
−		2
	(3)	(6)

2. Explain to children that they need to subtract to solve. Ask a volunteer to write 38 − 2 in vertical form. **Which numbers are the ones?** (8, 2)

3. Subtract the ones first. **What is 8 − 2?** (6) **Where do we write this number?** (in the ones column)

4. **Is there a number to subtract from 3 tens?** (no) **We still have 3 tens, so what number do we write in the tens column?** (3) **What is 38 − 2?** (36)

---

③ Practice

Independent Practice

Children complete **Exercises 1–12** independently.

Problem Solving

After children complete **Exercise 13**, call on volunteers to share their answers. Use the **Talk About It** in **Exercise 14** to discuss how children arrived at their answers.

Common Error

Subtracting the Ones from the Tens

Children may subtract the ones from the tens. Review the difference between the ones place and the tens place, then have children model subtracting ones from ones and tens from tens.

④ Assess and Close

In the subtraction problem 76 − 2, what number do you subtract from 6 ones? (2) What number do you subtract from 7 tens? (There is no number to subtract from 7.)

Keeping a Journal

Write a story problem for 57 − 5. Show how you solve the problem.

Hands-On: Subtract Two-Digit Numbers

PLANNING THE LESSON

MATHEMATICS OBJECTIVE
Subtract two-digit numbers.

Use Lesson Planner CD-ROM for Lesson 22.3.

Meeting North Carolina's Standards
Prepare for Grade 2 Standard 1.04 Develop fluency with multi-digit addition and subtraction through 999 using multiple strategies.

Daily Routines

Calendar
Point to a date and have children identify it as a one- or two-digit number. Then have them tell how many tens and ones are in the number.

Sunday	Monday	Tuesday	Wednesday	Thursday	Friday	Saturday
				1	2	3	4
5	6	7	8	9	10	11
12	13	14	15	16	17	18
19	20	21	22	23	24	25
26	27	28	29	30	31	

Vocabulary
Write the numbers 1, 4, 6, 23, 48, and 99 on the board in random order. Ask children to identify the *one-digit* numbers and the *two-digit* numbers.

Vocabulary Cards

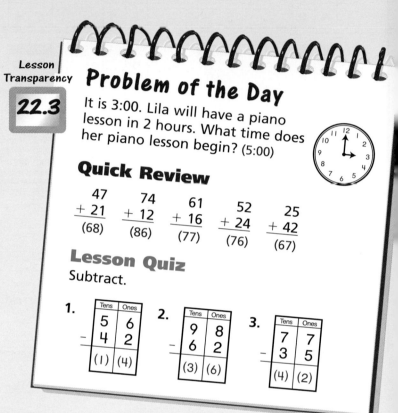

Lesson Transparency 22.3

Problem of the Day
It is 3:00. Lila will have a piano lesson in 2 hours. What time does her piano lesson begin? (5:00)

Quick Review

$$47 + 21 \quad (68)$$
$$74 + 12 \quad (86)$$
$$61 + 16 \quad (77)$$
$$52 + 24 \quad (76)$$
$$25 + 42 \quad (67)$$

Lesson Quiz
Subtract.

1.
Tens	Ones
5	6
4	2
(1)	(4)

2.
Tens	Ones
9	8
6	2
(3)	(6)

3.
Tens	Ones
7	7
3	5
(4)	(2)

LEVELED PRACTICE

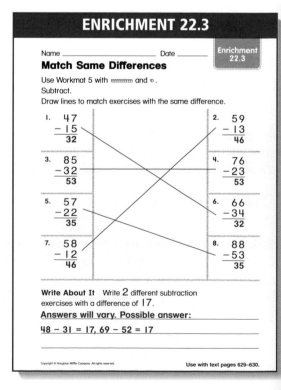

RETEACH 22.3

Name _____ Date _____   Reteach 22.3

Subtract Two-Digit Numbers
Find 47 − 23.

Step 1 Show 47.

Tens	Ones
4	7
− 2	3

Step 2 Subtract the ones.

Tens	Ones
4	7
− 2	3
	4

Step 3 Subtract the tens.

Tens	Ones
4	7
− 2	3
2	4

Use Workmat 5 with ▭▭▭ and ▫.
Subtract. Write the difference.

1.
Tens	Ones
6	7
− 3	4
3	3

2.
Tens	Ones
9	5
− 4	1
5	4

3.
Tens	Ones
5	8
− 1	3
4	5

4.
Tens	Ones
7	6
− 2	2
5	4

5.
Tens	Ones
8	3
− 5	1
3	2

6.
Tens	Ones
4	9
− 1	4
3	5

Use with text pages 629–630.

PRACTICE 22.3

Name _____ Date _____   Practice 22.3

Subtract Two-Digit Numbers
Use Workmat 5 with ▭▭▭ and ▫. Subtract.
Write the difference.

1.
Tens	Ones
5	6
− 2	3
3	3

2.
Tens	Ones
4	7
− 2	2
2	5

3.
Tens	Ones
4	4
− 1	3
3	1

4.
Tens	Ones
6	9
− 4	8
2	1

5.
Tens	Ones
5	3
− 4	1
1	2

6.
Tens	Ones
7	8
− 1	7
6	1

7.
Tens	Ones
7	7
− 3	6
4	1

8.
Tens	Ones
6	4
− 2	2
4	2

9.
Tens	Ones
8	8
− 3	6
5	2

10.
Tens	Ones
9	6
− 3	1
6	5

11.
Tens	Ones
8	3
− 4	2
4	1

12.
Tens	Ones
9	8
− 2	2
7	6

Test Prep

Fill in the ○ for the correct answer.
NH means Not Here.

13. A box has 27 apples and 15 pears.
How many more apples than pears
are in the box?

4   32   13   12   NH
○   ○   ○   ●   ○

Use with text pages 629–630.

ENRICHMENT 22.3

Name _____ Date _____   Enrichment 22.3

Match Same Differences
Use Workmat 5 with ▭▭▭ and ▫.
Subtract.
Draw lines to match exercises with the same difference.

1.
$$47 - 15 = 32$$

2.
$$59 - 13 = 46$$

3.
$$85 - 32 = 53$$

4.
$$76 - 23 = 53$$

5.
$$57 - 22 = 35$$

6.
$$66 - 34 = 32$$

7.
$$58 - 12 = 46$$

8.
$$88 - 53 = 35$$

Write About It   Write 2 different subtraction exercises with a difference of 17.
Answers will vary. Possible answer:
$$48 - 31 = 17, 69 - 52 = 17$$

Use with text pages 629–630.

Practice Workbook Page 149

Reaching All Learners

Differentiated Instruction

English Learners

Worksheet 22.3 introduces the word *faster*. English-language learners will need to understand this word in order to complete the Explain Your Thinking activity.

Special Needs

VISUAL, TACTILE

Materials: *place-value blocks, Workmat 5, tens and ones charts (LT 6)*

- Write 38 − 15 on a chart. Have the child model 38 on the workmat.
- Guide the child through the subtraction with models and then with pencil and paper.
- Repeat with other exercises.

Gifted and Talented

TACTILE, VISUAL

Materials: *index cards*

- Have children write four two-digit subtraction problems that have a difference of 13, three that have a difference of 12, and 2 that have a difference of 11.
- Have children exchange cards and solve each other's exercises.

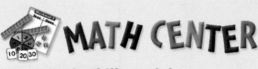

TECHNOLOGY

Spiral Review

You can prepare students for standardized tests with **customized** spiral review on key skills using the *Ways to Assess CD-ROM.*

Lesson Planner

You can use the **Lesson Planner CD-ROM** to create a report of the lessons and standards you have taught.

eBook

eMathBook allows students to review lessons and do homework without carrying their textbooks home.

ScienceConnection

Explain that children have 20 baby teeth. Usually between the ages of 6 and 12, children lose their baby teeth and grow 28 permanent teeth. Have children subtract to find how many more permanent teeth people have than baby teeth.

MATH CENTER

Basic Skills Activity

Motivate children to build basic skills. Use this activity to address multiple learning styles using hands-on activities related to the skills of this lesson.

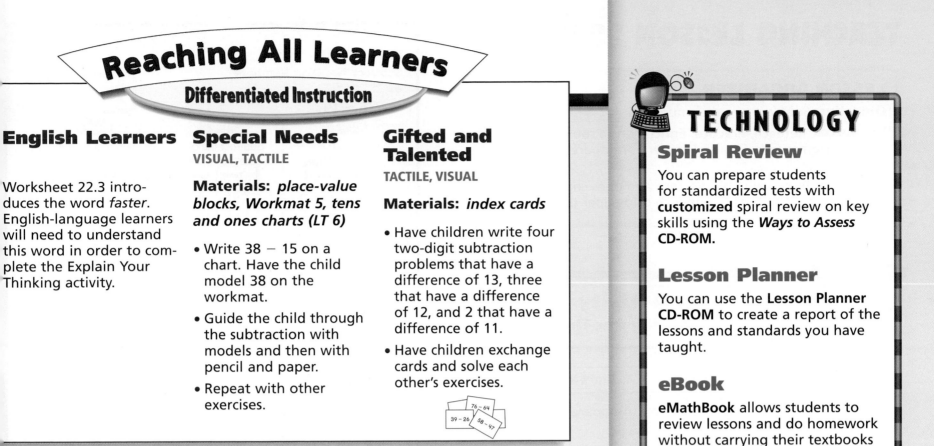

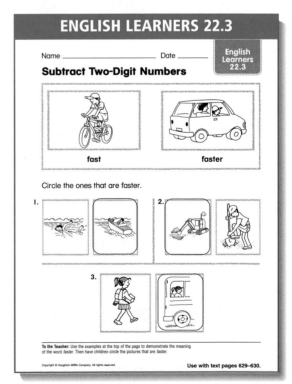

TEACHING LESSON 22.3

LESSON ORGANIZER

Objective Subtract two-digit numbers.

Resources Reteach, Practice, Enrichment, Problem Solving, Homework, English Learners, Transparencies, Math Center

Materials Place-value blocks, tens and ones chart transparency, Workmat 5, one-inch grid paper (LT 28)

Warm-Up Activity
Model Subtracting One-Digit Numbers

iiii Whole Group	⏱ 5 minutes	Auditory, Visual

1. Draw a tens and ones chart on the board. Write 48 − 6.

2. **What do we subtract first, the tens or the ones?** (ones) **What is 8 − 6?** (2) **Is there a number to subtract from 4 tens?** (no)

3. Explain that there are still 4 tens, so you have to write a 4 in the tens place. **What is 48 − 6?** (42)

4. Repeat with 57 − 2.

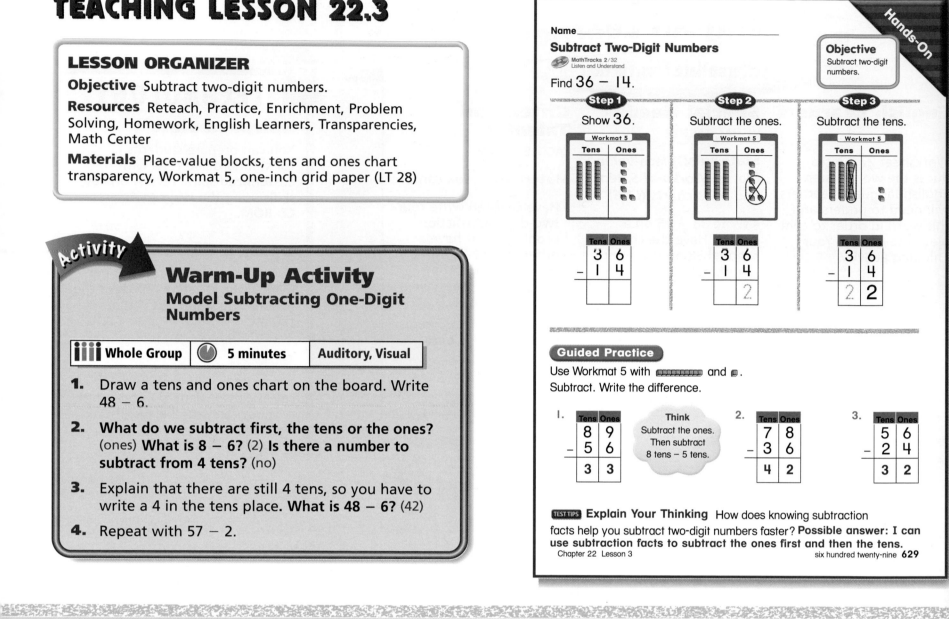

1 Introduce

Activity

Discuss Subtracting Two-Digit Numbers

iiii Whole Group	⏱ 10–15 minutes	Visual, Auditory

Materials: *place-value blocks, Workmat 5, tens and ones chart transparency*

1. Write 47 − 12 on the transparency. Display tens and ones blocks to show 47. Have children model 47 with place-value blocks on their workmats.

2. Tell children to subtract the ones first. **I'll circle and cross out the blocks we are subtracting. How many ones should I cross out?** (2) Children remove 2 ones. **What is 7 − 2?** (5) Emphasize the placement of the 5 in the ones place as you record it.

3. Now we subtract the tens. **How many tens should I cross out?** (1) Have children remove 1 ten. **What is 4 tens − 1 ten?** (3 tens) Record 3 in the tens column. **What is 47 − 12?** (35)

2 Develop

Guided Learning

Teaching Example Introduce the objective to children. Guide them through the three steps, showing 36 with blocks, then explain how to subtract the ones then the tens.

Guided Practice

Have children complete **Exercises 1–3** as you observe. Give children the opportunity to answer the Explain Your Thinking question. Then discuss their responses with the class.

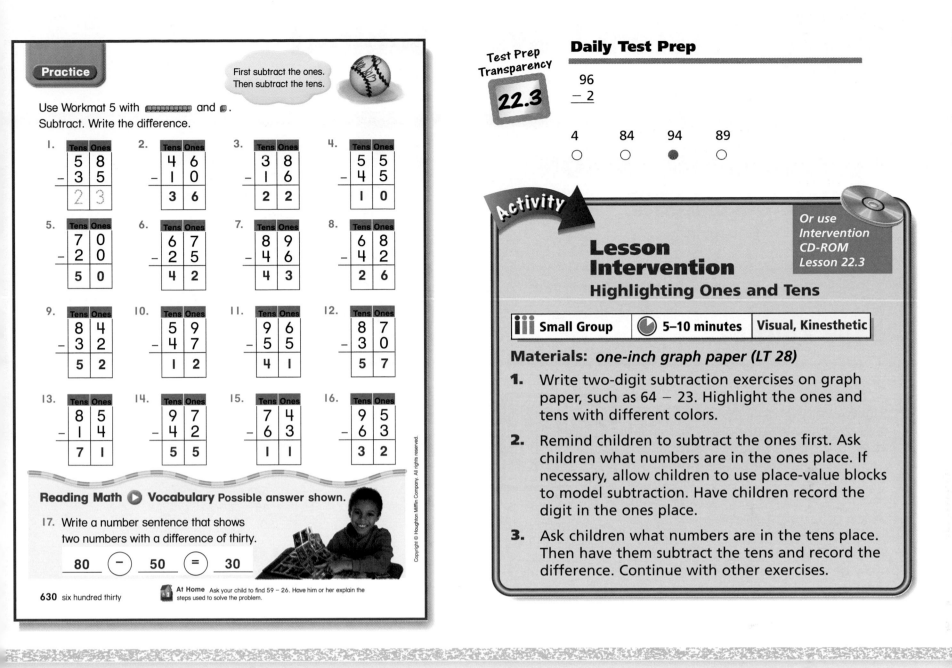

First subtract the ones.
Then subtract the tens.

Use Workmat 5 with ▭ and ▫.
Subtract. Write the difference.

	Tens	Ones			Tens	Ones			Tens	Ones			Tens	Ones
1.	5	8		2.	4	6		3.	3	8		4.	5	5
−	3	5		−	1	0		−	1	6		−	4	5
	2	3			3	6			2	2			1	0

	Tens	Ones			Tens	Ones			Tens	Ones			Tens	Ones
5.	7	0		6.	6	7		7.	8	9		8.	6	8
−	2	0		−	2	5		−	4	6		−	4	2
	5	0			4	2			4	3			2	6

	Tens	Ones			Tens	Ones			Tens	Ones			Tens	Ones
9.	8	4		10.	5	9		11.	9	6		12.	8	7
−	3	2		−	4	7		−	5	5		−	3	0
	5	2			1	2			4	1			5	7

	Tens	Ones			Tens	Ones			Tens	Ones			Tens	Ones
13.	8	5		14.	9	7		15.	7	4		16.	9	5
−	1	4		−	4	2		−	6	3		−	6	3
	7	1			5	5			1	1			3	2

Reading Math ▶ Vocabulary Possible answer shown.

17. Write a number sentence that shows
two numbers with a difference of thirty.

80 − **50** = **30**

At Home Ask your child to find 59 − 26. Have him or her explain the steps used to solve the problem.

Daily Test Prep

Test Prep Transparency **22.3**

$$96$$
$$-\ 2$$

4   84   94   89
○   ○   ●   ○

Activity

Or use Intervention CD-ROM Lesson 22.3

Lesson Intervention
Highlighting Ones and Tens

Small Group	5–10 minutes	Visual, Kinesthetic

Materials: *one-inch graph paper (LT 28)*

1. Write two-digit subtraction exercises on graph paper, such as 64 − 23. Highlight the ones and tens with different colors.

2. Remind children to subtract the ones first. Ask children what numbers are in the ones place. If necessary, allow children to use place-value blocks to model subtraction. Have children record the digit in the ones place.

3. Ask children what numbers are in the tens place. Then have them subtract the tens and record the difference. Continue with other exercises.

---

❸ Practice

Independent Practice

Children complete **Exercises 1–16** independently.

Reading Math

After children complete **Exercise 17**, call on several volunteers to share their sentences. Write the different sentences on the board and discuss why there is more than one correct answer.

Common Error

Subtracting from Left to Right
Children may subtract the tens before the ones. Remind them that the ones are subtracted first. Provide exercises with the ones column highlighted as a reminder.

❹ Assess and Close

James has 97 stamps. He uses 83 stamps. How many stamps does he have left? (14)

✎ Keeping a Journal

Show and write about the steps you use to find the difference for 89 − 45.

Different Ways to Subtract

PLANNING THE LESSON

MATHEMATICS OBJECTIVE
Use different ways to subtract.

Use Lesson Planner CD-ROM for Lesson 22.4.

Daily Routines

Calendar

Have a volunteer circle the first ten days of the current month. Ask children to find how many groups of ten days are in the entire month.

Sunday	Monday	Tuesday	Wednesday	Thursday	Friday	Saturday
				1	2	3	4
5	6	7	8	9	10	11
12	13	14	15	16	17	18
19	20	21	22	23	24	25
26	27	28	29	30	31	

Vocabulary

Ask a volunteer to write a subtraction sentence on the board. Ask another volunteer to identify how he or she would solve the subtraction. Discuss the different methods: *mental math, tens and ones blocks*, and *pencil and paper*.

Vocabulary Cards

Meeting North Carolina's Standards
Prepare for Grade 2 Standard 1.04 Develop fluency with multi-digit addition and subtraction through 999 using multiple strategies.

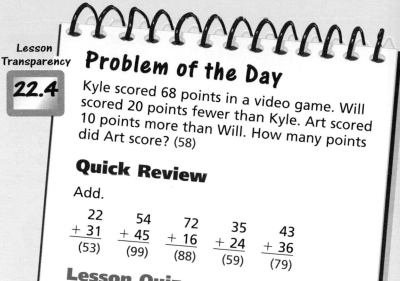

Lesson Transparency 22.4

Problem of the Day
Kyle scored 68 points in a video game. Will scored 20 points fewer than Kyle. Art scored 10 points more than Will. How many points did Art score? (58)

Quick Review
Add.

$$\begin{array}{c} 22 \\ +\ 31 \\ \hline (53) \end{array} \qquad \begin{array}{c} 54 \\ +\ 45 \\ \hline (99) \end{array} \qquad \begin{array}{c} 72 \\ +\ 16 \\ \hline (88) \end{array} \qquad \begin{array}{c} 35 \\ +\ 24 \\ \hline (59) \end{array} \qquad \begin{array}{c} 43 \\ +\ 36 \\ \hline (79) \end{array}$$

Lesson Quiz
$$1. \begin{array}{c} 78 \\ -\ 2 \\ \hline (76) \end{array} \qquad 2. \begin{array}{c} 90 \\ -\ 70 \\ \hline (20) \end{array} \qquad 3. \begin{array}{c} 66 \\ -\ 35 \\ \hline (31) \end{array}$$

LEVELED PRACTICE

RETEACH 22.4

Name _____ Date _____
Reteach 22.4

Different Ways to Subtract
You can use different ways to subtract.

Use mental math. Think of a basic fact to subtract.	Use pencil and paper. Subtract the ones first. Then subtract the tens.	Use tens and ones blocks. Show the numbers.
Think 9 − 6 = 3 $\begin{array}{c} 90 \\ -\ 60 \\ \hline 30 \end{array}$	 $\begin{array}{c} 48 \\ -\ 32 \\ \hline 16 \end{array}$	 $\begin{array}{c} 73 \\ -\ 20 \\ \hline 53 \end{array}$

Choose a way to subtract.
Write the difference.

	Tens	Ones		Tens	Ones		Tens	Ones		Tens	Ones
1.	5	7	2.	8	0	3.	7	5	4.	9	9
	− 2	5		− 4	0		− 3	4		−	5
	3	2		4	0		4	1		9	4

$$5. \begin{array}{c} 38 \\ -\ 7 \\ \hline 31 \end{array} \quad 6. \begin{array}{c} 56 \\ -\ 14 \\ \hline 42 \end{array} \quad 7. \begin{array}{c} 48 \\ -22 \\ \hline 26 \end{array} \quad 8. \begin{array}{c} 65 \\ -20 \\ \hline 45 \end{array} \quad 9. \begin{array}{c} 89 \\ -\ 4 \\ \hline 85 \end{array}$$

Use with text pages 631–632.

PRACTICE 22.4

Name _____ Date _____
Practice 22.4

Different Ways to Subtract

I can use mental math. I can use paper and pencil. I can use tens and ones blocks.

Choose a way to subtract.
Write the difference.

	Tens	Ones		Tens	Ones		Tens	Ones		Tens	Ones
1.	7	4	2.	3	8	3.	9	0	4.	5	4
	− 3	1		−	7		− 7	0		−	3
	4	3		3	1		2	0		5	1

$$5. \begin{array}{c} 98 \\ -67 \\ \hline 31 \end{array} \quad 6. \begin{array}{c} 65 \\ -\ 2 \\ \hline 63 \end{array} \quad 7. \begin{array}{c} 78 \\ -26 \\ \hline 51 \end{array} \quad 8. \begin{array}{c} 66 \\ -30 \\ \hline 36 \end{array}$$

$$9. \begin{array}{c} 70 \\ -50 \\ \hline 20 \end{array} \quad 10. \begin{array}{c} 76 \\ -12 \\ \hline 64 \end{array} \quad 11. \begin{array}{c} 99 \\ -68 \\ \hline 31 \end{array} \quad 12. \begin{array}{c} 87 \\ -\ 3 \\ \hline 84 \end{array}$$

13. 80 − 30 = <u>50</u>   14. 42 − 2 = <u>40</u>

15. 46 − 6 = <u>40</u>   16. 73 − 3 = <u>70</u>

Test Prep

17. Joel finds 10 large stones and 25 small stones. He gives 4 stones to his sister. How many stones does he have now? <u>31</u> stones

Draw or write to explain.

Use with text pages 631–632.

ENRICHMENT 22.4

Name _____ Date _____
Enrichment 22.4

Find the Greatest Differences

Choose a way to subtract for each exercise.
Write the differences.
Circle the greatest difference in each row.

$$1. \begin{array}{c} 46 \\ -33 \\ \hline \boxed{13} \end{array} \quad \begin{array}{c} 54 \\ -31 \\ \hline \boxed{23} \end{array} \quad \begin{array}{c} 69 \\ -26 \\ \hline \boxed{43} \end{array} \quad \begin{array}{c} 87 \\ -54 \\ \hline \boxed{33} \end{array}$$

$$2. \begin{array}{c} 90 \\ -40 \\ \hline \boxed{50} \end{array} \quad \begin{array}{c} 96 \\ -24 \\ \hline \boxed{72} \end{array} \quad \begin{array}{c} 55 \\ -10 \\ \hline \boxed{45} \end{array} \quad \begin{array}{c} 87 \\ -34 \\ \hline \boxed{53} \end{array}$$

$$3. \begin{array}{c} 78 \\ -25 \\ \hline \boxed{53} \end{array} \quad \begin{array}{c} 66 \\ -15 \\ \hline \boxed{51} \end{array} \quad \begin{array}{c} 35 \\ -20 \\ \hline \boxed{15} \end{array} \quad \begin{array}{c} 64 \\ -12 \\ \hline \boxed{52} \end{array}$$

Write About It Write the differences in Exercise 1 in order from least to greatest. What pattern do you see in the numbers?

<u>13</u> <u>23</u> <u>33</u> <u>43</u>

<u>Answers will vary. Possible answer: The ones stay</u>
<u>the same and the tens increase by 1 ten.</u>

Use with text pages 631–632.

Practice Workbook Page 150

Reaching All Learners
Differentiated Instruction

English Learners

English-language learners may be confused by the similar words *different* and *difference*. Use Worksheet 22.4 to help them distinguish between the two words.

Special Needs
AUDITORY, TACTILE

- Write 54 − 23, 38 − 6, and 90 − 20 vertically.
- Have the child describe mental math, using tens and ones models, and finding the difference with pencil and paper.
- Help the child, as necessary, choose a method for each of the exercises. Try more than one method to compare.

Gifted and Talented
TACTILE, VISUAL

Materials: *index cards*

- Prepare sets of index cards with one of the following numbers on each card: 4, 6, 15, 22, 33, 44, 50.
- Have each child choose a number and write subtraction problems that have the number as the difference.
- Have children exchange papers to check each others subtraction.

TECHNOLOGY

Spiral Review

Create **customized** spiral review worksheets for individual students using the *Ways to Assess* CD-ROM.

Education Place

You can visit **Education Place** at **eduplace.com/math/mw/** for teacher support materials.

Art Connection

Give each child a subtraction sentence, such as 48 − 25. Have children find the difference and use that many links to make a paper chain pattern. Display the chains and have children describe or identify the patterns.

MATH CENTER

Basic Skills Activity

Motivate children to build basic skills. Use this activity to address multiple learning styles using hands-on activities related to the skills of this lesson.

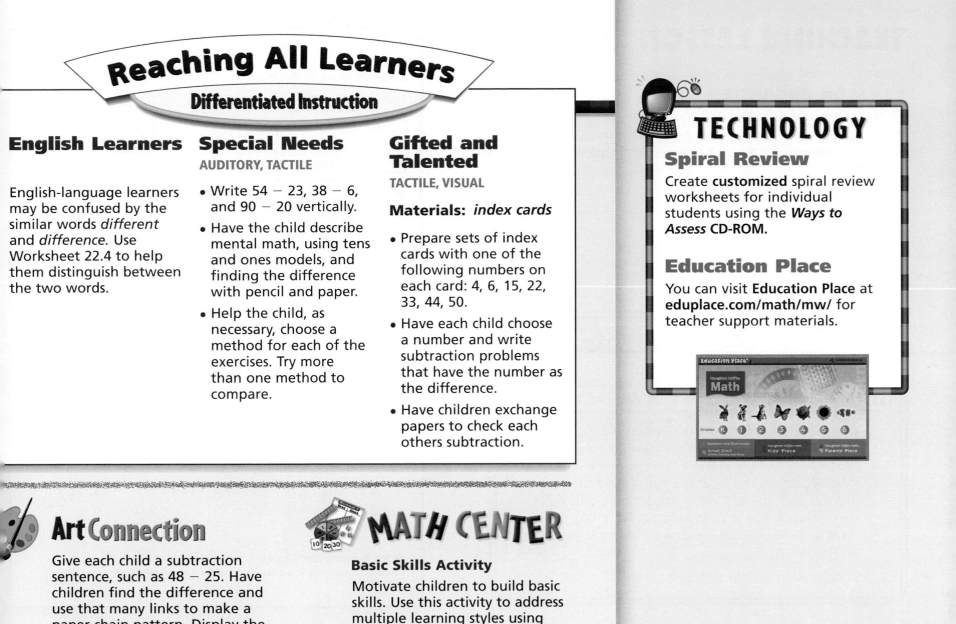

Homework Workbook Page 150

TEACHING LESSON 22.4

LESSON ORGANIZER

Objective Use different ways to subtract.

Resources Reteach, Practice, Enrichment, Problem Solving, Homework, English Learners, Transparencies, Math Center

Materials Place-value blocks

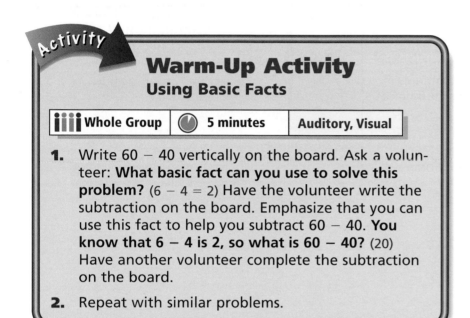

Warm-Up Activity
Using Basic Facts

iiii Whole Group	⏱ 5 minutes	Auditory, Visual

1. Write 60 − 40 vertically on the board. Ask a volunteer: **What basic fact can you use to solve this problem?** (6 − 4 = 2) Have the volunteer write the subtraction on the board. Emphasize that you can use this fact to help you subtract 60 − 40. **You know that 6 − 4 is 2, so what is 60 − 40?** (20) Have another volunteer complete the subtraction on the board.

2. Repeat with similar problems.

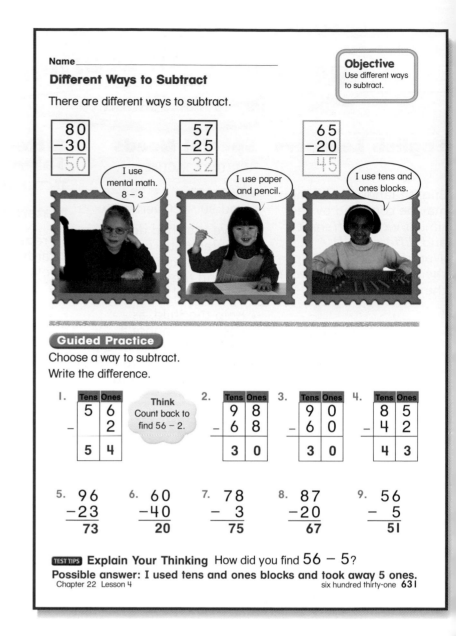

Name_____

Different Ways to Subtract

There are different ways to subtract.

Objective Use different ways to subtract.

$$\begin{array}{r} 80 \\ -30 \\ \hline 50 \end{array}$$
I use mental math. 8 − 3

$$\begin{array}{r} 57 \\ -25 \\ \hline 32 \end{array}$$
I use paper and pencil.

$$\begin{array}{r} 65 \\ -20 \\ \hline 45 \end{array}$$
I use tens and ones blocks.

Guided Practice

Choose a way to subtract.
Write the difference.

	Tens	Ones			Tens	Ones		Tens	Ones		Tens	Ones
1.	5	6		2.	9	8	3.	9	0	4.	8	5
−		2	Think Count back to find 56 − 2.	−	6	8	−	6	0	−	4	2
	5	4			3	0		3	0		4	3

5. $\begin{array}{r} 96 \\ -23 \\ \hline 73 \end{array}$ 6. $\begin{array}{r} 60 \\ -40 \\ \hline 20 \end{array}$ 7. $\begin{array}{r} 78 \\ -3 \\ \hline 75 \end{array}$ 8. $\begin{array}{r} 87 \\ -20 \\ \hline 67 \end{array}$ 9. $\begin{array}{r} 56 \\ -5 \\ \hline 51 \end{array}$

TEST TIPS Explain Your Thinking How did you find 56 − 5?
Possible answer: I used tens and ones blocks and took away 5 ones.
Chapter 22 Lesson 4   six hundred thirty-one **631**

1 Introduce
Discuss Different Ways to Subtract

iiii Whole Group	⏱ 10–15 minutes	Visual, Auditory

Materials: *place-value blocks*

1. Explain that you are going to use different ways to subtract.

2. Write 50 − 20 vertically on the board. **Can you use mental math to find the difference?** (yes) **What basic fact will help you?** (5 − 2 = 3) **If 5 − 2 = 3, then what is 50 − 20?** (30)

3. Write 78 − 35 vertically on the board. **Can you use mental math?** (Answers may vary.) **What numbers do you subtract first?** (the ones) **What is 8 − 5?** (3) **What do you do next?** (subtract the tens) **What is 7 tens − 3 tens?** (4 tens) **What is 78 − 35?** (43)

4. Write 67 − 53 vertically on the board. Model with tens and ones blocks. Work through the subtraction, allowing children to guide you through the steps.

2 Develop

Guided Learning

Teaching Example Introduce the objective to children. Guide them through the example, pointing out the three ways that can be used to subtract—using mental math, paper and pencil, and tens and ones blocks. Encourage children to use the method that works best for them and for the problem.

Guided Practice

Have children complete **Exercises 1–9** as you observe. Give children the opportunity to answer the Explain Your Thinking question. Emphasize that there is not just one correct method to use. Any of the three methods are acceptable.

Choose a way to subtract.
Write the difference.

Ways to Subtract
Use mental math.
Use paper and pencil.
Use tens and ones blocks.

1.
Tens	Ones
5	6
− 2	5
3	**1**

2.
Tens	Ones
7	0
− 4	0
	3 0

3. 98
   − 3
   95

4. 76
   −24
   52

5. 59
   − 9
   50

6. 67
   −35
   32

7. 46
   −20
   26

8. 80
   −30
   50

9. 45
   −13
   32

10. 97
    −63
    34

11. 75
    − 2
    73

12. 50
    −10
    40

13. 86 − 3 = **83**   14. 58 − 2 = **56**   15. 90 − 20 = **70**

16. 50 − 40 = **10**   17. 75 − 1 = **74**   18. 60 − 40 = **20**

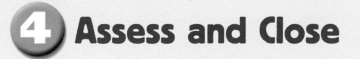

Problem Solving ▶ Reasoning

19. **Multistep** Ana has 30 marbles
in one box and 40 marbles
in another box. She gives
10 marbles to Max. How many
marbles does she have now?

Draw or write to explain.

_____ **60** _____ marbles

At Home Ask your child to subtract 75 − 35 and explain
how he or she found the difference.

Go on ▶

ACHIEVING
Mathematical Proficiency

Learning Algorithms for Operations

An algorithm is a systematic method for carrying
out a computation. Algorithms are important in
elementary school mathematics because they help
children understand basic arithmetic operations.
They are also important in teaching such concepts
as place value. The subtraction algorithm, based on
the base-10 numeration system, uses place value as
the "rule." Subtraction of two-digit numbers is
developed sequentially. Children subtract multiples
of ten; then they use the subtraction algorithm to
subtract two-digit numbers without regrouping.

In this chapter, children use subtraction facts to
subtract tens. They learn that 90 − 40 is the same as
9 tens − 4 tens. Then they use the subtraction
algorithm to subtract. Understanding and using the
subtraction algorithm in this way is an important
component of elementary mathematics.

---

③ Practice

Independent Practice

Children complete **Exercises 1–18** independently.

Problem Solving

After children complete **Exercise 19**, call on volunteers to
share their solutions and explain the steps they used to find
the answer.

Common Error

Omitting Part of the Difference
Children may forget to write the tens in the difference
after they have written the ones. Remind them that they
need to write both the tens and the ones in the difference.

④ Assess and Close

Kim found 24 sand crabs on the beach. Hannah found 47
sand crabs. How many more sand crabs did Hannah find?
(23) **Will you use mental math to solve?** (Answers will vary.)

✎ Keeping a Journal

List the three different ways you can use to
subtract. Then solve 98 − 36 and tell how you
found the difference.

Lesson continues

Daily Test Prep

May 1 is Monday.
What day is May 4?

MAY						
Sunday	Monday	Tuesday	Wednesday	Thursday	Friday	Saturday
	1	2	3	4	5	6
7	8	9	10	11	12	13
14	15	16	17	18	19	20
21	22	23	24	25	26	27
28	29	30	31			

Sunday ○   Tuesday ○   Thursday ●   Friday ○

Activity

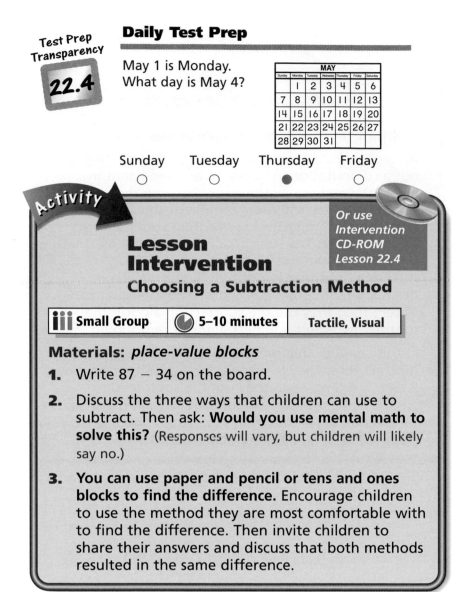

Or use
Intervention
CD-ROM
Lesson 22.4

Lesson Intervention

Choosing a Subtraction Method

👥 Small Group	🕐 5–10 minutes	Tactile, Visual

Materials: *place-value blocks*

1. Write 87 − 34 on the board.

2. Discuss the three ways that children can use to subtract. Then ask: **Would you use mental math to solve this?** (Responses will vary, but children will likely say no.)

3. **You can use paper and pencil or tens and ones blocks to find the difference.** Encourage children to use the method they are most comfortable with to find the difference. Then invite children to share their answers and discuss that both methods resulted in the same difference.

Name_____

Now Try This Subtract Money Amounts

Subtract money the same way you subtract numbers.
Think of dimes and pennies as tens and ones.

Subtract.

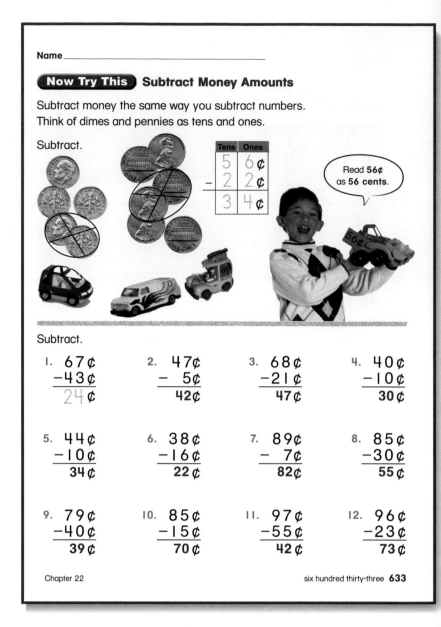

Read 56¢ as 56 cents.

Subtract.

1. 67¢ −43¢ 24¢	2. 47¢ − 5¢ 42¢	3. 68¢ −21¢ 47¢	4. 40¢ −10¢ 30¢
5. 44¢ −10¢ 34¢	6. 38¢ −16¢ 22¢	7. 89¢ − 7¢ 82¢	8. 85¢ −30¢ 55¢
9. 79¢ −40¢ 39¢	10. 85¢ −15¢ 70¢	11. 97¢ −55¢ 42¢	12. 96¢ −23¢ 73¢

Chapter 22   six hundred thirty-three **633**

Now Try This

Subtract Money Amounts

INTRODUCE Tell children that subtracting money is the same as subtracting two-digit numbers. First you subtract the ones, then the tens. Point out that the difference is that there is a cents sign after the numbers.

DEVELOP Have children complete **Exercises 1–4** as you observe. Provide coins to students who may need to use them.

PRACTICE Have children complete **Exercises 5–12** independently.

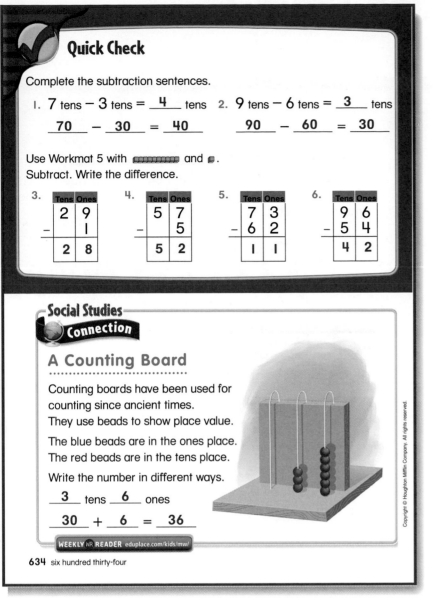

Quick Check

Complete the subtraction sentences.

1. 7 tens − 3 tens = __4__ tens

   __70__ − __30__ = __40__

2. 9 tens − 6 tens = __3__ tens

   __90__ − __60__ = __30__

Use Workmat 5 with ▭▭▭▭ and ▫.
Subtract. Write the difference.

3.
Tens	Ones
2	9
−	1
2	8

4.
Tens	Ones
5	7
−	5
5	2

5.
Tens	Ones
7	3
− 6	2
1	1

6.
Tens	Ones
9	6
− 5	4
4	2

Social Studies Connection

A Counting Board

Counting boards have been used for counting since ancient times.
They use beads to show place value.

The blue beads are in the ones place.
The red beads are in the tens place.

Write the number in different ways.

__3__ tens __6__ ones

__30__ + __6__ = __36__

WEEKLY WR READER eduplace.com/kids/mw/

634 six hundred thirty-four

Quick Check

Have children complete the Quick Check exercises independently to assess their understanding of concepts and skills taught in **Lessons 1–4**.

Item	Lesson	Error Analysis	Intervention
1–2	22.1	Children may omit zeros.	Reteach Resource 22.1 *Ways to Success* 22.1
3–4	22.2	Children may subtract the ones from the tens.	Reteach Resource 22.2 *Ways to Success* 22.2
5–6	22.3	Children may subtract from left to right.	Reteach Resource 22.3 *Ways to Success* 22.3
3–6	22.4	Children may omit part of the difference.	Reteach Resource 22.4 *Ways to Success* 22.4

Social Studies Connection

Introduce the counting board to the children. Tell them that this tool is believed to have been first used in the Middle East. Discuss how the counting board is used. **What color are the beads in the ones place?** (blue) **How many ones are shown?** (6) **What color are the beads in the tens place?** (red) **How many tens are there?** (3) **What is another name for 3 tens 6 ones?** (36) Explain that there are more beads on the other side of the counting board. You can slide beads over from the other side if you want to add ones or tens. You can slide beads away if you want to subtract tens or ones. **If you want to find the difference of 36 − 10 on the abacus, what would you do?** (Take away 1 red bead.) **If you want to show the sum of 36 + 3, what would you do?** (Add 3 more blue beads from the other side.)

Two-Digit Subtraction Practice

PLANNING THE LESSON

MATHEMATICS OBJECTIVE
Practice two-digit subtraction.

Use Lesson Planner CD-ROM for Lesson 22.5.

Meeting North Carolina's Standards
Prepare for Grade 2 Standard 1.04 Develop fluency with multi-digit addition and subtraction through 999 using multiple strategies.

Daily Routines

Calendar
With the class, count the number of children whose birthdays occur during the month. Help children subtract that number from 26.

Sunday	Monday	Tuesday	Wednesday	Thursday	Friday	Saturday
				1	2	3	4
5	6	7	8	9	10	11
12	13	14	15	16	17	18
19	20	21	22	23	24	25
26	27	28	29	30	31	

Vocabulary
Write a two-digit number, such as 52, on the board. Ask children to identify the **tens** and the **ones**. Repeat with other two-digit numbers.

Vocabulary Cards

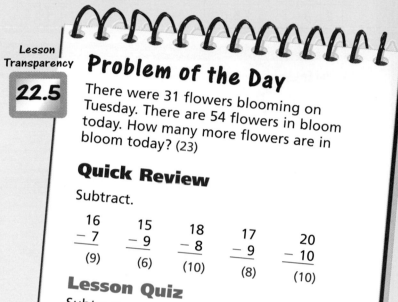

Lesson Transparency 22.5

Problem of the Day
There were 31 flowers blooming on Tuesday. There are 54 flowers in bloom today. How many more flowers are in bloom today? (23)

Quick Review
Subtract.

$$\begin{array}{r} 16 \\ -\ 7 \\ \hline (9) \end{array} \qquad \begin{array}{r} 15 \\ -\ 9 \\ \hline (6) \end{array} \qquad \begin{array}{r} 18 \\ -\ 8 \\ \hline (10) \end{array} \qquad \begin{array}{r} 17 \\ -\ 9 \\ \hline (8) \end{array} \qquad \begin{array}{r} 20 \\ -\ 10 \\ \hline (10) \end{array}$$

Lesson Quiz
Subtract.

1.
$$\begin{array}{r} 80 \\ -30 \\ \hline (50) \end{array}$$
2.
$$\begin{array}{r} 95 \\ -74 \\ \hline (21) \end{array}$$
3.
$$\begin{array}{r} 77 \\ -\ 5 \\ \hline (72) \end{array}$$
4.
$$\begin{array}{r} 58 \\ -34 \\ \hline (24) \end{array}$$

LEVELED PRACTICE

RETEACH 22.5

Name _____ Date _____ **Reteach 22.5**

Two-Digit Subtraction Practice

Find $65 - 42$.

Step 1 Subtract the ones.	**Step 2** Subtract the tens.
$\begin{array}{r} 65 \\ -42 \\ \hline 3 \end{array}$ 	$\begin{array}{r} 65 \\ -42 \\ \hline 23 \end{array}$

Write the difference.

1. $\begin{array}{r} 47 \\ -16 \\ \hline 31 \end{array}$ **2.** $\begin{array}{r} 98 \\ -25 \\ \hline 73 \end{array}$ **3.** $\begin{array}{r} 65 \\ -54 \\ \hline 11 \end{array}$ **4.** $\begin{array}{r} 77 \\ -\ 5 \\ \hline 72 \end{array}$

5. $\begin{array}{r} 53 \\ -12 \\ \hline 41 \end{array}$ **6.** $\begin{array}{r} 60 \\ -10 \\ \hline 50 \end{array}$ **7.** $\begin{array}{r} 83 \\ -41 \\ \hline 42 \end{array}$ **8.** $\begin{array}{r} 39 \\ -17 \\ \hline 22 \end{array}$

9. $78 - 23 = \underline{55}$ **10.** $70 - 50 = \underline{20}$

11. $49 - 2 = \underline{47}$ **12.** $64 - 41 = \underline{23}$

13. $68 - 5 = \underline{63}$ **14.** $90 - 30 = \underline{60}$

15. $80 - 20 = \underline{60}$ **16.** $95 - 42 = \underline{53}$

Use with text pages 635–636.

PRACTICE 22.5

Name _____ Date _____ **Practice 22.5**

Two-Digit Subtraction Practice

Write the difference.

1. $\begin{array}{r} 21 \\ -11 \\ \hline 10 \end{array}$ **2.** $\begin{array}{r} 40 \\ -30 \\ \hline 10 \end{array}$ **3.** $\begin{array}{r} 58 \\ -32 \\ \hline 26 \end{array}$ **4.** $\begin{array}{r} 74 \\ -12 \\ \hline 62 \end{array}$ **5.** $\begin{array}{r} 96 \\ -\ 4 \\ \hline 92 \end{array}$

6. $\begin{array}{r} 64 \\ -\ 3 \\ \hline 61 \end{array}$ **7.** $\begin{array}{r} 95 \\ -24 \\ \hline 71 \end{array}$ **8.** $\begin{array}{r} 55 \\ -33 \\ \hline 22 \end{array}$ **9.** $\begin{array}{r} 96 \\ -43 \\ \hline 53 \end{array}$ **10.** $\begin{array}{r} 26 \\ -14 \\ \hline 12 \end{array}$

11. $\begin{array}{r} 74 \\ -42 \\ \hline 32 \end{array}$ **12.** $\begin{array}{r} 65 \\ -41 \\ \hline 24 \end{array}$ **13.** $\begin{array}{r} 86 \\ -35 \\ \hline 51 \end{array}$ **14.** $\begin{array}{r} 76 \\ -\ 5 \\ \hline 71 \end{array}$ **15.** $\begin{array}{r} 49 \\ -\ 5 \\ \hline 44 \end{array}$

16. $\begin{array}{r} 36 \\ -23 \\ \hline 13 \end{array}$ **17.** $\begin{array}{r} 54 \\ -33 \\ \hline 21 \end{array}$ **18.** $\begin{array}{r} 90 \\ -20 \\ \hline 70 \end{array}$ **19.** $\begin{array}{r} 79 \\ -13 \\ \hline 66 \end{array}$ **20.** $\begin{array}{r} 87 \\ -45 \\ \hline 42 \end{array}$

Test Prep

Fill in the ○ for the correct answer.
NH means Not Here.

21. Zack has 33 stickers. His sister Kayla has 21 stickers. How many more stickers does Zack have than Kayla?

12 14 54 NH
● ○ ○ ○

Use with text pages 635–636.

ENRICHMENT 22.5

Name _____ Date _____ **Enrichment 22.5**

Same Differences

Look at the number.
Write 3 two-digit subtraction exercises with the number shown as the difference.
Answers will vary. Possible answers shown.

1. 52
$\begin{array}{r} \boxed{96} \\ -\boxed{44} \\ \hline 52 \end{array}$ $\begin{array}{r} \boxed{68} \\ -\boxed{16} \\ \hline 52 \end{array}$ $\begin{array}{r} \boxed{55} \\ -\boxed{3} \\ \hline 52 \end{array}$

2. 40
$\begin{array}{r} \boxed{60} \\ -\boxed{20} \\ \hline 40 \end{array}$ $\begin{array}{r} \boxed{70} \\ -\boxed{30} \\ \hline 40 \end{array}$ $\begin{array}{r} \boxed{50} \\ -\boxed{10} \\ \hline 40 \end{array}$

3. 33
$\begin{array}{r} \boxed{66} \\ -\boxed{33} \\ \hline 33 \end{array}$ $\begin{array}{r} \boxed{76} \\ -\boxed{43} \\ \hline 33 \end{array}$ $\begin{array}{r} \boxed{87} \\ -\boxed{54} \\ \hline 33 \end{array}$

Write About It Choose a two-digit number. Write 3 subtraction exercises with that number as the difference.
Answers will vary. Possible answer:
$26; 59 - 33 = 26, 38 - 12 = 26, 77 - 51 = 26.$

Use with text pages 635–636.

Practice Workbook Page 151

Reaching All Learners

Differentiated Instruction

English Learners

English-language learners may not have the language skills to explain the process behind their thinking. Use Worksheet 22.5 to provide children with sentence frames they can use to complete the Explain Your Thinking activity.

Special Needs
TACTILE, VISUAL

Materials: *index cards, number cube 10–16, place-value blocks*

- Write 57, 46, 39, 28, on four cards.
- Have the child choose a card and model the number. Then have the child roll the cube and take away that many tens and ones.
- Write the subtraction and have the child read it aloud.

Gifted and Talented
AUDITORY, TACTILE

- Have pairs of children discuss the things they see on the way to school, such as trees, signs, cars, and buses.
- Have each child write a subtraction story problem about a set of things mentioned in the discussion.
- Have partners exchange problems and solve.

TECHNOLOGY

Spiral Review
Using the *Ways to Assess* CD-ROM, you can create **customized** spiral review worksheets covering any lessons you choose.

Lesson Planner
You can customize your teaching plan or meet your curriculum requirements with the **Lesson Planner CD-ROM.**

eBook
An electronic version of this lesson can be found in **eMathBook.**

Education Place
Recommend that parents visit **Education Place** at **eduplace.com/parents/mw/** for parent support activities.

ScienceConnection

Discuss pumpkins with children. Explain that pumpkins are a source of Vitamin A, and pumpkin seeds can be a crunchy, healthy snack. Have children make up subtraction story problems about pumpkins.

MATH CENTER

Cross-Curricular Activity

As you use this activity to relate the mathematics of this lesson to another curriculum area, children will see how math can help them with other subjects.

PROBLEM SOLVING 22.5

Name _____ Date _____ Problem Solving 22.5

Two-Digit Subtraction Practice

Solve.

	Draw or write to explain.
1. Brad buys a box of 48 dog treats. He gives his dogs 16 treats. How many dog treats are left?	**32** dog treats
2. There are 65 books in Pat's bookcase. She has read 41 of the books. How many books has she not read?	**24** books
3. Ken has 96 white rocks in his rock collection. He has 25 black rocks. How many more white rocks than black rocks does Ken have?	**71** more white rocks
4. There are 39 fish and 22 snails in a fish tank. How many more fish than snails are there?	**17** more fish

Copyright © Houghton Mifflin Company. All rights reserved.   Use with text pages 635–636.

HOMEWORK 22.5

Name _____ Date _____ Homework 22.5

Two-Digit Subtraction Practice

Find 69 − 34.

Subtract the ones.
```
  69
− 34
   5
```
Subtract the tens.
```
  69
− 34
  35
```

Subtract.

1. 88 − 24 = 64
2. 47 − 17 = 30
3. 80 − 50 = 30
4. 39 − 11 = 28
5. 75 − 4 = 71
6. 56 − 45 = 11
7. 31 − 10 = 21
8. 94 − 62 = 32
9. 98 − 20 = 78
10. 39 − 6 = 33
11. 65 − 23 = 42
12. 82 − 2 = 80

13. Marco has 32 baseball cards. He gives 12 cards to Ken. How many cards does Marco have left?

20 cards   Draw or write to explain.

Copyright © Houghton Mifflin Company. All rights reserved.   Use with text pages 635–636.

ENGLISH LEARNERS 22.5

Name _____ Date _____ English Learners 22.5

Practice Two-Digit Subtraction

```
        68
    6 tens 8 ones
```

How do you get the difference for 73 − 3?

First, I subtract the ones.

3 − 3 = **0**

I write **0** in the ones column.

Then I subtract the tens.

7 − 0 = **7**

I write **7** in the tens column.

73 − 3 = **70**

To the Teacher: Use the example at the top of the page to reinforce children's understanding of place value. Then read the sentences with children and have them complete each one.

Copyright © Houghton Mifflin Company. All rights reserved.   Use with text pages 635–636.

TEACHING LESSON 22.5

LESSON ORGANIZER

Objective Practice two-digit subtraction.

Resources Reteach, Practice, Enrichment, Problem Solving, Homework, English Learners, Transparencies, Math Center

Materials Number cubes, index cards, blank transparency, dimes, pennies

Activity

Warm-Up Activity
Modeling Subtraction Methods

| 👤👤👤 Small Group | 🕐 5–10 minutes | Visual, Tactile |

Materials: *number cubes, index cards*

1. In advance, write two-digit numbers on index cards that have both digits equaling 5 or above. Label cubes with the numbers 5, 4, 2, 10, 12, and 22.

2. Give each group a cube and some cards. Have one child in each group choose a card and roll the cube. Tell each child to subtract the number on the cube from the number on the card as you observe. Encourage children to use any strategy they need to find the difference.

3. Ask another child in each group to check the difference. Have that child continue the activity by choosing a card and rolling the cube. Repeat the activity until all children have had a turn.

Name_____

Two-Digit Subtraction Practice

Find 86 − 25.

Step 1	Step 2
Subtract the ones.	Subtract the tens.
$\begin{array}{r} 86 \\ -25 \\ \hline \end{array}$	$\begin{array}{r} 86 \\ -25 \\ \hline 61 \end{array}$

Guided Practice

Write the difference.

1. $\begin{array}{r} 47 \\ -35 \\ \hline 12 \end{array}$
Think Subtract the ones first. Then subtract 4 tens − 3 tens.

2. $\begin{array}{r} 68 \\ -\ 5 \\ \hline 63 \end{array}$

3. $\begin{array}{r} 89 \\ -45 \\ \hline 44 \end{array}$

4. $\begin{array}{r} 35 \\ -\ 4 \\ \hline 31 \end{array}$

5. $\begin{array}{r} 56 \\ -\ 3 \\ \hline 53 \end{array}$

6. $\begin{array}{r} 87 \\ -13 \\ \hline 74 \end{array}$

7. $\begin{array}{r} 94 \\ -52 \\ \hline 42 \end{array}$

8. $\begin{array}{r} 75 \\ -\ 2 \\ \hline 73 \end{array}$

9. $\begin{array}{r} 90 \\ -50 \\ \hline 40 \end{array}$

10. $67 - 3 = \underline{64}$ 11. $80 - 50 = \underline{30}$ 12. $59 - 2 = \underline{57}$

13. $50 - 40 = \underline{10}$ 14. $80 - 20 = \underline{60}$ 15. $73 - 3 = \underline{70}$

TEST TIPS **Explain Your Thinking** How did you find the difference for $73 - 3$? **Possible answer: I started with 73 and counted back 3. 72, 71, 70.**

---

① Introduce *Activity*

Discuss Subtracting Two-Digit Numbers

| 👤👤👤👤 Whole Group | 🕐 10–15 minutes | Visual, Auditory |

Materials: *blank transparency*

1. Write $85 - 4$ in vertical form on the transparency. Ask a volunteer to read the subtraction aloud.

2. **What number are we starting with?** (85) **What are we subtracting?** (4) **What do we subtract first?** (the ones) **What is $5 - 4$?** (1)

3. Direct children's attention to the tens column. **What do we subtract from 8 tens?** (nothing) **What number do I put in the tens place?** (8) Make sure children understand that the 8 must be put into the tens place.

4. Repeat the activity with $76 - 42$ and $60 - 50$.

② Develop

Guided Learning

Teaching Example Introduce the objective to the children. Guide them through the example to review how to follow the steps to subtract two-digit numbers.

Guided Practice

Have children complete **Exercises 1–15** as you observe. Give children the opportunity to answer the Explain Your Thinking question. Then discuss their responses with the class.

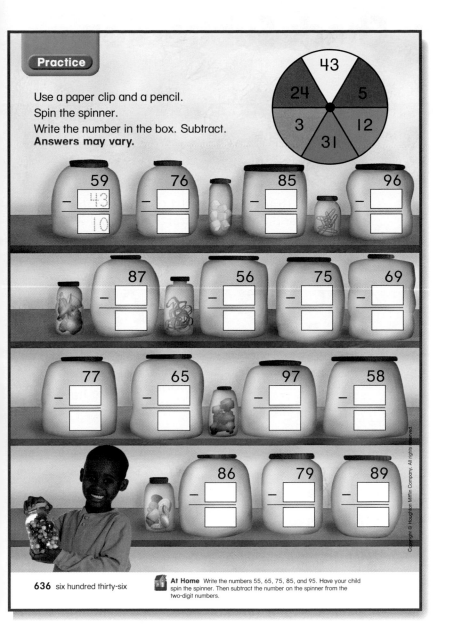

Practice

Use a paper clip and a pencil.
Spin the spinner.
Write the number in the box. Subtract.
Answers may vary.

Spinner: 43, 5, 12, 31, 3, 24

59 − 43 = 10

76 − ☐

85 − ☐

96 − ☐

87 − ☐

56 − ☐

75 − ☐

69 − ☐

77 − ☐

65 − ☐

97 − ☐

58 − ☐

86 − ☐

79 − ☐

89 − ☐

636 six hundred thirty-six

At Home Write the numbers 55, 65, 75, 85, and 95. Have your child spin the spinner. Then subtract the number on the spinner from the two-digit numbers.

Daily Test Prep

52
+22

54 ○   72 ○   74 ●   NH ○

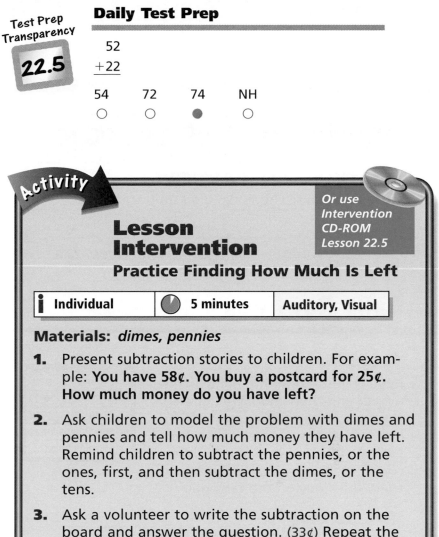

Activity

Or use Intervention CD-ROM Lesson 22.5

Lesson Intervention

Practice Finding How Much Is Left

| Individual | 5 minutes | Auditory, Visual |

Materials: *dimes, pennies*

1. Present subtraction stories to children. For example: **You have 58¢. You buy a postcard for 25¢. How much money do you have left?**

2. Ask children to model the problem with dimes and pennies and tell how much money they have left. Remind children to subtract the pennies, or the ones, first, and then subtract the dimes, or the tens.

3. Ask a volunteer to write the subtraction on the board and answer the question. (33¢) Repeat the activity for other subtraction stories.

3 Practice

Independent Practice

Have children complete the exercises on page 636 independently.

Common Error

Subtracting Horizontal Exercises Incorrectly
If children appear to make subtraction errors for a horizontal exercise, rewrite the exercises vertically so they can identify the tens and ones.

4 Assess and Close

Twenty-nine children ride on the bus. Six children ride in the van. How many more children ride on the bus? (23)

Laura rides on the bus for 15 minutes. Bill rides in the van for 25 minutes. Whose ride is longer? (Bill's ride) **How much longer?** (10 minutes)

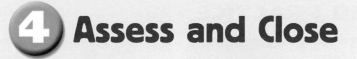

Keeping a Journal

Write a subtraction sentence with the numbers 86 and 5. Then write the difference.

Algebra Readiness: Check Subtraction

PLANNING THE LESSON

MATHEMATICS OBJECTIVE
Use addition to check two-digit subtraction.

Use Lesson Planner CD-ROM for Lesson 22.6.

Meeting North Carolina's Standards
Prepare for Grade 2 Standard 1.04 Develop fluency with multi-digit addition and subtraction through 999 using multiple strategies.

Daily Routines

Calendar
Have children read the name of the month and then count the letters in the name. Have them count off and mark the same number of days on the calendar. For example, children count 3 letters in May and mark every third day on the calendar.

Sunday	Monday	Tuesday	Wednesday	Thursday	Friday	Saturday
			1	2	3	4
5	6	7	8	9	10	11
12	13	14	15	16	17	18
19	20	21	22	23	24	25
26	27	28	29	30	31	

Vocabulary
Write a subtraction fact and its related addition fact on the board. Have children identify the **sum** and the **difference**.

Vocabulary Cards

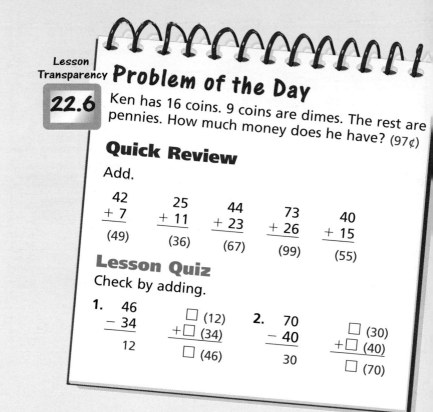

Lesson Transparency 22.6

Problem of the Day
Ken has 16 coins. 9 coins are dimes. The rest are pennies. How much money does he have? (97¢)

Quick Review
Add.

42	25	44	73	40
+ 7	+ 11	+ 23	+ 26	+ 15
(49)	(36)	(67)	(99)	(55)

Lesson Quiz
Check by adding.

1.
```
   46
 - 34
 ────
   12
```
☐ (12)
+☐ (34)
☐ (46)

2.
```
   70
 - 40
 ────
   30
```
☐ (30)
+☐ (40)
☐ (70)

LEVELED PRACTICE

RETEACH 22.6

Name _____ Date _____ Reteach 22.6

Check Subtraction

Add to check subtraction.

Subtract.	Check by adding.	The sum should equal the number you subtracted from.
56 −21	56 −21 ── 35 + 35 21	56 −21 ── 35 + 35 21 56

Subtract. Check by adding.

1. 57
   − 23
   ────
    34   + 34 → 23 → 57

2. 85
   − 54
   ────
    31   + 31 → 54 → 85

3. 59
   − 16
   ────
    43   + 43 → 16 → 59

4. 96
   − 41
   ────
    55   + 55 → 41 → 96

Copyright © Houghton Mifflin Company. All rights reserved.   Use with text pages 637–638.

PRACTICE 22.6

Name _____ Date _____ Practice 22.6

Check Subtraction

Subtract. Check by adding.

1. 78
   − 6
        + [6] 72
        [72]   78

2. 60
   − 10
        + 10 50
         50   60

3. 64
   − 23
        + 23 41
         41   64

4. 58
   − 30
        + 30 28
         28   58

Test Prep

Fill in the ○ for the correct answer.
NH means Not Here.

5. How many fewer children like grapes than apples?

Best Fruit Votes		Total
Apples	卌 卌 卌 卌 卌 卌 卌 III	38
Grapes	卌 卌 卌 卌 卌 III	28
Oranges	卌 卌 卌 卌	20

38 − 20 = 18   38 − 28 = 10   28 − 20 = 8   NH
     ○   ●   ○

Copyright © Houghton Mifflin Company. All rights reserved.   Use with text pages 637–638.

ENRICHMENT 22.6

Name _____ Date _____ Enrichment 22.6

Subtract and Match

Find the difference.
Match the subtraction sentence with the related addition sentence.

1. 59 − 50 = _9_

2. 74 − 33 = _41_

3. 68 − 48 = _20_

4. 85 − 30 = _55_

5. 79 − 64 = _15_

6. 96 − 82 = _14_

41 + 33 = 74

55 + 30 = 85

9 + 50 = 59

15 + 64 = 79

14 + 82 = 96

20 + 48 = 68

Write About It Explain how you can check subtraction by adding. Use pictures or words.
Answers will vary. Possible answer: Add the difference and the number that was subtracted from the first number.

Copyright © Houghton Mifflin Company. All rights reserved.   Use with text pages 637–638.

Practice Workbook Page 152

Reaching All Learners

Differentiated Instruction

English Learners

The word *check* has several meanings in English. Use Worksheet 22.6 to help children understand that when you check something, you make sure you did it correctly.

Inclusion
AUDITORY, TACTILE

Materials: *2 spinners (LT 38), place-value blocks*

- Prepare two spinners:

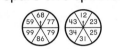

- Have the child spin and subtract the lesser number from the greater number by using models.
- Write the subtraction and then guide the child in checking by adding.

Gifted and Talented
TACTILE, VISUAL

Materials: *index cards*

- For each child prepare cards with 2-digit addition exercises that do not require regrouping.
- Have children solve the problems. Then have them create two related subtraction exercises for each addition.
- Allow children to exchange and review cards.

TECHNOLOGY

Spiral Review

To reinforce skills on lessons taught earlier, create **customized** spiral review worksheets using the *Ways to Assess* CD-ROM.

Education Place

Visit **Data Place** at **eduplace.com/dataplace/** to take a survey and see graphs of the results.

Games

Students can practice their computational skills using the **Rock Hopper** math game, available on the *Ways to Success* CD-ROM.

Social Studies Connection

Discuss postage stamps. Present subtraction problems comparing the cost of stamps based on the chart.

U.S. Postage Stamps	
Date	Cost
1932	3¢
1963	5¢
1974	10¢
1981	20¢
1988	25¢
1995	32¢
2002	37¢

MATH CENTER

Basic Skills Activity

Motivate children to build basic skills. Use this activity to address multiple learning styles using hands-on activities related to the skills of this lesson.

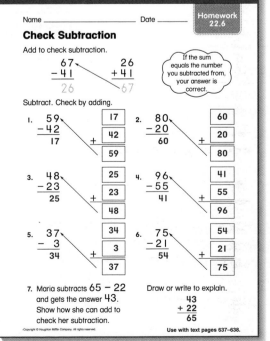

PROBLEM SOLVING 22.6

Name _____ Date _____

Problem Solving 22.6

Check Subtraction

Subtract to solve.
Then check by adding.

Draw or write to explain.

1. There are 86 apples on the tree. Tony picks 5 apples. How many apples are left on the tree?

   __81__ apples

2. The pet store fish tank has 34 fish. The store sells 12 fish. How many fish are left in the fish tank?

   __22__ fish

3. There are 29 cars and 15 trucks in the parking lot. How many more cars than trucks are there?

   __14__ more cars

4. Franco's dog weighs 63 pounds. His dog weighs 21 more pounds than Lisa's dog. How many pounds does Lisa's dog weigh?

   __42__ pounds

Use with text pages 637–638.

HOMEWORK 22.6

Name _____ Date _____

Homework 22.6

Check Subtraction

Add to check subtraction.

$$\begin{array}{r} 67 \\ -41 \\ \hline 26 \end{array} \qquad \begin{array}{r} 26 \\ +41 \\ \hline 67 \end{array}$$

If the sum equals the number you subtracted from, your answer is correct.

Subtract. Check by adding.

1. $\begin{array}{r} 59 \\ -42 \\ \hline 17 \end{array}$ 17 + 42 → 59

2. $\begin{array}{r} 80 \\ -20 \\ \hline 60 \end{array}$ 60 + 20 → 80

3. $\begin{array}{r} 48 \\ -23 \\ \hline 25 \end{array}$ 25 + 23 → 48

4. $\begin{array}{r} 96 \\ -55 \\ \hline 41 \end{array}$ 41 + 55 → 96

5. $\begin{array}{r} 37 \\ -3 \\ \hline 34 \end{array}$ 34 + 3 → 37

6. $\begin{array}{r} 75 \\ -21 \\ \hline 54 \end{array}$ 54 + 21 → 75

7. Maria subtracts 65 − 22 and gets the answer 43. Show how she can add to check her subtraction.

   Draw or write to explain.
   $$\begin{array}{r} 43 \\ +22 \\ \hline 65 \end{array}$$

Use with text pages 637–638.

ENGLISH LEARNERS 22.6

Name _____ Date _____

English Learners 22.6

Check Subtraction

I **check** to see if I brought my book.
I **make sure** I brought my book.

I draw a **check** on my paper.

Draw a picture of yourself checking to make sure you did something right.

Drawing of a child checking to make sure he or she did something correctly

Use with text pages 637–638.

TEACHING LESSON 22.6

LESSON ORGANIZER

Objective Use addition to check two-digit subtraction.

Resources Reteach, Practice, Enrichment, Problem Solving, Homework, English Learners, Transparencies, Math Center

Materials Place-value blocks, blank transparency

Activity
Warm-Up Activity
Modeling Related Facts

| ⅲⅲ Whole Group | ⏱ 5 minutes | Auditory, Kinesthetic |

1. Have 12 children stand in front of the board. Ask a volunteer to count the children. Then have 8 children sit down. Have a volunteer count the remaining children. **What number sentence shows what happened?** ($12 - 8 = 4$) Write the number sentence.

2. Ask the 8 children that sat down to go back to the group. Have a child count the total number of children standing. **What number sentence shows what happened?** ($4 + 8 = 12$) Write the sentence.

3. Have children look at both number sentences. **How are the number sentences the same?** (They both use the same three numbers.) Continue with other numbers.

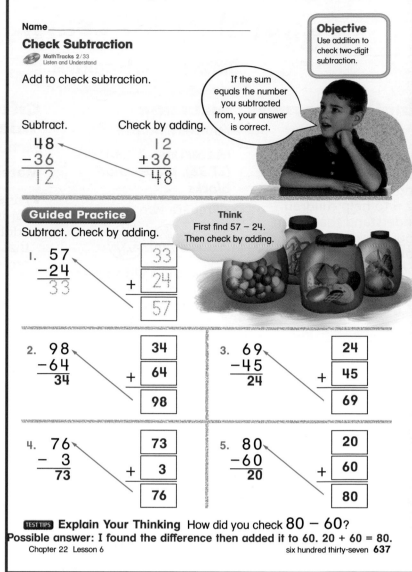

Name_____

Check Subtraction

MathTracks 2/33
Listen and Understand

Add to check subtraction.

If the sum equals the number you subtracted from, your answer is correct.

Subtract.   Check by adding.

```
  48                      12
- 36                    + 36
  12                      48
```

Guided Practice
Subtract. Check by adding.

Think
First find 57 − 24.
Then check by adding.

1.
```
  57        33
- 24     +  24
  33        57
```

2.
```
  98        34
- 64     +  64
  34        98
```

3.
```
  69        24
- 45     +  45
  24        69
```

4.
```
  76        73
-  3     +   3
  73        76
```

5.
```
  80        20
- 60     +  60
  20        80
```

TEST TIPS **Explain Your Thinking** How did you check $80 - 60$?
Possible answer: I found the difference then added it to 60. $20 + 60 = 80$.

Chapter 22 Lesson 6   six hundred thirty-seven **637**

---

1 Introduce
Activity
Discuss Checking Subtraction

| ⅲⅲ Whole Group | ⏱ 10–15 minutes | Visual, Auditory |

Materials: *place-value blocks, blank transparency*

1. Have a volunteer model 26 with tens and ones blocks. **How many tens are there?** (2) **How many ones?** (6)

2. **How can I take away 14?** (Take away 4 ones and then 1 ten.) **What is left?** (1 ten 2 ones) Write $26 - 14 = 12$ in vertical form. **We can check our work by adding back the number that we subtracted.**

3. Have a volunteer add back the 1 ten and the 4 ones to the 1 ten and 2 ones. **How many are there altogether?** (26) Write $12 + 14 = 26$. Relate the addition to the subtraction to demonstrate why addition can be used to check subtraction.

2 Develop

Guided Learning

Teaching Example Introduce the objective to the children. Guide them through the example to show how to check subtraction by adding.

Guided Practice

Have children complete **Exercises 1–5** as you observe. Give children the opportunity to answer the Explain Your Thinking question. Then discuss their responses with the class.

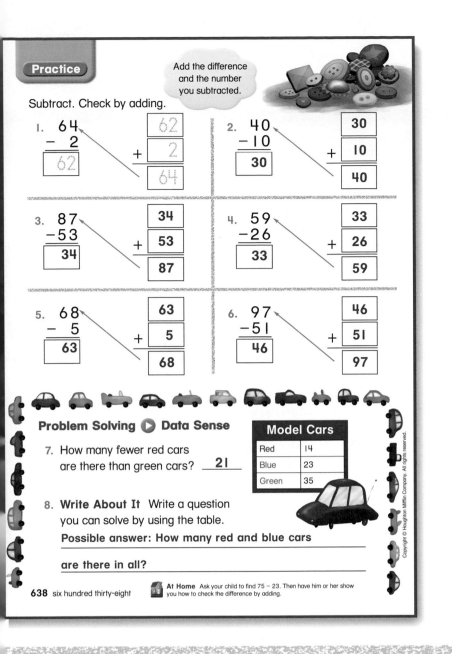

Subtract. Check by adding.

Add the difference and the number you subtracted.

1.
```
  64
-  2
  62
```
+ 62 → 2 → 64

2.
```
  40
- 10
  30
```
+ 30 → 10 → 40

3.
```
  87
- 53
  34
```
+ 34 → 53 → 87

4.
```
  59
- 26
  33
```
+ 33 → 26 → 59

5.
```
  68
-  5
  63
```
+ 63 → 5 → 68

6.
```
  97
- 51
  46
```
+ 46 → 51 → 97

Problem Solving ▶ Data Sense

Model Cars	
Red	14
Blue	23
Green	35

7. How many fewer red cars are there than green cars? __21__

8. **Write About It** Write a question you can solve by using the table.

Possible answer: How many red and blue cars are there in all?

At Home Ask your child to find 75 − 23. Then have him or her show you how to check the difference by adding.

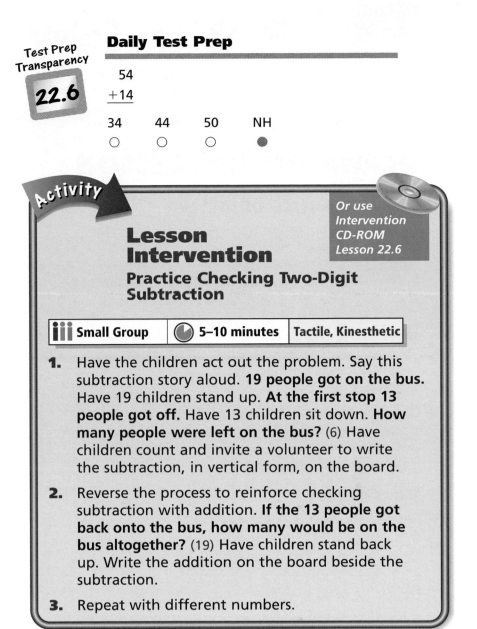

Daily Test Prep

Test Prep Transparency **22.6**

```
  54
+ 14
```

34 ○   44 ○   50 ○   NH ●

Activity

Or use Intervention CD-ROM Lesson 22.6

Lesson Intervention

Practice Checking Two-Digit Subtraction

👥 Small Group	⏱ 5–10 minutes	Tactile, Kinesthetic

1. Have the children act out the problem. Say this subtraction story aloud. **19 people got on the bus.** Have 19 children stand up. **At the first stop 13 people got off.** Have 13 children sit down. **How many people were left on the bus?** (6) Have children count and invite a volunteer to write the subtraction, in vertical form, on the board.

2. Reverse the process to reinforce checking subtraction with addition. **If the 13 people got back onto the bus, how many would be on the bus altogether?** (19) Have children stand back up. Write the addition on the board beside the subtraction.

3. Repeat with different numbers.

---

3 Practice

Independent Practice

Children complete **Exercises 1–6** independently.

Problem Solving

After children complete **Exercises 7–8**, call on volunteers to share their solutions and the questions they wrote using the data in the table.

Common Error

Confusing Which Numbers Must Be Equal in a Check
Children may have difficulty knowing which numbers must be equal in a subtraction/addition check. Have children write the number they begin with and the sum of the addition check in red.

4 Assess and Close

38 people carried flags in the parade. 22 flags were green. The rest were yellow. How many flags were yellow? (16)

What addition sentence can you use to check this problem? (16 + 22 = 38)

📓 Keeping a Journal

Write a subtraction sentence with the numbers 67 and 14. Find the difference. Then write an addition sentence to check your subtraction.

Problem Solving: Choose the Operation

PLANNING THE LESSON

MATHEMATICS OBJECTIVE
Choose the operation to solve word problems.

Use Lesson Planner CD-ROM for Lesson 22.7.

Daily Routines

Calendar
Direct children's attention to the classroom calendar. After pointing out today's date, ask how many days there are until Saturday.

Sunday	Monday	Tuesday	Wednesday	Thursday	Friday	Saturday
			1	2	3	4
5	6	7	8	9	10	11
12	13	14	15	16	17	18
19	20	21	22	23	24	25
26	27	28	29	30	31	

Vocabulary
Review **addition** and **subtraction** as operations that can be used to solve story problems. Have volunteers tell an addition story and a subtraction story.

Vocabulary Cards

Meeting North Carolina's Standards
Prepare for Grade 2 Standard **1.05** Create and solve problems using strategies such as modeling, composing and decomposing quantities, using doubles, and making tens and hundreds.

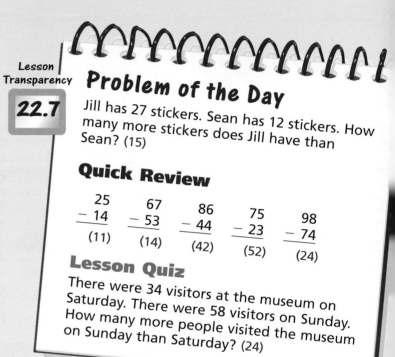

Lesson Transparency **22.7**

Problem of the Day
Jill has 27 stickers. Sean has 12 stickers. How many more stickers does Jill have than Sean? (15)

Quick Review

$$\begin{array}{r} 25 \\ -14 \\ \hline (11) \end{array} \qquad \begin{array}{r} 67 \\ -53 \\ \hline (14) \end{array} \qquad \begin{array}{r} 86 \\ -44 \\ \hline (42) \end{array} \qquad \begin{array}{r} 75 \\ -23 \\ \hline (52) \end{array} \qquad \begin{array}{r} 98 \\ -74 \\ \hline (24) \end{array}$$

Lesson Quiz
There were 34 visitors at the museum on Saturday. There were 58 visitors on Sunday. How many more people visited the museum on Sunday than Saturday? (24)

LEVELED PRACTICE

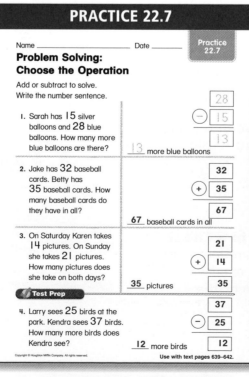

RETEACH 22.7

Name _____ Date _____ Reteach 22.7

Problem Solving
Choose the Operation

Read It Look for information.
Jessica has **84** postcards.
She puts **32** postcards in an album.
How many postcards are not in the album?

Picture It Here is a model of the problem.

Postcards in all	
Postcards in album	Postcards not in album

Solve It Use the model to solve the problem.

84 postcards in all	
32 postcards in album	_____ postcards not in album

1. Circle the sign you will use to solve the problem.
   + ⊖

2. Solve.

$$\begin{array}{r} 84 \\ -\ 32 \\ \hline 52 \end{array}$$

3. How many postcards are not in the album?
   52 postcards

Copyright © Houghton Mifflin Company. All rights reserved.
Use with text pages 639–641.

PRACTICE 22.7

Name _____ Date _____ Practice 22.7

Problem Solving:
Choose the Operation

Add or subtract to solve.
Write the number sentence.

1. Sarah has **15** silver balloons and **28** blue balloons. How many more blue balloons are there?

   28 ⊖ 15 = 13
   13 more blue balloons

2. Jake has **32** baseball cards. Betty has **35** baseball cards. How many baseball cards do they have in all?

   32 + 35 = 67
   67 baseball cards in all

3. On Saturday Karen takes **14** pictures. On Sunday she takes **21** pictures. How many pictures does she take on both days?

   21 + 14 = 35
   35 pictures

▶ **Test Prep**

4. Larry sees **25** birds at the park. Kendra sees **37** birds. How many more birds does Kendra see?

   37 ⊖ 25 = 12
   12 more birds

Copyright © Houghton Mifflin Company. All rights reserved.
Use with text pages 639–642.

ENRICHMENT 22.7

Name _____ Date _____ Enrichment 22.7

Problem Solving Choosing
Numbers that Make Sense

Complete the problem using two-digit numbers.
Add or subtract to solve. **Possible answers shown.**
Write the number sentence.

1. Chris collects **20** stones. There are **10** gray stones. The rest are white. How many stones are white?

   20 ⊖ 10 = 10
   10 white stones

2. Olivia has **15** pens. She collects **11** more pens. How many pens does Olivia have in all?

   15 + 11 = 26
   26 pens

3. Henry has **35** blue marbles. He has **22** green marbles. How many more marbles are blue?

   35 ⊖ 22 = 13
   13 marbles

4. Lily picks **32** blueberries and **20** strawberries. She eats **11** berries. How many berries does she have left?

   32 + 20 = 52
   52 ⊖ 11 = 41
   41 berries

Write About It In Exercise 3, do you put the greater number on the first or second line? How do you know?
I put the greater number first. The problem asks how many more are blue. So, the blue marbles are greater.

Copyright © Houghton Mifflin Company. All rights reserved.
Use with text pages 639–641.

Practice Workbook Page 153

Reaching All Learners
Differentiated Instruction

English Learners

Children will need to understand the meaning of the word *collects* in order to solve some word problems. Use Worksheet 22.7 to help children develop an understanding of the word.

Inclusion
TACTILE, AUDITORY

Materials: + − cards (LT 15)

- Give the child a plus sign and a minus sign card. Create an addition story problem using numbers to 10. Say it aloud. Have the child hold up the correct sign. Discuss why the child held up the plus sign.
- Repeat with addition and subtraction stories.

Gifted and Talented
TACTILE, VISUAL

Materials: index cards

- Give each child a card containing numbers for a fact family.
- Ask each child to write two word problems for each fact family, one that uses addition to solve and one that uses subtraction to solve.
- Have children exchange problems and solve.

TECHNOLOGY

Spiral Review

Help students remember skills they learned earlier by creating **customized** spiral review worksheets using the *Ways to Assess* CD-ROM.

Lesson Planner

Use the **Lesson Planner CD-ROM** to see how lesson objectives for this chapter are correlated to standards.

Intervention

Use the *Ways to Success* intervention software to support students who need more help in understanding the concepts and skills taught in this chapter.

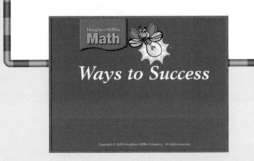

Literature Connection

Refer to *Lights Out!* by Lucille Recht Penner. Remind children that the girl counted the lights in the apartment building across the street. Present word problems about lights in windows.

MATH CENTER

Number of the Week Activity

Display the Number of the Week to motivate children to use their problem-solving skills. The exercises cover topics across all math strands.

PROBLEM SOLVING 22.7

Name _____ Date _____   Problem Solving 22.7

Choose the Operation

Ms. Jensen has 23 red markers.
She has 11 blue markers.
How many markers does she have in all?
How many more red markers than blue markers does she have?

| UNDERSTAND | What do I know? | the number of red markers and the number of blue markers. |

| PLAN | What operation do I use to find how many in all? | addition |
| | What operation can I use to find how many more? | subtraction |

SOLVE	Add to find how many markers in all.	23 + 11 = 34
	__34__ markers in all.	
	Subtract to find how many more red markers.	23 − 11 = 12
	__12__ more red markers	

| LOOK BACK | Did I answer both questions? | |

Copyright © Houghton Mifflin Company. All rights reserved.   Use with text pages 639–641.

HOMEWORK 22.7

Name _____ Date _____   Homework 22.7

**Problem Solving
Choose the Operation**

You can use addition or subtraction to help you solve problems.

The Kwan family likes macaroni.
They have 11 boxes of long macaroni.
They have 8 boxes of short macaroni.
How many boxes do they have?

$$\begin{array}{r} 11 \text{ boxes} \\ (+)\ 8 \text{ boxes} \\ \hline 19 \text{ boxes} \end{array}$$

Add to solve.   __19__ boxes of macaroni

1. The King family has 15 cans of soup. They have 7 cans of chicken soup. The rest are tomato soup. How many cans of tomato soup do they have?

$$\begin{array}{r} 15 \text{ cans} \\ (-)\ 7 \text{ cans} \\ \hline 8 \text{ cans} \end{array}$$

__8__ cans of tomato soup

2. Brendan counts 48 fish in the water. Then 17 fish swim away. How many fish are left?

$$\begin{array}{r} 48 \\ (-)\ 17 \\ \hline 31 \end{array}$$

__31__ fish

Copyright © Houghton Mifflin Company. All rights reserved.   Use with text pages 639–641.

ENGLISH LEARNERS 22.7

Name _____ Date _____   English Learners 22.7

Choose the Operation

Jim **collects** marbles.   Sara **collects** shells.

Draw pictures of two things you would like to collect.

| Drawing of something you can collect | Drawing of something you can collect |
| | |

To the Teacher: Use the pictures and sentences at the top of the page to help children understand the meaning of the word *collects*. Then have children draw pictures of things they would like to collect.

Use with text pages 639–641.

Homework Workbook Page 153

TEACHING LESSON 22.7

LESSON ORGANIZER

Objective Choose the operation to solve word problems.

Resources Reteach, Practice, Enrichment, Problem Solving, Homework, English Learners, Transparencies, Math Center

Materials Dimes, pennies, Part-Part-Whole Mat transparency, index cards, game board, game pieces

Activity

Warm-Up Activity
Modeling Solving Word Problems

👥 Whole Group	⏱ 5 minutes	Auditory, Tactile

Materials: *dimes, pennies*

1. Draw a key chain with the price tag 43¢ on the board. Say this story aloud to children: **Carlo wants to buy the key chain. He has 6 dimes and 5 pennies. How much money will he have left after he buys the key chain?**

2. **What does the problem ask?** (How much money will Carlo have left?) **What do we know?** (Carlo has 65¢. The key chain costs 43¢.) **What can we do to solve the problem?** (Subtract 43¢ from 65¢.) Have children use the dimes and pennies to solve the problem. **How much money will Carlo have left?** (22¢)

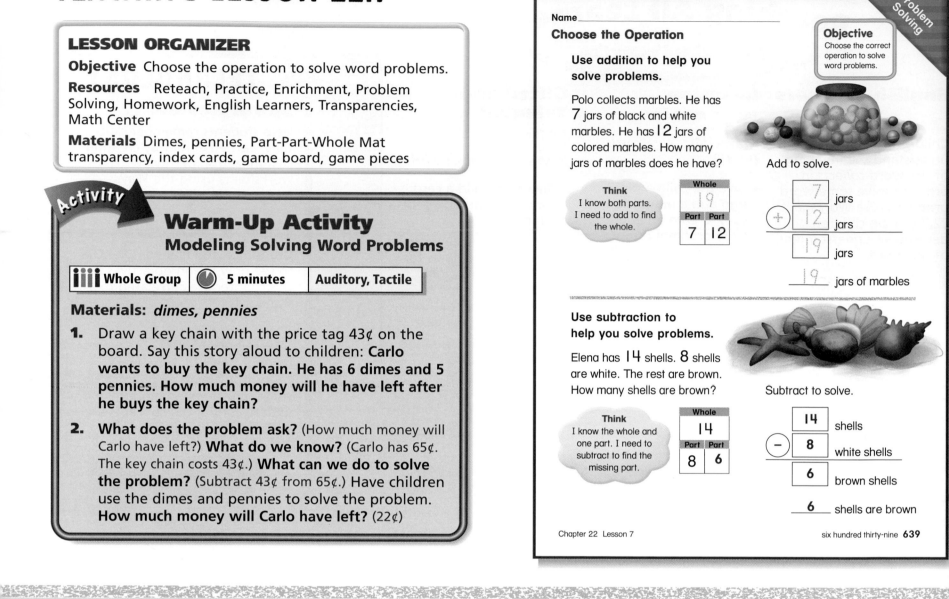

Name_____

Choose the Operation

Objective Choose the correct operation to solve word problems.

Use addition to help you solve problems.

Polo collects marbles. He has 7 jars of black and white marbles. He has 12 jars of colored marbles. How many jars of marbles does he have?

Add to solve.

Think I know both parts. I need to add to find the whole.

Whole
19

Part	Part
7	12

```
     7  jars
 +  12  jars
 _____
    19  jars
```

19 jars of marbles

Use subtraction to help you solve problems.

Elena has 14 shells. 8 shells are white. The rest are brown. How many shells are brown?

Subtract to solve.

Think I know the whole and one part. I need to subtract to find the missing part.

Whole
14

Part	Part
8	6

```
    14  shells
 -   8  white shells
 _____
     6  brown shells
```

6 shells are brown

Chapter 22 Lesson 7   six hundred thirty-nine **639**

---

① Introduce
Discuss Choosing the Operation

👥 Whole Group	⏱ 10–15 minutes	Visual, Auditory

Materials: *Part-Part-Whole Mat transparency*

1. Say the following story aloud: **Jason has 8 baseball cards. After his birthday, he has 17 baseball cards. How many baseball cards did Jason get for his birthday?**

2. **What does the problem ask?** (How many baseball cards did Jason get?) **What information does the problem give?** (Jason had 8 baseball cards; now he has 17 cards.) Write the 17 and 8 in the appropriate places on the transparency. **How can we solve this problem?** (Subtract 8 from 17.) **How much is 17 − 8?** (9)

3. Repeat the activity, and say a new story using addition. Then summarize by pointing out that children should read carefully to decide what operation to use to solve a problem.

② Develop

Guided Learning

Teaching Example Introduce the objective to the children. Guide them through the two examples to show how to use part-part-whole to organize the information in the problem. Be sure children understand that they add to find the whole then subtract to find the missing part.

Guided Practice

Have children complete **Exercises 1–2** on page 640 as you observe.

Guided Practice

Add or subtract to solve.

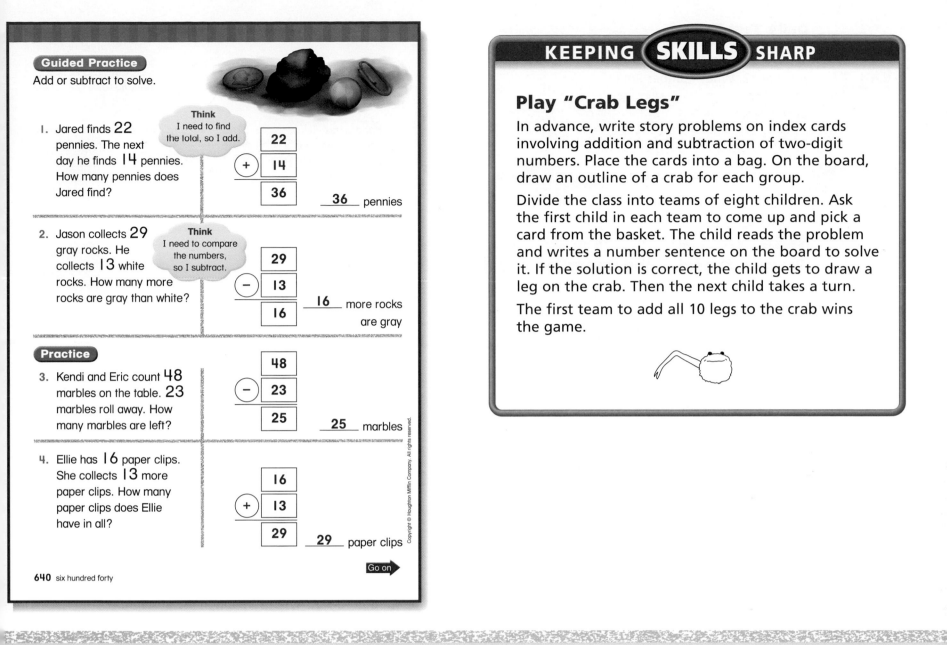

1. Jared finds 22 pennies. The next day he finds 14 pennies. How many pennies does Jared find?

   Think
   I need to find the total, so I add.

22
+	14
36

   __36__ pennies

2. Jason collects 29 gray rocks. He collects 13 white rocks. How many more rocks are gray than white?

   Think
   I need to compare the numbers, so I subtract.

29
−	13
16

   __16__ more rocks are gray

Practice

3. Kendi and Eric count 48 marbles on the table. 23 marbles roll away. How many marbles are left?

48
−	23
25

   __25__ marbles

4. Ellie has 16 paper clips. She collects 13 more paper clips. How many paper clips does Ellie have in all?

16
+	13
29

   __29__ paper clips

640 six hundred forty

Go on ▶

Play "Crab Legs"

In advance, write story problems on index cards involving addition and subtraction of two-digit numbers. Place the cards into a bag. On the board, draw an outline of a crab for each group.

Divide the class into teams of eight children. Ask the first child in each team to come up and pick a card from the basket. The child reads the problem and writes a number sentence on the board to solve it. If the solution is correct, the child gets to draw a leg on the crab. Then the next child takes a turn.

The first team to add all 10 legs to the crab wins the game.

---

3 Practice

Independent Practice

Children complete **Exercises 3–4** on page 640 independently.

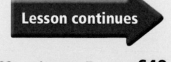
Lesson continues

Daily Test Prep

I am a two-digit number. If you subtract 5 from me, you get 12. What number am I?

17   16   7   NH
●   ○   ○   ○

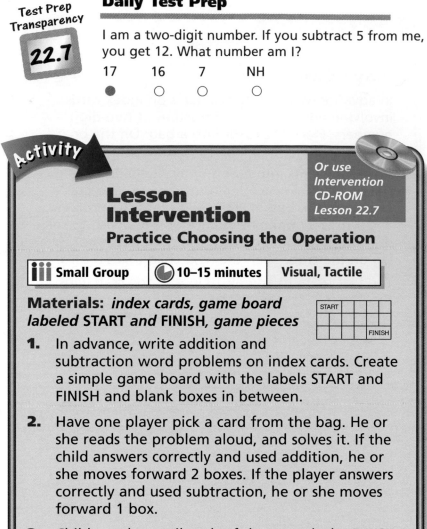

Activity

Or use Intervention CD-ROM Lesson 22.7

Lesson Intervention

Practice Choosing the Operation

| 👥 Small Group | 🕐 10–15 minutes | Visual, Tactile |

Materials: *index cards, game board labeled* START *and* FINISH, *game pieces*

1. In advance, write addition and subtraction word problems on index cards. Create a simple game board with the labels START and FINISH and blank boxes in between.

2. Have one player pick a card from the bag. He or she reads the problem aloud, and solves it. If the child answers correctly and used addition, he or she moves forward 2 boxes. If the player answers correctly and used subtraction, he or she moves forward 1 box.

3. Children play until each of them reach the FINISH.

Name_____

Choose a Strategy

Strategies
Act It Out With Models
Write a Number Sentence
Draw a Picture

Solve.

1. Kendra has 20 acorns. She finds 9 more at the park. How many acorns does she have in all?

   Draw or write to explain. **Allow children to use any strategy or method they want.**

   _29_ acorns

   acorn

2. There are 28 pine cones on the ground. 13 blow away. How many pine cones are on the ground?

   _15_ pine cones

   pine cone

3. 27 pebbles have stripes. 20 have spots. How many more pebbles have stripes than have spots?

   _7_ pebbles

   pebbles

4. **Multistep** Jon finds 15 white shells and 10 black shells. He gives away 3 shells. How many shells does he have now?

   _22_ shells

   shell

Chapter 22   **At Home** Ask your child how he or she decided to solve each problem above.

six hundred forty-one **641**

---

③ Practice

Mixed Strategy Practice

Read the problem-solving strategies with children. Make sure children can read and comprehend the problems in **Exercises 1–4** on page 641. If necessary, pair more proficient readers with less proficient readers. Encourage them to discuss the problems before solving.

Common Error

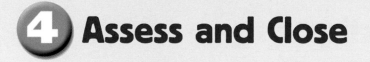

Adding Instead of Subtracting
Children may add when they should subtract to solve a problem. Discuss the words and phrases in story problems that mean to add and the words and phrases that mean to subtract.

④ Assess and Close

Troy and his brother collected 16 shells in one week and 23 shells the next week. How many shells did they collect in all? (39)

What operation did you use to solve the problem? Why? (addition; *in all* means to add)

✏️ Keeping a Journal

Write an addition or subtraction story using two-digit numbers. Solve it.

Listen to your teacher read the problem. Solve.

1. Mrs. Rosen takes Henry to the park. He counts 48 leaves on the ground. 13 leaves blow away. How many leaves are left on the ground?

Show your work using pictures, numbers, or words.

35 leaves

2. There are 8 buttons in the jar. The teacher puts 11 more buttons in the jar. How many buttons are in the jar now?

19 buttons

Listen to your teacher read the problem. Choose the correct answer.

3. ● 65 shells   ○ 63 shells   ○ 56 shells   ○ 43 shells

4. ○ 8 chains   ○ 10 chains   ● 11 chains   ○ 18 chains

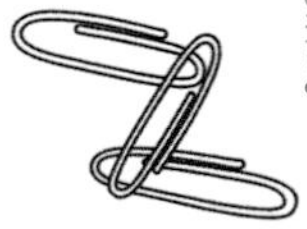

642 six hundred forty-two

Problem-Solving for Tests

Listening Skills

This page provides children practice with the oral problem-solving format used in some standardized test items.

You may want to read each item only once to mimic the style of oral tests.

Use With Items 1 and 2

Listening Strategy: Read the problem silently while the teacher reads it aloud.

- *This problem is on the page. Read it to yourself while I read it aloud.*
- *Listen to the whole problem. Wait until I finish reading to start writing.*

Use With Item 3

Listening Strategy: Listen as the teacher reads the problem. Listen for numbers and important words.

- *Look at me and listen as I read the problem.*

  Anita finds 51 shells on the beach. She finds 14 shells in the water. How many shells does she find in all?

- *You can write numbers or words now. Then mark your answer.*

Use With Item 4

Listening Strategy: Listen for important facts and numbers.

- *Listen for the question the problem asks.*

  Albert makes 19 paper clip chains. He gives 8 of the chains to Sonia. How many chains does he have left?

- *Use the numbers to solve the problem. Then mark your answer.*

Quick Check

Have children complete the Quick Check exercises independently to assess their understanding of concepts and skills taught in **Lessons 5–7.**

Item	Lesson	Error Analysis	Intervention
1–6	22.5	Children may subtract incorrectly when exercises are presented horizontally.	Reteach Resource 22.5 *Ways to Success* 22.5
7–10	22.6	Children may confuse which numbers must be equal in a check.	Reteach Resource 22.6 *Ways to Success* 22.6
11	22.7	Children may add instead of subtract.	Reteach Resource 22.7 *Ways to Success* 22.7

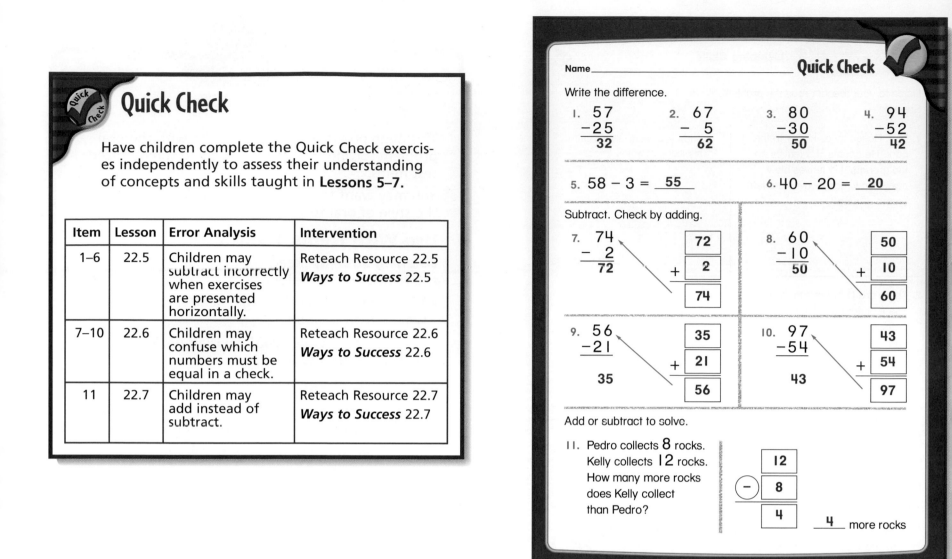

Name_____

Quick Check

Write the difference.

1. $\begin{array}{r} 57 \\ -25 \\ \hline 32 \end{array}$ 2. $\begin{array}{r} 67 \\ -5 \\ \hline 62 \end{array}$ 3. $\begin{array}{r} 80 \\ -30 \\ \hline 50 \end{array}$ 4. $\begin{array}{r} 94 \\ -52 \\ \hline 42 \end{array}$

5. $58 - 3 = \underline{55}$ 6. $40 - 20 = \underline{20}$

Subtract. Check by adding.

7. $\begin{array}{r} 74 \\ -2 \\ \hline 72 \end{array}$ 72 + 2 = 74

8. $\begin{array}{r} 60 \\ -10 \\ \hline 50 \end{array}$ 50 + 10 = 60

9. $\begin{array}{r} 56 \\ -21 \\ \hline 35 \end{array}$ 35 + 21 = 56

10. $\begin{array}{r} 97 \\ -54 \\ \hline 43 \end{array}$ 43 + 54 = 97

Add or subtract to solve.

11. Pedro collects 8 rocks. Kelly collects 12 rocks. How many more rocks does Kelly collect than Pedro?

12 ⊖ 8 = 4   ___4___ more rocks

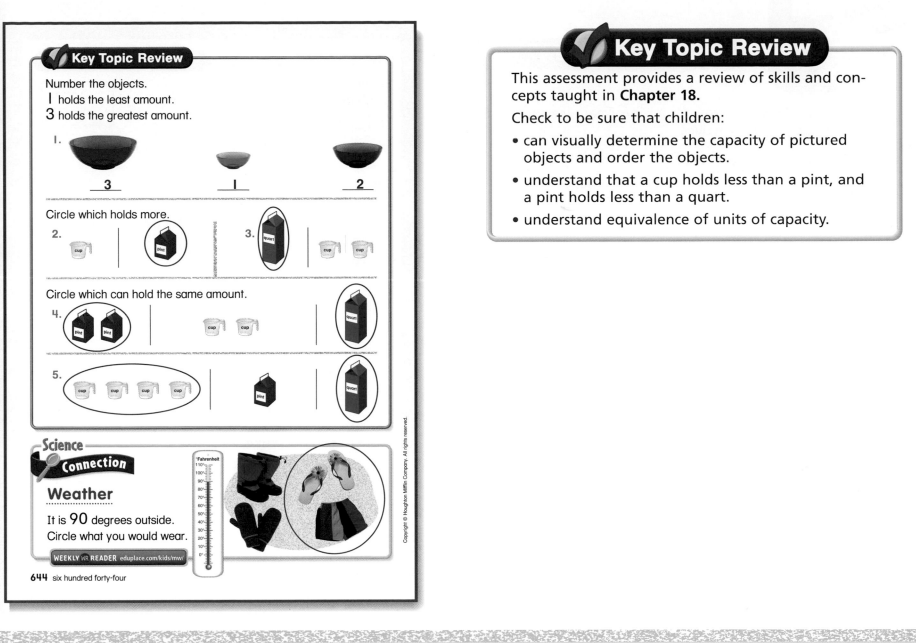

Key Topic Review

Number the objects.
1 holds the least amount.
3 holds the greatest amount.

1.

3   1   2

Circle which holds more.

2.   cup | pint

3.   quart | cup   cup

Circle which can hold the same amount.

4.   pint pint | cup cup | quart

5.   cup cup cup cup | pint | quart

Science Connection

Weather

It is **90** degrees outside.
Circle what you would wear.

°Fahrenheit

WEEKLY WR READER eduplace.com/kids/mw/

Key Topic Review

This assessment provides a review of skills and concepts taught in **Chapter 18**.

Check to be sure that children:

- can visually determine the capacity of pictured objects and order the objects.
- understand that a cup holds less than a pint, and a pint holds less than a quart.
- understand equivalence of units of capacity.

Science Connection

Weather

Discuss children's answers to the question. **How do you know that shorts and sandals is the best answer?** (Ninety degrees is very hot, so shorts and sandals would be cooler.) **When it is 90°, what season is it likely to be?** (summer) **What are some activities you might do when it is 90°?** (Possible answers: go swimming, go to the beach, have a cookout.)

Chapter Review/Test

Purpose: This test provides an informal assessment of the Chapter 22 objectives.

Chapter Test Items 1–20

To assign a numerical grade for this Chapter Test, use 5 points for each test item.

Check Understanding

Use children's work on word problems to informally assess progress on chapter content.

Customizing Your Instruction

For children who have not yet mastered these objectives, you can use the reteaching resources listed in the chart below.

✓ Assessment Options

A summary test for this chapter is also provided in the Unit Resource Folder.

Name_____ ✓ Chapter Review/Test

Vocabulary *Glossary*

Complete the sentence.

difference
subtract

1. I ___subtract___ to find $38 - 5$.

2. The answer to a subtraction problem is the ___difference___.

Concepts and Skills

Complete the subtraction sentences.

3.
$6 - 3 = \underline{3}$
$6 \text{ tens} - 3 \text{ tens} = \underline{3} \text{ tens}$
$\underline{60} - \underline{30} = \underline{30}$

4.
$5 - 4 = \underline{1}$
$5 \text{ tens} - 4 \text{ tens} = \underline{1} \text{ ten}$
$\underline{50} - \underline{40} = \underline{10}$

5. $9 \text{ tens} - 2 \text{ tens} = \underline{7} \text{ tens}$
$\underline{90} - \underline{20} = \underline{70}$

6. $4 \text{ tens} - 2 \text{ tens} = \underline{2} \text{ tens}$
$\underline{40} - \underline{20} = \underline{20}$

Use Workmat 5 with ▭ and ▪.
Subtract. Write the difference.

7.
Tens	Ones
3	7
−	5
3	2

8.
Tens	Ones
8	3
−	2
8	1

9.
Tens	Ones
5	9
− 2	8
3	1

10.
Tens	Ones
4	5
− 3	3
1	2

11. $48 - 5 = \underline{43}$

12. $30 - 20 = \underline{10}$

Chapter 22   six hundred forty-five **645**

Reteaching Support

Chapter Test Items	Summary Test Items	Chapter Objectives Tested	TE Pages	Use These Reteaching Resources
1–2	1–2	**22A** Develop and use math vocabulary relating to subtracting two-digit numbers.	625A–628	Reteach Resources and *Ways to Success* CD: 22.1, 22.2 Skillsheet 160
3–17	3–14	**22B** Subtract two-digit numbers, including money amounts, without regrouping.	625A–630	Reteach Resources and *Ways to Success* CD: 22.1–22.3 Skillsheet 161
18–19	15–18	**22C** Use different ways to subtract and use addition to check two-digit subtraction	631A–632, 635A–638	Reteach Resources and *Ways to Success* CD: 22.4–22.6 Skillsheet 162
20	19–20	**22D** Choose the correct operation to solve word problems.	639A–642	Reteach Resource and *Ways to Success* CD: 22.7 Skillsheet 163

CHAPTER SUMMARY TEST

Name_____ Date_____ Chapter 22 Test

Look at the vocabulary words.
Fill in the blank.

Vocabulary
difference
basic fact
subtraction

1. $89 - 4 = 85$.
85 is the ___difference___.

2. Use addition to check ___subtraction___.

Complete the subtraction sentences.

3. $7 \text{ tens} - 2 \text{ tens} = \underline{5} \text{ tens}$
$70 - 20 = \underline{50}$

4. $8 \text{ tens} - 4 \text{ tens} = \underline{4} \text{ tens}$
$80 - 40 = \underline{40}$

5. $6 \text{ tens} - 5 \text{ tens} = \underline{1} \text{ ten}$
$60 - 50 = \underline{10}$

6. $9 \text{ tens} - 3 \text{ tens} = \underline{6} \text{ tens}$
$90 - 30 = \underline{60}$

Subtract.
Write the difference.

7.
Tens	Ones
7	6
−	4
7	2

8.
Tens	Ones
9	8
−	5
9	3

9.
Tens	Ones
6	5
−	3
6	2

10.
Tens	Ones
8	9
−	2
8	7

11.
94
-54
40

12.
89
-31
58

13.
$66¢$
$-43¢$
$23¢$

14.
$89¢$
$- 2¢$
$87¢$

Go on

Subtract.
Write the difference.

13. 80 − 40 = __40__   14. 82 − 10 = __72__

15. 85¢
    −53¢
     32 ¢

16. 18¢
    − 7¢
     11¢

17. 70¢
    −40¢
     30¢

Copyright © Houghton Mifflin Company. All rights reserved.

Use the End of Grade Test Prep Assessment Guide to help familiarize your children with the format of standardized tests.

Subtract.
Check by adding.

18. 49
    −25
     24

24
+	25
49

19. 60
    −30
     30

30
+	30
60

Problem Solving
Add or subtract to solve.

20. Zach finds 46 shells at the beach. He gives 23 to Leah. How many shells does he have left?

46
−	23
23

__23__ shells

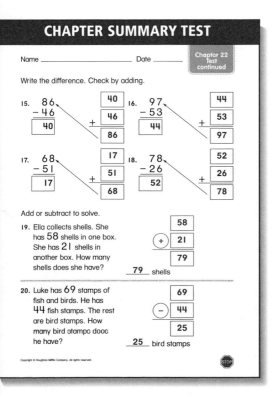

CHAPTER SUMMARY TEST

Name _____ Date _____

Chapter 22
Test
continued

Write the difference. Check by adding.

15. 86
    −46
     40

| 40 |
| 46 |
| 86 |

16. 97
    −53
     44

| 44 |
| 53 |
| 97 |

17. 68
    −51
     17

| 17 |
| 51 |
| 68 |

18. 78
    −26
     52

| 52 |
| 26 |
| 78 |

Add or subtract to solve.

19. Ella collects shells. She has 58 shells in one box. She has 21 shells in another box. How many shells does she have?

| 58 |
+ | 21 |
| 79 |

__79__ shells

20. Luke has 69 stamps of fish and birds. He has 44 fish stamps. The rest are bird stamps. How many bird stamps does he have?

| 69 |
− | 44 |
| 25 |

__25__ bird stamps

STOP

Social Studies Connection

PURPOSE

To use two-digit addition and subtraction.

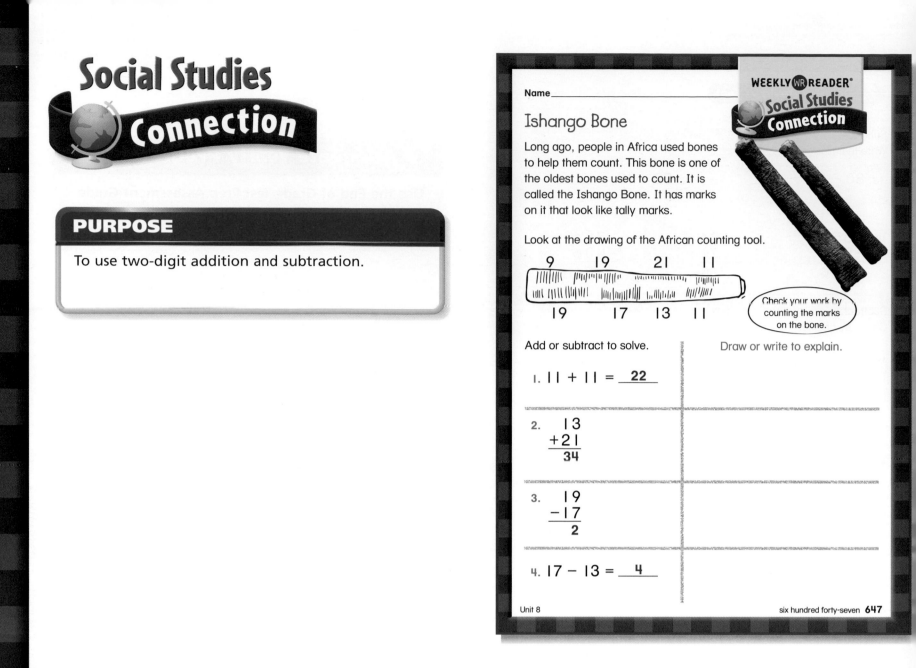

WEEKLY WR READER®
Social Studies Connection

Name_____

Ishango Bone

Long ago, people in Africa used bones to help them count. This bone is one of the oldest bones used to count. It is called the Ishango Bone. It has marks on it that look like tally marks.

Look at the drawing of the African counting tool.

9   19   21   11

19   17   13   11

Check your work by counting the marks on the bone.

Add or subtract to solve.   Draw or write to explain.

1. 11 + 11 = __22__

2. 13
   +21
   ―――
    34

3. 19
   −17
   ―――
     2

4. 17 − 13 = __4__

Using These Pages

Discussion Topics

- Tell children that the Ishango Bone is the second oldest known mathematical tool. The oldest is called the Lebombo Bone, and it was made about 37,000 years ago! There are 29 tally marks on the Lebombo Bone. **How many more tally marks are on the Lebombo Bone than in the largest tally group on the Ishango Bone?** (8) **Explain how you know.** (29 − 21 = 8)

- Refer children to the drawing of the Ishango Bone. **Which number has a 1 in the ones place and a 1 in the tens place?** (11)

- **How many groups of 11 are on the tool?** (2) **What is 11 + 11?** (22)

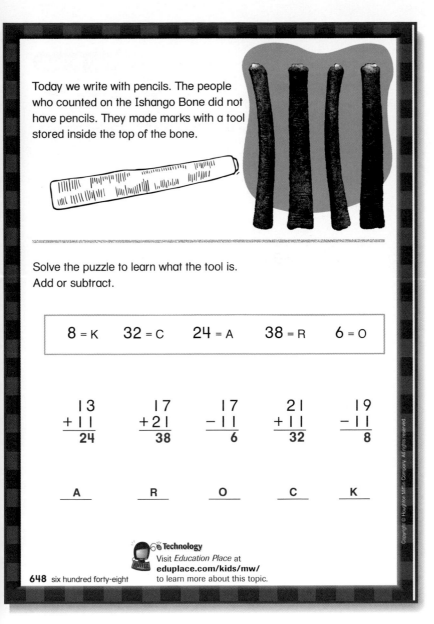

Today we write with pencils. The people who counted on the Ishango Bone did not have pencils. They made marks with a tool stored inside the top of the bone.

Solve the puzzle to learn what the tool is. Add or subtract.

8 = K	32 = C	24 = A	38 = R	6 = O

$$\begin{array}{r} 13 \\ +11 \\ \hline 24 \end{array} \qquad \begin{array}{r} 17 \\ +21 \\ \hline 38 \end{array} \qquad \begin{array}{r} 17 \\ -11 \\ \hline 6 \end{array} \qquad \begin{array}{r} 21 \\ +11 \\ \hline 32 \end{array} \qquad \begin{array}{r} 19 \\ -11 \\ \hline 8 \end{array}$$

  A   R   O   C   K

Technology
Visit *Education Place* at
eduplace.com/kids/mw/
to learn more about this topic.

648 six hundred forty-eight

Wrap Up the Unit Project

- Ask each child to record the number of books he or she has read in a week. Then help children determine the total for the week.

- Ask children how many books were read in two given weeks, or how many more books were read in one week than in another.

- Have children tell how many books were read in all.

PURPOSE

This test provides an informal assessment of the Unit 8 objectives.

Unit Test Items 1–30

To assign a numerical grade for this Unit Test, use 3 points for each test item and add 10 to the score.

Customizing Your Instruction

For children who have not yet mastered these objectives, you can use the **Reteaching Resources** listed in the chart below. **Ways to Success** is Houghton Mifflin's Intervention program available in CD-ROM and blackline master formats.

Name_____ ✓ **Unit 8 Test**

Vocabulary 🔵 Glossary

Match the word to the correct statement.

1. **difference** —— a fact that adds the same two numbers
2. **double** —— $100 = 10$ of these
3. **tens** —— the answer to a subtraction problem

Concepts and Skills

Find the sum.

4.	5.	6.	7.	8.
7 +7 —— 14	9 +10 —— 19	4 +5 —— 9	10 + 3 —— 13	6 +5 —— 11

9.	10.	11.	12.	13.
6 4 +2 —— 12	2 9 +1 —— 12	9 4 +4 —— 17	7 3 +2 —— 12	6 6 +2 —— 14

Find the difference.

14.	15.	16.	17.	18.
16 − 8 —— 8	18 − 9 —— 9	14 −10 —— 4	12 − 9 —— 3	17 − 8 —— 9

Complete the fact family.

19.

16		
9	7	

$$\begin{array}{r} 9 \\ +7 \\ \hline 16 \end{array}$$ $$\begin{array}{r} 7 \\ + \boxed{9} \\ \hline \boxed{16} \end{array}$$ $$\begin{array}{r} 16 \\ - 9 \\ \hline 7 \end{array}$$ $$\begin{array}{r} \boxed{16} \\ - \boxed{7} \\ \hline 9 \end{array}$$

Unit 8   six hundred forty-nine **649**

Reteaching Support

Unit Test Item		Unit Objectives Tested		TE Pages	Use These Reteaching Resources
p. 649–650 2–13, 19	Tests A & B 1–7	8A	Use addition concepts and strategies to find the sum of two and three addends to 20.	557A–562, 581A–582	Reteach Resources and *Ways to Success*, 19.1–19.3, 20.1
1, 14–18	8–10	8B	Subtract from 20 using subtraction concepts and strategies.	557A–558, 591A–594	Reteach Resources and *Ways to Success*, 19.1, 20.5, 20.6
20–23	11–16	8C	Add 2-digit numbers, including money amounts, without regrouping.	605A–608, 611A–614	Reteach Resources and *Ways to Success*, 21.2, 21.3, 21.5
24–29	17–22	8D	Subtract 2-digit numbers, including money amounts, without regrouping.	625A–632, 635A–638	Reteach Resources *and Ways to Success*, 22.1–22.6
30	23–25	8E	Apply skills and strategies to solve problems.	595A–596, 639A–642	Reteach Resources and *Ways to Success*, 20.7, 22.7

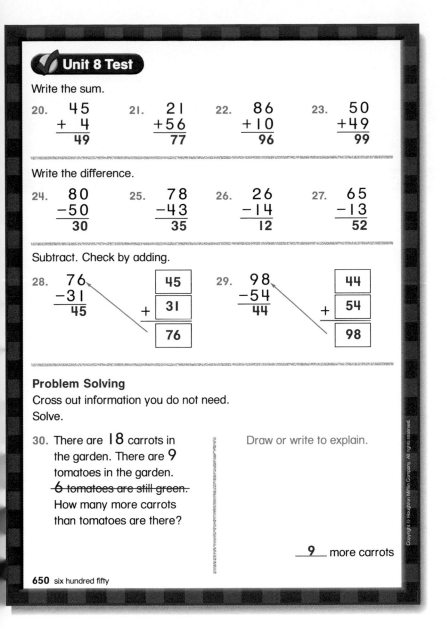

Unit 8 Test

Write the sum.

20.
$$\begin{array}{r} 45 \\ +\ 4 \\ \hline 49 \end{array}$$

21.
$$\begin{array}{r} 21 \\ +56 \\ \hline 77 \end{array}$$

22.
$$\begin{array}{r} 86 \\ +10 \\ \hline 96 \end{array}$$

23.
$$\begin{array}{r} 50 \\ +49 \\ \hline 99 \end{array}$$

Write the difference.

24.
$$\begin{array}{r} 80 \\ -50 \\ \hline 30 \end{array}$$

25.
$$\begin{array}{r} 78 \\ -43 \\ \hline 35 \end{array}$$

26.
$$\begin{array}{r} 26 \\ -14 \\ \hline 12 \end{array}$$

27.
$$\begin{array}{r} 65 \\ -13 \\ \hline 52 \end{array}$$

Subtract. Check by adding.

28.
$$\begin{array}{r} 76 \\ -31 \\ \hline 45 \end{array}$$
$$\begin{array}{r} 45 \\ +\ 31 \\ \hline 76 \end{array}$$

29.
$$\begin{array}{r} 98 \\ -54 \\ \hline 44 \end{array}$$
$$\begin{array}{r} 44 \\ +\ 54 \\ \hline 98 \end{array}$$

Problem Solving

Cross out information you do not need.
Solve.

30. There are 18 carrots in
the garden. There are 9
tomatoes in the garden.
~~6 tomatoes are still green.~~
How many more carrots
than tomatoes are there?

Draw or write to explain.

_____9_____ more carrots

650 six hundred fifty

Monitoring Student Progress

Assessment Options

Formal Tests for this unit are also provided in the
Unit Resource Folder.

- **Unit 8 Test A (Open Response)**
- **Unit 8 Test B (Multiple Choice)**

Performance Assessment

You may want to use the Performance Assessment
instead of, or in addition to, the Unit Test. Three
Performance Assessment tasks can be found on
Student Book pages 265–266.

Adequate Yearly Progress

Use the *End of Grade Test Prep Assessment
Guide* to help familiarize your children with the
format of standardized tests.

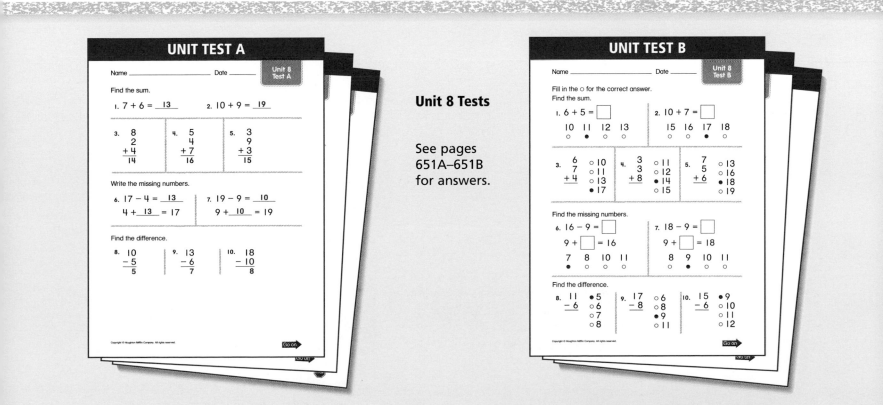

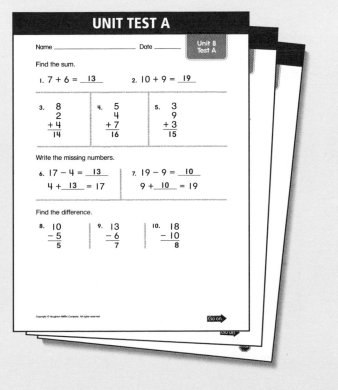

Unit 8 Tests

See pages
651A–651B
for answers.

Two-Digit Addition and Subtraction   **650**

Unit Test Answers: Form A

UNIT TEST A

Name _____ Date _____

Unit 8
Test A

Find the sum.

1. 7 + 6 = __13__   2. 10 + 9 = __19__

3. 8 2 +4 __14__	4. 5 4 +7 __16__	5. 3 9 +3 __15__

Write the missing numbers.

6. 17 − 4 = __13__   7. 19 − 9 = __10__

  4 + __13__ = 17   9 + __10__ = 19

Find the difference.

8. 10 − 5 __5__	9. 13 − 6 __7__	10. 18 − 10 __8__

Go on

UNIT TEST A

Name _____ Date _____

Unit 8
Test A
continued

Write the sum.

11. 15 + 83 __98__	12. 20 + 50 __70__	13. 14 + 62 __76__
14. 53¢ + 25¢ __78¢__	15. 75¢ + 20¢ __95¢__	16. 44¢ + 33¢ __77¢__

Write the difference.

17. 88 − 45 __43__	18. 94 − 51 __43__	19. 80 − 30 __50__
20. 79¢ − 5¢ __74¢__	21. 57¢ − 34¢ __23¢__	22. 96¢ − 23¢ __73¢__

Go on

UNIT TEST A

Name _____ Date _____

Unit 8
Test A
continued

Solve.

23. Cindy sees 15 robins on Monday. Cindy sees 10 robins on Tuesday. How many robins does she see in all? Write the number sentence.

Draw or write to explain.

```
  15
+ 10
  25
```

__25__ robins

24.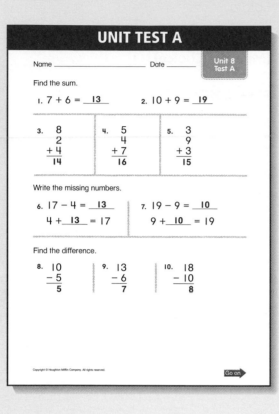

18   24   32   56
Bag A   Bag B   Bag C   Bag D

Mrs. Santos buys beads to make bracelets. She wants 50 beads. Which two bags does she buy?

Bag __A__ and Bag __C__

25. Kayla and Nick collect 39 cans. They collect 16 bottles. How many more cans than bottles do they collect? Write the number sentence.

```
  39
− 16
  23
```

__23__ more cans

STOP

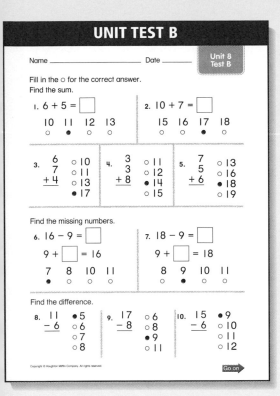

UNIT TEST B

Name _____ Date _____

Unit 8 Test B

Fill in the ○ for the correct answer.
Find the sum.

1. 6 + 5 = ☐
   10 11 12 13
   ○   ●   ○   ○

2. 10 + 7 = ☐
   15 16 17 18
   ○   ○   ●   ○

3. 6
    7
   +4
   ○ 10
   ○ 11
   ○ 13
   ● 17

4. 3
    3
   +8
   ○ 11
   ○ 12
   ● 14
   ○ 15

5. 7
    5
   +6
   ○ 13
   ○ 16
   ● 18
   ○ 19

Find the missing numbers.

6. 16 − 9 = ☐
   9 + ☐ = 16
   7   8   10   11
   ●   ○   ○   ○

7. 18 − 9 = ☐
   9 + ☐ = 18
   8   9   10   11
   ○   ●   ○   ○

Find the difference.

8. 11
   − 6
   ● 5
   ○ 6
   ○ 7
   ○ 8

9. 17
   − 8
   ○ 6
   ○ 8
   ● 9
   ○ 11

10. 15
    − 6
   ● 9
   ○ 10
   ○ 11
   ○ 12

Copyright © Houghton Mifflin Company. All rights reserved.

Go on →

UNIT TEST B

Name _____ Date _____

Unit 8 Test B continued

Find the sum.

11. 24
    +71
   ○ 85
   ○ 93
   ● 95
   ○ 96

12. 30
    +40
   ○ 60
   ● 70
   ○ 80
   ○ 90

13. 37
    +52
   ○ 69
   ○ 79
   ○ 88
   ● 89

14. 62¢
    +31¢
   ○ 31¢
   ○ 33¢
   ● 93¢
   ○ 94¢

15. 43¢
    + 4¢
   ○ 44¢
   ○ 46¢
   ● 47¢
   ○ 57¢

16. 25¢
    +32¢
   ○ 37¢
   ○ 55¢
   ● 57¢
   ○ 59¢

Find the difference.

17. 79
    −57
   ○ 12
   ○ 21
   ● 22
   ○ 32

18. 68
    − 7
   ○ 60
   ● 61
   ○ 62
   ○ 75

19. 90
    −50
   ○ 30
   ● 40
   ○ 50
   ○ 60

20. 57¢
    − 5¢
   ● 52¢
   ○ 53¢
   ○ 54¢
   ○ 55¢

21. 77¢
    −32¢
   ○ 44¢
   ● 45¢
   ○ 46¢
   ○ 54¢

22. 84¢
    −64¢
   ● 20¢
   ○ 22¢
   ○ 24¢
   ○ 28¢

Copyright © Houghton Mifflin Company. All rights reserved.

Go on →

UNIT TEST B

Name _____ Date _____

Unit 8 Test B continued

Solve.

23. Colleen has 18 stamps. Tim has 8 stamps. How many fewer stamps does Tim have? Choose the correct number sentence.
   ○ 18 − 10 = 8
   ○ 18 − 9 = 9
   ○ 18 + 8 = 26
   ● 18 − 8 = 10

24. Meg saves 55¢. Her brother Matt saves 34¢. How much more money does Meg save? Choose the correct number sentence.
   ○ 55¢ − 34¢ = 11¢
   ● 55¢ − 34¢ = 21¢
   ○ 34¢ − 4¢ = 31¢
   ○ 54¢ + 34¢ = 89¢

25. Jody buys stickers for her notebook. She needs 48 stickers. Which two sheets of stickers does she buy?

   16   20   32   36
   Sheet A   Sheet B   Sheet C   Sheet D

   ○ A and B   ● A and C   ○ B and C   ○ C and D

Copyright © Houghton Mifflin Company. All rights reserved.

STOP

Performance Assessment

PURPOSE

This assessment focuses on addition and subtraction. Children use addition and subtraction concepts and strategies to find the sum of three addends, subtract from 20 or less, and add two-digit numbers to solve problems.

Name_____

Performance Assessment

1. Find 6 + 5 + 4.

Show your work using pictures, numbers, or words.

15

2. Find 18 − 9.

Show your work using pictures, numbers, or words.

9

Unit 8   six hundred fifty-one **651**

Using These Pages

- Show 15 pennies and 11 nickels on the overhead. Tell children the following problem: *Samantha has 15 pennies. Kyle has 11 nickels. How many more coins does Samantha have than Kyle?* **Do you add or subtract to solve the problem?** (subtract) **How do you know?** (I am finding how many more and that means to subtract.) Write the number sentence to show subtraction. (15 − 11 = 4)

- Direct children's attention to assessment tasks. You may wish to read the directions aloud to the children.

- Observe children as they work to complete the tasks.

Exercise One

In Exercise 1, children should be able to add three addends. (15)

Exercise Two

In Exercise 2, children should be able to subtract through 20. (9)

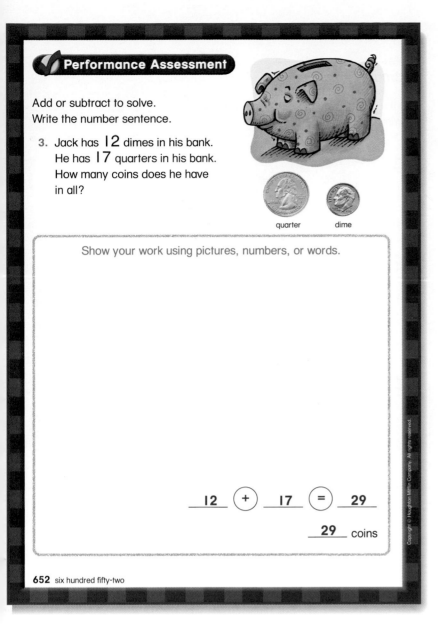

Add or subtract to solve.
Write the number sentence.

3. Jack has 12 dimes in his bank.
He has 17 quarters in his bank.
How many coins does he have
in all?

quarter   dime

Show your work using pictures, numbers, or words.

12 (+) 17 (=) 29

29 coins

652 six hundred fifty-two

Exercise Three

In Exercise 3, children should be able to decide
whether they need to add or subtract to solve the
problem. Children should also be able to write the
number sentence. (12 + 17 = 29; 29 coins)

Assessing Student Work

Use the **Scoring Rubric** to evaluate children's
performance on these tasks.

Scoring Rubric

4 EXEMPLARY

Represents the addition and subtraction
correctly and finds the correct sum and
difference, and applies skills and strategies
to solve problems correctly.

3 PROFICIENT

Represents the addition and subtraction
correctly and finds the correct sum and
difference. Solution to problems
demonstrates mathematical reasoning,
although the number sentence is faulty.

2 ACCEPTABLE

Represents the addition and subtraction
correctly and finds the correct sum and
difference. Solution to problems is incorrect
or incomplete.

1 LIMITED

Represents the addition and subtraction
incorrectly or finds the incorrect sum or
difference. Solution to problems provides
no mathematical reasoning or number
sentence.

UNIT 8

Enrichment

▶ Estimate Sums

PURPOSE

This page provides an opportunity for children to apply their understanding of two-digit addition by having them estimate sums.

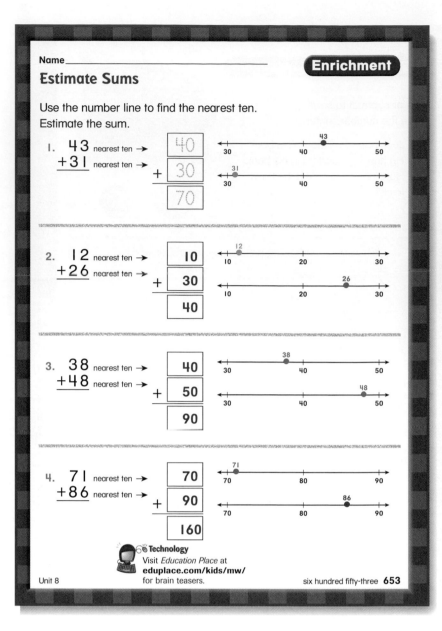

Using This Page

Discussion Topics

- This page extends Chapter 21 by having children estimate the sums of pairs of two-digit numbers.

- Read directions with the children. Tell them that they are not going to add the numbers, but instead they are going to find the nearest 10 for each number and estimate the sum.

- Remind children that when finding the nearest 10, they need to look at the number in the ones column to decide whether they look forward or back on the number line. **If the ones are 5 or more, look forward. If the ones are 4 or less, look back.**

- Have children work individually or in pairs to complete the page. Children working in pairs can take turns solving the exercises and then check each other's work.

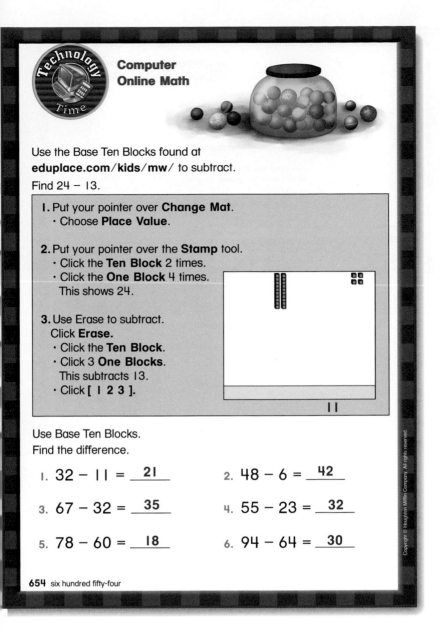

Use the Base Ten Blocks found at
eduplace.com/kids/mw/ to subtract.

Find 24 – 13.

1. Put your pointer over **Change Mat**.
   · Choose **Place Value**.

2. Put your pointer over the **Stamp** tool.
   · Click the **Ten Block** 2 times.
   · Click the **One Block** 4 times.
   This shows 24.

3. Use Erase to subtract.
   Click **Erase.**
   · Click the **Ten Block**.
   · Click 3 **One Blocks**.
   This subtracts 13.
   · Click **[1 2 3]**.

Use Base Ten Blocks.
Find the difference.

1. 32 – 11 = __21__   2. 48 – 6 = __42__

3. 67 – 32 = __35__   4. 55 – 23 = __32__

5. 78 – 60 = __18__   6. 94 – 64 = __30__

654 six hundred fifty-four

ONLINE MATH

PURPOSE

To provide an opportunity for children to use a computer when subtracting.

Using This Page

Discussion Topics

● This is another way for the children to work with subtraction.

● You may want to review how to move the cursor.

● Work through the example with the children.

What is the answer to a subtraction problem called? (difference)

● Read the remaining questions and allow time for the children to complete. When the page is completed, have children share answers with a partner.

Cumulative Test Prep

▶ Practice Test

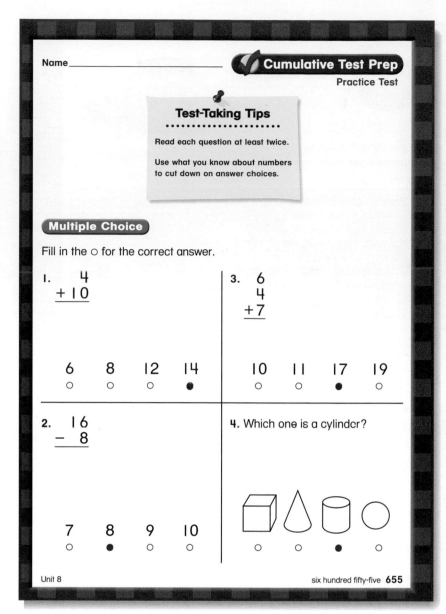

Name_____

Cumulative Test Prep
Practice Test

Test-Taking Tips
· · · · · · · · · · · · · · · ·
Read each question at least twice.

Use what you know about numbers to cut down on answer choices.

Multiple Choice

Fill in the ○ for the correct answer.

1. 4
    +10

   6   8   12   14
   ○   ○   ○   ●

2. 16
    − 8

   7   8   9   10
   ○   ●   ○   ○

3. 6
    4
   +7

   10   11   17   19
   ○   ○   ●   ○

4. Which one is a cylinder?

   ○   ○   ●   ○

Unit 8   six hundred fifty-five **655**

Test-Taking TIPS

Review the test-taking tips with children before they begin the test. Remind children to use what they know to cut down on answer choices.

- Remind children to be sure their answer fits what the question asked.
- Discuss similar answer choices, and encourage children to use visual discrimination to determine which is correct.

- Emphasize that children should ignore extra information that they don't need to solve a problem.
- Remind children that NH means Not Here. Tell them that this means that the correct answer is not shown.

Fill in the ○ for the correct answer.
N means Not Here.

5. 42¢
   +37¢

   15¢   69¢   79¢   95¢
    ○   ○   ●   ○

6. Which container holds about
   1 quart?

   ○   ●   ○   N ○

7. 56
   −14

   31   52   60   N
   ○   ○   ○   ●

Solve.

8. Cross out information you
   do not need.

   Roberto finds 12 clams.
   He gives 5 clams to Lee.
   ~~Each clam has 2 shells.~~
   How many clams does
   Roberto have now?

   ___7___ clams

9. How much in all?

   ___72___ ¢

10. Mrs. Chang finds chopsticks
    in boxes of 8, 12, and 24.
    She only needs 32 chopsticks
    for a party. Which two boxes
    should she buy?

    box of __8__

    and box of __24__

Test Prep on the Net
Visit *Education Place* at **eduplace.com/kids/mw/**
for more test prep practice.

Test-Taking Vocabulary

- Review the term *doubles* with children. Have volunteers give examples of doubles facts. Make a list of the examples on the board.

- Ask volunteers to define *sum* and *difference* and use the words in sentences.

- Write the numbers 56 and 14 on the board. Have a volunteer tell how many *tens* and how many *ones* in 56 and 14. Repeat with other numbers to 99.

National and state tests may present subtraction sentences horizontally as well as vertically.

UNIT 1

AUNT FLOSSIE'S HATS (and Crab Cakes Later)

By Elizabeth Fitzgerald Howard

On Sunday afternoons, Sarah and I go to see Great-great-aunt Flossie. Sarah and I love Aunt Flossie's house. It is crowded full of stuff and things. Books and pictures and lamps and pillows . . .

Plates and trays and old dried flowers . . .
And boxes
and boxes
and boxes
of HATS!

On Sunday afternoons when Sarah and I go to see Aunt Flossie, she says,
"Come in, Susan. Come in, Sarah.
Have some tea. Have some cookies.
Later we can get some crab cakes!"

We sip our tea and eat our cookies, and then Aunt Flossie lets us look in her hatboxes.

We pick out hats and try them on.
Aunt Flossie says they are her
memories, and each hat has its story.

Hats, hats, hats, hats!
A stiff black one with bright red ribbons. A soft brown one with silver buttons. Thin floppy hats that hide our eyes. Green or blue or pink or purple. Some have fur and some have feathers. Look! This hat is just one smooth soft rose, but here's one with a trillion flowers! Aunt Flossie has so many hats!

One Sunday afternoon, I picked out a wooly winter hat, sort of green, maybe. Aunt Flossie thought a minute. Aunt Flossie almost always thinks a minute before she starts a hat story. Then she sniffed the wooly hat.
"Just a little smoky smell now," she said.
Sarah and I sniffed the hat, too.
"Smoky smell, Aunt Flossie?"

"The big fire," Aunt Flossie said.
"The big fire in Baltimore. Everything smelled of smoke for miles around. For days and days. Big fire. Didn't come near our house on Centre Street, but we could hear fire engines racing down St. Paul.

Horses' hooves clattering.
Bells! Whistles!
Your great-grandma and I couldn't sleep. We grabbed our coats and hats and ran outside. Worried about Uncle Jimmy's grocery store, worried about the terrapins and crabs. Big fire in Baltimore."

Aunt Flossie closed her eyes. I think she was seeing long ago. I wondered about crab cakes. Did they have crab cakes way back then?

Then Sarah sniffed Aunt Flossie's hat.
"No more smoky smell," she said. But I thought I could smell some, just a little.

Then Sarah tried a different hat. Dark, dark blue, with a red feather.
"This one, Aunt Flossie! This one!"
Aunt Flossie closed her eyes and thought a minute.

AUNT FLOSSIE'S HATS (and Crab Cakes Later) continued

"Oh my, yes, my, my. What an exciting day!"

We waited, Sarah and I.
"What happened, Aunt Flossie?" I asked.

"Big parade in Baltimore."

"Ooh! Parade!" said Sarah. "We love parades."

"I made that hat," Aunt Flossie said, "to wear to watch that big parade. Buglers bugling. Drummers drumming.

Flags flying everywhere. The boys— soldiers, you know—back from France. Marching up Charles Street. Proud. Everyone cheering, everyone shouting! The Great War was over! The Great War was over!"

"Let's have a parade!" I said. Sarah put on the dark blue hat. I found a red one with a furry pompom. We marched around Aunt Flossie's house.

"March with us, Aunt Flossie!" I called. But she was closing her eyes. She was seeing long ago.
"Maybe she's dreaming about crab cakes," Sarah said.

Then we looked in the very special box.
"Look, Aunt Flossie! Here's your special hat." It was the big straw hat with the pink and yellow flowers and green velvet ribbon. Aunt Flossie's favorite best Sunday hat! It's our favorite story, because we are in the story, and we can help Aunt Flossie tell it!

Aunt Flossie smiled.
"One Sunday afternoon," she said, "we were going out for crab cakes. Sarah and Susan . . ."
"And Mommy and Daddy," I said.
"And Aunt Flossie," said Sarah.
Aunt Flossie nodded.
"We were walking by the water. And the wind came."

"Let me tell it," I said. "The wind came and blew away your favorite best Sunday hat!"
"My favorite best Sunday hat," said Aunt Flossie.
"It landed in the water."
"It was funny," said Sarah.
"I didn't think so," said Aunt Flossie.

"And Daddy tried to reach it," I said, "but he slid down in the mud. Daddy looked really surprised, and everybody laughed."
"He couldn't rescue my favorite, favorite best Sunday hat," said Aunt Flossie.

"And Mommy got a stick and leaned far out. She almost fell in, but she couldn't reach it either. The water rippled, and your favorite best Sunday hat just floated by like a boat!"

"Now comes the best part, and I'll tell it!" said Sarah. "A big brown dog came. It was walking with a boy.
'May we help you?' the boy asked.
'My dog Gretchen can get it.'
The boy threw a small, small stone.
It landed in Aunt Flossie's hat!
'Fetch, Gretchen, fetch!
Fetch, Gretchen, fetch!'

AUNT FLOSSIE'S HATS (and Crab Cakes Later) *continued*

Gretchen jumped into the water and she
swam. She swam and she got it!
Gretchen got Aunt Flossie's hat!
'Hurray for Gretchen!'
We all jumped up and down.
'Hurray for Aunt Flossie's hat!'"

"It was very wet," said Aunt Flossie,
"but it dried just fine . . . almost like new.
My favorite, favorite best Sunday hat."

"I like that story," I said.
"So do I," said Sarah.
"And I like what happened next! We went to
get crab cakes!"

"Crab cakes!" said Aunt Flossie.
"What a wonderful idea! Sarah, Susan,
telephone your parents. We'll go get some
crab cakes right now!"

I think Sarah and I will always agree about
one thing: Nothing in the whole wide world
tastes as good as crab cakes.

But crab cakes taste best after stories . . .
stories about Aunt Flossie's hats!

Literature Selections

UNIT 2

BUG FUN!

by Sarah Curran

It is night, there is no sun.
The time has come to have some fun.
I'll get the others as I fly.
How many bugs do you spy?

_____ bugs

3 little ants soon strike out.
The others give a great big shout.
Now 4 ants wait to hit the ball.
How many ants are there in all?

$3 + 4 =$ _____ ants

One little spider sings a song.
2 more spiders play along.
They'll sing and play their songs tonight.
How many spiders in the bright moonlight?

$1 + 2 =$ _____ spiders

8 little ladybugs like to chat,
Telling stories about this and that.
Then 5 little ladybugs fly away.
How many ladybugs are left to play?

$8 - 5 =$ _____ ladybugs

All the grasshoppers take a dip.

They are careful not to slip.
Then 2 grasshoppers hop away.
How many grasshoppers stay to play?

$6 - 2 =$ _____ grasshoppers

Oh, now look at the great big sun.
This is the end of our night of fun.
7 fireflies look around.
5 fly off without a sound.
How many fireflies are on the ground?

$7 - 5 =$ _____ fireflies

UNIT 4

100 DAYS OF SCHOOL

by Trudy Harris

If you go to school for 95 days, and then go 5 more days, what do you get?
   Smarter and smarter. And…
   (how cool)
   100 DAYS OF SCHOOL!

If 10 tired children all take off their shoes, what do you get?
   Lots of bare feet! And…
   (I suppose)
   100 toes!

If you find a tiny bug with 50 legs on one side and 50 on the other, what do you get?
   100 legs. And…
   (yes, indeed)
   a centipede.

If 20 children each drop 5 papers on the floor, what do you get?
   100 papers. And…
   (I would guess)
   an awful mess.

If you eat 10 salty peanuts every minute for 10 minutes, what do you get?
   100 peanuts. And…
   (big mistake)
   a tummy ache!

If 99 dots are on a clown's suit, what do you get?
   100 polka dots. Those…
   (on his clothes)
   plus 1 on his nose.

If 25 bees fly out of a hive, then 25 more and 25 more and 25 MORE, what do you get?
   100 bees. And…
   (no surprise)
   some exercise!

If you put 10 candles on a birthday cake, and then add 90 more, what do you get?
   100 candles. And…
   (with ALL those)
   a fire hose!

If every day you save 1 penny for 100 days, what do you get?
   100 pennies! Or…
   (better still)
   1 dollar bill!

If you pick 75 blackberries, and your mom picks 25 more, what do you get?
   100 berries. And…
   (Oh, my)
   blackberry pie!

If a train goes by with 99 cars and then 1 red caboose, what do you get?
   100 cars. And…
   (my friend)
   the end!

Literature Selections

UNIT 5

MY BIG NIGHT
by Harold Mitchell

Tonight at 7 o'clock
I'll be acting in a a play.
But it's only _____ o'clock.
It's still 6 hours away.

Tonight at 7 o'clock
I'll be singing in play.
But it's only ___ o'clock.
It's still 5 hours away.

Tonight at 7 o'clock
I'll be dancing in a play.
But it's only ___ o'clock.
It's still 4 hours away.

Tonight at 7 o'clock
I'll be roaring in a play.
But it's only ___ o'clock.
It's still 2 hours away.

It's Saturday at ___ o'clock.
It's time to start the play.
I've got butterflies in my stomach.
I wish they'd go away!

It's Saturday at ___ o'clock
I just completed the play.
I smile so wide and take a bow,
While the crowd shouts out, "Hooray!"

Literature Selections

READING MATH

UNIT 6

TWENTY IS TOO MANY

by Kate Duke

Twenty guinea pigs can be too many.
Twenty guinea pigs can start to sink.
But twenty sinking guinea pigs
minus ten diving guinea pigs
leaves ten
floating guinea pigs.   **20 − 10 = 10**

Ten floating guinea pigs
minus one ballooning guinea pig
leaves nine
waving guinea pigs.   **10 − 1 = 9**

Nine waving guinea pigs
minus one swinging guinea pig
leaves eight
seasick guinea pigs.   **9 − 1 = 8**

Eight seasick guinea pigs
minus one exploring guinea pig
leaves seven
excited guinea pigs.   **8 − 1 = 7**

Seven excited guinea pigs
minus one sneaky guinea pig
leaves six
yelling guinea pigs.   **7 − 1 = 6**

Six yelling guinea pigs
minus one fishing guinea pig
leaves five
flabbergasted guinea pigs.   **6 − 1 = 5**

Five flabbergasted guinea pigs
minus one surfing guinea pig
leaves four
copycatting guinea pigs.   **5 − 1 = 4**

Four copycatting guinea pigs
minus one belly-flopping guinea pig
leaves three
wet guinea pigs.   **4 − 1 = 3**

Three wet guinea pigs
minus one greedy guinea pig
leaves two
thirsty guinea pigs.   **3 − 1 = 2**

Two thirsty guinea pigs
minus one sleepy guinea pig
leaves just one guinea pig.
And one . . .   **2 − 1 = 1**
can be fun.

Literature Selections

READING MATH

UNIT 8

ONE WATERMELON SEED

by Celia Barker Lottridge

Max and Josephine planted a garden.

1 They planted one watermelon seed . . .
    and it grew.
They planted two pumpkin seeds . . .
    and they grew.   **2**

3 Max planted three eggplants . . .
    and they grew.
Josephine planted four pepper seeds . . .
    and they grew.   **4**

5 Then she planted five tomato plants . . .
    and they grew.
Max planted six blueberry bushes . . .
    and they grew.   **6**

7 And seven strawberry plants . . .
    and they grew.
Josephine planted eight bean seeds . . .
    and they grew.   **8**

9 And nine seed potatoes . . .
    and they grew.
They planted ten corn seeds . . .
    and they grew.   **10**

The rain fell and the sun shone. The seeds and the leaves, the stalks and the vines grew and grew and grew.

Max and Josephine weeded and watered and waited. One day they looked at their garden and saw there was plenty to pick. So . . .

10 They picked ten watermelons, big and green.
And twenty pumpkins, glowing orange. **20**

30 Max picked thirty eggplants, dark and purple,
and forty peppers, shiny yellow.   **40**

50 They both picked fifty tomatoes, plump and juicy
and sixty blueberries, small and round.   **60**

70 Josephine picked seventy strawberries, sweet and red.
Max picked eighty stringbeans, thin and crisp.   **80**

90 Josephine dug ninety potatoes, nobby and brown.
And they picked one hundred ears of corn. **100**

It was not ordinary corn. Max and Josephine saved it for cold winter nights, when the garden was covered with snow. Then they turned it into hundreds and thousands of big white crunchy puffs because that corn was POPCORN!

Glossary ....

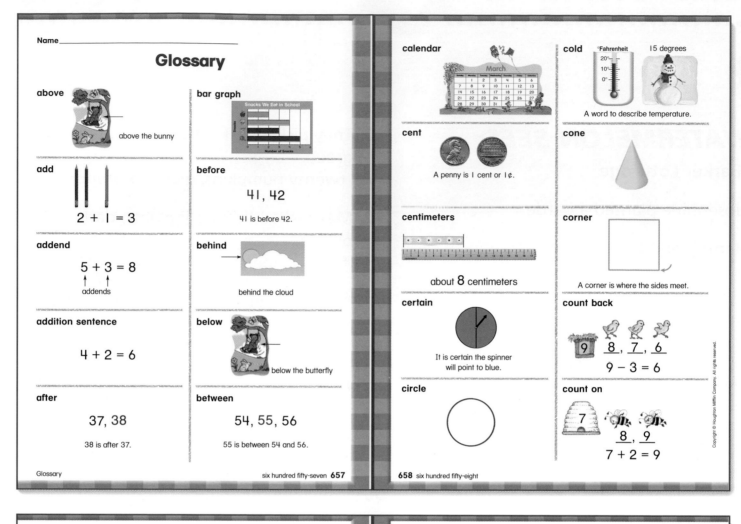

Name_____

Glossary

above

above the bunny

bar graph

Snacks We Eat in School

add

$2 + 1 = 3$

before

41, 42

41 is before 42.

addend

$5 + 3 = 8$
↑   ↑
addends

behind

behind the cloud

addition sentence

$4 + 2 = 6$

below

below the butterfly

after

37, 38

38 is after 37.

between

54, 55, 56

55 is between 54 and 56.

Glossary   six hundred fifty-seven **657**

---

calendar

March

cold

°Fahrenheit   15 degrees

A word to describe temperature.

cent

A penny is 1 cent or 1¢.

cone

centimeters

about **8** centimeters

corner

A corner is where the sides meet.

certain

It is certain the spinner
will point to blue.

count back

9   8, 7, 6

$9 - 3 = 6$

circle

count on

7   8, 9

$7 + 2 = 9$

658 six hundred fifty-eight

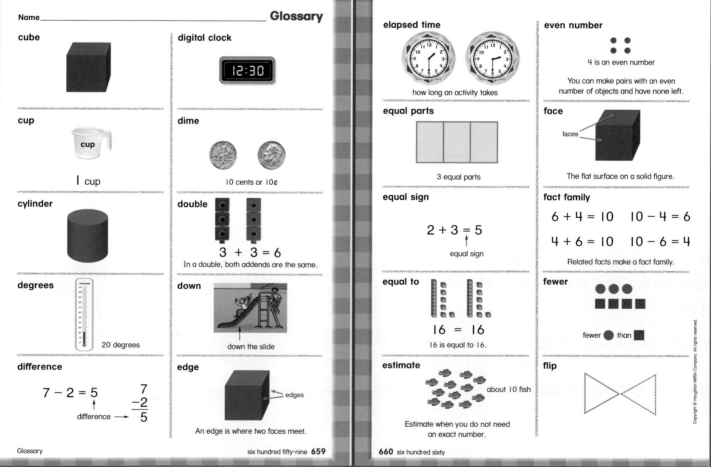

Name_____ **Glossary**

cube

digital clock

12:30

cup

cup

1 cup

dime

10 cents or 10¢

cylinder

double

$3 + 3 = 6$

In a double, both addends are the same.

degrees

20 degrees

down

down the slide

difference

$7 - 2 = 5$ $\begin{array}{r} 7 \\ -2 \\ \hline 5 \end{array}$
↑
difference

edge

edges

An edge is where two faces meet.

Glossary   six hundred fifty-nine **659**

---

elapsed time

how long an activity takes

even number

4 is an even number

You can make pairs with an even
number of objects and have none left.

equal parts

3 equal parts

face

faces

The flat surface on a solid figure.

equal sign

$2 + 3 = 5$
↑
equal sign

fact family

$6 + 4 = 10$ $10 - 4 = 6$

$4 + 6 = 10$ $10 - 6 = 4$

Related facts make a fact family.

equal to

$16 = 16$

16 is equal to 16.

fewer

fewer ● than ■

estimate

about 10 fish

Estimate when you do not need
an exact number.

flip

660 six hundred sixty

T58   **Glossary**

Glossary ....

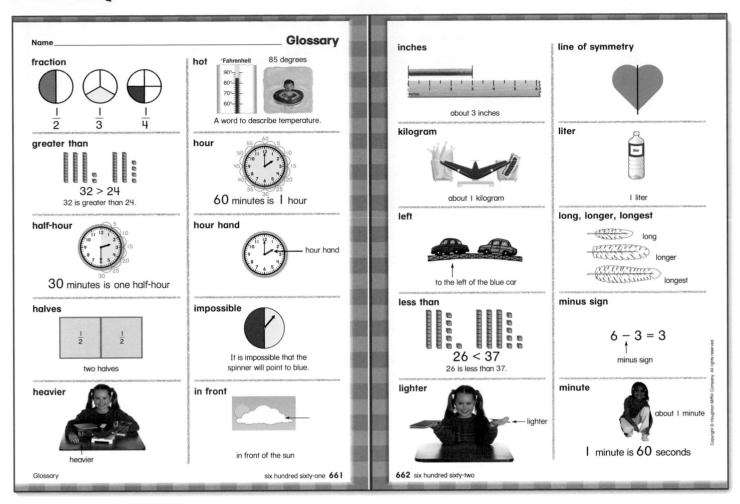

Name _____ **Glossary**

fraction

$\frac{1}{2}$ $\frac{1}{3}$ $\frac{1}{4}$

greater than

$32 > 24$
32 is greater than 24.

half-hour

30 minutes is one half-hour

halves

$\frac{1}{2}$ | $\frac{1}{2}$
two halves

heavier

heavier

hot

°Fahrenheit   85 degrees
A word to describe temperature.

hour

60 minutes is 1 hour

hour hand

← hour hand

impossible

It is impossible that the spinner will point to blue.

in front

in front of the sun

inches

about 3 inches

kilogram

about 1 kilogram

left

to the left of the blue car

less than

$26 < 37$
26 is less than 37.

lighter

← lighter

line of symmetry

liter

1 liter

long, longer, longest

long
longer
longest

minus sign

$6 - 3 = 3$
↑
minus sign

minute

about 1 minute

1 minute is 60 seconds

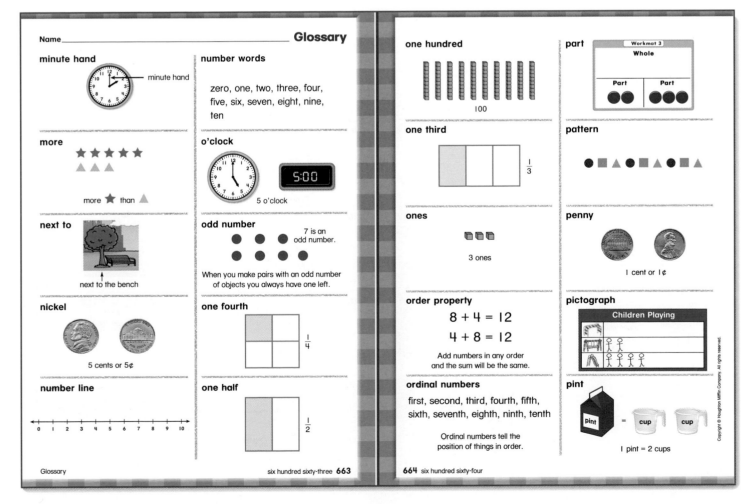

Name _____ **Glossary**

minute hand

← minute hand

more

★ ★ ★ ★ ★
▲ ▲ ▲
more ★ than ▲

next to

next to the bench

nickel

5 cents or 5¢

number line

0 1 2 3 4 5 6 7 8 9 10

number words

zero, one, two, three, four, five, six, seven, eight, nine, ten

o'clock

5:00
5 o'clock

odd number

7 is an odd number.

When you make pairs with an odd number of objects you always have one left.

one fourth

$\frac{1}{4}$

one half

$\frac{1}{2}$

one hundred

100

one third

$\frac{1}{3}$

ones

3 ones

order property

$8 + 4 = 12$
$4 + 8 = 12$
Add numbers in any order and the sum will be the same.

ordinal numbers

first, second, third, fourth, fifth, sixth, seventh, eighth, ninth, tenth

Ordinal numbers tell the position of things in order.

part

Workmat 3
Whole
Part | Part

pattern

● ■ ▲ ● ■ ▲ ● ■ ▲

penny

1 cent or 1¢

pictograph

Children Playing

pint

pint = cup cup
1 pint = 2 cups

Glossary ....

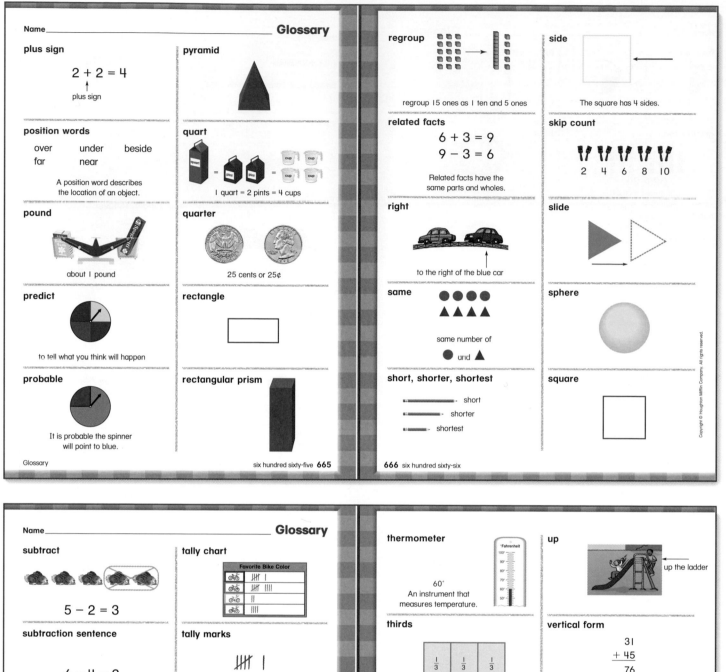

Name_____ **Glossary**

plus sign

$$2 + 2 = 4$$

↑ plus sign

position words

over   under   beside

far   near

A position word describes the location of an object.

pound

about 1 pound

predict

to tell what you think will happen

probable

It is probable the spinner will point to blue.

pyramid

quart

1 quart = 2 pints = 4 cups

quarter

25 cents or 25¢

rectangle

rectangular prism

regroup

regroup 15 ones as 1 ten and 5 ones

related facts

$$6 + 3 = 9$$
$$9 - 3 = 6$$

Related facts have the same parts and wholes.

right

to the right of the blue car

same

same number of

● and ▲

short, shorter, shortest

- short

- shorter

- shortest

side

The square has 4 sides.

skip count

2   4   6   8   10

slide

sphere

square

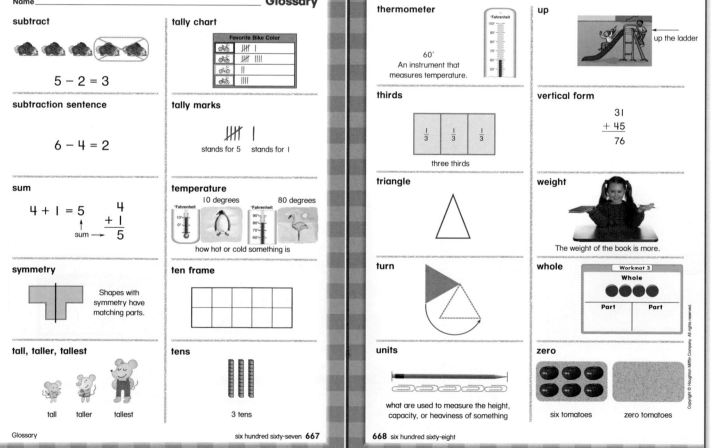

Name_____ **Glossary**

subtract

$$5 - 2 = 3$$

subtraction sentence

$$6 - 4 = 2$$

sum

$$4 + 1 = 5 \qquad \begin{array}{r} 4 \\ + 1 \\ \hline 5 \end{array}$$

↑ sum

symmetry

Shapes with symmetry have matching parts.

tall, taller, tallest

tall   taller   tallest

tally chart

Favorite Bike Color	
🚲	卌 I
🚲	卌 IIII
🚲	II
🚲	IIII

tally marks

卌 I

stands for 5   stands for 1

temperature

10 degrees   80 degrees

how hot or cold something is

ten frame

tens

3 tens

thermometer

60°
An instrument that measures temperature.

thirds

1/3	1/3	1/3

three thirds

triangle

turn

units

what are used to measure the height, capacity, or heaviness of something

up

up the ladder

vertical form

$$\begin{array}{r} 31 \\ + 45 \\ \hline 76 \end{array}$$

weight

The weight of the book is more.

whole

Workmat 3

Whole

Part   Part

zero

six tomatoes   zero tomatoes

WEEKLY WR READER® Activity Almanac

Houghton Mifflin Math and *Weekly Reader* have worked together to provide you with enriching real-world activities and internet connections for your students. The *Weekly Reader Activity Almanac* includes a map activity designed to link math and map skills along with data-related information and activities for each unit.

The Weekly Reader Activity Almanac presents intriguing information about North Carolina and provides Data Hunt activities that encourage learning about historic sites, national and state parks, plants and animals, and other fascinating topics related to North Carolina. The Weekly Reader Web Connections found throughout the student book provide safe access to more information about many cross-curricular connections and math topics on Houghton Mifflin's Education Place Web site: **www.eduplace.com/kids/mw/**.

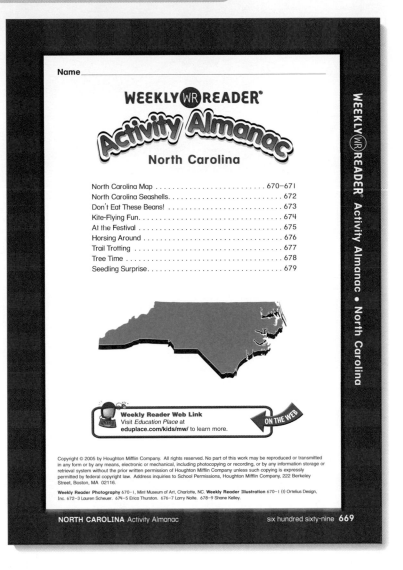

Name _____

WEEKLY WR READER®
Activity Almanac
North Carolina

Weekly Reader Web Link
Visit *Education Place* at
eduplace.com/kids/mw/ to learn more.
ON THE WEB

Weekly Reader Photography 670–1, Mint Museum of Art, Charlotte, NC. **Weekly Reader Illustration** 670–1 (t) Ortelius Design, Inc. 672–3 Lauren Scheuer. 674–5 Erica Thurston. 676–7 Larry Nolte. 678–9 Shane Kelley.

NORTH CAROLINA Activity Almanac   six hundred sixty-nine **669**

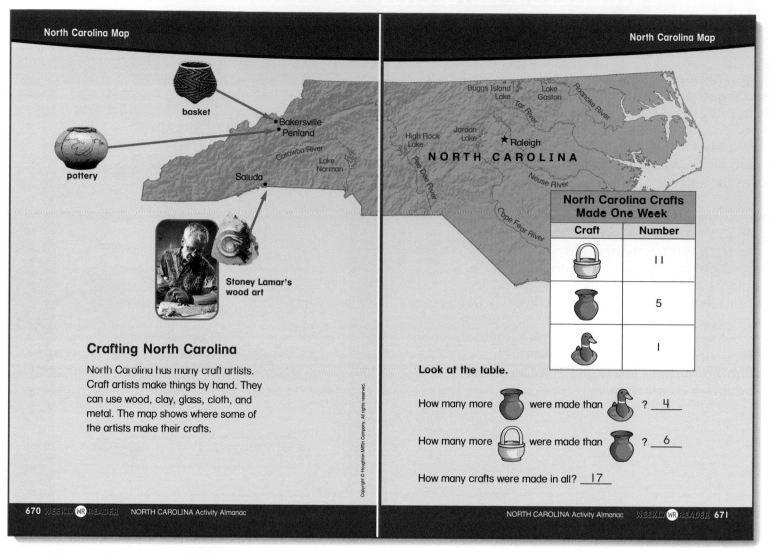

Crafting North Carolina

North Carolina has many craft artists. Craft artists make things by hand. They can use wood, clay, glass, cloth, and metal. The map shows where some of the artists make their crafts.

basket

pottery

Stoney Lamar's wood art

North Carolina Crafts Made One Week

Craft	Number
	11
	5
	1

Look at the table.

How many more [pottery] were made than [duck] ? __4__

How many more [basket] were made than [pottery] ? __6__

How many crafts were made in all? __17__

North Carolina Map

Teacher's Notes

Pottery can be objects such as vases, pots, bowls, or plates shaped from moist clay and hardened by heat. Sometimes a potter's wheel is used to help shape the clay by hand. Baskets are typically weaved from materials such as plant stems or twigs. Pottery and baskets can be decorative or used as containers to carry items such as water and food.

Stoney Lamar is an artist who uses objects such as wood and metal to create sculptures. Wet wood works best for his sculpture. He works on five to six pieces at a time and allows them to dry in stages prior to finishing them. His work has been shown in many museums in Atlanta, New York, Los Angeles, and Washington, DC.

Children should be able to read the information in the table, then use addition and subtraction to answer the questions.

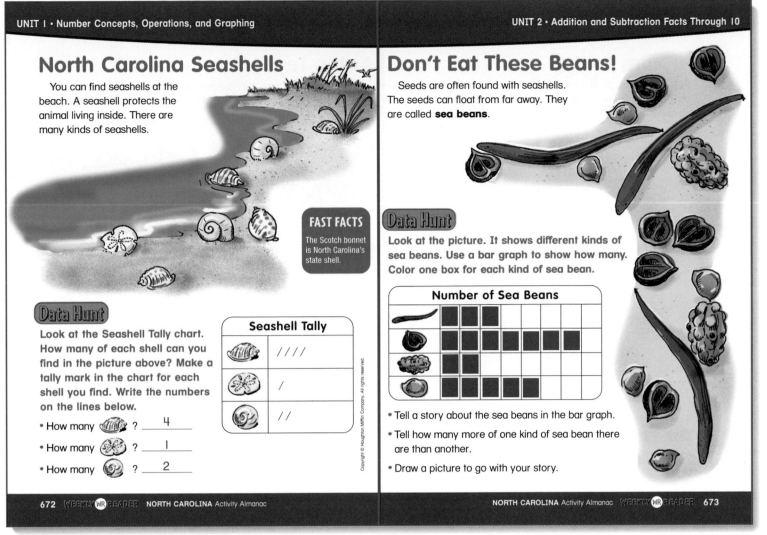

North Carolina Seashells

You can find seashells at the beach. A seashell protects the animal living inside. There are many kinds of seashells.

FAST FACTS

The Scotch bonnet is North Carolina's state shell.

Data Hunt

Look at the Seashell Tally chart. How many of each shell can you find in the picture above? Make a tally mark in the chart for each shell you find. Write the numbers on the lines below.

Seashell Tally	
🐚	////
🪨	/
🐌	//

- How many 🐚 ? ___4___
- How many 🪨 ? ___1___
- How many 🐌 ? ___2___

Don't Eat These Beans!

Seeds are often found with seashells. The seeds can float from far away. They are called **sea beans**.

Data Hunt

Look at the picture. It shows different kinds of sea beans. Use a bar graph to show how many. Color one box for each kind of sea bean.

Number of Sea Beans

- Tell a story about the sea beans in the bar graph.
- Tell how many more of one kind of sea bean there are than another.
- Draw a picture to go with your story.

Unit 1

Unit 2

Teacher's Notes

The tally chart shows three shells. The first is the scotch bonnet, the second is the sand dollar, and the third is the moon shell. The scotch bonnet and moon shell are used as homes to many types of snails. The sand dollar is also known as a keyhole urchin. These three shells can be found all along the East Coast.

Teacher's Notes

The illustration shows four different types of sea beans found in North Carolina.

The coin plant looks like a misshapen coin. The red mangrove has a long tube shape. The blister pod has bumps that look like blisters. The black walnut looks like a walnut.

Check children's stories and drawings.

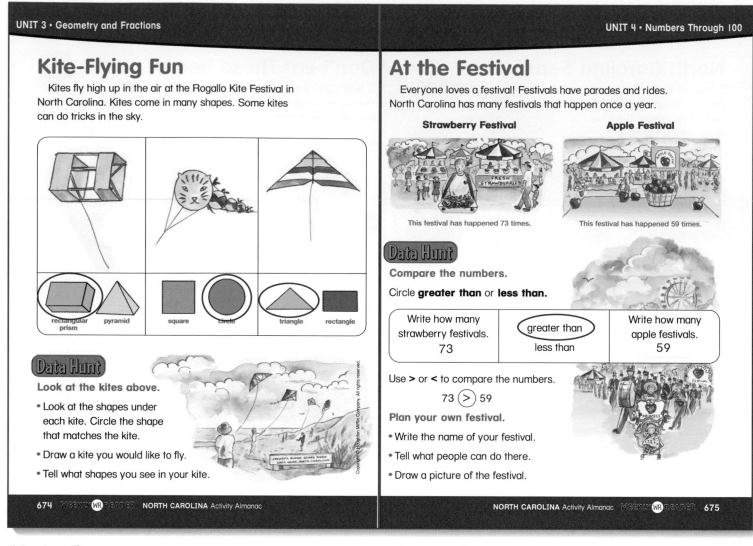

Kite-Flying Fun

Kites fly high up in the air at the Rogallo Kite Festival in North Carolina. Kites come in many shapes. Some kites can do tricks in the sky.

rectangular prism   pyramid   square   circle   triangle   rectangle

Data Hunt

Look at the kites above.

- Look at the shapes under each kite. Circle the shape that matches the kite.
- Draw a kite you would like to fly.
- Tell what shapes you see in your kite.

At the Festival

Everyone loves a festival! Festivals have parades and rides. North Carolina has many festivals that happen once a year.

Strawberry Festival   **Apple Festival**

This festival has happened 73 times.   This festival has happened 59 times.

Data Hunt

Compare the numbers.

Circle **greater than** or **less than**.

Write how many strawberry festivals. 73	greater than / less than	Write how many apple festivals. 59

Use > or < to compare the numbers.

73 (>) 59

Plan your own festival.

- Write the name of your festival.
- Tell what people can do there.
- Draw a picture of the festival.

Unit 3

Unit 4

Teacher's Notes

The Rogallo Kite Festival takes place annually at Jockey's Ridge State Park in Nags Head, North Carolina — the site of the highest sand dune on the East Coast. Kites of all shapes and sizes are entered in the festival. There are events for different kinds of kites. Sport kites perform tricks. There is music, food, contests, and kite-flying lessons.

Teacher's Notes

The number of times the North Carolina Apple and Strawberry Festivals have happened is up-to-date as of 2003.

You may wish to explain to children what a festival is. Ask children if they have ever been to a festival. Discuss the type of attractions they might see. They might see a parade, animals in animal shows, contests, food, music groups, and dancing.

WEEKLY (WR) READER   Activity Almanac

Horsing Around

There are lots of horses at the Carolina Horse Park. The horses perform in contests. First, a rider puts a saddle on the horse. Then the rider climbs on the horse. Finally, the horse and the rider are ready to perform!

Riding a Horse

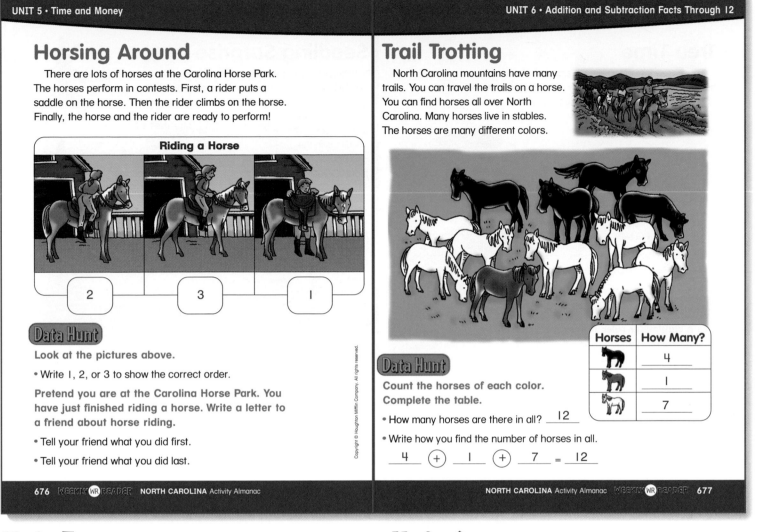

2   3   1

Data Hunt

Look at the pictures above.

• Write 1, 2, or 3 to show the correct order.

Pretend you are at the Carolina Horse Park. You have just finished riding a horse. Write a letter to a friend about horse riding.

• Tell your friend what you did first.

• Tell your friend what you did last.

Trail Trotting

North Carolina mountains have many trails. You can travel the trails on a horse. You can find horses all over North Carolina. Many horses live in stables. The horses are many different colors.

Horses	How Many?
🐴	4
🐴	1
🐴	7

Data Hunt

Count the horses of each color. Complete the table.

• How many horses are there in all? ___12___

• Write how you find the number of horses in all.

___4___ (+) ___1___ (+) ___7___ = ___12___

Unit 5   Unit 6

Teacher's Notes

This lesson explains the order of events for riding a horse. You may wish to explain what a saddle is to the children. Tell them that a saddle is used to ride horses. Riders usually sit on the saddle when they are on the horse.

Teacher's Notes

This lesson shows the different colors of horses found at a North Carolina stable. Explain to children that a stable is a shelter where animals live. You may wish to tell children that most horses come in various shades of brown, black, grey, and white.

WEEKLY (WR) READER   Activity Almanac

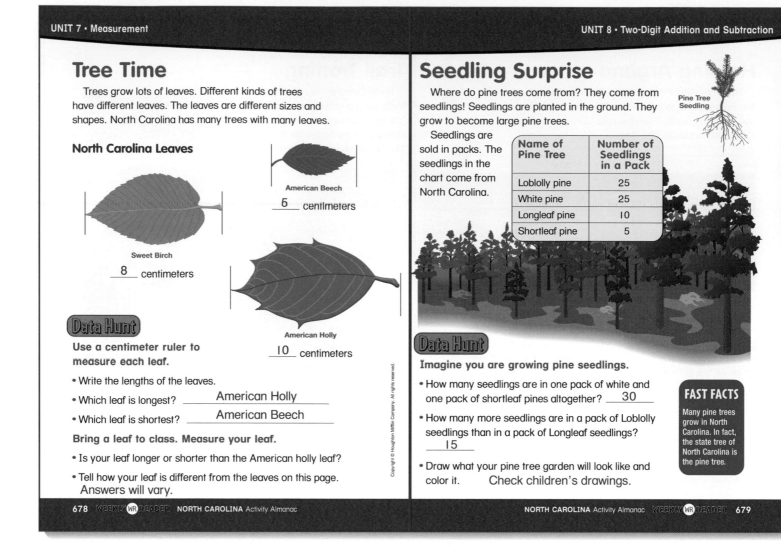

Tree Time

Trees grow lots of leaves. Different kinds of trees have different leaves. The leaves are different sizes and shapes. North Carolina has many trees with many leaves.

North Carolina Leaves

American Beech
_6_ centimeters

Sweet Birch
_8_ centimeters

American Holly
_10_ centimeters

Data Hunt

Use a centimeter ruler to measure each leaf.

• Write the lengths of the leaves.
• Which leaf is longest? _American Holly_
• Which leaf is shortest? _American Beech_

Bring a leaf to class. Measure your leaf.

• Is your leaf longer or shorter than the American holly leaf?
• Tell how your leaf is different from the leaves on this page.
  Answers will vary.

Seedling Surprise

Where do pine trees come from? They come from seedlings! Seedlings are planted in the ground. They grow to become large pine trees.

Seedlings are sold in packs. The seedlings in the chart come from North Carolina.

Pine Tree Seedling

Name of Pine Tree	Number of Seedlings in a Pack
Loblolly pine	25
White pine	25
Longleaf pine	10
Shortleaf pine	5

Data Hunt

Imagine you are growing pine seedlings.

• How many seedlings are in one pack of white and one pack of shortleaf pines altogether? _30_

• How many more seedlings are in a pack of Loblolly seedlings than in a pack of Longleaf seedlings? _15_

• Draw what your pine tree garden will look like and color it.   Check children's drawings.

FAST FACTS

Many pine trees grow in North Carolina. In fact, the state tree of North Carolina is the pine tree.

Unit 7   Unit 8

Teacher's Notes

American Hollies have bright, round, red berries. They grow in the autumn and stay on all winter. American Beeches grow best in mountain coves. The leaves are found towards the ends of branches. Sweet Birches make scaly, oval-shaped fruit. The stems of their leaves are hairy.

Teacher's Notes

Seedlings can be purchased from the North Carolina Tree Seedling Nursery Program. They are sold to agencies and landowners that support the planting of trees in North Carolina.

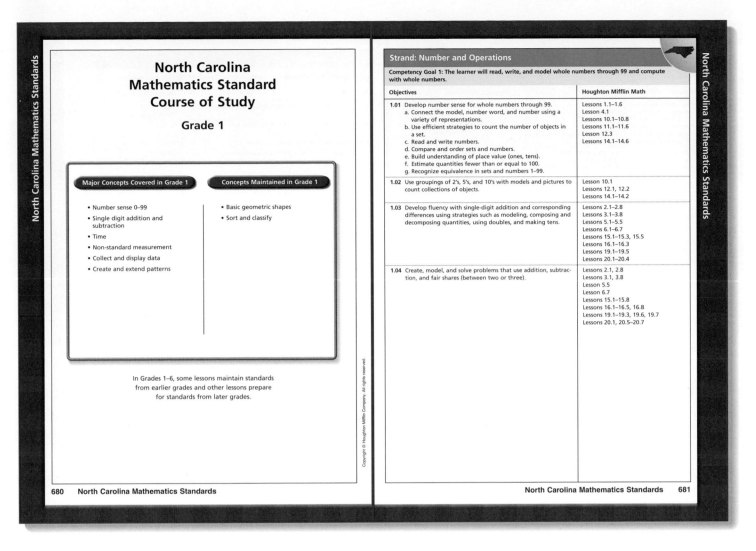

North Carolina
Mathematics Standard
Course of Study

Grade 1

Major Concepts Covered in Grade 1

- Number sense 0–99
- Single digit addition and subtraction
- Time
- Non-standard measurement
- Collect and display data
- Create and extend patterns

Concepts Maintained in Grade 1

- Basic geometric shapes
- Sort and classify

In Grades 1–6, some lessons maintain standards from earlier grades and other lessons prepare for standards from later grades.

Strand: Number and Operations

Competency Goal 1: The learner will read, write, and model whole numbers through 99 and compute with whole numbers.

Objectives	Houghton Mifflin Math
1.01 Develop number sense for whole numbers through 99. a. Connect the model, number word, and number using a variety of representations. b. Use efficient strategies to count the number of objects in a set. c. Read and write numbers. d. Compare and order sets and numbers. e. Build understanding of place value (ones, tens). f. Estimate quantities fewer than or equal to 100. g. Recognize equivalence in sets and numbers 1–99.	Lessons 1.1–1.6 Lesson 4.1 Lessons 10.1–10.8 Lessons 11.1–11.6 Lesson 12.3 Lessons 14.1–14.6
1.02 Use groupings of 2's, 5's, and 10's with models and pictures to count collections of objects.	Lesson 10.1 Lessons 12.1, 12.2 Lessons 14.1–14.2
1.03 Develop fluency with single-digit addition and corresponding differences using strategies such as modeling, composing and decomposing quantities, using doubles, and making tens.	Lessons 2.1–2.8 Lessons 3.1–3.8 Lessons 5.1–5.5 Lessons 6.1–6.7 Lessons 15.1–15.3, 15.5 Lessons 16.1–16.3 Lessons 19.1–19.5 Lessons 20.1–20.4
1.04 Create, model, and solve problems that use addition, subtraction, and fair shares (between two or three).	Lessons 2.1, 2.8 Lessons 3.1, 3.8 Lesson 5.5 Lesson 6.7 Lessons 15.1–15.8 Lessons 16.1–16.5, 16.8 Lessons 19.1–19.3, 19.6, 19.7 Lessons 20.1, 20.5–20.7

Meeting the Standards

The North Carolina Department of Education has developed the Mathematics Standard Course of Study for the teaching of mathematics across all grade levels. These standards reflect an approach for teaching mathematics that will prepare today's students for living and working in tomorrow's world.

These pages in the Student Book will help you show parents how your classroom teaching reflects the Strands and Competency Goals of the Standard Course of Study. This should help both parents and students understand how a particular lesson contributes to a student's overall achievement of the Competency Goals for Mathematics.

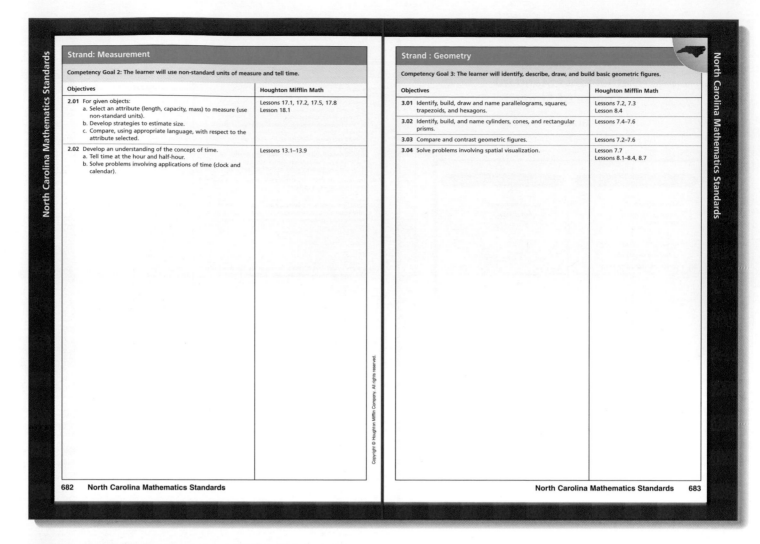

Strand: Measurement

Competency Goal 2: The learner will use non-standard units of measure and tell time.

Objectives	Houghton Mifflin Math

2.01 For given objects:
  a. Select an attribute (length, capacity, mass) to measure (use non-standard units).
  b. Develop strategies to estimate size.
  c. Compare, using appropriate language, with respect to the attribute selected.
	Lessons 17.1, 17.2, 17.5, 17.8
	Lesson 18.1

2.02 Develop an understanding of the concept of time.
  a. Tell time at the hour and half-hour.
  b. Solve problems involving applications of time (clock and calendar).
	Lessons 13.1–13.9

Strand : Geometry

Competency Goal 3: The learner will identify, describe, draw, and build basic geometric figures.

Objectives	Houghton Mifflin Math
3.01 Identify, build, draw and name parallelograms, squares, trapezoids, and hexagons.	Lessons 7.2, 7.3 Lesson 8.4
3.02 Identify, build, and name cylinders, cones, and rectangular prisms.	Lessons 7.4–7.6
3.03 Compare and contrast geometric figures.	Lessons 7.2–7.6
3.04 Solve problems involving spatial visualization.	Lesson 7.7 Lessons 8.1–8.4, 8.7

Strand: Data Analysis and Probability

Competency Goal 4: The learner will understand and use data and simple probability concepts.

Objectives	Houghton Mifflin Math
4.01 Collect, organize, describe and display data using line plots and tallies.	Lesson 4.1 Lesson 9.5
4.02 Describe events as certain, impossible, more likely, or less likely to occur.	Lessons 9.5–9.6

Strand: Algebra

Competency Goal 5: The learner will demonstrate an understanding of classification and patterning.

Objectives	Houghton Mifflin Math
5.01 Sort and classify objects by two attributes.	Lesson 7.3
5.02 Use Venn diagrams to illustrate similarities and differences in two sets.	Lesson 7.5
5.03 Create and extend patterns, identify the pattern unit, and translate into other forms.	Lessons 8.5, 8.6, 8.8 Lesson 9.6 Lessons 12.1, 12.2, 12.5 Lesson 16.7

Workmats ....

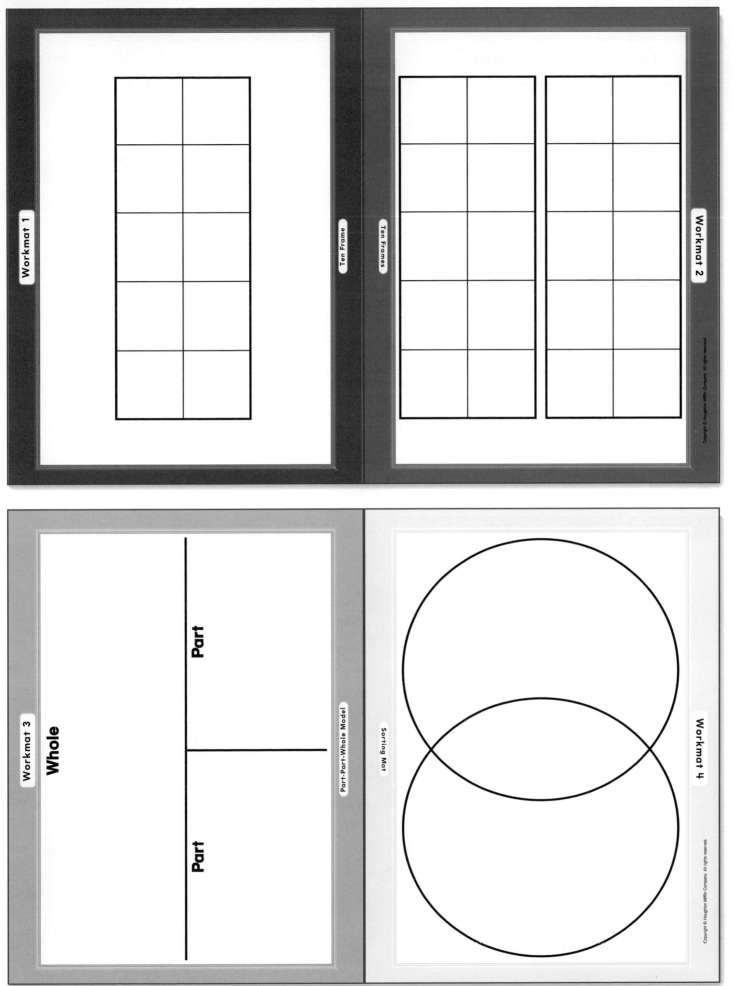

Workmat 1

Ten Frame

Ten Frames

Workmat 2

Workmat 3

Whole

Part

Part

Part-Part-Whole Model

Sorting Mat

Workmat 4

Workmats

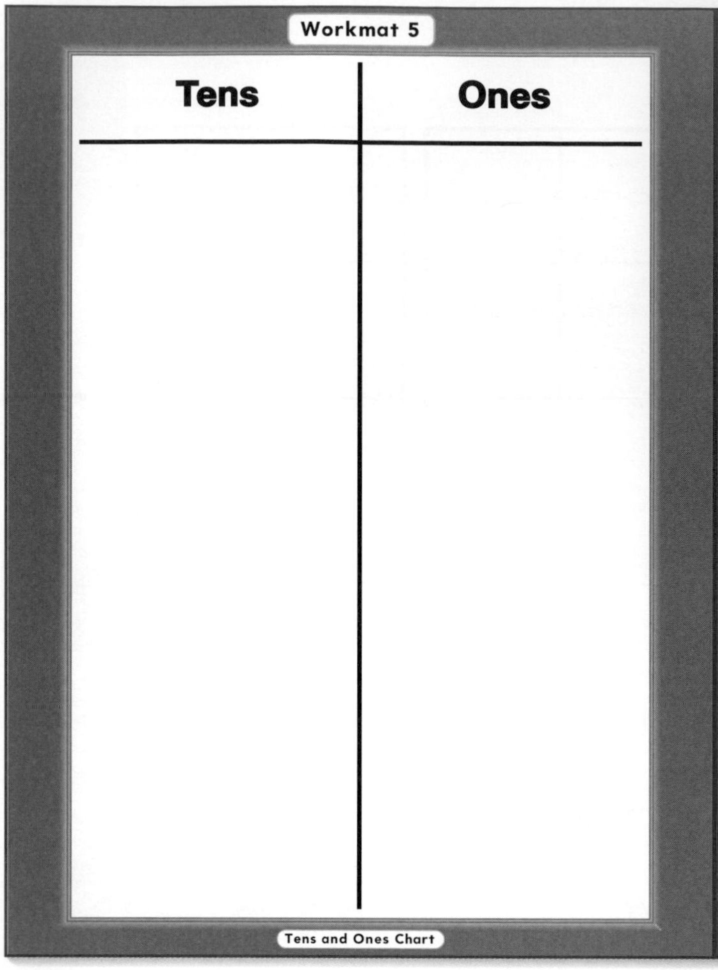

Workmat 5

Tens	Ones

Tens and Ones Chart

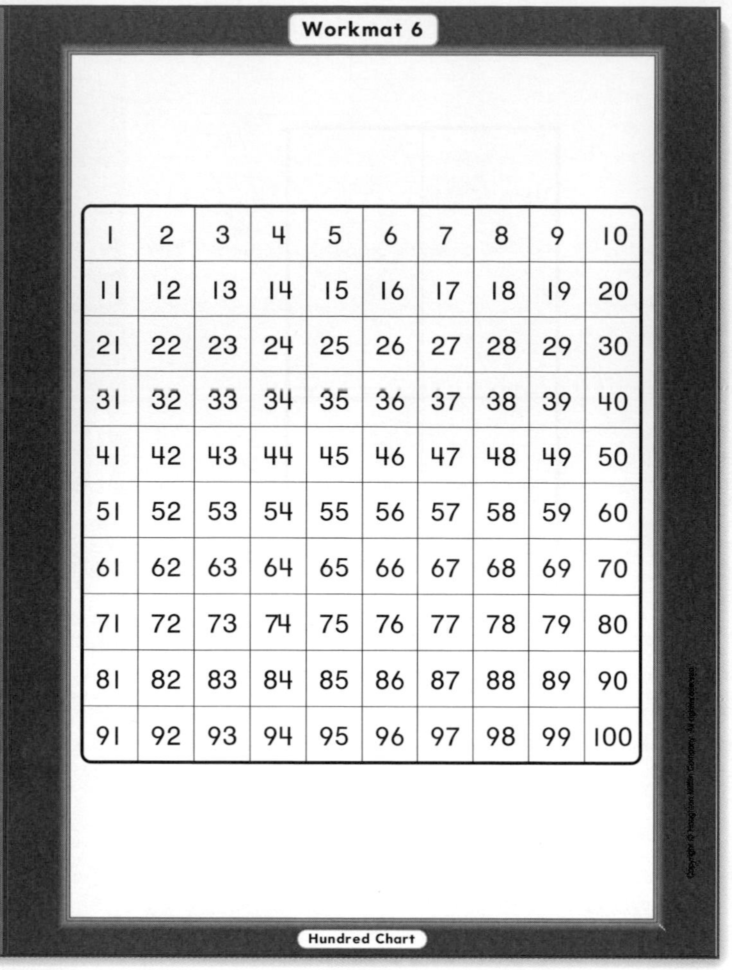

Workmat 6

1	2	3	4	5	6	7	8	9	10
11	12	13	14	15	16	17	18	19	20
21	22	23	24	25	26	27	28	29	30
31	32	33	34	35	36	37	38	39	40
41	42	43	44	45	46	47	48	49	50
51	52	53	54	55	56	57	58	59	60
61	62	63	64	65	66	67	68	69	70
71	72	73	74	75	76	77	78	79	80
81	82	83	84	85	86	87	88	89	90
91	92	93	94	95	96	97	98	99	100

Hundred Chart

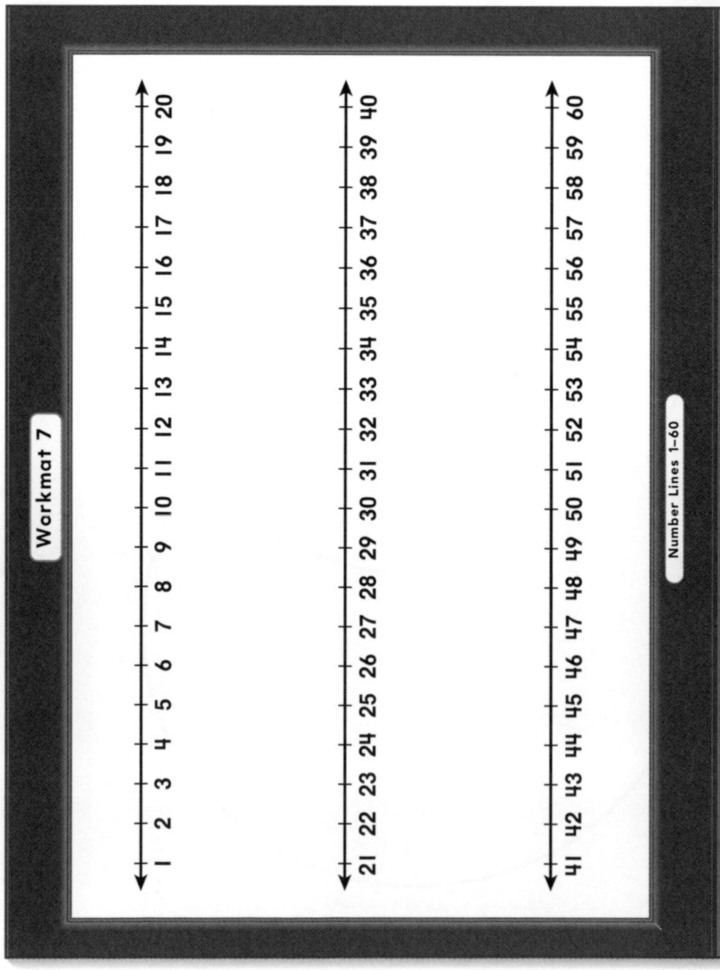

Workmat 7

1 2 3 4 5 6 7 8 9 10 11 12 13 14 15 16 17 18 19 20

21 22 23 24 25 26 27 28 29 30 31 32 33 34 35 36 37 38 39 40

41 42 43 44 45 46 47 48 49 50 51 52 53 54 55 56 57 58 59 60

Number Lines 1–60

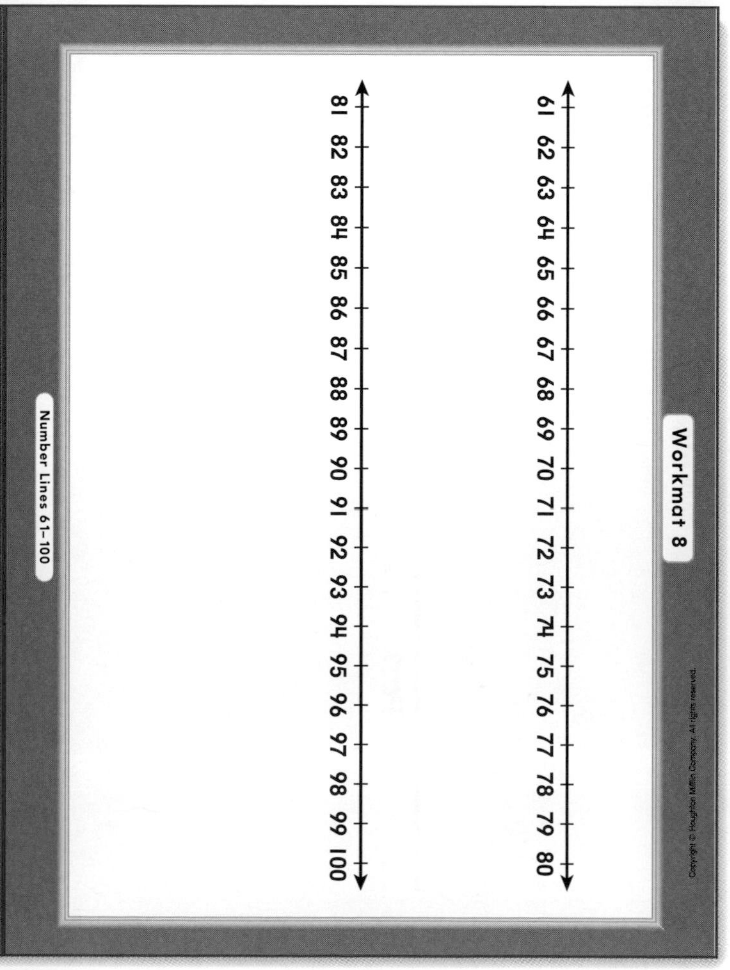

Number Lines 61–100

Workmat 8

61 62 63 64 65 66 67 68 69 70 71 72 73 74 75 76 77 78 79 80

81 82 83 84 85 86 87 88 89 90 91 92 93 94 95 96 97 98 99 100

Teacher Support Handbook

References for a number of professional resources are presented in this section of your Teacher's Edition. These materials reflect the needs expressed by classroom teachers around the country for additional resources to help them enrich their teaching or enhance their understanding of mathematics.

Math and Literature Bibliography

Addition Annie
by David Gisler
Children's Press, 2002
Annie counts everything around her, from trees to knees to peas.

Aunt Flossie's Hats (and Crab Cakes Later)
by Elizabeth Fitzgerald Howard
Clarion, 1991
A picture book about two African-American girls that can be connected to numbers, sorting, and graphing.

*A Bag Full of Pups
by Dick Gackenbach
Houghton Mifflin, 1983
Most of Mr. Mullin's pups go to people who want a dog to do tasks for them, but one little boy just wants a pet to love.

The Best Vacation Ever
by Stuart J. Murphy
HarperCollins, 1997
As a family decides where to go on vacation, the narrator gathers all of their ideas in a chart.

Can You Count Ten Toes?
by Lezlie Evans
Houghton Mifflin, 1999
You can learn to count in ten different languages in this counting book.

*Cat Up a Tree
by John and Ann Hassett
Houghton Mifflin, 2003
Nana Quimby has too many cats stuck in her tree, but the people she asks for help will not help rescue the cats.

A Collection for Kate
by Barbara deRubertis
Econo-Clad Books, 2000
It's Collection Week at Kate's school and she doesn't have a collection. What can she do?

Count on Pablo
by Barbara deRubertis
Econo-Clad Books, 1999
Pablo shows how good he is at counting when he helps his grandmother, his "abuela," sell vegetables.

Counting Cranes
by Mary Beth Owens
Little, Brown & Company, 1993
A counting book that describes the characteristics and behaviors of a whooping crane.

*Dim Sum for Everyone!
by Grace Lin
Random House Children's Books, 2001
On a visit to a Chinatown restaurant with her family, a child describes all the different dishes of dim sum.

Dinner at the Panda Palace
by Stephanie Calmenson
Bt Bound, 1999
Mr. Panda greets a growing list of guests arriving at his restaurant in this counting rhyme.

The Doorbell Rang
by Pat Hutchins
Greenwillow, 1986
Every time the doorbell rings, more friends arrive to share the cookies that Ma has made.

Each Orange Had 8 Slices: A Counting Book
by Paul Giganti, Jr.
Pearson Learning, 1992
Have fun counting, adding, or multiplying your way through the math hiding in the world around you.

Eating Fractions
by Bruce McMillan
Scholastic, 1991
A boy and a girl discover halves, thirds, and fourths as they divide bananas, pizza, and strawberry pie.

The Eentsy, Weentsy Spider: Fingerplays and Action Rhymes
by Joanna Cole and Stephanie Calmenson
Econo-Clad Books, 1991
Say, sing, and act out this collection of favorite fingerplays and action rhymes.

*Feast for 10
by Cathryn Falwell
Houghton Mifflin Company, 1995
A counting book that features a family shopping for, and preparing, a meal.

Fish Eyes: A Book You Can Count On
by Lois Ehlert
Harcourt, 2001
Brightly colored fish introduce children to counting.

Gator Pie
by Louise Mathews
Sundance, 1995
A group of alligators divide a pie into smaller and smaller fractional parts.

The Grapes of Math: Mind-Stretching Math Riddles
by Greg Tang
Scholastic, 2001
Use visual clues to solve a variety of math riddles.

How Long?
by Elizabeth Dale
Orchard Books, 1998
Caroline the dormouse wants to find out how long a minute is so she paints a line. She continues playing to find out how long 10 minutes and 15 minutes are.

How Many Feet In the Bed?
by Dianne Johnston Hamm
Simon & Schuster, 1994
Count feet as five family members tumble in and out of bed.

Inch by Inch
by Leo Lionni
Bt Bound, 1999
An inchworm is proud of his ability to measure everything under the sun.

*Just a Little Bit
by Ann Tompert
Houghton Mifflin, 1993
Mouse and Elephant are playing on a seesaw and need help from lots of animal friends to balance the scales.

Just Enough Carrots
by Stuart J. Murphy
Scott Foresman, 1997
Count and compare food in shopping carts while a bunny and his mother shop.

Just One More
by Michelle Koch
Greenwillow Books, 1991
A counting book from one to fifteen that also explores the concept of "one more."

Lemonade for Sale
by Stuart J. Murphy
HarperCollins, 1997
The Elm Street Kids' Club wants to fix up their clubhouse, so they decide to sell lemonade and use a graph to track their sales.

Let's Fly a Kite
by Stuart J. Murphy
HarperCollins, 2000
Bob and Hannah learn about symmetry as they build and fly a kite.

Lights Out!
by Lucille Recht Penner
Econo-Clad Books, 2000
A young girl counts the lights as each is turned out in the apartment building across from hers.

*Look Inside
by Lilly Ernesto
DC Heath, 1989
Take a look inside different buildings and find out who is there.

Lulu's Lemonade
by Barbara deRubertis
Econo-Clad Books, 2000
Three children make special lemonade on a hot day and squabble over which ingredients and what quantities to use.

Me Counting Time
by Joan Sweeney
Crown Books for Young Readers, 2000
Describes the relationship between various measurements of time.

*Also available in the Math Trade Book Literature Library

Math and Literature Bibliography

Measuring Penny
by Loreen Leedy
Econo-Clad Books, 2000
For homework, Lisa decides to measure her dog, Penny. She uses all sorts of units, including pounds, inches, dog biscuits, and cotton swabs.

Missing Mittens
by Stuart J. Murphy
Econo-Clad Books, 2001
Children are introduced to odd and even numbers as they unravel the mitten mystery on Farmer Bill's farm.

*The Mitten
adapted and illustrated
by Jan Brett
Putnam, 1996
Nicki accidentally drops his mitten in the snow and several animals sleep inside it.

Musical Chairs and Dancing Bears
by Joanne Rocklin
Holt, 1993
Bears play musical chairs to demonstrate simple subtraction.

Numbers (Math Counts)
by Henry Arthur Pluckrose
Scholastic Library Publishing, 1995
Using the Math Counts series, children can become mathematical problem solvers.

100 Days of School
by Trudy Harris
Millbrook Press, 1999
Children celebrate 100 days of school. Using fun examples, kids will learn many of the ways to reach 100 through groupings.

One Hundred is a Family
by Pam Muñoz Ryan
Hyperion, 1994
Groups making up different types of families introduce numbers from one to ten, and then by tens to one hundred.

one less fish
by Kim Michelle Toft
Charlesbridge, 1998
Learn about threatened tropical fish in the Great Barrier Reef as you count down from twelve to zero.

One More Bunny
by Rick Walton
HarperCollins, 2001
Bunnies introduce the numbers one through ten as they play.

1 + 1 Take Away Two!
by Michael Berenstain
Golden Books, 1991
Single-digit addition and subtraction equations are modeled with jungle animal illustrations.

One Watermelon Seed
by Celia Barker Lottridge
Oxford University Press, 1988
Two children plant a garden and then harvest the fruits and vegetables they have grown. Practice counting up to ten and then by tens up to one hundred.

Over in the Meadow, a Rhyme
illustrated
by Ezra Jack Keats
Penguin Group, 1999
Animal mothers and their babies introduce the numbers one through ten in this favorite counting rhyme.

*The Pig Is in the Pantry, the Cat Is on the Shelf
by Shirley Mozelle
Houghton Mifflin, 2000
When Mr. McDuffel goes shopping and forgets to lock his house, eight farm animals take it over and cause chaos.

Probably Pistachio
by Stuart J. Murphy
HarperCollins, 2000
Everything is going wrong for Jack today, and during the course of the day he learns all about probability.

The Purse
by Kathy Caple
Houghton Mifflin, 1986
Kathy spends all of her money to buy a purse, but then must earn the money to put in it.

A Quarter From the Tooth Fairy
by Caren Holtzman
Econo-Clad Books, 1995
A young boy gets a quarter from the Tooth Fairy and has trouble deciding how to spend it.

The Right Number of Elephants
by Jeff Sheppard
HarperCollins, 1992
A girl decides how many elephants are needed for several projects.

Sea Sums
by Joy N. Hulme
Hyperion, 1996
Changing numbers of sea creatures are added and subtracted as they swim in the shallows of a coral reef.

Shape (Math Counts)
by Henry Arthur Pluckrose
Scholastic, 1995
Using the Math Counts series, children can become mathematical problem solvers.

So Many Cats!
by Beatrice Schenk de Regniers
Houghton Mifflin, 1991
One lonely cat turns into twelve in this counting story.

Take Off with Numbers
by Sally Hewitt
Raintree Publishers, 1996
Use everyday objects and situations to explore the world of numbers.

Ten Little Mice
by Joyce Dunbar
Harcourt, 1990
Ten mischievous mice play happily outside and then scurry home, one by one.

12 Ways to Get to 11
by Eve Merriam
Simon & Schuster, 1993
Various combinations of items are added together to reach the number eleven.

Twenty Is Too Many
by Kate Duke
Penguin Putnam, 2000
One by one twenty guinea pigs jump ship in this book about subtraction.

Two of Everything
by Lily Toy Hong
Whitman, 1993
Mr. and Mrs. Haktak become rich after discovering a brass pot that doubles everything that's put into it.

What's a Pair? What's a Dozen?
by Stephen R. Swinburne
Boyds Mills Press, 2000
Introduce children to number-related words. Using lively photos children are then asked to identify what they've learned.

What Time Is It, Mr. Wolf?
by Bob Beeson
Hambleton-Hill Publishing, Inc., 1994
Children will learn about time on the hour, using analog and digital clocks.

Where the Sidewalk Ends
by Shel Silverstein
HarperCollins Children's Books
A collection of humorous poetry, including One Inch Tall.

Where's That Bone
by Lucille Recht Penner
The Kane Press, 2000
When Jill's dog Bingo buries his bones to hide them from Hulk the cat, Jill keeps track of where they are with a map.

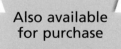

Also available
for purchase

*Math Trade Book
Literature Library*

Professional Resources Bibliography

Bresser, R., and C. Holtzman. *Developing Number Sense –Grades 3-6.* Math Solutions Publications, 1999.

Brodie, J. P. *Constructing Ideas About Large Numbers.* Creative Publications, 1995.

Burns, Marilyn. *About Teaching Mathematics: A K–8 Resource,* 2nd Ed. Sausalito, CA: Math Solutions Publications, 2000.

Butterworth, B. *The Mathematical Brain.* Macmillan, 1999.

Carpenter, Thomas P., Elizabeth Fennema, Megan Loef Franke, Linda Levi, and Susan P. Empson. *Children's Mathematics: Cognitively Guided Instruction.* Portsmouth, NH: Heinemann, 1999.

Cathcart. W., Y. Pothier, J. Vance, and N. Bezuk. *Learning Mathematics in Elementary and Middle Schools.* Merrill: Prentice-Hall, Inc., 2000.

Childs, L., and L Choate. *Nimble with Numbers.* Dale Seymour Publications, 1999.

Clapham, C. *Concise Dictionary of Mathematics.* Oxford University Press, 1996.

Coates, G., and J. Stenmark. *Family Math for Young Children.* Lawrence Hall of Science, 1997.

Cowan, T., and J. Maguire. *Timelines of African-American History: 500 Years of Black Achievement.* Berkley Publishing Group, 1994.

Crawford, M., and M. Witte. *"Strategies for Mathematics: Teaching in Context."* Educational Leadership, Vol. 57, ASCD, November 1999.

Eby, J., and E. Kujawa. *Reflective Planning, Teaching and Evaluation: K-12.* Merrill: Macmillan Publishing Company, 1994.

Flournoy, V., et al. *The Patchwork Quilt.* Scholastic, 1996.

Franco, B., et al. *Understanding Geometry.* Great Source Education Group, 1998.

Garland, T. Fibonacci *Fun: Fascinating Activities with Intriguing Numbers.* Dale Seymour Publications, 1998.

Geary, D. C. *Children's Mathematical Development: Research and Practical Applications.* Washington, D.C., 1994.

Gelfand, I., and A. Shen. *Algebra.* Birkhauser, 1993.

Ginsburg, H.P., Greenes, C., and Balfanz, R. *Big Math for Little Kids.* Dale Seymour Publications, 2003

Ginsburg, H. P., Greenes, C., Balfanz, R., Glassman, B., ed. *Macmillan Visual Almanac.* Blackbirch Press, 1996.

Greenes, C., and G. Immerzeel. *Problem Solving Focus: Time and Money.* Dale Seymour Publications, 1993.

Hiebert, J., T. Carpenter, E. Fennema, K. Fuson, D. Wearne, H. Murray, A. Olivier, and P. Humam. *Making Sense: Teaching and Learning Mathematics with Understanding.* Heinemann, 1997.

Hoffman, P. *The Man Who Loved Only Numbers: The Story of Paul Erdos and the Search for Mathematical Truth.* Hyperion, 1998.

Karp, Karen, E. Todd Brown, Linda Allen, and Candy Allen. *Feisty Females: Inspiring Girls to Think Mathematically.* Portsmouth, NH: Heinemann, 1998.

Kovalik, Susan J., and Karen D. Olsen. *Exceeding Expectations: A User's Guide to Implementing Brain Research in the Classroom,* 2nd Ed. Covington, WA: Books for Educators, Inc., 2001.

Lamon. Susan J. *Teaching Fractions and Ratios for Understanding.* Mahwah, NJ: Lawrence Erlbaum Associates, 1999.

Lee, M., and M. Miller. *Great Graphing.* Scholastic Professional Books, 1993.

Ma, Liping. *Knowing and Teaching Elementary Mathematics.* Lawrence Erlbaum Associates, 1999.

Mamchur, C. *A Teacher's Guide to Cognitive Type Theory and Learning Style.* ASCD, 1996.

The Math Learning Center. *"Fractions on a Geoboard," in Opening Eyes to Mathematics,* Volume 3. 1995.

McIntosh, A., B. Reys, R. Reys, and J. Hope. *Number SENSE: Simple Effective Number Sense Experiences, Grades 4-6.* Dale Seymour Publications, 1997.

Means, B., C. Chelener, and M. Knapp. *Teaching Advanced Skills to At-Risk Students.* Jossey-Bass Inc., 1991.

Mendlesohn, E. *Teaching Primary Math with Music.* Dale Seymour Publications, 1990.

Miller, D., and A. McKinnon. *The Beginning School Mathematics Project.* ASCD, 1995.

Miller, E. *Read It! Draw It! Solve It! Problem Solving for Primary Grades.* Dale Seymour Publications, 1997.

Myren, C. *Posing Open-Ended Questions in the Primary Classroom.* Teaching Resource Center, 1997.

Professional Resources Bibliography

National Council of Teachers of Mathematics. *Principles and Standards for School Mathematics* (2000)
    See also these NCTM products:
        Addenda Series
        Navigations Series
        Yearbook

National Research Council. *Adding It Up: Helping Children Learn Mathematics.* Washington, DC, National Academy Press, 2001.

Newman, V. *Math Journals, Grades K-5.* Teaching Resource Center, 1994.

Norton-Wolf, S. *Base-Ten Block Activities.* Learning Resources, 1990.

Ohanian, S. *Garbage, Pizza, Patchwork Quilts, and Math Magic.* W. H. Freeman and Co., 1992.

Pappas, T. *The Magic of Mathematics – Discovering the Spell of Mathematics.* Wide World Publishing/Tetra, 1994.

Parker, M., ed. *She Does Math! – Real-Life Problems from Women on the Job.* The Mathematical Association of America, 1995.

Piccirilli, R. *Mental Math: Computation Activities for Anytime.* Scholastic Professional Books, 1996.

Rich, D. *MegaSkills.* Houghton Mifflin Company, 1992.

Salvin, R. E., N. L. Karweit, and B. A. Wasik, eds. *Preventing Early School Failure: Research, Policy, and Practice.* Boston: Allyn and Bacon. 1994.

Satariano, P. *Storytime, Mathtime: Math Explorations in Children's Literature.* Dale Seymour Publications, 1997.

Schechter, B. *My Brain Is Open: The Mathematical Journeys of Paul Erdos.* Simon & Schuster, 1998.

Schoenfeld, A. *"When Good Teaching Leads to Bad Results: The Disasters of Well-Taught Mathematics Courses,"* Educational Psychologist, Vol. 23, 145-66. 1998.

Schullman, D., and E. Rebeka. *Growing Mathematical Ideas in Kindergarten.* Math Solutions Publications, 1999.

Sheffield, Linda Jensen. *Extending the Challenge in Mathematics: Developing Mathematical Promise in K–8 Students.* Thousand Oaks, CA: Corwin Press, Inc., 2002.

Singer, Margie, et al. *Between Never and Always.* Dale Seymour Publications, 1997.

Skinner, P. *It All Adds Up! Math Solutions Publications* (Adapted by Permission of Addison-Wesley Longman, Australia), 1999.

Sparrow, Len, and Paul Swan. *Learning Math with Calculators: Activities for Grades 3–8.* Sausalito, CA: Math Solutions Publications, 2001.

Sternberg, R., and W. Williams. *How to Develop Student Creativity.* ASCD. 1996

Stewart, K., and K. Walker. *20 Thinking Questions for Base-Ten Blocks, Grades 3-6.* Creative Publications, 1995.

Tomlinson, Carol Ann. *How to Differentiate Instruction in Mixed-Ability Classrooms.* ASCD, 1995.

Trafton, P., and D. Thiesen. *Learning Through Problems: Number Sense and Computational Strategies/A Resource for Teachers.* Heinemann, 1999.

Van De Walle, J. *Elementary and Middle School Mathematics: Teaching Developmentally,* Fourth Edition. Dale Seymour Publications, 2000.

Wahl, Mark. *Math for Humans: Teaching Math Through 8 Intelligences,* 2nd Ed. Vernon Hills, IL: LivnLern Press, 1999.

Webb, N., and T. Romberg. *Reforming Mathematics Education in America's Cities: The Urban Mathematics Collaborative Project.* Teachers College Press, 1994.

Zaslavsky, C. *Fear of Math – How to Get Over It and Get On with Your Life.* Rutgers University Press, 1994.

Zemelman, S., H. Daniels, and A. Hyde. *Best Practice: New Standards for Teaching and Learning in America's Schools.* Heinemann, 1998.

Research Support* for Unit 1

TO: First Grade Teachers

SUBJECT: Basic Facts Are Still Fundamental

The mastery of lower-order skills instills confidence for higher-order mathematics. According to Chinese teaching tradition, how teachers help students learn basic facts is most important. One reason that Chinese children appear to master basic facts well is the difference in the way numbers are written and spoken in Chinese versus English.

Chinese numeration highlights grouping by ten, and encourages children to view two-digit numbers as "tens" and "ones." This, in turn, promotes "ten" as a "bridge" when performing addition and subtraction.

In America, addition is taught by "adding on." Chinese children are taught to "make ten."

Example: 9 + 4 = ?

Chinese teaching: 9 + ? = 10

$9 + 1 = 10$ Make a ten using 1.

$4 = 1 + 3$ See how many more need to be added.

$10 + 3 = 13$ Add 3 to the 10 made from 9 and 1.

So, 9 + 4 is the same as 10 + + 3, or 13.

By using ten as a bridge in both addition and subtraction, children are encouraged to rely on understanding about facts that they have used repeatedly.

TRY IT OUT!

The creative teacher can employ an "adding-on" strategy in the introduction of addition, or a "take-away" strategy with subtraction. Later, with two-digit numbers, the Chinese approach of "making or removing ten" can be used to advantage.

CHECK IT OUT!

Horvath, Tara (2005). Number concepts, operations, and graphing. *Professional Resources Handbook—Grade 1*. Boston: Houghton-Mifflin.

Howard, K. (1979). *I can count to 100...can you?* New York: Random House.

Ma, L. (1999). *Knowing and teaching elementary mathematics*. Mahwah, NJ: Lawrence Erlbaum.

* For more information about the research base for this unit of *Houghton Mifflin Math*, see *Professional Resources Handbook, Grade 1*.

Research Support* for Unit 2

TO: **First Grade Teachers**

SUBJECT: **Working Out Facts You Don't Remember**

The use of counting materials such as bottle caps, sticks, rods, and other manipulatives is essential in laying the cognitive foundations for addition and subtraction of whole numbers through 10. While children should be encouraged to "work out" a basic fact by "combining" or "taking away" collections of counters, most teachers expect children eventually to memorize basic facts. Many children, however, cannot recall every basic fact reliably.

Children should be taught to "work out" facts, not just with manipulatives but with various fact generation strategies based upon fundamental properties of arithmetic. For example, "7" facts are notoriously difficult for some children.

The fact for $7 + 5 = 12$ is especially troublesome; however, if 7 is rewritten as $2 + 5$, then the fact becomes $2 + 5 + 5 = 12$ and is more easily remembered by making 10.

> **Some of the most useful "fact generation" strategies include:**
>
> **1) The order property of addition**
>
> **2) The grouping property of addition**
>
> **3) The "one more" or "one less" strategies.**

For example, if the fact $8 + 3$ is remembered, then $3 + 8$ can be "generated" using the order property. Similarly, if $8 + 3 = 11$ is recalled, then $8 + 4 = 12$ can be "generated" since 4 is one more than 3.

TRY IT OUT!

Play the "related facts" game—it's almost like bingo! Distribute blank addition tables to your class. Each table should have rows and columns from 0 through 10.

Place one entry on an overhead copy of the grid. For example, you might write 11 in the intersection of the 5 row and 6 column.

Children must begin with this entry. To make another entry, they must use a "generation strategy"; for example, the grid square to the left of 11 can be filled with "10" since $5 + 5$ is one less than $5 + 6$. What strategy could be used to fill the shaded square? $[6 + 7 = 5 + 1 + 6 + 1 = 5 + 6 + 2]$

The first child to complete an entire row, column or diagonal calls "bingo" and explains how they found the entries by beginning only with 11.

Go to the next grid and enter another sum to repeat the game.

Ask where a sum could be entered to make it very easy or very hard to call "bingo."

CHECK IT OUT!

Bergeron, J. C., & Herscovice, N. (1990). Kindergartners' knowledge of the precepts of number. In L. P. Steff & T. Wood (Eds.), *Transforming children's mathematics education: International perspectives* (pp. 125-134). Hillsdale, NJ: Erlbaum.

Han, Annie Yi and Peskoff, Fred (2005). Addition and subtraction facts through ten. *Professional Resources Handbook—Grade 1*. Boston: Houghton-Mifflin.

Moser, J. (1992). Arithmetic operations on whole numbers: Addition and subtraction. In T. Post (Ed.), *Teaching mathematics in grades K-8* (pp. 123-155). Needham Heights, MA: Allyn & Bacon.

* For more information about the research base for this unit of *Houghton Mifflin Math,* see *Professional Resources Handbook, Grade 1.*

Research Support * for Unit 3

TO: **First Grade Teachers**

SUBJECT: **Developing Spatial Skills**

Froebel (1782-1852) was among the first to emphasize that experience with everyday objects was an integral part of children's intellectual development. Froebel's teaching materials or "gifts" were geometric solids—spheres, cubes, cylinders—that were part of the real world of the child. Piaget and Inhelder (1967) underscored Froebel's belief in concrete geometric experiences; however, they believed that children's concepts of space develop sequentially from the most general (closed, connected) to the most specific (congruent, similar).

In the first grade, teachers should build upon the child's out-of-school geometric knowledge by emphasizing play and experimentation with actual objects rather than focusing exclusively upon memorizing terms and definitions.

Geometric play and experimentation are especially important for girls since some assessments show that girls may have less well-developed special skills than boys. Activities with blocks or with computer or video games may help build special skills; for example, geometric puzzles that require children to "visualize" the number of blocks in various configurations are useful to promote visual thinking.

TRY IT OUT!

Construct a "Puzzle of the Day" from wood or plastic cubes. Leave holes and cavities that are not hidden from external view. Then ask children how they solved the puzzle.

CHECK IT OUT!

Nickson, M. (2000). *Teaching and learning mathematics: A teacher's guide to recent research.* London: Cassell.

Sisul, J. (2002). Fostering flexibility with number in the primary grades. *Teaching Children Mathematics*, 9(4), 212-217.

Walker, Erica (2005). Geometry and fractions. *Professional Resources Handbook— Grade 1*. Boston: Houghton-Mifflin.

*   For more information about the research base for this unit of *Houghton Mifflin Math,* see *Professional Resources Handbook, Grade 1.*

Research Support* for Unit 4

TO: **First Grade Teachers**

SUBJECT: **Fun with Place Value Cards**

"Numeration" is the process of associating some symbolic representation with a collection of objects. Ordinarily "standard" numerals such as 1, 7 or 12 are used. Other "names" for standard numerals are often used too; for example, 5 + 2 is another name for 7. Expressions such as 5 + 2 are not readily accepted by children as just another name for 7.

This close association can be emphasized by using not only the standard numeral for numbers greater than 10, but also the expanded form. For example:

10 + 8 for 18

70 + 3 for 73

When the expanded form is used in conjunction with sticks bundled by tens or place-value pockets, the importance of the position of a digit within a standard numeral is clarified.

Using collections of counters and their basic counting skills, children can count without knowledge of place value. For very large collections, confusion in keeping track of the association between the words and the objects being counted forces the use of some form of grouping—into tens, hundreds, etc. A number of commercial teaching aids may be helpful in teaching place value numeration, but simple teacher-made material can serve equally well.

TRY IT OUT!

Make a set of place-value numeration cards—for 11 – 20, twenty cards are required: 10, 11, 12, 13, 14, 15, 16, 17, 18, 19, 20, 10 + 0, 10 + 1, 10 + 2, 10 + 3, 10 + 4, 10 + 5, 10 + 6, 10 + 7, 10 + 8, 10 + 9. Each number has two cards, such as 12 and 10 + 2.

Shuffle and deal one card to each student. The first player writes his numeral(s) on the chalkboard and asks who has the same number. Ask the children to make cards for 20 – 30, 30 – 40, 40 – 50, etc. To avoid the expense of 3 × 5 cards, cut paper into strips, and then cut each strip into three cards.

CHECK IT OUT!

Howard, K. (1979). *I can count to 100...can you?* New York; Random House.

Ness, Daniel (2005). Numbers through 100. *Professional Resources Handbook—Grade 1*. Boston: Houghton-Mifflin.

Sztajn, P. (2002). Celebrating 100 with number sense. *Teaching Children Mathematics*, 9(4), 212-217.

* **For more information about the research base for this unit of *Houghton Mifflin Math*, see *Professional Resources Handbook, Grade 1*.**

Research Support * for Unit 5

TO: **First Grade Teachers**

SUBJECT: **How Big Is a Nickel?**

Time and money are two of the most relevant topics in the primary curricula. Children arrive in first grade with informal out-of-school experience with both time and money, but usually this experience is quite incomplete.

Telling time or reading a clock is not the same as understanding time, its sequence, its duration, and its relativity (Mock, 1999). Children should learn to associate concrete events with the passing of time. Egg timers or hourglasses can be used to "time" games, songs or other classroom activities.

One difficulty associated with teaching about money is the lack of a relationship between the size of coins and their value (Botula, 1999). Thus coins are abstract models when used to teach values rather than concrete ones. Some educators suggest the use of proportionally-sized models of coins. For example, a cut-out dime would be about ten times the area of a cut-out penny. Other coins would also be proportional to the size of the model penny.

TRY IT OUT!

Introduce coin names by using proportional coins. Cut out a model penny about 1 inch in diameter from copper-colored construction paper. Cut out nickel and dime models that are about 2 inches and 3 inches in diameter, respectively, and label them "Nickel 5¢" and "Dime 10¢." A proportional model quarter would be about 5 inches in diameter. Use the proportional models in buying and making change activities to establish understanding of the relative values of the coins.

CHECK IT OUT!

Baroody, A. J., & Wilkins, J. L. (1999). The development of informal counting, number, and arithmetic skills and concepts. In J. V. Copley (Ed.), *Mathematics in the early years* (pp. 48-65). Reston, VA: National Council of Teachers of Mathematics.

Esposito, Linda (2005). Time and money. *Professional Resources Handbook—Grade 1.* Boston: Houghton-Mifflin.

Friederwitzer, F. J., & Berman, B. (1999). The language of time. *Teaching Children Mathematics, 6*(4), 254-259.

* For more information about the research base for this unit of *Houghton Mifflin Math,* see *Professional Resources Handbook, Grade 1.*

Research Support* for Unit 6

TO: **First Grade Teachers**

SUBJECT: **Planning a "Double Facts" Day!**

Much early research on the teaching of arithmetic concentrated upon which basic addition and subtraction facts were the most difficult for children and how much repetition was needed for memorization (Brownell, 1941). More recent research indicates that "doubles facts," "make ten," and "ten combination" facts are among the easiest for children to master (Baroody, 1984). Repetition does not insure mastery unless a rationale for the fact is present.

These research results are especially useful for facts involving 11 and 12. The doubles fact $6 + 6 = 12$ and the related subtraction fact $12 - 6 = 6$ are easily remembered when the "doubles" rationale is stressed. Similarly, the "ten combinations" $10 + 1 = 11$ and $10 + 2 = 12$ together with the subtraction facts $11 - 1 = 10$ and $12 - 2 = 10$ lead directly to a "make ten" rationale for extended facts; for example, $12 + 7 = 10 + 2 + 7 = 10 + 9 = 19$. This strategy emphasizes the use of 10 as a base. While these strategies require application of the grouping (associative) property, at the first grade level this important property need not be made explicit.

TRY IT OUT!

Plan a "double facts" day! Make index cards for each "doubles fact" through 12. Put the related subtraction fact on the back of each card. For example, $7 + 7 = 14$ on one side of a card and $14 - 7 = 7$ on the other side of the card.

Distribute each of the twelve cards to groups of two or three children. Each group then makes up two story problems—one for their "addition doubles fact" and one for the related subtraction fact.

CHECK IT OUT!

Ginsburg, H. P. (1989). *Children's arithmetic: How they learn it and how you teach it.* Austin, TX: Pro-Ed.

Lin, Chia-ling (2005). Addition and subtraction facts through 12. *Professional Resources Handbook—Grade 1.* Boston: Houghton-Mifflin.

Steffe, L. P., & Cobb, P. (1988). *Construction of arithmetical meanings and strategies.* New York: Springer-Verlag.

* For more information about the research base for this unit of *Houghton Mifflin Math,* see *Professional Resources Handbook, Grade 1.*

Research Support* for Unit 7

TO: **First Grade Teachers**

SUBJECT: **Use Your Math Books to Measure Length**

Children's ability to measure is dependent upon their understanding of the concept of a unit of measure. Activities with non-standard units are important prerequisites for measurement with standard units. Often children will compare lengths measured with different non-standard units by counting the units in each case, but will not recognize that the numbers alone provide little information about the relative size of the objects measured.

Children need to understand that useful measurements require the use of identical units when comparisons are to be made. Activities with multiple non-standard units are helpful in overcoming the reluctance of children to consider a unit only of a single entity.

TRY IT OUT!

Put two equal 8–10 ft pieces of masking tape on the floor in different parts of the classroom. Partition the class into two groups, say, boys and girls. Have one group "measure" the length of the tape by placing their mathematics books side-by-side along the tape, and have the other group measure the second tape by placing their books end-to-end as shown.

Count the books in each case. Which tape is longer in the sense that the book count is larger? Why is that not a good way to compare the lengths of the two tapes?

Now let's try to use the books to measure the width (length) of the classroom. There are not enough books! Try it by opening each book.

How many "books"-wide is the classroom? Each "unit" here is really as wide as two unopened books.

CHECK IT OUT!

Cloherty, Helen (2005). Measurement. *Professional Resources Handbook—Grade 1*. Boston: Houghton-Mifflin.

Kamii, C., Lewis, B., & Livingston, S. (1993). Primary arithmetic: Children inventing their own procedures. *Arithmetic Teacher*, 41, 200-203.

Lindquist, M., & Kuvba, V. (1989). Measurement. In M. M. Lindquist (Ed.), *Results from the Fourth Mathematics Assessment of the National Assessment of Educational Progress* (pp. 35-43). Reston, VA: National Council of Teachers of Mathematics.

*   For more information about the research base for this unit of *Houghton Mifflin Math*, see *Professional Resources Handbook, Grade 1.*

Research Support* for Unit 8

TO: **First Grade Teachers**

SUBJECT: **Making 10's and 20's**

Research indicates that many children have difficulty applying algorithms for multi-digit addition and subtraction, especially when regrouping is required. Many children rely instead on various thinking strategies. The number sense promoted by these strategies is an important asset in applying mathematics in the world outside the classroom.

A common theme in these strategies is the decomposition of one or more of the given numbers to reduce the problem by one requiring basic facts the child knows; for example, the use of expanded form alters the problem $15 + 12$ to $10 + 5 + 10 + 2$. The child thinks of the addends in a different way.

$$15 + 12 \text{ to } 10 + 5 + 10 + 2$$

The child then rearranges the problem to add tens and then add units:

$$15 + 12 = 10 + 5 + 10 + 2 = 10 + 10 + 5 + 2 = 20 + 7 = 27$$

This use of expanded form is the basis of the standard algorithm, however, the same decomposition thinking strategy can be used in other ways. For example:

$$15 + 12 = 15 + 5 + 7 = 20 + 7 = 27$$

Here, a "make 20" strategy avoids use of expanded form as well as the formal algorithm.

TRY IT OUT!

Use a "make 20" strategy to add:

$$17 + 9 = ? \qquad 13 + 18 = ?$$

Use a "make 30" strategy to add:

$$28 + 8 = ? \qquad 17 + 15 = ?$$

CHECK IT OUT!

Evered, Lisa (2005). Two-digit addition and subtraction. *Professional Resources Handbook—Grade 1*. Boston: Houghton-Mifflin.

Isaacs, A. C., & Carroll, W. M. (1999). Strategies for basic-facts instruction. *Teaching Children Mathematics, 5*, 508-515.

Leutzinger, L. P. (1999). Developing thinking strategies for addition facts. *Teaching Children Mathematics, 6*, 14-18.

* For more information about the research base for this unit of *Houghton Mifflin Math*, see *Professional Resources Handbook, Grade 1*.

Grade 1 Index

A

Access Prior Knowledge
Literature Activity, 2, 120, 178, 272, 354, 424, 494, 552

Achieving Mathematical Proficiency,
10, 18, 26, 43, 69, 93, 136, 151, 213, 224, 242, 248, 252, 329, 366, 401, 406, 437, 440, 448, 474, 528, 572, 587, 608, 632

Activities
Home School, 1D, 119D, 177D, 271D, 353D, 423D, 493D, 551D
Lesson Intervention, 8, 12, 16, 19, 22, 24, 36, 38, 40, 42, 46, 48, 50, 53, 62, 64, 66, 68, 72, 74, 76, 79, 88, 90, 92, 96, 99, 103, 126, 128, 130, 134, 137, 146, 148, 150, 154, 156, 158, 161, 184, 186, 189, 192, 194, 196, 199, 208, 210, 212, 218, 220, 222, 226, 229, 238, 240, 243, 246, 249, 253, 278, 280, 282, 285, 288, 290, 292, 295, 304, 306, 309, 312, 314, 316, 324, 326, 328, 332, 335, 360, 362, 364, 368, 371, 374, 376, 378, 381, 390, 392, 394, 396, 402, 404, 407, 430, 432, 434, 436, 442, 444, 446, 449, 458, 460, 462, 466, 468, 470, 472, 475, 500, 502, 504, 506, 510, 512, 514, 516, 524, 526, 529, 532, 534, 558, 560, 562, 566, 568, 570, 574, 582, 584, 586, 590, 592, 594, 596, 604, 606, 609, 612, 614, 617, 626, 629, 630, 633, 636, 638, 641
Prior Knowledge, 7, 9, 13, 17, 21, 23, 25, 35, 37, 39, 41, 45, 47, 49, 51, 61, 63, 65, 67, 71, 73, 75, 77, 87, 89, 91, 95, 97, 101, 125, 127, 129, 133, 135, 145, 147, 149, 153, 155, 157, 159, 183, 185, 187, 191, 193, 195, 197, 207, 209, 211, 215, 219, 221, 223, 227, 237, 239, 241, 245, 247, 251, 277, 279, 281, 283, 287, 289, 291, 293, 303, 305, 307, 311, 313, 315, 323, 325, 327, 331, 333, 359, 361, 363, 365, 369, 373, 375, 377, 379, 389, 391, 393, 395, 399, 403, 405, 429, 431, 433, 435, 439, 443, 445, 447, 457, 459, 461, 465, 467, 469, 471, 473, 499, 501, 503, 505, 509, 511, 513, 515, 523, 525, 527, 531, 533, 557, 559, 567, 565, 567, 569, 571, 581, 583, 585, 589, 591, 593, 595, 603, 605, 607, 611, 613, 615, 625, 627, 629, 631, 635, 627,

639
Unit Vocabulary, 1D, 119D, 177D, 271D, 353D, 423D, 493D, 551D

Activity lessons 9, 13, 35, 61, 87, 97, 191, 215, 247, 361, 499, 503, 509, 511, 513, 523, 525, 527

Addition
2-digit numbers, 607-608, 609, 611-612, 613-614
addends, missing, 130, 156, 432, 445-446, 568, 604
concepts, 37-38, 39-40
counting on to add, 125-126, 133-134, 429-430, 439, 559, 611-612
doubles plus one, 129, 130, 131, 132, 133-134, 439, 557-558
doubles, 129-130, 131, 132, 133-134, 439, 557-558, 565, 568, 569
families, 47-48, 155-156, 431-432, 433 434, 435 436
in any order, 45-46, 48, 435-436, 443-444, 569
make a ten, 559-560, 561-562, 565, 569
meaning of, 35-36, 37-38, 39-40, 45-46, 49-50, 51-52
modeling, 37-38, 39-40, 41-42, 45-46, 47-48, 49-50, 125-126, 129, 277-278, 431-432, 433-434, 435, 445-446, 559, 561, 565, 603-604, 605, 607, 609
money, 609
of 10s, 603-604
on a number line, 127-128, 429-430
part-part-whole, 37-38, 44, 135, 565, 567-568
practice, 439-442, 565-566, 611-612, 613-614
problem solving with, 51-52, 135-137
related to subtraction, 153-154, 157-158, 455-456, 462, 465-466, 560, 581-586, 587, 591-594
sentence, 42, 43, 45-46, 47-48, 51-52, 135-136, 434, 437, 454, 559, 560, 571-572
stories, 35-36, 43. 437
strategies, 133-134, 439-440, 446, 565-566, 611-612
three numbers, 443-444, 569-570
using symbols, 39-40, 42, 43, 51-52, 135-136, 437, 449, 559, 587, 610
vertical form, 49-50, 435-436, 439-442, 443, 558, 560, 562, 569-570
with 2-digit numbers, 605-606, 609, 611-612, 613-614
with zero, 41-42, 44

After, 17-20, 303-304, 359-360

Algebra and Algebraic Thinking
charts, 87-88
Choose the Operation, 159-160, 639-640
comparing numbers, 21-22, 23-24, 127-128, 313-314, 429-430
coordinate grid, 211-212
doubles, 129-130, 131, 132, 133-134, 439, 557-558, 565, 568, 569
functions, 46
graphs, 89-90, 91-92, 93, 95-96, 97-98, 99, 100, 101-102
missing addends, 130, 156, 432, 445-446, 568, 604
missing numbers, 590
number sentences, 67-68, 72, 73-74, 75-76, 90, 151, 470, 560, 584, 592
patterns, 50, 219-222, 227-230, 332, 333-336, 378, 472
    properties, 48
related facts, 439
    relating addition and subtraction, 153-154, 455-456, 467-470, 581, 560, 594, 595, 637-638
    using $>$ and $<$ and $=$, 23-24, 313-314, 566

Algebra Readiness
missing addends, 130, 156, 432, 445-446, 568, 604

Alternative Teaching Strategies, 7B, 8, 12, 13B, 16, 17B, 19, 21B, 22, 23B, 24, 25B, 35B, 36, 37B, 38, 39B, 40, 41B, 42, 45B, 46, 47B, 48, 49B, 50, 51B, 53, 61B, 62, 63B, 64, 65B, 66, 67B, 68, 71B, 72, 73B, 74, 75B, 76, 77B, 79, 87B, 88, 89B, 90, 91B, 92, 95B, 96, 97B, 99, 101B, 103, 125B, 126, 127B, 128, 129B, 130, 133B, 134, 135B, 137, 145B, 146, 147B, 148, 149B, 150, 153B, 154, 155B, 156, 157B, 158, 159B, 161, 183B, 184, 185B, 186, 187B, 189, 191B, 192, 193B, 194, 195B, 196, 197B, 199, 207B, 208, 209B, 210, 211B, 212, 215B, 218, 219B, 220, 221B, 222, 223B, 226, 227B, 229, 237B, 238, 239B, 240, 241B, 243, 245B, 246, 247B, 249, 251B, 253, 277B, 278, 279B, 280, 281B, 282, 283B, 285, 287B, 288, 289B, 290, 291B, 292, 293B, 295, 303B, 304, 305B, 306, 307B, 309, 311B, 312, 313B, 314, 315B, 316, 323B, 324, 325B, 326, 327B, 328, 331B, 332, 333B, 335, 359B, 360, 361B, 362, 363B, 364, 365B, 368, 369B, 371, 373B, 374, 375B, 376, 377B, 378, 379B, 381, 389B, 390, 391B, 392, 393B, 394,

half-dollar, 402
nickel, 389-390, 391-392, 395-396,
   399-402
penny, 389-390, 391-392, 393-394,
   395-396, 399-402
quarter, 399-402
counting, 395-396, 558
identifying, 389
equal amounts of, 403-404
subtracting, 633
value of, 389-390, 391-392, 393-394,
   395-396, 397, 399-401, 405-408, 582

Month, 377-378

More
capacity and, 523-524
fewer, same and, 7-8
how many, 149-150
quantity and, 7-9

More than, 327-328

Music Connection, 67B, 82, 147B, 195B,
237B, 327B, 393B, 443B, 511B, 559B,
591B

Names for numbers, 471-472, 567-568

Nickels
and pennies, 391-392
counting, 395-396
value of, 389-390, 395-396

Nonstandard units, 501-502, 509-510,
523-524

North Carolina Standards, 7A, 9A, 13A,
17A, 21A, 23A, 25A, 35A, 37A, 39A, 41A,
45A, 47A, 49A, 51A, 61A, 63A, 65A, 67A,
71A, 73A, 75A, 77A, 87A, 89A, 91A, 95A,
97A, 101A, 125A, 127A, 129A, 133A,
135A, 145A, 147A, 149A, 153A, 155A,
157A, 159A, 183A, 185A, 187A, 191A,
193A, 195A, 197A, 207A, 209A, 211A,
215A, 219A, 221A, 223A, 227A, 237A,
239A, 241A, 245A, 247A, 251A, 277A,
279A, 281A, 283A, 287A, 289A, 291A,
293A, 303A, 305A, 307A, 311A, 313A,
315A, 323A, 325A, 327A, 331A, 333A,
359A, 361A, 363A, 365A, 369A, 373A,
375A, 377A, 379A, 389A, 391A, 393A,
395A, 399A, 403A, 405A, 429A, 431A,
433A, 435A, 439A, 443A, 445A, 447A,
457A, 459A, 461A, 465A, 467A, 469A,
471A, 473A, 499A, 501A, 503A, 505A,
509A, 511A, 513A, 515A, 523A, 525A,
527A, 531A, 533A, 557A, 559A, 561A,
565A, 567A, 569A, 571A, 581A, 583A,
585A, 589A, 591A, 593A, 595A, 603A,

605A, 607A, 611A, 613A, 615A, 625A,
627A, 629A, 631A, 635A, 637A, 639A

Now Try This, 19, 189, 226, 243, 249, 368,
402, 609, 633

Number line
to add, 127-128, 429-430
to subtract, 147-148, 157-158, 457-458

Number of the Week Activity
Math Center, 25B, 51B, 77B, 101B, 135B,
159B, 197B, 227B, 251B, 293B, 315B,
333B, 379B, 405B, 447B, 473B, 515B,
533B, 571B, 595B, 615B, 639B

Number sentence. *See* Addition *and*
Subtraction.

Numbers
0 through 9, 9-12
10 through 20, 13-16
comparing, 21-22, 23-24, 30, 326
even, 331-332
greater than, 23-24, 311-314
less than, 23-24, 311-314
missing numbers, 18, 327
names for, 471-472, 567-568
odd, 331-332
one-to-one correspondence, 7-8
order, 303-304
ordinal, 305-306, 318
problem solving, 571-572
through 50, 281-282
through 99, 283-285, 287-288
through 100, 291-292
using symbols to compare, 313-314
See also Patterns *and* Place value.

Odd numbers, 331-332

One fourth, 241-242, 243, 245-246

One half, 239-240, 243, 245-246

One third, 243-244, 245-246

Ones
add, 35-36, 37-38, 39-40, 41-42, 45-46,
47-48, 49-50, 51-53
and tens, 279-280, 281-282, 283-285,
287-288, 289-290, 291-292, 293-295
count back, 145-146, 147-148
count on, 125-126, 127-128
doubles plus one, 129, 130, 131, 132,
133-134, 439, 557-558
less, 311-312
more, 311-312
subtracting, 61-62, 63-64, 65-66, 67-69,
71-72, 73-74, 75-76, 77-79

One-to-one correspondence, 7-8

Operations. *See* Addition *and* Subtraction.

Order, 17-18
events, 359-360, 438, 532
of addition, 45-46

Order property, 45-46

Ordering numbers. *See* Numbers.

Ordinal numbers, 305-306, 318

Organizing data. *See* Data.

Part-part-whole
addition, 37-38, 44, 135, 565, 567-568
subtraction, 63-64, 153-154, 155-156,
459-460, 461-461, 583-584, 585, 589

Patterns
analyze, 219, 221, 222
color, 183-184, 219-220, 221-222, 332
create, 219-220, 221-222, 332
describe and extend, 219-220, 222
doubles. See Addition.
growing, 267
number, 220, 327-328, 332, 333-334
shape, 184-188, 192-196
using, 227-230
See also Problem Solving Lessons, Find a
Pattern.

Pennies
and dimes, 393-394
and nickels, 391-392
counting, 395-396
value of, 389-390, 395-396

Performance Assessment
scoring rubric, 113-114, 171-172, 265-
266, 347-348, 417-418, 487-488, 545-
546, 651-652

Pictograph. *See* Data *and* Graphs.

Picture Glossary. *See* Glossary.

Pint, 525-526

Place value
ordering numbers, 303-304, 311-312,
349
to one hundred, 277-278, 279-280, 281-
282, 283-285, 287-288, 289-290, 291-
292, 293-295

Plane shapes
circle, 184, 185-186, 187-188, 195-196
classifying and sorting, 183-184, 187-188,
189, 193-194, 196
congruent, 226
corners, 185-186, 187-188, 192-193
line of symmetry, 223-225
rectangle, 185-186, 187-188, 195-196

603B, 605B, 607B, 611B, 613B, 615B,
625B, 627B, 629B, 631B, 635B, 637B,
639B

Gifted and Talented, 7B, 13B, 17B, 23B,
35B, 37B, 41B, 47B, 51B, 61B, 75B,
77B, 89B, 97B, 101B, 127B, 133B,
135B, 145B, 147B, 159B, 183B, 187B,
191B, 197B, 211B, 223B, 227B, 237B,
247B, 279B, 283B, 293B, 303B, 305B,
307B, 315B, 325B, 331B, 363B, 369B,
377B, 379B, 391B, 393B, 399B, 405B,
435B, 443B, 457B, 461B, 465B, 467B,
473B, 501B, 503B, 505B, 515B, 523B,
525B, 559B, 561B, 565B, 567B, 571B,
581B, 583B, 589B, 591B, 595B, 603B,
605B, 607B, 613B, 615B, 629B, 631B,
635B, 637B, 639B

Inclusion, 7B, 13B, 21B, 35B, 41B, 47B,
51B, 61B, 65B, 67B, 89B, 95B, 101B,
127B, 145B, 149B, 155B, 157B, 159B,
185B, 193B, 195B, 209B, 211B, 219B,
239B, 251B, 277B, 293B, 303B, 307B,
311B, 315B, 363B, 365B, 377B, 379B,
391B, 403B, 405B, 431B, 433B, 435B,
447B, 461B, 465B, 501B, 509B, 515B,
523B, 525B, 531B, 533B, 557B, 559B,
565B, 569B, 571B, 583B, 585B, 591B,
595B, 607B, 613B, 615B, 637B, 639B

Special Needs, 9B, 17B, 25B, 37B, 39B,
45B, 49B, 63B, 71B, 73B, 75B, 77B,
87B, 91B, 97B, 125B, 129B, 133B,
135B, 147B, 153B, 183B, 187B, 191B,
197B, 207B, 215B, 221B, 223B, 227B,
237B, 241B, 245B, 247B, 2 79B, 281B,
283B, 287B, 289B, 291B, 305B, 313B,
323B, 325B, 327B, 331B, 333B, 359B,
361B, 369B, 373B, 375B, 389B, 393B,
395B, 399B, 429B, 439B, 443B, 445B,
457B, 459B, 467B, 469B, 471B, 473B,
499B, 503B, 505B, 511B, 513B, 527B,
561B, 567B, 581B, 589B, 593B, 603B,
605B, 611B, 625B, 627B, 629B, 631B,
635B

Reading Math
Vocabulary, 42, 72, 210, 280, 306, 312,
460, 506, 586, 630

Real-Life Activity
Math Center, 13B, 41B, 49B, 97B, 125B,
193B, 209B, 211B, 245B, 247B, 277B,
289B, 303B, 327B, 359B, 365B, 373B,
391B, 393B, 395B, 399B, 435B, 469B,
501B, 503B, 505B, 523B, 531B, 569B,
591B, 605B, 611B

Reasoning
logical, 515-516

Rectangle, 185-186, 187-188, 195-196

Rectangular prism, 191-192, 193-194,

195-196

Review
Key Topic Review, 30, 56, 82, 106, 140,
164, 202, 256, 298, 318, 338, 384, 410,
452, 478, 518, 536, 576, 598, 620, 644

Quick Review, 7A, 9A, 13A, 17A, 21A,
23A, 25A, 35A, 37A, 39A, 41A, 45A,
47A, 49A, 51A, 61A, 63A, 65A, 67A,
71A, 73A, 75A, 77A, 87A, 89A, 91A,
95A, 97A, 101A, 125A, 127A, 129A,
133A, 135A, 145A, 147A, 149A, 153A,
155A, 157A, 159A, 183A, 185A, 187A,
191A, 193A, 195A, 197A, 207A, 209A,
211A, 215A, 219A, 221A, 223A, 227A,
237A, 239A, 241A, 245A, 247A, 251A,
277A, 279A, 281A, 283A, 287A, 289A,
291A, 293A, 303A, 305A, 307A, 311A,
313A, 315A, 323A, 325A, 327A, 331A,
333A, 359A, 361A, 363A, 365A, 369A,
373A, 375A, 377A, 379A, 389A, 391A,
393A, 395A, 399A, 403A, 405A, 429A,
431A, 433A, 435A, 439A, 443A, 445A,
447A, 457A, 459A, 461A, 465A, 467A,
469A, 471A, 473A, 499A, 501A, 503A,
505A, 509A, 511A, 513A, 515A, 523A,
525A, 527A, 531A, 533A, 557A, 559A,
561A, 565A, 567A, 569A, 571A, 581A,
583A, 585A, 589A, 591A, 593A, 595A,
603A, 605A, 607A, 611A, 613A, 615A,
625A, 627A, 629A, 631A, 635A, 637A,
639A

Rubric, scoring. *See* Performance
Assessment.

Rulers
centimeter, 505-506, 507
inch, 503-504, 547

Schedule. *See* Data.

Science Connection, 13B, 21B, 37B, 51B,
56, 73B, 91B, 101B, 106, 129B, 140,
157B, 164, 183B, 191B, 209B, 223B,
245B, 281B, 287B, 293B, 305B, 310,
333B, 359B, 377B, 391B, 438, 445B,
457B, 463, 467B, 469B, 505B, 509B,
531B, 567B, 569B, 589B, 598, 605B, 610,
615B, 629B, 635B, 644

Scope and Sequence, T14-T29

Shapes. *See* Plane shapes *and* Solid
shapes.

Sides. *See* Plane shapes.

Skills Games. *See* Keeping Skills Sharp.

Skills Trace, 5A, 33A, 59A, 85A, 123A,

143A,181A,205A,235A,275A, 301A,
321A, 357A, 387A, 427A, 455A, 497A,
521A, 555A, 579A, 601A, 623A

Skip count
by 2s, 323-324, 329
by 5s, 325-326, 329

Slides, 215-218

Social Studies Connection, 7B, 23B, 30,
35B, 47B, 71B, 87B, 97B, 135B, 155B,
159B, 185B, 187B, 202, 207B, 215B,
227B, 247B, 251B, 277B, 289B, 291B,
303B, 313B, 318, 331B, 361B, 373B, 384,
389B, 395B, 399B, 447B, 452, 459B,
499B, 515B, 518, 523B, 527B, 536, 565B,
581B, 583B, 603B, 625B, 634, 637B

Solid shapes
classifying and sorting, 193-194
cone, 191-192, 193-194, 195-196
corners, 192
cube, 191-192, 193-194, 195-196
cylinder, 191-192, 193-194, 195-196
edges, 192, 193-194
identifying faces, 191-192, 193-194, 195-
196
pyramid, 191-192, 193-194, 195-196
rectangular prism, 191-192, 193-194,
195-196
related to plane figures, 194-196
sphere, 191-192, 193-194, 195-196

Sorting and classifying
attributes, 183-186, 189
by number of corners, 187-188, 192
by plane shape, 183-184
by size, 183-184
color, 183-184
solid shapes, 191-192, 193-194
See also Data.

Special Needs, 9B, 17B, 25B, 37B, 39B,
45B, 49B, 63B, 71B, 73B, 75B, 77B, 87B,
91B, 97B, 125B, 129B, 133B, 135B, 147B,
153B, 183B, 187B, 191B, 197B, 207B,
215B, 221B, 223B, 227B, 237B, 241B,
245B, 247B, 279B, 281B, 283B, 287B,
289B, 291B, 305B, 313B, 323B, 325B,
327B, 331B, 333B, 359B, 361B, 369B,
373B, 375B, 389B, 393B, 395B, 399B,
429B, 439B, 443B, 445B, 457B, 459B,
467B, 469B, 471B, 473B, 499B, 503B,
505B, 511B, 513B, 527B, 561B, 567B,
581B, 589B, 593B, 603B, 605B, 611B,
625B, 627B, 629B, 631B, 635B

Sphere, 191-192, 193-194, 195-196

Square, 184, 185-186, 187-188, 195-196

Standards. *See* North Carolina Standards.

279A, 281A, 283A, 287A, 289A, 291A,
293A, 303A, 305A, 307A, 311A, 313A,
315A, 323A, 325A, 327A, 331A, 333A,
359A, 361A, 363A, 365A, 369A, 373A,
375A, 377A, 379A, 389A, 391A, 393A,
395A, 399A, 403A, 405A, 429A, 431A,
433A, 435A, 439A, 443A, 445A, 447A,
457A, 459A, 461A, 465A, 467A, 469A,
471A, 473A, 499A, 501A, 503A, 505A,
509A, 511A, 513A, 515A, 523A, 525A,
527A, 531A, 533A, 557A, 559A, 561A,
565A, 567A, 569A, 571A, 581A, 583A,
585A, 589A, 591A, 593A, 595A, 603A,
605A, 607A, 611A, 613A, 615A, 625A,
627A, 629A, 631A, 635A, 637A, 639A
Listening Skills for, 28, 54, 80, 104, 138,
162, 200, 230, 254, 296, 336, 382, 408,
450, 476, 574, 618, 642
Quick Check, 20, 29, 44, 55, 70, 81, 94,
105, 132, 139, 152, 163, 190, 201, 214,
231, 244, 255, 286, 297, 310, 317, 330,
337, 372, 383, 409, 438, 451, 463, 477,
508, 517, 530, 535, 564, 575, 588, 597,
610, 619, 634, 643
Unit Test, 111-112, 169-170, 263-264,
345-346, 415-416, 485-486, 543-544,
649-650

est Tips. *See* Explain Your Thinking in
each lesson.

est-Taking Tips. *See* Cumulative Test
Prep.

hermometer, 531-532, 534

hirds, 243-244, 245-246

me
calendar, 19, 375-378
clocks
analog, 363-364, 365-367, 368, 369-
371, 373-374, 628
digital, 363-364, 365-367, 370-371,
373-374
hour hand, 363-364, 365-366
minute hand, 363-364, 365-366, 368,
628
elapsed, 369-371, 379-380
estimate, 361-362
half-hour, 365, 367, 369-371, 373-374,
628
hour, 363-364, 365, 367, 369-371, 373-
374
minute, 361-362, 368
order events, 359-360
tell time, 363-364, 365-367, 368, 369-
371, 373-374, 628
See also Days, Month, *and* Week.

ade Book References. *See*
Bibliographies.

Triangle, 184-185, 186, 187-188, 195-196

Turns, 215-218

Two-digit addition, 605-606, 607-608,
610, 611-612, 613-614, 615-617

Two-digit subtraction, 627-628, 629-630,
631-633, 635-636, 637-638, 639-641

Unit Activity, 1D, 119D, 177D, 271D,
353D, 423D, 493D, 551D

Unit at a Glance, 1A, 119A, 177A, 271A,
353A, 423A, 493A, 551A

Unit Bibliography, 2, 120, 178, 272, 354,
424, 494, 552

Unit Literature, 1-3, 119-121, 177-179,
271-273, 353-355, 423-425, 493-495,
551-553

Unit Project
Connecting to the Unit Project, 5D, 33D,
59D, 85D, 123D, 143D, 181D, 205D,
235D, 275D, 301D, 321D, 357D. 387D,
427D, 455D, 497D, 521D, 555D, 579D,
601D, 623D
Wrap Up the Unit Project, 110, 168, 262,
344, 414, 484, 542, 648

Units of Measurement. *See* Measurement.

Unit Test. *See* Tests.

Unit Vocabulary Activity. *See* Activities.

Vertical form
for addition, 49-50, 435-436, 439-442,
443, 558, 560, 562, 569-570
for subtraction, 75-76

Vocabulary
Building Strategies, 4, 122, 180, 274, 356,
426, 496, 554
Daily Routines, 7A, 9A, 13A, 17A, 21A,
23A, 25A, 35A, 37A, 39A, 41A, 45A,
47A, 49A, 51A, 61A, 63A, 65A, 67A,
71A, 73A, 75A, 77A, 87A, 89A, 91A,
95A, 97A, 101A, 125A, 127A, 129A,
133A, 135A, 145A, 147A, 149A, 153A,
155A, 157A, 159A, 183A, 185A, 187A,
191A, 193A, 195A, 197A, 207A, 209A,
211A, 215A, 219A, 221A, 223A, 227A,
237A, 239A, 241A, 245A, 247A, 251A,
277A, 279A, 281A, 283A, 287A, 289A,
291A, 293A, 303A, 305A, 307A, 311A,
313A, 315A, 323A, 325A, 327A, 331A,

333A, 359A, 361A, 363A, 365A, 369A,
373A, 375A, 377A, 379A, 389A, 391A,
393A, 395A, 399A, 403A, 405A, 429A,
431A, 433A, 435A, 439A, 443A, 445A,
447A, 457A, 459A, 461A, 465A, 467A,
469A, 471A, 473A, 499A, 501A, 503A,
505A, 509A, 511A, 513A, 515A, 523A,
525A, 527A, 531A, 533A, 557A, 559A,
561A, 565A, 567A, 569A, 571A, 581A,
583A, 585A, 589A, 591A, 593A, 595A,
603A, 605A, 607A, 611A, 613A, 615A,
625A, 627A, 629A, 631A, 635A, 637A,
639A
Our Math Bulletin Board, 4, 122, 180, 274,
356, 426, 496, 554
Reading Math, 42, 72, 210, 280, 306, 312,
460, 506, 586, 630
Unit Vocabulary Activity. *See* Activities.

Vocabulary Activity
Math Center, 7B, 21B, 23B, 39B, 91B,
185B, 215B, 239B, 241B, 281B, 283B,
291B, 305B, 311B, 331B, 361B, 363B,
369B, 375B, 377B, 389B, 471B, 511B,
513B, 525B, 527B, 567B

Week, 375-376, 378

Weight
comparing, 509-510
measuring, 509-510
pound, 511-512

Write About It, 24, 97, 510, 512, 514, 529,
592

Zero
addition with, 41-42, 44
subtraction with, 71-72

Grade 1 Credits ....

PERMISSIONS ACKNOWLEDGMENTS

Houghton Mifflin Mathematics © 2005, Grade 1 PE/TE

1/1 *Aunt Flossie's Hats (and Crab Cakes Later)*, by Elizabeth Fitzgerald Howard, illustrated by James Ransome. Text copyright © 1991 by Elizabeth Fitzgerald Howard. Illustrations copyright © 1991 by James Ransome. Reproduced by permission of Clarion Books/Houghton Mifflin Company. All rights reserved.

1/4 *100 Days of School*, by Trudy Harris, illustrated by Beth Griffis Johnson. Text copyright © 1999 by Trudy Harris. Illustrations copyright © 1999 by Beth Griffis Johnson. Reprinted by permission of the Millbrook Press, Inc.

1/6 *Twenty Is Too Many*, by Kate Duke. Copyright © 2000 by Kate Duke. Reprinted by permission of Penguin Putnam Books for Young Readers, a division of Penguin Putnam Inc. All rights reserved.

1/7 "One Inch Tall" from *Where the Sidewalk Ends*, by Shel Silverstein. Copyright © 1974 by Evil Eye Music, Inc. All rights reserved. Reprinted by permission of HarperCollins Publishers.

1/8 *One Watermelon Seed*, by Ceila Barker Lottridge, illustrated by Karen Patkau. Text copyright © 1986 by Ceila Barker Lottridge. First published by Oxford University Press. All rights reserved. Reprinted by permission of Fitzhenry & Whiteside Limited, Ontario, Canada

COVER © HMCo./Bruton Stroube Studios. (puppy) © Ron Kimball Studios.

PHOTOGRAPHY

27 (t) Royalty Free/CORBIS. (mt) PhotoDisc/Getty Images. (mb) Courtesy of the Topps Company, Inc. **53** PhotoDisc/Getty Images. **56-7** PhotoDisc/Getty Images. **62, 65-66, 70-72, 75-76** PhotoDisc/Getty Images **79** (t) PhotoDisc/Getty Images. (b) Iconotec.com. **81** (t) (mt) (mb) PhotoDisc/Getty Images. **82** (m) (r) PhotoDisc/Getty Images. (l) Creatas. **86** © Underwood & Underwood/CORBIS. **103** (t) ©Jack Hollingsworth/Getty Images. (m) ©Mike Brinson/Getty Images. (b) © Richard Hamilton Smith/CORBIS. **105** PhotoDisc/Getty Images. (carrot) Iconotec.com. **109** © Peter Beck/CORBIS. **110** © Nicholas DeVore/Getty Images. **137** (t) (mb) (b) PhotoDisc/Getty Images. (mt) © Wayne Lawler; Ecoscene/CORBIS. **140** PhotoDisc/Getty Images. **144** (t) © Julian Calder/CORBIS. (b) PhotoDisc/Getty Images. **159** PhotoDisc/Getty Images. **161** PhotoDisc/Getty Images. **164** © Fritz Polking; Frank Lane Picture Agency/CORBIS . **167** © D. Robert & Lorri Franz/CORBIS. **168** © Reuters NewMedia, Inc./CORBIS. **190** PhotoDisc/Getty Images. **206** (l) © Lawrence Manning/CORBIS. (r) Library of Congress. **229** (t) © Janis Christie/Getty Images. (mt) PhotoDisc/Getty Images. **232** PhotoDisc/Getty Images. **253** (t) PhotoDisc/Getty Images. (m) © Jonathan Blair/CORBIS. (b) PhotoDisc/Getty Images. **256** Painting by Bruce Gray/ www.brucegray.com. **298** Krimmer/eStock Photography/PictureQuest. **310** © Chase Swift/CORBIS. **335** (t) (mb) (b) PhotoDisc/Getty Images. (mt) © Kelly-Mooney Photography/CORBIS. **343** © Gallo Images/CORBIS. **344** © Michael & Patricia Fogden/CORBIS. **369** © Elan Sunstar/PictureQuest. **381** (t) © Charles O'Rear/CORBIS. (mt) CORBIS Royalty Free. (mb) © FRANK CEZUS/Getty Images. (b) © Alan Schein Photography/CORBIS. **384** © Philip Gould/CORBIS. **388** © Bettmann/CORBIS. **393** (t), **395** (b), **407** (t) (mb), **412** (r) PhotoDisc/Getty Images. **413** Courtesy of Pete Quasius. **449** (t) (mt) Royalty Free/CORBIS. (mb) © Pat O'Hara/CORBIS. (b) © Arthur Morris/CORBIS. **456** © Bettmann/CORBIS. **464** (l) PhotoDisc/Getty Images. **475** (t) © Ariel Skelley/CORBIS. (mt) © Philip James Corwin/CORBIS. (mb) Royalty Free/CORBIS . (b) © Mug Shots/CORBIS. **483** Royalty-Free/Corbis. Courtesy of The President's Challenge. **484** © Norbert Schaefer/CORBIS. **499** (bl) © HMCo film archive. (bm) Photospin. (br) PhotoDisc/Getty Images. **502** (ball), **506** (button), **510** (tiger), **514** (l) (r), **520** (apple, ball, melon, orange) PhotoDisc/Getty Images. **514** (m) © Wegner, Jorg & Petra/Animals Animals/Earth Scenes. **518** © Paul Barton/CORBIS. **522** (t) Courtesy of the Presser Foundation.

524 (t) (b) (c) HMCo film archive. **532** (l) (m) PhotoDisc/Getty Images. **536** © Massimo Mastrorillo/CORBIS. **541** © Sea World of California/CORBIS. **542** © Jeffrey L. Rotman/CORBIS. **571**© Tim Pannell/CORBIS. **572, 573** (mb) PhotoDisc/Getty Images. **57**(t)(mt)(b) (c) HMCo film archive. **595** © Jane Burton/Bruce Coleman U.S.A. **598** © Brandon D. Cole/CORBIS. **602** Michael Justice/Mercury Pictures. **610** © LYTHGOE/Getty Images. **617** (t) (mb) Royalty Free/CORBIS. (mt) © DiMaggio/Kalish/CORBIS. (b) © John Conrad/CORBIS. **620** © Kelly-Mooney Photography/CORBIS **641** PhotoDisc/Getty Images. **644** (b) PhotoDisc/Getty Images. **647-8** Copyright Thierry Hubin, Museum of Natural Sciences Brussels. **T3** © Ariel Skelley/CORBIS. **T33** © PhotoDisc/Getty Images.

ASSIGNMENT PHOTOGRAPHY

xxii © HMCo./Joel Benjamin

9, 27 (b)**, 30 , 37, 39, 45, 49 , 90, 99-100 ,191, 195 ,219, 221, 223, 229** (mb)**, 237, 250-251, 287, 289, 315 , 321-322, 327, 329, 331, 333,359, 361, 366-368, 373, 385, 387** (child)**, 389, 391, 394** (b)**, 395** (t)**, 397, 401, 403-404** (b)**,445,463, 465** (r)**,499** (t)**, 500** (tr)**, 507** (b)**, 509** (t)**, 519** (desk)**,522** (b)**, 523, 525** (t)**, 527** (child)**, 532** (r)**, 533** (r)**, 559, 561, 603, 611, 623, 625, 630, 631, 633** (r)**, 636, 637** © HMCo./Cheryl Clegg.

184, 193, 199, 204, 229 (b)**, 235, 295, 362, 387**(objects)**, 390, 392, 393** (b)**, 394** (t)**, 396, 399-400, 401** (t)**, 402, 405-406, 407** (mt)(b)**, 409-411, 412** (l) **,498, 500** (objects)**, 501, 502** (all objects except ball)**, 503, 505, 506** (top three)**, 508, 509** (b)**, 510** (except tiger)**, 513, 517, 519** (except desk)**, 520** (feather, backpack)**,523** (b)**, 524** (mt) (mb)**, 527** (objects)**, 529, 533** (l) (m)**, 534-535, 537, 538, 633** (l) (ml) (mr)**, 644** (t) © HMCo./Brian Harris.

xxiii, xxiv © HMCo./Allan Landau.

ILLUSTRATION

318 Argosy. **5-8, 10-27, 30-31** Marla Bagetta. **85-99, 101-103** Hector Borlasca. **54, 10** (b)**, 450, 500** (bl) Scott Brooks. **427-440, 442-448, 451, 454** Mircea Catusanu. **301-31 319-320, 478** Dave Clegg. **205, 207-218, 220-225, 227, 230, 232, 233** Steve Cox. **363 374, 382, 510** (b)**, 511** (t) (b)**, 513, 516, 518, 520** (t) (b) Rob Dunlavey. **104** (t)**,107-10 408** (t)**, 524** (b)**, 528, 574, 642** Ruth Flanigan. **34, 39-42, 43** (t)**, 44** (b) **428** Rusty Fletcher. **623-624, 626-632, 634-640** Barry Gott. **236-243, 245-246, 248** Tim Haggerty. **143, 145-160, 162, 164-165** Diane Dawson Hearn. **59-65, 67-70, 73, 75-78, 80, 82, 83** Ben Mahan. **579-582, 584-587, 589-594, 596-597, 600** Cheryl Mendenhall. **33, 35-38, 40** (t) (bkgd)**, 41** (m)**, 43** (bkgd)**, 44** (t)**, 46-48, 50-52** Judith Moffat. **357-360, 362-363, 364** (b)**, 365, 372, 385** Alex Steele Morgan. **497-500** (br)**, 502-504, 506** (t)**, 511** (m)**, 512, 514-515, 516, 517** (t) Ellen Mueller. **183-186, 188, 193-194, 196, 202, 364** (t)**, 369-371, 374-380, 383, 386** John Nez. **521, 524** (t)**, 526** (b)**, 529-532, 534-535, 538** Laura Ovresat. **555-562, 564-571, 576** Lizzy Rockwell. **45! 457, 459-462, 466-473, 476** Margaret Sanfilippo. **601-609, 611-614** Barbara Schaffer. **506** (b)**, 618** Denise Shea. **123-136, 138, 140** Jerry Smath. **181-189, 191-197, 203** Ari Vangsgard. **321-328, 331-334, 336, 338** Bruce Van Patter. **275-294, 296, 451** Bari Weissman.

All tech art by Pronk & Associates.

WEEKLY READER

Photography Credits: 670-1 Mint Museum of Art, Charlotte, NC.
Illustration Credits: 670-71 (t) Ortelius Design, Inc. **672-3** Lauren Scheuer.
674-5 Erica Thurston. **676-7** Larry Nolte. **678-9** Shane Kelley.

Credits